OF THE ELEMENTS

							18 VIIIA
							2 Helium **He** 4.00

			13 IIIA	14 IVA	15 VA	16 VIA	17 VIIA	
			5 Boron **B** 10.81	6 Carbon **C** 12.01	7 Nitrogen **N** 14.01	8 Oxygen **O** 16.00	9 Fluorine **F** 19.00	10 Neon **Ne** 20.18
10	11 IB	12 IIB	13 Aluminum **Al** 26.98	14 Silicon **Si** 28.09	15 Phos- phorus **P** 30.97	16 Sulfur **S** 32.06	17 Chlorine **Cl** 35.45	18 Argon **Ar** 39.95
28 Nickel **Ni** 58.69	29 Copper **Cu** 63.54	30 Zinc **Zn** 65.37	31 Gallium **Ga** 69.72	32 Germa- nium **Ge** 72.61	33 Arsenic **As** 74.92	34 Selenium **Se** 78.96	35 Bromine **Br** 79.91	36 Krypton **Kr** 83.80
46 Palladium **Pd** 106.42	47 Silver **Ag** 107.87	48 Cadmium **Cd** 112.41	49 Indium **In** 114.82	50 Tin **Sn** 118.69	51 Antimony **Sb** 121.75	52 Tellurium **Te** 127.60	53 Iodine **I** 126.90	54 Xenon **Xe** 131.29
78 Platinum **Pt** 195.08	79 Gold **Au** 196.97	80 Mercury **Hg** 200.59	81 Thallium **Tl** 204.37	82 Lead **Pb** 207.19	83 Bismuth **Bi** 208.98	84 Polonium **Po** (209)	85 Astatine **At** (210)	86 Radon **Rn** (222)

65 Terbium **Tb** 158.92	66 Dys- prosium **Dy** 162.50	67 Holmium **Ho** 164.93	68 Erbium **Er** 167.26	69 Thulium **Tm** 168.93	70 Ytterbium **Yb** 173.04	71 Lutetium **Lu** 174.97
97 Berkelium **Bk** (247)	98 Califor- nium **Cf** (251)	99 Einstei- nium **Es** (252)	100 Fermium **Fm** (257)	101 Mende- levium **Md** (258)	102 Nobelium **No** (259)	103 Lawren- cium **Lr** (260)

Foundations of Inorganic, Organic, & Biological Chemistry

ROBERT L. CARET

Towson State University

KATHERINE J. DENNISTON

Towson State University

JOSEPH J. TOPPING

Towson State University

WCB Wm. C. Brown Publishers

Dubuque. IA Bogota Boston Buenos Aires Caracas Chicago
Guilford. CT London Madrid Mexico City Sydney Toronto

Book Team

Editor *Megan Johnson*
Developmental Editor *John Berns*
Publishing Services Coordinator *Julie Avery Kennedy*

Wm. C. Brown Publishers
A Division of Wm. C. Brown Communications, Inc.

Vice President and General Manager *Beverly Kolz*
Vice President, Publisher *Earl McPeek*
Vice President, Director of Sales and Marketing *Virginia S. Moffat*
Vice President, Director of Production *Colleen A. Yonda*
National Sales Manager *Douglas J. DiNardo*
Marketing Manager *Jane Ducham*
Advertising Manager *Janelle Keeffer*
Production Editorial Manager *Renée Menne*
Publishing Services Manager *Karen J. Slaght*
Royalty/Permissions Manager *Connie Allendorf*

Wm. C. Brown Communications, Inc.

President and Chief Executive Officer *G. Franklin Lewis*
Senior Vice President, Operations *James H. Higby*
Corporate Senior Vice President, President of WCB Manufacturing *Roger Meyer*
Corporate Senior Vice President and Chief Financial Officer *Robert Chesterman*

Cover Image © by Irving Geis

Copyediting, Design, Permissions, and Production by York Production Services

Composition by York Graphic Services

The credits section for this book is on page 574 and is considered
an extension of the copyright page.

A Times Mirror Company

Library of Congress Catalog Card Number: 94-71225

ISBN 0-697-21242-4

Printed in the United States of America by Wm. C. Brown Communications, Inc.,
2460 Kerper Boulevard, Dubuque, IA 52001

10 9 8 7 6 5 4 3 2 1

To Liz,
For standing by me.

RLC

To my parents, Peg and Guy,
who taught me that I could do anything if I tried hard enough.
And to Andrew and Amanda,
whom I hope to teach the same lesson.

KJD

In memory of my parents, Virginia and Joseph,
for all their support.
And to John Topping,
a very special uncle.

JJT

Brief Contents

Detailed Contents

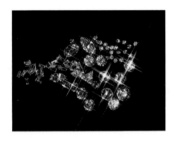

3
Structure and Properties of Ionic and Covalent Compounds   56

4
Calculations and the Chemical Equation   83

5
Energy Relationships and States of Matter   104

6

Solutions 132

7

Chemical Reactions 152

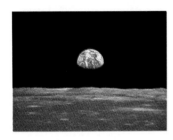

8

Radioactivity and
Nuclear
Medicine   176

9

An Introduction to
Organic Chemistry:
The
Hydrocarbons   197

10

Oxygen- and Sulfur-Containing Organic Compounds   230

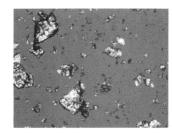

11

Carbohydrates   259

12

Carboxylic Acids and Carboxylic Acid Derivatives   283

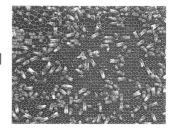

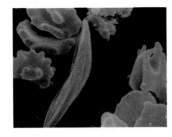
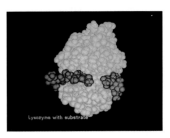

16
Carbohydrate Metabolism   386

17
Aerobic Respiration and Energy Production   412

Preface

AUDIENCE

Foundations of Inorganic, Organic, & Biological Chemistry serves two primary audiences: those students in health-related majors who will be challenged to cover all of chemistry in one semester, as well as students who take a one semester survey course as a foundation. This course necessarily emphasizes applications. Students are exposed to the practical aspects of chemistry as they relate to the health sciences and the environment. Therefore, *Foundations of Inorganic, Organic, & Biological Chemistry* strikes a balance between theoretical and practical chemistry, while emphasizing material unique to health-related studies. It is written at a level intended for the student whose goals in life do not include a mastery of chemistry, but for whom an understanding of the principles and their practical applications is a necessity.

PHILOSOPHY

Chemistry is a unified discipline. In this text we will, of course, treat the individual disciplines of inorganic, organic, and biological chemistry. However, the emphasis will be on the integration of these areas to help the student understand the inter-relatedness of these three disciplines. We believe this approach will provide a sound foundation in the principles of chemistry. At the same time, the students will learn that life is not a magical property, but rather is the result of a set of chemical reactions that obey the laws of chemistry (and physics). We want the students to develop a "feel" for each of the following concepts:

◆ the importance of chemistry in the normal biochemical function of the cell and the body as a whole.

◆ the medical ramifications that result when such reactions go awry.

◆ the action of drugs in the body.

◆ the application of chemistry to alleviate disease and suffering.

Indeed, these are the aspects of chemistry that are most critical in health-related occupations.

The approach to writing the book has been to provide an interesting and logical sequence that will develop the very basic principles of inorganic and organic chemistry and an in-depth understanding of the basic biological molecules that make up the cell and the biochemical reactions that allow it to function.

ORGANIZATION AND CONTENT

When organizing the contents of this text one of our major concerns was the challenge of covering all aspects of inorganic, organic, and biological chemistry in a meaningful way—in a single semester. One approach we have adopted is to closely tie together the related topics of organic and biochemistry. In this way the chemistry of a class of organic molecules need only be covered once. Then it can be immediately applied to the appropriate class of biological molecules. We have tried to avoid the temptation to cover "a little of everything" or to present material for its own sake. Topics have been chosen or omitted on the basis of whether or not the material will be useful to the students in later chapters or in their future careers.

We have attempted to provide a comfortable flow of material and have maintained a rather traditional organization. The first eight chapters supply the type of background that is generally found in a two semester science major's chemistry course, but the material is intended to be covered in less than one half a semester. The chapters that follow (Chapters 9 and 10) present the fundamental principles of organic chemistry: basics of nomenclature, hydrocarbon structure and chemistry, and common functional groups. Immediately thereafter we introduce the more biochemistry-oriented, organic chemistry. Specifically, carbohydrate chemistry (Chapter 11) immediately follows the discussion of alcohols, ketones, and aldehydes (Chapter 10). This allows the students to apply what they have just learned about ketones and aldehydes to the important group of biological molecules that *are* polyhydroxyketones and polyhydroxyaldehydes. Chapter 13 (Lipids) builds on the material presented in Chapter 12 (Carboxylic Acids). Chapter 15 (Protein Structure and Enzymes) naturally follows Chapter 14 (Amines and Amides). This intermingling of organic and biochemistry softens the boundary between the two areas. Furthermore, this approach allows the instructor to begin coverage of biochemistry earlier in the course. This provides a solution to one of the common problems encountered in teaching this type of course, namely, that there is so much material that it is difficult to adequately cover the focal point of the course—the biochemistry. The book is designed to allow the instructor flexibility in the organization of the course. For instance, the instructor may choose to teach the discipline of chemistry sequentially: inorganic chemistry (Chapters 1–8), organic chemistry (Chapters 9, 10, 12, and 14), and biochemistry (Chapters 11, 13, 15–19). Alternatively, the instructor may choose to follow the organization of the text, alternating the study of organic and biological molecules characterized by a particular functional group.

PEDAGOGY

The text includes a variety of pedagogical devices. In designing these we asked ourselves the question, "If we were students, what would help us organize and understand the material covered in this chapter?" We chose the following pedagogical supports:

1. **Learning Goals:** Students have the opportunity to preview the material and become aware of the information and ideas that they are expected to learn. These chapter goals are also useful as a self-test after the chapter has been read.

2. **Detailed Chapter Outline:** Topics are divided and subdivided in outline form to help students organize the material in their own minds. These chapter outlines also give the instructor a quick summary of the topics found in the chapter and help to organize lecture material.

3. **Boxed Readings—A "Chemistry Connection":** These beginning essays connect the content of each chapter to an interesting application.

4. **Perspectives** relate the chapter subject matter to the real world. Depending on the nature of the topic, these are called Human, Clinical, Medical, or Environmental Perspectives. The perspectives provide practical and relevant applications of the chemistry covered in the text.

5. **In-Chapter Examples, Solutions, and Problems:** Because problem-solving is most easily learned by example and practice, we have included throughout the text a number of examples that show the student, step-by-step, precisely how to properly determine the correct answer. Whenever possi-

ble, the solved examples are followed by in-text problems that allow the students to test their mastery of the information just covered and to build self-confidence.

6. **In-Chapter and End-of-Chapter Problems:** These include a wide variety of problems. The answers to the odd-numbered questions will be found in the back of the book as reinforcement for students as they develop problem-solving skills. However, students must then be able to apply the same principles to the related even-numbered problem.

7. **Chapter Cross-References:** Often a discussion in the text demands an understanding of key principles and concepts described previously. These cross-references are also used to alert students to upcoming topics that require an understanding of the information currently being studied and help students locate the pertinent background material.

8. **Detailed End-of-Chapter Summary:** These summaries serve as a "mini-study guide." Each covers the major concepts in the chapter.

9. **End-of-Chapter Key Terms:** Each key term is accompanied by the chapter section number so that students can quickly find the definition in the text.

10. **End-of-Chapter Vocabulary Quiz:** There is a set of ten vocabulary review questions at the end of each chapter. These will help students learn the language of chemistry.

11. **End-of-Book Glossary of Key Terms:** All new terms are in boldface and each term is defined in the alphabetized glossary at the end of the textbook.

12. **Appendix Material:** Appendixes have been selected because the information will be useful to students in doing basic work or because they extend information introduced in the chapter.
    Appendix A: Review of Mathematics Applied to Problem-Solving in Chemistry
    Appendix B: Table of Formula Weights
    Appendix C: Stereochemistry and Stereoisomers Revisited
    Appendix D: Lipid-Soluble Vitamins
    Appendix E: Water-Soluble Vitamins
    Appendix F: Minerals and Cellular Function
    Answers to the Odd-Numbered Questions and Problems
    Answers to the Vocabulary Quizzes

13. **Color Coding Scheme:** Because it is difficult for students to understand the chemical changes that occur in complex reactions, we have color coded reactions so that chemical groups being added or removed in a reaction can be quickly and clearly seen. This is particularly useful in the organic and biochemistry chapters.

14. **Illustrations:** Each chapter is amply illustrated using figures, tables, and chemical formulas. All of these illustrations are carefully annotated for clarity.

Supplementary Materials

An extensive supplemental package has been designed to support this text. It includes the following elements.

1. **Instructor's Manual:** The Instructor's Manual contains the printed test item file, solutions to the even-numbered problems, and a list of the transparencies. Written by the authors, this unique ancillary also contains suggestions for organizing lectures, additional "Perspectives," and a list of each chapter's key problems and concepts.

2. **Student's Study Guide/Solutions Manual:** A separate Student's Study Guide/Solution Manual is available. It contains the answers and complete solutions for the odd-numbered problems. It also offers students a variety of exercises and keys for testing their comprehension of basic, as well as difficult, concepts.

3. **Transparencies:** A set of over 100 transparencies is available to help the instructor coordinate the lecture with key illustrations from the text.

4. **Customized Transparency Service:** For those adopters interested in receiving acetates of text figures not included in the standard transparency package, a select number of acetates will be custom made upon request.

5. **Microtest:** This computerized classroom management system/service includes a database of test questions, reproducible student self-quizzes, and a grade-recording program. Disks are available for IBM and Macintosh computers, and require no programming experience.

6. **Laboratory Manual:** Written by Charles H. Henrickson, Larry C. Byrd, and Norman W. Hunter, all of Western Kentucky University, "Experiments in Inorganic, Organic, and Biochemistry," carefully and safely guides students through the process of scientific inquiry. The manual features 26 self-contained experiments that can easily be reorganized to suit individual course needs. In addition, you can delete experiments and/or add your own materials to create a custom manual to fit your students' precise needs.

7. **Laboratory Resource Guide:** This helpful prep guide contains the hints that the authors have learned over the years to ensure student success.

8. **Is Your Math Ready for Chemistry?** Developed by Walter Gleason of Bridgewater State College, this unique booklet provides a diagnostic test that measures your students' math ability. Part II of the booklet provides helpful hints on the necessary math skills needed to successfully complete a chemistry course.

9. **Problem Solving Guide to General Chemistry:** Written by Ronald DeLorenzo of Middle Georgia College, this exceptional supplement provides your students with over 2,500 problems and questions. The guide holds students' interests by integrating the solution of chemistry problems with real-life applications, analogies, and anecdotes.

10. **How to Study Science:** Written by Fred Drewes of Suffolk County Community College, this excellent workbook offers students helpful suggestions for meeting the considerable challenges of a science course. It offers tips on how to take notes and how to overcome science anxiety. The book's unique design helps to stir critical thinking skills, while facilitating careful notetaking on the part of the student.

11. **Exploring Chemistry Video Tapes:** Narrated by Ken Hughes of the University of Wisconsin-Oshkosh, the tapes provide six hours of laboratory demonstrations. Many of the demonstrations are of high interest experiments, too expensive or dangerous to be performed in the typical freshman laboratory.

12. **Doing Chemistry Videodisc:** This critically acclaimed image database contains 136 experiments and demonstrations. It can be used as a prelab demonstration of equipment setup, laboratory techniques, and safety precautions. It may also be used as a substitute for lab experiences for which time or equipment is not available.

13. **ChemTALK Lecture Presentation Software:** This unique presentation software contains lecture outlines and numerous color illustrations and animations designed to bring the basic concepts of chemistry to life. Three software programs have been developed to be used in a variety of introductory courses including general chemistry, preparatory chemistry, and allied health chemistry. The programs are available on both Windows and Macintosh formats. Less cumbersome than writing on a blackboard, this software will allow you to present material to your students at the pace that you choose, while integrating full-color illustrations and animations into your lecture. Students may purchase the corresponding lecture notebook which contains all the material from the software. Using the notebook to follow the lecture, students will spend more time listening and absorbing information.

14. **Student Study Art Notebook:** Free with each new text, the Student Study Art Notebook contains all of the full color art included in the transparency set. The notebook allows students to focus on the lecture rather than trying to recopy art being displayed in class.

Acknowledgments

We are grateful to our families, whose patience and support made it possible for us to undertake this project. We thank our colleagues at Wm. C. Brown Publishers especially our Developmental Editor, John Berns, and our Acquisitions Editor, Megan Johnson. We also thank Molly Kelchen, Editorial Secretary, and Julie Kennedy, Publishing Services Coordinator, who have worked quietly behind the scenes to ensure that the book is both accurate and elegant. Finally we extend our sincere gratitude and appreciation to Mary Jo Gregory of York Production Services. She and her colleagues guided us patiently through the winding paths of textbook publication; they have prodded us gently to meet our deadlines; and, above all, they have always insisted on excellence in the quality of the science, the writing, the artwork, and the overall process of publication.

Johanne Artman
Del Mar College

Tom J. Baldus
Northwest Iowa Community College

John T. Barbas
Valdosta State University

Thomas Berke
Brookdale Community College

Michael J. Collins
Viterbo College, LaCrosse, Wisconsin

Brian E. Cox
Cochise College

Jack L. Dalton
Boise State University

Cheryl Donlon
Northeast Iowa Community College

John Ferrara
Cuyahoga Community College

Patrick Flash
Kent State—Ashtabula Campus

Bill Flurkey
Indiana State University

A. Fredrick Goellner
CCCAC—South Campus

Craig R. Johnson
Carlow College

Betty Klapper
Columbus State Community College

F. H. Kruse
University of Toledo

Stephen L. Monts
Kankakee Community College

Deb Nycz
Broward Community College

Fred Redmore
Highland Community College

Art Serianz
St. Ambrose University

Frank B. Slezak
Mercer County Community College

David Speckhard
Loras College

Justine Walhout
Rockford College

Alan S. Wingrove
Towson State University

1
Chemistry: Methods and Measurement

LEARNING GOALS

◆ Understand the definition of chemistry, and know its major subfields.

◆ Know the approach to science, the scientific method.

◆ Distinguish among the terms *hypothesis, theory,* and *scientific law.*

◆ Know both the differences and relationships between science and technology.

◆ Distinguish between data and results.

◆ Learn the major units of measure in the English and metric systems, and be able to convert from one system to another.

◆ Understand the distinction among the terms *error, accuracy, precision,* and *uncertainty.*

◆ Report data and results using scientific notation and the proper number of significant figures.

◆ Calculate the density of an object from mass and volume data and calculate the specific gravity of an object from its density.

Chance Favors the Prepared Mind

Most of you have chosen a career in medicine because you want to help others. In medicine, helping others means easing pain and suffering by treating or curing diseases. One important part of the practice of medicine involves observation. The physician must carefully observe the patient and listen to his or her description of symptoms to arrive at a preliminary diagnosis. Then appropriate tests must be done to determine whether the diagnosis is correct. During recovery the patient must be carefully observed for changes in behavior or symptoms. These changes are clues that the treatment or medication needs to be modified.

These practices are also important in science. The scientist makes an observation and comes up with a preliminary hypothesis or explanation for the observed phenomenon. Experiments are then carried out to determine whether the hypothesis is correct. When performing the experiment and analyzing the data, the scientist must look for any unexpected results that indicate that the original hypothesis must be modified.

Several important discoveries in medicine and the sciences have arisen from accidental observations. A health care worker or scientist may see something quite unexpected. Whether this results in an important discovery or is ignored depends on the training and preparedness of the observer.

It was Louis Pasteur, a chemist and microbiologist, who said, "Chance favors the prepared mind." In the history of science and medicine there are many examples of individuals who have made important discoveries because they recognized the value of an unexpected observation.

One such example is the use of ultraviolet (UV) light to treat infant jaundice. Infant jaundice is a condition in which the skin and the whites of the eyes appear yellow because of high levels of the bile pigment bilirubin in the blood. Bilirubin is a breakdown product of the oxygen-carrying blood protein hemoglobin. If bilirubin builds up in the body, it can cause brain damage and death. The immature liver of the baby cannot remove the bilirubin.

An observant nurse in England noticed that when jaundiced babies were exposed to sunlight, the jaundice faded. Research based on her observation showed that the UV light changes the bilirubin into another substance that can be excreted. To this day, jaundiced newborns are treated with UV light.

The Pap smear test for the early detection of cervical and uterine cancer was also developed because of an accidental observation. Dr. George Papanicolaou, affectionately called Dr. Pap, was studying changes in the cells of the vagina during the stages of the menstrual cycle. In one sample he recognized cells that looked like cancer cells. Within five years, Dr. Pap had perfected a technique for staining cells from vaginal fluid and observing them microscopically for the presence of any abnormal cells. The lives of countless women have been saved because a routine Pap smear showed early stages of cancer.

In this first chapter of your study of chemistry you will learn more about the importance of observation and accurate, precise measurement in medical practice and scientific study. You will also study the scientific method, the process of developing hypotheses to explain observations, and the design of experiments to test those hypotheses.

INTRODUCTION

When you awoke this morning, a flood of chemicals called neurotransmitters were sent from cell to cell in your nervous system. As these chemical signals accumulated, you gradually became aware of your surroundings. Chemical signals from your nerves to your muscles propelled you out of your warm bed to prepare for your day.

For breakfast you had a glass of milk, two eggs, and buttered toast, thus providing your body with needed molecules in the form of carbohydrates, proteins, lipids, vitamins, and minerals. As you ran out the door, enzymes of your digestive tract were dismantling the macromolecules of your breakfast. Other enzymes in your cells were busy converting the chemical energy of food molecules into ATP (adenosine triphosphate), the universal energy currency of all cells.

As you continue through your day, thousands of biochemical reactions will keep your cells functioning optimally. Hormones and other chemical signals will regulate the conditions within your body. They will let you know if you are hungry or thirsty. If you injure yourself or come into contact with a disease-causing microorganism, chemicals in your body will signal cells to begin the necessary repair or defense processes.

Life is an organized array of large, carbon-based molecules maintained by biochemical reactions. To understand and appreciate the nature of a living being, we must understand the principles of science and chemistry as they apply to biological molecules.

Chemistry has been described as the "central science." In this chapter we will learn how science works and see how chemistry and the other sciences are related.

1.1 CHEMISTRY: AN OVERVIEW

Definition of chemistry

Chemistry is the study of matter and the changes that matter undergoes. **Matter** is anything that has mass and occupies space. The changes that matter undergoes always involve either gain or loss of energy. **Energy** is nonmaterial and is the ability to do work to accomplish some change.

The study of chemistry involves matter, energy, and their interrelationship. Matter and energy are at the heart of chemistry.

Major areas of chemistry

Chemistry is a broad area of study covering everything from the basic parts of an atom to interactions between huge biological molecules. Because of this, chemistry encompasses the following specialties.

Biochemistry is the study of life at the molecular level and the processes associated with life, such as reproduction, growth, and respiration. **Organic chemistry** is the study of matter that is composed principally of carbon and hydrogen. Organic chemists study methods of preparing such diverse substances as plastics, drugs, solvents, and a host of industrial chemicals. **Inorganic chemistry** is the study of matter that consists of all of the elements other than carbon and hydrogen and their combination. Inorganic chemists have been responsible for the development of unique substances such as semiconductors and high-temperature ceramics for industrial use. **Analytical chemistry** involves the analysis of matter to determine its composition and the quantity of each kind of matter that is present. Analytical chemists detect traces of toxic chemicals in water and air. They also develop methods to analyze human body fluids for drugs, poisons, and levels of medication. **Physical chemistry** is a discipline that attempts to explain the way in which matter behaves. Physical chemists develop theoretical concepts and try to prove them experimentally. This helps us understand how chemical systems behave.

1.2 THE METHODOLOGY

The scientific method

How do we learn about the properties of matter, the way it behaves in nature, and how it can be modified to make useful products? Chemists do this by using the **scientific method** to study the way in which matter changes under carefully controlled conditions.

The scientific method is not a "cookbook recipe" that, if followed faithfully, will yield new discoveries; rather, it is an organized approach to solving scientific problems. Every scientist brings his or her own curiosity, creativity, and imagination to scientific study. But scientific inquiry still involves some of the "cookbook approach." For example, in the laboratory you may use a procedure that was developed by others to measure certain physical properties of matter, such as measuring the density of urine to determine the amount of sugar present. By doing this, you are applying part of the scientific method.

The scientific method consists of five processes:

1. *Observation.* The description of the color, taste, or odor of a substance is a result of observation. The measurement of the temperature of a liquid or the size or mass of a solid results from observation.

2. *Pattern recognition.* If a scientist finds a cause-and-effect relationship, it may be the basis of a generalized explanation of substances and their behavior.

3. *Developing theories.* When scientists observe a phenomenon, they want to explain it. The process of explaining observed behavior begins with a **hypothesis,** which is an educated guess. If many experiments show that this hypothesis is true, it may attain the status of a theory. A **theory** is a hypothesis supported by testing (experimentation) that explains scientific facts and can predict new facts.

4. *Experimentation.* Proving that theories are correct is the heart of the scientific method. This is done by carrying out carefully designed experiments that will either prove or disprove the theory or hypothesis.

5. *Summarizing information.* A scientific **law** is nothing more than the summary of a large quantity of information. For example, the law of conservation of matter states that matter cannot be created or destroyed, only converted from one form to another. This statement represents a massive quantity of chemical information gathered from experiments.

The discovery of penicillin by Alexander Fleming is an example of the scientific method at work. Fleming was studying the growth of bacteria. One day, his experiment was ruined because colonies of mold were growing on his plates. From this failed experiment, Fleming made an observation that would change the practice of medicine: Bacterial colonies could not grow in the area around the mold colonies. Fleming hypothesized that the mold was making a chemical compound that inhibited the growth of the bacteria. He performed a series of experiments designed to test this hypothesis.

The key to the scientific method is the design of carefully controlled experiments that will either prove or disprove the hypothesis. This is exactly what Fleming did.

> A properly designed experiment looks at only one variable at a time. To ensure this, a second experiment, the control, is also performed. This experiment is identical to the first in every way but one: The variable being studied is not present. So if the results of the two experiments differ, the difference must be due to the variable. In Fleming's experiment, the variable was the culture of mold cells.

In one experiment he used two sets of tubes containing sterile nutrient broth. To one set he added mold cells. The second set (the control tubes) remained sterile. The mold was allowed to grow for several days. Then the broth from each of the tubes (experimental and control) were passed through a filter to remove any mold cells. Next, bacteria were placed in each tube. If Fleming was correct, the tubes in which the mold had grown would contain the chemical that inhibits growth, and the bacteria would not grow. On the other hand, the control tubes (which were never used to grow mold) would allow bacterial growth. This is exactly what Fleming observed.

Within a few years this *antibiotic,* penicillin, was being used to treat bacterial infections in patients.

Another example of the scientific method is Isaac Newton's discovery of the theory of gravity in 1687. According to the story, Newton saw an apple fall from a tree while having tea in the garden. From this observation he developed a cause-and-effect relationship: There is a universal attractive force between bodies. He called this force *gravity.* His experiments and calculations proved his hypothesis. It became the *theory* of gravitational attraction, and centuries of experiments have supported this theory. We now call Newton's observed relationship *the law of gravity.* A **law** is a statement of observed behavior for which no exceptions have been found. It summarizes the similar behavior of all matter.

The scientific method involves the interactive use of hypotheses, development of theories, and thorough testing of theories using well-designed experiments. The approach is summarized in Figure 1.1.

FIGURE 1.1
The scientific method, an organized way of doing science. A degree of trial and error is apparent here. If experimentation does not support the hypothesis, one must begin the cycle again.

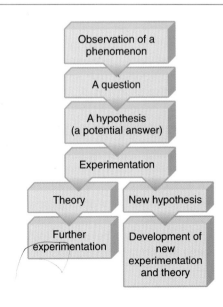

Hypotheses, theories, and laws are frequently expressed by using mathematical equations. These equations may confuse all but the best of mathematicians. For this reason a *model* of a chemical unit or system is often used to make ideas more clear. A good model based on everyday experience, although imperfect, gives a great deal of information in a simple fashion. Consider the fundamental unit of methane, the major component of natural gas, which is composed of one carbon atom (symbolized by C) and four hydrogen atoms (symbolized by H).

A geometrically correct model of methane can be constructed from balls and sticks. The balls represent the individual units (atoms) of hydrogen and carbon, and the sticks correspond to the attractive forces that hold the hydrogen and carbon together. The model consists of four balls representing hydrogen symmetrically arranged around a center ball, representing carbon. The "carbon" ball is attached to each "hydrogen" ball by sticks, as seen below:

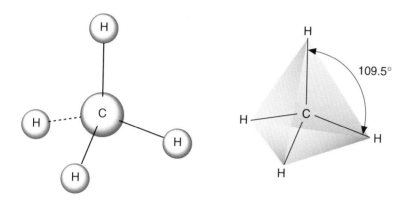

Color-coding the balls distinguishes one type of matter from another; all of the angles and dimensions of a tetrahedron, the geometrical form of the model, are the same for each methane unit found in nature. Methane is certainly not a collection of balls and sticks; but such models are valuable because they help us understand the chemical behavior of methane and other, more complex substances.

Science and technology

The development of the scientific method has played a major role in the rapid growth of civilization in the last two centuries. In fact, more profound changes have occurred in the short period of time since the Industrial Revolution in eighteenth century Europe than in all of previous history. It is true that the human race had achieved a certain level of sophistication in its earlier history. Fire, the wheel, manufacturing of tools and weapons from metals, and tanning of hides for protective clothing are prominent examples. In later times the process of photography was developed without any real understanding of the chemical process. However, this technological progress was slow and sporadic without science to aid in the understanding of the underlying principles.

Technology is the conversion of a material or information from its current form to a more useful form. Many would describe technology as *applied science,* the use of scientific principles to meet human needs. For example, a few drops of petroleum may be converted into a life-saving drug. Some do not view all technological conversions as "more useful." Is the paper used for advertising "more useful" than the tree from which it was made? All of these processes do, however, fulfill some human need.

Clearly, science breeds technology with both its benefits and its potential dangers. For example, Enrico Fermi's discovery that the atom could be "split," producing enormous amounts of energy, has given rise to clearly beneficial applications (nuclear radiation used as a treatment for cancer) as well as developments that pose serious threats to society (nuclear arms). Many spinoffs of the space program are in routine use today; flame-resistant materials, voice-controlled wheelchairs, reading machines for the blind, solar energy devices, and portable X-ray units are only a few of the technological rewards of this scientific venture.

1.3 DATA, RESULTS, AND UNITS

A scientific experiment produces **data.** Each piece of data is the individual result of a single measurement or observation. Examples include the *mass* of a sample and the *time* required for a chemical reaction to occur. Mass, length, volume, time, temperature, and energy are common types of data obtained from chemical experiments.

Results are the outcome of an experiment. Data and results may be identical, but more often several pieces of data are combined, and reason is used to produce a result.

EXAMPLE 1.1

Distinguishing between Data and Results

In many cases, a drug is less stable if moisture is present, and excess moisture can hasten the breakdown of the active ingredient, leading to loss of potency. Therefore we may wish to know how much water a certain quantity of a drug gains when exposed to air. To do this experiment, we must first weigh the drug sample, then expose it to the air for a period of time and reweigh it. The change in weight,

$$[\text{weight}_{final} - \text{weight}_{initial}] = \text{weight difference}$$

indicates the weight of water taken up by the drug formulation. The initial and final weights are individual bits of *data;* by themselves they do not answer the question, but they do provide the information necessary to calculate the answer: the results. The difference in weight and the conclusions based on the observed change in weight are the *results* of the experiment.

The experiment described in the above example was really not a very good experiment because there were many other environmental conditions that were not measured. Measurement of the temperature and humidity of the atmosphere and the length of time that the drug was exposed to the air (the creation of a more complete set of data) would make the results less ambiguous.

Any measurement made in the experiment must also specify the units of that measurement. An initial weight of 3 *ounces* is clearly quite different than 3 *pounds*. A **unit** defines the basic quantity of mass, volume, time, or whatever quantity is being measured. A number that is not followed by the correct unit usually conveys no useful information.

1.4 MEASUREMENT IN CHEMISTRY

English and metric units

In the *English system of measurement* the standard *pound* (lb) is the basic unit of weight. The fundamental unit of *length* is the standard *yard* (yd), and the basic unit of *volume* is the standard *gallon* (gal). The English system is used in the United States in business and industry. However, it is not used in scientific work, primarily because it is difficult to convert from one unit to another. For example,

$$1 \text{ foot} = 12 \text{ inches} = 0.33 \text{ yard} = \frac{1}{5280} \text{ mile} = \frac{1}{6} \text{ fathom}$$

Clearly, operations such as the conversion of 1.62 yards to inches are not easily done. In fact, the English ''system'' is not really a system at all. It is simply a collection of measures accumulated throughout English history. Since they have no functional relationship, it is not surprising that conversion from one unit to another is not straightforward.

The United States, the last major industrial country to retain the English system, has now begun efforts to convert totally to the metric system. Since the *metric system* is a decimal-based system, it is inherently simpler to use and less ambiguous. For example, the length of an object may be represented as

$$1 \text{ meter} = 10 \text{ decimeters} = 100 \text{ centimeters} = 1000 \text{ millimeters}$$

No arithmetic is needed! Only the decimal point moves in the conversion from one unit to another.

TABLE 1.1 Some Common Prefixes Used in the Metric System

Prefix	Multiple	Decimal Equivalent
mega (M)	10^6	1,000,000.
kilo (k)	10^3	1,000.
deka (da)	10^1	10.
deci (d)	10^{-1}	0.1
centi (c)	10^{-2}	0.01
milli (m)	10^{-3}	0.001
micro (μ)	10^{-6}	0.000001
nano (n)	10^{-9}	0.000000001

The metric system was originally developed in France just before the French Revolution in 1789. The modern version of this system is the *Système International,* or *S.I. system.* Although the S.I. system has been in existence for over 40 years, it has yet to gain widespread acceptance. To make the S.I. system truly systematic, it utilizes certain units, especially those for pressure, that many find difficult to use.

In this text we will use the metric system, not the S.I. system, and we will use the English system only to the extent of converting *from* it to the more scientifically useful metric system.

In the metric system there are three basic units. Mass is represented as the *gram,* length as the *meter,* and volume as the *liter.* Any subunit or multiple unit contains one of these units preceded by a prefix indicating the power of ten by which the base unit is to be multiplied to form the subunit or multiple unit. The most common metric prefixes are shown in Table 1.1.

The same prefix may be used for volume, mass, length, time, and so forth. Consider the following examples:

$$1 \text{ milliliter (mL)} = \frac{1}{1000} \text{ liter} = 0.001 \text{ liter} = 10^{-3} \text{ liter}$$

Appendix A

or

$$1 \text{ microliter (}\mu\text{L)} = \frac{1}{1,000,000} \text{ liter} = 0.000001 \text{ liter} = 10^{-6} \text{ liter}$$

A volume unit is indicated by the base unit, liter, and the prefix milli-, which indicates that the unit is one thousandth of the base unit, or micro-, which indicates that the unit is one millionth of the base unit. In the same way,

$$1 \text{ milligram (mg)} = \frac{1}{1000} \text{ gram} = 0.001 \text{ gram} = 10^{-3} \text{ gram}$$

or

$$1 \text{ microgram (}\mu\text{g)} = \frac{1}{1,000,000} \text{ gram} = 0.000001 \text{ gram} = 10^{-6} \text{ gram}$$

and

$$1 \text{ millimeter (mm)} = \frac{1}{1000} \text{ meter} = 0.001 \text{ meter} = 10^{-3} \text{ meter}$$

or

$$1 \text{ micrometer (}\mu\text{m)} = \frac{1}{1,000,000} \text{ meter} = 0.000001 \text{ meter} = 10^{-6} \text{ meter}$$

Additionally,

$$1 \text{ kilogram (kg)} = 1000 \text{ grams} = 10^3 \text{ grams}$$

and

$$1 \text{ decigram (dg)} = \frac{1}{10} \text{ gram} = 0.1 \text{ gram} = 10^{-1} \text{ gram}$$

Other measurements can be treated in the same way; for example, a millisecond is $\frac{1}{1000}$ of a second, and so forth.

Unit conversion: English and metric systems

To convert from one unit to another, we must have a **conversion factor** or series of conversion factors that relate two units. The proper use of these conversion factors is called the *factor-label method*.

This method is used for two kinds of conversions: to convert from one unit to another within the *same system* or to convert units from *one system to another*.

Conversion of units within the same system

We know, for example, that in the English system,

$$1 \text{ gallon} = 4 \text{ quarts}$$

Since dividing both sides of the equation by the same term does not change its identity,

$$\frac{1 \text{ gallon}}{1 \text{ gallon}} = \frac{4 \text{ quarts}}{1 \text{ gallon}}$$

The expression on the left is equal to unity (1); therefore

$$1 = \frac{4 \text{ quarts}}{1 \text{ gallon}} \quad \text{or} \quad \frac{1 \text{ gallon}}{4 \text{ quarts}}$$

Now, multiplying any other expression by the ratio 4 quarts/1 gallon will not change the value of the term, because multiplication of any number by 1 produces the original value. However, there is one important difference: The units will have changed.

EXAMPLE 1.2

Using Conversion Factors

Convert 8 gallons to units of quarts.

Solution

$$8 \text{ gal} \times \frac{4 \text{ qt}}{1 \text{ gal}} = 32 \text{ qt}$$

The conversion factor, (4 qt/1 gal), serves as a bridge, or linkage, between the unit that was given (gallons) and the unit that was sought (quarts).

The conversion factor in Example 1.2 may be written as 4 qt/1 gal or 1 gal/4 qt, since both are equal to 1. However, only the first factor, (4 qt/1 gal), will give us the units we need to solve the problem. If we had set up the problem incorrectly, we would get

$$8 \text{ gal} \times \frac{1 \text{ gal}}{4 \text{ qt}} = 2 \frac{\text{gal}^2}{\text{qt}}$$

Incorrect units

Clearly, units of gal²/qt are not those asked for in the problem, nor are they reasonable units. The factor-label method is therefore a self-indicating system; the correct units (those required by the problem) will result only if the factor is set up properly.

Table 1.2 lists a variety of commonly used English system relationships that may serve as the basis for useful conversion factors.

TABLE 1.2 Some Common Relationships Used in the English System

A. Weight	1 pound = 16 ounces
	1 ton = 2000 pounds
B. Length	1 foot = 12 inches
	1 yard = 3 feet
	1 mile = 5280 feet
C. Volume	1 gallon = 4 quarts
	1 quart = 2 pints
	1 quart = 32 fluid ounces

Conversion of units within the metric system may be accomplished by using the factor-label method as well. Unit prefixes that dictate the conversion factor facilitate unit conversion (refer to Table 1.1).

EXAMPLE 1.3

Using Conversion Factors

Convert 10 centimeters to meters.

Solution

First, recognize that the prefix *centi-* means $\frac{1}{100}$ of the base unit, the meter. Thus our conversion factor is either

$$\frac{1 \text{ meter}}{100 \text{ cm}} \quad or \quad \frac{100 \text{ cm}}{1 \text{ meter}}$$

each being equal to 1. Only one, however, will result in proper cancellation of units, producing the correct answer to the problem. If we proceed as follows:

$$10 \cancel{\text{ cm}} \times \frac{1 \text{ meter}}{100 \cancel{\text{ cm}}} = 0.10 \text{ meter}$$

Data given	Conversion factor	Desired result

we obtain the desired units, meters (m). If we had used the conversion factor 100 cm/1 m, the answer would have been incorrect:

$$10 \text{ cm} \times \frac{100 \text{ cm}}{1 \text{ m}} = 1000 \frac{\text{cm}^2}{\text{m}}$$

Incorrect units

The units are meaningless.

QUESTION 1.1

Convert 1 liter to each of the following units, using the factor-label method:

a. milliliters

b. microliters

c. kiloliters

d. centiliters

e. dekaliters

Convert 1 gram to each of the following units:

a. micrograms
b. milligrams
c. kilograms
d. centigrams
e. decigrams

Conversion of units from one system to another

The conversion of a quantity expressed in units of one system to an equivalent quantity in the other system (English to metric or metric to English) requires a *bridging* conversion unit. For example:

Quantity	English		Metric
Mass	1 pound	=	454 grams
	2.2 pounds	=	1 kilogram
Length	1 inch	=	2.54 centimeters
	1 yard	=	0.91 meter
Volume	1 quart	=	0.946 liter
	1 gallon	=	3.78 liters

English and metric conversions are shown in Tables 1.1 and 1.2.

The conversion may be represented as a three-step process:

1. Conversion from the units given in the problem to a bridging unit.
2. Conversion to the other system using the bridge.
3. Conversion within the desired system to units required by the problem.

EXAMPLE 1.4

Using Conversion Factors Between Systems

Convert 4.00 ounces to kilograms.

Solution

Step 1. A convenient bridging unit for mass is 1 lb = 454 grams. To use this conversion factor, we relate ounces (given in the problem) to pounds:

$$4.00 \; \text{ounces} \times \frac{1 \text{ pound}}{16 \text{ ounces}} = 0.250 \text{ pound}$$

Step 2. Using the bridging unit conversion, we get

$$0.250 \; \text{pound} \times \frac{454 \text{ grams}}{1 \text{ pound}} = 114 \text{ grams}$$

Step 3. Grams may then be directly converted to kilograms, the desired unit:

$$114 \; \text{grams} \times \frac{1 \text{ kilogram}}{1000 \text{ grams}} = 0.114 \text{ kilogram}$$

The calculation may also be done in a single step by arranging the factors in a chain:

$$4.00 \; \text{oz} \times \frac{1 \text{ lb}}{16 \text{ oz}} \times \frac{454 \text{ g}}{1 \text{ lb}} \times \frac{1 \text{ kg}}{1000 \text{ g}} = 0.114 \text{ kg}$$

QUESTION 1.3

a. Convert 0.50 inch to meters.

b. Convert 0.75 quart to liters.

c. Convert 56.8 grams to ounces.

QUESTION 1.4

a. Convert 0.50 inch to centimeters.

b. Convert 0.75 quart to milliliters.

c. Convert 56.8 milligrams to ounces.

Error is the difference between the true value and our estimation, or measurement, of the value. **Accuracy** is the degree of agreement between the true value and the measured value. **Uncertainty** is the degree of doubt in a single measurement.

Only discrete quantities, such as the number of pages in this book or the number of quarters in your pocket, can be measured with perfect certainty. For example, there are 50 pages in your notebook, *exactly* 50, not $50\frac{1}{2}$ or $49\frac{1}{2}$. In measuring quantities that show continuous variation, for example, the weight of this page or the volume of one of your quarters, some doubt or uncertainty is present because the answer cannot be expressed with an infinite number of meaningful digits. The number of meaningful digits is determined by the measuring device. The presence of some error is a natural consequence of any measurement.

Simply dividing $\frac{2}{3}$ can produce a variety of answers that depend on the device used to perform the calculation: pencil and paper, calculator, computer. The answer might be

0.67

0.667

0.6667

and so forth. All are correct, but each value has a different level of uncertainty. The first number listed, 0.67, has the greatest uncertainty.

It is always best to measure a quantity several times. Modern scientific instruments are designed to perform measurements rapidly; this allows many more measurements to be completed in a reasonable time period. Replicate measurements of the same quantity minimize the uncertainty of the result. **Precision** is a measure of the agreement of replicate measurements.

It is important to recognize that accuracy and precision are not the same thing. It is possible to have one without the other. However, when scientific measurements are carefully made, the two most often go hand in hand; high-quality data are characterized by high levels of precision and accuracy.

In Figure 1.2, bullseye (a) shows the goal of all experimentation: accuracy *and* precision. Bullseye (b) shows the results to be repeatable (good precision); however, some error in the experimental procedure has caused the results to center on an incorrect value. This error is consistent, occurring in each replicate measurement. Occasionally, an experiment may show ''accidental'' accuracy. The precision is poor, but the average of these replicate measurements leads to a correct value. We don't want to rely on accidental success; this experiment should be repeated until the precision inspires faith in the accuracy of the method. Modern measuring devices in chemistry, equipped with powerful computers with immense storage capacity, are capable of making literally thousands of individual replicate measurements to enhance the quality of the result. Bullseye (c) describes the most common situation. A low level of precision is all-too-often associated with poor accuracy.

1.5 ERROR, ACCURACY, PRECISION, AND UNCERTAINTY

FIGURE 1.2
An illustration of precision and accuracy in replicate experiments

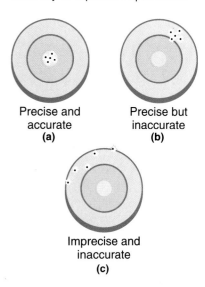

Precise and accurate
(a)

Precise but inaccurate
(b)

Imprecise and inaccurate
(c)

1.6 SIGNIFICANT FIGURES AND SCIENTIFIC NOTATION

Data and results arising from a scientific experiment convey information about the way in which the experiment was conducted. The degree of uncertainty or doubt associated with a measurement or series of measurements is indicated by the number of figures used to represent the information.

Significant figures

Consider the following situation: A student was asked to obtain the length of a section of wire. In the chemistry laboratory, several different types of measuring devices are usually available. Not knowing which was most appropriate, the student decided to measure the object using each device that was available in the laboratory. The following data were obtained:

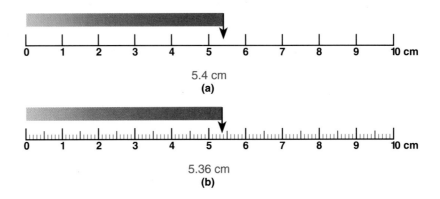

5.4 cm

(a)

5.36 cm

(b)

Two questions should immediately come to mind:

Are the two answers equivalent?

If not, which answer is correct?

In fact, the two answers are *not* equivalent, but *both* are correct. How do we explain this apparent contradiction?

The data are not equivalent because each is known to a different degree of certainty. The answer, 5.36 cm, containing three significant figures, specifies the length of the object more exactly than 5.4 cm, which contains only two significant figures. The term **significant figures** is defined to be all digits in a number representing data or results that are known with certainty *plus the first uncertain digit.*

In case (a) we are certain that the object is at least 5 cm long and equally certain that it is *not* 6 cm long because the end of the object falls between the calibration lines 5 and 6. We can only estimate between 5 and 6, since there are no calibration indicators between 5 and 6. The end of the wire appears to be approximately four tenths of the way between 5 and 6, hence 5.4 cm. The 5 is known with certainty, and 4 is estimated; there are two significant figures.

In case (b) the ruler is calibrated in tenths of centimeters. The end of the wire is at least 5.3 cm and not 5.4 cm. Estimation of the second decimal place between the two closest calibration marks leads to 5.36 cm. In this case, 5.3 is certain, and the 6 is estimated (or uncertain), leading to three significant digits.

Both answers are correct because each is consistent with the measuring device used to generate the data. An answer of 5.36 cm obtained from a measurement using ruler (a) would be *incorrect* because the measuring device is not capable of that exact specification. On the other hand, a value of 5.4 cm obtained from ruler (b) would be erroneous as well; in that case the measuring device is capable of generating a higher level of certainty (more significant digits) than are actually reported.

In summary, the number of significant figures associated with a measurement is determined by the measuring device. Conversely, the number of significant figures reported is an indication of the sophistication of the measurement itself.

Only *significant* digits should be reported as data or results. However, are all digits, as written, significant digits? Let's look at a few examples.

Recognition of significant figures

EXAMPLE 1.5

7.314 has *four* significant digits.

RULE: All nonzero digits are significant. ▪

EXAMPLE 1.6

73.14 has *four* significant digits.

RULE: The number of significant digits is independent of the position of the decimal point. ▪

EXAMPLE 1.7

60.052 has *five* significant figures.

RULE: Zeros located between nonzero digits are significant. ▪

EXAMPLE 1.8

4.70 has *three* significant figures.

RULE: Zeros at the end of a number (often referred to as trailing zeros) are significant if the number contains a decimal point. ▪

EXAMPLE 1.9

100 has *one* significant figure.

RULE: Trailing zeros are insignificant because the number does not contain a decimal point. ▪

EXAMPLE 1.10

0.0032 has *two* significant figures.

RULE: Zeros to the left of the first nonzero integer are not significant; they serve only to locate the position of the decimal point. ▪

QUESTION 1.5

How many significant figures are contained in each of the following numbers?

a. 7.26   3
b. 726   3
c. 700.2   4
d. 7.0   2
e. 0.0720   3

> **QUESTION 1.6**
>
> How many significant figures are contained in each of the following numbers?
>
> a.   0.042   *two*
>
> b.   4.20   3
>
> c.   24.0   3
>
> d.   240   2
>
> e.   204   3

Scientific notation

Appendix A

It is often difficult to express very large numbers to the proper number of significant figures using conventional notation. Consider the number fifteen thousand, which might have resulted from a measurement capable of generating three significant figures. Writing the number in a conventional fashion as 15,000. (note the presence of a decimal point) shows five digits that, if written, must be assumed to be significant. Alternatively, writing 15,000 (no decimal point) indicates only two significant figures. How can we express such a number using only the desired number (in this case, three) of significant figures? The solution lies in the use of **scientific notation,** also referred to as *exponential notation,* which involves the representation of a number as a power of ten.

If we consider the number 15,000, it is equivalent to 15×1000 which is also 15×10^3. In fact 15,000 could be represented as

$$15,000 \times 10^0$$

$$1500 \quad \times 10^1 \quad \text{(decimal moved *one* place to the left)}$$

$$150 \quad \times 10^2 \quad \text{(decimal moved *two* places to the left)}$$

$$15 \quad \times 10^3 \quad \text{(decimal moved *three* places to the left)}$$

$$1.5 \quad \times 10^4 \quad \text{(decimal moved *four* places to the left)}$$

All appear to be correct; however, when we superimpose our initial requirement that the data point, fifteen thousand, has three significant figures, 15.0×10^3 or 1.50×10^4 is the logical choice. 1.50×10^4 would be preferred; the usual convention shows the decimal point in standard position—to the right of the leading digit.

RULE: To convert a number greater than 1 to scientific notation, the original decimal point is moved x places to the left, and the resulting number is multiplied by 10^x. The exponent (x) is a *positive* number equal to the number of places the original decimal point was moved. ■

Scientific notation is also useful in representing numbers less than 1. For example, the mass of a single helium atom is

$$0.00000000000000000000000006692 \text{ gram}$$

a rather cumbersome number as written. Scientific notation would represent the mass of a single helium atom as 6.692×10^{-24} gram. The conversion is illustrated by using a simpler number:

$$0.0062 = 6.2 \times \frac{1}{1000} = 6.2 \times \frac{1}{10^3} = 6.2 \times 10^{-3}$$

or

$$0.0534 = 5.34 \times \frac{1}{100} = 5.34 \times \frac{1}{10^2} = 5.34 \times 10^{-2}$$

RULE: To convert a number less than 1 to scientific notation, the original decimal point is moved x places to the right, and the resulting number is multiplied by 10^{-x}. The exponent ($-x$) is a *negative* number equal to the number of places the original decimal point was moved. ■

QUESTION 1.7

Represent each of the following numbers in the most proper form, using scientific notation to show only significant digits:

a. 0.0024 24×10^{-3}

b. 0.0180 180×10^{-2}

c. 224

QUESTION 1.8

Represent each of the following numbers in the most proper form, using scientific notation to show only significant digits:

a. 48.20 4820×10^{2}

b. 480.0 480×10^{1}

c. 0.126 126×10^{-1}

Addition and subtraction

If we combine the following numbers:

$$37.68 \quad \text{liters}$$

$$108.428 \quad \text{liters}$$

$$6.71862 \quad \text{liters}$$

our calculator will show a final result of

$$152.82662 \quad \text{liters}$$

Clearly, the answer, with eight digits, defines the volume of total material much more accurately than *any* of the individual quantities being combined. This cannot be correct; *the answer cannot have greater significance than any of the quantities that produced the answer.* We rewrite the problem:

$$
\begin{array}{ll}
37.68xxx & \text{liters} \\
108.428xx & \text{liters} \\
+ \quad 6.71862 & \text{liters} \\
\hline
152.82662 & \text{(should be 152.83) liters}
\end{array}
$$

where x = no information; x may be any integer from 0 to 9. Adding 2 to two unknown numbers (in the right column) produces no information. Similar logic prevails for the next two columns. Thus five digits remain, all of which are significant. Conventional rules for rounding off would dictate a final answer of 152.83.

QUESTION 1.9

Report the result of each of the following to the proper number of significant figures:

a. $4.26 + 3.831 = 8.09$

b. $8.321 - 2.4 =$

c. $16.262 + 4.33 - 0.40 =$

QUESTION 1.10

Report the result of each of the following to the proper number of significant figures:

a. $7.939 + 6.26 =$

b. $2.4 - 8.321 =$

c. $2.333 + 1.56 - 0.29 =$

Significant figures in calculation of results

Remember the distinction between the words *zero* and *nothing*. *Zero* is one of the ten digits and conveys as much information as 1, 2, and so forth. *Nothing* implies no information; the digits in the positions indicated by x's could be 0, 1, 2, or any other.

Multiplication and division

In the above discussion of addition and subtraction the position of the decimal point in the quantities being combined has a bearing on the number of significant figures in the answer. In multiplication and division this is not the case. The decimal point position is irrelevant. It is the number of significant figures that is important. Consider

$$\frac{4.237 \times 1.21 \times 10^{-3} \times 0.00273}{11.125} = 1.26 \times 10^{-6}$$

The answer is limited to three significant figures; the answer can have *only* three significant figures because two numbers in the calculation, 1.21×10^{-3} and 0.00273, have three significant figures and ''limit'' the answer. Remember, *the answer can be no more precise than the* least *precise number from which the answer is derived.*

QUESTION 1.11

Report the results of each of the following operations using the proper number of significant figures:

a. $63.8 \times 0.80 =$ 51.0

b. $\dfrac{63.8}{0.80} =$ 79.6

c. $\dfrac{53.8 \times 0.90}{0.3025} =$ 160

QUESTION 1.12

Report the results of each of the following operations using the proper number of significant figures:

a. $\dfrac{27.2 \times 15.63}{1.84} =$

b. $\dfrac{13.6}{18.02 \times 1.6} =$

c. $\dfrac{12.24 \times 6.2}{18.02 \times 1.6} =$

Appendix A

Exponents

Now consider the determination of the proper number of significant digits in the results when a value is multiplied by any power of ten. In each case the number of significant figures in the answer is identical to the number contained in the original term. Therefore

$$(8.314 \times 10^2)^3 = 574.7 \times 10^6 = 5.747 \times 10^8$$

and

$$(8.314 \times 10^2)^{1/2} = 2.883 \times 10^1$$

Section 1.8

Each answer contains four significant figures.

It is important to note, in operating with significant figures, that defined or counted numbers do *not* determine the number of significant figures. Two examples follow:

1 pen costs \$1.98. What is the cost of 4 pens?

$$4 \text{ pens} \times \frac{\$1.98}{1 \text{ pen}} = \$7.92 \quad \text{(3 significant figures)}$$

4 is a counted, hence an exact, number. The \$1.98 determines the number of significant digits.

If you purchased these four pens in a store, you would feel cheated if you were required to pay \$8 (1 significant figure) rather than \$7.92 (3 significant figures).

Also,

How many grams are contained in 0.240 kg?

$$0.240 \text{ kg} \times \frac{1000 \text{ g}}{1 \text{ g}} = 240 \text{ g}$$

The "1" in the conversion factor is defined, or exact, and does not limit the number of significant digits.

A good rule of thumb to follow: The quantity being converted, not the conversion factor, determines the number of significant figures.

Rounding off numbers

The use of an electronic calculator generally produces more digits for a result than are justified by the rules of significant figures on the basis of the data input. For example, on your calculator,

$$3.84 \times 6.72 = 25.8048$$

The most correct answer would be 25.8, dropping 048.

The generally accepted rule for rounding off states that if the first digit dropped is 5 or greater, we raise the last significant digit to the next higher number. If the first digit dropped is 4 or less, the last significant digit remains unchanged.

EXAMPLE 1.11

Round Each of the Following to Three Significant Figures

Solution

a. 63.6$\underline{69}$ becomes 63.7. *Rationale:* 6 > 5.
b. 8.77$\underline{15}$ becomes 8.77. *Rationale:* 1 < 5.
c. 2.22$\underline{45}$ becomes 2.22. *Rationale:* 4 < 5.
d. 0.00041$\underline{09}$ becomes 0.000411. *Rationale:* 9 > 5.

Symbol $x > y$ implies "x greater than y."
Symbol $x < y$ implies "x less than y."

QUESTION 1.13

Round off each of the following numbers to three significant figures.

a. 61.40   61.4
b. 6.171   6.17
c. 0.066494   0.066

QUESTION 1.14

Round off each of the following numbers to three significant figures.

a. 6.2262   6.23
b. 3895   390
c. 6.885   6.89

Thus far we have discussed the scientific method and its role in acquiring data and converting the data to obtain the results of the experiment. We have seen that such data must be reported in the proper units with the appropriate number of significant figures. The quantities that are most often determined include mass, length, volume, time, temperature, and energy. Now let's look at each of these quantities in more detail.

1.7 EXPERIMENTAL QUANTITIES

Mass

Mass describes the quantity of matter in an object. The terms *weight* and *mass,* in common usage, are often considered synonymous. They are not, in fact. **Weight** is the force of gravity on an object:

$$\text{Weight} = \text{mass} \times \text{acceleration due to gravity}$$

When gravity is constant, mass and weight are directly proportional. But gravity is not constant; it varies as a function of the distance from the center of the earth. Therefore weight cannot be used for scientific measurement because the weight of an object may vary from one place on the earth to the next.

Mass, on the other hand, is independent of gravity; it is a result of a comparison of an unknown mass with a known mass called a *standard mass.* Balances are instruments used to measure the mass of materials.

Examples of common balances used for the determination of mass are shown in Figure 1.3. The common conversion units for mass are as follows:

$$1 \text{ gram (g)} = 1 \times 10^{-3} \text{ kilogram (kg)} = \frac{1}{454} \text{ pound (lb)}$$

In chemistry, in talking about incredibly small bits of matter such as individual atoms or molecules, units such as grams and even micrograms are much too large. We don't say that a 100-pound individual weighs 0.0500 ton; the unit does not fit the quantity being described. Similarly, an atom of a substance such as hydrogen is very tiny. Its mass is only 1.66×10^{-24} gram.

One *atomic mass unit* (**amu**) is a more convenient way to represent the mass of one hydrogen atom, rather than 1.66×10^{-24} gram:

$$1 \text{ amu} = 1.66 \times 10^{-24} \text{ g}$$

Units should be chosen to suit the quantity being described. This can easily be done by choosing a unit that gives an exponential term closest to 10^{0}.

FIGURE 1.3
Illustration of three common balances that are useful for the measurement of mass. (a) A two-pan comparison balance for approximate mass measurement suitable for routine work requiring accuracy to 0.1 g (or perhaps 0.01 g). (b) A top-loading single-pan electronic balance that is similar in accuracy to (a) but has the advantages of speed and ease of operation. The revolution in electronics over the past 20 years has resulted in electronic balances largely supplanting the two-pan comparison balance in routine laboratory usage. (c) An analytical balance that is capable of precise mass measurement (three to five significant figures beyond the decimal point). A balance of this type is used when the highest level of precision and accuracy is required.

(a)

(b)

(c)

The standard metric unit of length is the meter. Large distances are measured conveniently in   **Length**
kilometers; smaller distances are measured in millimeters or centimeters. Very small distances
such as the distances between atoms on a surface are measured in *nanometers (nm):*

$$1 \text{ nm} = 10^{-7} \text{ cm} = 10^{-9} \text{ m}$$

Common conversions for length are as follows:

$$1 \text{ meter (m)} = 1 \times 10^2 \text{ centimeters (cm)} = 3.94 \times 10^1 \text{ inch (in)}$$

The standard metric unit of volume is the liter. A liter is the volume occupied by 1000 grams of   **Volume**
water at 4° Celsius (°C). The volume, 1 liter, also corresponds to:

$$1 \text{ liter (L)} = 1000 \text{ milliliters (mL)} = 1.06 \text{ quarts (qt)}$$

Typical laboratory glassware used for volume measurement is shown in Figure 1.4. The volumetric flask is designed to *contain* a specified volume, and the pipet and buret *dispense* a desired
volume of liquid.

The standard metric unit of time is the second. The need for accurate measurement of time by   **Time**
chemists may not be as apparent as that associated with mass, length, and volume. It is necessary, however, in many applications. In fact, matter may be characterized by measuring the time   *See Section 5.3*
required for a certain process to occur. The rate of a chemical reaction is a measure of change as
a function of time.

Temperature is the degree of "hotness" of an object. This may not sound like a very "scien-   **Temperature**
tific" definition, and, in a sense, it is not. We know intuitively the difference between a "hot"
and a "cold" object, but developing a precise definition to explain this is not easy. We may
think of the temperature of an object as a measure of the amount of heat in the object. However,
this is not strictly true. An object increases in temperature because its heat content has increased   *Section 5.1 describes the distinction*
and vice versa; however, the relationship between heat content and temperature depends on the   *between heat and temperature*
composition of the material.

Many substances, such as mercury, expand as their temperature increases, and this expansion provides us with a way to measure temperature and temperature changes. If the mercury is
contained within a sealed tube, as it is in a thermometer, the height of the mercury is proportional to the temperature. A mercury thermometer may be calibrated, or scaled, in different

FIGURE 1.4
Common laboratory equipment used for the measurement of volume. Graduated cylinders (a), pipets (b), and burets (c) are
used for the delivery of liquids; volumetric flasks (d) are used to contain a specific volume. A graduated cylinder is usually
used for measurement of approximate volumes; it is less accurate and precise than either pipets or burets.

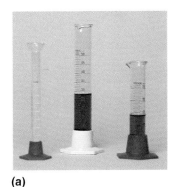
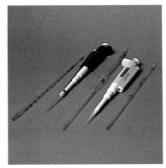

(a)   **(b)**   **(c)**   **(d)**

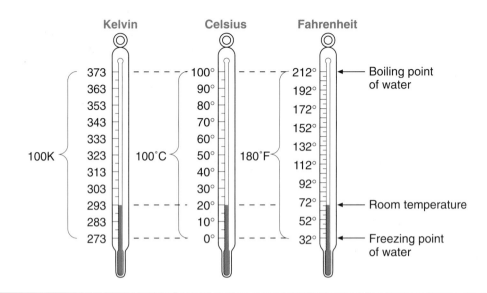

FIGURE 1.5
The freezing point and boiling point of water expressed in the three common units of temperature.

units, just as a ruler can be. Three common temperature scales are *Fahrenheit (°F), Celsius (°C), and Kelvin (K).* Two convenient reference temperatures that are used to calibrate a thermometer are the freezing and boiling temperatures of water. Figure 1.5 shows the relationship between the scales and these reference temperatures.

Although Fahrenheit temperature is most familiar to us, Celsius and Kelvin temperature are used exclusively in scientific measurements. It is often necessary to convert a temperature reading from one scale to another. To convert from Fahrenheit to Celsius, we use the following formula:

Appendix A

$$°C = \tfrac{5}{9}(°F - 32)$$

To convert from Celsius to Fahrenheit, we use the formula

$$°F = \tfrac{9}{5}°C + 32$$

The Kelvin symbol does not have a degree sign.

To convert from Celsius to Kelvin, we use the formula

$$K = °C + 273$$

EXAMPLE 1.12

Converting from Fahrenheit to Celsius and Kelvin

Normal body temperature is 98.6°F. Calculate the corresponding temperature in degrees Celsius:

Solution

$$°C = \tfrac{5}{9}(°F - 32)$$
$$°C = \tfrac{5}{9}(98.6 - 32) = \tfrac{5}{9}(66.6)$$
$$°C = 37.0$$

Calculate the corresponding temperature in Kelvin units:

Solution

$$K = °C + 273$$
$$K = 37.0 + 273$$
$$K = 310 \ K$$

QUESTION 1.15

The freezing temperature of water is 32°F. Calculate the freezing temperature of water in:

a. Celsius units

b. Kelvin units

(handwritten: a. 0° ; b. 273)

(handwritten: $°C = \frac{5}{9}(°F - 32)$ 5/9(32-32) $\frac{5}{9}(0) = 0$ $K = C + 273$ K = 0+273 = 273)

QUESTION 1.16

When a patient is ill, his or her temperature may increase to 104°F. Calculate the temperature of this patient in:

(handwritten: $C = \frac{5}{9}(104 - 32)$ $\frac{5}{9}(72) = 40$)

a. Celsius units *(handwritten: 40°)*

b. Kelvin units *(handwritten: 313°)*

Energy

Energy, the ability to do work, may be categorized as either **kinetic energy,** the energy of motion, or **potential energy,** the energy of position. Kinetic energy may be considered as energy in process; potential energy is stored energy. All energy is either kinetic or potential.

Another useful way of classifying energy is by form. The principal forms of energy include light, heat, electrical, mechanical, and chemical energy. All of these forms of energy share the following set of characteristics:

◆ In chemical reactions, energy cannot be created or destroyed.

◆ Energy may be converted from one form to another.

◆ Energy conversion always occurs with less than 100% efficiency.

◆ All chemical reactions involve either a ''gain'' or a ''loss'' of energy.

Energy absorbed or liberated in chemical reactions is usually in the form of heat energy. Heat energy may be represented in units of calories or joules, their relationship being

$$1 \text{ calorie (cal)} = 4.18 \text{ joules (J)}$$

One calorie is defined as the amount of heat energy required to increase the temperature of one gram of water 1°C.

Heat energy measurement is a quantitative measure of heat content, whereas temperature, as we have mentioned, is relative. Not all substances have the same capacity for holding heat; 1 gram of iron and 1 gram of water, even if they are at the same temperature, do *not* contain the same amount of heat energy. One gram of iron will absorb and store 0.108 calorie of heat energy when the temperature is raised 1°C. In contrast, one gram of water will absorb almost ten times as much energy, 1.00 calorie, when the temperature is increased an equivalent amount.

Units for other forms of energy will be introduced in later chapters.

The *kilocalorie* (kcal) is the familiar nutritional calorie. It is also known as the large Calorie; note that in this term the ''C'' is uppercase to distinguish it from the normal calorie. The large calorie is 1000 small calories. Refer to Section 5.2 and A Medical Perspective: Food Calories for more information.

Water in the environment (lakes, oceans, and streams) has a powerful effect on the climate due to its ability to store large quantities of energy. In summer, water stores heat energy, moderating temperatures of the surrounding area. In winter, some of this stored energy is released to the air as the water temperature falls; this prevents the surroundings from experiencing extreme changes in temperature.

Concentration

Concentration is a measure of the number of particles of a substance, or the mass of those particles, that are contained in a specified volume. Concentration is a widely used way of representing mixtures of different substances. Examples include:

◆ The concentration of oxygen in the air

◆ Pollen counts, given during the hay fever seasons, which are simply the number of grains of pollen contained in a measured volume of air

◆ The amount of an illegal drug in a certain volume of blood, indicating the extent of drug abuse

◆ The proper dose of an antibiotic, based on a patient's weight

We will see many situations in which concentration is used to predict useful information about chemical reactions (Sections 6.4 and 7.4, for example). In Chapter 6 we calculate a numerical value for concentration from experimental data.

A HUMAN PERSPECTIVE

Food Calories

The body gets its energy through the processes known collectively as metabolism, which will be discussed in detail in subsequent chapters on biochemistry and nutrition. The primary energy sources for the body are carbohydrates, fats, and proteins, which we obtain from the foods we eat. The amount of energy available from a given foodstuff is related to the Calories (C) available in the food. Calories are a measure of the energy and heat content that can be derived from the food. One (food) Calorie (symbolized by C) equals 1000 (metric) calories (symbolized by c):

$$1 \text{ Calorie} = 1000 \text{ calories} = 1 \text{ kilocalorie}$$

The energy available in food can be measured by totally burning the food; in other words, we are using the food as a fuel. The energy given off in the form of heat is directly related to the amount of chemical energy that is available in the food and that the food could provide to the body through the various metabolic pathways.

The classes of food molecules are not equally energy rich. For instance, when oxidized via metabolic pathways, carbohydrates and proteins provide the cell with 4 Calories per gram, while fats generate approximately 9 Calories per gram.

In addition, as with all processes, not all the available energy can be efficiently extracted from the food; a certain percentage is always lost. The average person requires between 2000 and 3000 Calories per day to maintain normal body functions such as the regulation of body temperature, muscle movement, and so on. If a person takes in more Calories than the body uses, the Calorie-containing substances will be stored as fat, and the person will gain weight. Conversely, if a person uses more Calories than are ingested, the individual will lose weight.

Excess Calories are stored in the form of fat, the form that provides the greatest amount of energy per gram. Too many

Calories lead to too much fat. Similarly, a lack of Calories (in the form of food) forces the body to raid its storehouse, the fat. Weight is lost in this process as the fat is consumed. Unfortunately, it always seems easier to add fat to the storehouse than to remove it.

The "rule of thumb" is that 3500 Calories are equivalent to approximately 1 pound of body weight. You have to take in 3500 Calories more than you use to gain a pound, and you have to lose 3500 Calories above what you normally use to lose a pound. If you eat as little as 100 Calories a day above your body's needs, you could gain about 10–11 pounds per year:

$$\frac{100 \text{ C}}{\text{day}} \times \frac{365 \text{ day}}{1 \text{ year}} \times \frac{1 \text{ lb}}{3500 \text{ C}} = \frac{10.4 \text{ lb}}{\text{year}}$$

A frequently recommended procedure for increasing the rate of weight loss involves a combination of dieting (taking in fewer Calories) and exercise. The numbers of Calories used in several forms of exercise are provided below:

Activity	Energy Output (C/min)
Running	19.4
Swimming	11.0
Jogging	10.0
Bicycling	8.0
Tennis	7.1
Walking	5.2
Golfing	5.0
Driving a car	2.8
Standing or sitting	1.9
Sleeping	1.0

Density and specific gravity

Appendix A

Both mass and volume are a function of the *amount* of material present. **Density,** the ratio of mass to volume,

$$d = \frac{\text{mass}}{\text{volume}} = \frac{m}{V}$$

is *independent* of the amount of material. Density is a useful way to characterize a substance because each substance has a unique density (Figure 1.6).

One milliliter of air and one milliliter of iron do not weigh the same amount. There is much more mass in 1 milliliter of iron; its density is greater.

Density measurements were used to discriminate between real gold and "fool's gold" during the gold-rush era. Today the measurement of the density of a substance is still a valuable analytical technique. The densities of a number of common substances may be found in Table 1.3.

TABLE 1.3   Densities of Some Common Materials

Substance	Density (g/mL)	Substance	Density (g/mL)
Air	0.00129 (at 0°C)	Methyl alcohol	0.792
Ammonia	0.00771 (at 0°C)	Milk	1.028–1.035
Benzene	0.879	Oxygen	0.00143 (at 0°C)
Bone	1.7–2.0	Rubber	0.9–1.1
Carbon dioxide	0.01963 (at 0°C)	Turpentine	0.87
Ethyl alcohol	0.789	Urine	1.005–1.03
Gasoline	0.66–0.69	Water	1.000 (at 4°C)
Gold	19.3	Water	0.998 (at 20°C)
Hydrogen	0.00090 (at 0°C)	Wood	0.3–0.98
Kerosene	0.82	(balsa, least dense; ebony and	
Lead	11.3	teak, most dense)	
Mercury	13.6		

FIGURE 1.6
Density (mass/volume) is a unique property of a material. A mixture of wood, water, brass, and mercury is shown, with the cork—the least dense—floating on water. Additionally, brass, with a density greater than water but less than liquid mercury, floats on the interface between these two liquids.

In density calculations the mass is usually represented in grams, and volume is given in either milliliters (mL) or cubic centimeters (cm³ or cc):

$$1 \text{ mL} = 1 \text{ cm}^3 = 1 \text{ cc}$$

The unit of density would therefore be g/mL, g/cm³, or g/cc.

Calculating the Density of a Solid

2.00 cm³ of aluminum are found to weigh 5.40 g. Calculate the density of aluminum in units of g/cm³.

Solution

$$d = \frac{m}{V} = \frac{\text{g}}{\text{cm}^3}$$

$$d = \frac{5.40 \text{ g}}{2.00 \text{ cm}^3}$$

$$d = 2.70 \text{ g/cm}^3$$

Calculating the Mass of a Gas from Its Density

Air has a density of 0.0013 g/mL. What is the mass of a 6.0-L sample of air?

Solution

$$0.0013 \text{ g/mL} = 1.3 \times 10^{-3} \text{ g/mL}$$

(The decimal point is moved three positions to the right.) This problem can be solved by using conversion factors:

$$6.0 \text{ L air} \times \frac{10^3 \text{ mL air}}{1 \text{ L air}} \times \frac{1.3 \times 10^{-3} \text{ g air}}{\text{mL air}} = 7.8 \text{ g air}$$

EXAMPLE 1.15

Using the Density to Calculate the Mass of a Liquid

Calculate the mass, in grams, of 10.0 mL of mercury if the density of mercury is 13.6 g/mL.

Solution

Using the density as a conversion factor from volume to mass, we have

$$m = (10.0 \, \text{mL})\left(13.6 \, \frac{\text{g}}{\text{mL}}\right)$$
$$m = 136 \, \text{g}$$

EXAMPLE 1.16

Using the Density to Calculate the Volume of a Liquid

Calculate the volume, in milliliters, of a liquid that has a density of 1.20 g/mL and a mass of 5.00 grams.

Solution

Using the density as a conversion factor from mass to volume, we have

$$V = (5.00 \, \text{g})\left(\frac{1 \, \text{mL}}{1.20 \, \text{g}}\right)$$
$$V = 4.17 \, \text{mL}$$

QUESTION 1.17

The density of ethyl alcohol (200 proof, or pure alcohol) is 0.789 g/mL at 20°C. Calculate the mass of a 30.0-mL sample.

QUESTION 1.18

Calculate the volume, in milliliters, of 10.0 g of a saline solution that has a density of 1.05 g/mL.

For convenience, values of density are often related to a standard, well-known reference, the density of pure water at 4°C. This "referenced" density is called the **specific gravity,** the ratio of the density of the object in question to the density of pure water at 4°C.

$$\text{specific gravity} = \frac{\text{density of object (g/mL)}}{\text{density of water (g/mL)}}$$

Specific gravity is a *unitless* term. Since the density of water at 4.0°C is 1.00 g/mL, the numerical values for the density and specific gravity of a substance are equal. That is, an object with a density of 2.00 g/mL has a specific gravity of 2.00 at 4°C.

Routine hospital tests involving the measurement of the specific gravity of urine and blood samples are frequently used as diagnostic tools. For example, diseases such as kidney disorders and diabetes change the composition of urine. This compositional change results in a corresponding change in the specific gravity. This change is easily measured and provides the basis for a quick preliminary diagnosis. This topic is discussed in greater detail in the Clinical Perspective: Diagnosis Based on Waste.

A CLINICAL PERSPECTIVE

Diagnosis Based on Waste

Any archaeologist would say that you can learn a great deal about the activities and attitudes of a society by finding the remains of their dump sites and studying their waste.

Similarly, urine, a waste product consisting of a wide variety of metabolites, may be analyzed to indicate abnormalities in various metabolic processes or even unacceptable behavior (recall the steroid tests in the most recent Olympics).

Many of these tests must be performed by using sophisticated and sensitive instrumentation. However, a very simple test, the measurement of the specific gravity of urine, can be an indicator of diabetes mellitus or Bright's disease. The normal range for human urine specific gravity is 1.010–1.030.

A hydrometer, a weighted glass bulb inserted in a liquid, may be used to determine specific gravity. The higher it floats in the liquid, the more dense the liquid. A hydrometer that is calibrated to indicate the specific gravity of urine is called a urinometer.

Although hydrometers have been replaced by more modern measuring devices that use smaller samples, these newer instruments operate on the same principles as the hydrometer.

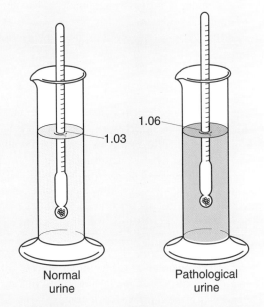

A hydrometer, used in the measurement of the specific gravity of urine.

SUMMARY

1.1 Chemistry: An Overview

Chemistry is the study of matter and the changes that matter undergoes. *Matter* is anything that has mass and occupies space. The changes that matter undergoes always involve either gain or loss of energy. *Energy* is nonmaterial and is the ability to do work (to accomplish some change). Thus, a study of chemistry involves matter, energy, and their interrelationship.

The major areas of chemistry include *biochemistry, organic chemistry, inorganic chemistry, analytical chemistry,* and *physical chemistry.*

1.2 The Methodology

The scientific method consists of five distinct processes: *observation, pattern recognition, development of theories* from *hypotheses, experimentation,* and *summarizing information.* A *law* summarizes a large quantity of information.

The development of the scientific method has played a major role in civilization's rapid growth in the last two centuries.

Technology is the conversion of a material from its current form to a more useful form. Many consider technology to be applied science, the use of scientific principles to fulfill human needs.

1.3 Data, Results, and Units

A scientific experiment produces *data.* Each piece of data is the individual result of a single measurement. Mass, length, volume, time, temperature, and energy are the most common types of data obtained from chemical experiments.

Results are the outcome of an experiment. Usually, several pieces of data are combined, using a mathematical equation, to produce a result.

A *unit* defines the basic quantity of mass, volume, time, and so on. A number that is not followed by the correct unit usually conveys no useful information.

1.4 Measurement in Chemistry

The metric system is a decimal-based system. In the metric system, mass is represented as the gram, length as the meter, and volume as the liter. Any subunit or multiple unit contains one of these units preceded by a prefix indicating the power of ten by which the base unit is to be multiplied to form the subunit or multiple unit.

To convert one unit to another, we must set up a *conversion factor* or series of conversion factors that relate two units. The proper use of these conversion factors is referred to as the factor-label method. This method is used either to convert from one unit to another within the same system or to convert units from one system to another.

1.5 Error, Accuracy, Precision, and Uncertainty

Error is defined as the difference between the true value and our estimation, or measurement, of the value. *Accuracy* is the degree of agreement between the true and measured value. *Uncertainty* is the degree of doubt in a single measurement. The number of meaningful digits in a measurement is determined by the measuring device. Precision is a measure of the agreement of replicate measurements.

1.6 Significant Figures and Scientific Notation

Significant figures are all digits in a number representing data or results that are known with certainty plus the first uncertain digit. The number of significant figures associated with a measurement is determined by the measuring device.

Very large and very small numbers may be represented with the proper number of significant figures by using *scientific notation*.

1.7 Experimental Quantities

Mass describes the quantity of matter in an object. The terms weight and mass are often used interchangeably, but they are not equivalent. *Weight* is the force of gravity on an object. The fundamental unit of mass in the metric system is the gram. One atomic mass unit (amu) is equal to 1.66×10^{-24} g.

The standard metric unit of length is the meter. Large distances are measured in kilometers; smaller distances are measured in millimeters or centimeters. Very small distances (on the atomic scale) are measured in nanometers (nm). The standard metric unit of volume is the liter. A liter is the volume occupied by 1000 grams of water at 4 degrees Celsius. The standard metric unit of time is the second, a unit that is used in the English system as well.

Temperature is the degree of "hotness" of an object. Many substances, such as liquid mercury, expand as their temperature increases, and this expansion provides us with a way to measure temperature and temperature changes. Three common temperature scales are Fahrenheit (°F), Celsius (°C), and Kelvin (K).

Energy, the ability to do work, may be categorized as either *kinetic energy*, the energy of motion, or *potential energy*, the energy of position. The principal forms of energy are light, heat, mechanical, electrical, nuclear, and chemical energy.

Energy absorbed or liberated in chemical reactions is most often in the form of heat energy. Heat energy may be represented in units of calories or joules: 1 calorie (cal) = 4.18 joules (J). One calorie is defined as the amount of heat energy required to change the temperature of one gram of water 1°C.

Concentration is a measure of the number of particles of a substance, or the mass of those particles, that are contained in a specified volume. Concentration is a widely used way of representing relative quantities of different substances in a mixture of those substances.

Density is the ratio of mass to volume and is a useful way of characterizing a substance. Values of density are often related to a standard reference, the density of pure water at 4°C. This "referenced" density is the *specific gravity*, the ratio of the density of the object in question to the density of pure water at 4°C.

KEY TERMS

accuracy (1.5)
analytical chemistry (1.1)
biochemistry (1.1)
chemistry (1.1)
concentration (1.7)
conversion factor (1.4)
data (1.3)
density (1.7)
energy (1.1)
error (1.5)
hypothesis (1.2)
inorganic chemistry (1.1)
kinetic energy (1.7)
law (1.2)
mass (1.7)
matter (1.1)
organic chemistry (1.1)
physical chemistry (1.1)
potential energy (1.7)

precision (1.5)
results (1.3)
scientific method (1.2)
scientific notation (1.6)
significant figures (1.6)
specific gravity (1.7)
technology (1.2)
temperature (1.7)
theory (1.2)
uncertainty (1.5)
unit (1.3)
weight (1.7)

QUESTIONS AND PROBLEMS

Fundamental Concepts

1.19 Define each of the following terms:
   a. chemistry   **d.** hypothesis
   b. matter   **e.** theory
   c. energy   **f.** law

1.20 Define each of the following terms:
   a. precision   **d.** results
   b. accuracy   **e.** mass
   c. data   **f.** weight

1.21 Give the base unit for each of the following in the metric system:
   a. mass
   b. volume
   c. length

1.22 Give the base unit for each of the following in the metric system:
   a. time
   b. temperature
   c. energy

1.23 Discuss the difference between the terms *mass* and *weight*.

1.24 Discuss the difference between the terms *data* and *results*.

1.25 Distinguish between specific gravity and density.

1.26 Distinguish between kinetic energy and potential energy.

1.27 Discuss the meaning of the term *scientific method*.

1.28 Describe an application of reasoning involving the scientific method that has occurred in your day-to-day life.

Conversion Factors

1.29 Convert 2.0 pounds to:
   a. ounces   **d.** milligrams
   b. tons   **e.** dekagrams
   c. grams

1.30 Convert 5.0 quarts to:
  a. gallons **d.** milliliters
  b. pints **e.** microliters
  c. liters

1.31 Convert 3.0 grams to:
  a. pounds **d.** centigrams
  b. ounces **e.** milligrams
  c. kilograms

1.32 Convert 3.0 meters to:
  a. yards **d.** centimeters
  b. inches **e.** millimeters
  c. feet

1.33 Convert 50°F to:
  a. °C
  b. K

1.34 Convert −10°F to:
  a. °C
  b. K

1.35 Convert 20°C to:
  a. K
  b. °F

1.36 Convert 300 K to:
  a. °C
  b. °F

1.37 A 150-lb adult has approximately 9 pints of blood. How many liters of blood does the individual have?

1.38 If a drop of blood has a volume of 0.05 mL, how many drops of blood are in the adult described in Problem 1.37?

1.39 A patient's temperature is found to be 38.5°C. To what Fahrenheit temperature does this correspond?

1.40 A newborn is 21 inches in length and weighs 6 lb 9 oz. Describe the baby in metric units.

Significant Figures

1.41 How many significant figures are contained in each of the following numbers?
  a. 10.0 **d.** 2.062
  b. 0.214 **e.** 10.50
  c. 0.120 **f.** 1050

1.42 How many significant figures are contained in each of the following numbers?
  a. 3.8×10^{-3} **d.** 24
  b. 5.20×10^{2} **e.** 240
  c. 0.00261 **f.** 2.40

1.43 Round the following numbers to three significant figures:
  a. 3.873×10^{-3} **d.** 24.3387
  b. 5.202×10^{-2} **e.** 240.1
  c. 0.002616 **f.** 2.407

1.44 Round the following numbers to three significant figures:
  a. 123700 **d.** 53.2995
  b. 0.00285792 **e.** 16.96
  c. 1.421×10^{-3} **f.** 507.5

1.45 Perform each of the following arithmetic operations, reporting the answer with the proper number of significant figures:
  a. (23)(657) **d.** 1157.23 − 17.812
  b. 0.00521 + 0.236 **e.** $\dfrac{(1.987)(298)}{0.0821}$
  c. $\dfrac{18.3}{3.0576}$

1.46 Perform each of the following arithmetic operations, reporting the answer with the proper number of significant figures:
  a. $\dfrac{(16.0)(0.1879)}{45.3}$ **d.** 18 + 52.1
  b. $\dfrac{(76.32)(1.53)}{0.052}$ **e.** 58.17 − 57.79
  c. (0.0063)(57.8)

The Factor-Label Method and Scientific (Exponential) Notation

1.47 Express the following numbers in scientific notation (use the proper number of significant figures):
  a. 12.3 **e.** 92,000,000
  b. 0.0569 **f.** 0.005280
  c. −1527 **g.** 1.279
  d. 0.000000789 **h.** −531.77

1.48 Using scientific notation, express the number two thousand in terms of:
  a. one significant figure **d.** four significant figures
  b. two significant figures **e.** five significant figures
  c. three significant figures

1.49 Express each of the following numbers in decimal notation:
  a. 3.24×10^{3} **e.** -8.21×10^{-2}
  b. 1.50×10^{-4} **f.** 2.9979×10^{8}
  c. 4.579×10^{-1} **g.** 1.50×10^{0}
  d. -6.83×10^{5} **h.** 6.02×10^{23}

1.50 Which of the following numbers have two significant figures? Three significant figures? Four significant figures?
  a. 327 **e.** 7.8×10^{3}
  b. 1.049×10^{4} **f.** 1507
  c. 1.70 **g.** 4.8×10^{2}
  d. 0.000570 **h.** 7.389×10^{15}

Experimental Quantities

1.51 Calculate the density of a 3.00×10^{2}-g object that has a volume of 50.0 mL.

1.52 What volume, in liters, will 8.00×10^{2} g of air occupy if the density of air is 1.29 g/L?

1.53 What is the mass, in grams, of a piece of iron that has a volume of 1.50×10^{2} mL and a density of 7.20 g/mL?

1.54 What is the mass of a femur (leg bone) having a volume of 118 cm³? The density of bone is 1.8 g/cm³.

1.55 You are given a piece of wood that is either maple, teak, or oak. The piece of wood has a volume 1.00×10^{2} cm³ and a mass of 98 g. The densities of maple, teak, and oak are as follows:

Wood	Density (g/cm³)
Maple	0.70
Teak	0.98
Oak	0.85

What is the identity of the piece of wood?

1.56 The specific gravity of a patient's urine sample was measured to be 1.008. Given that the density of water is 1.000 g/mL at 4°C, what is the density of the urine sample?

Further Problems

1.57 The density of grain alcohol is 0.789 g/mL. Given that the density of water at 4°C is 1.00 g/mL, what is the specific gravity of grain alcohol?

1.58 The density of mercury is 13.6 g/mL. If a sample of mercury weighs 272 g, what is the volume of the sample in milliliters?

1.59 You are given three bars of metal. Each is labeled with its identity (lead, uranium, platinum). The lead bar has a mass of 5.0×10^2 g and a volume of 6.36 cm^3. The uranium bar has a mass of 75 g and a volume of 3.97 cm^3. The platinum bar has a mass of 2140 g and a volume of 1.00×10^2 cm^3. Which of these metals has the lowest density? Which has the greatest density?

1.60 Refer to Problem 1.59. Suppose that each of the bars had the same mass. How could one determine which bar had the lowest density or highest density?

VOCABULARY QUIZ

1.1 _____ is the nearness of an experimental value to the true value.

1.2 The study of matter and the changes that matter undergoes is referred to as _Chemistry_.

1.3 _____ is a group of facts resulting from an experiment.

1.4 An ''educated guess'' at the explanation of observed behavior of our surroundings is a(n) _Hypothesis_

1.5 A(n) _Natural law_ is a statement of observed behavior for which no exceptions have been found.

1.6 Stored energy is called _Potential energy_

1.7 The degree of agreement between replicate measurements of the same quantity is the _Accuracy_ of the measurement.

1.8 The ratio of the density of a substance to the density of water at the same temperature is called the _Specific gravity_

1.9 A(n) _Theory_ is a hypothesis developed to explain observed behavior of matter that has been verified by using the scientific method.

1.10 _____ is a force exerted on an object by gravity.

2

The Structure of the Atom and the Periodic Table

L E A R N I N G   G O A L S

◆ Recognize the interrelationships of the structure of matter and its physical and chemical properties.

◆ Understand the current model of modern atomic structure including the major particles that comprise the atom: protons, neutrons, and electrons.

◆ Have a historical overview of the development of atomic theory, especially Dalton's theory and the Bohr theory.

◆ Distinguish among atoms, ions, and isotopes.

◆ Recognize the important subdivisions of the periodic table: periods, groups (families), metals, and nonmetals.

◆ Obtain information about an element from the periodic table, such as the mass, number of protons, neutrons, and electrons in an atom of any element.

◆ Use the periodic table and its predictive power to estimate the relative sizes of atoms and ions, as well as relative magnitudes of ionization energy and electron affinity.

◆ Use the octet rule to predict the charge of common cations and anions.

◆ Understand the value of ionization energies and electron affinities in predicting bond formation.

CHEMISTRY CONNECTION

Curiosity, Science, and Medicine

Curiosity is one of the most important human traits. Small children constantly ask why. As we get older, our questions become more complex, but the curiosity remains.

Curiosity is also the basis of the scientific method. A scientist observes an event, wonders why it happens, and sets out to answer the question. Dr. Michael Zasloff's curiosity may lead to the development of an entirely new class of antibiotics. When he was a geneticist at the National Institutes of Health, his experiments involved surgical removal of the ovaries of African clawed frogs. After surgery he sutured (sewed up) the incision and put the frogs back in their tanks. These water-filled tanks were teeming with bacteria, but the frogs healed quickly, and the incisions did not become infected!

Of all the scientists to observe this remarkable healing, only Zasloff was curious enough to ask whether there were chemicals in the frogs' skin that defended the frogs against bacterial infections—a new type of antibiotic. All of the current antibiotics are produced by fungi or are synthesized in the laboratory. One big problem in medicine today is the fact

that more and more pathogenic (disease-causing) bacteria are becoming resistant to these antibiotics. Zasloff hoped to find an antibiotic that worked in an entirely new way so that the problems with antibiotic resistance might be overcome.

Dr. Zasloff found two molecules in frog skin that can kill bacteria. Both are small proteins. Zasloff named them magainins, from the Hebrew word for shield. Most of the antibiotics that we now use enter bacteria and kill them by stopping some biochemical process inside the cell. Magainins are more direct; they simply punch holes in the bacterial membrane, and the bacteria explode.

One of the magainins, now chemically synthesized in the laboratory so that no frogs are harmed, may be available to the public in the near future. This magainin can kill a wide variety of bacteria (broad-spectrum antibiotic), and it has passed the Phase I human trials. If this compound passes all the remaining tests, it will be used in treating deep infected wounds and ulcers, providing an alternative to traditional therapy.

INTRODUCTION

In Chapter 1 we defined chemistry as the study of matter and the changes that matter undergoes. In this chapter we will expand and enhance our understanding of matter. We can deal with visible quantities of matter such as an ounce of silver or a pint of blood. However, we can also describe matter at the level of individual particles that make up matter. For instance, one atom of silver is the smallest amount of silver that retains the properties of the bulk material. This is important because the description of matter at the atomic level can be used to explain the behavior of the larger, visible quantities of the same material.

Why does ice float on water? Why don't oil and water mix? Why does blood transport oxygen to our cells, while carbon monoxide inhibits this process? Questions such as these are best explained by understanding the behavior of substances at the atomic level.

2.1 MATTER AND PROPERTIES

Properties are characteristics of matter. These properties are classified as either physical or chemical. In this section we will learn the meaning of physical and chemical properties and how they are used to characterize matter.

Matter and physical properties

There are three **states of matter: the gaseous state,** the **liquid state,** and the **solid state.** A gas is made up of particles that are widely separated. In fact, a gas will expand to fill any container; it has no definite shape or volume. In contrast, particles of a liquid are closer together; a liquid has a definite volume but no definite shape; it takes on the shape of its container. A solid consists of particles that are close together and that often have a regular and predictable pattern of particle arrangement (crystalline). A solid has both fixed volume and fixed shape. Attractive forces, which exist between all particles, are strongest in solids and weakest in gases.

The states of matter are distinguishable by differences in **physical properties.** These characteristics (the physical properties) enable us to identify different kinds of matter without changing the identity (chemical composition) of the sample. Examples of physical properties include color, odor, taste, melting and boiling temperatures, and compressibility. Even the relative ability to store energy is considered a physical property.

(a)　　　　　　　　　(b)　　　　　　　　　(c)

FIGURE 2.1
The three states of matter exhibited by water: (a) solid, as ice; (b) liquid, as ocean water; (c) gas, as humidity in the air.

Water is the most common example of a substance that can exist in all three states over a reasonable temperature range (Figure 2.1). Conversion of ice to liquid water (melting) or liquid water to the gaseous state (boiling) are examples of *physical change*. A **physical change** does not alter the composition or identity of the substance undergoing change. The particles making up ice, liquid water, and steam are identical units. Each unit consists of two *hydrogen atoms* (H) and one *oxygen atom* (O) held together by attractive forces referred to as *chemical bonds*. It is described by the familiar chemical formula H_2O. The continual interconversion of the three states of water in the environment (snow, rain, and humidity) clearly demonstrates the retention of the identity of water particles or *molecules*.

We have noted that physical properties can be exhibited, measured, or observed without any change in identity or composition. In contrast, **chemical properties** do result in a change in composition and can be observed only through chemical reactions. A **chemical reaction** is a process of rearranging, replacing, or adding atoms to produce new substances. For example, the process of photosynthesis can be shown as

Matter and chemical properties

$$\text{carbon dioxide} + \text{water} \xrightarrow[\text{Chlorophyll}]{\text{Light}} \text{sugar} + \text{oxygen}$$

This chemical reaction involves the conversion of carbon dioxide and water (the **reactants**) to a sugar and oxygen (the **products**). The products and reactants are clearly different. We know that carbon dioxide and oxygen are gases at room temperature and water is a liquid at this temperature; the sugar is a solid white powder. A chemical property of carbon dioxide is its ability to form sugar under certain conditions. The process of formation of this sugar is the *chemical change*.

Light is the energy needed to make the reaction happen. Chlorophyll is the energy absorber, converting light energy to chemical energy. Chapter 5 discusses energy in chemical reactions.

QUESTION 2.1

Classify each of the following as either a chemical property or a physical property:

a.　color ~physical~　d.　odor ~physical~
b.　flammability ~chem~　e.　taste ~physical~
c.　hardness ~phy~

QUESTION 2.2

Classify each of the following as either a chemical change or a physical change:

a.　water boiling to become steam ~physi~
b.　butter becoming rancid ~chem~
c.　combustion of wood ~chem~
d.　melting of ice in spring ~phy~
e.　decay of leaves in winter ~phy~

Intensive and extensive properties

It is important to recognize the fundamental difference between properties such as density and specific gravity and properties such as mass and volume. Density and specific gravity are intensive properties. An **intensive property** is *independent* of the *quantity* of the substance. For example, the density of one drop of water is exactly the same as the density of a liter of water. On the other hand, mass and volume are extensive properties. An **extensive property** depends on the quantity of a substance.

Classification of matter

Chemists look for similarities in properties among various types of materials. Recognizing these likenesses simplifies learning the subject and allows us to predict the behavior of new substances on the basis of their relationship to substances already known and characterized.

Many classification systems exist. The most useful system, based on composition, is described below (see also Figure 2.2).

All matter is either *a pure substance or a mixture.* A **pure substance** is a form of matter that has uniform composition and physical and chemical properties throughout. Pure water is a pure substance. It is made up only of particles containing two hydrogen atoms and one oxygen atom, that is, water molecules (H_2O). A **mixture** is a combination of two or more pure substances in which each substance retains its own identity. Alcohol and water can be combined in a mixture. They coexist as pure substances because they do not undergo a chemical reaction; they exist as thoroughly mixed discrete molecules. This collection of dissimilar particles is the mixture. A mixture has variable composition; there are an infinite number of combinations of quantities of alcohol and water that can be mixed. For example, the mixture may contain a small amount of alcohol and a large amount of water or vice versa. Each is, however, an alcohol-water mixture.

A mixture may be either *homogeneous or heterogeneous* (Figure 2.3). A **homogeneous mixture** has uniform composition. Its particles are well-mixed, or thoroughly intermingled. The above example, alcohol and water, is homogeneous. A homogeneous mixture, such as alcohol and water, is described as a *solution.* Air, a mixture of gases, is an example of a gaseous solution. A **heterogeneous mixture** has a nonuniform composition. A mixture of salt and pepper is a good example of a heterogeneous mixture. Concrete is also composed of a heterogeneous mixture of materials (various types and sizes of stone and sand present in a nonuniform mixture).

There are different types of pure substances. Elements and compounds are both pure substances. An **element** is a pure substance that cannot be changed into a simpler form of matter by any chemical reaction. Hydrogen and oxygen, for example, are elements. Alternatively, a **compound** is a substance resulting from the combination of two or more elements in a definite, reproducible way. The elements hydrogen and oxygen, as noted earlier, may combine to form the compound water, H_2O.

A detailed discussion of solutions (homogeneous mixtures) and their properties is presented in Chapter 6.

At present, more than 100 elements have been characterized. A complete listing of the elements and their symbols, in the form of the periodic table, is found on the inside front cover of this textbook.

FIGURE 2.2
Classification of matter. All matter is either a pure substance or a mixture of pure substances. Pure substances are either elements or compounds, and mixtures may be either homogeneous (uniform composition) or heterogeneous (nonuniform composition).

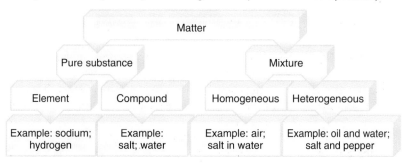

QUESTION 2.3

Is each of the following materials a pure substance, a homogeneous mixture, or a heterogeneous mixture?

a. ethyl alcohol   *homogeneous mixture.*
b. blood   *pure substance*
c. Alka Seltzer dissolved in water   *heterogeneous mixture*
d. oxygen in a hospital oxygen tank   *element*

QUESTION 2.4

Is each of the following materials a pure substance, a homogeneous mixture, or a heterogeneous mixture?

a. air   *homogeneous*
b. paint
c. perfume
d. carbon monoxide

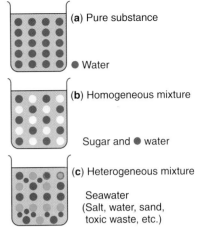

(a) Pure substance
● Water

(b) Homogeneous mixture

Sugar and ● water

(c) Heterogeneous mixture

Seawater
(Salt, water, sand, toxic waste, etc.)

FIGURE 2.3
Schematic representation of some classes of matter. A pure substance (a) consists of a single component. A homogeneous mixture (b) has a uniform distribution of components. A heterogeneous mixture (c) has a nonuniform distribution of components.

Chemists and physicists have used the observed properties of matter to develop models of the individual units of matter. These models collectively make up what we now know as the atomic theory of matter.

These models have developed from experimental observations over the past 200 years. Thus theory and experiment reinforce each other. We must gain some insight into atomic structure to appreciate the behavior of the atoms themselves as well as larger aggregates of atoms: compounds.

The structure-properties concept has advanced so far that compounds are designed and synthesized in the laboratory with the hope that they will perform very specific functions, such as curing diseases that have been resistant to other forms of treatment.

The theory of atomic structure has progressed rapidly, from a very primitive level to its present point of sophistication, in a relatively short period of time. A brief summary of our present knowledge of the composition of the atom is presented below, coupled with an outline of the significant scientific discoveries that brought about major progress in the historical development of atomic theory. Before we proceed, let us insert a note of caution. We must not think of the present picture of the atom as final. Scientific inquiry continues, and we should view the present theory as a step in an evolutionary process. *Theories are subject to constant refinement,* as was noted in our discussion of the scientific method.

Electrons, protons, and neutrons

The basic structural unit of an element is the **atom,** which is the smallest unit of an element that retains the chemical properties of that element. A tiny sample of the element copper, too small to be seen by the naked eye, is composed of billions of copper atoms arranged in some orderly fashion. Each atom is incredibly small. Only recently have we been able to "see" atoms using modern instruments such as the scanning tunneling microscope (see Figure 2.4).

We know from experience that certain kinds of atoms can "split" into smaller particles and release large amounts of energy; this process is *radioactive decay*. We also know that the atom is composed of three primary particles: the *electron,* the *proton,* and the *neutron*. While other

2.2 MATTER AND STRUCTURE

As we saw in Section 1.3, models allow us to make ideas more clear and enable us to predict behavior; this is their main value.

Atomic structure

Section 1.2

Radioactivity and radioactive decay are discussed in Chapter 8.

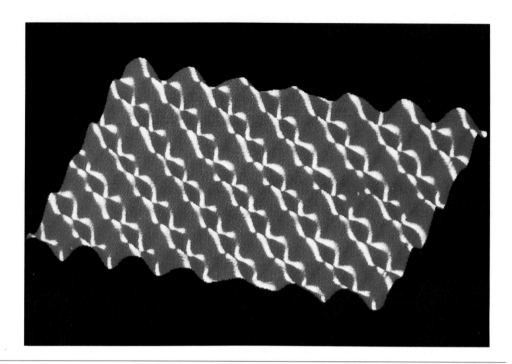

FIGURE 2.4
Sophisticated techniques, such as scanning tunneling electron microscopy, provide visual evidence for the structure of molecules. The planar nature of graphite, a commonly used lubricant, is shown here; the peaks are images of carbon atoms.

subatomic fragments with unusual names (neutrinos, gluons, quarks, and so forth) have also been discovered, we shall concern ourselves only with the primary particles: the protons, neutrons, and electrons.

We can consider the atom to be composed of two distinct regions:

1. The **nucleus** is a small, dense, positively charged region in the center of the atom. The nucleus is composed of positively charged **protons** and uncharged **neutrons.**

2. Surrounding the nucleus is a diffuse region of negative charge populated by **electrons,** the source of the negative charge. Electrons are tiny in comparison to the protons and neutrons.

The properties of these particles are summarized in Table 2.1.

Atoms of various types differ in their number of protons, neutrons, and electrons. The number of protons determines the identity of the atom. As such, the number of protons is *characteristic* of the element. When the number of protons is equal to the number of electrons, the atom is neutral because the charges are balanced and effectively cancel one another.

We may represent an element symbolically as follows:

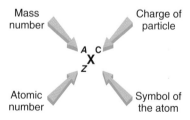

TABLE 2.1 Selected Properties of the Three Basic Subatomic Particles

Name	Charge	Mass (amu)	Mass (grams)
Electron (e)	-1	5.4×10^{-4}	9.11×10^{-28}
Proton (p)	$+1$	1.00	1.67×10^{-24}
Neutron (n)	0	1.00	1.67×10^{-24}

The **atomic number** (Z) is equal to the number of protons in the atom, and the **mass number** (A) is equal to the *sum* of the number of protons and neutrons (the mass of the electrons is so small as to be insignificant in comparison to the nucleus).

If

$$\text{number of protons} + \text{number of neutrons} = \text{mass number}$$

then, if the number of protons is subtracted from each side,

$$\text{number of neutrons} = \text{mass number} - \text{number of protons}$$

or, since the number of protons equals the atomic number,

$$\text{number of neutrons} = \text{mass number} - \text{atomic number}$$

For an atom, in which positive and negative charges cancel, the number of protons and electrons must be equal and identical to the atomic number.

EXAMPLE 2.1

Calculating the Composition of an Atom

Calculate the numbers of protons, neutrons, and electrons in an atom of fluorine.

Solution

The atomic symbol for the fluorine atom is

$$_{9}^{19}\text{F}$$

We know that the mass number 19 is telling us that the total number of protons + neutrons is 19. The atomic number, 9, represents the number of protons. The difference, $19 - 9$, or 10, is the number of neutrons. The number of electrons must be the same as the number of protons, hence 9, for a neutral fluorine atom.

QUESTION 2.5

Calculate the number of protons, neutrons, and electrons in each of the following atoms:

a. $_{16}^{32}\text{S}$ ~~protons 16, neutrons 16, electrons 16~~

b. $_{11}^{23}\text{Na}$ ~~protons 11, neutrons 12, elec 11~~

QUESTION 2.6

Calculate the number of protons, neutrons, and electrons in each of the following atoms:

a. $_{1}^{1}\text{H}$

b. $_{94}^{244}\text{Pu}$

Isotopes

Isotopes are atoms of the same element having different masses *due to different numbers of neutrons.* In other words, isotopes have different mass numbers. For example, all of the following are isotopes of hydrogen:

$$_{1}^{1}\text{H} \qquad _{1}^{2}\text{H} \qquad _{1}^{3}\text{H}$$

Hydrogen   Deuterium   Tritium

The existence of isotopes explains why the mass numbers, measured in atomic mass units (amu), of the various elements are not whole numbers. This is contrary to what we would expect from proton and neutron masses, which are whole numbers to three significant figures.

Consider, for example, the mass of one chlorine atom, containing 17 protons (atomic number) and 18 neutrons:

$$17 \text{ protons} \times \frac{1.00 \text{ amu}}{\text{proton}} = 17.00 \text{ amu}$$

$$18 \text{ neutrons} \times \frac{1.00 \text{ amu}}{\text{neutron}} = 18.00 \text{ amu}$$

$$17.00 \text{ amu} + 18.00 \text{ amu} = 35.00 \text{ amu (mass of chlorine atom)}$$

Inspection of the periodic table reveals that the mass number of chlorine is actually 35.45 amu, *not* 35.00 amu. The existence of isotopes accounts for this difference. A natural sample of chlorine is composed principally of two isotopes, $^{35}_{17}Cl$ and $^{37}_{17}Cl$, in approximately a 3:1 ratio, and the tabulated mass is the *weighted average* of the two isotopes. In our calculation above, the chlorine atom referred to was the isotope that has a mass number of 35 amu.

The weighted average of the masses of all of the isotopes of an element is the **atomic mass** and should be distinguished from the mass number, which is the sum of the number of protons and neutrons in a single isotope of the element.

Isotopes are often written with the name of the element followed by the mass number. For example, the isotopes $^{12}_{6}C$ and $^{14}_{6}C$ may be written as carbon-12 and carbon-14, respectively.

Certain isotopes (radioactive isotopes) of elements emit particles and energy that can be used to trace the behavior of biochemical systems. These isotopes otherwise behave identically to any other isotope of the same element. Their chemical behavior is identical; it is their nuclear behavior that is unique. As a result, a radioactive isotope can be substituted for the "nonradioactive" isotope, and its biochemical activity can be followed by monitoring the particles or energy emitted by the isotope as it passes through the body.

Ions

Ions are electrically charged particles that result from a gain of one or more electrons by the parent atom (forming negative ions, or **anions**) or a loss of one or more electrons from the parent atom (forming positive ions, or **cations**).

Formation of an anion may occur as follows:

$$^{19}_{9}F + 1e^- \longrightarrow {}^{19}_{9}F^-$$

The neutral atom gains an electron   The fluorine anion is formed

Alternatively, formation of a cation of sodium may proceed as follows:

$$^{23}_{11}Na \longrightarrow 1e^- + {}^{23}_{11}Na^+$$

The neutral atom loses an electron   The sodium cation is formed

Note that the electrons gained are written to the left of the reaction arrow (they are reactants), while the electrons lost are written as products to the right of the reaction arrow. For simplification the atomic and mass numbers are often omitted, since they do not change during ion formation. For example, the sodium cation would be written as Na^+ and the anion of fluorine as F^-.

The weighted average is not a true average but is corrected by the relative amounts (the weighting factor) of each isotope present in nature.

A detailed discussion of the use of radioactive isotopes in the diagnosis and treatment of disease is found in Chapter 8.

2.3 DEVELOPMENT OF THE ATOMIC THEORY

With this overview of our current understanding of the structure of the atom, we now look at a few of the most important scientific discoveries that led to the modern atomic theory.

Dalton's theory

The first experimentally based theory of atomic structure was proposed by John Dalton, an English schoolteacher, in the early 1800s. Dalton proposed the following ideas:

1. All matter consists of tiny particles called atoms.
2. An atom cannot be created, divided, destroyed, or converted to any other type of atom.

3. All atoms of a particular element have identical properties.

4. Atoms of different elements have different properties.

5. Atoms combine in simple whole-number ratios.

6. Chemical change involves joining, separating, or rearranging atoms.

Even though Dalton's theory was founded on a small amount of experimental information, we regard much of it as correct today. Postulates 1, 4, 5, and 6 are still thought to be true. However, the discovery of nuclear fusion (''joining'' of atoms), fission (''splitting'' of atoms), and radioactivity have disproved the postulate that atoms cannot be created or destroyed. Postulate 3, that the atoms of a particular element are identical, was disproven by the discovery of isotopes.

Section 2.2

The next major discoveries occurred almost a century later (1879–1897). Although Dalton pictured atoms as indivisible, various experiments, particularly those of William Crookes and Eugene Goldstein, indicated that the atom was composed of charged (+ and −) particles. Later experiments by J. J. Thomson demonstrated the electrical and magnetic properties of these positive and negative particles. It was also demonstrated that these particles, now known as *protons* and *electrons,* respectively, are characteristic of all matter.

Electrons, protons, and neutrons

The third fundamental atomic particle is the *neutron.* It has a mass virtually equal to that of the proton and zero charge. The neutron was first postulated in the early 1920s, but it was not until 1932 that James Chadwick demonstrated its existence.

In the early 1900s it was believed that protons and electrons were uniformly distributed throughout the atom. However, an experiment by Hans Geiger led Ernest Rutherford (in 1911) to propose that the majority of the mass and positive charge of the atom was actually located in a small, dense region, the *nucleus,* with small, negatively charged electrons spread across a much larger volume outside of the nucleus.

The nucleus

The significance of Rutherford's contribution cannot be understated. His discovery of the nucleus is fundamental to our understanding of chemistry.

The nucleus is described in detail in Chapter 8.

Rutherford's idea of the atom was a tiny, dense, positively charged nucleus containing protons and surrounded by electrons. The electron arrangement, or **electron configuration,** was not understood. More information was needed regarding the organization of the electrons around the nucleus.

The Bohr atom

Because the dimensions of an atom are on the order of 10^{-10} m (0.1 nm), we cannot simply measure the location of subatomic particles. But we can use the measurement of *energy* rather than the *position* of the atomic particles to determine structure. For example, information obtained from the absorption or emission of *light* by atoms (energy changes) can yield valuable insight into structure. Such studies are referred to as *spectroscopy.* The term spectroscopy means the measurement of the spectrum of light. The spectrum is simply a collection of light of different colors or *wavelengths.* The spectrum is termed the *electromagnetic spectrum* because the light has both electrical and magnetic properties.

The emission of light by hydrogen atoms placed in an electric field was explained by *Niels Bohr.* His explanation gave rise to a totally new model of the atom that emphasized the arrangement of electrons around the nucleus. Bohr hypothesized that surrounding each atomic nucleus were certain fixed **energy levels** that could be occupied by electrons. He also believed that each level was defined by a circular **orbit** around the nucleus, located at a specific distance from the nucleus. The concept of certain fixed energy levels is referred to as the *quantization* of energy. The implication is that electrons can be located only in these **quantum levels,** or orbits.

The Environmental Perspective, Electromagnetic Radiation and Its Effects on Our Everyday Lives, contains a number of examples of practical technology resulting from our understanding of this radiation.

When an atom *absorbs* energy, an electron may be *excited.* When this happens, it may ''jump'' from an orbit closer to the nucleus (lower energy) to one farther from the nucleus (higher energy). This process is termed **promotion.** Similarly, the release of energy from an atom, **relaxation,** occurs when an electron falls into an orbit closer to the nucleus (lower energy level).

Promotion and relaxation processes are called **electronic transitions.** The amount of energy absorbed in jumping from one energy level to a higher energy level is a precise quantity (hence the term *quantum*), and that energy exactly equals the energy difference between the two orbits. Electron promotion resulting from absorption of energy results in an **excited state** atom;

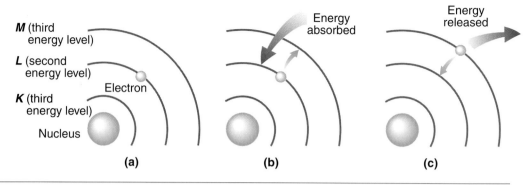

FIGURE 2.5
(a) The Bohr atom. (b) Excitation involves promotion of an electron to a higher energy level by absorption of energy.
(c) Relaxation is the reverse process, whereby an atom returns to the ground state as the electron moves to a lower energy level and energy is released.

the process of relaxation allows the atom to return to the **ground state** (Figure 2.5) with the simultaneous emission of energy that is sometimes perceived as visible light. When scientists excited atoms using an electric field and allowed them to return to the ground state, the light energy that was released appeared as a series of emission lines (the emission spectrum).

The theory that Bohr developed after evaluating the data from many experiments showed the atom to have a series of concentric orbits surrounding the nucleus. The orbits are identified by two different systems, one using numbers ($n = 1, 2, 3, \ldots$) and the other using letters (K, L, M, . . .). The number n is referred to as a **quantum number.** The quantum number $n = 1$ corresponds to a K shell, $n = 2$ is L, and so forth. As the quantum number increases, the energy difference between adjacent levels decreases.

2.4 MODERN ATOMIC THEORY

The Bohr model was an immensely important contribution to the understanding of atomic structure. The idea that electrons exist in specific energy states around the nucleus gave a much clearer picture of the atom. However, this model's limitations quickly became apparent. Although it explained the behavior of the hydrogen atom, it failed to explain more complex atoms.

Bohr's concept of principal energy levels is still valid; however, limiting electrons to fixed orbits is too restrictive. The fact is, we don't know exactly where the electron is at any time. We can only approximate where it is. When we can estimate a location, time, or any other quantity, it can be described in terms of probability. So too with electrons.

We speak of the *probability* of finding an electron in a region of space within the principal energy level. The rapid movement of electrons spreads the charge into a *cloud* of charge. This cloud is more *dense* in certain regions, the density being proportional to the probability of finding the electron in that region of space. Because these regions are within the principal energy levels, they are referred to as sublevels. Each sublevel contains *orbitals* designated by letters *s*, *p*, *d*, *f*, and so forth. The shapes of the *s* and *p* orbitals are shown in Figure 2.6.

2.5 THE PERIODIC LAW AND THE PERIODIC TABLE

In 1869, Dimitri Mendeleev, a Russian, and Lothar Meyer, a German, working independently, found ways of arranging elements in order of increasing atomic mass such that elements with similar properties were grouped together in a *table of elements*. Mendeleev's statement, ''the elements if arranged according to their atomic weights (masses), show a distinct *periodicity* (regular variation) of their properties,'' is the **periodic law.** The *periodic table* (Figure 2.7) is a visual representation of the periodic law.

Chemical and physical properties of elements correlate with the electronic structure of the atoms that make up these elements. In turn, the electronic structure correlates with position on the periodic table.

A thorough familiarity with the arrangement of the periodic table allows one to predict electronic structure and physical and chemical properties of the various elements. It also serves as the basis for understanding chemical bonding.

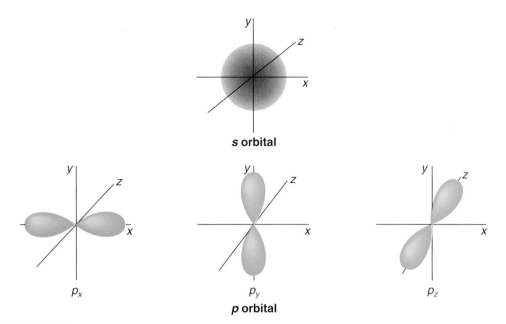

FIGURE 2.6
Atomic orbitals from wave-mechanical calculation.

FIGURE 2.7
Classification of the elements: the periodic table.

1 Group IA																	18 VIIIA
1 **H** 1.008	2 IIA											13 IIIA	14 IVA	15 VA	16 VIA	17 VIIA	2 **He** 4.00
3 **Li** 6.94	4 **Be** 9.01											5 **B** 10.81	6 **C** 12.01	7 **N** 14.01	8 **O** 16.00	9 **F** 19.00	10 **Ne** 20.18
11 **Na** 22.99	12 **Mg** 24.31	3 IIIB	4 IVB	5 VB	6 VIB	7 VIIB	8	9 VIIIB	10	11 IB	12 IIB	13 **Al** 26.98	14 **Si** 28.09	15 **P** 30.97	16 **S** 32.06	17 **Cl** 35.45	18 **Ar** 39.95
19 **K** 39.10	20 **Ca** 40.08	21 **Sc** 44.96	22 **Ti** 47.90	23 **V** 50.94	24 **Cr** 52.00	25 **Mn** 54.94	26 **Fe** 55.85	27 **Co** 58.93	28 **Ni** 58.69	29 **Cu** 63.54	30 **Zn** 65.37	31 **Ga** 69.72	32 **Ge** 72.61	33 **As** 74.92	34 **Se** 78.96	35 **Br** 79.91	36 **Kr** 83.80
37 **Rb** 85.47	38 **Sr** 87.62	39 **Y** 88.91	40 **Zr** 91.22	41 **Nb** 92.91	42 **Mo** 95.94	43 **Tc** (98)	44 **Ru** 101.07	45 **Rh** 102.90	46 **Pd** 106.42	47 **Ag** 107.87	48 **Cd** 112.41	49 **In** 114.82	50 **Sn** 118.69	51 **Sb** 121.75	52 **Te** 127.60	53 **I** 126.90	54 **Xe** 131.29
55 **Cs** 132.91	56 **Ba** 137.34	57 **La*** 138.91	72 **Hf** 178.49	73 **Ta** 180.95	74 **W** 183.85	75 **Re** 186.21	76 **Os** 190.2	77 **Ir** 192.22	78 **Pt** 195.08	79 **Au** 196.97	80 **Hg** 200.59	81 **Tl** 204.37	82 **Pb** 207.19	83 **Bi** 208.98	84 **Po** (209)	85 **At** (210)	86 **Rn** (222)
87 **Fr** (223)	88 **Ra** 226.03	89 **Ac**† 227.03	104 **Rf** (261)	105 **Ha** (262)	106 **(Sg)** (263)	107 **Ns** (262)	108 **Hs** (265)	109 **Mt** (266)									

Representative elements · Metalloids · Noble gases · Lathanides · Transition metals · Actinides

Atomic number · Symbol · Atomic mass
6 **C** 12.01

*Lanthanides	58 **Ce** 140.12	59 **Pr** 140.91	60 **Nd** 144.24	61 **Pm** (145)	62 **Sm** 150.36	63 **Eu** 151.96	64 **Gd** 157.25	65 **Tb** 158.92	66 **Dy** 162.50	67 **Ho** 164.93	68 **Er** 167.26	69 **Tm** 168.93	70 **Yb** 173.04	71 **Lu** 174.97
†Actinides	90 **Th** 232.04	91 **Pa** 231.04	92 **U** 238.03	93 **Np** (237)	94 **Pu** (244)	95 **Am** (243)	96 **Cm** (247)	97 **Bk** (247)	98 **Cf** (251)	99 **Es** (252)	100 **Fm** (257)	101 **Md** (258)	102 **No** (259)	103 **Lr** (260)

Note: The symbol for element 106 is provisional.

AN ENVIRONMENTAL PERSPECTIVE

Electromagnetic Radiation and Its Effects on Our Everyday Lives

From the preceding discussion of the interaction of electromagnetic radiation with matter—spectroscopy—one might be left with the impression that the utility of such radiation is limited to theoretical studies of atomic structure. While this is a useful application that has enabled us to learn a great deal about the structure and properties of matter, it is by no means the only application. Useful, everyday applications of the theories of light energy and transmission are all around us. Let's look at just a few examples.

Transmission of sound and pictures is conducted at radio frequencies or radio wavelengths. We are immersed in radio waves from the day we are born. A radio or television is our "detector" of these waves. Radio waves are believed to cause no physical harm because of their very low energy, although some concern for people who live very close to transmission towers has resulted from recent research.

X-rays are electromagnetic radiation, and they travel at the speed of light just like radio waves. However, because of their higher energy, they can pass through the human body and leave an image of the body's interior on a photographic film. X-ray photographs are invaluable for medical diagnosis. However, caution is advised in exposing oneself to X-rays, since the high energy is capable of actually removing electrons from biological molecules, causing subtle and potentially harmful changes in their chemistry.

The sunlight that passes through our atmosphere provides the basis for a potentially useful technology for providing heat and electricity: *solar energy.* Light is captured by absorbers, referred to as solar collectors, which convert the light energy into heat energy. This heat can be transferred to water circulating beneath the collectors to provide heat and hot water for homes or industry. Wafers of a silicon-based material can convert light energy to electrical energy; many believe that if the efficiency of these processes can be improved, such approaches may provide at least a partial solution to the problems of rising energy costs and pollution associated with our fossil-fuel-based energy economy.

Microwave radiation for cooking, *infrared* lamps for heating and remote sensing, *ultraviolet* lamps used to kill microorganisms on environmental surfaces, *gamma radiation* from nu-

The intensity of infrared radiation from a solid or liquid is an indicator of relative temperature. This has been used to advantage in the design of infrared cameras, which can obtain images without the benefit of visible light, as is necessary with conventional cameras. The infrared photograph shows the coastline surrounding the city of San Francisco.

The concept of "periodicity" may be illustrated by examining a portion of the modern periodic table (Figure 2.7). The elements in the second row (beginning with lithium, Li, and proceeding to the right) show a marked difference in properties. However, sodium (Na) has properties similar to those of lithium, and sodium is therefore placed below lithium; once lithium is fixed in this position, the elements Mg through Ar have properties remarkably similar to those of the elements just above them. The same is true throughout the complete periodic table.

Mendeleev arranged the elements in his original periodic table in order of increasing atomic mass. However, as our knowledge of atomic structure increased, atomic numbers became the basis for the organization of the table.

The modern periodic law states that *the physical and chemical properties of the elements are periodic functions of their atomic numbers.*

Not all of the elements are of equal importance to an introductory study of chemistry. Table 2.2 summarizes 25 of the elements that are most important to biological systems, along with their symbols and a brief description of their functions.

We will use the periodic table as our "map," just as a traveler would use a road map. A short time spent learning how to read the map (and remembering to carry it along on your trip!)

clear waste, the *visible* light from the lamp you are using to read this chapter—all are forms of the same type of energy that, for better or worse, plays such a large part of our twentieth century technological society.

Electromagnetic radiation and spectroscopy also play a vital role in the field of diagnostic medicine. They are routinely used as diagnostic and therapeutic tools in the detection and treatment of disease.

The radiation therapy used in the treatment of many types of cancer has been responsible for saving many lives and extending the span of many others. When radiation is used as a treatment, it destroys cancer cells. This topic will be discussed in detail in Chapter 8.

As a diagnostic tool, spectroscopy has the benefit of providing data quickly and reliably; it can also provide information that might not be available through any other means. Additionally, these are often nonsurgical, outpatient proce-

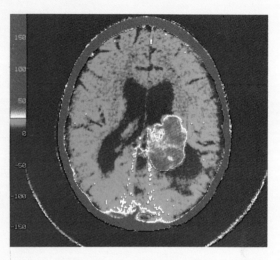

An image of a tumor detected by a CT scan.

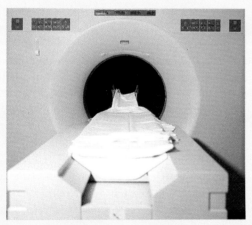

The CT scanner is a device used for diagnostic purposes.

dures. Such procedures are safer, can be more routinely performed, and are more acceptable to the general public than surgical procedures. The potential cost savings due to the elimination of many unnecessary surgical procedures is an added benefit.

The most commonly practiced technique utilizes the CT scanner, an acronym for *computer-accentuated tomography*. In this technique, X-rays are directed at the tissue of interest. As the X-rays pass through the tissue, detectors surrounding the tissue gather the signal, compare it to the original X-ray beam, and, using the computer, produce a three-dimensional image of the tissue.

is much easier than memorizing every highway and intersection. The information learned about one element relates to an entire family of elements grouped as a recognizable unit within the table.

Periods and families

A horizontal row of elements in the periodic table is referred to as a **period.** The periodic table consists of seven periods containing 2, 8, 8, 18, 18, and 32 elements. The seventh period is still incomplete but potentially holds 32 elements. Note that the **lanthanide series** is a part of period six. It is written separately for convenience of presentation. We could insert it between lanthanum (La), atomic number 57, and hafnium (Hf), atomic number 72. Similarly, the **actinide series** inserts between actinium, atomic number 89, and rutherfordium, atomic number 104.

The columns of elements in the periodic table are called **groups** or *families*. The elements of a particular family share many similarities, as in a human family. The similarities extend to physical and chemical properties that are related to similarities in electronic structure (that is, the way in which electrons are arranged in an atom). The various groups are labeled with Roman numerals, and each is subtitled with the letter A or B.

TABLE 2.2   Summary of the Most Important Elements

Element	Symbol	Significance
Hydrogen	H	
Carbon	C	
Oxygen	O	Components of
Nitrogen	N	major biological
Phosphorus	P	molecules
Sulfur	S	
Potassium	K	Produce electrolytes responsible
Sodium	Na	for fluid balance and
Chlorine	Cl	nerve transmission
Calcium	Ca	
Magnesium	Mg	Bones, nerve function
Aluminum	Al	
Strontium	Sr	
Iron	Fe	Essential trace
Copper	Cu	metals in human
Cobalt	Co	metabolism
Manganese	Mn	
Cadmium	Cd	"Heavy metals"
Mercury	Hg	toxic to living
Lead	Pb	systems

Group A elements are called **representative elements,** and Group B elements are **transition elements.** Certain families have common names as well as a Roman numeral and letter designation. For example, Group IA elements are also known as the **alkali metals;** Group IIA, the **alkaline earth metals;** Group VIIA, the **halogens;** and Group VIIIA, the **noble gases.**

Metals and nonmetals

Many metals, as positive ions, are essential nutrients in biological systems. The Clinical Perspective: Copper Deficiency and Wilson's Disease gives but one example.

A closer inspection of the periodic table reveals a bold zigzag line running from top to bottom of the table beginning to the left of boron (B) and ending between polonium (Po) and astatine (At). This line acts as the boundary between **metals,** to the left, and **nonmetals,** to the right. Elements straddling the boundary, such as germanium, Ge, and arsenic, As, have properties intermediate between those of metals and nonmetals. These elements are referred to as **metalloids.**

Atomic number and atomic mass

The atomic number is the number of protons in the nucleus of an atom of an element. It also corresponds to the nuclear charge, the positive charge from the nucleus. Both the atomic number and atomic mass of each element are readily available from the periodic table. For example,

$$
\begin{array}{ll}
20 & \longleftarrow \quad \text{atomic number} \\
\text{Ca} & \longleftarrow \quad \text{symbol} \\
\text{calcium} & \longleftarrow \quad \text{name} \\
40.08 & \longleftarrow \quad \text{atomic mass}
\end{array}
$$

More detailed periodic tables may also include such information as the electron arrangement, relative sizes of atoms and ions, and most probable ion charges.

QUESTION 2.7

Referring to the periodic table (Figure 2.7), find the following information:

a.   the symbol of the element with an atomic number of 40   Zr

b.   the mass of the element sodium (Na)   22.99

c.   the element whose atom contains 24 protons   Cr

d. the known element that should most resemble the as-yet-undiscovered element with an atomic number of 115

QUESTION 2.8

Referring to the periodic table (Figure 2.7), find the following information:

a. the symbol of the noble gas in period 3
b. the lightest element in group IVA
c. the only metalloid in group IIIA
d. the element representing an atom containing 18 protons

QUESTION 2.9

For each of the following elemental symbols, give the name of the element, its atomic number, and its atomic mass:

a. He   Helium
b. F   Flourine
c. Mn   Manganese

QUESTION 2.10

For each of the following elemental symbols, give the name of the element, its atomic number, and its atomic mass:

a. Mg   Magnesium
b. Ne   Neon
c. Se   Selenium

A primary objective of studying chemistry is to understand the way in which atoms join together to form chemical compounds. The most important factor in this *bonding process* is the arrangement of the electrons in the atoms that are combining. The periodic table is helpful because it provides us with a great deal of information about the electron arrangement or **electronic configuration** of atoms.

Electron arrangement and the periodic table

2.6 VALENCE ELECTRONS

If we picture two spherical objects that we wish to join together, perhaps with glue, the glue can be applied to the surface, and the two objects can then be brought into contact. We can extend this analogy to two atoms that are modeled as spherical objects. Although this is not a perfect analogy, it is apparent that the surface interaction is of primary importance. Although the positively charged nucleus and "interior" electrons certainly play a role in bonding, we can most easily understand the process by considering only the outermost electrons. We refer to these as **valence electrons.**

For representative elements the number of valence electrons in an atom corresponds to the number of the *group* or *family* in which the atom is found. For example, elements such as hydrogen and sodium (in fact, all alkali metals, Group IA) have a valence of 1 (or one valence electron). Reading from left to right in period 2, beryllium, Be (Group IIA), has two valence electrons; boron, B (Group IIIA), has three; carbon, C (Group IVA), has four; and so forth.

We have seen that an atom may have several energy levels, or regions where electrons are located. These energy levels are symbolized by n, the lowest energy level being assigned a value of $n = 1$. Each energy level may contain up to a fixed maximum number of electrons. For example, the $n = 1$ energy level contains a maximum of two electrons. Thus hydrogen (atomic number = 1) has one electron and helium (atomic number = 2) has two electrons in the $n = 1$

Metals tend to have fewer valence electrons, and nonmetals tend to have more valence electrons.

level. Only these elements have electrons *exclusively* in the first energy level:

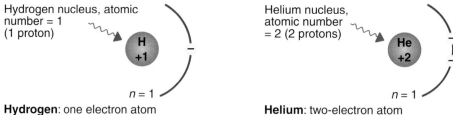

Hydrogen: one electron atom   **Helium**: two-electron atom

These two elements make up the first period of the periodic table. Period 1 contains all elements whose *maximum* energy level is $n = 1$. In other words, the $n = 1$ level is the *outermost* electron region for hydrogen and helium. Hydrogen has one electron and helium has two electrons in the $n = 1$ level.

The valence electrons of elements in the second period are in the $n = 2$ energy level. (Remember that you must fill the $n = 1$ level with two electrons before adding electrons to the next level.) The third electron of lithium (Li) and the remaining electrons of the second period elements must be in the $n = 2$ level and are considered the valence electrons for lithium and the remaining second period elements.

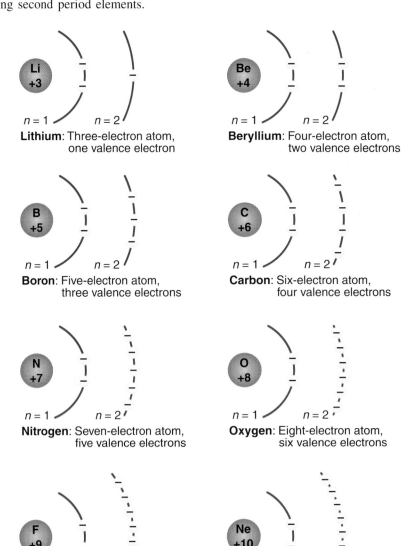

Lithium: Three-electron atom, one valence electron

Beryllium: Four-electron atom, two valence electrons

Boron: Five-electron atom, three valence electrons

Carbon: Six-electron atom, four valence electrons

Nitrogen: Seven-electron atom, five valence electrons

Oxygen: Eight-electron atom, six valence electrons

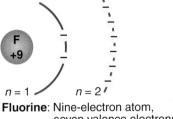

Fluorine: Nine-electron atom, seven valence electrons

Neon: Ten-electron atom, eight valence electrons

TABLE 2.3　The Electron Distribution for the First 20 Elements of the Periodic Table

Element Symbol and Name	Total Number of Electrons (Valence Electrons)	Electrons in $n = 1$	Electrons in $n = 2$	Electrons in $n = 3$	Electrons in $n = 4$
H, hydrogen	1 (1)	1	0	0	0
He, helium	2 (2)	2	0	0	0
Li, lithium	3 (1)	2	1	0	0
Be, beryllium	4 (2)	2	2	0	0
B, boron	5 (3)	2	3	0	0
C, carbon	6 (4)	2	4	0	0
N, nitrogen	7 (5)	2	5	0	0
O, oxygen	8 (6)	2	6	0	0
F, fluorine	9 (7)	2	7	0	0
Ne, neon	10 (8)	2	8	0	0
Na, sodium	11 (1)	2	8	1	0
Mg, magnesium	12 (2)	2	8	2	0
Al, aluminum	13 (3)	2	8	3	0
Si, silicon	14 (4)	2	8	4	0
P, phosphorus	15 (5)	2	8	5	0
S, sulfur	16 (6)	2	8	6	0
Cl, chlorine	17 (7)	2	8	7	0
Ar, argon	18 (8)	2	8	8	0
K, potassium	19 (1)	2	8	8	1
Ca, calcium	20 (2)	2	8	8	2

The electron configuration (arrangement) of the first 20 elements of the periodic table is given in Table 2.3.

Two general rules of electron configuration are based on the periodic law:

Rule 1　The number of valence electrons in an atom equals the *group* number for all representative (A group) elements.

Rule 2　The energy level ($n = 1$, 2, etc.) in which the valence electrons are located corresponds to the *period* in which the element may be found.

For example,

Group IA	Group IIA	Group IIIA	Group VIIA
Li	Ca	Al	Br
one valence electron in period 2 $n = 2$	two valence electrons in period 4 $n = 4$	three valence electrons in period 3 $n = 3$	seven valence electrons in period 4 $n = 4$

EXAMPLE 2.2

Determining Electron Arrangement

Provide the total number of electrons, total number of valence electrons, and energy levels in which the valence electrons are found for the silicon (Si) atom.

Solution

Step 1　Determine the position of silicon in the periodic table. Silicon is found in Group IVA and period 2 of the table. Silicon has an atomic number of 14.

Step 2   The atomic number provides the number of electrons in an atom. Silicon there-fore has 14 electrons.

Step 3   Since silicon is in Group IV, only four of the 14 electrons are valence electrons.

Step 4   Silicon has two electrons in $n = 1$, eight electrons in $n = 2$, and four electrons in the $n = 3$ level.

QUESTION 2.11

For each of the following elements, provide the *total* number of electrons and *valence* electrons in its atom:

a. Na   d. Cl
b. Mg   e. Ar
c. S

QUESTION 2.12

For each of the following elements, provide the *total* number of electrons and *valence* electrons in its atom:

a. K   d. O
b. F   e. Ca
c. P

The octet rule

We may think of stability as a type of contentment; the atom does not need to rearrange its electrons or lose or gain any electrons to get to a more stable, lower-energy, or more "contented" configuration.

Elements in the last family, the noble gases, have either two valence electrons (helium) or eight valence electrons (neon, argon, krypton, xenon, and radon). These elements, are extremely stable and were often termed inert gases. They do not readily bond to other elements, although they can be made to do so under extreme experimental conditions. A full $n = 1$ energy level (as in helium) or an outer *octet* of electrons (eight valence electrons, as in all of the other noble gases) is responsible for this unique stability.

It follows that atoms of elements in other groups are more reactive than the noble gases because they are, in the process of chemical reaction, trying to achieve a more stable "noble gas" configuration by gaining or losing electrons. This is the basis of the **octet rule.** Elements usually react in such a way as to attain the electron configuration of the noble gas closest to them in the periodic table (a stable octet of electrons). In chemical reactions they will gain, lose, or share the minimum number of electrons necessary to attain this more stable energy state. The octet rule, although simple in concept, is a remarkably reliable predictor of chemical change, especially for representative elements.

Ion formation and the octet rule

Metals and nonmetals differ in the way in which they form ions. Metallic elements (located at the left of the periodic table) tend to form positively charged ions called *cations*. Positive ions are formed when an atom loses one or more electrons, for example,

$$\text{Na} \longrightarrow \text{Na}^+ + e^-$$

Sodium atom   Sodium ion
($11e^-$)   ($10e^-$)

$$\text{Mg} \longrightarrow \text{Mg}^{2+} + 2e^-$$

Magnesium atom   Magnesium ion
($12e^-$)   ($10e^-$)

$$\text{Al} \longrightarrow \text{Al}^{3+} + 3e^-$$

Aluminum atom　　　　Aluminum ion
　(13e$^-$)　　　　　　　(10e$^-$)

In each of these cases the atom has lost *all* of its valence electrons. The resulting ion has the same number of electrons as the nearest noble gas atom:

Na$^+$ (10e$^-$)	Ne (10e$^-$)
Sodium ion	Neon atom
Mg^{2+} (10e$^-$)	Ne (10e$^-$)
Magnesium ion	Neon atom
Al^{3+} (10e$^-$)	Ne (10e$^-$)
Aluminum ion	Neon atom

These ions are more stable than their corresponding neutral atoms. Each ion is **isoelectronic** (that is, it has the same number of electrons) with its nearest noble gas neighbor and has an octet of electrons in its outermost energy level.

Sodium is typical of each element in its group. Knowing that sodium forms a 1+ ion leads to the prediction that H, Li, K, Rb, Cs, and Fr will form 1+ ions as well. Furthermore, magnesium, which forms a 2+ ion, is typical of each element in its group. Be^{2+}, Ca^{2+}, Sr^{2+}, and so forth are the resulting ions.

Nonmetallic elements, located at the right of the periodic table, tend to gain electrons to become isoelectronic with the nearest noble gas element, forming negative ions called *anions*. Consider:

$$\text{F} + 1e^- \longrightarrow \text{F}^-　\quad\text{(isoelectronic with Ne, 10e}^-\text{)}$$

Fluorine atom　　　　　Fluoride ion
　(9e$^-$)　　　　　　　　(10e$^-$)

$$\text{O} + 2e^- \longrightarrow \text{O}^{2-}　\quad\text{(isoelectronic with Ne, 10e}^-\text{)}$$

Oxygen atom　　　　　　Oxide ion
　(8e$^-$)　　　　　　　　(10e$^-$)

$$\text{N} + 3e^- \longrightarrow \text{N}^{3-}　\quad\text{(isoelectronic with Ne, 10e}^-\text{)}$$

Nitrogen atom　　　　Nitride ion
　(7e$^-$)　　　　　　　(10e$^-$)

Section 3.2 discusses the naming of ions. The ion of fluorine is the *fluoride ion*; the ion of oxygen is the *oxide ion*; and the ion of nitrogen is the *nitride* ion.

As in the case of positive ion formation, each of the negative ions listed above has an octet of electrons in its outermost energy level.

The element fluorine, forming F$^-$, indicates that the other halogens, Cl, Br, and I, behave as a true family and form Cl$^-$, Br$^-$, and I$^-$ ions. Also, oxygen and the other nonmetals in its group form 2$^-$ ions; nitrogen and phosphorus form 3$^-$ ions.

QUESTION 2.13

Give the charge of the most probable ion resulting from each of the following elements. With what element is the ion isoelectronic?

a.　Ca　　d.　Mg
b.　Sr　　e.　P
c.　S

QUESTION 2.14

Which of the following pairs of atoms and ions are isoelectronic?

a. Cl^-, Ar   d. Li^+, Ne

b. Na^+, Ne   e. O^{2-}, F^-

c. Mg^{2+}, Na^+

The transition metals tend to form positive ions by losing electrons, just like the representative metals. Metals, whether representative or transition, share this characteristic. However, the transition elements are characterized as "variable valence" elements; depending on the type of substance with which they react, they may form more than one stable ion. For example, iron has two stable ionic forms:

$$Fe^{2+} \quad \text{and} \quad Fe^{3+}$$

copper can exist as

$$Cu^+ \quad \text{and} \quad Cu^{2+}$$

and elements such as vanadium, V, and manganese, Mn, each have four different stable ions.

Predicting the charge of an ion or the various possible ions for a given transition metal is not an easy task. Energy differences between valence electrons are small and not easily predicted from the position of the element in the periodic table. In fact, in contrast to representative metals, the transition metals show great similarities within a *period* as well as within a *group*.

2.7 TRENDS IN THE PERIODIC TABLE

Atomic size

If our model of the atom is a tiny sphere whose radius is determined by the distance between the center of the nucleus and the boundary of the region where the valence electrons are located, the size of the atom will be determined principally by two factors:

1. The energy level (*n*-level) in which the outermost electron(s) is (are) located increases as we go *down* a group. (Recall that the outermost *n*-level correlates with period number.) Thus the size of atoms should increase from top to bottom of the periodic table as we fill successive energy levels of the atoms with electrons (see Figure 2.8).

2. As the magnitude of the positive charge of the nucleus increases, its "pull" on all of the electrons increases, and the electrons are drawn closer to the nucleus. This results in a contraction of the atomic radius and therefore a decrease in atomic size. This effect is

---

FIGURE 2.8
Variation in the size of atoms as a function of their position in the periodic table. Note particularly the decrease in size from left to right in the periodic table and the increase in size as we proceed down the table, although some exceptions do exist. [Lanthanide and actinide elements are not included here.]

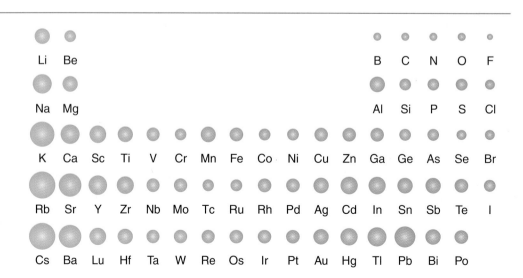

apparent as we go *across* the periodic table within a period. Atomic size decreases from left to right in the periodic table (see Figure 2.8).

Positive ions (cations) are smaller than the parent atom. The cation has more protons than electrons (an increased nuclear charge). The excess nuclear charge pulls the remaining electrons closer to the nucleus.

Ion size

Negative ions (anions) are larger than the parent atom. The anion has more electrons than protons. Owing to the excess negative charge, the nuclear ''pull'' on each individual electron is reduced. The electrons are held less tightly, resulting in a larger anion radius in contrast to the neutral atom.

Ions with multiple positive charge (such as Cu^{2+}) are even *smaller* than their corresponding monopositive ion (Cu^{+}); ions with multiple negative charge (such as O^{2-}) are *larger* than their corresponding less negative ion. This follows directly from Rules 1 and 2 above.

Figure 2.9 depicts the relative sizes of several atoms and their corresponding ions.

The energy required to remove an electron from an isolated atom is the **ionization energy.** The process for sodium is represented as follows:

Ionization energy

$$Na \;\; + \;\; ionization \;\; \longrightarrow \;\; Na^{+} \;\; + \;\; e^{-}$$
$$energy$$

The magnitude of the ionization energy should correlate with the strength of the attractive force between the nucleus and the outermost electron.

◆ Reading *down* a group, the ionization energy decreases, since the atom's size is increasing. The outermost electron is progressively farther from the nuclear charge, hence easier to remove.

◆ Reading *across* a period, atomic size decreases, since the outermost electrons are closer to the nucleus, more tightly held, and more difficult to remove. Therefore the ionization energy must increase.

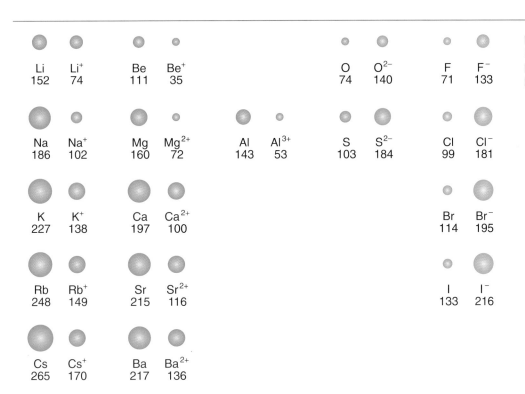

FIGURE 2.9
Relative size of ions and their parent atoms. Atomic radii are provided in units of picometers.

A MEDICAL PERSPECTIVE

Copper Deficiency and Wilson's Disease

An old adage tells us that we should consume all things in moderation. This is very true of many of the trace minerals, such as copper. Too much copper in the diet causes toxicity, and too little copper results in a serious deficiency disease.

Copper is extremely important for the proper functioning of the body. It aids in the absorption of iron from the intestine and facilitates iron metabolism. It is critical for the formation of hemoglobin and red blood cells in the bone marrow. Copper is also necessary for the synthesis of collagen, a protein that is a major component of the connective tissue. It is essential to the central nervous system in two important ways. First, copper is needed for the synthesis of norepinephrine and dopamine, two chemicals that are necessary for the transmission of nerve signals. Second, it is required for the deposition of the myelin sheath (a layer of insulation) around nerve cells. Release of cholesterol from the liver depends on copper, as does bone development and proper function of the immune and blood clotting systems.

The estimated safe and adequate daily dietary intake (ESADDI) for adults is 1.5–3.0 mg. Meats, cocoa, nuts, legumes, and whole grains provide significant amounts of copper. The accompanying table shows the amount of copper in some common foods.

Although getting enough copper in the diet would appear to be relatively simple, it is estimated that Americans often ingest only marginal levels of copper, and we absorb only 25–40% of that dietary copper. Despite these facts, it appears that copper deficiency is not a serious problem in the United States.

Individuals who are at risk for copper deficiency include people who are recovering from abdominal surgery, which causes decreased absorption of copper from the intestine. Others at risk are premature babies and people who are sustained solely by intravenous feedings that are deficient in copper. In addition, people who ingest high doses of antacids or take excessive supplements of zinc, iron, or vitamin C can develop copper deficiency due to reduced copper absorption. Because copper is involved in so many processes in the body, it is not surprising that the symptoms of copper deficiency are many and diverse. They include anemia; decreased red and white blood cell counts; heart disease; increased levels of serum cholesterol; loss of bone; defects in the nervous system, immune system, and connective tissue; and abnormal hair.

Some of these symptoms are seen among people who suffer from the rare genetic disease known as Menkes' kinky hair syndrome. The symptoms of this disease, which is caused by a defect in the ability to absorb copper from the intestine, include very low copper levels in the serum, kinky white hair, slowed growth, and degeneration of the brain.

Just as too little copper causes serious problems, so does an excess of copper. At doses greater than about 15 mg, copper causes toxicity that results in vomiting. The effects of

Copper in One-Cup Portions of Food

Food	One-Cup Portion of Food (mg)
Sesame seeds	5.88
Cashews	3.04
Oysters	2.88
Sunflower seeds	2.52
Peanuts, roasted	1.85
Crabmeat	1.71
Walnuts	1.28
Almonds	1.22
Cereal, All Bran	0.98
Tuna fish	0.93
Wheat germ	0.70
Prunes	0.69
Kidney beans	0.56
Dried apricots	0.56
Lentils, cooked	0.54
Sweet potato, cooked	0.53
Dates	0.51
Whole milk	0.50
Raisins	0.45
Cereal, C. W. Post, Raisins	0.40
Grape Nuts	0.38
Whole-wheat bread	0.34
Cooked cereal, Roman Meal	0.32

Source: From David C. Nieman, Diane E. Butterworth, and Catherine N. Nieman, *Nutrition,* Revised First Edition. Copyright © 1992 Wm. C. Brown Communications, Inc., Dubuque, Iowa. All Rights Reserved. Reprinted by permission.

extended exposure to excess copper are apparent when we look at Wilson's disease. This is a genetic disorder in which excess copper cannot be removed from the body and accumulates in the cornea of the eye, liver, kidneys, and brain. The symptoms include a greenish ring around the cornea, cirrhosis of the liver, copper in the urine, dementia and paranoia, drooling, and progressive tremors. As a result of the condition, the victim generally dies in early adolescence. Wilson's disease can be treated with moderate success if it is recognized early, before permanent damage has occurred to any tissues. The diet is modified to reduce the intake of copper; for instance, such foods as chocolate are avoided. In addition, the drug penicillamine is administered. This compound is related to the antibiotic penicillin but has no antibacterial properties; rather it has the ability to bind to copper in the blood and enhance its excretion by the kidneys into the urine. In this way the brain degeneration and tissue damage that are normally seen with the disease can be lessened.

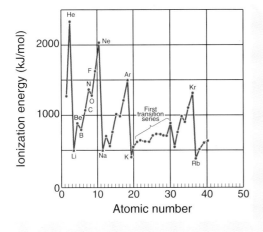

FIGURE 2.10
The ionization energies of the first 40 elements versus their atomic numbers. Note the very high values for elements located to the right of the periodic table, and low values for those to the left. Some exceptions to the trends are evident.

A correlation does indeed exist between trends in atomic size and ionization energy. Atomic size *decreases* from bottom to top of a group and from left to right in a period. Ionization energies *increase* in the same periodic way. Note also that ionization energies are highest for the noble gases (see Figure 2.10). A high value for ionization energy means that it is difficult to remove electrons from the atom, and this, in part, accounts for the extreme stability and nonreactivity of the noble gases.

The energy released when a single electron is added to an isolated atom is the **electron affinity.** **Electron affinity**
If we consider ionization energy in relation to positive ion formation (remember that the magnitude of the ionization energy tells us the ease of *removal* of an electron, hence the ease of forming positive ions), then electron affinity provides a measure of the ease of forming negative ions. A large electron affinity (energy released) indicates that the atom becomes more stable as it becomes a negative ion (through gaining an electron). Consider the gain of an electron by a bromine atom:

$$Br + e^- \longrightarrow Br^- + energy$$

electron affinity

Periodic trends for electron affinity are as follows:

◆ Electron affinities generally decrease as we go down a group.
◆ Electron affinities generally increase going across a period.

Remember these trends are not absolute. Exceptions exist, as seen in Figure 2.11.

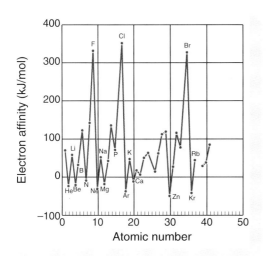

FIGURE 2.11
The periodic variation of electron affinity. Note the very low values for the noble gases and the elements to the far left of the periodic table. These elements do not form negative ions. F, Cl, and Br, in contrast, readily form negative ions.

QUESTION 2.15

Rank Be, N, and F in order of increasing

a. atomic size

b. ionization energy

c. electron affinity

QUESTION 2.16

Rank Cl, Br, I, and F in order of increasing

a. atomic size

b. ionization energy

c. electron affinity

SUMMARY

2.1 Matter and Properties

Properties (characteristics) of matter may be classified as either physical or chemical. Physical properties can be observed without changing the chemical composition of the sample. *Chemical properties* result in a change in composition and can be observed only through *chemical reactions. Intensive properties* are independent of the quantity of the substance. *Extensive properties* depend on the quantity of a substance.

Three states of matter exist (solid, liquid, and gas); these states of matter are distinguishable by differences in physical properties.

All matter is classified as either a *pure substance* or a *mixture.* A pure substance has identical composition and physical and chemical properties throughout. A mixture is a combination of two or more pure substances in which the combined substances retain their identity.

A *homogeneous mixture* has uniform composition. Its particles are well mixed. A *heterogeneous mixture* has a nonuniform composition.

An *element* is a pure substance that cannot be converted into a simpler form of matter by any chemical reaction. A *compound* is a substance produced from the combination of two or more elements in a definite, reproducible fashion.

2.2 Matter and Structure

The basic structural unit of an element is the *atom,* which is the smallest unit of an element that retains the chemical properties of that element. The atom is composed of three primary particles: the electron, the proton, and the neutron.

The atom has two distinct regions. The *nucleus* is a small, dense, positively charged region in the center of the atom composed of positively charged *protons* and uncharged *neutrons.* Surrounding the nucleus is a diffuse region of negative charge made up of *electrons,* the source of the negative charge. Electrons are tiny in comparison to protons and neutrons.

The *atomic number* (Z) is equal to the number of protons in the atom. The *mass number* (A) is equal to the sum of the protons and neutrons (the mass of the electrons is insignificant).

Isotopes are atoms of the same element that have different masses because they have different numbers of neutrons (different mass numbers). Isotopes have chemical behavior identical to that of any other isotope of the same element.

Ions are electrically charged particles that result from a gain or loss of one or more electrons by the parent atom. *Anions,* negative ions, are formed by a gain of one or more electrons by the parent atom. *Cations,* positive ions, are formed by a loss of one or more electrons from the parent atom.

2.3 Development of the Atomic Theory

The first experimentally based theory of atomic structure was proposed by John Dalton. Although Dalton pictured atoms as indivisible, the experiments of William Crookes, Eugene Goldstein, and J. J. Thomson indicated that the atom is composed of charged particles: protons and electrons. The third fundamental atomic particle is the neutron. An experiment conducted by Hans Geiger led Ernest Rutherford to propose that the majority of the mass and positive charge of the atom was located in a small, dense region, the *nucleus,* with small, negatively charged electrons spread across a much larger, diffuse area outside of the nucleus.

Niels Bohr proposed an atomic model that described the atom as a nucleus surrounded by fixed *energy levels* (or *quantum levels*) that can be occupied by electrons. He believed that each level was defined by a circular *orbit* located at a specific distance from the nucleus.

Promotion and relaxation processes are referred to as *electronic transitions.* Electron promotion resulting from absorption of energy results in an *excited state* atom; the process of relaxation allows the atom to return to the *ground state.*

2.4 Modern Atomic Theory

The modern view of the atom describes the probability of finding an electron in a region of space within the principal energy level, referred to as an *atomic orbital.* The rapid movement of the electrons spreads them into a cloud of charge. This cloud is more dense in certain regions, the density being proportional to the probability of finding the electron at any point in time. The arrangement of electrons in atomic orbitals is the *electron configuration.*

2.5 The Periodic Law and the Periodic Table

The *periodic law* is an organized "map" of the elements that relates their structure to their chemical and physical properties. It states that the elements, when arranged according to their atomic numbers, show a distinct periodicity (regular variation) of their properties. The periodic table is the result of the periodic law.

A horizontal row of elements in the periodic table is referred to as a *period.* The periodic table consists of seven periods. The *lanthanide series* is a part of period 6; the *actinide series* is a part of period 7.

The columns of elements in the periodic table are called *groups* or *families.* The elements of a particular family share many similarities in physical and chemical properties because of the similarities in electronic structure. The various groups are labeled with Roman numerals, and each is subtitled with the letter A or B. Some of the most important groups are named as well; for example the *alkali metals* (IA), *alkaline earth metals* (IIA), the *halogens* (VIIA), and the *noble gases* (VIII).

Group A elements are called *representative elements;* Group B elements are *transition elements.* A bold zigzag line runs from top to bottom of the table, beginning to the left of boron (B) and ending between polonium (Po) and astatine (At). This line acts as the boundary between *metals* to the left and *nonmetals* to the right. Elements straddling the boundary, *metalloids,* have properties intermediate between those of metals and nonmetals.

2.6 Valence Electrons

The outermost electrons in an atom are *valence electrons.* For representative elements the number of valence electrons in an atom corresponds to the group or family number. Metals tend to have fewer valence electrons than nonmetals.

Elements in the last family, the noble gases, have either two valence electrons (helium) or eight valence electrons (neon, argon, krypton, xenon, and radon). Their most important properties are their extreme stability and lack of reactivity. A full valence level is responsible for this unique stability. The *octet rule* tells us that in chemical reactions, elements will gain, lose, or share the minimum number of electrons necessary to achieve the electron configuration of the nearest noble gas.

Metallic elements tend to form cations. The ion is *isoelectronic* with its nearest noble gas neighbor and has a stable octet of electrons in its outermost energy level. Nonmetallic elements tend to gain electrons to become isoelectronic with the nearest noble gas element, forming anions.

2.7 Trends in the Periodic Table

Atomic size decreases from left to right and from bottom to top in the periodic table. Cations are smaller than the parent atom. Anions are larger than the parent atom. Ions with multiple positive charge are even smaller than their corresponding monopositive ion; ions with multiple negative charge are larger than their corresponding less negative ion.

The energy required to remove an electron from the atom is the *ionization energy.* Descending a group, the ionization energy generally decreases. Proceeding across a period, the ionization energy generally increases.

The energy released when a single electron is added to a neutral atom in the gaseous state is known as the *electron affinity.* Electron affinities generally decrease proceeding down a group and increase proceeding across a period.

KEY TERMS

actinide series (2.5)
alkali metal (2.5)
alkaline earth metals (2.5)
anion (2.2)
atom (2.2)
atomic mass (2.2)
atomic number (2.2)
cation (2.2)
chemical properties (2.1)
chemical reaction (2.1)
compound (2.1)
electron (2.2)
electron affinity (2.7)
electron configuration (2.3, 2.6)
electronic transition (2.3)
element (2.1)
energy level (2.3)
excited state (2.3)
extensive property (2.1)
family (2.5)
gaseous state (2.1)
ground state (2.3)
group (2.5)
halogens (2.5)
heterogeneous mixture (2.1)
homogeneous mixture (2.1)
intensive property (2.1)
ion (2.2)
ionization energy (2.7)
isoelectronic (2.6)

isotopes (2.2)
lanthanide series (2.5)
liquid state (2.1)
mass number (2.2)
metalloids (2.5)
metals (2.5)
mixture (2.1)
neutron (2.2)
noble gases (2.5)
nonmetals (2.5)
nucleus (2.2)
octet rule (2.6)
orbit (2.3)
period (2.5)
periodic law (2.5)
physical change (2.1)
physical property (2.1)
product (2.1)
promotion (2.3)
proton (2.2)
pure substance (2.1)
quantum level (2.3)
quantum number (2.3)
reactants (2.1)
relaxation (2.3)
representative elements (2.5)
solid state (2.1)
states of matter (2.1)
transition elements (2.5)
valence electrons (2.6)

QUESTIONS AND PROBLEMS

Matter and Properties

2.17 Describe what is meant by a physical property.

2.18 Describe what is meant by a physical change.

2.19 Label each of the following as either a physical change or a chemical change:

a. An iron nail rusts.

b. An ice cube melts.

c. A puddle of water evaporates.

d. Food is digested.

e. Wood is burned.

2.20 Label each of the following properties of sodium as either a physical property or a chemical property:

a. Sodium is a soft metal (can be cut with a knife).

b. Sodium reacts violently with water to produce hydrogen gas and sodium hydroxide.

c. When exposed to air, sodium forms a white oxide.

d. Sodium melts at 98°C.

e. The density of sodium metal at 25°C is 0.97 g/cm^3.

2.21 Describe several chemical properties of matter.

2.22 Describe what is meant by chemical change.

2.23 Distinguish between a pure substance and a mixture.

2.24 Label each of the following as either a pure substance or a mixture:

a. water

b. table salt (sodium chloride)

c. blood

d. sucrose (table sugar)

e. orange juice

2.25 Distinguish between a homogeneous mixture and a heterogeneous mixture.

2.26 Label each of the following as either a homogeneous mixture or a heterogeneous mixture:

a. a soft drink

b. a saline solution

c. concrete

d. gasoline

e. vegetable soup

Matter and Structure

2.27 Calculate the number of protons, neutrons, and electrons in:

a. $^{16}_{8}O$

b. $^{31}_{15}P$

2.28 Calculate the number of protons, neutrons, and electrons in:

a. $^{136}_{56}Ba$

b. $^{209}_{84}Po$

2.29 What are isotopes?

2.30 Describe the similarities and differences among carbon-12, carbon-13, and carbon-14.

Development of Atomic Theory

2.31 What are the major postulates of Dalton's atomic theory?

2.32 What are the major points of the Bohr Theory?

2.33 Fill in the blanks:

Symbol	No. of Protons	No. of Neutrons	No. of Electrons	Charge
Example:				
$^{40}_{20}Ca$	20	20	20	0
$^{23}_{11}Na$	11	_____	11	0
$^{32}_{16}S^{2-}$	16	16	_____	2−
_____	8	8	8	0
$^{24}_{12}Mg^{2+}$	12	12	12	2+
_____	19	20	18	_____

2.34 Fill in the blanks:

a. An isotope of an element differs in mass from another isotope of the same element because the atom has a different number of _____.

b. The atomic number gives the number of _____ in the nucleus.

c. The mass number of an atom is due to the number of _____ and _____ in the nucleus.

d. An atom that has lost one or more electrons is called a(n) _____.

e. Electrons surround the _____ and have a _____ charge.

The Periodic Law and the Periodic Table

2.35 Label each of the following statements as true or false:

a. Elements of the same group have similar properties.

b. Atomic size decreases from left to right across a period.

c. Ionization energy increases from top to bottom within a group.

2.36 For each of the elements Na, Ni, Al, P, Cl, and Ar, provide the following information:

a. Which are metals?

b. Which are representative metals?

c. Which tend to form positive ions?

d. Which are inert or noble gases?

2.37 Provide the name of the element represented by each of the following symbols:

a. Na

b. K

c. Mg

2.38 Provide the name of the element represented by each of the following symbols:

a. Ca

b. Cu

c. Co

2.39 Which group of the periodic table is known as the alkali metals? List the elements in this group.

2.40 Which group of the periodic table is known as the halogens? List the elements in this group.

Electron Arrangement

2.41 How many valence electrons are in each of the following?

a. H   d. F

b. Na   e. Ne

c. B   f. He

2.42 Give the most probable ion formed from each of the following elements:

a. Li   d. Br

b. O   e. S

c. Ca   f. Al

2.43 Which of the following pairs of atoms and/or ions are isoelectronic with one another?

a. O^{2-}, Ne

b. S^{2-}, Cl^-

c. F^-, Cl^-

d. K^+, Ar

2.44 Which atom or ion in each of the following groups would you expect to be most stable?

a. Na, Na^+, Na^-

b. S^{2-}, S^-, S^+

c. Cl, Cl^-, Cl^+

2.45 Arrange each of the following lists of elements in order of increasing ionization energy:
a. N, O, F
b. Li, K, Cs
c. Cl, Br, I

2.46 Arrange each of the following lists of elements in order of decreasing electron affinity:
a. N, O, F
b. Br, F, Cl
c. S, O, Se

2.47 Arrange each of the following lists of elements in order of increasing atomic size:
a. N, O, F
b. Li, K, Cs
c. Cl, Br, I

2.48 Arrange each of the following lists of elements in order of increasing atomic size:
a. Al, Si, P, Cl, S
b. In, Ga, Al, B, Tl
c. Sr, Ca, Ba, Mg, Be
d. P, N, Sb, Bi, As

Further Problems

2.49 Provide several examples of physical properties of matter.

2.50 On the basis of your everyday experience, give specific examples of processes involving physical change.

2.51 List several examples of chemical properties.

2.52 Provide frequently encountered examples of chemical change.

2.53 What process results in the formation of a cation?

2.54 What process results in the formation of an anion?

2.55 Which of Dalton's postulates are no longer considered true?

2.56 How does the Bohr Theory differ from what we know today?

VOCABULARY QUIZ

2.1 The _____ occupy group IA of the periodic table.

2.2 A(n) _proton_ is a positively charged particle.

2.3 The properties of a substance that relate to the participation of that substance in a chemical reaction are _chemical_ properties.

2.4 A(n) _electron_ is a negatively charged particle outside of the nucleus of an atom.

2.5 A(n) _Element_ is a substance that cannot be decomposed into simpler substances by chemical or physical means.

2.6 The _gaseous_ state is a physical state of matter characterized by the lack of fixed shape or volume and ease of compressibility.

2.7 A _homogenous_ consists of two or more substances and is characterized by uniform composition.

2.8 Atoms of the same element that differ in mass because they contain different numbers of neutrons are called _Isotopes_.

2.9 A(n) _neutron_ is an uncharged particle in the nucleus of an atom that has the same mass as the proton.

2.10 A positively charged particle in the nucleus of an atom is called a(n) _____.

3

Structure and Properties of Ionic and Covalent Compounds

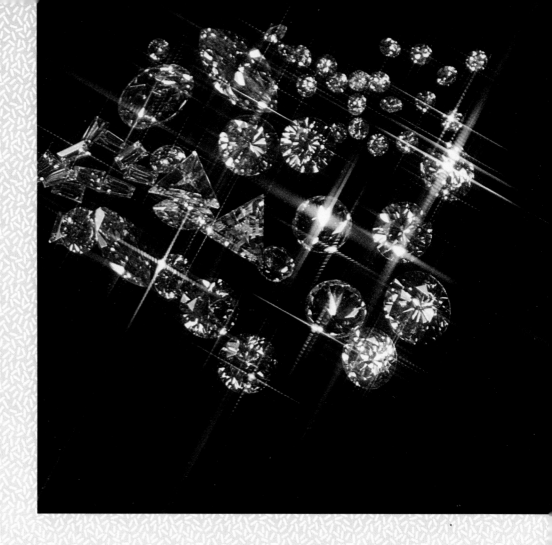

LEARNING GOALS

◆ Name common inorganic compounds using the I.U.P.A.C. convention and recognize the common names of frequently-used substances.

◆ Write the formulas of compounds, when provided with the name of the compound.

◆ Draw Lewis structures for covalent compounds and complex inorganic ions.

◆ Predict the geometry of molecules and ions using the octet rule and Lewis structure.

◆ Recognize the differences in physical state, melting and boiling points, solid-state structure, and solution chemistry that result from differences in bonding.

◆ Know the relationship between stability and bond energy.

◆ Understand the role that molecular geometry plays in determining the solubility and melting and boiling points of compounds.

CHEMISTRY CONNECTION

Magnets and Migration

All of us, at one time or another, have wondered at the magnificent sight of thousands of migrating birds, flying in formation, heading south for the winter and returning each spring.

Less visible, but no less impressive, are the schools of fish that travel thousands of miles, returning to the same location year after year. Almost instantly, when faced with some external stimulus such as a predator, they snap into a formation that rivals an army drill team for precision.

The questions of how these life forms know when and where they are going and how they establish their formations have perplexed scientists for many years. The explanations so far are really just hypotheses—educated guesses.

Some clues to the mystery may be hidden in very tiny particles of magnetite, Fe_3O_4. Magnetite contains iron that is naturally magnetic, and collections of these particles behave like a compass needle; they line up in formation aligned with the earth's magnetic field.

Magnetotactic bacteria contain magnetite in the form of magnetosomes, small particles of Fe_3O_4. The normal habitat of these bacteria is either fresh water or the ocean; the bacteria orient themselves to the earth's magnetic field and swim to the nearest pole (north or south). This causes them to swim into regions of nutrient-rich sediment.

Could the directional device, the simple F_3O_4 unit, also be responsible for direction finding in higher organisms in much the same way that an explorer uses a compass? Perhaps so! Recent studies have shown evidence of magnetosomes in the brains of birds, tuna, green turtles, and dolphins.

Most remarkably, at least one study has shown evidence that magnetite is present in the human brain.

These preliminary studies offer hope of unraveling some of the myth and mystery of guidance and communication in living systems. The answers may involve a very basic compound that is like those we will study in this chapter.

INTRODUCTION

A chemical compound is formed when two or more atoms of different elements are joined by attractive forces called chemical bonds. These bonds result from either a transfer of electrons from one atom to another (the ionic bond) or a sharing of electrons between two atoms (the covalent bond). The elements, once converted to a compound, cannot be recovered by any physical process. A chemical reaction must take place to regenerate the individual elements. The chemical and physical *properties* of a compound are related to the *structure* of the compound, and this structure is, in turn, determined by the arrangement of electrons in the atoms that produced the compounds. Properties such as solubility, boiling point, and melting point correlate well with the shape and charge distribution in the individual units of the compound.

We need to learn how to properly name and write formulas for ionic and covalent compounds when given their names. We should become familiar with some of their properties and be able to relate these properties to the structure and bonding of the compounds.

3.1 CHEMICAL BONDING

When two atoms form a chemical compound, the force of attraction between the two atoms is the **chemical bond.** The attraction is the force that overcomes the repulsion of the positively charged nuclei of the two atoms.

Interactions involving valence electrons are responsible for the chemical bond. We shall focus our attention on these electrons and the electron arrangement of atoms both before and after bond formation.

Lewis symbols

The **Lewis symbol,** developed by G. N. Lewis early in this century, is a convenient way of representing atoms singly or in combination. Its principal advantage is that *only* valence electrons (those that may participate in bonding) are shown.

Recall that the number of valence electrons is equal to the group number for representative elements as determined from the periodic table (Figure 2.7).

To draw Lewis structures, the chemical symbol of the atom is written; this symbol represents the nucleus and all of the lower-energy nonvalence electrons. The valence electrons are indicated by dots arranged around the atomic symbol, as illustrated below:

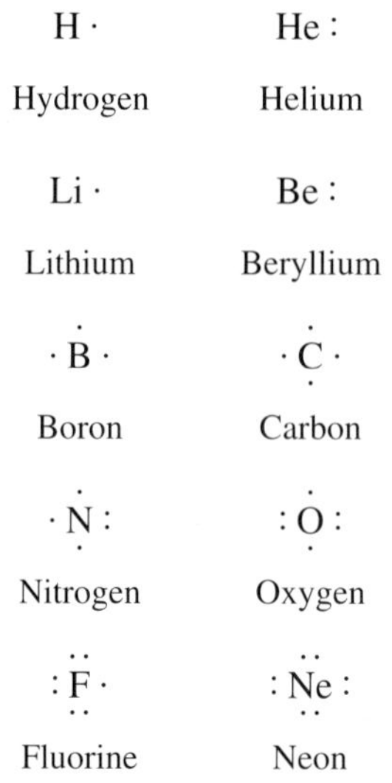

$$H \cdot \qquad He :$$
Hydrogen   Helium

$$Li \cdot \qquad Be :$$
Lithium   Beryllium

$$\cdot \overset{\cdot}{B} \cdot \qquad \cdot \overset{\cdot}{C} \cdot$$
Boron   Carbon

$$\cdot \overset{\cdot}{N} : \qquad : \overset{\cdot}{O} :$$
Nitrogen   Oxygen

$$: \overset{\cdot\cdot}{F} \cdot \qquad : \overset{\cdot\cdot}{Ne} :$$
Fluorine   Neon

Note particularly that the number of dots corresponds to the number of valence electrons in the outermost shell of the atoms of the element.

Types of chemical bonds: ionic and covalent

Two principal classes of chemical bonds exist: ionic and covalent bonds. Both involve valence electrons.

Ionic bonding involves a transfer of one or more electrons leading to bond formation. **Covalent bonding** involves a sharing of electrons resulting in the covalent bond.

Before discussing each type, we should recognize that the distinction between ionic and covalent bonding is not always clear-cut. Some compounds are clearly ionic, and some are clearly covalent, but many others possess both ionic and covalent characteristics.

Ionic bonding

Consider the reaction of a sodium atom and a chlorine atom to produce sodium chloride:

$$Na + Cl \longrightarrow NaCl$$

Recall that the sodium atom:

◆ has a low ionization energy (it readily loses an electron);
◆ has a low electron affinity (it does not want more electrons).

If sodium loses its valence electron, it will become isoelectronic (same number of electrons) with neon, a very stable noble gas atom. This tells us that the sodium atom would be a good electron donor, forming the sodium ion:

$$Na \cdot \longrightarrow Na^+ + e^-$$

Recall that the chlorine atom:

◆ has a high ionization energy (it will not easily give up an electron);
◆ has a high electron affinity (it readily accepts another electron).

Chlorine will gain one more electron. By doing so, it will complete an octet (eight outermost electrons) and be isoelectronic with argon, a stable noble gas. Therefore chlorine behaves as a

Refer to Section 2.7 for a discussion of ionization energy and electron affinity.

willing electron acceptor, forming a chloride ion:

$$: \overset{..}{\underset{..}{Cl}} \cdot + \; e^- \longrightarrow [\; : \overset{..}{\underset{..}{Cl}} : \;]^-$$

The electron released by sodium *(electron donor)* is the electron received by chlorine *(electron acceptor):*

$$Na \cdot \longrightarrow Na^+ + e^-$$

$$e^- + \; \cdot \overset{..}{\underset{..}{Cl}} : \longrightarrow [\; : \overset{..}{\underset{..}{Cl}} : \;]^-$$

The resulting ions of opposite charge, Na^+ and Cl^-, are attracted to each other (opposite charges attract) and held together by this *electrostatic force* as an **ion pair:** Na^+Cl^-.

This electrostatic force, the attraction of opposite charges, is quite strong and holds the ion pair together. It is the ionic bond.

The essential features of ionic bonding are the following:

◆ Atoms of elements with low ionization energy and low electron affinity tend to form positive ions.

◆ Atoms of elements with high ionization energy and high electron affinity tend to form negative ions.

◆ Ion formation takes place by an electron transfer process.

◆ The positive and negative ions are held together by the electrostatic force between ions of opposite charge in an ionic bond.

◆ Reactions between representative metals and nonmetals (elements far to the left and right, respectively, in the periodic table) tend to result in ionic bonds.

Covalent bonding

Consider the bond formed between two hydrogen atoms, producing the diatomic form of hydrogen: H_2. Individual hydrogen atoms are not stable, and two hydrogen atoms readily combine to produce diatomic hydrogen:

$$H + H \longrightarrow H_2$$

If a hydrogen atom were to gain a second electron, it would be isoelectronic with the stable electron configuration of helium. However, since two identical hydrogen atoms have an equal tendency to gain or lose electrons, an electron transfer from one atom to the other is unlikely to occur under normal conditions. Each atom may attain a noble gas structure only by *sharing* its electron with the other. This is shown below using Lewis symbols:

$$H \cdot \; + \; \cdot H \longrightarrow H : H$$

When electrons are shared rather than transferred, the *shared electron pair* is referred to as a *covalent bond.* Compounds characterized by covalent bonding are called *covalent compounds.* Covalent bonds tend to form from atoms with similar tendencies to gain or lose electrons. The most obvious examples are the diatomic molecules H_2, N_2, O_2, F_2, Cl_2, Br_2, and I_2. Bonding in these molecules is *totally covalent* because there can be no net tendency for electron transfer between identical atoms. The formation of F_2, for example, may be represented as

$$: \overset{..}{\underset{..}{F}} \cdot \; + \; \cdot \overset{..}{\underset{..}{F}} : \longrightarrow \; : \overset{..}{\underset{..}{F}} : \overset{..}{\underset{..}{F}} :$$

Fourteen valence electrons are arranged in such a way that each fluorine atom is surrounded by eight electrons. The octet rule is satisfied for each fluorine atom.

As in H_2, a single covalent bond is formed. The bonding electron pair is said to be *localized,* or largely confined to the region between the two fluorine nuclei.

Two atoms do not have to be identical to form a covalent bond. Consider compounds such as the following:

$$H\!:\!\ddot{F}\!:\qquad H\!:\!\ddot{O}\!:\!H\qquad H\!:\!\underset{H}{\overset{H}{C}}\!:\!H\qquad H\!:\!\ddot{N}\!:\!H$$

Hydrogen fluoride	Water	Methane	Ammonia
$7e^-$ from F	$6e^-$ from O	$4e^-$ from C	$5e^-$ from N
$1e^-$ from H	$2e^-$ from 2H	$4e^-$ from 4H	$3e^-$ from 3H
$8e^-$ for F	$8e^-$ for O	$8e^-$ for C	$8e^-$ for N
$2e^-$ for H	$2e^-$ for H	$2e^-$ for H	$2e^-$ for H

In each of these cases, bond formation satisfies the octet rule. There is a total of eight electrons around each atom other than hydrogen. Hydrogen has only two electrons (corresponding to the electronic structure of helium).

3.2 NAMING COMPOUNDS AND WRITING FORMULAS OF COMPOUNDS

Ionic compounds

Understanding **nomenclature,** the assignment of a correct and unambiguous name to each and every chemical compound, is a necessary first step in any discussion of these compounds.

The "shorthand" symbol for a compound is its formula, for example,

$$\text{NaCl} \quad \text{and} \quad \text{MgBr}_2$$

The formula identifies the number and type of the various atoms that make up the compound unit. The number of like atoms in the unit is shown by the use of a subscript. The presence of only one atom is understood when no subscript is present.

The formula NaCl indicates that each ion pair consists of one sodium cation (Na^+) and one chloride anion (Cl^-). Similarly, the formula $MgBr_2$ indicates that one magnesium ion and two bromide ions combine to form the compound.

In Chapter 2 we learned that positive ions were formed from elements that:

◆　are located at the left of the periodic table;

◆　are referred to as *metals;*

◆　have low ionization energies and low electron affinities, hence easily *lose* electrons.

Elements that form negative ions, on the other hand:

◆　are located at the right of the periodic table (but exclude the noble gases);

◆　are referred to as *nonmetals;*

◆　have high ionization energies and high electron affinities, hence easily *gain* electrons.

In short, metals and nonmetals usually react to produce ionic compounds resulting from the transfer of one or more electrons from the metal to the nonmetal.

Although we refer to ionic compounds as ion pairs, in the solid state these ion pairs do not actually exist as individual units. The positive ions exert attractive forces on several negative ions, and the negative ions are attracted to several positive centers. Positive and negative ions arrange themselves in a regular three-dimensional repeating array to produce a stable arrangement known as a **crystal lattice.** The lattice structure for sodium chloride is shown from three different perspectives in Figure 3.1. The simplest repeating unit of an ionic compound is the *formula unit* or simply the **formula.**

Writing formulas of ionic compounds given the identities of the component ions

It is important to be able to write the formula of an ionic compound when provided with the identities of the ions that make up the compound. The charge of each ion can be determined from the group (family) of the periodic table in which the parent element is found. The cations and anions must combine in such a way that the resulting formula unit has a net charge of zero.

Consider the following examples.

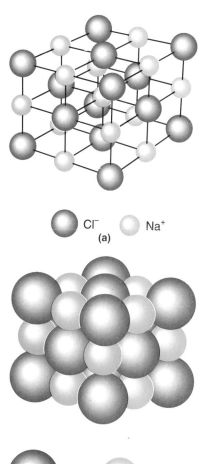

Cl^- Na^+
(a)

EXAMPLE 3.1

Predicting the Formula of an Ionic Compound

Predict the formula of the ionic compound formed from the reaction of sodium and oxygen atoms.

Solution

Sodium is in group IA; it has *one* valence electron. Loss of this electron produces Na^+. Oxygen is in group VIA; it has *six* valence electrons. A gain of two electrons (to create a stable octet) produces O^{2-}. Two positive charges are necessary to counterbalance two negative charges on the oxygen anion. Since each sodium ion carries a 1+ charge, two sodium ions are needed for each O^{2-}. The subscript 2 is used to indicate that the formula unit contains two sodium ions. Thus the formula of the compound is Na_2O.

EXAMPLE 3.2

Predicting the Formula of an Ionic Compound

Predict the formula of the compound formed by the reaction of aluminum and oxygen atoms.

Solution

Aluminum is in group IIIA of the periodic table; therefore it has three valence electrons. Loss of these electrons produces Al^{3+}. Oxygen is in group VIA of the periodic table and has six valence electrons. A gain of two electrons (to create a stable octet) produces O^{2-}. How can we combine Al^{3+} and O^{2-} to yield a unit of zero charge? It is necessary that *both* the cation and anion be multiplied by factors that will result in a zero net charge:

$$2 \times (+3) = +6 \quad \text{and} \quad 3 \times (-2) = -6$$

$$2 \times Al^{3+} = +6 \quad \text{and} \quad 3 \times O^{2-} = -6$$

hence Al_2O_3.

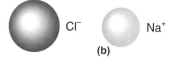

Cl^- Na^+
(b)

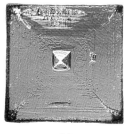

(c)

QUESTION 3.1

Predict the formula of the compounds formed from the combination of ions of the following elements:

a. lithium and bromine

b. calcium and bromine

c. calcium and nitrogen

QUESTION 3.2

Predict the formula of the compounds formed from the combination of ions of the following elements:

a. potassium and chlorine

b. magnesium and bromine

c. magnesium and nitrogen

FIGURE 3.1
The arrangement of ions in a crystal of NaCl (sodium chloride or table salt). (a) Microscopic arrangement of ions as point charges. (b) Microscopic arrangement of the spherical ions in crystal lattice. (c) A macroscopic view of a crystal of sodium chloride.

TABLE 3.1   Systematic and Common Names for Iron and Copper Ions

| Formula | For systematic name: | | |
	+ Ion Charge	Cation Name	Compound Name
$FeCl_2$	2+	Iron(II)	Iron(II) chloride
$FeCl_3$	3+	Iron(III)	Iron(III) chloride
Cu_2O	1+	Copper(I)	Copper(I) oxide
CuO	2+	Copper(II)	Copper(II) oxide

| Formula | For common nomenclature: | | |
	+Ion Charge	Cation Name	Common -ous/ic Name
$FeCl_2$	2+	Ferrous	Ferrous chloride
$FeCl_3$	3+	Ferric	Ferric chloride
Cu_2O	1+	Cuprous	Cuprous oxide
CuO	2+	Cupric	Cupric oxide

Writing names of ionic compounds given the formula of the compound

Nomenclature, the way in which compounds are named, is based on their formulas. The name of the cation appears first, followed by the name of the anion. The positive ion is simply the name of the element; the negative ion is named by using the *stem* of the name of the element joined to the suffix *-ide*. Some examples follow.

Formula	+ion	and	−ion stem	+	ide	=	compound name
NaCl	sodium		chlor	+	ide		sodium chloride
Na_2O	sodium		ox	+	ide		sodium oxide
Li_2S	lithium		sulf	+	ide		lithium sulfide
$AlBr_3$	aluminum		brom	+	ide		aluminum bromide
CaO	calcium		ox	+	ide		calcium oxide

If the cation and anion exist in only one common charged form, there is no ambiguity between formula and name. Sodium chloride *must be* NaCl, and lithium sulfide *must be* Li_2S, so that the sum of positive and negative charges is zero. With many elements, such as the transition metals, several ions of different charge may exist. Fe^{2+}, Fe^{3+} and Cu^+, Cu^{2+} are two common examples. Clearly, an ambiguity exists if we use the name iron for both Fe^{2+} and Fe^{3+} or copper for both Cu^+ and Cu^{2+}. Two systems have been developed to avoid this problem: the *Stock system* and the *common nomenclature system*.

In the Stock system (systematic name) a Roman numeral indicates the magnitude of the cation's charge. In the older common nomenclature system the suffix *-ous* indicates the lower ionic charge, and the suffix *-ic* indicates the higher ionic charge. Consider the examples in Table 3.1.

Systematic names are easier and less ambiguous than common names. Whenever possible, we will use this system of nomenclature. The older, common names (-ous, -ic) are less specific; furthermore, they often use the Latin names of the elements (for example, iron compounds use *ferr-*, from *ferrum*, the Latin word for iron).

Ions consisting of a single atom are called **monatomic ions.** Common monatomic ions are listed in Table 3.2. The ions that are particularly important in biological systems are highlighted in blue.

Polyatomic ions, such as the hydroxide ion, OH^-, are composed of two or more atoms bonded together. These ions, although bonded to other ions with ionic bonds, are themselves held together by covalent bonds.

The polyatomic ion has an *overall* positive or negative charge. Some common polyatomic ions are listed in Table 3.3. The formulas, charges, and names of these polyatomic ions, especially those highlighted in blue, should be memorized.

TABLE 3.2   Common Monatomic Cations and Anions

Cation	Name
H^+	Hydrogen
Li^+	Lithium
Na^+	Sodium
K^+	Potassium
Cs^+	Cesium
Be^{2+}	Beryllium
Mg^{2+}	Magnesium
Ca^{2+}	Calcium
Ba^{2+}	Barium
Al^{3+}	Aluminum
Ag^+	Silver

Anion	Name
H^-	Hydride
F^-	Fluoride
Cl^-	Chloride
Br^-	Bromide
I^-	Iodide
O^{2-}	Oxide
S^{2-}	Sulfide
N^{3-}	Nitride
P^{3-}	Phosphide

The ions of principal importance are highlighted in blue.

Examples of formulas of several compounds containing polyatomic ions are shown below.

Formula	Cation	Anion	Name
NH_4Cl	NH_4^+	Cl^-	ammonium chloride
$Ca(OH)_2$	Ca^{2+}	OH^-	calcium hydroxide
Na_2SO_4	Na^+	SO_4^{2-}	sodium sulfate
$NaHCO_3$	Na^+	HCO_3^-	sodium bicarbonate

Sodium bicarbonate may also be named sodium hydrogen carbonate, a preferred and less ambiguous name. Likewise, Na_2HPO_4 is named sodium hydrogen phosphate, and other ionic compounds are named similarly.

QUESTION 3.3

Name each of the following compounds:

a. KCN

b. MgS

c. CH_3COOLi

QUESTION 3.4

Name each of the following compounds:

a. Li_2CO_3

b. $FeBr_2$

c. NH_4OH

Writing formulas of ionic compounds given the name of the compound

It is also important to be able to write the correct formula when given the compound name. To do this, we must be able to predict the charge of monatomic ions and remember the charge and formula of polyatomic ions. Equally important, the relative number of positive and negative ions in the unit must result in a net (compound) charge of zero. Two examples follow.

EXAMPLE 3.3

Writing a Formula When Given the Name of the Compound

Write the formula of sodium sulfate.

Solution

Step 1 The sodium ion is Na^+ (group I element). The sulfate ion is SO_4^{2-} (from Table 3.3).

Step 2 Two positive charges, two sodium ions, are needed to cancel the charge on one sulfate ion (two negative charges).

Hence the formula is Na_2SO_4.

EXAMPLE 3.4

Writing a Formula When Given the Name of the Compound

Write the formula of ammonium sulfide.

Solution

Step 1 The ammonium ion is NH_4^+ (from Table 3.3). The sulfide ion is S^{2-} (from its position on the periodic table).

Step 2 Two positive charges are necessary to cancel the charge on one sulfide ion (two negative charges).

Hence the formula is $(NH_4)_2S$.

Note that parentheses must be used whenever a subscript accompanies a polyatomic ion.

TABLE 3.3 Common Polyatomic Cations and Anions

Ion	Name
NH_4^+	Ammonium
NO_2^-	Nitrite
NO_3^-	Nitrate
SO_3^{2-}	Sulfite
SO_4^{2-}	Sulfate
HSO_4^-	Hydrogen sulfate
OH^-	Hydroxide
CN^-	Cyanide
PO_4^{3-}	Phosphate
HPO_4^{2-}	Hydrogen phosphate
$H_2PO_4^-$	Dihydrogen phosphate
CO_3^{2-}	Carbonate
HCO_3^-	Bicarbonate
ClO^-	Hypochlorite
ClO_2^-	Chlorite
ClO_3^-	Chlorate
ClO_4^-	Perchlorate
CH_3COO^-	Acetate
MnO_4^-	Permanganate
$Cr_2O_7^{2-}$	Dichromate
CrO_4^{2-}	Chromate
O_2^{2-}	Peroxide

The most commonly encountered ions are highlighted in blue.

QUESTION 3.5

Write the formula for each of the following compounds:

a. calcium carbonate

b. sodium bicarbonate

QUESTION 3.6

Write the formula for each of the following compounds:

a. sodium phosphate

b. potassium bromide

Covalent compounds

Naming covalent compounds

Most covalent compounds are formed by the reaction of nonmetals. Compounds characterized by covalent bonding are referred to as **molecules.** We saw earlier that ionic compounds are not composed of single units but are a part of a massive three-dimensional crystal structure in the solid state. Covalent compounds exist as independent molecules in the solid, liquid, and gas states. This is a distinctive feature of covalently bonded substances.

The conventions for naming covalent compounds follow:

1. The names of the elements are written in the order in which they appear in the formula.

2. A prefix (see Table 3.4) indicating the number of each kind of atom found in the unit is placed before the name of the element.

By convention the prefix mono- is often omitted (dinitrogen oxide, not dinitrogen monoxide). In other cases, common usage retains the prefix (carbon monoxide, not carbon oxide).

3. If only one atom of a particular kind is present in the molecule, the prefix mono- is usually omitted.

4. The stem of the name of the last element is used with the suffix -ide.

EXAMPLE 3.5

Naming a Covalent Compound

Name the covalent compound N_2O_4.

Solution

Step 1	two nitrogen atoms	four oxygen atoms
Step 2	di-	tetra-
Step 3	dinitrogen	tetr(a)oxide

The final vowel in a prefix is often dropped before a vowel in the stem name, hence, dinitrogen tetroxide.

The name is dinitrogen tetroxide.

Examples of other covalent compounds are given below.

Formula	Name
N_2O	dinitrogen oxide
NO_2	nitrogen dioxide
SiO_2	silicon dioxide
CO_2	carbon dioxide
CO	carbon monoxide

TABLE 3.4 Prefixes Used to Denote Numbers of Atoms in a Compound

Prefix	Number of Atoms
Mono-	1
Di-	2
Tri-	3
Tetra-	4
Penta-	5
Hexa-	6
Hepta-	7
Octa-	8

QUESTION 3.7

Name each of the following compounds:

a. B_2O_3 c. ICl

b. NO   d. PCl_3

QUESTION 3.8

Name each of the following compounds:

a. H_2S c. PCl_5
b. CS_2 d. P_2O_5

Writing formulas of covalent compounds

Many compounds are so familiar to us that their *common names* are used. For example, H_2O is water, NH_3 is ammonia, C_2H_5OH (ethanol) is alcohol, and $C_6H_{12}O_6$ is glucose. It is useful to be able to correlate both systematic and common names with the corresponding molecular formula and vice versa.

When common names are used, formulas of covalent compounds can be written *only* from memory. You *must* remember that water is H_2O, ammonia is NH_3, and so forth. This is the major disadvantage of common names. Because of their widespread use, however, they cannot be avoided.

Compounds named by using Greek prefixes are easily converted to formulas. Consider the following examples.

EXAMPLE 3.6

Writing the Formula of a Covalent Compound

Write the formula of nitrogen monoxide.

Solution

Nitrogen has no prefix; one is understood. Oxide has the prefix mono—one oxygen. Hence the formula is NO.

EXAMPLE 3.7

Writing the Formula of a Covalent Compound

Write the formula of dinitrogen tetroxide.

Solution

Nitrogen has the prefix "di"—two nitrogen atoms. Oxygen has the prefix "tetr(a)"—four oxygen atoms. Hence the formula is N_2O_4.

QUESTION 3.9

Write the formula of each of the following compounds:

a. diphosphorus pentoxide
b. silicon dioxide

QUESTION 3.10

Write the formula of each of the following compounds:

a. nitrogen trifluoride
b. carbon monoxide

3.3 PROPERTIES OF IONIC AND COVALENT COMPOUNDS

The differences in ionic and covalent bonding result in markedly different properties for ionic and covalent compounds. Because covalent molecules are distinct units, they have less tendency to form an extended structure in the solid state. Ionic compounds, with ions joined by electrostatic attraction, do not have definable units but form a crystal lattice composed of enormous numbers of positive and negative ions in an extended three-dimensional network.

The effects of this basic structural difference are summarized below.

Physical state

All ionic compounds (for example, NaCl, KCl, NaNO$_3$) are solids at room temperature; covalent compounds may be solids (sugar), liquids (H$_2$O, ethanol), or gases (carbon monoxide, carbon dioxide). The three-dimensional crystal structure that is characteristic of ionic compounds holds them in a rigid, solid arrangement, while molecules of covalent compounds may be more mobile, a characteristic of liquids and gases.

Melting and boiling points

The **melting point** is the temperature at which a solid is converted to a liquid and the **boiling point** is the temperature at which a liquid is converted to a gas. It requires considerable energy to break apart an ionic crystal lattice with uncountable numbers of ionic interactions and convert the ionic substance to a liquid or a gas. As a result, the melting and boiling temperatures for ionic compounds are generally higher than those of covalent compounds, whose molecules interact less strongly in the solid state. A typical ionic compound, sodium chloride, has a melting point of 801°C; methane, a covalent compound, melts at −182°C.

See Table 9.1.

Structure of compounds in the solid state

Ionic solids are *crystalline,* characterized by a regular structure, whereas covalent solids may either be crystalline or have no regular structure. In the latter case they are said to be *amorphous.*

Solutions of ionic and covalent compounds

In the first chapter we saw that mixtures are either heterogeneous or homogeneous. A homogeneous mixture is a solution. Many ionic solids dissolve in solvents, such as water. An ionic solid, if soluble, will **dissociate** in solution to form positive and negative ions.

Because ions in water are capable of carrying (conducting) a current of electricity, we refer to these compounds as **electrolytes,** and the solution is termed an **electrolytic solution.** Covalent solids dissolved in solution retain their neutral character and are **nonelectrolytes.** The solution is not an electrical conductor.

The role of the solvent in the dissolution of solids is discussed in Section 6.5.

3.4 DRAWING LEWIS STRUCTURES OF IONS AND MOLECULES

In Section 3.1 we used Lewis structures to represent the bonding process. To explain the relationship of molecular structure and molecular properties, we must develop rules for representing more complex compounds.

An example, using carbon dioxide, CO$_2$, follows.

Rule 1: Draw a skeletal structure of the molecule, arranging the atoms in their most probable order.

For CO$_2$, two possibilities exist:

$$C—O—O \quad \text{and} \quad O—C—O$$

It is sometimes difficult to decide which of a number of possibilities is correct, even for a practicing chemist! Generally, you will be provided with the most suitable structure. For CO$_2$, experiments have shown O—C—O to be correct.

Rule 2: Determine the number of valence electrons on each atom, and add them together to get the total for the compound.

For CO$_2$,

$$1 \text{ C atom} \times 4 \text{ valence electrons} = 4 \text{ e}^-$$
$$\underline{2 \text{ O atoms} \times 6 \text{ valence electrons} = 12 \text{ e}^-}$$
$$16 \text{ e}^- \text{ total}$$

Rule 3: Distribute the electrons around the atoms (in pairs if possible) in an attempt to satisfy the octet rule, eight electrons around each element (remember, H and He can have only two electrons).

For CO$_2$, several possibilities exist:

(a) $:\!\overset{..}{\underset{..}{O}}\!:\!\overset{..}{\underset{}{C}}\!:\!\overset{..}{\underset{..}{O}}\!:$ (b) $:\!\overset{..}{\underset{..}{O}}\!:\!\overset{..}{\underset{}{C}}\!:\!\overset{..}{\underset{..}{O}}\!:$ (c) $\overset{..}{\underset{..}{O}}\!:\!\overset{}{\underset{}{C}}\!:\!\overset{..}{\underset{..}{O}}$

A CLINICAL PERSPECTIVE:

Blood Pressure and the Sodium/Potassium Ratio

When you have a physical exam, the physician measures your blood pressure. This indicates the pressure of blood against the walls of the blood vessels each time the heart pumps. A blood pressure reading is always characterized by two numbers. With every heartbeat there is an increase in pressure; this is the systolic blood pressure. When the heart relaxes between contractions, the pressure drops; this is the diastolic pressure. Thus the blood pressure is expressed as two values—for instance, 117/72—measured in millimeters of mercury. Hypertension is simply defined as high blood pressure. To the body it means that the heart must work too hard to pump blood, and this can lead to heart failure or heart disease.

Heart disease accounts for 50% of all deaths in the United States. Epidemiological studies correlate the following major risk factors with heart disease: heredity, sex, race, age, diabetes, cigarette smoking, high blood cholesterol, and hypertension. Obviously, we can do little about our age, sex, and genetic heritage, but we can stop smoking, limit dietary cholesterol, and maintain a normal blood pressure.

The number of Americans with hypertension is alarmingly high: 60 million adults and children. More than 10 million of these individuals take medication to control blood pressure, at a cost of nearly $2.5 billion each year. In many cases, blood pressure can be controlled without medication by increasing physical activity, losing weight, decreasing consumption of alcohol, and limiting intake of sodium.

It has been estimated that the average American ingests 7.5–10 g of salt (NaCl) each day. Since NaCl is about 40% sodium, this amounts to 3–4 g of sodium daily. Until 1989 the Food and Nutrition Board of the National Academy of Sciences National Research Council defined an established safe and adequate daily dietary intake (ESADDI) of sodium as 1.1–3.3 g. Clearly, Americans exceed this recommendation.

Recently, studies have shown that excess sodium is not the sole consideration in the control of blood pressure. More important is the sodium/potassium (Na/K) ratio. That ratio should be about 0.6; in other words, our diet should contain about 40% more potassium than sodium. Does the typical American diet fall within this limit? Definitely not! Young American males (25–30 years old) consume a diet with a Na/K = 1.07, while the diet of females of the same age range has a Na/K = 1.04. It is little wonder that so many Americans suffer from hypertension.

How can we restrict sodium in the diet, while simultaneously increasing the potassium? The following table lists a variety of foods that are low in sodium and high in potassium. These include fresh fruits and vegetables and fruit juices, a variety of cereals, unsalted nuts, and cooked dried beans (legumes). The table also notes some high-sodium, low-potassium foods. Notice that most of these are processed or prepared foods. This points out how difficult it can be to control sodium in the diet. The majority of the sodium that we ingest comes from commercially prepared foods. The consumer must read the nutritional information printed on cans and packages to determine whether the sodium levels are within acceptable limits.

Low-Sodium, High-Potassium Foods

Food Category	Examples
Fruit and fruit juices	Pineapple, grapefruit, pears, strawberries, watermelon, raisins, bananas, apricots, oranges
Low-sodium cereals	Oatmeal (unsalted), Roman Meal Hot Cereal, Shredded Wheat
Nuts (unsalted)	Hazelnuts, macadamia nuts, almonds, peanuts, cashews, coconut
Vegetables	Summer squash, zucchini, eggplant, cucumber, onions, lettuce, green beans, broccoli
Beans (dry, cooked)	Great Northern beans, lentils, lima beans, red kidney beans

High-Sodium, Low-Potassium Foods

Food Category	Examples
Fats	Butter, margarine, salad dressings
Soups	Onion, mushroom, chicken noodle, tomato, split pea
Breakfast cereals	Many varieties; consult the label for specific nutritional information.
Breads	Most varieties
Processed meats	Most varieties
Cheese	Most varieties

Structure (a) does not satisfy the octet rule for either the carbon atom (only 6 electrons) or the oxygen atom on the right (only 6 electrons). Structure (b) satisfies the oxygen atoms but not the carbon atom (only 4 electrons). Structure (c) satisfies the carbon atom but not either oxygen atom. However, when structure (b) is modified by moving two electrons from each oxygen to a position between C and O, each oxygen and carbon is

(d) $\;\ddot{O} :: C :: \ddot{O}\;$

surrounded by eight electrons. The octet rule is satisfied, and (d) is the most probable Lewis structure for CO_2. In this structure, four electrons (two electron pairs) are located between C and each O, and these electrons are shared in covalent bonds. Since a **single bond** is composed of two electrons (one electron pair) and since four electrons "bond" the carbon atom to each oxygen atom in this structure, there must be two bonds between each oxygen atom and the carbon atom, a **double bond:**

Single bond: : is equivalent to —

Double bond: : : is equivalent to =

We may write CO_2 as structure (d) above or as

$$\overline{O}{=}C{=}\overline{O}$$

Rule 4: After completion of the Lewis structure the *nonbonding electrons* are often omitted.

When this is done,

$$O{=}C{=}O$$

is a satisfactory structure for CO_2.

In the above example we created a "pool" of electrons. We gathered all of the valence electrons together, whether or not they were originally on carbon or oxygen, and distributed them to satisfy the octet rule for all the atoms in the compound. We concern ourselves not so much with the origin of the electrons as with their final arrangement. It is this radical change in electron arrangement that accounts for the differences in properties of a compound when it is compared to the elements from which it is formed. As just one example, carbon dioxide is formed at high temperature from carbon and oxygen:

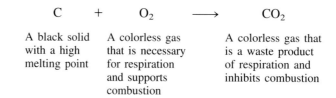

C	+	O$_2$	$\longrightarrow$	CO$_2$
A black solid with a high melting point		A colorless gas that is necessary for respiration and supports combustion		A colorless gas that is a waste product of respiration and inhibits combustion

Consider the covalent bonding in ammonia, NH_3:

◆   The skeletal structure is

$$\begin{array}{c} H \\ | \\ H{-}N{-}H \end{array}$$

◆   There are five valence electrons in nitrogen and one in each of the three hydrogens, for a total of eight valence electrons.

◆   The distribution of valence electrons is

$$\begin{array}{c} H \\ H : \ddot{N} : H \end{array}$$

This satisfies the octet rule for nitrogen (eight electrons around N) and hydrogen (two electrons around each H) and is an acceptable structure for ammonia. Ammonia may also be written as

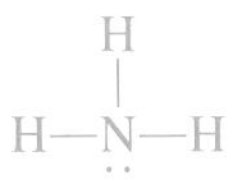

$$
\begin{array}{ccc}
\text{H} & & \text{H} \\
| & & | \\
\text{H---N---H} & \quad \text{or simply} \quad & \text{H---N---H} \\
\cdot\cdot & &
\end{array}
$$

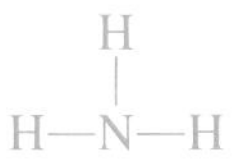

Note the pair of nonbonding electrons on the nitrogen atom. These are often called a **lone pair** or *unshared* pair of electrons. As we will see later in the chapter, lone pair electrons have a profound effect on molecular geometry. The geometry, in turn, affects the reactivity of the molecule.

QUESTION 3.11

Draw a Lewis structure for each of the following covalent compounds:

a. H_2O (water)

b. CH_4 (methane)

QUESTION 3.12

Draw a Lewis structure for each of the following covalent compounds:

a. C_2H_6 (ethane)

b. N_2 (nitrogen gas)

The rules for writing the Lewis structures of ions are similar to those for neutral compounds. There is, however, one major difference. The charge on the ion must be accounted for in computing the total number of valence electrons.

Consider the sulfate ion SO_4^{2-}, which has the following skeletal structure and charge:

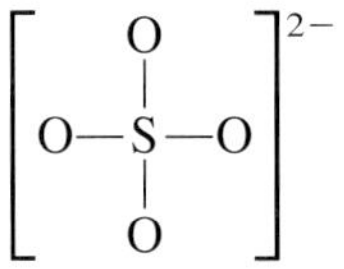

$$
\left[\begin{array}{c} \text{O} \\ | \\ \text{O---S---O} \\ | \\ \text{O} \end{array} \right]^{2-}
$$

The total number of valence electrons is

$$
\begin{array}{rcl}
1\ \text{S atom} \times 6\ \text{valence electrons} & = & 6\ e^- \\
4\ \text{O atoms} \times 6\ \text{valence electrons} & = & 24\ e^- \\
+\ \text{2 negative charges} & = & 2\ e^- \\
\hline
& & 32\ e^-\ \text{total}
\end{array}
$$

Applying our rules as before yields

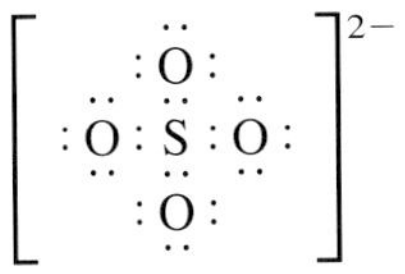

$$
\left[\begin{array}{c}
\cdot\cdot \\
:\ddot{\text{O}}: \\
:\ddot{\text{O}}:\ddot{\text{S}}:\ddot{\text{O}}: \\
:\ddot{\text{O}}: \\
\cdot\cdot
\end{array} \right]^{2-}
$$

For positive ions the same logic prevails; however, we *subtract* one valence electron for each unit of positive charge. Consider the ammonium ion NH_4^+:

$$
\begin{array}{rcl}
1\ \text{N atom} \times 5\ \text{valence electrons} & = & 5\ e^- \\
4\ \text{H atoms} \times 1\ \text{valence electron} & = & 4\ e^- \\
-\ \text{1 electron for} +1\ \text{charge} & = & -1\ e^- \\
\hline
& & 8\ e^-\ \text{total}
\end{array}
$$

Distribution of these eight electrons around our skeletal structure yields

$$\left[\begin{array}{c} H \\ | \\ H-N-H \\ | \\ H \end{array}\right]^{+}$$

$$\left[\begin{array}{c} H \\ \ddots \\ H:N:H \\ \ddots \\ H \end{array}\right]^{+}$$

The skeletal structure only indicates the relative positions of atoms in the molecule or ion. Bonding information results from the Lewis structure.

A commonly encountered anion, the acetate ion CH_3COO^-, has a skeletal structure that is more complex:

$$\left[\begin{array}{c} H \quad O \\ | \quad \; | \\ H-C-C-O \\ | \\ H \end{array}\right]^{-}$$

The pool of valence electrons is determined:

$$
\begin{array}{lll}
2 \text{ C atoms} \times 4 \text{ valence electrons} & = & 8 \text{ e}^- \\
3 \text{ H atoms} \times 1 \text{ valence electron} & = & 3 \text{ e}^- \\
2 \text{ O atoms} \times 6 \text{ valence electrons} & = & 12 \text{ e}^- \\
+ \; 1 \text{ negative charge} & = & 1 \text{ e}^- \\
\hline
& & 24 \text{ e}^- \text{ total}
\end{array}
$$

Distributing these 24 electrons around our skeletal structure gives

$$\left[\begin{array}{c} H \qquad \ddot{O} \\ \ddots \quad \ddots \\ H:\ddot{C}:C \\ \ddots \qquad \ddot{O} \\ H \end{array}\right]^{-}$$

This Lewis structure satisfies the octet rule for carbon and oxygen and surrounds each hydrogen with two electrons. All 24 electrons are used in this process.

QUESTION 3.13

Draw the Lewis structure for each of the following ions:

a. H_3O^+ (the hydronium ion)

b. OH^- (the hydroxide ion)

QUESTION 3.14

Draw the Lewis structure for each of the following ions:

a. CN^- (the cyanide ion)

b. CO_3^{2-} (the carbonate ion)

Lewis structure, stability, multiple bonds, and bond energies

Hydrogen, oxygen, and nitrogen are present in the atmosphere as diatomic gases, H_2, O_2, and N_2. All are covalent molecules. Their stability and reactivity, however, are quite different. Hydrogen is an explosive material, sometimes used as a fuel. Oxygen, although more stable than hydrogen, reacts with fuels in combustion. The explosion of the space shuttle *Challenger* resulted from the reaction of massive amounts of hydrogen and oxygen. Nitrogen, on the other hand, is extremely nonreactive. Since nitrogen makes up about 80% of the atmosphere, it dilutes the oxygen, which accounts for only about 20% of the atmosphere.

Breathing pure oxygen for long periods, although necessary in some medical situations, would cause the breakdown of nasal and lung tissue over time. Oxygen diluted with nonreactive nitrogen is an ideal mixture for humans and animals to breathe.

Why is there such a great difference in reactivity (or stability) among these three gases? We can explain this, in part, in terms of their bonding characteristics. The Lewis structure for H_2 (two valence electrons) is

$$H_2 \quad \text{or} \quad H:H \quad \text{or} \quad H\text{—}H$$

For oxygen (12 valence electrons, six on each atom), the only Lewis structure that satisfies the octet rule is

$$O_2 \quad \text{or} \quad \ddot{O}::\ddot{O} \quad \text{or} \quad O\text{=}O$$

The Lewis structure of N_2 (ten total valence electrons) must be

$$N_2 \quad \text{or} \quad :N:::N: \quad \text{or} \quad N{\equiv}N$$

Therefore

N_2 has a *triple bond* (six bonding electrons).

O_2 has a *double bond* (four bonding electrons).

H_2 has a *single bond* (two bonding electrons).

A **triple bond,** in which three pairs of electrons are shared by two atoms, is very stable. More energy is required to break a triple bond than a double bond. Stability is related to the **bond energy.** The bond energy is the amount of energy, in kilocalories, required to break a bond holding two atoms together. Bond energy is therefore a *measure* of stability. The values of bond energies decrease in the order *triple bond > double bond > single bond*.

The bond length is related to the presence or absence of multiple bonding. The distance of separation of two nuclei is greatest for a single bond, less for a double bond, and still less for a triple bond. The *bond length* decreases in the order *single bond > double bond > triple bond*.

QUESTION 3.15

Contrast a single and double bond with regard to:

a. distance of separation of the bonded nuclei

b. strength of the bond

QUESTION 3.16

Two nitrogen atoms in a nitrogen molecule are held together more strongly than the two chlorine atoms in a chlorine molecule. Explain this fact by comparing their respective Lewis structures.

The shape of a molecule plays a large role in determining its properties and reactivity. The shape of a molecule can be predicted by inspecting its Lewis structure and determining the position of its electron pairs. The location of electron pairs in covalent molecules gives the molecules a characteristic shape.

Lewis structures and molecular geometry

Consider the series of molecules whose Lewis structures are shown below:

$$BeH_2 \quad H:Be:H$$

$$BF_3 \qquad \begin{array}{c} :\ddot{F}: \\ :\ddot{F}:B:\ddot{F}: \end{array}$$

$$CH_4 \qquad H : \overset{\overset{\displaystyle H}{\displaystyle \cdot\cdot}}{\underset{\displaystyle H}{C}} : H$$

$$NH_3 \qquad H : \overset{\cdot\cdot}{\underset{\displaystyle H}{N}} : H$$

$$H_2O \qquad H : \overset{\cdot\cdot}{\underset{\cdot\cdot}{O}} : H$$

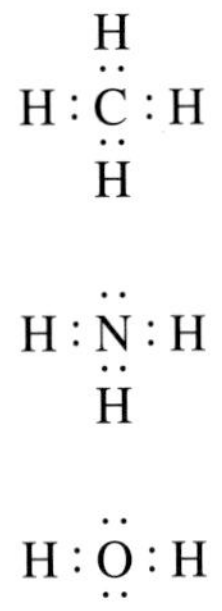

An analysis of these structures shows that the electron pairs around the central atom of the molecule arrange themselves to minimize electronic repulsion. This means that the electron pairs arrange themselves so that they can be as far as possible from each other. We may use this fact to predict molecular shape. This approach is termed the *Valence Shell Electron Pair Repulsion Theory (VSEPR Theory).*

Let's see how the VSEPR theory can be used to describe the bonding and structure of each of the molecules shown above.

BeH$_2$

Beryllium hydride has two shared electron pairs around the beryllium atom. These electron pairs have minimum repulsion if they are located as far apart as possible while still bonding the hydrogen to the central atom. This condition is met if the electron pairs are located on opposite sides of the molecule, resulting in a *linear* structure, 180° apart:

$$H : Be : H$$

or

$$H\!-\!Be\!-\!H$$
$$180°$$

The *bond angle,* the angle between H—Be and Be—H bonds, formed by the two bonding pairs is 180°.

BF$_3$

Boron trifluoride has three shared electron pairs around the central atom. Locating the electron pairs in a plane, forming a triangle, minimizes the electron pair repulsion in this molecule:

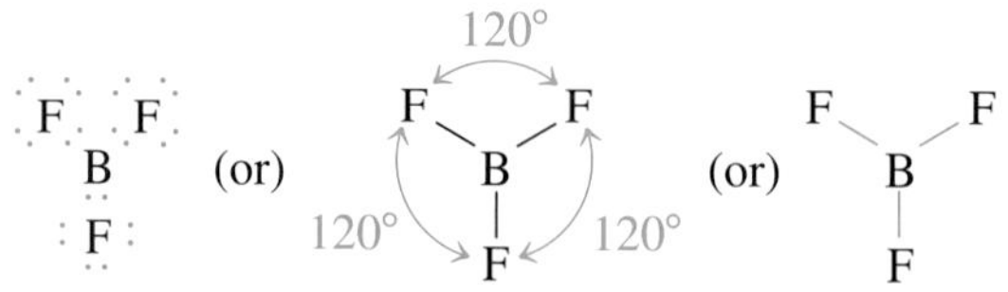

Such a structure is *trigonal planar,* and each F—B—F bond angle is 120°. We also find that compounds with central atoms in the same group of the periodic table will have similar geometry. Aluminum, in the same group as boron, produces compounds such as AlH$_3$, which is also trigonal planar.

CH$_4$

Methane has four shared pairs of electrons. Here, minimum electron repulsion is achieved by arranging the electrons at the corners of a tetrahedron (see Figure 3.2). Each H—C—H bond angle is 109.5°. Methane has a three-dimensional **tetrahedral structure.** Silicon, in the same group as carbon, forms compounds such as SiCl$_4$ and SiH$_4$ that also have tetrahedral structures.

NH₃

Ammonia also has four electron pairs about the central atom. In contrast to methane, in which all four pairs are bonding, ammonia has three pairs of bonding electrons and one non-bonding lone pair of electrons. We might expect CH_4 and NH_3 to have electron pair arrangements that are similar but not identical. The lone pair in ammonia is more negative than the bonding pairs; some of the negative charge on the bonding pairs is offset by the presence of the hydrogen atoms with their positive nuclei. Thus the arrangement of electron pairs in ammonia is distorted. The resulting distribution appears as

Angle a is greater than angle b. The hydrogen atoms in ammonia are pushed closer together than in methane. The bond angle, b, is 107°. When we represent the structure, we normally do not show the nonbonding electrons, but we must not forget their effect on the structure.

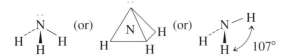

The structure is termed *trigonal pyramidal* and the molecule is termed a trigonal pyramidal, or **pyramidal molecule.**

H₂O

Water also has four electron pairs around the central atom; two pairs are bonding, and two pairs are nonbonding. These four electron pairs are approximately tetrahedral to each other; however, because of the difference between bonding and nonbonding electrons, noted earlier, the tetrahedral relationship is only approximate:

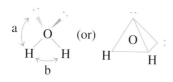

angle a > angle b

If we choose not to write the nonbonding electron pairs, we get the following structure:

This **angular** or *bent* structure has a bond angle of 104.5°, 5° smaller than the tetrahedral angle, because of the repulsive effects of the lone pairs of electrons.

The characteristics of linear, trigonal planar, and tetrahedral structures are summarized in Table 3.5.

Periodic structural relationships

The molecules considered above contain the central atoms Be (group IIA), B (group IIIA), C (group IVA), N (group VA), and O (group VIA). We may expect that a number of other compounds, containing the same central atom, will have structures with similar geometries. This is an approximation, not always true, but still useful in expanding our ability to write reasonable, geometrically accurate structures for a large number of compounds.

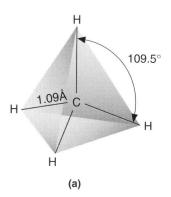

(a)

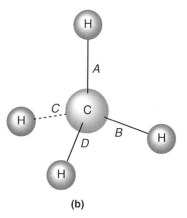

(b)

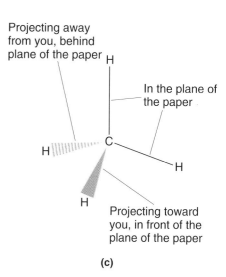

(c)

FIGURE 3.2
Representations of the three-dimensional structure of methane, CH_4. (a) Tetrahedral methane structure. (b) Ball and stick model of tetrahedral methane. (c) Three-dimensional representation of structure (b).

Molecules with five and six electron pairs also exist. They may have structures that are *trigonal bipyramidal* (forming a six-sided figure) or *octahedral* (forming an eight-sided figure).

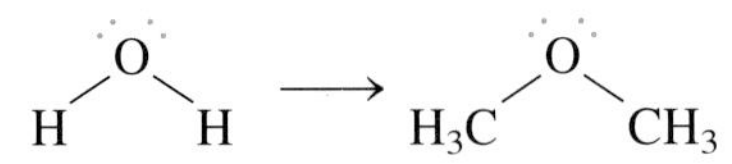

Known bond angle, 104°   Predicted bond angle is approximately 104°

FIGURE 3.3
A comparison of the bonding in water and dimethyl ether.

TABLE 3.5   Molecular Structure: The Geometry of a Molecule Is Affected by the Number of Valence Electron Pairs Around the Central Atom

Electron Pairs	Electron Pair Structure	Bonding Pairs	Nonbonding Pairs	Bond Angle	Molecular Structure	Example
2	Linear	2	0	180°	Linear	CO_2
3	Equilateral triangle	3	0	120°	Trigonal planar	SO_3
		2	1	<109°	Angular	SO_2
4	Tetrahedral	4	0	~109°	Tetrahedral	CH_4
		3	1	<107°	Trigonal pyramidal	NH_3
		2	2	<104.5°	Angular	H_2O

The periodic similarity of group members is also useful in predictions involving bonding. Consider Group VI, oxygen, sulfur, and selenium (Se). Each has six valence electrons. Each needs two more electrons to complete its octet. Each should react with hydrogen, forming

$$H_2O$$

$$H_2S$$

$$H_2Se$$

If we recall that H_2O is an angular molecule with the following Lewis structure:

$$H : \overset{..}{\underset{..}{O}} :$$
$$H$$

it follows that H_2S and H_2Se would also be angular molecules with similar Lewis structures:

$$H : \overset{..}{\underset{..}{S}} : \qquad \text{and} \qquad H : \overset{..}{\underset{..}{Se}} :$$
$$H \qquad\qquad\qquad H$$

This logic applies equally well to the other A group elements.

More complex molecules

A molecule such as dimethyl ether, $CH_3—O—CH_3$, has two different central atoms: oxygen and carbon. Recalling that carbon gives rise to a tetrahedral geometry, we could picture the parts of the molecule containing the CH_3 group (commonly referred to as the methyl group) as exhibiting tetrahedral geometry (analogous to methane):

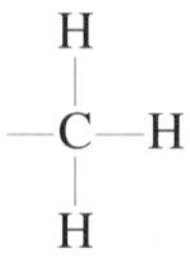

The part of the molecule connecting these two methyl groups (the oxygen) would have a bond angle similar to that of water (in which oxygen is also the central atom), approximately 104°, as seen in Figure 3.3. This is a reasonable way to represent the molecule dimethyl ether.

Trimethylamine, $(CH_3)_3N$, is a member of the amine family. As in the case of ether, two different central atoms are present. Carbon and nitrogen determine the geometry of amines. In this case the methyl group should assume the tetrahedral geometry of methane, and the nitrogen atom should have the methyl groups in a pyramidal arrangement, similar to the hydrogen atoms in ammonia, as seen in Figure 3.4. This creates a pyramidal geometry around nitrogen. H—N—H bond angles in ammonia are 107°; experimental information shows a very similar C—N—C bond angle in trimethylamine.

Ethers are a family of organic compounds that you will study in Chapter 10.

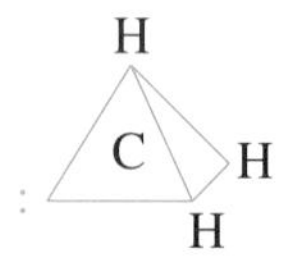

The structure and properties of amines are discussed in Chapter 14.

QUESTION 3.17

Sketch the geometry of each of the following molecules (basing your structure on the Lewis electron dot representation of the molecule):

a. PH_3

b. SiH_4

QUESTION 3.18

Sketch the geometry of each of the following molecules (basing your structure on the Lewis electron dot representation of the molecule):

a. C_2H_4

b. C_2H_2

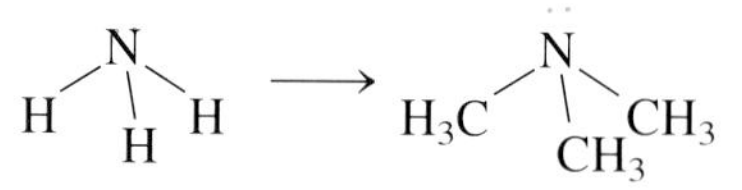

Known bond angle, 107°

Predicted bond angle is approximately 107°

FIGURE 3.4
A comparison of the bonding in ammonia and trimethylamine.

Lewis structures and polarity

A molecule is *polar* if its centers of positive and negative charges do not coincide. Molecules whose positive and negative charges are separated when the molecules are placed in an electric field will align themselves with the field. The molecule behaves as a *dipole* (having two "poles" or ends, one pole is more negative and the other pole is more positive) and is said to be polar.

Nonpolar molecules will not align with the electric field because their positive and negative centers are the same; no dipole exists. These molecules are nonpolar.

The hydrogen molecule is the simplest nonpolar molecule:

$$H : H \quad \text{or} \quad H\text{—}H$$

Both electrons, on average, are located at the center of the molecule and positively charged nuclei are on either side. The center of both positive and negative charge is at the center of the molecule; therefore the bond is nonpolar.

We may arrive at the same conclusion by considering the equality of electron sharing between the atoms being bonded. Electron sharing is related to the concept of electronegativity. **Electronegativity** is the ability of an atom in a molecule to attract electrons to itself. Electronegativity is represented by a scale derived from the measurement of energies of chemical bonds. The scale was developed by Linus Pauling, and values range from 4.0 (most electronegative element) to 0.7 (least electronegative element). The periodic trends for electronegativity, which decrease from top to bottom and increase from left to right, are similar to both ionization energy and electron affinity and are summarized in Figure 3.5.

Remember: Electronegativity deals with atoms in molecules, whereas electron affinity and ionization energy deal with isolated atoms.

The atoms of H_2 are identical; their electronegativity (electron pulling power) is the same. Thus the electrons remain at the center of the molecule, and the molecule is nonpolar.

Similarly, O_2, N_2, Cl_2, and F_2 are nonpolar molecules with nonpolar bonds. Arguments analogous to those made for hydrogen explain these observations as well (see Figure 3.6 on page 76).

Let's next consider hydrogen fluoride, HF. Fluorine is more electronegative than hydrogen. This indicates that the electrons are more strongly attracted to a fluorine atom than they are to a hydrogen atom. This results in a bond and molecule that are polar. The symbol

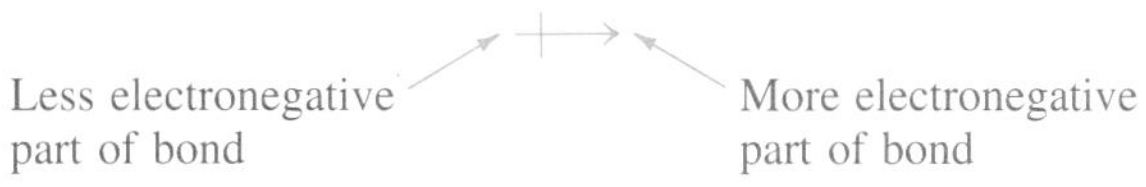

Less electronegative part of bond

More electronegative part of bond

placed below a bond indicates the direction of polarity. The more electronegative end of the bond is near the head of the arrow, and the less electronegative end of the bond is next to the tail of the arrow. Symbols, utilizing the Greek letter "delta" may also be used to designate polarity. In this system the more electronegative end of the bond is designated δ^- (partial negative), and

1A																	
H 2.2	**2A**												**3A**	**4A**	**5A**	**6A**	**7A**
Li 1.0	**Be** 1.6												**B** 2.0	**C** 2.6	**N** 3.0	**O** 3.4	**F** 4.0
Na 0.9	**Mg** 1.3	**3B**	**4B**	**5B**	**6B**	**7B**		8B		**1B**	**2B**		**Al** 1.6	**Si** 1.9	**P** 2.2	**S** 2.6	**Cl** 3.2
K 0.8	**Ca** 1.0	**Sc** 1.4	**Ti** 1.5	**V** 1.6	**Cr** 1.7	**Mn** 1.6	**Fe** 1.8	**Co** 1.9	**Ni** 1.9	**Cu** 1.9	**Zn** 1.7	**Ga** 1.8	**Ge** 2.0	**As** 2.2	**Se** 2.6	**Br** 3.0
Rb 0.8	**Sr** 1.0	**Y** 1.2	**Zr** 1.3	**Nb** 1.6	**Mo** 2.2	**Tc** 1.9	**Ru** 2.2	**Rh** 2.3	**Pd** 2.2	**Ag** 1.9	**Cd** 1.7	**In** 1.8	**Sn** 2.0	**Sb** 2.1	**Te** 2.1	**I** 2.7
Cs 0.8	**Ba** 0.9	**La*** 1.1	**Hf** 1.3	**Ta** 1.5	**W** 2.4	**Re** 1.9	**Os** 2.2	**Ir** 2.2	**Pt** 2.3	**Au** 2.5	**Hg** 2.0	**Tl** 2.0	**Pb** 2.3	**Bi** 2.0	**Po** 2.0	**At** 2.2
Fr 0.7	**Ra** 0.9	**Ac†** 1.1															

Below 1.0
1.0–3.0
Above 3.0

Alkali metals

*Lathanides: 1.1 – 1.3
†Actinides: 1.3 – 1.5

FIGURE 3.5
Electronegativities of the elements.

FIGURE 3.6
Nonpolar bonds. Molecules are depicted to emphasize their symmetry. (a) The hydrogen molecule. (b) The oxygen molecule. (c) The nitrogen molecule. (d) The chlorine molecule.

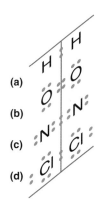

(a)
(b)
(c)
(d)

The "pulling power" or electron attracting power of the two atoms composing the bond is the same.

The electrons making up the bond are symmetrically distributed about the molecule.

One side of the molecule is a "mirror image" of the other.

the less electronegative end is designed δ^+ (partial positive). The symbols are applied to the hydrogen fluoride molecule as follows:

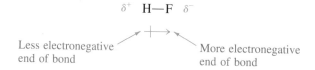

$$\delta^+ \quad H—F \quad \delta^-$$

Less electronegative end of bond   More electronegative end of bond

HF is a **polar covalent molecule** characterized by **polar covalent bonding.** This implies that the electrons are shared unequally.

A molecule containing all nonpolar bonds must also be nonpolar. In contrast, a molecule containing polar bonds may be either polar or nonpolar depending on the relative arrangement of the bonds and any lone pairs of electrons.

Let's now examine the bonding in methane. All four bonds of CH_4 are polar because of the electronegativity difference between C and H. However, because of the symmetrical arrangement of the four C—H bonds, their polarities cancel, and the molecule is nonpolar covalent:

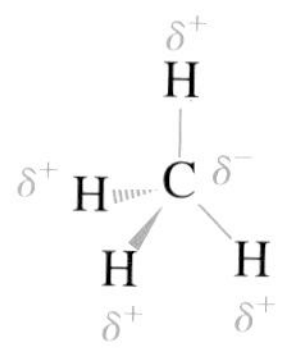

Now look at H_2O. Because of its angular (bent) structure, the polar bonds do not cancel, and the molecule is polar covalent:

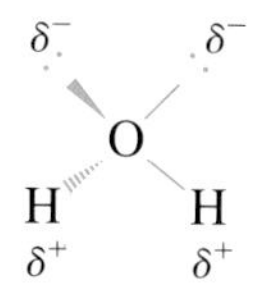

The electron density is shifted away from the hydrogens toward oxygen in the water molecule. In methane, equal electron ''pull'' in all directions results in a nonpolar covalent molecule.

QUESTION 3.19

Predict which of the following bonds are polar, and, if polar, in which direction the electrons are pulled:

a. O—S

b. C≡N

c. Cl—Cl

d. I—Cl

QUESTION 3.20

Predict which of the following bonds are polar, and, if polar, in which direction the electrons are pulled:

a. Si—Cl

b. S—Cl

c. H—C

d. C—C

QUESTION 3.21

Predict whether each of the following molecules is polar:

a. BCl_3

b. NH_3

c. HCl

d. $SiCl_4$

QUESTION 3.22

Predict whether each of the following molecules is polar:

a. CO_2

b. SCl_2

c. BrCl

d. CS_2

3.5 PROPERTIES BASED ON MOLECULAR GEOMETRY

The polarity of a molecule determines many of its physical and chemical properties. The degree of polarity affects the strength of attractive forces between individual molecules of a compound. These forces between molecules are called **intermolecular forces.**

Intermolecular and intramolecular forces should not be confused. **Intramolecular forces** are attractive forces within a molecule. It is the *intermolecular* forces that determine such properties as the solubility of one substance in another and the freezing and boiling points of liquids.

Solubility

The *solute* is the substance that is present in lesser quantity, and the *solvent* is the substance that is present in the greater amount (see Section 7.1).

The interaction of water and ammonia is an example of a particularly strong intermolecular force, the hydrogen bond; this phenomenon is discussed in Chapter 5.

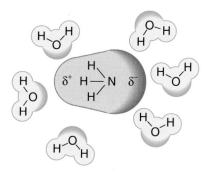

FIGURE 3.7
The interaction of polar covalent water molecules (the solvent) with polar covalent solute molecules such as ammonia, resulting in the formation of a solution.

Solubility is defined as the maximum amount of solute that dissolves in a given amount of solvent at a specified temperature. Polar molecules are most soluble in polar solvents, while nonpolar molecules are most soluble in nonpolar solvents. This is the rule of *"like dissolves like."* Substances of similar polarity are mutually soluble, and large differences in polarity lead to insolubility.

Case I: ammonia and water

Ammonia is soluble in water because both ammonia and water are polar molecules:

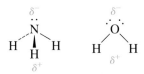

Dissolution of ammonia in water is a consequence of the intermolecular forces present among the ammonia and water molecules. The δ^- end (a nitrogen) of the ammonia molecule is attracted to the δ^+ end (a hydrogen) of the water molecule; at the same time the δ^+ end (a hydrogen) of the ammonia molecule is attracted to the δ^- end (an oxygen) of the water molecule. These attractive forces thus "pull" ammonia into water (and water into ammonia), and the ammonia molecules are randomly distributed throughout the solvent, forming a homogeneous solution (Figure 3.7).

Case II: oil and water

Oil and water don't mix; oil is a nonpolar substance composed primarily of molecules containing carbon and hydrogen. Water molecules, on the other hand, are quite polar. The potential solvent, water molecules, have partially charged ends, whereas the molecules of oil do not. As a result, water molecules exert their attractive forces on other water molecules, not on the molecules of oil; the oil remains insoluble, and because it is less dense than water, the oil simply floats on the surface of the water. This is illustrated in Figure 3.8.

Boiling points of liquids and melting points of solids

See Section 5.8.

Boiling a liquid requires energy. The energy is used to overcome the intermolecular attractive forces in the liquid, driving the molecules into the less associated gas phase. The amount of energy required to accomplish this is related to the boiling temperature. This, in turn, depends on the strength of the intermolecular attractive forces in the liquid, which parallel the polarity. This is not the only determinant of boiling point. Molecular mass is also an important consideration. The larger the mass of the molecule, the more difficult it becomes to convert the collection of molecules to the gas phase.

A similar argument can be made for the melting points of solids. The ease of conversion of a solid to a liquid also depends on the magnitude of the attractive forces in the solid. The situation actually becomes very complex for ionic solids because of the complexity of the crystal lattice.

As a general rule, polar compounds have strong attractive (intermolecular) forces, and their boiling and melting points tend to be higher than those of nonpolar substances of similar molecular mass.

Melting and boiling points of a variety of substances are included in Table 3.6.

TABLE 3.6 Melting and Boiling Points of Selected Compounds in Relation to Their Bonding Type

Formula (Name)	Bonding Type	M.P. (°C)	B.P. (°C)
N_2 (nitrogen)	Nonpolar covalent	−210	−196
O_2 (oxygen)	Nonpolar covalent	−219	−183
NH_3 (ammonia)	Polar covalent	−78	−33
H_2O (water)	Polar covalent	0	100
NaCl (sodium chloride)	Ionic	801	1413
KBr (potassium bromide)	Ionic	730	1435

QUESTION 3.23

Predict which compound in each of the following groups should have the higher melting and boiling points:

a. H_2O and C_2H_4

b.   CO and CH_4

c. NH_3 and N_2

d. Cl_2 and ICl

QUESTION 3.24

Predict which compound in each of the following groups should have the higher melting and boiling points:

a. C_2H_6 and CH_4

b.   CO and NO

c. F_2 and Br_2

d. $CHCl_3$ and CCl_4

FIGURE 3.8
The interaction of polar water molecules and nonpolar "oil" molecules. The familiar salad dressing, oil and vinegar, forms two layers. The oil does not dissolve in vinegar, an aqueous solution of acetic acid.

SUMMARY

3.1 Chemical Bonding

When two atoms are joined together to make a chemical compound, the force of attraction between the two atoms is the *chemical bond. Ionic bonding* is characterized by an electron transfer process occurring before bond formation, forming an *ion pair.* In *covalent bonding,* electrons are shared between atoms in the bonding process. The *Lewis symbol,* showing only valence electrons, is a convenient way of representing atoms singly or in combination.

3.2 Naming Compounds and Writing Formulas of Compounds

The "shorthand" symbol for a compound is its *formula.* The formula identifies the number and type of atoms in the compound.

An ion that consists of only a single atom is said to be *monatomic. Polyatomic ions,* such as the hydroxide ion, OH^-, are composed of two or more atoms bonded together.

Names of ionic compounds are derived from the names of their ions. The name of the cation appears first, followed by the name of the anion. In the Stock system for naming an ion (the systematic name), a Roman numeral indicates the charge of the cation. In the older common nomenclature system the suffix *-ous* indicates the lower of the ionic charges, and the suffix *-ic* indicates the higher ionic charge.

Most covalent compounds are formed by the reaction of nonmetals. Covalent compounds exist as *molecules.*

The convention used for naming covalent compounds is as follows:

◆   The names of the elements are written in the order in which they appear in the formula.

◆   A prefix indicating the number of each kind of atom found in the unit is placed before the name of the element.

◆ The stem of the name of the last element is used with the suffix *-ide*.

Many compounds are so familiar to us that their common names are used. It is useful to be able to correlate both systematic and common names with the corresponding molecular formula.

3.3 Properties of Ionic and Covalent Compounds

Covalently bonded molecules are discrete units, and they have less tendency to form an extended structure in the solid state. Ionic compounds, with ions joined by electrostatic attraction, do not have definable units but form a *crystal lattice* composed of positive and negative ions in an extended three-dimensional network.

The *melting point* is the temperature at which a solid is converted to a liquid; the *boiling point* is the temperature at which a liquid is converted to a gas. Melting and boiling temperatures for ionic compounds are generally higher than those of covalent compounds.

Ionic solids are crystalline, whereas covalent solids may be either crystalline or amorphous.

Many ionic solids dissolve in water, *dissociating* into positive and negative ions (an *electrolytic solution*). Because these ions can carry (conduct) a current of electricity, they are called *electrolytes*. Covalent solids in solution retain their neutral character and are *nonelectrolytes*.

3.4 Drawing Lewis Structures of Ions and Molecules

The procedure for drawing Lewis structures of molecules involves writing a skeletal structure of the molecule, arranging the atoms in their most probable order, determining the number of valence electrons on each atom, and combining them to get the total for the compound. The electrons are then distributed around the atoms (in pairs if possible) in an attempt to satisfy the octet rule. After completion of the Lewis structure the nonbonding electrons (*lone pairs* of electrons) are often omitted.

Stability of a covalent compound is related to the *bond energy*. The magnitude of the bond energy decreases in the order *triple bond > double bond > single bond*. The bond length decreases in the order *single bond > double bond > triple bond*.

Electron pairs around the central atom of the molecule arrange themselves to minimize electronic repulsion; the electrons orient themselves as far as possible from each other. Two electron pairs around the central atom lead to a *linear* arrangement of the attached atoms; three indicate a *trigonal planar* arrangement, and four result in a *tetrahedral* geometry. Molecules with five and six electron pairs also exist. They may have structures that are trigonal, bipyramidal, or octahedral.

A molecule is polar if its centers of positive and negative charges do not coincide. A *polar covalent* molecule has at least one *polar covalent bond*. An understanding of the concept of

electronegativity, the relative electron-attracting power of atoms in molecules, helps us to assess the polarity of a bond.

A molecule containing all nonpolar bonds must be nonpolar. A molecule containing polar bonds may be either polar or nonpolar, depending on the relative position of the bonds.

3.5 Properties Based on Molecular Geometry

Attractions between molecules are called *intermolecular forces. Intramolecular forces,* on the other hand, are the attractive forces within molecules. It is the intermolecular forces that determine such properties as the solubility of one substance in another and the freezing and boiling points of liquids.

Solubility is the maximum amount of solute that dissolves in a given amount of solvent at a specified temperature. Polar molecules are most soluble in polar solvents; nonpolar molecules are most soluble in nonpolar solvents. This is the rule of ''like dissolves like.''

As a general rule, polar compounds have strong intermolecular forces, and their boiling and melting points tend to be higher than nonpolar compounds of similar molecular mass.

KEY TERMS

angular molecule (3.4)	Lewis symbol (3.1)
boiling point (3.3)	linear molecule (3.4)
bond energy (3.4)	lone pair (3.4)
chemical bond (3.1)	melting point (3.3)
covalent bond (3.1)	molecule (3.2)
crystal lattice (3.2)	monatomic ion (3.2)
dissociation (3.3)	nomenclature (3.2)
double bond (3.4)	nonelectrolyte (3.3)
electrolyte (3.3)	polar covalent bond (3.4)
electrolytic solution (3.3)	polar covalent molecule (3.4)
electronegativity (3.4)	polyatomic ion (3.2)
formula (3.2)	pyramidal molecule (3.4)
intermolecular force (3.5)	single bond (3.4)
intramolecular force (3.5)	solubility (3.5)
ionic bond (3.1)	tetrahedral molecule (3.4)
ion pair (3.1)	triple bond (3.4)

QUESTIONS AND PROBLEMS

Chemical Bonding

3.25 Classify each of the following compounds as ionic or covalent:
a. $MgCl_2$ c. H_2S
b. CO_2 d. NO_2

3.26 Classify each of the following compounds as ionic or covalent:
a. NaCl   c. ICl
b. CO   d. H_2

3.27 Using Lewis symbols, write an equation predicting the product of the reaction of:
a. Li + Br
b. Mg + Cl

3.28 Using Lewis symbols, write an equation predicting the product of the reaction of:
  a. Na + O
  b. Na + S

3.29 Give the Lewis structure for each of the following compounds:
  a. NCl_3 **b.** CH_3OH **c.** CS_2

3.30 Give the Lewis structure for each of the following compounds:
  a. HNO_3 **b.** CCl_4 **c.** PBr_3

Naming Compounds and Writing Formulas of Compounds

3.31 Name each of the following ions:
  a. Na^+
  b. Cu^+
  c. Mg^{2+}
  d. Fe^{2+}
  e. Fe^{3+}

3.32 Name each of the following ions:
  a. S^{2-}
  b. Cl^-
  c. CO_3^{2-}
  d. NH_4^+
  e. CH_3COO^-

3.33 Write the formula for each of the following monatomic ions:
  a. the potassium ion
  b. the bromide ion
  c. the calcium ion
  d. the chromium(VI) ion

3.34 Write the formula for each of the following complex ions:
  a. the sulfate ion
  b. the nitrate ion
  c. the phosphate ion
  d. the bicarbonate ion

3.35 Write the correct formula for each of the following:
  a. sodium chloride
  b. magnesium bromide
  c. copper(II) oxide
  d. iron(III) oxide
  e. aluminum chloride

3.36 Write the correct formula for each of the following:
  a. silver cyanide
  b. ammonium chloride
  c. silver oxide
  d. magnesium carbonate
  e. magnesium bicarbonate

3.37 Name each of the following compounds:
  a. $MgCl_2$
  b. $AlCl_3$
  c. CaS
  d. Na_2O
  e. $Fe(OH)_3$

3.38 Name each of the following covalent compounds:
  a. NO_2
  b. SO_3
  c. PCl_3
  d. N_2O_4
  e. CCl_4

3.39 Predict the formula of a compound formed from:
  a. aluminum and oxygen
  b. lithium and sulfur
  c. boron and hydrogen
  d. magnesium and phosphorus

3.40 Predict the formula of a compound formed from:
  a. carbon and oxygen
  b. sulfur and oxygen
  c. calcium and oxygen
  d. silicon and hydrogen

Properties of Ionic and Covalent Compounds

3.41 Contrast ionic and covalent compounds with respect to the nature of the solid state.

3.42 Contrast ionic and covalent compounds with respect to their relative melting points.

Drawing Lewis Structures of Ions and Molecules

3.43 Draw the appropriate Lewis structure for each of the following atoms:
  a. H   **c.** C
  b. He   **d.** N

3.44 Draw the appropriate Lewis structure for each of the following atoms:
  a. Be   **c.** F
  b. B   **d.** S

3.45 Draw the appropriate Lewis structure for each of the following ions:
  a. Li^+ **c.** Cl^-
  b. Mg^{2+} **d.** P^{3-}

3.46 Draw the appropriate Lewis structure for each of the following ions:
  a. Be^{2+} **c.** O^{2-}
  b. Al^{3+} **d.** S^{2-}

Properties Based on Molecular Geometry

3.47 What is the relationship between the polarity of a bond and the polarity of the molecule?

3.48 What effect does polarity have on the solubility of a compound in water?

3.49 What effect does polarity have on the melting point of a pure compound?

3.50 What effect does polarity have on the boiling point of a pure compound?

Further Problems

3.51 Give the Lewis structure for each of the following ions:
  a. CO_3^{2-} **b.** SO_3^{2-} **c.** NH_4^+

3.52 Give the Lewis structure for each of the following ions:
  a. NO_3^- **b.** OH^- **c.** CN^-

3.53 Supply the missing charge for each of the following ions:
   a. CO_3 **c.** PO_4
   b. SO_4 **d.** NO_3

3.54 Supply the missing charge for each of the following ions:
   a. MnO_4 **c.** CN
   b. HCO_3 **d.** OH

VOCABULARY QUIZ

3.1 A(n) _____ is a region of electron density with a principal energy level that has a maximum capacity of two electrons.

3.2 A(n) _____ is a unit of a solid characterized by a regular arrangement of components.

3.3 A material that dissolves in water to produce a solution that conducts an electrical current is a(n) _____.

3.4 _____ are attractive forces that occur between molecules.

3.5 A(n) _____ is a diagram of an atom, ion, or molecule showing valence electron arrangement.

3.6 A(n) _____ is an electron pair that is not involved in bonding.

3.7 A covalent bond in which the electrons are not equally shared is referred to as a(n) _____ bond.

3.8 A(n) _____ is an ion containing a number of atoms.

3.9 A molecule consisting of four groups attached to a central atom usually has a(n) _____ structure.

3.10 A bond in which three pairs of electrons are shared by two atoms is called a(n) _____.

4

Calculations and the Chemical Equation

LEARNING GOALS

◆ Know the relationship between the mole and Avogadro's number as well as the usefulness of these quantities.

◆ Know the major function served by the chemical equation, the basis for chemical calculations.

◆ Write chemical formulas for common inorganic substances.

◆ Perform calculations using Avogadro's number and the mole.

◆ Balance chemical equations given the identity of products and reactants.

◆ Perform calculations involving conversions from moles to grams or grams to moles.

◆ Calculate the number of moles of product resulting from a given number of moles of reactants or the number of moles of reactant needed to produce a certain number of moles of product.

◆ Perform computations involving more complex systems that may involve conversion from volume to mass or the reverse, one mass unit to another, and mass to moles or the reverse.

CHEMISTRY CONNECTION

The Chemistry of Automobile Air Bags

Each year, thousands of individuals are killed or seriously injured in automobile accidents. Perhaps most serious is the front-end collision. The car decelerates or stops virtually on impact; the momentum of the passengers, however, does not stop, and the driver and passengers are thrown forward toward the dashboard and the front window. Suddenly, passive parts of the automobile, such as control knobs, the rear view mirror, the steering wheel, the dashboard, and the windshield, become lethal weapons.

Automobile engineers have been aware of these problems for a long time. They have instituted a series of design improvements to lessen the potential problems associated with front-end impact. Smooth switches rather than knobs, recessed hardware, and padded dashboards are examples. These changes, coupled with the use of lap and shoulder belts, which help to immobilize occupants of the car, have lessened the frequency and severity of the impact and decreased the death rate for this type of accident.

An almost ideal protection would be a soft, fluffy pillow, providing a cushion against impact. Such a device, an air bag inflated only on impact, is now available for the protection of the driver and front seat passenger.

How does it work? Ideally, it inflates only when severe front-end impact occurs; it inflates very rapidly (in approxi-

mately 40 milliseconds), then deflates to provide a steady deceleration, cushioning the occupants from impact. A remarkably simple chemical reaction makes this a reality.

When solid sodium azide (NaN_3) is detonated (mechanical energy produced by an electric current), it decomposes to form solid sodium and nitrogen gas:

$$2NaN_3(s) \longrightarrow 2Na(s) + 3N_2(g)$$

The nitrogen gas inflates the air bag, cushioning the driver and front-seat passenger.

The solid sodium azide has a high density (characteristic of solids) and thus occupies a small volume. It can easily be stored in the center of a steering wheel or in the dashboard. The rate of the detonation (Chapter 5) is very rapid. In milliseconds it produces three moles of N_2 gas for every two moles of NaN_3. The N_2 gas occupies a relatively large volume because its density is low. (Recall from Chapter 1 that this is a general property of gases.)

Figuring out how much sodium azide is needed to produce enough nitrogen to properly inflate the bag is an example of a practical application of the chemical arithmetic that we are learning in this chapter.

INTRODUCTION

We often need to predict the quantity of a product produced from the reaction of a given amount of material. It is equally possible to calculate how much of a material would be necessary to produce a desired amount of product. One of many examples was shown in the story at the beginning of this chapter: the need to solve a very practical problem.

What is required is a recipe: a procedure to follow. The basis for our recipe is the *chemical equation.* A properly written chemical equation provides all of the necessary information for the chemical calculation. That critical information is the *combining ratio* of elements or compounds that must occur to produce a certain amount of product or products.

The calculation of chemical quantities based on chemical equations is the application of arithmetic to chemical systems to answer a typical question such as the following:

"A pharmaceutical company wishes to manufacture 1000 kg of a product next year. How much of each of the starting materials must be ordered? If the starting materials cost $20/gram, how much money must be budgeted for the project?"

In this chapter we define the mole, the fundamental unit of measure of chemical arithmetic, learn to write and balance chemical equations, and use these tools to perform calculations of chemical quantities.

4.1 THE MOLE CONCEPT AND ATOMS

Atoms are exceedingly small, yet their masses have been experimentally determined for each of the elements. The unit of measurement for these determinations is the **atomic mass unit,** abbreviated amu:

$$1 \text{ amu} = 1.66 \times 10^{-24} \text{ gram}$$

The periodic table provides atomic masses in atomic mass units. For example, the average mass of a helium atom is 4.003 amu, which corresponds to 6.65×10^{-24} gram.

The mole and Avogadro's number

In everyday work, chemists use much larger quantities of matter (typically, grams or kilograms). A more practical unit for defining a ''collection'' of atoms is the **mole:**

$$1 \text{ mole of atoms} = 6.02 \times 10^{23} \text{ atoms of an element}$$

This number is **Avogadro's number.** Amadeo Avogadro, a nineteenth-century scientist, conducted a series of experiments that provided the basis for the mole concept.

The practice of defining a unit for a quantity of small objects is common; a *dozen* eggs, a *ream* of paper, and a *gross* of pencils are well-known examples. Similarly, a mole is 6.02×10^{23} individual units of anything. We could, if we desired, speak of a mole of eggs or a mole of pencils. However, in chemistry we use the mole to represent a specific quantity of atoms, ions, or molecules.

The mole (mol) and the atomic mass unit (amu) are related. The atomic mass of an element corresponds to the average mass of a single atom in amu *and* the mass of a mole of atoms in grams.

Consider this relationship for sodium in Example 4.1.

EXAMPLE 4.1

Relating Avogadro's Number to Mass

Calculate the mass, in grams, of Avogadro's number of sodium atoms.

Solution

The average mass of one sodium atom is 22.99 amu. As noted above, one amu is 1.66×10^{-24} gram, and 6.02×10^{23} atoms of sodium is Avogadro's number.

Formatting this information as a series of conversion factors, using the factor-label method, we have

$$22.99 \, \frac{\cancel{amu}}{\cancel{\text{atom Na}}} \times 1.66 \times 10^{-24} \, \frac{\text{g Na}}{\cancel{amu}} \times 6.02 \times 10^{23} \, \frac{\cancel{\text{atoms Na}}}{\text{mol Na}} = 22.99 \, \frac{\text{g Na}}{\text{mol Na}}$$

Section 1.4

The average mass of one *atom* of sodium, in units of amu, is *numerically identical* to the mass of *Avogadro's number of atoms,* expressed in units of grams.

The example shown above for sodium is not unique. It is true for every element in the periodic table.

Since Avogadro's number of particles (atoms) is one mole, it follows that

The average mass of one atom of hydrogen is 1.008 amu

and

The mass of one mole of hydrogen atoms is 1.008 grams

or

The average mass of one atom of carbon is 12.01 amu

and

The mass of one mole of carbon atoms is 12.01 grams

and so forth. One mole of atoms of *any element* contains the same number, Avogadro's number, of atoms.

The difference in mass of a mole of two different elements can be quite striking (see Figure 4.1). For example, a mole of hydrogen atoms is 1.008 grams, and a mole of lead atoms is 207.19 grams.

FIGURE 4.1
The comparison of approximately one mole each of silver (as Morgan and Peace dollars), gold (as Canadian Maple Leaf coins), and copper (as pennies) shows the considerable difference in mass (as well as economic value) of equivalent moles of different substances.

Calculating atoms, moles, and mass

Performing calculations based on the chemical equation requires a facility for relating the number of atoms of an element to a corresponding number of moles of that element and ultimately to their mass in grams. Such calculations involve the use of conversion factors. This type of calculation was first described in Chapter 1. Some examples follow.

EXAMPLE 4.2

Conversion of Moles to Atoms

How many iron atoms are present in 3.0 moles of iron metal?

Solution

The calculation is based on the development of the appropriate conversion factor. The relationship

$$\frac{6.02 \times 10^{23} \text{ atoms Fe}}{1 \text{ mol Fe}}$$

follows directly from

$$1 \text{ mol Fe} = 6.02 \times 10^{23} \text{ atoms Fe}$$

Using this conversion factor, we have

$$\text{Number of atoms of Fe} = 3.0 \text{ mol Fe} \times \frac{6.02 \times 10^{23} \text{ atoms Fe}}{1 \text{ mol Fe}}$$

$$= 18 \times 10^{23} \text{ atoms of Fe, or}$$

$$= 1.8 \times 10^{24} \text{ atoms of Fe}$$

EXAMPLE 4.3

Conversion of Atoms to Moles

Calculate the number of moles of sulfur represented by 1.81×10^{24} atoms of sulfur.

Solution

$$1.8 \times 10^{24} \text{ atoms S} \times \frac{1 \text{ mol S}}{6.02 \times 10^{23} \text{ atoms S}} = 3.0 \text{ mol S}$$

Note that this conversion factor is the inverse of that used in the previous problem. Remember, the conversion factor must cancel units that should not appear in the final answer.

EXAMPLE 4.4

Conversion of Moles of a Substance to Mass in Grams

What is the mass, in grams, of 3.01 moles of sulfur?

Solution

We know that one mole of sulfur has a mass of 32.06 grams. Setting up a suitable conversion factor between grams and moles results in

$$3.01 \text{ mol S} \times \frac{32.06 \text{ g S}}{1 \text{ mol S}} = 96.5 \text{ grams S}$$

EXAMPLE 4.5

Conversion of Kilograms to Moles

Calculate the number of moles of sulfur in 1.00 kilogram of sulfur.

Solution

$$1.00 \text{ kg S} \times \frac{1000 \text{ g S}}{1 \text{ kg S}} \times \frac{1 \text{ mol S}}{32.06 \text{ g S}} = 30.7 \text{ mol S}$$

EXAMPLE 4.6

Conversion from Grams to Atoms

Calculate the number of atoms of sulfur in 1.00 gram of sulfur.

Solution

$$1.00 \cancel{\text{g S}} \times \frac{1 \cancel{\text{mol S}}}{32.06 \cancel{\text{g S}}} \times \frac{6.02 \times 10^{23} \text{ atoms S}}{1 \cancel{\text{mol S}}} = 1.88 \times 10^{22} \text{ atoms S}$$

All of the above examples use a sequence of conversion factors to proceed from the information *provided* in the problem to the information *requested* by the problem.

It is generally useful to map out a pattern for the required conversion. In Example 4.6 we are given the number of grams and need the number of atoms that correspond to that mass. Begin by "tracing a path" to the answer:

$$\text{grams} \xrightarrow[\text{1}]{\text{Step}} \text{moles} \xrightarrow[\text{2}]{\text{Step}} \text{atoms}$$

Two transformations, or conversions, are required:

Step 1   Grams to moles.

Step 2   Moles to atoms.

For the first conversion we could consider either

$$\frac{1 \text{ mol S}}{32.06 \text{ g S}}$$

or the inverse

$$\frac{32.06 \text{ g S}}{1 \text{ mol S}}$$

If we want grams to cancel, (a) is the correct choice, resulting in

$$1.000 \cancel{\text{g S}} \times \frac{1 \text{ mol S}}{32.06 \cancel{\text{g S}}} = \text{value in mol S}$$

For the second conversion, moles to atoms, the moles of S must cancel; therefore

$$\cancel{\text{mol S}} \times \frac{6.02 \times 10^{23} \text{ atom S}}{1 \cancel{\text{mol S}}} = \text{number of atoms S}$$

which are the desired units, those requested in the problem.

QUESTION 4.1

a.   How many oxygen atoms are present in 2.50 moles of oxygen atoms?

b.   How many oxygen atoms are present in 2.50 moles of oxygen molecules?

QUESTION 4.2

How many moles of sodium are represented by 9.03×10^{23} atoms of sodium?

QUESTION 4.3

What is the mass, in grams, of 3.50 moles of the element helium?

QUESTION 4.4

How many oxygen atoms are present in 40.0 grams of oxygen?

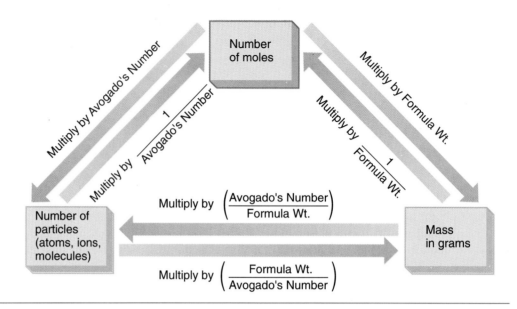

FIGURE 4.2
Interconversion between numbers
of moles, particles, and grams.

The conversion between the three principal measures of quantity of matter—the number of grams (mass), the number of moles, and the number of individual particles (atoms, ions, or molecules)—is essential to the art of problem solving in chemistry. Their interrelationship is depicted in Figure 4.2.

4.2 COMPOUNDS

The chemical formula

Chapter 1

Compounds are pure substances that are composed of two or more elements that are chemically combined. They are represented by their **chemical formula,** a combination of symbols of the various elements that make up the compounds. The chemical formula is based on the **formula unit.** This is the smallest collection of atoms that provides the following information:

1. the identity of the atoms present in the compound and
2. the relative numbers of each type of atom.

Let's look at the following formulas:

Hydrogen gas, H_2.   This indicates that two atoms of hydrogen are chemically bonded as a unit, hence the subscript 2.

Water, H_2O.   Water is composed of individual units containing two atoms of hydrogen (subscript 2) and one atom of oxygen (lack of a subscript means *one* atom).

Sodium chloride, NaCl.   One atom of sodium and one atom of chlorine combine to make a unit (an ion pair) of sodium chloride.

Calcium hydroxide, $Ca(OH)_2$.   One unit of calcium hydroxide contains one atom of calcium and two atoms each of oxygen and hydrogen. The subscript outside the parentheses applies to *all* atoms inside the parentheses.

Ammonium sulfate, $(NH_4)_2SO_4$.   Ammonium sulfate contains two units of the ammonium ion (NH_4^+) and one sulfate ion (SO_4^{2-}). Each ammonium ion contains one nitrogen and four hydrogen atoms. The formula unit is therefore composed of two nitrogen atoms, eight hydrogen atoms, one sulfur atom, and four oxygen atoms.

Copper sulfate pentahydrate, $CuSO_4 \cdot 5H_2O$.   This is an example of a compound that, as a part of the formula unit, has water incorporated in its structure. Copper sulfate pentahydrate has five units of water (or ten H atoms and five O atoms) in addition to one copper atom, one sulfur atom, and four oxygen atoms for a total atomic composition of:

1 copper atom
1 sulfur atom
9 oxygen atoms
10 hydrogen atoms

Note that the symbol for water in the hydrate is preceded by a "dot," indicating that although the water is a formula unit capable of standing alone, it is, in this case, a part of a larger crystalline structure.

Just as a mole of atoms is based on the atomic mass, a mole of a compound is based on the formula mass or **formula weight.** The formula weight is calculated by adding the masses of all the atoms of which the compound is composed. To calculate the formula weight of a compound, the formula unit must be known.

4.3 THE MOLE CONCEPT APPLIED TO COMPOUNDS

EXAMPLE 4.7

Calculation of Formula Weight

Calculate the formula weight of water, H_2O.

Solution

Each water molecule contains two hydrogen atoms and one oxygen atom. The formula weight is

$$\begin{array}{r} 2 \text{ atoms of hydrogen} \times \ \ 1.008 \text{ amu/atom} = \ \ 2.016 \text{ amu} \\ \underline{1 \text{ atom of oxygen} \quad \times 16.00 \text{ amu/atom} \ = 16.00 \text{ amu}} \\ 18.02 \text{ amu} \end{array}$$

The average mass of a single unit of H_2O is 18.02 amu/formula unit. Therefore the mass of a mole of H_2O formula units is 18.02 grams.

In the example of H_2O we are describing a covalent compound, and individual units of covalent compounds are molecules. It is therefore appropriate to refer to the formula weight of molecular species as the **molecular weight.**

EXAMPLE 4.8

Calculation of Formula Weight

Calculate the formula weight of sodium sulfate.

Solution

The sodium ion is Na^+, and the sulfate ion is SO_4^{2-}. Two sodium ions must be present to neutralize the negative charges on sulfate. The formula is Na_2SO_4. Sodium sulfate contains two sodium atoms, one sulfur atom, and four oxygen atoms. The formula weight is

$$\begin{array}{r} 2 \text{ atoms of sodium} \times 22.99 \text{ amu/atom} = \ \ 45.98 \text{ amu} \\ 1 \text{ atom of sulfur} \quad \times 32.06 \text{ amu/atom} = \ \ 32.06 \text{ amu} \\ \underline{4 \text{ atoms of oxygen} \times 16.00 \text{ amu/atom} = \ \ 64.00 \text{ amu}} \\ 142.04 \text{ amu} \end{array}$$

The average mass of a single unit of Na_2SO_4 is 142.04 amu/formula unit. Therefore the mass of a mole of Na_2SO_4 formula units is 142.04 grams/mole.

In the above example, Na_2SO_4 is an ionic compound. As we have seen, it is not technically correct to describe ionic compounds as molecules; similarly, the term *molecular weight* is not appropriate for Na_2SO_4. The term *formula weight* may be used to describe ions, ion pairs, or molecules. We shall use the term *formula weight* in a general way to represent each of these species.

Figure 4.3 illustrates the difference between molecules and ion pairs.

FIGURE 4.3
Formula units of (a) sodium chloride, an ionic compound, and (b) methane, a covalent compound.

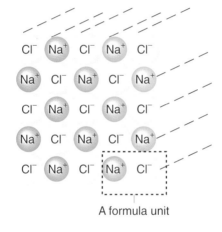

A formula unit

(a) Ionic

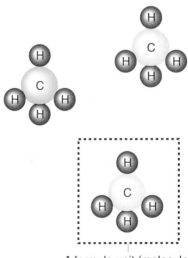

A formula unit (molecule)

(b) Covalent

EXAMPLE 4.9

Calculation of Formula Weight

Calculate the formula weight of calcium phosphate.

Solution

The calcium ion is Ca^{2+}, and the phosphate ion is PO_4^{3-}. To form a neutral unit, $3Ca^{2+}$ must combine with $2PO_4^{3-}$; $[3 \times (+2)]$ calcium ion charges are balanced by $[2 \times (-3)]$, the phosphate ion charge. Thus for calcium phosphate, $Ca_3(PO_4)_2$, the subscript 2 for phosphate dictates that there are two phosphorus atoms and eight oxygen atoms (2×4) in the formula unit. Therefore

$$\begin{array}{l} 3 \text{ atoms of Ca} \times 40.08 \text{ amu/atom} = 120.24 \text{ amu} \\ 2 \text{ atoms of P} \;\; \times 30.97 \text{ amu/atom} = \;\; 61.94 \text{ amu} \\ \underline{8 \text{ atoms of O} \;\; \times 16.00 \text{ amu/atom} = 128.00 \text{ amu}} \\ \hspace{5cm} 310.18 \text{ amu} \end{array}$$

The formula weight is 310.18 grams/mole.

Calculate the formula weight of each of the following compounds:

a. NH_3 (ammonia)

b. $C_6H_{12}O_6$ (a sugar, glucose)

c. $CoCl_2 \cdot 6H_2O$ (cobalt chloride hexahydrate)

Calculate the formula weight of each of the following compounds:

a. $C_2F_2Cl_4$ (a freon gas)

b. C_3H_7OH (isopropyl alcohol, rubbing alcohol)

c. CH_3Br (bromomethane)

4.4 THE CHEMICAL EQUATION AND THE INFORMATION IT CONVEYS

A recipe for chemical change

The **chemical equation** is the shorthand notation for a chemical reaction. It describes all of the substances that react to produce the product(s). **Reactants,** or starting materials, are all substances that undergo change in a chemical reaction; **products** are substances produced by a chemical reaction.

The chemical equation also describes the physical state of the reactants and products as solid, liquid, or gas. It tells us whether the reaction occurs and identifies the solvent and experimental conditions employed, such as heat, light, or electrical energy added to the system.

Most important, the relative number of moles of reactants and products appears in the equation. According to the **law of conservation of mass,** matter cannot be either gained or lost in the process of a chemical reaction. The total mass of the products must be equal to the total mass of the reactants. In other words, the law of conservation of mass tells us that we must have a balanced chemical equation.

Features of a chemical equation

Consider the decomposition of calcium carbonate:

$$CaCO_3(s) \xrightarrow{\Delta} CaO(s) + CO_2(g)$$

$$\text{Calcium carbonate} \qquad \text{Calcium oxide} \quad \text{Carbon dioxide}$$

The factors involved in writing this equation are the following.

1. ***The identity of products and reactants must be specified.*** In some cases it is possible to predict the products of a reaction. More often, the fate of a reactant must be verified by chemical analysis. (Generally, you will be given information regarding the identity of the reactants and products.)

2. ***Reactants are written to the left of the reaction arrow ($\rightarrow$), and products are written to the right.*** The direction in which the arrow points indicates the direction in which the reaction proceeds. In the preceding example the reactant on the left ($CaCO_3$) is converted to products on the right ($CaO + CO_2$) during the course of the reaction.

3. ***The physical state of reactants and products may be shown in parentheses.*** For example:
   - $Cl_2(g)$ or $Cl_2\uparrow$ means that chlorine is in the gaseous state.
   - $Mg(s)$ or $Mg\downarrow$ indicates that magnesium is a solid.
   - $Br_2(l)$ indicates that bromine is present as a liquid.
   - $NH_3(aq)$ tells us that ammonia is present as an aqueous solution (dissolved in water).

4. ***The symbol Δ over the reaction arrow means that heat energy is necessary for the reaction to occur.*** Often, other special conditions are noted above or below the reaction arrow. For example, ''light'' means that a light source provides energy necessary for the reaction. Such reactions are termed photochemical reactions.

5. ***The equation must be balanced.*** We will treat this topic in detail later in this chapter.

According to the considerations outlined above, the equation for the decomposition of calcium carbonate is written as

$$CaCO_3(s) \xrightarrow{\Delta} CaO(s) + CO_2(g)$$

The equation tells us that solid calcium carbonate, when heated, decomposes to solid calcium oxide and gaseous carbon dioxide. Furthermore, this equation shows that one mole of calcium carbonate produces one mole of calcium oxide and one mole of carbon dioxide.

The experimental basis of a chemical equation

The chemical equation must represent a real chemical transformation. Evidence for the reaction may be based on observations such as the following:

- the release of carbon dioxide gas when an acid is added to a carbonate,
- the formation of a solid (or precipitate) when a solution of iron ions is made basic,
- the production of heat,
- the change in color of a solution upon addition of a second substance.

Many reactions are not so obvious. Sophisticated instruments are now available to the chemist. These instruments allow the detection of subtle changes in chemical systems that would otherwise go unnoticed. Such instruments may measure:

- heat or light absorbed or emitted,
- changes in the way the sample behaves in an electric or magnetic field,
- changes in electrical properties.

Whether we use our senses or a $100,000 computerized instrument, the ''bottom line'' is the same: We are measuring a change in one or more chemical or physical properties in an effort to understand the changes taking place in a chemical system.

Disease can be described as a chemical system (actually a biochemical system) gone awry. Here too, the underlying changes may not be obvious. Just as technology has helped chemists see subtle chemical changes in the laboratory, medical diagnosis has been revolutionized in our lifetimes using very similar technology. One such technique is described in the Clinical Perspective, Magnetic Resonance Imaging.

A CLINICAL PERSPECTIVE

Magnetic Resonance Imaging

It has been known for some time that nuclei, like electrons, exist in different energy states or energy levels. Furthermore, under the influence of electromagnetic radiation, transitions involving absorption of radiation can occur between the various nuclear states. This is analogous to the behavior of the electron in an atom. However, electronic transitions occur under the influence of ultraviolet and visible radiation, whereas the nuclear transitions occur in the microwave region of the electromagnetic spectrum under the influence of a magnetic field. The nuclei of hydrogen atoms may be affected in different ways, depending on their position in a molecule. These differences give rise to unique patterns of energy absorption (called absorption spectra), and the technique of nuclear magnetic resonance (NMR) has become a useful tool for the study of molecules containing hydrogen.

Human organs and tissue are made up of compounds containing hydrogen atoms. In the 1970s and 1980s this experimental technique was extended beyond tiny laboratory samples of pure compounds to the most complex sample possible—the human body. The result of these experiments is termed "magnetic resonance imaging (MRI)."

MRI is noninvasive to the body; requires no use of radioactive substances; and is quick, safe, and painless. A person is placed in a cavity surrounded by a magnetic field, and an image (based on the extent of microwave energy absorption) is generated, stored, and sorted in a computer. Differences between normal and malignant tissue, atherosclerotic thickening of an aortal wall, and a host of other problems may clearly be seen in the final image.

Advances in MRI technology have provided medical practitioners with a powerful new tool in diagnostic medicine. This is but one more example of basic science leading to technological advancement.

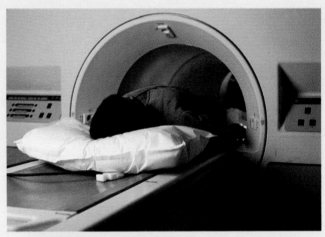

A patient entering an MRI scanner.

Dr. Paul Barnett of the Greater Baltimore Medical Center studies images obtained using MRI.

4.5 BALANCING CHEMICAL EQUATIONS

The chemical equation also shows the *molar quantity* of reactants needed to produce a certain *molar quantity* of products. The chemical equation expresses these quantities in terms of moles.

The number of moles of each product and reactant is indicated by placing a whole-number *coefficient* before the formula of each substance in the chemical equation. A coefficient of 2 (for example, $2NaCl$) indicates that two moles of sodium chloride are involved in the reaction. $3NH_3$ signifies three moles of ammonia; it also means that three moles of nitrogen atoms and 3×3 or nine moles of hydrogen atoms are involved in the reaction. The coefficient 1 is understood, not written. H_2SO_4 would therefore be interpreted as one mole of sulfuric acid, or two moles of hydrogen atoms, one mole of sulfur atoms, and four moles of oxygen atoms.

The equation

$$CaCO_3(s) \xrightarrow{\Delta} CaO(s) + CO_2(g)$$

is balanced as written. On the reactant side we have

1 mole of Ca
1 mole of C
3 moles of O

On the product side there are

$$1 \text{ mole of Ca}$$
$$1 \text{ mole of C}$$
$$3 \text{ moles of O}$$

Therefore the law of conservation of mass is obeyed.
Now consider the reaction of hydrogen chloride gas with solid calcium metal:

$$HCl(g) + Ca(s) \longrightarrow CaCl_2(s) + H_2(g)$$

The equation, as written, is not balanced.

Reactants	*Products*
1 mole H atoms	2 moles H atoms
1 mole Cl atoms	2 moles Cl atoms
1 mole Ca atoms	1 mole Ca atoms

We need two moles of both H and Cl on the left, or reactant, side. An *incorrect* way of balancing the equation is as follows:

$$H_2Cl_2(g) + Ca(s) \longrightarrow CaCl_2(s) + H_2(g)$$

Not a correct equation

The equation satisfies the law of conservation of mass; however, we have altered one of the reacting species. Hydrogen chloride is HCl, not H_2Cl_2. We must remember that *we cannot alter any chemical species in the process of balancing the equation.* We can *only* introduce coefficients into the equation. To do anything else would misrepresent the chemistry of the reaction. The equation must represent the reaction accurately. The correct equation is

$$2HCl(g) + Ca(s) \longrightarrow CaCl_2(s) + H_2(g)$$

Correct equation

This process is illustrated in Figure 4.4.
Many equations are balanced by trial and error. If the identity of the products and reactants, the physical state, and the reaction conditions are known, the following steps provide a method for correctly balancing a chemical equation:

Step 1 Count the number of moles of atoms of each element on both product and reactant side.

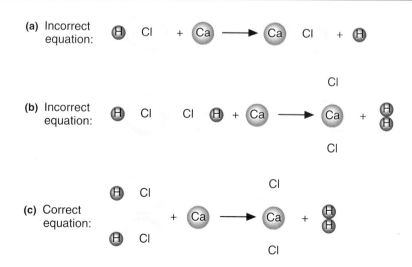

(a) Incorrect equation:

(b) Incorrect equation:

(c) Correct equation:

FIGURE 4.4
Balancing the equation HCl + Ca→CaCl₂ + H₂. (a) Neither product is the correct chemical species. (b) The reactant, HCl, is incorrectly represented as H_2Cl_2. (c) This equation is correct; all species are correct, and the law of conservation of mass is obeyed.

Step 2 Determine which elements are not balanced.

Step 3 Balance one element at a time using coefficients.

Step 4 After you believe that you have successfully balanced the equation, check, as in Step 1, to be certain that mass conservation has been achieved.

Let us apply these steps to the reaction of calcium with hydrogen chloride gas:

$$HCl(g) + Ca(s) \longrightarrow CaCl_2(s) + H_2(g)$$

Step 1 *Reactants*   *Products*

1 mole H atoms   2 moles H atoms

1 mole Cl atoms   2 moles Cl atoms

1 mole Ca atoms   1 mole Ca atoms

Step 2 The numbers of moles of H and Cl are not balanced.

Step 3 Insertion of a 2 before HCl on the reactant side should balance the equation:

$$2HCl(g) + Ca(s) \longrightarrow CaCl_2(s) + H_2(g)$$

Step 4 Check for mass balance:

Reactants   *Products*

2 moles H atoms   2 moles H atoms

2 moles Cl atoms   2 moles Cl atoms

1 mole Ca atoms   1 mole Ca atoms

Hence the equation is balanced.

EXAMPLE 4.10

Balancing Equations

Balance the following equation: Hydrogen gas and oxygen gas react explosively to produce water vapor.

Solution

Recall that hydrogen and oxygen are diatomic molecules; therefore

$$H_2(g) + O_2(g) \longrightarrow H_2O(g)$$

Note that the moles of hydrogen atoms are balanced but the moles of oxygen atoms are not; therefore we must first balance the moles of oxygen atoms:

$$H_2(g) + O_2(g) \longrightarrow 2H_2O(g)$$

Balancing moles of oxygen atoms creates an imbalance in the number of moles of hydrogen atoms, so

$$2H_2(g) + O_2(g) \longrightarrow 2H_2O(g)$$

The equation is balanced, with four moles of hydrogen atoms and two moles of oxygen atoms on each side of the reaction arrow.

EXAMPLE 4.11

Balancing Equations

Balance the following equation: Propane gas, C_3H_8, a fuel, reacts with oxygen to produce carbon dioxide and water vapor. The reaction is

Section 9.2

$$C_3H_8(g) + O_2(g) \longrightarrow CO_2(g) + H_2O(g)$$

Solution

First, balance carbon; there are three moles of carbon atoms on the left and only one mole of carbon atoms on the right:

$$C_3H_8(g) + O_2(g) \longrightarrow 3CO_2(g) + H_2O(g)$$

Next, we balance the hydrogen; there are two moles of hydrogen atoms on the right and eight on the left. We need $4H_2O$ on the right:

$$C_3H_8(g) + O_2(g) \longrightarrow 3CO_2(g) + 4H_2O(g)$$

There are now ten moles of oxygen atoms on the right and two on the left. To balance, we must have $5O_2$ on the left side of the equation:

$$C_3H_8(g) + 5O_2(g) \longrightarrow 3CO_2(g) + 4H_2O(g)$$

The balanced equation

Remember: In every case, be sure to check the final equation for mass balance.

QUESTION 4.7

Balance each of the following chemical equations:

a. $Fe(s) + O_2(g) \longrightarrow Fe_2O_3(s)$

b. $C_6H_6(l) + O_2(g) \longrightarrow CO_2(g) + H_2(g)$

QUESTION 4.8

Balance each of the following chemical equations:

a. $S_2Cl_2(s) + NH_3(g) \longrightarrow N_4S_4(s) + NH_4Cl(s) + S_8(s)$

b. $C_2H_5OH(l) + O_2(g) \longrightarrow CO_2(g) + H_2O(g)$

4.6 CALCULATIONS USING THE CHEMICAL EQUATION

General principles

The calculation of quantities of products and reactants based on a balanced chemical equation is important in many fields. The synthesis of drugs and other complex molecules on a large scale is conducted on the basis of a balanced equation. This minimizes the waste of expensive chemical compounds used in these reactions. Similarly, the ratio of fuel and air in a home furnace or automobile must be adjusted carefully, according to their combining ratio, to maximize energy conversion, minimize fuel consumption, and minimize pollution.

In carrying out chemical calculations we apply the following rules.

Rule 1. The basis for the calculations is a balanced equation. If the equation is not properly balanced, the calculation is meaningless.

Rule 2. The calculations are performed in terms of moles. The coefficients in the balanced equation represent the relative number of moles of products and reactants.

Rule 3. The conservation of mass must be obeyed. We have seen that the number of moles of products and reactants often differ in a balanced equation. For example,

$$C(s) + O_2(g) \longrightarrow CO_2(g)$$

is a balanced equation. Two moles of reactants combine to produce one mole of product:

$$(1 \text{ mole of C} + 1 \text{ mole of } O_2 \longrightarrow 1 \text{ mole of } CO_2)$$

However, one mole of C *atoms* and two moles of O *atoms* produce one mole of C *atoms* and two moles of O *atoms*. In other words, the number of moles of reactants and products may differ, but the number of moles of atoms cannot. The formation of CO_2 from C and O_2 may be described as follows:

$$C(s) + O_2(g) \longrightarrow CO_2(g)$$

$$1 \text{ mole C} + 1 \text{ mole } O_2 \longrightarrow 1 \text{ mole } CO_2$$

$$12.0 \text{ g C} + 32.0 \text{ g } O_2 \longrightarrow 44.0 \text{ g } CO_2$$

The mole is the basis of our calculations. However, moles are generally measured in grams (or kilograms). A facility for interconversion of moles and grams is fundamental to chemical arithmetic.

Use of conversion factors

Conversion between moles and grams

Conversion from moles to grams, and vice versa, requires only the formula weight of the compound of interest. Consider the following examples.

EXAMPLE 4.12

Conversion between Moles and Grams

a.   Convert one mole of oxygen to grams.

Solution

The formula weight of oxygen (O_2) is

$$\frac{32.0 \text{ g } O_2}{1 \text{ mol } O_2}$$

Therefore

$$1 \text{ mol } O_2 \times \frac{32.0 \text{ g } O_2}{1 \text{ mol } O_2} = 32.0 \text{ g } O_2$$

b.   How many grams of carbon dioxide are contained in 10.0 moles of carbon dioxide?

Solution

The formula weight of CO_2 is

$$\frac{44.0 \text{ g } CO_2}{1 \text{ mol } CO_2}$$

and

$$10.0 \text{ mol } CO_2 \times \frac{44.0 \text{ g } CO_2}{1 \text{ mol } CO_2} = 4.40 \times 10^2 \text{ grams } CO_2$$

c.   How many moles of sodium atoms are contained in 1 lb (454 g) of sodium metal?

Solution

$$454 \text{ g Na} \times \frac{1 \text{ mol Na}}{23.0 \text{ g Na}} = 19.7 \text{ mol Na}$$

QUESTION 4.9

Perform each of the following conversions:

a.   5.00 moles of water to grams of water
b.   25.0 grams of LiCl to moles of LiCl

QUESTION 4.10

Perform each of the following conversions:

a. 1.00×10^{-5} mole of $C_6H_{12}O_6$ to micrograms of $C_6H_{12}O_6$

b.   35.0 grams of $MgCl_2$ to moles of $MgCl_2$

Conversion of moles of reactants to moles of products

In Example 4.11 we balanced the equation for the reaction of propane and oxygen as follows:

$$C_3H_8(g) + 5O_2(g) \longrightarrow 3CO_2(g) + 4H_2O(g)$$

In this reaction, one mole of C_3H_8 corresponds to, or results in,

five moles of O_2 being consumed, or

three moles of CO_2 being formed, or

four moles of H_2O being formed.

This information may be written in the form of a conversion factor or ratio:

1 mol C_3H_8/5 mol O_2

Translated: One mole of C_3H_8 reacts with five moles of O_2.

1 mol C_3H_8/3 mol CO_2

Translated: One mole of C_3H_8 produces three moles of CO_2.

1 mol C_3H_8/4 mol H_2O

Translated: One mole of C_3H_8 produces four moles of H_2O.

Conversion factors, based on the chemical equation, permit us to perform a variety of calculations.

EXAMPLE 4.13

Calculating Reacting Quantities

Calculate the number of grams of O_2 that will react with one mole of C_3H_8.

Solution

Two conversion factors are necessary to solve this problem:

1.   conversion from moles of C_3H_8 to moles of O_2 and

2.   conversion of moles of O_2 to grams of O_2.

$$1 \text{ mol } C_3H_8 \times \frac{5 \text{ mol } O_2}{1 \text{ mol } C_3H_8} \times \frac{32.0 \text{ g } O_2}{1 \text{ mol } O_2} = 1.60 \times 10^2 \text{ g } O_2$$

EXAMPLE 4.14

Calculating Grams of Product from Moles of Reactant

Calculate the number of grams of CO_2 produced from the combustion of one mole of C_3H_8.

Solution

Employing logic similar to that used in Example 4.13, we get

$$1 \text{ mol } C_3H_8 \times \frac{3 \text{ mol } CO_2}{1 \text{ mol } C_3H_8} \times \frac{44.0 \text{ g } CO_2}{1 \text{ mol } CO_2} = 132 \text{ g } CO_2$$

EXAMPLE 4.15

Relating Masses of Reactants and Products

Calculate the number of grams of C_3H_8 required to produce 36.0 g of H_2O.

Solution

It is necessary to convert:

1. grams of H_2O to moles of H_2O,
2. moles of H_2O to moles of C_3H_8,
3. moles of C_3H_8 to grams of C_3H_8.

$$36.0 \text{ g } H_2O \times \frac{1 \text{ mol } H_2O}{18 \text{ g } H_2O} \times \frac{1 \text{ mol } C_3H_8}{4 \text{ mol } H_2O} \times \frac{44.0 \text{ g } C_3H_8}{1 \text{ mol } C_3H_8} = 22.0 \text{ g } C_3H_8$$

QUESTION 4.11

Given the balanced equation for the combustion of ethyl alcohol:

$$C_2H_5OH(l) + 3O_2(g) \longrightarrow 2CO_2(g) + 3H_2O(g)$$

a. How many moles of O_2 will react with one mole of ethyl alcohol?
b. How many grams of O_2 will react with one mole of ethyl alcohol?

QUESTION 4.12

How may grams of CO_2 will be produced by the combustion of one mole of ethyl alcohol (see Question 4.11)?

Let's consider an example that requires us to write and balance the chemical equation, use conversion factors, and calculate the amount of a reactant consumed in the chemical reaction.

EXAMPLE 4.16

Calculating a Quantity of Reactant

The reaction between an acid and a base produces a salt and water (Section 7.4).

Calcium hydroxide may be used to neutralize (completely react with) hydrochloric acid. Calculate the number of grams of hydrochloric acid that would be neutralized by 0.50 mol of calcium hydroxide.

Solution

The formula for calcium hydroxide is $Ca(OH)_2$, and that for hydrochloric acid is HCl. The unbalanced equation produces calcium chloride and water as products:

$$Ca(OH)_2(s) + HCl(aq) \longrightarrow CaCl_2(aq) + H_2O(l)$$

First, balance the equation:

$$Ca(OH)_2(s) + 2HCl(aq) \longrightarrow CaCl_2(aq) + 2H_2O(l)$$

Next, determine the necessary conversion:

1. moles of $Ca(OH)_2$ to moles of HCl and
2. moles of HCl to grams of HCl.

$$0.500 \text{ mol } Ca(OH)_2 \times \frac{2 \text{ mol } HCl}{1 \text{ mol } Ca(OH)_2} \times \frac{36.5 \text{ g } HCl}{1 \text{ mol } HCl} = 36.5 \text{ g } HCl$$

This reaction is illustrated in Figure 4.5.

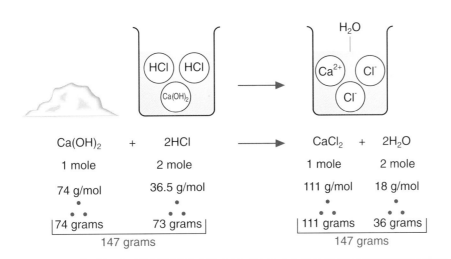

FIGURE 4.5
An illustration of the law of conservation of mass. In this example, one mole of calcium hydroxide and two moles of hydrogen chloride react to produce three moles of product (two moles of water and one mole of calcium chloride). The mass (grams) of product produced is provided. The total mass, in grams, of reactant(s) consumed is equal to the total mass, in grams, of product(s) formed. *Note:* In reality, HCl does not exist as discrete molecules in water. The HCl separates to form H^+ and Cl^-. Ionization in water will be discussed with the chemistry of acids and bases in Chapter 7.

EXAMPLE 4.17

Calculating Reactant Quantities

What mass of sodium hydroxide, NaOH, would be required to produce 8.00 grams of the antacid milk of magnesia, $Mg(OH)_2$, by the reaction of $MgCl_2$ with NaOH?

Solution

$$MgCl_2(aq) + 2NaOH(aq) \longrightarrow Mg(OH)_2(s) + 2NaCl(aq)$$

The equation tells us that two moles of NaOH form one mole of $Mg(OH)_2$. If we calculate the number of moles of $Mg(OH)_2$ in 8 grams of $Mg(OH)_2$, we can determine the number of moles of NaOH necessary and then the mass of NaOH required:

$$\text{Mass of } Mg(OH)_2 \longrightarrow \text{Moles of } Mg(OH)_2 \longrightarrow \text{Moles of } NaOH \longrightarrow \text{Mass of } NaOH$$

$$58.3 \text{ g of } Mg(OH)_2 = 1 \text{ mol of } Mg(OH)_2$$

Therefore

$$8.00 \text{ g } Mg(OH)_2 \times \frac{1 \text{ mol } Mg(OH)_2}{58.3 \text{ g } Mg(OH)_2} = 0.137 \text{ mol } Mg(OH)_2$$

Two moles of NaOH react to give one mole of $Mg(OH)_2$. Therefore

$$0.137 \text{ mol } Mg(OH)_2 \times \frac{2 \text{ mol } NaOH}{1 \text{ mol } Mg(OH)_2} = 0.274 \text{ mol } NaOH$$

40.0 g of NaOH = 1 mol of NaOH. Therefore

$$0.274 \text{ mol } NaOH \times \frac{40.0 \text{ g } NaOH}{1 \text{ mol } NaOH} = 11.0 \text{ g } NaOH$$

QUESTION 4.13

Metallic iron reacts with O_2 gas to produce iron(III) oxide.

a. Write and balance the equation.

b. Calculate the number of grams of iron needed to produce 5.00 grams of product.

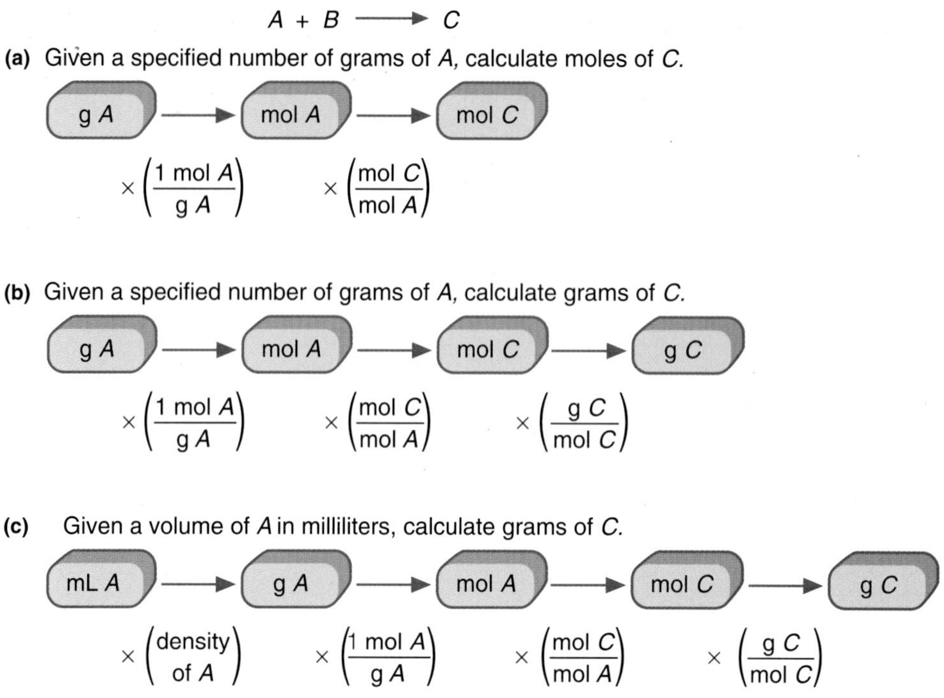

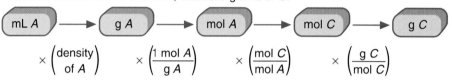

$$A + B \longrightarrow C$$

(a) Given a specified number of grams of *A*, calculate moles of *C*.

gA $\longrightarrow$ mol A $\longrightarrow$ mol C

$\times \left(\dfrac{1 \text{ mol } A}{g\,A} \right)$ $\times \left(\dfrac{\text{mol } C}{\text{mol } A} \right)$

(b) Given a specified number of grams of *A*, calculate grams of *C*.

gA $\longrightarrow$ mol A $\longrightarrow$ mol C $\longrightarrow$ gC

$\times \left(\dfrac{1 \text{ mol } A}{g\,A} \right)$ $\times \left(\dfrac{\text{mol } C}{\text{mol } A} \right)$ $\times \left(\dfrac{g\,C}{\text{mol } C} \right)$

(c) Given a volume of *A* in milliliters, calculate grams of *C*.

mL A $\longrightarrow$ gA $\longrightarrow$ mol A $\longrightarrow$ mol C $\longrightarrow$ gC

$\times \left(\dfrac{\text{density}}{\text{of } A} \right)$ $\times \left(\dfrac{1 \text{ mol } A}{g\,A} \right)$ $\times \left(\dfrac{\text{mol } C}{\text{mol } A} \right)$ $\times \left(\dfrac{g\,C}{\text{mol } C} \right)$

FIGURE 4.6
A general problem-solving strategy using molar quantities.

QUESTION 4.14

Barium carbonate decomposes upon heating to barium oxide and carbon dioxide.

a.   Write and balance the equation.

b.   Calculate the number of grams of carbon dioxide produced by heating 50.0 grams of barium carbonate.

A general problem-solving strategy is summarized in Figure 4.6.

SUMMARY

4.1 The Mole Concept and Atoms

Atoms are exceedingly small, yet their masses have been experimentally determined for each of the elements. The unit of measurement for these determinations is the *atomic mass unit*, abbreviated amu:

$$1 \text{ amu} = 1.66 \times 10^{-24} \text{ gram}$$

The periodic table provides atomic masses in atomic mass units.

A more practical unit for defining a "collection" of atoms is the *mole*:

$$1 \text{ mol of atoms} = 6.02 \times 10^{23} \text{ atoms of an element}$$

This number is often referred to as *Avogadro's number*.

The mole and the atomic mass unit are related. The atomic mass of a given element corresponds to the average mass of a single atom in atomic mass units and the mass of a mole of atoms in grams. One mole of atoms of any element contains the same number, Avogadro's number, of atoms.

4.2 Compounds

Compounds are pure substances that are composed of two or more elements that are chemically combined. They are represented by their *chemical formula,* a combination of symbols of the various elements that make up the compounds. The chemical formula is based on the *formula unit.* This is the smallest collection of atoms that provides the identity of the atoms present in the compound and the relative numbers of each type of atom.

4.3 The Mole Concept Applied to Compounds

Just as a mole of atoms is based on the atomic mass, a mole of a compound is based on the formula mass or *formula weight.* The formula weight is calculated by addition of the masses of all the atoms or ions of which the unit is composed. To calculate the formula weight, the formula unit must be known.

4.4 The Chemical Equation and the Information It Conveys

The *chemical equation* is the shorthand notation for a chemical reaction. It describes all of the substances that react to produce the product(s). *Reactants,* or starting materials, are all substances that undergo change in a chemical reaction; *products* are substances produced by a chemical reaction.

According to the *law of conservation of mass,* matter cannot be either gained or lost in the process of a chemical reaction. The law of conservation of mass states that we must have a balanced chemical equation.

Features of a suitable equation include the following:

◆ The identity of products and reactants must be specified.

◆ Reactants are written to the left of the reaction arrow ($\rightarrow$) and products to the right.

◆ The physical states of reactants and products are shown in parentheses.

◆ The symbol Δ over the reaction arrow means that heat energy is necessary for the reaction to occur.

◆ The equation must be balanced.

4.5 Balancing Chemical Equations

The chemical equation shows the molar quantity of reactants needed to produce a certain molar quantity of products. The chemical equation expresses these quantities in terms of moles.

The number of moles of each product and reactant is indicated by placing a whole-number coefficient before the formula of each substance in the chemical equation.

Many equations are balanced by trial and error. If the identity of the products and reactants, the physical state, and the reaction conditions are known, the following steps provide a method for correctly balancing a chemical equation:

◆ Count the number of atoms of each element on both product and reactant side.

◆ Determine which atoms are not balanced.

◆ Balance one atom at a time using coefficients.

◆ After you believe that you have successfully balanced the equation, check to be certain that mass conservation has been achieved.

4.6 Calculations Using the Chemical Equation

Calculations involving chemical quantities are based on the following requirements:

◆ The basis for the calculations is a balanced equation

◆ The calculations are performed in terms of moles.

◆ The conservation of mass must be obeyed.

The mole is the basis for calculations. However, masses are generally measured in grams (or kilograms). Therefore, you must be able to interconvert moles and grams to perform chemical arithmetic.

KEY TERMS

atomic mass unit (4.1)
Avogadro's number (4.1)
chemical equation (4.4)
chemical formula (4.2)
formula unit (4.2)
formula weight (4.3)
law of conservation of mass (4.4)
mole (4.1)
molecular weight (4.3)
product (4.4)
reactant (4.4)

QUESTIONS AND PROBLEMS

The Mole Concept and Atoms

4.15 What is the mass in grams of one mole of helium atoms?

4.16 What is the mass in grams of one mole of nitrogen atoms?

4.17 Calculate the number of moles corresponding to:
a. 20.0 g He
b. 0.040 kg Na
c. 3.0 g Cl

4.18 Calculate the number of moles corresponding to:
a. 0.10 lb Ca
b. 4.00 g Fe
c. 2.00 kg C

Chemical Compounds

4.19 Distinguish between the terms *molecule* and *ion pair.*

4.20 Distinguish between the terms *formula weight* and *molecular weight.*

4.21 Calculate the formula weight, in grams per mole, of each of the following formula units:
a. NaCl
b. Na_2SO_4
c. $Fe_3(PO_4)_2$

4.22 Calculate the formula weight, in grams per mole, of each of the following formula units:
a. S_8
b. $(NH_4)_2SO_4$
c. CO_2

The Mole Concept Applied to Compounds

4.23 Calculate the number of moles corresponding to:
a. 15.0 g NaCl
b. 15.0 g Na_2SO_4

4.24 Calculate the number of moles corresponding to:
a. 15.0 g NH_3
b. 16.0 g O_2

4.25 Calculate the mass in grams corresponding to:
a. 1.000 mole H_2O
b. 2.000 moles NaCl

4.26 Calculate the mass in grams corresponding to:
a. 0.400 mole NH_3
b. 0.800 mole $BaCO_3$

4.27 Calculate the mass in grams corresponding to:
a. 10.0 moles He
b. 1.00×10^2 moles H_2

4.28 Calculate the mass in grams corresponding to:
  a. 2.00 moles CH_4
  b. 0.400 mole $Ca(NO_3)_2$

4.29 How many grams are required to have 0.100 mole of each of the following compounds?
  a. Mg
  b. $CaCO_3$
  c. $C_6H_{12}O_6$ (glucose)
  d. NaCl

4.30 How many grams are required to have 0.100 mole of each of the following compounds?
  a. NaOH
  b. H_2SO_4
  c. C_2H_5OH (ethanol)
  d. $Ca_3(PO_4)_2$

4.31 How many moles are in 50.0 g of each of the following compounds?
  a. KBr
  b. $MgSO_4$
  c. Br_2
  d. NH_4Cl

4.32 How many moles are in 50.0 g of each of the following compounds?
  a. CS_2
  b. $Al_2(CO_3)_3$
  c. $Sr(OH)_2$
  d. $LiNO_3$

4.33 How many molecules are found in each of the following?
  a. 0.100 mole CO_2
  b. 18.9 g of glucose, $C_6H_{12}O_6$

4.34 How many molecules are found in each of the following?
  a. 15.0 g of NH_3
  b. 5.20×10^{-4} g of H_2O

The Chemical Equation and the Information It Conveys

4.35 What is the ultimate basis for a correct chemical equation?

4.36 List the general types of information that a chemical equation provides.

Balancing Chemical Equations

4.37 Write a balanced equation for each of the following reactions:
  a. Ammonia is formed by the reaction of nitrogen and hydrogen.
  b. Hydrochloric acid reacts with sodium hydroxide to produce water and sodium chloride.

4.38 Write a balanced equation for each of the following reactions:
  a. Nitric acid reacts with calcium hydroxide to produce water and calcium nitrate.
  b. Butane (C_4H_{10}) reacts with oxygen to produce water and carbon dioxide.

4.39 Write a balanced equation for each of the following reactions:
  a. Glucose, a sugar, $C_6H_{12}O_6$, is oxidized (reacts with oxygen) in the body to produce water and carbon dioxide.
  b. Sodium carbonate, upon heating, produces sodium oxide and carbon dioxide.

4.40 Write a balanced equation for each of the following reactions:
  a. Sulfur, present as an impurity in coal, is burned in oxygen to produce sulfur dioxide.

  b. Hydrofluoric acid (HF) reacts with glass (SiO_2) in the process of etching to produce silicon tetrafluoride and water.

Calculations Using the Chemical Equation

4.41 How many grams of boron oxide B_2O_3 can be produced from 20.0 grams of diborane (B_2H_6)?

$$B_2H_6 + 3O_2 \longrightarrow B_2O_3 + 3H_2O$$

4.42 How many grams of Al_2O_3 can be produced from 15.0 grams of Al?

$$4Al + 3O_2 \longrightarrow 2Al_2O_3$$

4.43 Calculate the amount of $CrCl_3$ that could be produced from 50.0 grams of Cr_2O_3 according to the equation

$$Cr_2O_3 + 3CCl_4 \longrightarrow 2CrCl_3 + 3COCl_2$$

4.44 3.50 grams of water are reacted according to the following equation:

$$3H_2O + PCl_3 \longrightarrow H_3PO_3 + 3HCl$$

How many grams of H_3PO_3 are produced?

4.45 For the reaction

$$N_2(g) + H_2(g) \longrightarrow NH_3(g)$$

  a. Balance the equation.
  b. How many moles of H_2 would react with one mole of N_2?
  c. How many moles of product would form from one mole of N_2?
  d. If 14.0 g of N_2 were initially present, calculate the number of moles of H_2 required to react with all of the N_2.
  e. For conditions outlined in part (d), how many grams of product would form?

4.46 Aspirin (acetylsalicylic acid) may be formed from salicylic acid and acetic acid as follows:

$$C_7H_6O_3 + CH_3COOH \longrightarrow C_9H_8O_4 + H_2O$$

Salicylic   Acetic   Aspirin
acid   acid

  a. Is this equation balanced? If not, complete the balancing.
  b. How many moles of aspirin may be produced from 1.00×10^2 moles of salicylic acid?
  c. How many grams of aspirin may be produced from 1.00×10^2 moles of salicylic acid?
  d. How many grams of acetic acid would be required to completely react with the 1.00×10^2 moles of salicylic acid?

Further Problems

4.47 The protein in our bodies is composed of various molecules called amino acids. One amino acid is methionine; its molecular formula is $C_5H_{11}NO_2S$. Calculate:
  a. the formula weight of methionine
  b. the number of oxygen atoms in a mole of this compound
  c. the mass of oxygen in a mole of the compound
  d. the mass of oxygen in 50.0 grams of the compound

4.48 Triglycerides (Chapters 13 and 18) are used in biochemical systems to store energy; they can be formed from glycerol. The molecular formula of glycerol is $C_3H_8O_3$. Calculate:
  a. the formula weight of glycerol
  b. the number of oxygen atoms in a mole of this compound
  c. the mass of oxygen in a mole of the compound
  d. the mass of oxygen in 50.0 grams of the compound

4.49 Joseph Priestley discovered oxygen in the eighteenth century by using heat to decompose mercury(II) oxide:

$$2HgO \xrightarrow{\Delta} 2Hg + O_2$$

How much oxygen is produced from 1.00×10^2 grams of HgO?

4.50 Dinitrogen monoxide (also known as nitrous oxide and used as an anesthetic) can be made by heating ammonium nitrate:

$$NH_4NO_3(s) \longrightarrow N_2O(g) + 2H_2O(g)$$

How much dinitrogen monoxide can be made from 1.00×10^2 grams of ammonium nitrate?

4.51 The burning of acetylene (C_2H_2) in oxygen is the reaction in the oxyacetylene torch. How much oxygen is needed to burn 20.0 kg of acetylene? The unbalanced equation is

$$C_2H_2(g) + O_2(g) \longrightarrow CO_2(g) + H_2O(g)$$

4.52 The reaction of calcium hydride with water can be used to prepare hydrogen gas:

$$CaH_2(s) + 2H_2O(l) \longrightarrow Ca(OH)_2(aq) + 2H_2(g)$$

How many moles of hydrogen gas are produced by reacting 1.00×10^2 g of calcium hydride with water?

4.53 Which of the following has fewer moles of carbon? 100 g of $CaCO_3$ or 0.5 mole of CCl_4

4.54 Which of the following has fewer moles of carbon? 6.02×10^{22} molecules of C_2H_6 or 88 g of CO_2

4.55 How many molecules are found in each of the following?
  a. 1.0 lb of sucrose, $C_{12}H_{22}O_{11}$ (table sugar)
  b. 1.57 kg of N_2O (anesthetic)

4.56 How many molecules are found in each of the following?
  a. 4×10^5 tons of SO_2 (produced by the 1980 eruption of the Mount St. Helens volcano)
  b. 25.0 lb of SiO_2 (major constituent of sand)

VOCABULARY QUIZ

4.1 _____ is 6.02×10^{23} particles of matter contained in 1 mole of a substance.

4.2 A record of chemical change showing the conversion of reactants to products is called a(n) _____.

4.3 A(n) _____ is the representation of a compound or ion in which elemental symbols represent types of atoms and subscripts show the relative numbers of atoms.

4.4 The smallest collection of atoms from which the formula of a compound can be established is called _____.

4.5 The mass of a formula unit of a compound relative to a standard (carbon-12) is called _____.

4.6 In chemical change, "matter cannot be created or destroyed" is a statement of the _____.

4.7 A(n) _____ is the amount of substance containing Avogadro's number of particles.

4.8 The _____ is the mass of a molecule relative to a standard (carbon-12).

4.9 _____ result from a chemical reaction and appear on the right side of a chemical equation.

4.10 _____ are starting materials for a chemical reaction, appearing on the left side of a chemical equation.

5

Energy Relationships and States of Matter

LEARNING GOALS

◆ State the meaning of the terms *enthalpy, entropy,* and *free energy* and know their implications.

◆ Describe experiments that yield thermochemical information and calculate fuel values based on experimental data.

◆ Know what is meant by the rate of a reaction and the role of kinetics in chemical and physical change.

◆ Know what is meant by the terms *activation energy* and the *activated complex.*

◆ Develop a "feel" for the way reactant structure, concentration, temperature, and catalysis affect the rate of a chemical reaction.

◆ Understand what is meant by the term *equilibrium,* and relate LeChatelier's Principle to the concept of reversibility.

◆ Understand the relationships expressed in the gas laws: Boyle's Law, Charles's Law, Avogadro's Law, the ideal gas law, and Dalton's Law.

◆ Understand properties of the liquid state: compressibility, viscosity, surface tension, and vapor pressure.

◆ Describe the processes of melting, boiling, evaporation, and condensation.

◆ Know the properties of the various classes of solids: ionic, covalent, molecular, and metallic.

CHEMISTRY CONNECTION

Getting Nothing for Something

Would you pay something for nothing? Most would reply, "Certainly not!" However, all of us do exactly that every day of our lives. Energy is nonmaterial—technically, nothing. But its cost is a significant fraction of everyone's budget.

When we purchase gasoline for our automobiles or oil for the furnace, we are certainly buying matter. That matter is only a storage device; we are really purchasing the nonmaterial energy stored in the chemical bonds. Combustion, burning in oxygen, releases the stored potential energy in a form suited to its function: mechanical energy to power a vehicle or heat energy to warm a home.

If we are paying a considerable price for "nothing," it would be nice to believe that we are at least getting full value for our expenditure. Even that is not the case. Removal of energy from molecules also extracts a price. For example, a properly tuned automobile engine is perhaps 30% efficient. That means that less than one-third of the available energy actually moves the car. The other two-thirds is released into the atmosphere as wasted energy, mostly heat energy. The energy is not destroyed (the law of conservation of energy, Section 1.7), but it is certainly not available to us in a useful form.

Can we build a 100% efficient energy transfer system? Is there such a thing as free energy? No, on both counts. It is theoretically impossible, and the laws of thermodynamics, which we discuss in this chapter, tell us why this is so.

INTRODUCTION

In the previous chapter we discussed chemical change assuming that all of the reacting material was consumed and that only products of the reaction remain at the end of the reaction. Often, this is not true. Furthermore, not all chemical reactions take place at the same speed; some occur almost instantaneously (explosions), while others may proceed for many years (corrosion).

Two concepts play important roles in determining the extent and speed of a chemical reaction: *thermodynamics,* which deals with energy changes in chemical reactions, and *kinetics,* which describes the rate or speed of a chemical reaction.

Although both thermodynamics and kinetics involve energy, they are two separate considerations. A reaction may be thermodynamically favored but very slow; conversely, a reaction may be very fast because it is kinetically favorable yet produce very little (or no) product because it is thermodynamically unfavorable.

In this chapter we investigate the fundamentals of thermodynamics and kinetics, with an emphasis on the critical role that energy changes play in chemical reactions. We consider physical change as well as chemical change, including the conversions that take place among the states of matter (solid, liquid, and gas).

5.1 THERMODYNAMICS

Thermodynamics is the study of energy, work, and heat. It may be applied to chemical change, such as the calculation of the quantity of heat obtainable from the combustion of one gallon of fuel oil. Similarly, energy produced or consumed in physical change, such as the boiling or freezing of water, may be determined.

There are three basic laws of thermodynamics; only the first two will be of concern here. They help us to understand why some chemical reactions occur readily, while others do not. For instance, a mixture of concentrated solutions of hydrochloric acid and sodium hydroxide reacts violently producing a large quantity of heat. On the other hand, nitrogen and oxygen have coexisted in the atmosphere for thousands of years with no significant chemical reaction occurring.

The chemical reaction and energy

Section 2.3

John Dalton believed that chemical change involved joining, separating, or rearranging atoms. Almost 200 years later, this statement stands as an accurate description of chemical reactions. However, we now know much more about the nonmaterial energy changes that are an essential part of every reaction.

Throughout the discussion of thermodynamics and kinetics it will be useful to remember the following:

◆ Molecules and atoms in a reaction mixture are in constant, random motion.

◆ These molecules and atoms frequently collide with each other.

◆ Only some collisions, those with sufficient energy, will break bonds in molecules.

◆ When reactant bonds are broken, new bonds are formed and products result.

Exothermic and endothermic reactions: enthalpy

The first law of thermodynamics states that the energy of the universe is constant; this is the law of conservation of energy. The study of energy changes that occur in chemical reactions is a very practical application of the first law. Consider, for example, the generalized reaction:

$$A\!-\!B + C\!-\!D \longrightarrow A\!-\!D + C\!-\!B$$

Each chemical bond is stored chemical energy (potential energy). In order for the reaction to take place, bond $A\!-\!B$ and bond $C\!-\!D$ must break; this process *always* requires energy. At the same time, bonds $A\!-\!D$ and $C\!-\!B$ must form; this process always releases energy.

If the energy required to break the $A\!-\!B$ and $C\!-\!D$ bonds is *less* than the energy given off when the $A\!-\!D$ and $C\!-\!B$ bonds form, the reaction will release the excess energy; the energy is a *product,* and the reaction is termed **exothermic** (*Gr. exo,* out, and *Gr. therm,* heat). This conversion of chemical energy to heat energy is represented in Figure 5.1a.

An example of an exothermic reaction is the combustion of methane:

$$CH_4(g) + 2O_2(g) \longrightarrow CO_2(g) + 2H_2O(g) + 211 \text{ kcal}$$

Exothermic reaction

On the other hand, if the energy required to break the $A\!-\!B$ and $C\!-\!D$ bonds is *greater* than the energy released when the $A\!-\!D$ and $C\!-\!B$ bonds form, the reaction will need an external supply of energy (perhaps from a Bunsen burner). Insufficient energy is available in the system to initiate the bond-breaking process. Such reactions are termed **endothermic** (*Gr. endo,* to take on, and *Gr. therm,* heat), and energy is a *reactant.* The conversion of heat energy into chemical energy is represented in Figure 5.1b.

The decomposition of ammonia into nitrogen and oxygen is one example:

$$22 \text{ kcal} + 2NH_3(g) \longrightarrow N_2(g) + 3H_2(g)$$

Endothermic reaction

The examples used here show the energy absorbed or released as heat energy. Depending on the reaction and the conditions under which the reaction is run, the energy may take the form of light energy or electrical energy. A firefly releases energy as a soft glow of light on a summer evening. An electrical current results from a chemical reaction in a battery, enabling your car to start.

Enthalpy is the term used to represent heat energy. The *change in enthalpy* is the energy difference between the products and reactants of a chemical reaction and is symbolized as $\Delta H°$. By convention, energy released is represented with a negative sign (indicating an exothermic reaction), and energy absorbed is shown with a positive sign (indicating an endothermic reaction).

For the combustion of methane, an exothermic process,

$$\Delta H° = -211 \text{ kcal}$$

For the decomposition of ammonia, an endothermic process,

$$\Delta H° = +22 \text{ kcal}$$

FIGURE 5.1
(a) An exothermic reaction. ΔE represents the energy released during the progress of the exothermic reaction: $A + B \rightarrow C + D + \Delta E$. (b) An endothermic reaction. ΔE represents the energy absorbed during the progress of the endothermic reaction: $\Delta E + A + B \rightarrow C + D$.

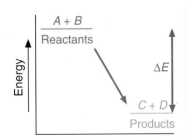

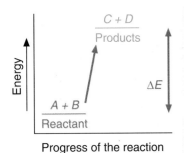

Spontaneous reactions are just that: They occur without any external energy input. Nonspontaneous reactions must be persuaded; they need an input of energy.

It seems that all exothermic reactions should be spontaneous. After all, an external supply of energy does not appear to be necessary; in fact, energy is a product of the reaction. It also seems that all endothermic reactions should be nonspontaneous: Energy is a reactant that we must provide. However, these hypotheses are not supported by experimentation.

Experimental measurement has shown that most *but not all* exothermic reactions are spontaneous; likewise, most *but not all,* endothermic reactions are not spontaneous. There must be some factor in addition to enthalpy that will help us to explain the less obvious cases, nonspontaneous exothermic reactions and spontaneous endothermic reactions. This other factor is entropy.

The first law of thermodynamics considers the enthalpy of chemical reactions. The second law states that the universe spontaneously tends toward increasing disorder or randomness. A measure of the randomness of a chemical system is its **entropy.** The entropy of a substance is represented by the symbol $S°$. A random, or disordered, system is characterized by *high entropy;* a well-organized system has *low entropy.*

Entropy

A *system* is a part of the universe upon which we wish to focus our attention. For example, it may be a beaker containing reactants and products.

What we do mean by disorder in chemical systems? Disorder is simply the absence of a regular repeating pattern. Disorder or randomness increases as we convert from the solid to the liquid to the gaseous state. As we shall see, solids often have an ordered crystalline structure, and liquids have, at best, a loose arrangement, while gas particles are virtually random in their distribution. Therefore gases are substances with high entropy, and crystalline solids have very low entropy.

The second law describes the entire universe. On a more personal level, we all fall victim to the law of increasing disorder. Chaos in our room or workplace is certainly not our intent! It happens almost effortlessly. However, reversal of this process requires work and energy. The same is true at the molecular level. The gradual deterioration of our cities' infrastructure (roads, bridges, water mains, and so forth) is an all-too-familiar example; millions of dollars (translated into energy and work) are needed annually just to try to maintain the status quo.

The entropy of a reaction is measured as a difference, $\Delta S°$, between the entropies, $S°$, of products and reactants.

The drive toward increased entropy, along with a tendency to achieve a lower potential energy, is responsible for spontaneous chemical reactions. Reactions that are exothermic and whose products are more disordered (higher in entropy) will occur spontaneously, while endothermic reactions producing products of lower entropy will not be spontaneous. If they are to take place at all, they will need some energy input.

The two situations described above are clear-cut and unambiguous. In any other situation the reaction may or may not be spontaneous; it depends on the relative size of the enthalpy and entropy values.

The energy value, **free energy,** symbolized by $\Delta G°$, represents the combined contribution of the enthalpy *and* entropy values for a chemical reaction. Thus free energy is the ultimate predictor of reaction spontaneity.

Free energy is expressed as

$$\Delta G° = \Delta H° - T\Delta S°$$

$\Delta H°$ represents the change in enthalpy between products and reactants, $\Delta S°$ represents the change in entropy between products and reactants, and T is the Kelvin temperature of the reaction.

The measurement of heat energy changes in a chemical reaction is **calorimetry.** This technique involves the measurement of the change in the temperature of a quantity of water that is in contact with the reaction of interest and isolated from the surroundings. A device used for these measurements is a *calorimeter,* which measures heat changes in calories.

A styrofoam coffee cup is a simple design for a calorimeter, and it produces surprisingly

A HUMAN PERSPECTIVE

Triboluminescence: Sparks in the Dark with Candy

Generations of children have inadvertently discovered the phenomenon of triboluminescence. Crushing a wintergreen candy (Lifesavers®) with the teeth in a dark room (in front of a few friends or a mirror) or simply rubbing two pieces of candy together may produce the effect—transient sparks of light!

Triboluminescence is simply the production of light upon fracturing a solid. It is easily observed and straightforward to describe but difficult to explain. It is believed to result from charge separation produced by the disruption of a crystal lattice. The charge separation has a very short lifetime; when the charge distribution returns to equilibrium, energy is released, and that energy is the light that is observed.

Dr. Linda M. Sweeting and several other groups of scientists are trying to reproduce these events under controlled circumstances. Crystals similar to the sugars in wintergreen candy are prepared with a very high level of purity. Some theories attribute the light emission to impurities in a crystal rather than to the crystal itself. Devices have been constructed that will crush the crystal with a uniform and reproducible force. Light-measuring devices, spectrophotometers, accurately measure the various wavelengths of light and the intensity of the light at each wavelength.

Through the application of careful experimentation and measurement of light-emitting properties of a variety of re-lated compounds, these scientists hope to develop a theory of light emission from fractured solids.

This is one more example of the scientific method improving our understanding of everyday occurrences.

Charles Schultz's "Peanuts" vision of triboluminescence.
Reprinted by permission of UFS, Inc.

---

accurate results. It is a good insulator, and, when filled with solution, it can be used to measure temperature changes taking place as the result of a chemical reaction (Figure 5.2). The change in the temperature of the solution, caused by the reaction, can be used to calculate the gain or loss of heat energy for the reaction taking place in solution.

For an exothermic reaction, heat released by the reaction is absorbed by the surrounding water. The **specific heat of water** is defined as the number of calories of heat needed to raise the temperature of 1 gram of water 1 degree Celsius. This, along with the total number of grams of water and the temperature increase (measured as the difference between the final and initial temperatures of the water), enables the experimenter to calculate the heat released during the reaction.

The water behaves as a ''trap'' or ''sink'' for energy released in the exothermic process; the temperature increase indicates a gain in heat energy. Endothermic reactions, on the other hand, take heat energy away from the water, lowering its temperature.

The quantity of heat absorbed or released by the reaction (Q) is the product of the mass of water in the calorimeter (m_w), the specific heat of the water (SH_w) and the change in temperature (ΔT) of the water as the reaction proceeds from the initial to final state.

The heat is calculated by using the following equation:

$$Q = m_w \times \Delta T_w \times SH_w$$

with units

$$\text{calories} = \cancel{\text{gram}} \times \cancel{°C} \times \frac{\text{calorie}}{\cancel{\text{gram-°C}}}$$

The details of the experimental approach are illustrated below.

FIGURE 5.2
A "coffee cup" calorimeter used for the measurement of heat flow in chemical change. The concentric Styrofoam cups insulate the system from its surroundings. Heat released by the chemical reaction enters the water, raising its temperature, which is measured by using a thermometer.

- Thermometer
- Stirrer
- Rubber stopper
- Concentric styrofoam cups. The inner cup contains the reactant being studied and the solvent, water.

EXAMPLE 5.1

Calorimeter Calculations

If 0.050 mole of hydrochloric acid (HCl) is mixed with 0.050 mole of sodium hydroxide (NaOH) in a "coffee cup" calorimeter, the temperature of 1.00×10^2 grams of water surrounding the reaction increases from 25.0°C to 31.5°C. If the specific heat of water is 1.00 calorie/gram-°C, calculate the quantity of energy involved in the reaction. Also, is the reaction endothermic or exothermic?

Solution

The change in temperature is

$$\Delta T_w = T_{w_{final}} - T_{w_{initial}}$$

$$\Delta T_w = 31.5°C - 25.0°C = 6.5°C$$

$$Q \text{ calories} = 1.00 \times 10^2 \text{ grams water} \times 6.5°C \times \frac{1.00 \text{ calorie}}{\text{gram-}°C}$$

$$Q \text{ calories} = 6.5 \times 10^2 \text{ calories}$$

6.5×10^2 calories (or 0.65 kilocalorie) of heat energy were released by this acid-base reaction; the reaction is exothermic.

QUESTION 5.1

Referring to Example 5.1, calculate the temperature change that would have been observed if 50.0 g of water were in the calorimeter instead of 1.00×10^2 g of water.

QUESTION 5.2

Referring to Example 5.1, calculate the temperature change that would have been observed if 1.00×10^2 g of another liquid, with a specific heat of 0.800 calorie/gram-°C, was substituted for the water in the calorimeter.

Many chemical reactions that produce heat are combustion reactions. In our bodies many food substances (principally carbohydrates and fats, Chapters 16 and 17) are oxidized to produce energy. The amount of energy per gram of food is its **fuel value.**

The fuel value of food is an important concept in nutrition science. The fuel value is generally reported in units of **nutritional Calories.** One nutritional Calorie is equivalent to one kilocalorie (1000 calories). It is also known as the *large Calorie* (uppercase C).

Energy necessary for our daily activity and bodily function comes largely from the "combustion" of carbohydrates. Chemical energy from foods that is not used to maintain normal body temperature or in muscular activity is stored as fat. Thus "high-calorie" foods are implicated in obesity.

Note: Refer to "Human Perspective: Food Calories," Section 1.7.

A special type of calorimeter, a *bomb calorimeter,* is useful for the measurement of the fuel value (Calories) of foods. Such a device is illustrated in Figure 5.3. Its design is similar, in principle, to that of the "coffee cup" calorimeter discussed earlier. It incorporates the insulation from the surroundings, water pool, reaction chamber, and thermometer. Oxygen gas is added as one of the reactants, and an electrical igniter is inserted to initiate the reaction. However, it is not open to the atmosphere. In the sealed container the reaction continues until the sample is completely oxidized. All of the heat energy released during the reaction is captured in the water.

EXAMPLE 5.2

Calculating the Fuel Value of Foods

One gram of glucose (a common sugar or carbohydrate) was burned in a bomb calorimeter. The temperature of 1.00×10^3 grams of water was raised from 25.0°C to 28.8°C. Calculate the fuel value of glucose.

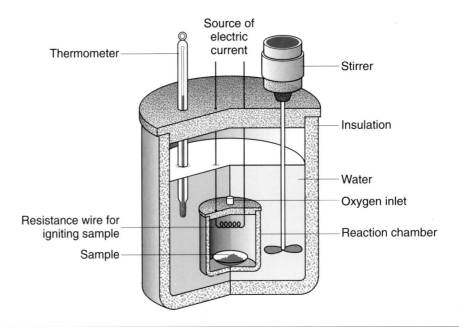

FIGURE 5.3
A bomb calorimeter that may be used to measure heat released upon combustion of a sample. This is commonly used to determine the fuel value of foods. The bomb calorimeter is similar to the "coffee cup" calorimeter. However, note the electrical device necessary to initiate the combustion reaction.

Solution

Recalling that the fuel value is the number of nutritional Calories liberated by the combustion of one gram of material and one gram of material was burned in the calorimeter,

$$\text{Fuel value} = Q = m_w \times \Delta T \times SH_w$$

$$\text{Fuel value} = \text{gram water} \times {}^\circ C \times \frac{1.00 \text{ calories}}{\text{gram-}^\circ C}$$

$$\text{Fuel value} = 1.00 \times 10^3 \text{ gram water} \times 3.8 {}^\circ C \times \frac{1.00 \text{ calories}}{\text{gram-}^\circ C}$$

$$\text{Fuel value} = 3.8 \times 10^3 \text{ calories}$$

and

$$3.8 \times 10^3 \text{ calories} \times \frac{1 \text{ nutritional Calorie}}{10^3 \text{ calories}} = 3.8 \text{ C (nutritional Calories)}$$

The fuel value of glucose is 3.8 nutritional Calories/gram of glucose.

QUESTION 5.3

A 1.0-g sample of a candy bar (which contains lots of sugar!) was burned in a bomb calorimeter. A 3.0°C temperature increase was observed for 1.00×10^3 grams of water. The entire candy bar weighed 2.5 ounces. Calculate the fuel value (in nutritional Calories) of the sample as well as the total caloric content of the candy bar.

QUESTION 5.4

If the fuel value of 1.00 g of a certain carbohydrate (sugar) is 3.00 nutritional Calories, how many grams of water must be present in the calorimeter to record a 5.00°C change in temperature?

A CLINICAL PERSPECTIVE

Hot and Cold Packs

Hot and cold packs are in common use today for the treatment of injuries and the reduction of swelling (cold packs) and for "instant warmth" for hikers and skiers and treatment of injuries such as pulled muscles (hot packs).

These useful items are an excellent example of basic science producing a technologically useful product. (Recall our discussion in Chapter 1 of the relationship of science and technology.)

Both hot and cold packs depend on large energy changes taking place during a chemical reaction. Cold packs rely on an endothermic reaction, while hot packs generate heat energy from an exothermic reaction.

A cold pack is fabricated as two separate compartments within a single package. One compartment contains NH_4NO_3, and the other contains water. When the package is squeezed, the inner boundary between the two compart-

ments ruptures, allowing the components to mix, and the following reaction occurs:

$$6.7 \text{ kcal/mol} + NH_4NO_3(s) \longrightarrow NH_4^+(aq) + NO_3^-(aq)$$

This reaction is endothermic; heat taken from the surroundings produces the cooling effect.

The design of a hot pack is similar. Here, finely divided iron powder is mixed with oxygen. Production of iron oxide results in the evolution of heat:

$$4Fe + 3O_2 \longrightarrow 2Fe_2O_3 + 198 \text{ kcal/mol}$$

This reaction occurs via an oxidation-reduction mechanism (Chapter 7). The rate of the reaction is slow; therefore the heat is liberated gradually over a period of several hours.

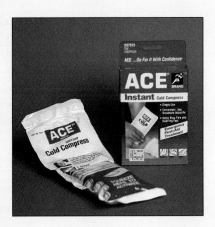

5.3 KINETICS

The first two laws of thermodynamics help us to decide whether a chemical reaction will take place. Knowing that a reaction can occur tells us nothing about the time that it may take.

Chemical **kinetics** is the study of the **rate** or speed of a chemical reaction. Kinetics also gives an indication of the *mechanism* of a reaction, a step-by-step description of how reactants become products.

Information about the rate at which various chemical processes occur is useful. For example, what is the "shelf life" of processed foods? When will slow changes in composition make food unappealing or even unsafe? Many drugs lose their potency with time because the active ingredient decomposes into other substances. The rate of hardening of dental filling material (via a chemical reaction) influences the dentist's technique. Our very lives depend on the rapid and efficient transport of oxygen to each of our cells and the rapid use of the oxygen for energy-producing reactions.

Let's see what actually happens when two chemical compounds "react" and what experimental conditions affect the rate of a reaction.

The chemical reaction

Consider the exothermic reaction that we discussed in Section 5.1:

$$CH_4(g) + 2O_2(g) \longrightarrow CO_2(g) + 2H_2O(l) + \boxed{211\ kcal}$$

In order for the reaction to proceed, C—H and O—O bonds must be broken, and C—O and H—O bonds must be formed. Sufficient energy must be available to cause the bonds to break if the reaction is to take place. This energy is provided by the collision of two or more molecules. If sufficient energy is available at the temperature of the reaction, one or more bonds will break, and the atoms will recombine in a lower energy arrangement, in this case as carbon dioxide and water. A collision producing one or more product molecules is termed an *effective collision.* Only effective collisions lead to chemical reaction.

Activation energy and the activated complex

The minimum amount of energy required to produce a chemical reaction is called the **activation energy** for the reaction.

We can picture the chemical reaction in terms of the changes in potential energy that occur during the reaction. Figure 5.4a graphically shows these changes for an exothermic reaction. Important characteristics of this graph include the following:

◆   The reaction proceeds from reactants to products through an extremely unstable state that we term the **activated complex.** The activated complex cannot be isolated from the reaction mixture but may be thought of as a short-lived group of atoms structured in such a way that it quickly and easily breaks apart into the products of the reaction.

◆   Formation of the activated complex requires energy. The difference between the energy of reactants and that of the activated complex is the activation energy. This energy must be provided by the collision of the reacting molecules or atoms at the temperature of the reaction.

◆   As this is an exothermic reaction, the overall energy change must be a *net* release of energy. The *net* release of energy is the difference in energy between products and reactants.

For an endothermic reaction, such as the decomposition of water,

$$\boxed{energy} + 2H_2O(l) \longrightarrow 2H_2(g) + O_2(g)$$

This reaction will take place when an electrical current is passed through water. The process is termed electrolysis.

the variation of potential energy with reaction time is shown in Figure 5.4b.

Liquid water is *stable* because the products are less stable (higher energy) than the reactants; furthermore, the reaction takes place slowly because of the large activation energy required for the conversion of water into the elements hydrogen and oxygen.

FIGURE 5.4
(a) The change in potential energy as a function of reaction time for an exothermic chemical reaction. Note particularly the energy barrier associated with the formation of the activated complex. This energy barrier *is* the activation energy.
(b) The change in potential energy as a function of reaction time for an endothermic chemical reaction. In contrast to the exothermic reaction (a) the energy of the products is greater than the energy of the reactants.

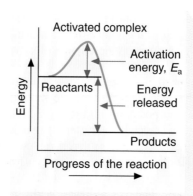

(a)

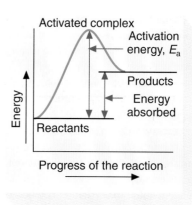

(b)

Five major experimental conditions influence reaction rate.

◆ Structure of the reacting species

◆ The concentration of reactants

◆ The temperature of reactants

◆ The physical state of reactants

◆ The presence of a catalyst

Structure of the reacting species

Owing to electrostatic attraction, oppositely charged species often react more rapidly than neutral species. Ions with the same charge do not react, owing to the repulsion of like charges. In contrast, oppositely charged ions attract one another and are often reactive.

The bond strength certainly plays a role in determining reaction rates as well, for the magnitude of the activation energy, or energy barrier, is related to the bond strength.

The size and shape of reactant molecules influence the rate of the reaction. Large molecules, containing bulky groups of atoms, may block the reactive part of the molecule from interacting with another reactive substance, causing the reaction to proceed slowly.

The concentration of reactants

The rate of a chemical reaction is often a complex function of the concentration of one or more of the reacting substances. The rate will generally *increase* as concentration *increases* simply because a higher concentration means more reactant molecules in a given volume and therefore a greater number of collisions per unit time. Assuming that other variables are held constant, a larger number of collisions leads to a larger number of effective collisions. The explosion (very fast exothermic reaction) of gunpowder is a dramatic example of a rapid rate at high reactant concentration.

Concentration is introduced in Section 1.7, and units and calculations are discussed in Sections 6.2 and 6.3.

The temperature of reactants

The rate of a reaction *increases* as the temperature increases, since the kinetic energy of the reacting particles is directly proportional to the Kelvin temperature. Increasing the speed of particles increases the likelihood of collision, and the higher kinetic energy means that a higher percentage of these collisions will result in product formation (effective collisions). A 10°C rise in temperature, on average, has been found to double the reaction rate.

The physical state of reactants

The rate of a reaction depends on the physical state of the reactants: solid, liquid, or gas. Distance of separation between particles, strength of attractive forces, and particle mobility are related to the physical state of the reactants. These factors all affect reaction rates, as we have shown.

We consider these factors in greater detail in our discussion of the states of matter (Section 5.5).

The presence of a catalyst

A **catalyst** is a substance that *increases* the reaction rate. If added to a reaction mixture, the catalytic substance undergoes no net change, nor does it alter the outcome of the reaction. However, the catalyst interacts with the reactants to create an alternative pathway for production of products. This alternative path has a lower activation energy. This makes it easier for the reaction to take place and thus increases the rate. This effect is illustrated in Figure 5.5.

Catalysis is important industrially; it may often make the difference between profit and loss in the sale of a product. For example, catalysis is useful in converting double bonds to single bonds. An important application of this principle involves the process of hydrogenation. Hydrogenation converts unsaturated fats such as corn oil (containing a double bond between two carbons) to saturated fats (all single bonds) such as margarine. The use of a metal catalyst, such as nickel, in contact with the reaction mixture dramatically increases the rate of the reaction.

Sections 9.3 and 13.2.

Some reactions that would occur only once in 10,000 years may be required to occur 10,000 times each second in the cells of our bodies. Thousands of essential biochemical reactions in our bodies are controlled and speeded up by biological catalysts called *enzymes*.

Sections 15.5 through 15.9

Examples of chemical reactions that are exothermic *and* very fast are shown in Figure 5.6a and 5.6b.

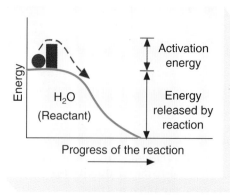
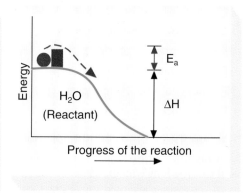

(a) Noncatalyzed reaction   (b) Catalyzed reaction

FIGURE 5.5
The effect of a catalyst on the magnitude of the activation energy of a chemical reaction. Note that the presence of a catalyst decreased the activation energy, thus increasing the rate of the reaction.

FIGURE 5.6
The rapid reaction of magnesium metal and oxygen (in air) is a graphic example of a highly exothermic reaction. Hydrogen and oxygen react to produce the massive amounts of energy necessary for liftoff of the U.S. Space Shuttle.

5.4 CHEMICAL EQUILIBRIUM AND THE REVERSIBILITY OF REACTIONS

The concept of equilibrium

Many chemical reactions do not proceed to completion. A *complete* reaction is one in which all reactants have been converted to products. A reaction that has measurable quantities of both reactants and products remaining is an **equilibrium** reaction.

After a period of time, determined by the kinetics of the reaction, the concentration of reactants no longer decreases, and the concentration of products ceases to increase. At this point, a mixture of products and reactants exists, and its composition would remain *constant* unless the experimental conditions were changed. This mixture is in a state of *chemical equilibrium.*

Reversibility of chemical and physical processes

In our representation of chemical reactions thus far we have placed reactants to the left and products to the right of the reaction arrow. However, many reactions can proceed in either direction, left to right *or* right to left, depending on the experimental conditions. Such reactions are **reversible.** For example, consider the reaction of nitrogen gas and hydrogen gas to produce ammonia:

$$N_2(g) + 3H_2(g) \rightleftharpoons 2NH_3(g)$$

The double arrow ($\rightleftharpoons$) shows that the reaction is reversible.

Beginning with a mixture of hydrogen and nitrogen, the rate of the reaction is initially rapid, since the reactant concentration is high; as the reaction proceeds, the concentration of reactants decreases. At the same time the concentration of the product, ammonia, is increasing. At equilibrium the *rate of depletion* of hydrogen and nitrogen *is equal to* the *rate of depletion* of ammonia. In other words, *the rates of the forward and reverse reactions are equal.*

Chemists often use the term **dynamic equilibrium** when referring to the situation described above. The concentration of the various species is fixed at equilibrium because product is being *consumed and formed at the same rate*. In other words, the reaction continues indefinitely (dynamic), but the concentrations of products and reactants is fixed (equilibrium). This is a *dynamic equilibrium*.

The composition of this reaction mixture as a function of time is depicted in Figure 5.7.

Dynamic equilibrium can be particularly dangerous for living cells because it represents a situation in which nothing is getting done. There is no gain. Let us consider an exothermic reaction designed to produce a net gain of energy for the cell. In a dynamic equilibrium the rate of the forward (energy-producing) reaction is equal to the rate of the backward (energy-requiring) reaction. Thus there is no net gain of energy to fuel cellular activity, and the cell will die.

The concept of equilibrium applies equally well to chemical change (as shown above) and to physical change. We shall see that physical states of substances may also be in equilibrium.

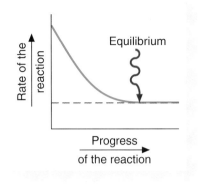

FIGURE 5.7
The change of the rate of reaction as a function of time. The rate of reaction, initially rapid, decreases as the concentration of reactants decreases and approaches a limiting value at equilibrium.

The most precise description of an equilibrium process is through the use of the equilibrium constant, K_{eq}.

Consider again the reaction that we have been discussing:

$$N_2(g) + 3H_2(g) \rightleftharpoons 2NH_3(g)$$

We may subdivide this expression into two reactions: a forward reaction,

$$N_2(g) + 3H_2(g) \longrightarrow 2NH_3(g)$$

and a reverse reaction,

$$2NH_3(g) \longrightarrow N_2(g) + 3H_2(g)$$

If the extent of each reaction is related to the concentration of the reactants remaining, at equilibrium these concentrations will become invariant. The ratio of the concentrations (actually, the concentrations raised to a power equal to the coefficient in the balanced equation) will itself be constant. This ratio is *defined* as the equilibrium constant, K_{eq}.

$$K_{eq} = \frac{[\text{concentration of reactants in the reverse reaction}]^x}{[\text{concentration of reactants in the forward reaction}]^y}$$

For the decomposition of ammonia (above),

$$K_{eq} = \frac{[NH_3]^2}{[N_2][H_2]^3}$$

◆ *Products* of the overall equilibrium reaction are in the numerator, and *reactants* are in the denominator.

◆ [ ] represents molar concentration, *M*.

◆ The exponents correspond to the *coefficients* of the balanced equation.

It does not matter what initial amounts (concentrations) of reactants or products we choose. When the system reaches equilibrium, the calculated value of K_{eq} will not change. The magnitude of K_{eq} can be altered only by changing the temperature; thus K_{eq} is temperature dependent. The chemical industry uses this fact to advantage by choosing a reaction temperature that will maximize the yield of a desired product.

The equilibrium constant

Section 5.7

LeChatelier's Principle

Chapters 1 and 6

In the nineteenth century the French chemist LeChatelier discovered that changes in equilibrium depend on the amount of "stress" applied to the system. The stress may take the form of an increase or decrease of the temperature of the system at equilibrium or perhaps the amount of reactant or product present in a fixed volume (the concentration of reactant or product).

LeChatelier's Principle states that if a stress is placed on a system at equilibrium, the system will respond by altering the equilibrium in such a way as to minimize the stress.

Consider the equilibrium situation discussed earlier:

$$N_2(g) + 3H_2(g) \rightleftharpoons 2NH_3(g)$$

If the reactants and products are present in a fixed volume (such as 1 L) and more NH_3 (the *product*) is introduced into the container, the system will be stressed—the equilibrium will be disturbed. The system will try to alleviate the stress (as we all do) by *removing* as much of the added material as possible. How can it accomplish this? By converting some NH_3 to H_2 and N_2. The equilibrium shifts to the left ($\leftarrow$), and the dynamic equilibrium is soon reestablished.

Had we added extra H_2 or N_2, the stress would have been applied to the other side of the equilibrium. To minimize the stress, the system would "use up" some of the excess H_2 or N_2 to make product, NH_3. The equilibrium would shift to the right ($\rightarrow$).

In summary,

$$N_2(g) + 3H_2(g) \rightleftharpoons 2NH_3(g)$$

Product introduced: $\xleftarrow{\text{equilibrium shifted}}$

Reactant introduced: $\xrightarrow{\text{equilibrium shifted}}$

What would happen if we *removed* some of the ammonia molecules from the system? The loss of ammonia represents a stress on the system; to remove that stress, the ammonia would be replenished by the reaction of hydrogen and nitrogen. The equilibrium would shift to the right.

QUESTION 5.5

For the hypothetical equilibrium reaction

$$A(g) + B(g) \rightleftharpoons C(g) + D(g)$$

predict whether the amount of A in a 5.0-L container would increase, decrease, or remain the same if:

a. excess B were added
b. excess C were added
c. some D were removed

QUESTION 5.6

For the hypothetical equilibrium reaction

$$A(g) + B(g) \rightleftharpoons C(g) + D(g)$$

predict whether the amount of A in a 5.0-L container would increase, decrease, or remain the same if:

a. some B were removed
b. some C were removed
c. excess D were added

We have learned that the major differences between solids, liquids, and gases are:

◆ the average distance of separation of particles in each state,

◆ the strength of the attractive forces between the particles, and

◆ the degree of organization of particles.

5.5 ENERGY AND THE STATES OF MATTER

Section 3.3

We have already discovered that the solid state is the most organized, with particles close together and with large attractive forces exerted among the particles. This results in high melting and boiling points for solid substances. Large amounts of energy are needed to overcome the attractive forces and disrupt the orderly structure.

Substances that are gases at room temperature and atmospheric pressure, on the other hand, are disordered, with particles widely separated and weak attractive forces. Their melting and boiling points are relatively low. Gases at room temperature must be cooled a great deal in order for them to liquefy or solidify. For example, the melting and boiling points of N_2 are $-210°C$ and $-196°C$, respectively.

Liquids are intermediate in character. The molecular organization, spacing, and attractive forces among the molecules place liquid properties in a transition position between solids and gases.

5.6 THE GASEOUS STATE

The fundamental model of particle behavior in the gas phase is the **kinetic-molecular theory.** This theory describes an **ideal gas,** in which gas particles exhibit no interactive or repulsive forces and the volumes of the individual gas particles are assumed to be negligible.

The term *kinetic* indicates motion, and the kinetic-molecular theory is a model of gas particles in motion. The theory is summarized as follows:

The term particle is a general term that may represent a molecule such as O_2 or a monatomic gas such as He.

1. A gas consists of particles that are far apart. The volume of the individual particles is assumed to be small in comparison to the average distance between the particles.

2. The gas particles are in continuous, rapid, random motion. Particles change direction only as a result of collision with other particles or the wall of the container.

3. Upon collision there is no net loss of energy; energy may only be *transferred* from one particle to another.

4. The velocity (speed) of the particles is directly proportional to the square root of the Kelvin temperature; as a result, the average kinetic energy is directly proportional to the absolute temperature.

Kinetic energy (K.E.) is equal to $\frac{1}{2}mv^2$, where m = mass and v = velocity. Thus increased velocity correlates with an increase in kinetic energy.

The kinetic-molecular theory is the basis for the various gas laws, which we discuss next.

The gas laws

The most important gas laws (Boyle's Law, Charles's Law, Dalton's Law, and the ideal gas law) involve the relationships between pressure (P), volume (V), temperature (T), and number of moles (n) of gas. We are already familiar with the measurement of temperature and quantity from our laboratory experience. Measurement of pressure is perhaps not as obvious.

Gas pressure is a result of the force exerted by the collision of particles with the walls of the container. **Pressure** is force per unit area. The pressure of a gas may be measured with a **barometer,** invented by Evangelista Torricelli in the mid-1600s. The most common type of barometer is the mercury barometer depicted in Figure 5.8. A tube, sealed at one end, is filled with mercury and inverted in a dish of mercury. The pressure of the atmosphere pushing down on the mercury surface in the dish supports the column of mercury. The height of the column is proportional to the atmospheric pressure. The tube can be calibrated to give a numerical reading in millimeters, centimeters, or inches of mercury. A commonly used unit of measurement is the atmosphere (atm). One standard atmosphere (1 atm) of pressure is equivalent to a height of mercury of

One mole of a gas contains Avogadro's number of particles (6.02 × 10²³ particles). We are dealing with a *very* large number of particles.

760 mm Hg (millimeters of mercury)

76.0 cm Hg (centimeters of mercury)

1 mm of Hg is also = 1 torr, in honor of Torricelli.

Only torr, cm Hg, and mm Hg will be used throughout this book.

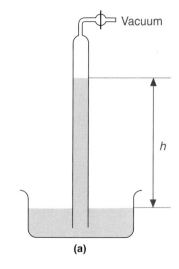

Vacuum

h

(a)

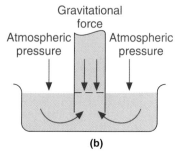

Gravitational force

Atmospheric pressure   Atmospheric pressure

(b)

FIGURE 5.8
A mercury barometer of the type invented by Torricelli. (a) The height of the column of mercury (h) is a function of the magnitude of the surrounding atmospheric pressure. (b) The mercury in the tube is supported by atmospheric pressure.

Appendix A

The English system equivalent is a pressure of 14.7 lb/in^2 (pounds per square inch) or 30 in Hg (inches of mercury). A recommended, yet less frequently used, systematic unit is the pascal (or kilopascal), named in honor of Blaise Pascal, a seventeenth century French mathematician and scientist:

$$1 \text{ atm} = 1.01 \times 10^5 \text{ Pa (pascal)} = 101 \text{ kPa (kilopascal)}$$

Atmospheric pressure is due to the cumulative force of the air molecules (N_2 and O_2, for the most part) attracted to the earth's surface by gravity.

QUESTION 5.7

Express each of the following in units of atmospheres:

a. 725 mm Hg

b. 29.0 cm Hg

c. 555 torr

QUESTION 5.8

Express each of the following in units of atmospheres:

a. 10.0 torr

b. 61.0 cm Hg

c. 275 mm Hg

Boyle's Law

The English scientist Robert Boyle found that the volume of a gas varies _inversely_ with the pressure exerted by the gas if the number of moles and temperature of gas are held constant. This relationship is known as **Boyle's Law.**

Mathematically, the _product_ of pressure (P) and volume (V) is a constant:

$$PV = k_1$$

Consider a gas occupying a volume of 10.0 L at 1.00 atmosphere of pressure. The product, $PV = (10.0 \text{ L})(1.00 \text{ atm})$, is a constant, k_1. Doubling the pressure, to 2.0 atm, decreases the volume to 5.0 L:

$$(2.0 \text{ atm})(V_x) = (10.0 \text{ L})(1.00 \text{ atm})$$

$$V_x = 5.0 \text{ L}$$

Tripling the pressure decreases the volume by a factor of three:

$$(3.0 \text{ atm})(V_x) = (10.0 \text{ L})(1.00 \text{ atm})$$

$$V_x = 3.3 \text{ L}$$

These relationships are illustrated in Figure 5.9.

Boyle's Law is often used to calculate the volume resulting from a pressure change or vice versa. We consider

$$P_i V_i = k_1$$

the _initial_ condition and

$$P_f V_f = k_1$$

the _final_ condition. Since PV, initial or final, is constant and is equal to k_1,

$$P_i V_i = P_f V_f$$

Examples of the application of this useful relationship follow.

EXAMPLE 5.3

Calculating a Final Pressure

A certain mass of oxygen, at 25°C, occupies a volume of 5.00×10^2 mL at 1.50 atm pressure. What pressure must be applied to compress the gas to a volume of 1.50×10^2 mL, assuming no temperature change?

Solution

Boyle's Law applies directly, as there is no change in temperature or number of moles (mass is constant). Begin by identifying each term in the Boyle's Law expression:

$$P_i = 1.50 \text{ atm}$$

$$V_i = 5.00 \times 10^2 \text{ mL}$$

$$V_f = 1.50 \times 10^2 \text{ mL}$$

$$P_i V_i = P_f V_f$$

and solve

$$P_f = \frac{P_i V_i}{V_f}$$

$$P_f = \frac{(1.50 \text{ atm})(5.00 \times 10^2 \text{ mL})}{1.50 \times 10^2 \text{ mL}}$$

$$P_f = 5.00 \text{ atm}$$

The calculation can be done with volume units of milliliters or liters. It is important only that the units be the *same* on both sides of the equation.

QUESTION 5.9

Complete the following table:

	Initial Pressure (atm)	Final Pressure (atm)	Initial Volume (L)	Final Volume (L)
a.	X	5.0	1.0	7.5
b.	5.0	X	1.0	0.20

QUESTION 5.10

Complete the following table:

	Initial Pressure (atm)	Final Pressure (atm)	Initial Volume (L)	Final Volume (L)
a.	1.0	0.50	X	0.30
b.	1.0	2.0	0.75	X

Charles's Law

Jacques Charles, a French scientist, studied the relationship between gas volume and temperature. This relationship, **Charles's Law,** states that the volume of a gas varies *directly* with the absolute temperature (K) if pressure and number of moles of gas are constant.

Mathematically, the *ratio* of volume (V) and temperature (T) is a constant:

$$\frac{V}{T} = k_2$$

Consider a gas occupying a volume of 10.0 L at 273 K. The ratio $V/T = 10.0 \text{ L}/273 \text{ K} = 0.0366$ L/K, a constant, k_2. Doubling the temperature, to 546 K, increases the volume to 20.0 L

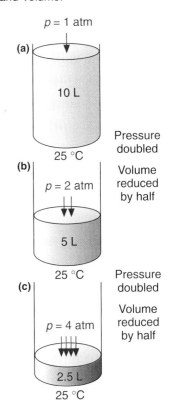

FIGURE 5.9
An illustration of Boyle's Law. Note the inverse relationship of pressure and volume.

as shown here:

$$\frac{V_x}{546 \text{ K}} = 0.0366 \text{ L/K}$$

$$V_x = 20.0 \text{ L}$$

Tripling the temperature, to 819 K, increases the volume by a factor of three:

$$\frac{V_x}{819 \text{ K}} = 0.0366 \text{ L/K}$$

$$V_x = 30.0 \text{ L}$$

These relationships are illustrated in Figure 5.10.

In a way analogous to Boyle's Law, we may establish a set of initial conditions:

$$\frac{V_i}{T_i} = k_2$$

and final conditions,

$$\frac{V_f}{T_f} = k_2$$

Since k_2 is a constant, we may equate them, resulting in

$$\frac{V_i}{T_i} = \frac{V_f}{T_f}$$

and use this expression to solve some practical problems.

FIGURE 5.10
An illustration of Charles's Law. Note the direct relationship between volume and temperature.

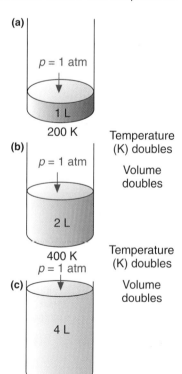

(a) p = 1 atm
1 L
200 K

Temperature (K) doubles
Volume doubles

(b) p = 1 atm
2 L
400 K
p = 1 atm

Temperature (K) doubles
Volume doubles

(c)
4 L
800 K

EXAMPLE 5.4

Calculating a Final Volume

A balloon filled with helium has a volume of 4.0×10^3 L at 25°C. What volume will the balloon occupy at 50°C if the pressure surrounding the balloon remained constant?

Solution

Remember, the temperature must be converted to Kelvin before Charles's Law is applied:

$$T_i = 25°C + 273 = 298 \text{ K}$$

$$T_f = 50°C + 273 = 323 \text{ K}$$

$$V_i = 4.0 \times 10^3 \text{ L}$$

$$V_f = ?$$

Using

$$\frac{V_i}{T_i} = \frac{V_f}{T_f}$$

and substituting our data, we get

$$V_f = \frac{(V_i)(T_f)}{T_i} = \frac{(4.0 \times 10^3 \text{ L})(323 \text{ K})}{298 \text{ K}} = 4.3 \times 10^3 \text{ L}$$

QUESTION 5.11

A sample of nitrogen gas has a volume of 3.00 L at 25°C. What volume will it occupy at each of the following temperatures if the pressure is constant?

a.   100°C   b.   150°F   c.   273 K

QUESTION 5.12

A sample of nitrogen gas has a volume of 3.00 L at 25°C. What volume will it occupy at each of the following temperatures if the pressure is constant?

a. 546 K

b. 0.00°C

c. 373 K

The behavior of a hot-air balloon is a commonplace consequence of Charles's Law. The balloon rises because air expands when heated (Figure 5.11). The volume of the balloon is fixed; as a result, some of the air is forced out as its volume expands. Hence the density of the remaining air is less (less mass contained in the same volume), and the balloon rises. Turning down the heat reverses the process, and the balloon descends.

Avogadro's Law

The relationship between the volume and number of moles of a gas is known as **Avogadro's Law.** This law states that equal volumes of a gas contain the same number of moles if measured under the same conditions of temperature and pressure.

Mathematically, the *ratio* of volume (V) and number of moles (n) is a constant:

$$\frac{V}{n} = k_3$$

Consider one mole of gas occupying a volume of 10.0 L; using logic similar to the application of Boyle's and Charles's Laws, two moles of the gas would occupy 20.0 L, three moles would occupy 30.0 L, and so forth. As we have done with the previous laws, we can formulate a useful expression relating initial and final conditions:

$$\frac{V_i}{n_i} = \frac{V_f}{n_f}$$

FIGURE 5.11
Charles's Law predicts that the volume of air in the balloon will increase when heated. We assume that the volume of the balloon is fixed; consequently, some air will be pushed out. The air remaining in the balloon is less dense (same volume, less mass) and the balloon will rise. When the heater is turned off the air cools, the density increases, and the balloon returns to earth.

Molar volume of a gas

The volume occupied by *one mole* of any gas is referred to as its **molar volume.** At **standard temperature and pressure (STP)** the molar volume of any gas is 22.4 L. STP conditions are defined as follows:

$$T = 273 \text{ K (or } 0°C)$$

$$P = 1 \text{ atm}$$

Appendix A

Thus one mole of N_2, O_2, H_2, and He all occupy the *same volume, 22.4 L at STP.*

It is also possible to compute the density of various gases at STP. If one recalls that density is the mass/unit volume:

$$d = \frac{m}{V}$$

and one mole of helium weighs 4.00 g, then

$$d_{He} = \frac{4.00 \text{ g}}{22.4 \text{ L}} = 0.178 \text{ g/L at STP}$$

or, since one mole of nitrogen weighs 28.0 g, then

$$d_{N_2} = \frac{28.0 \text{ g}}{22.4 \text{ L}} = 1.25 \text{ g/L at STP}$$

The large difference in gas densities of helium and nitrogen (which makes up about 80% of the air) accounts for the lifting power of helium. A balloon filled with helium will rise through a

Heating a gas, such as air, will decrease its density and have a lifting effect as well. (See Figure 5.11 for this familiar application of the gas laws.)

predominantly nitrogen atmosphere because its gas density is less than 15% of the density of the surrounding atmosphere:

$$\frac{0.178 \text{ g/L}}{1.25 \text{ g/L}} \times 10^2 = 14.2\%$$

The ideal gas law

Boyle's Law (relating volume and pressure), Charles's Law (relating volume and temperature), and Avogadro's Law (relating volume to the number of moles) may be combined into a single expression relating all four terms. This expression is the **ideal gas law:**

$$PV = nRT$$

where R, based on k_1, k_2, and k_3, is a constant and is referred to as the *ideal gas constant:*

$$R = 0.0821 \text{ L-atm K}^{-1} \text{ mol}^{-1}$$

if the units

Remember that 0.0821 L-atm/K mol is identical to 0.0821 L-atm K^{-1} mol^{-1}.

P in atmospheres

V in liters

n in number of moles

T in Kelvins

are used.

Consider some examples of the application of the ideal gas equation.

EXAMPLE 5.5

Calculating a Molar Volume

Demonstrate that the molar volume of oxygen gas at STP is 22.4 L.

Solution

$$PV = nRT$$

$$V = \frac{nRT}{P}$$

If standard pressure

$$P = 1.00 \text{ atm}$$

standard temperature

$$T = 273 \text{ K}$$

$$n = 1.00 \text{ mole}$$

$$R = 0.0821 \text{ L-atm K}^{-1} \text{ mol}^{-1}$$

then

$$V = \frac{(1.00 \text{ mol})(0.0821 \text{ L-atm K}^{-1} \text{ mol}^{-1})(273 \text{ K})}{(1.00 \text{ atm})}$$

$$V = 22.4 \text{ L}$$

EXAMPLE 5.6

Calculating the Number of Moles of a Gas

Calculate the number of moles of helium in a 1.00-L balloon at 27°C and 1.00 atm of pressure.

Solution

$$PV = nRT$$

$$n = \frac{PV}{RT}$$

If

$$P = 1.00 \text{ atm}$$

$$V = 1.00 \text{ L}$$

$$T = 27°C + 273 = 300 \text{ K}$$

$$R = 0.0821 \text{ L atm K}^{-1} \text{ mol}^{-1}$$

then

$$n = \frac{(1.00 \text{ atm})(1.00 \text{ L})}{(0.0821 \text{ L atm K}^{-1} \text{ mol}^{-1})(300 \text{ K})}$$

$$n = 0.0406 \text{ or } 4.06 \times 10^{-2} \text{ mole}$$

EXAMPLE 5.7

Converting Mass to Volume

Oxygen used in hospitals and laboratories is often obtained from cylinders containing liquefied oxygen. If a cylinder contained 1.00×10^2 kg of liquid oxygen, how many liters of oxygen could be produced at 1.00 atmosphere of pressure at room temperature (20.0°C)?

Solution

$$PV = nRT$$

$$V = \frac{nRT}{P}$$

Using conversion factors,

$$n_{O_2} = 1.00 \times 10^2 \text{ kg O}_2 \times \frac{10^3 \text{ g O}_2}{1 \text{ kg O}_2} \times \frac{1 \text{ mol O}_2}{32 \text{ g O}_2}$$

then

$$n = 313 \times 10^3 \text{ moles O}_2$$

and

$$T = 20.0°C + 273 = 293 \text{ K}$$

$$P = 1.00 \text{ atm}$$

then

$$V = \frac{(3.13 \times 10^3 \text{ moles})(0.0821 \text{ L-atm K}^{-1} \text{ mol}^{-1})(293 \text{ K})}{1.00 \text{ atm}}$$

$$V = 75.2 \times 10^3 \text{ L}$$

QUESTION 5.13

What is the volume occupied by 10.0 grams of N_2 at 30°C and a pressure of 750 torr?

QUESTION 5.14

A 20.0-L gas cylinder contains 4.80 grams of H_2 at 25°C. What is the pressure of this gas?

QUESTION 5.15

How many moles of N_2 gas will occupy a 5.00-L container at standard temperature and pressure?

QUESTION 5.16

At what temperature will 2.00 moles of He fill a 2.00-L container at standard pressure?

Dalton's Law of partial pressures

Our discussion of gases so far has presumed that we are working with a single pure gas. A *mixture* of gases exerts a pressure that is the *sum* of the pressures that each gas would exert if it were present alone under the same conditions. This is known as **Dalton's Law of partial pressures.**

Stated another way, the total pressure of a mixture of gases is the sum of the **partial pressures.** That is,

$$P_t = p_1 + p_2 + p_3 + \cdots$$

where P_t = total pressure and $p_1, p_2, p_3, \ldots$, are the partial pressures of the component gases. For example, the total pressure of our atmosphere is equal to the sum of the pressures of N_2 and O_2 (the principal components of air):

$$P_{air} = p_{N_2} + p_{O_2}$$

Ideal gases versus real gases

To this point we have assumed, in both theory and calculations, that all gases behave as ideal gases. However, in reality there is no such thing as an ideal gas. Interactive forces, even between the widely spaced particles of gas, are not totally absent in any sample of gas.

Attractive forces are present in gases composed of polar molecules. Nonuniform charge distribution on polar molecules creates positive and negative regions, resulting in electrostatic attraction and deviation from ideality.

See Section 3.5 for a discussion of interactions of polar molecules.

Calculations involving polar gases such as HF, NO, and SO_2 using ideal gas equations (which presume no such interactions) are approximations. However, at low pressures, such approximations certainly provide useful information. Nonpolar molecules, on the other hand, are only weakly attracted to each other and behave much more ideally in the gas phase.

5.7 THE LIQUID STATE

Molecules in the liquid state are close to one another. Attractive forces are large enough to keep the molecules together in contrast to gases, whose cohesive forces are so low that a gas expands to fill any volume. However, these attractive forces in a liquid are not large enough to restrict movement, as in solids. Since each liquid has a different molecular structure, we would expect that their properties would differ as well. Let us look at the various properties of liquids in more detail.

Compressibility

Liquids are incompressible. In fact, the molecules are so close to one another that even the application of many atmospheres of pressure does not significantly decrease the volume. This makes liquids ideal for the transmission of force, as in the brake lines of an automobile. The force applied by the driver's foot on the brake pedal does not compress the brake fluid in the lines; rather, it transmits the force directly to the brake pads, and the friction between the brake pads and rotors (that are attached to the wheel) stops the car.

Viscosity

The **viscosity** of a liquid is a measure of its resistance to flow. Viscosity is a function of the attractive forces between molecules as well as the molecular geometry.

Complex molecules, which do not "slide" smoothly past each other, as well as polar molecules, tend to have higher viscosity than less structurally complex, less polar liquids. Glyc-

A CLINICAL PERSPECTIVE

Blood Gases and Respiration

The respiration process must deliver oxygen to the cells and the waste product, carbon dioxide, to the lungs to be exhaled. Dalton's Law of partial pressures helps to explain the way in which this process occurs.

Gases (such as O_2 and CO_2) will move from a region of higher partial pressure to one of the lower partial pressure in an effort to establish an equilibrium. At the interface of the lung, the membrane barrier between the blood and the surrounding atmosphere, the following situation exists: Atmospheric O_2 partial pressure is high, and atmospheric CO_2 partial pressure is low. The reverse is true on the other side of the membrane (blood). Thus CO_2 is efficiently removed from the blood, and O_2 is efficiently moved into the bloodstream.

At the other end of the line, capillaries are distributed in close proximity to the cells that need to expel CO_2 and gain O_2. The partial pressure of CO_2 is high in these cells, and the partial pressure of O_2 is low, having been used up by the energy-producing reaction, the oxidation of glucose:

$$C_6H_{12}O_6 + 6O_2 \longrightarrow 6CO_2 + 6H_2O + energy$$

The O_2 diffuses into the cells (from a region of high to low partial pressure), and the CO_2 diffuses from the cells to the blood (again from a region of high to low partial pressure).

The net result is a continuous process proceeding according to Dalton's Law. With each breath we take, oxygen is distributed to the cells and used to generate energy, and the waste product, CO_2, is expelled by the lungs.

erol, which is used in a variety of skin treatments, has the structural formula:

$$\delta+ \qquad \begin{array}{c} H \\ | \\ H-C-O-H \\ | \\ H-C-O-H \\ | \\ H-C-O-H \\ | \\ H \end{array} \qquad \delta-$$

It is quite viscous, owing to its polar nature, and this is certainly desirable in a skin treatment (its viscosity keeps it on the area being treated). Gasoline, on the other hand, is much less viscous and readily flows through the gas lines of your auto; it is composed of nonpolar molecules.

Viscosity generally decreases with increasing temperature. The increased kinetic energy at higher temperatures overcomes some of the intermolecular attractive forces. The temperature effect is an important consideration in the design of products that must remain fluid at low temperatures, such as motor oils and transmission fluids found in automobiles.

The **surface tension** of a liquid is a measure of the attractive forces exerted among molecules at the surface of a liquid. It is only the surface molecules that are not totally surrounded by other liquid molecules (the top of the molecule faces the atmosphere). These surface molecules are attracted by fewer liquid molecules; hence the resulting force on each molecule must be stronger.

This increased surface force is responsible for the spherical shape of drops of liquid. Drops of water "beading" on a polished surface, such as a waxed automobile, illustrate this effect.

Since surface tension is related to the attractive forces exerted among molecules, surface tension generally decreases with an increase in temperature or a decrease in the polarity of molecules that make up the liquid.

Substances known as **surfactants** can be added to a liquid to decrease surface tension. Common surfactants include soaps and detergents that reduce water's surface tension, increasing the interaction of the water with the fabric, making it easier to remove grease and dirt.

Surface tension

This analogy may help: Three people sharing $100 have more money for themselves than four people sharing the same amount!

Evaporation, condensation, and the meaning of the term "boiling point" are all related to the concept of liquid vapor pressure. Consider the following example. A liquid, such as water, is placed in a sealed container. After a period of time the contents of the container are analyzed.

Vapor pressure of a liquid

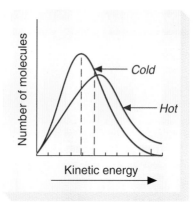

FIGURE 5.12
The average molecular kinetic energy increases with temperature. Note that the average values are indicated by dashed lines.

The process of evaporation of perspiration from the skin produces a cooling effect, as heat is stored in the evaporating molecules.

Section 5.6

Section 5.5

Both liquid water and water vapor are found at room temperature, when we might expect water to be found only as a liquid. In this closed system, some of the liquid water was converted to a gas:

$$H_2O(l) \longrightarrow H_2O(g)$$

How did this happen? The temperature is too low for boiling, the conversion of a liquid to a gas. According to the kinetic theory, liquid molecules are in continuous motion, with their *average* kinetic energy directly proportional to the Kelvin temperature. The word *average* is the key. Although the average kinetic energy is too low to allow "average" molecules to escape from the liquid phase to the gas phase, there exists a range of molecules with different energies, some low and some high, that make up the "average" (see Figure 5.12). Thus some of these high-energy molecules possess sufficient energy to escape from the bulk liquid.

At the same time a fraction of these gaseous molecules lose energy (perhaps by collision with the walls of the container) and return to the liquid state:

$$H_2O(g) \longrightarrow H_2O(l)$$

The process of conversion of liquid to gas, at a temperature too low to boil, is **evaporation.** The reverse process, conversion of the gas to the liquid state, is **condensation.** After some period of time the rates of evaporation and condensation become *equal,* and this sets up a dynamic equilibrium between liquid and vapor states. The **vapor pressure of a liquid** is defined as the pressure exerted by the vapor *at equilibrium.*

$$H_2O(g) \rightleftharpoons H_2O(l)$$

The equilibrium process of evaporation and condensation of water is depicted in Figure 5.13.

The boiling point of a liquid is defined as the temperature at which the vapor pressure of the liquid becomes equal to the atmospheric pressure. The "normal" atmospheric pressure is 760 torr, or 1 atmosphere, and the **normal boiling point** is the temperature at which the vapor pressure of the liquid is equal to 1 atmosphere.

It follows from the definition that the boiling point of a liquid is not constant. It depends on the atmospheric pressure. At high altitudes, where the atmospheric pressure is low, the boiling point of a liquid, such as water, is lower than the normal boiling point (for water, 100°C). High atmospheric pressure increases the boiling point.

Apart from its dependence on the surrounding atmospheric pressure, the boiling point depends on the nature of the attractive forces between the liquid molecules. Polar liquids, such as water, with large intermolecular attractive forces have *higher* boiling points than nonpolar liquids, such as gasoline, which exhibit weak attractive forces.

Hydrogen bonding

Typical forces in polar liquids, discussed above, are only about 1–2% as strong as ionic and covalent bonds. However, certain liquids have boiling points that are much higher than we would predict from these dipolar interactions alone. This indicates the presence of some strong

---

FIGURE 5.13
Liquid water in equilibrium with water vapor. (a) Initiation: process of evaporation exclusively. (b, c) After a time, both evaporation and condensation occur, but evaporation predominates. (d) Dynamic equilibrium established. Rates of evaporation and condensation are equal.

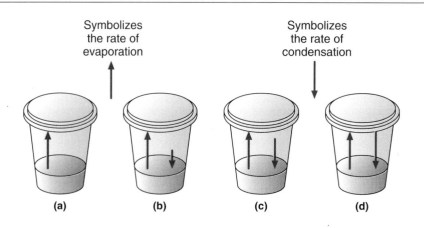

intermolecular force. This attractive force is due to **hydrogen bonding.** Molecules in which a hydrogen atom is bonded to a small, highly electronegative atom such as nitrogen, oxygen, or fluorine exhibit this effect. The presence of a highly electronegative atom bonded to a hydrogen atom creates a large dipole:

This arrangement of atoms produces a very polar bond, often resulting in a polar molecule with strong intermolecular attractive forces. Although the hydrogen bond is weaker than bonds formed *within* molecules (covalent and polar covalent *intra*molecular forces), it is the strongest attractive force *between* molecules (intermolecular force).

Consider the boiling points of four small molecules:

CH_4	NH_3	H_2O	HF
$-161°C$	$-33°C$	$+100°C$	$-19.5°$

Recall that the most electronegative elements are in the upper right corner of the periodic table, and these elements exert strong electron attraction in molecules as described in Chapter 3.

Clearly, ammonia, water, and hydrogen fluoride boil at significantly higher temperatures than methane. The N—H, O—H, and F—H bonds are far more polar than the C—H bond due to the high electronegativity of N, O, and F.

It is interesting to note that the boiling points increase as the electronegativity of the element bonded to hydrogen increases, with one exception: Fluorine, with the highest electronegativity should cause HF to have the highest boiling point. This is not the case. The order of boiling points is

water > hydrogen fluoride > ammonia > methane

not

hydrogen fluoride > water > ammonia > methane

Why? To answer this question we must look at the *number of potential bonding sites* in each molecule. Water has two partial positive sites and two partial negative sites; it can form hydrogen bonds at each site. This results in a complex network of attractive forces among water molecules in the liquid state and the strength of the forces holding this network together accounts for water's unusually high boiling point. This network is depicted in Figure 5.14.

Ammonia and hydrogen fluoride can form only one hydrogen bond per molecule. Ammonia

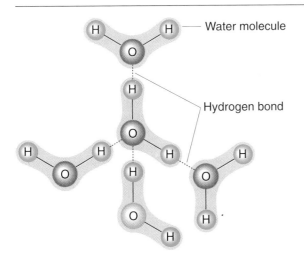

(a)

(b)

FIGURE 5.14
(a) An illustration of hydrogen bonding in water. The red dotted lines represent the hydrogen bonds between the hydrogen (δ^+) and oxygen (δ^-) ends of the water molecule. (b) Water has a unique structure and properties owing to the extensive hydrogen bonding. In this model, the blue units represent H atoms, and the violet units represent O atoms.

has three partial positive sites (three hydrogen atoms bonded to nitrogen) but only one partial negative site (the lone pair); the single lone pair is the limiting factor. One positive site and one negative site are needed for each hydrogen bond. Hydrogen fluoride has only one partial positive site and three partial negative sites. It too can form only one hydrogen bond per molecule. Consequently, the network of attractive forces in ammonia and hydrogen fluoride is much less extensive than that found in water and their boiling points are considerably lower than that found for water.

Hydrogen bonding has an extremely important influence on the behavior of many biological systems. Molecules, such as proteins and DNA, require extensive hydrogen bonding to maintain their structures and hence functions.

See Sections 10.1, 12.1, and 14.1

Intramolecular hydrogen bonding between polar regions helps keep proteins folded in their proper 3-dimensional structure.

5.8 THE SOLID STATE

The close packing of the particles of a solid results in attractive forces that are strong enough to restrict motion. The particles are "locked" together in a defined and highly organized fashion. This results in fixed shape and volume, although, at the atomic level, vibrational motion is observed.

Properties of solids

Solids are incompressible, owing to the small distance between particles. Most will convert to liquids at a higher temperature, when the increased heat energy overcomes some of the attractive forces within the solid. The temperature at which a solid is converted to the liquid phase is its **melting point.** The melting point depends on the strength of the attractive forces in the solid, hence its structure. As we might expect, polar solids have higher melting points than nonpolar solids of the same molecular weight.

Solids may be **crystalline,** having a regular repeating structure, or **amorphous,** having no organized structure. Diamond and sodium chloride (Figure 5.15) are examples of crystalline substances; glass, plastic, and wood are examples of amorphous solids.

Types of crystalline solids

Crystalline solids may exist in one of four general groups:

1. **Ionic solids.** The units that make up an **ionic solid** are positive and negative ions. Electrostatic forces hold the crystal together. They are generally high melting, hard, and brittle. A common example of an ionic solid is sodium chloride.

2. **Covalent solids.** The units that make up a **covalent solid** are atoms held together by covalent bonds. They have very high melting points (1200°C to 2000°C or more is not unusual) and are extremely hard. They are insoluble in most solvents. Diamond is a covalent solid composed of covalently bonded carbon atoms. Diamonds are used for industrial cutting because they are so hard and as gemstones because of their crystalline beauty.

Section 3.5

3. **Molecular solids.** The units composing **molecular solids,** molecules, are held together by intermolecular attractive forces. Molecular solids are usually soft and low melting. They are frequently volatile and are poor electrical conductors. A common example is ice (solid water).

FIGURE 5.15
Crystalline solids.

(a) The crystal structure of diamond.

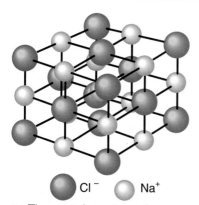

Cl⁻   Na⁺

(b) The crystal structure of sodium chloride.

4. **Metallic solids.** **Metallic solids** are composed of metal atoms held together by metallic bonds. **Metallic bonds** are formed by the overlap of orbitals of metal atoms, resulting in regions of high electron density surrounding the positive metal nuclei. Electrons in these regions are extremely mobile, resulting in the high *conductivity* (ability to carry electrical current) exhibited by many metallic solids. Silver and copper are common examples of metallic solids. Metals are easily shaped and are used for a variety of purposes. Most of these are practical applications such as hardware, cookware, and surgical and dental tools. Others are purely for enjoyment and decoration, such as silver and gold jewelry.

SUMMARY

5.1 Thermodynamics

Thermodynamics is the study of energy, work, and heat. Thermodynamics can be applied to the study of chemical reactions. *Exothermic reactions* produce energy and products that are lower in energy than the reactants. *Endothermic reactions* require energy in order to take place. Heat energy is represented as *enthalpy, $H°$.* The energy gain or loss is the change in enthalpy, $\Delta H°$, and is one factor that is useful in predicting whether a reaction is spontaneous or nonspontaneous.

Entropy, $S°$, is a measure of the randomness of a system. A random, or disordered system has high entropy; a well-ordered system has low entropy. The change in entropy in a chemical reaction, $\Delta S°$, is also a factor in predicting reaction spontaneity.

Free energy ($\Delta G°$) is a quantity that incorporates both factors, enthalpy and entropy; as such, it is an absolute predictor of the spontaneity of a chemical reaction.

5.2 Experimental Determination of Energy Change in Reactions

A *calorimeter* measures heat changes (in calories or joules) that occur in chemical reactions.

The *specific heat of water* is the number of calories of heat needed to raise the temperature of 1 gram of water 1 degree Celsius.

The amount of energy per gram of food is referred to as its *fuel value.* Fuel values are commonly reported in units of *nutritional Calories* (1 nutritional Calorie = 1 kcal). A bomb calorimeter is useful for measurement of the fuel value of foods.

5.3 Kinetics

Chemical *kinetics* is the study of the *rate* or speed of a chemical reaction. Energy for reactions is provided by molecular collisions. If this energy is sufficient, bonds may break, and atoms may recombine in a lower-energy arrangement, producing product. A collision producing one or more product molecules is termed an effective collision.

The minimum amount of energy needed for a reaction is the *activation energy.* The reaction proceeds from reactants to products through an intermediate state, the *activated complex.*

Experimental conditions influencing the reaction rate include the structure of the reacting species, the concentration of reactants, the temperature of reactants, the physical state of reactants, and the presence or absence of a catalyst.

A *catalyst* increases the rate of a reaction. The catalytic substance undergoes no net change in the reaction, nor does it alter the outcome of the reaction.

5.4 Chemical Equilibrium and the Reversibility of Reactions

Many chemical reactions do not completely convert reactants to products. A mixture of products and reactants exists, and its composition will remain constant until the experimental conditions are changed. This mixture is in a state of *chemical equilibrium.* The reaction continues indefinitely (dynamic), but the concentration of products and reactants are fixed (equilibrium). This is a *dynamic equilibrium.*

LeChatelier's Principle states that if a stress is placed on an equilibrium system, the system will respond by altering the equilibrium in such a way as to minimize the stress.

5.5 Energy and the States of Matter

The major difference between solids, liquids, and gases include the average distance between adjacent particles, the strength of the interparticle attractive forces, and the degree of organization of the particles.

5.6 The Gaseous State

The *kinetic molecular theory* describes an *ideal gas* in which gas particles exhibit no interactive or repulsive forces and the volumes of the individual gas particles are assumed to be negligible.

Boyle's Law states that the volume of a gas varies inversely with the pressure exerted by the gas if the number of moles and temperature of gas are held constant ($PV = k_1$).

Charles's Law states that the volume of a gas varies directly with the absolute temperature (K) if pressure and number of moles of gas are constant ($V/T = k_2$).

Avogadro's Law states that equal volumes of any gas contain the same number of moles if measured at constant temperature and pressure ($V/n = k_3$).

The volume occupied by one mole of any gas is its *molar volume.* At *standard temperature and pressure* (STP) the molar volume of any gas is 22.4 L. STP conditions are defined as 273 K (or 0°C) and 1 atmosphere pressure.

Boyle's Law, Charles's Law, and Avogadro's Law may be combined into a single expression relating all four terms, the *ideal gas law: PV = nRT. R* is the ideal gas constant (0.0821 L-atm K^{-1} mol^{-1}) if the units *P* (atmospheres), *V* (liters), *n* (number of moles), and *T* (Kelvin) are used.

Dalton's Law of *partial pressures* states that a mixture of gases exerts a pressure that is the sum of the pressure that each gas would exert if it were present alone under similar conditions ($P_t = p_1 + p_2 + p_3 + \ldots$).

5.7 The Liquid State

Liquids are incompressible because of the closeness of the molecules. The *viscosity* of a liquid is a measure of its resistance to flow. Viscosity generally decreases with increasing temperature. The *surface tension* of a liquid is a measure of the attractive forces at the surface of a liquid. *Surfactants* decrease surface tension.

The conversion of liquid to vapor at a temperature below the boiling point of the liquid is *evaporation.* Conversion of the gas to the liquid state is *condensation.* The *vapor pressure of the liquid* is defined as the pressure exerted by the vapor at equilibrium at a specified temperature. The *normal boiling point* of a liquid is the temperature at which the vapor pressure of the liquid is equal to one atmosphere.

Molecules in which a hydrogen atom is bonded to a highly electronegative atom such as nitrogen, oxygen, or fluorine exhibit *hydrogen bonding.* Hydrogen bonding in liquids is responsible for lower than expected vapor pressures and higher than normal boiling points.

5.8 The Solid State

Solids have fixed shapes and volumes. They are *incompressible,* owing to the closeness of the particles. Solids may be *crystalline,* having a regular, repeating structure, or *amorphous,* having no organized structure.

Crystalline solids may exist as *ionic solids, covalent solids, molecular solids,* or *metallic solids.* Electrons in metallic solids are extremely mobile, resulting in the high *conductivity* (ability to carry electrical current) exhibited by many metallic solids.

KEY TERMS

activated complex (5.3)	dynamic equilibrium (5.4)
activation energy (5.3)	endothermic reaction (5.1)
amorphous solid (5.8)	enthalpy (5.1)
Avogadro's Law (5.6)	entropy (5.1)
barometer (5.6)	equilibrium (5.4)
Boyle's Law (5.6)	evaporation (5.7)
calorimetry (5.2)	exothermic reaction (5.1)
catalyst (5.3)	free energy (5.1)
Charles's Law (5.6)	fuel value (5.2)
condensation (5.7)	hydrogen bonding (5.7)
covalent solid (5.8)	ideal gas (5.6)
crystalline solid (5.8)	ideal gas law (5.6)
Dalton's Law (5.6)	ionic solid (5.8)

kinetic-molecular theory (5.6)	rate of a reaction (5.3)
kinetics (5.3)	reversible reaction (5.4)
LeChatelier's Principle (5.4)	specific heat of water (5.2)
melting point (5.8)	standard temperature and
metallic bond (5.8)	pressure, STP (5.6)
metallic solid (5.8)	surface tension (5.7)
molar volume of a gas (5.6)	surfactant (5.7)
molecular solid (5.8)	thermodynamics (5.1)
normal boiling point (5.7)	vapor pressure of a liquid
nutritional Calorie (5.2)	(5.7)
partial pressure (5.6)	viscosity (5.7)
pressure (5.6)	

QUESTIONS AND PROBLEMS

Energy and Thermodynamics

5.17 Define or explain each of the following terms:
 a. exothermic reaction
 b. endothermic reaction
 c. calorimeter

5.18 Define or explain each of the following terms:
 a. entropy
 b. specific heat of water
 c. fuel value

5.19 Explain what is meant by the term *enthalpy.*

5.20 Explain what is meant by the term *entropy.*

5.21 5.00 g of octane are burned in a bomb calorimeter containing 2.00×10^2 g of water. How much energy, in calories, is released if the water temperature increases 6.00°C?

5.22 0.0500 mole of a nutrient substance is burned in a bomb calorimeter containing 2.00×10^2 g of water. If the formula weight of this nutrient substance is 114 g/mol, what is the fuel value if the temperature of the water increased 5.70°C.

5.23 Predict whether each of the following processes increases or decreases entropy, and explain your reasoning.
 a. melting of a solid metal
 b. boiling of water

5.24 Predict whether each of the following processes increases or decreases entropy, and explain your reasoning.
 a. burning a log in a fireplace
 b. condensation of water vapor on a cold surface

5.25 Explain why an exothermic reaction produces products that are more stable than the reactants.

5.26 Provide an example of entropy from your own life experience.

5.27 Isopropyl alcohol, commonly known as rubbing alcohol, feels cool when applied to the skin. Give an explanation.

5.28 Energy is required to break chemical bonds during the course of a reaction. When is energy released?

Kinetics and Equilibrium

5.29 Define or explain each of the following terms:
 a. activated complex
 b. rate of a reaction
 c. dynamic equilibrium
 d. product

5.30 Define or explain each of the following terms:
 a. activation energy
 b. catalyst
 c. reversible reaction
 d. reactant

5.31 Label each of the following statements as true or false, and explain why.
 a. A slow reaction is an incomplete reaction.
 b. The rates of forward and reverse reactions are never the same.

5.32 Label each of the following statements as true or false, and explain why.
 a. A reaction is at equilibrium when no reactants remain.
 b. A reaction at equilibrium is undergoing continual change.

States of Matter

5.33 List the major differences between the solid, liquid, and gaseous states.

5.34 Arrange the three states of matter in order of increasing entropy.

5.35 Define each of the following terms:
 a. ideal gas
 b. barometer
 c. viscosity
 d. surface tension

5.36 Define each of the following terms:
 a. partial pressure
 b. STP
 c. liquid vapor pressure
 d. evaporation

5.37 Calculate the volume of 2.00 g of SO_2 at STP.

5.38 Calculate the volume of N_2 that results when 1.00×10^2 mL of the gas at 25°C is heated to 75°C at constant pressure.

5.39 What is the volume of 0.500 mole of neon gas at 20°C and 735 torr?

5.40 Calculate the temperature at which 2.50 g of helium in a 5.00-L container will exert a pressure of 4.00 atm.

Further Problems

5.41 Cyclopropane, C_3H_6, is used as an anesthetic. If 1.00 mole of cyclopropane is released into a 2.00-L container at 25°C, what is the pressure?

5.42 Hydrogen sulfide, H_2S, has the characteristic odor of rotten eggs. If a sample of H_2S gas at 760 torr and 25.0°C in a 2.00-L container is allowed to expand into a 10.0-L container at 25.0°C, what is the pressure in the 10.0-L container?

5.43 Calculate the formula weight of each gas under the following conditions:
 a. 0.491 g of gas at STP in a 2.50×10^2 mL container.
 b. 1.72 g of gas at 0.500 atm and 298 K in a 2.00-L container.

5.44 Calculate the density of each of the gases in Problem 5.43.

5.45 Use LeChatelier's Principle to predict whether the amount of PCl_3 in a 1.00-L container is increased, is decreased, or remains the same if for the following equilibrium:

$$PCl_3(g) + Cl_2(g) \rightleftharpoons PCl_5(g) + heat$$

 a. PCl_5 is added
 b. Cl_2 is added
 c. PCl_5 is removed
 d. the temperature is decreased
 e. a catalyst is added

5.46 A clever device found in some homes is a figurine that is blue on dry, sunny days and pink on damp, rainy days. These figurines are coated with substances containing chemical species that undergo the following equilibrium:

$$Co(H_2O)_6{}^{2+} + 4Cl^- \longrightarrow CoCl_4{}^{2-} + 6H_2O$$

 a. Which substance is blue?
 b. Which substance is pink?
 c. How is LeChatelier's Principle applied here?

5.47 How do gas densities compare to the densities of liquids and solids?

5.48 Calculate the density of methane (CH_4) at STP.

5.49 Describe the difference between enthalpy and free energy.

5.50 The first law of thermodynamics tells us that heat will always travel from hotter to colder. With this statement in mind, why does a glass of iced tea feel cold?

VOCABULARY QUIZ

5.1 _____ is the threshold energy that must be overcome to produce a chemical reaction.

5.2 _____ solids have no organized, regular structure.

5.3 A(n) _____ is a device for measuring gas pressure.

5.4 A(n) _____ is a device for measuring heat.

5.5 A(n) _____ speeds up reactions without undergoing change.

5.6 _____ is the conversion of a gas to a liquid.

5.7 _____ processes absorb energy in a chemical change.

5.8 _____ is a tendency toward randomness or disorder.

5.9 _____ is the conversion of a liquid to a gas below the boiling point of the liquid.

5.10 A(n) _____ gas is one in which gas particles do not interact and the volume of the individual gas particles is assumed to be negligible.

6
Solutions

LEARNING GOALS

◆ Explain the meaning of the terms *solution, solute,* and *solvent.*

◆ Describe the types of solutions, and give examples of each.

◆ Discuss the importance of solution chemistry in chemical processes.

◆ Describe the relationship between solubility and equilibrium.

◆ Calculate solution concentration in the commonly used units: weight/volume percent, volume/volume percent, weight/weight percent, and molarity.

◆ Describe and explain concentration-dependent solution properties: vapor pressure lowering, freezing point depression, boiling point elevation, and osmotic pressure.

◆ List the chemical and physical properties of water that make it a truly unique solvent.

CHEMISTRY CONNECTION

Drug Delivery

When a doctor prescribes medicine to treat a disease or relieve its symptoms, the medication may be administered in a variety of ways. Drugs may be taken orally, injected into a muscle or a vein, or absorbed through the skin. Specific instructions are often provided to regulate what particular combination of drugs can or cannot be taken. The diet, both before and during the drug therapy, may be of special importance.

To appreciate why drugs are administered in a specific way, it is necessary to understand a few basic facts about medications and how they interact with the body.

Drugs function by undergoing one or more chemical reactions in the body. Few compounds react in only one way, to produce a limited set of products, even in the simple environment of a beaker or flask. Imagine the number of possible reactions that a drug can undergo in a complex chemical factory like the human body. In many cases a drug can react in a variety of ways other than its intended path. These alternative paths are side reactions, sometimes producing *side effects* such as nausea, vomiting, insomnia, or drowsiness. All are unpleasant and may actually interfere with the primary function of the drug.

The development of safe, effective medication, with minimal side effects, is a slow and painstaking process and determining the best drug delivery system is a critical step. For example, a drug that undergoes an unwanted side reaction in an acidic solution would not be very effective if administered orally. The acidic digestive fluids in the stomach could prevent the drug from even reaching the intended organ, let alone retaining its potency. The drug could be administered through a vein into the blood; blood is not acidic, in contrast to digestive fluids. In this way the drug may be delivered intact to the intended site in the body, where it is free to undergo its primary reaction.

Drug delivery has become a science in its own right. Pharmacology, the study of drugs and their uses in the treatment of disease, has a goal of creating drugs that are highly selective. In other words, they will undergo only one reaction, the intended reaction. Encapsulation of drugs, enclosing them within larger molecules or collections of molecules, may protect them from unwanted reactions as they are transported to their intended site.

In this chapter we will explore the fundamentals of solutions and solution reactions. Knowing a few basic concepts that govern reactions in beakers will help us to understand the conditions that affect the reactivity of a host of biochemically interesting molecules that we will encounter in later chapters.

INTRODUCTION

A majority of chemical reactions, and virtually all important organic and biochemical reactions, take place as reactants dissolved in solution. For this reason the major emphasis of this chapter will be on *solution reactions.*

We will see that the properties of solutions depend not only on the types of substances that make up the solution but also on the amount of each substance that is contained in a certain volume of the solution; the latter is termed the concentration of the solution.

6.1 PROPERTIES OF SOLUTIONS

A **solution** is a homogeneous (or uniform) mixture of two or more substances. A solution is composed of one or more **solutes,** dissolved in a **solvent.** For example, when sugar (the solute) is added to water (the solvent), the sugar dissolves in the water to produce a solution. In those instances in which the solvent is water, we refer to the homogeneous mixture as an **aqueous solution,** from the Latin *aqua,* meaning water.

The dissolution of a solid in a liquid is perhaps the most common example of solution formation. However, it is also possible to form solutions in gases and solids as well as in liquids. For example:

◆ Air is a gaseous mixture, but it is also a solution; oxygen and a number of trace gases are dissolved in the gaseous solvent, nitrogen.

◆ Alloys, such as brass and silver and the gold used to make jewelry, are also homogeneous mixtures of two or more kinds of metal atoms in the solid state.

When there is doubt as to which substance is the solute and which is the solvent, the common convention states that the solvent is always the substance that is present in the greater amount.

Although solid and gaseous solutions are important in many applications, our emphasis will be on *liquid solutions* because so many important chemical reactions take place in liquid solutions.

General properties of liquid solutions

Section 3.3

Recall that matter in solution, as in gases, is in continuous, random motion (Section 5.6).

Section 6.2

Liquid solutions are clear and transparent with no visible particles of solute. They may be colored or colorless, depending on the properties of the solute and solvent. Note that the terms *clear* and *colorless* do not mean the same thing; a clear solution has only one state of matter that can be detected; *colorless* simply means the absence of color.

Recall that solutions of **electrolytes** are formed from solutes that are soluble ionic compounds. These compounds dissociate in solution to produce ions that behave as charge carriers. Solutions of electrolytes are good conductors of electricity. In contrast, solutions of **nonelectrolytes** are formed from nondissociating *molecular* solutes (nonelectrolytes), and these solutions are nonconducting.

A *true solution* is a homogeneous mixture with uniform properties throughout. In a true solution the solute cannot be isolated from the solution by filtration; the particle size of the solute is about the same as that of the solvent, and solvent and solute pass directly through the filter paper. Furthermore, solute particles will not "settle out" after a period of time; all of the molecules of solute and solvent are intimately mixed. The continuous particle motion in solution maintains the homogeneous, random distribution of solute and solvent particles.

Volumes of solute and solvent are not additive; one liter of alcohol mixed with one liter of water does not result in exactly two liters of solution. The volume of pure liquid is determined by the way in which the individual molecules "fit together." When two or more kinds of molecules are mixed, the interactions become more complex. Solvent interacts with solvent, solute interacts with solvent, and solute may interact with other solute. This will be important to remember when we solve concentration problems later.

Solutions and colloids

See Section 7.2 for more information on precipitates.

How can you recognize a solution? A beaker containing a clear liquid may be a pure substance, a true solution, or a colloid. Only chemical analysis, determining the identity of all substances in the liquid, can distinguish between a pure substance and a solution. A pure substance has *one* component, pure water being an example. A true solution will contain more than one substance, with the tiny particles homogeneously intermingled.

A **colloidal suspension** also consists of solute particles distributed throughout a solvent. However, the distribution is not completely homogeneous, owing to the size of the colloidal particles. Particles with diameters of 1×10^{-9} m (1 nm) to 2×10^{-7} m (200 nm) are colloids. Particles smaller than 1 nm are solution particles; those larger than 200 nm are precipitates (solid in contact with solvent).

To the naked eye, a colloidal suspension and a true solution appear identical; neither solute nor colloid can be seen by the naked eye. However, a simple experiment, using only a bright light source, can readily make the distinction. Colloid particles are large enough to scatter light; solute particles are not. When a beam of light passes through a colloidal suspension, the particles are large enough to scatter light, and the liquid appears hazy. We see this effect in sunlight passing through fog. The haze is light scattered by droplets of water. You may have noticed that your automobile headlights are not very helpful in foggy weather. Visibility becomes worse rather than better because light scattering increases.

The light-scattering ability of colloidal suspensions is termed the *Tyndall effect*. True solutions, with very tiny particles, do not scatter light—no haze is observed—and true solutions are easily distinguished from colloidal suspensions by observing their light-scattering properties (Figure 6.1).

FIGURE 6.1
The Tyndall effect. The beaker on the left contains a colloidal suspension, which scatters the light. This scattered light is visible as a haze. The beaker on the right contains a true solution; no scattered light is observed.

In our discussion of the relationship of polarity and solubility the rule *"like dissolves like"* was described as the fundamental condition for solubility. Polar solutes are soluble in polar solvents, and nonpolar solutes are soluble in nonpolar solvents. Thus, knowing a little bit about the structure of the molecule enables us to predict qualitatively the solubility of the compound.

The degree of **solubility,** *how much* solute can dissolve in a given volume of solvent, is a quantitative measure of solubility. It is difficult to predict the solubility of each and every compound. However, general solubility trends are based on the following considerations:

◆ *The magnitude of difference between polarity of solute and solvent.* The greater the difference, the less soluble the solute.

◆ *Temperature.* An increase in temperature usually, but not always, increases solubility. Often, the effect is dramatic. For example, an increase in temperature from 0°C to 100°C increases the water solubility of KCl from 28 g/100 mL to 58 g/100 mL.

◆ *Pressure.* Pressure has little effect on the solubility of solids and liquids in liquids. However, the solubility of a gas in liquid is directly proportional to the applied pressure. Carbonated beverages, for example, are made by dissolving carbon dioxide in the beverage under high pressure (hence the term "carbonated").

When a solution contains all the solute that can be dissolved at a particular temperature, it is **saturated.** When solubility values are given, for example, 13.3 g of potassium nitrate in 100 mL of water at 24°C, they refer to the concentration of a saturated solution.

As we have already noted, *increasing* the temperature generally increases the amount of solute a given solution may hold. Conversely, *cooling* a saturated solution often results in a decrease in the amount of solute in solution; the excess solute falls to the bottom of the container as a **precipitate** (a solid in contact with the solution). Occasionally, however, on cooling, the excess solute may remain in solution for a period of time. Such a solution is described as a **supersaturated solution.** This type of solution is inherently unstable; with time, excess solute will precipitate, and the solution will revert to a saturated solution, which will be stable.

When an excess of solute is added to a solvent, it begins to dissolve and continues until it establishes a *dynamic equilibrium* between dissolved and undissolved solute.

Initially, the rate of dissolution is large. After a period of time the rate of the reverse process, precipitation, increases. The rates of dissolution and precipitation eventually become equal, and there is no further change in the composition of the solution. There is, however, a continual exchange of solute particles between solid and liquid phases because particles are in constant motion. The solution is saturated; the most precise definition of a saturated solution is a solution that is in equilibrium with undissolved solute.

Degree of solubility

Section 3.5

The term *qualitative* implies identity, and the term *quantitative* relates to quantity.

Solubility and equilibrium

Section 5.4

Solubility of gases: Henry's Law

The concept of partial pressure is a consequence of Dalton's Law, discussed in Section 5.6.

Chapter 5

See *"A Clinical Perspective: Blood Gases and Respiration,"* Chapter 5.

When a liquid and a gas are allowed to come to equilibrium, the amount of gas dissolved in the liquid reaches some maximum level. This quantity can be predicted from **Henry's Law,** which states that the number of moles of a gas dissolved in a liquid at a given temperature is proportional to the partial pressure of the gas. In other words, the gas solubility is directly proportional to the pressure of that gas in the atmosphere that is in contact with the liquid.

Carbonated beverages are bottled at high pressures of carbon dioxide. When the cap is removed, the fizzing results from the fact that the partial pressure of carbon dioxide in the atmosphere is much less than that used in the bottling process. As a result, the equilibrium quickly shifts to one of lower gas solubility.

Gases are most soluble at low temperatures, and the gas may be explosively released at higher temperatures. This explains many common observations; for example, a chilled container of carbonated beverage that is opened at room temperature quickly goes flat. As the beverage warms up, the solubility of the carbon dioxide decreases.

Henry's Law helps to explain the process of respiration. Respiration depends on a rapid and efficient exchange of oxygen and carbon dioxide between the atmosphere and the blood. This transfer occurs through the lungs. The process, oxygen entering the blood and carbon dioxide released to the atmosphere, is accomplished in air sacs called *alveoli,* which are surrounded by an extensive capillary system. Equilibrium is quickly established between alveolar air and the capillary blood. The temperature of the blood is effectively constant. Therefore the equilibrium concentration of both oxygen and carbon dioxide are determined by the partial pressures of the gases (Henry's Law). The oxygen is transported to cells, a variety of reactions take place, and the waste product of respiration, carbon dioxide, is brought back to the lungs to be expelled into the atmosphere.

6.2 CONCENTRATION OF SOLUTIONS: PERCENTAGE

The amount of solute dissolved in a given amount of solution is defined as the solution **concentration.** The concentration of a solution has a profound effect on the properties of a solution, both *physical* (melting and boiling points) and *chemical* (solution reactivity). Solution concentration may be expressed in many different units. Concentration units based on the concept of percentage are considered below.

Weight/volume percent

The concentration of a solution is defined as the amount of solute dissolved in a specified amount of solution,

$$\text{concentration} = \frac{\text{amount of solute}}{\text{amount of solution}}$$

If we define the amount of solute as the *mass* of solute (in grams) and the amount of solution in *volume* units (milliliters), concentration is expressed as the ratio

$$\text{concentration} = \frac{\text{grams of solute}}{\text{milliliters of solution}}$$

This concentration can then be expressed as a percentage by multiplying the ratio by the factor, 10^2. This results in

$$\% \text{ concentration} = \frac{\text{grams of solute}}{\text{milliliters of solution}} \times 10^2$$

The percent concentration expressed in this way is called **weight/volume percent,** or % **(W/V).** Thus

$$\% \frac{\text{W}}{\text{V}} = \frac{\text{grams of solute}}{\text{milliliters of solution}} \times 10^2$$

Consider the following examples.

A HUMAN PERSPECTIVE

Scuba Diving: Nitrogen and the Bends

A deep-water diver's worst fear is the interruption of the oxygen supply through equipment malfunction, forcing his or her rapid rise to the surface in search of air. If a diver must ascend too rapidly, he or she may suffer a condition known as "the bends."

Key to understanding this problem is recognition of the tremendous increase in pressure that divers withstand as they descend, due to the weight of the water above them. At the surface the pressure is approximately one atmosphere, which corresponds to 14.7 pounds/in². At a depth of 200 feet the pressure is approximately six times as great, or 90 pounds/in.².

At these pressures the solubility of nitrogen in the blood increases dramatically. Oxygen solubility increases as well, although its effect is less serious (O_2 is 20% of air, N_2 is 80%). As the diver quickly rises, the pressure decreases rapidly, and the nitrogen "boils" out of the blood, stopping blood flow and impairing nerve transmission. The joints of the body lock in a bent position, hence the name of the condition: the bends.

To minimize the problem, scuba tanks are often filled with mixtures of helium and oxygen rather than nitrogen and oxygen. Helium has a much lower solubility in blood and, like nitrogen, is inert.

EXAMPLE 6.1

Calculating Weight/Volume Percent

Calculate the percent composition, or % (W/V), of 3.00×10^2 mL of solution containing 15.0 g of glucose.

Solution

There are 15.0 g of glucose, the solute, and 3.00×10^2 mL of total solution. Therefore

$$\% \frac{W}{V} = \frac{15.0 \text{ grams glucose}}{3.00 \times 10^2 \text{ mL solution}} \times 10^2$$

or

$$\% \frac{W}{V} = 5.00\% \text{ glucose}$$

EXAMPLE 6.2

Calculating the Weight of Solute from a Weight/Volume Percent

Calculate the number of grams of NaCl in 5.00×10^2 mL of a 10.0% solution:

Solution

$$10.0\% \frac{W}{V} = \frac{X \text{ grams NaCl}}{5.00 \times 10^2 \text{ mL solution}} \times 10^2$$

$$X \text{ grams NaCl} \times 10^2 = \left(10.0\% \frac{W}{V}\right)(5.00 \times 10^2 \text{ mL solution})$$

$$X = 50.0 \text{ grams NaCl}$$

If the units of mass are other than grams, or if the solution volume is in units other than milliliters, the proper conversion factor must be used to arrive at the units used in the equation.

Section 1.4

QUESTION 6.1

Calculate the % (W/V) of 0.0600 L of solution containing 10.0 g NaCl.

QUESTION 6.2

Calculate the volume (in milliliters) of a 25.0% (W/V) solution containing 10.0 g NaCl.

QUESTION 6.3

Calculate the % (W/V) of 0.200 L of solution containing 15.0 g KCl.

QUESTION 6.4

Calculate the mass (in grams) of sodium hydroxide required to make 2.00 L of a 1.00% (W/V) solution.

Volume/volume percent

If the volume of solute is known, rather than its mass, it is often more convenient to represent solution concentration as **volume/volume percent,** or **% (V/V):**

$$\% \frac{V}{V} = \frac{\text{mL solute}}{\text{mL solution}} \times 10^2$$

The logic and calculations are the same as those we have used for % (W/V).

EXAMPLE 6.3

Calculating Volume/Volume Percent

Calculate the % (V/V) of ethyl alcohol if 5.00×10^{-1} mL of the alcohol is dissolved in 10.0 mL of solution:

Solution

$$\% \frac{V}{V} = \frac{\text{mL solute}}{\text{mL solution}} \times 10^2$$

$$\% \frac{V}{V} = \frac{5.00 \times 10^{-1} \text{ mL}}{10.0 \text{ mL}} \times 10^2$$

$$\% \frac{V}{V} = 5.00\% \text{ ethyl alcohol}$$

QUESTION 6.5

Calculate the % (V/V) of 1.00×10^2 mL of an aqueous solution that contains 5.00 mL of ethyl alcohol.

QUESTION 6.6

Calculate the % (V/V) of 2.50 L of aqueous solution that contains 50.0 g of a solute and that has a density of 1.20 g/mL. (*Hint:* Recall the use of density as a conversion factor.)

Weight/weight percent

The **weight/weight percent,** or **% (W/W),** is most useful for mixtures of solids, whose weights (masses) are easily obtained. The expression used to calculate weight/weight percentage is analogous in form to % (W/V) and % (V/V), discussed above:

$$\% \frac{W}{W} = \frac{\text{grams solute}}{\text{grams solution}} \times 10^2$$

EXAMPLE 6.4

Calculating Weight/Weight Percent

Calculate the % (W/W) of platinum in a gold ring that contains 14.00 grams of gold and 4.500 grams of platinum.

Solution

$$\% \frac{W}{W} = \frac{\text{grams solute}}{\text{grams solution}} \times 10^2$$

$$\% \frac{W}{W} = \frac{4.500 \text{ g platinum}}{4.500 \text{ g platinum} + 14.00 \text{ g gold}} \times 10^2$$

$$\% \frac{W}{W} = \frac{4.500 \text{ g}}{18.50 \text{ g}} \times 10^2 = 24.32\% \text{ platinum}$$

QUESTION 6.7

20.0 grams of oxygen gas are diluted with 80.0 grams of nitrogen gas in a 78.0-L container at standard temperature and pressure. Calculate:

a. % (W/V) of oxygen gas

b. % (V/V) of oxygen gas (*Hint:* Recall our discussion of gases in Chapter 5.)

c. % (W/W) of oxygen gas.

QUESTION 6.8

50.0 grams of argon gas are diluted with 80.0 grams of helium gas in a 476-L container at standard temperature and pressure. Calculate:

a. % (W/V) of argon gas

b. % (V/V) of argon gas (*Hint:* Recall our discussion of gases in Chapter 5.)

c. % (W/W) of argon gas

In our discussion of the chemical arithmetic of reactions in Chapter 4 we saw that the chemical equation represents the relative number of *moles* of two or more reactants producing products. When chemical reactions occur in solution, it is most useful to represent their concentrations on a *molar* basis.

The most common mole-based concentration unit is molarity. **Molarity,** symbolized **M**, is defined as the number of moles of solute per liter of solution, or

$$M = \frac{\text{moles solute}}{\text{L solution}}$$

6.3 CONCENTRATION OF SOLUTIONS: MOLES AND EQUIVALENTS

Molarity

EXAMPLE 6.5

Calculating Molarity from Moles

Calculate the molarity of 2.0 L of solution containing 5.0 moles of NaOH.

Solution

$$M_{\text{NaOH}} = \frac{5.0 \text{ moles solute}}{2.0 \text{ L solution}}$$

$$M_{\text{NaOH}} = 2.5 \ M$$

Remember the need for conversion factors to convert from mass to number of moles. Consider the following example.

EXAMPLE 6.6

Calculating Molarity from Mass

If 5.00 grams of glucose are dissolved in 1.00×10^2 mL of solution, calculate the M of the glucose solution.

Solution

The molecular weight of glucose is 1.80×10^2 grams/mole. Therefore

$$5.00 \text{ grams} \times \frac{1 \text{ mole}}{1.80 \times 10^2 \text{ grams}} = 2.78 \times 10^{-2} \text{ moles glucose}$$

and

$$1.00 \times 10^2 \text{ mL} \times \frac{1 \text{ L}}{1000 \text{ mL}} = 1.00 \times 10^{-1} \text{ L}$$

and

$$M \text{ (glucose)} = \frac{2.78 \times 10^{-2} \text{ moles}}{1.00 \times 10^{-1} \text{ L}}$$

$$M \text{ (glucose)} = 2.78 \times 10^{-1} M$$

EXAMPLE 6.7

Calculating Volume from Molarity

Calculate the volume of a 0.750 M sulfuric acid (H_2SO_4) solution containing 0.120 mole of solute.

Solution

Substituting in our basic expression, we get

$$0.750 \text{ } M \text{ } H_2SO_4 = \frac{0.120 \text{ mole } H_2SO_4}{X \text{ L}}$$

$$X \text{ } L = 0.160 \text{ L}$$

QUESTION 6.9

Calculate the number of moles of solute in 5.00×10^2 mL of 0.250 M HCl.

QUESTION 6.10

Calculate the number of grams of silver nitrate required to prepare 2.00 L of 0.500 M $AgNO_3$.

Laboratory reagents are often purchased as concentrated solutions (for example 12 M HCl, 6 M NaOH) for reasons of safety, economy, and space limitations. One must often *dilute* such a solution to a larger volume to prepare a less concentrated solution for the experiment at hand. The approach to such a calculation is outlined below.

We define

$$M_1 = \text{molarity of solution } prior \text{ } to \text{ dilution}$$

$$M_2 = \text{molarity of solution } after \text{ dilution}$$

$$V_1 = \text{volume of solution } prior \text{ } to \text{ dilution}$$

$$V_2 = \text{volume of solution } after \text{ dilution}$$

and

$$M = \frac{\text{moles solute}}{\text{L solution}}$$

and

$$\text{moles solute} = (M)(\text{L solution})$$

The number of moles of solute *prior to* and *after* dilution is unchanged, since dilution involves only addition of extra solvent:

$$\text{moles}_1 \text{ solute} = \text{moles}_2 \text{ solute}$$

Initial   Final
condition   condition

or

$$(M_1)(\text{L}_1 \text{ solution}) = (M_2)(\text{L}_2 \text{ solution})$$

$$(M_1)(V_1) = (M_2)(V_2)$$

Knowing any three of these terms enables one to calculate the fourth.

EXAMPLE 6.8

Calculating Molarity after Dilution

Calculate the molarity of a solution made by diluting 0.050 L of 0.10 M HCl solution to a volume of 1.0 L.

Solution

$$M_1 = 0.10 \ M$$

$$M_2 = X \ M$$

$$V_1 = 0.050 \ \text{L}$$

$$V_2 = 1.0 \ \text{L}$$

Then

$$(M_1)(V_1) = (M_2)(V_2)$$

$$M_2 = \frac{(M_1)(V_1)}{V_2}$$

$$X \ M = \frac{(0.10 \ M)(0.050 \ \text{L})}{(1.0 \ \text{L})}$$

$$X \ M = 0.0050 \ M \qquad \text{or} \qquad 5.0 \times 10^{-3} \ M \text{ HCl}$$

EXAMPLE 6.9

Calculating a Dilution Volume

Calculate the volume, in liters, of water that must be added to dilute 20.0 mL of 12.0 M HCl to 0.100 M HCl.

Solution

$$M_1 = 12.0 \ M$$

$$M_2 = 0.100 \ M$$

$$V_1 = 20.0 \ \text{mL} \ (0.0200 \ \text{L})$$

$$V_2 = V_{\text{final}}$$

Then

$$(M_1)(V_1) = (M_2)(V_2)$$

$$V_2 = \frac{(M_1)(V_1)}{(M_2)}$$

$$V_{\text{final}} = \frac{(12.0\ M)(0.0200\ \text{L})}{0.100\ M}$$

$$V_{\text{final}} = 2.40\ \text{L solution}$$

Note that this is the *total final volume*. The amount of water added equals this volume *minus* the original solution volume, or

$$2.40\ \text{L} - 0.0200\ \text{L} = 2.38\ \text{L water}$$

QUESTION 6.11

How would you prepare 1.0×10^2 mL of 2.0 M HCl, starting with concentrated (12.0 M) HCl?

QUESTION 6.12

What volume of 0.200 M sugar solution can be prepared from 50.0 mL of 0.400 M solution?

The dilution equation is valid with any concentration units, such as % (W/V) or % (V/V), *as well as* molarity, which was used in the above example. However, you must be certain to use the same units for both initial *and* final concentration values. Only in this way will proper unit cancellation occur.

Representation of concentration of ions in solution

The concentration of ions in solution may be represented in a variety of ways. The most common include moles per liter (molarity) and equivalents per liter.

Molarity emphasizes the number of individual ions. A 1 M solution of Na^+ contains Avogadro's number, 6.02×10^{23}, of Na^+. In contrast, equivalents per liter emphasizes charge; one equivalent of Na^+ contains Avogadro's number of positive charge.

We defined one mole as the number of grams of an atom, molecule, or ion corresponding to Avogadro's number of particles. One **equivalent** of an ion is the number of grams of the ion corresponding to Avogadro's number of electrical charges. Some examples follow:

1 mole Na^+ = 1 equivalent Na^+	(one Na^+ = 1 unit of charge/ion)
1 mole Cl^- = 1 equivalent Cl^-	(one Cl^- = 1 unit of charge/ion)
1 mole Ca^{2+} = 2 equivalents Ca^{2+}	(one Ca^{2+} = 2 units of charge/ion)
1 mole CO_3^{2-} = 2 equivalents CO_3^{2-}	(one CO_3^{2-} = 2 units of charge/ion)
1 mole PO_4^{3-} = 3 equivalents PO_4^{3-}	(one PO_4^{3-} = 3 units of charge/ion)

Changing from moles per liter to equivalents per liter (or the reverse) can be accomplished by using conversion factors.

EXAMPLE 6.10

Calculate the number of equivalents per liter of phosphate ion, PO_4^{3-}, in a solution that is 5.0×10^{-3} M phosphate.

Solution

$$\frac{5.0 \times 10^{-3}\ \text{mol } PO_4^{3-}}{1\ \text{L}} \times \frac{3\ \text{mol charge}}{1\ \text{mol } PO_4^{3-}} \times \frac{1\ \text{equivalent}}{1\ \text{mol charge}} = \frac{1.5 \times 10^{-2}\ \text{equivalent } PO_4^{3-}}{\text{L}}$$

Solution properties that are dependent on the *concentration of the solute particles,* rather than the *identity of the solute,* are **colligative properties.**

There are four colligative properties of solutions:

1. vapor pressure lowering
2. boiling point elevation
3. freezing point depression
4. osmotic pressure

Each of these properties has widespread practical application. We look at each in some detail in the following sections.

6.4 CONCENTRATION-DEPENDENT SOLUTION PROPERTIES

Vapor pressure lowering

Raoult's Law states that when a solute is added to a solvent, the vapor pressure of the solvent decreases in proportion to the concentration of the solute.

Recall that the concept of liquid vapor pressure was discussed in Section 5.7.

This observation may be explained in molecular terms by using the following logic: Vapor pressure of a solution results from the escape of solvent molecules from the liquid to the gas phase, thus increasing the partial pressure of the gas phase solvent molecules until the equilibrium vapor pressure is reached. Presence of solute molecules hinders the escape of solvent molecules, thus lowering the equilibrium vapor pressure (see Figure 6.2).

Perhaps the most important consequence of Raoult's Law is the effect of the solute on the freezing and boiling points of a solution.

Freezing point depression and boiling point elevation

When a nonvolatile solid is added to a solvent, the freezing point of the resulting solution decreases (a lower temperature is required to convert the liquid to a solid). The boiling point of the solution is found to increase (it requires a higher temperature to form the gaseous state).

The freezing point depression may be explained by equilibrium considerations. At the freezing point, ice is in equilibrium with liquid water:

$$H_2O(l) \underset{(r)}{\overset{(f)}{\rightleftharpoons}} H_2O(s)$$

The solute molecules interfere with the rate at which liquid water molecules associate to form the solid state. For a true equilibrium the rate of the forward (f) and reverse (r) processes must be equal. Lowering the temperature eventually slows the rate of the reverse (r) process sufficiently; at the lower temperature, equilibrium is established, and the solution freezes.

Section 5.4

The boiling point elevation can be explained by considering the definition of the boiling point, that is, the temperature at which the vapor pressure of the liquid equals the atmospheric pressure. Raoult's Law states that the vapor pressure of a solution is decreased by the presence of a solute. Therefore a higher temperature is necessary to raise the vapor pressure to the atmospheric pressure, hence the boiling point elevation.

The extent of the freezing point depression (ΔT_f) is proportional to the solute concentration over a limited range of concentration:

$$\Delta T_f = k_f \times (\text{solute concentration})$$

The boiling point elevation (ΔT_b) is also proportional to the solute concentration:

$$\Delta T_b = k_b \times (\text{solute concentration})$$

If the value of the proportionality factor (k_f or k_b) is known for the solvent of interest, the magnitude of the freezing point depression or boiling point elevation can be calculated for a solution of known concentration.

Solute concentration must be in *mole*-based units. The number of particles (molecules or ions) is critical here, not the mass of solute. One *heavy* molecule will have exactly the same effect on the freezing or boiling point as one *light* molecule. A mole-based unit, since it is related directly to Avogadro's number, will correctly represent the number of particles in solution.

FIGURE 6.2
An illustration of Raoult's Law: lowering of vapor pressure by addition of solute molecules. White units represent solvent molecules, and red units are solute molecules. Solute molecules present a barrier to escape of solvent molecules, thus decreasing the vapor pressure.

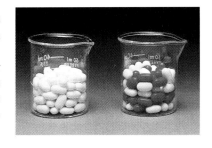

We have already worked with one mole-based unit, *molarity,* and this concentration unit can be used to calculate either the freezing point depression or the boiling point elevation.

A second mole-based concentration unit, molality, is more commonly used in these types of situations. *Molality* (symbolized *m*) is defined as the number of moles of solute per kilogram of solvent in a solution:

$$m = \frac{\text{moles solute}}{\text{kg solvent}}$$

Molality does not vary with temperature, whereas molarity is temperature dependent. For this reason, molality is the preferred concentration unit for studies such as freezing point depression and boiling point elevation, in which measurement of *change* in temperature is critical.

Practical applications that take advantage of freezing point depression of solutions by solutes include the following:

◆ Salt is spread on icy roads to melt the ice in winter. The salt lowers the freezing point of the water, so it exists in the liquid phase below its normal freezing point, 0°C or 32°F.

◆ Solutes such as ethylene glycol, "antifreeze," are added to auto radiators in the winter to prevent freezing by lowering the freezing point of the coolant.

We have referred to the concentration of *particles* in our discussion of colligative properties. Why did we stress this term? The reason is that there is a very important difference between electrolytes and nonelectrolytes. That difference is the way in which they behave when they dissolve. For example, if we dissolve one mole of glucose ($C_6H_{12}O_6$) in one liter of water,

$$1\ C_6H_{12}O_6(s) \xrightarrow{H_2O} 1\ C_6H_{12}O_6(aq)$$

one mole (Avogadro's number, 6.02×10^{23} particles) of glucose is present in solution. *Glucose is a covalently bonded nonelectrolyte.* Dissolving one mole of sodium chloride in one liter of water,

$$1\ NaCl(s) \xrightarrow{H_2O} 1\ Na^+(aq) + 1\ Cl^-(aq)$$

produces two moles of particles (one mole of sodium ions and one mole of chloride ions). *Sodium chloride is an ionic electrolyte.*

$$1\ \text{mole of glucose} \longrightarrow 1\ \text{mole of particles in solution}$$

$$1\ \text{mole of sodium chloride} \longrightarrow 2\ \text{moles of particles in solution}$$

It follows that one mole of sodium chloride will decrease the vapor pressure, increase the boiling point, or depress the freezing point of one liter of water *twice as much* as one mole of glucose in the same quantity of water.

Osmotic pressure

Certain types of thin films, or *membranes,* while appearing impervious to matter, actually contain a network of small holes or pores. These pores may be large enough to allow small *solvent* molecules, such as water, to pass from one side of the membrane to the other. On the other hand, *solute* molecules cannot cross the membrane because they are too large to fit through the pores. Membranes that allow the solvent and small molecules and ions, but not solute, to pass through are **semipermeable membranes.** Examples of semipermeable membranes range from synthetics, such as cellophane, to membranes of cells. When the pores are so small that only water molecules can pass through, they are termed osmotic membranes.

Osmosis is the movement of solvent from a *dilute solution* to a more *concentrated solution* through a *semipermeable membrane.* Pressure must be applied to the more concentrated solution to stop this flow, and the amount of pressure required to just stop the flow is the **osmotic pressure.**

The process of osmosis occurring between pure water and glucose (sugar) solution is illustrated in Figure 6.3. Note that the "driving force" for the osmotic process is the need to

---

Molarity is temperature dependent simply because it is expressed as mole/volume. Volume is temperature dependent—liquids expand when heated and contract when cooled. Molality is moles/mass; each is temperature independent.

Section 10.1

Biological membranes are discussed in Section 13.3.

The term *selectively permeable* or *differentially permeable* is used to describe biological membranes because they restrict passage of particles based both on size and charge. Even small ions, such as H^+, cannot pass freely across a cell membrane.

establish an equilibrium between the solutions on either side of the membrane. Pure solvent is entering the more concentrated solution in an effort to dilute it. If this process is successful, and concentrations on both sides of the membrane become equal, the "driving force," or concentration difference, disappears. A dynamic equilibrium is established, and the osmotic pressure difference between the two sides is equal to zero.

The osmotic pressure, like the pressure exerted by a gas, may be treated quantitatively. Osmotic pressure, symbolized by π, follows the same form as the ideal gas equation:

Ideal Gas	Osmotic Pressure
$PV = nRT$	$\pi V = nRT$
or	or
$P = \dfrac{n}{V}RT$	$\pi = \dfrac{n}{V}RT$
and since	and since
$M = \dfrac{n}{V}$	$M = \dfrac{n}{V}$
then	then
$P = MRT$	$\pi = MRT$

The osmotic pressure can be calculated from the solution concentration at any given temperature. How do we determine "solution concentration"? Recall that osmosis is a colligative property; it is dependent on the concentration of solute particles. Again, it becomes necessary to distinguish between solutions of electrolytes and nonelectrolytes. For example, a $1\,M$ glucose solution consists of one mole of particles per liter; glucose is a nonelectrolyte. A solution of $1\,M$ NaCl produces two moles of particles per liter (one mole of Na^+ and one mole of Cl^-). A $1\,M$ $CaCl_2$ solution is $3\,M$ in particles (one mole of Ca^{2+} and two moles of Cl^- per liter).

By convention the molarity of particles in solution is **osmolarity**, abbreviated **Osm**, for osmotic pressure calculations.

EXAMPLE 6.11

Calculating Osmolarity

Determine the osmolarity of $5.0 \times 10^{-3}\,M$ Na_3PO_4.

Solution

Na_3PO_4 is an ionic compound and produces an electrolytic solution:

$$Na_3PO_4 \xrightarrow{H_2O} 3Na^+ + PO_4{}^{3-}$$

$$5.0 \times 10^{-3}\frac{\text{mol } Na_3PO_4}{\text{liter solution}} \times \frac{4 \text{ mol particles}}{1 \text{ mol } Na_3PO_4} = 2.0 \times 10^{-2}\frac{\text{mol particles}}{\text{liter solution}}$$

and

$$2.0 \times 10^{-2}\frac{\text{mol particles}}{\text{liter solution}} = 2.0 \times 10^{-2} \text{ osm}$$

QUESTION 6.13

Determine the osmolarity of the following solution:

$$5.0 \times 10^{-3}\,M \text{ } NH_4NO_3 \text{ (electrolyte)}$$

QUESTION 6.14

Determine the osmolarity of the following solution:

$$5.0 \times 10^{-3}\,M \text{ } C_6H_{12}O_6 \text{ (nonelectrolyte)}$$

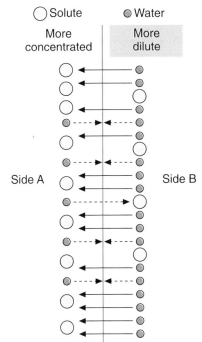

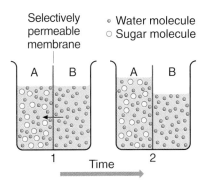

FIGURE 6.3
(a) Attainment of equilibrium by osmosis. Note that the solutions attain equilibrium when sufficient solvent has passed from the more dilute side (Side B) to equalize the concentrations on both sides of the membrane. Side A becomes more dilute, and side B becomes more concentrated. (b) An illustration of osmosis. A semipermeable membrane separates a solution of sugar in water from the pure solvent, water. Over a period of time, water diffuses from B to A in an attempt to equalize the concentration in the two compartments. The water level in side A will rise at the expense of side B because the net flow of water is from B to A.

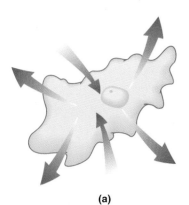

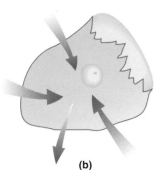

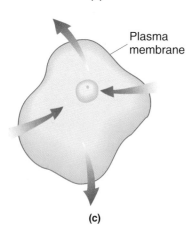

Plasma
membrane

FIGURE 6.4
The effect of hypertonic and
hypotonic solutions on the cell.
(a) Crenation occurs when blood
cells are surrounded by a
hypertonic solution (water
leaving > water entering). (b) Cell
rupture occurs when cells are
surrounded by a hypotonic solution
(water entering > water leaving).
(c) Cell size remains unchanged
when surrounded by an isotonic
solution (water entering = water
leaving).

6.5 WATER AS A SOLVENT

Section 3.4

EXAMPLE 6.12

Calculating Osmotic Pressure

Calculate the osmotic pressure of a $5.0 \times 10^{-2} M$ solution of NaCl at 25°C (298 K).

Solution

$$\pi = MRT$$

M should be represented as osmolarity:

$$M = 5.0 \times 10^{-2} \frac{\text{mol NaCl}}{\text{liter solution}} \times \frac{2 \text{ mol particles}}{1 \text{ mol NaCl}} = 1.0 \times 10^{-1} \frac{\text{mol particles}}{\text{liter solution}}$$

and

$$\pi = 1.0 \times 10^{-1} \frac{\text{mol particles}}{\text{liter solution}} \times 0.0821 \frac{\text{l-atm}}{\text{K-mol}} \times 298 \text{ K}$$

$$\pi = 2.4 \text{ atm}$$

QUESTION 6.15

Calculate the osmotic pressure of the solution described in Question 6.13. (Assume a temperature of 25°C.)

QUESTION 6.16

Calculate the osmotic pressure of the solution described in Question 6.14. (Assume a temperature of 25°C.)

Living cells contain aqueous solution (intracellular fluid) and the cells are surrounded by aqueous solution (intercellular fluid). Cell function (and survival!) depend on maintaining approximately the same osmotic pressure inside and outside the cell. If the solute concentration of the fluid surrounding red blood cells is higher than that inside the cell (a **hypertonic solution**), water flows from the cell, causing it to collapse. This process is **crenation.** On the other hand, if the solute concentration of this fluid is too low relative to the solution within the cell (a **hypotonic solution**), water will flow into the cells, causing cell rupture, **hemolysis.** To prevent either of these effects from taking place when fluids are administered to a patient intravenously, aqueous fluids [0.9% (W/W) NaCl, also referred to as physiological saline, or 5.0% (W/W) glucose] are prepared in such a way as to be **isotonic** with intracellular fluids (see Figure 6.4).

Two solutions are isotonic if they have identical osmotic pressures. In that way the osmotic pressure differential across the cell is zero, and no cell disruption occurs.

Practical examples of osmosis abound.

◆ A sailor, lost at sea in a lifeboat, dies of dehydration while surrounded by water. Seawater, because of its high salt concentration, dehydrates the cells of the body as a result of the large osmotic pressure difference between itself and intracellular fluids.

◆ A cucumber, soaked in brine, shrivels into a pickle. The water in the cucumber is drawn into the brine (salt) solution because of a difference in osmotic pressure (Figure 6.5).

Water is by far the most abundant substance on earth. It is an excellent solvent for most inorganic substances. In fact, it is often referred to as the "universal solvent." Water is the principal biological solvent. Approximately 60% of the adult human body is water. Maintenance of this level is essential for survival. These characteristics are a direct consequence of the molecular structure of water.

As we saw in our previous discussion, water is a bent molecule with a 104.5° bond angle. This angular structure, resulting from the effect of the two lone pairs of electrons around the

(a)   (b)

FIGURE 6.5
A cucumber (a) in an acidic salt
solution undergoes considerable
shrinkage on its way to becoming
a pickle (b) because of osmosis.

oxygen atom, is responsible for the polar nature of water. The polarity, in turn, gives water its unique properties.

Because water molecules are polar, water is an excellent solvent for other polar substances ("like dissolves like"). Since much of the matter on earth is polar, hence at least somewhat water soluble, water has been described as the universal solvent. It is readily accessible and easily purified. It is nontoxic and quite nonreactive. The high boiling point of water, 100°C, compared with molecules of similar size such as N_2 (b.p. = -196°C), is also explained by water's polar character. Strong dipole-dipole interactions between δ^+ hydrogen of one molecule and δ^- oxygen of a second, referred to as **hydrogen bonding,** create an interactive molecular network in the liquid phase (see Figure 5.14a). The strength of these interactions requires more energy (higher temperature) to cause water to boil. The higher than expected boiling point enhances water's value as a solvent; often, reactions are carried out at higher temperatures to increase their rate. Other solvents, with lower boiling points, would simply boil away, and the reaction would stop.

This idea is easily extended to our own chemistry—since 60% of our bodies is water, we should appreciate the polarity of water on a hot day. As a biological solvent in the human body, water is involved in the transport of oxygen, carbon dioxide, nutrients, and waste into and out of cells. Water is also the solvent for biochemical reactions in cells and the digestive tract. Water is a reactant or product in some biochemical processes.

Refer to Sections 3.4 and 3.5 for a more complete description of the bonding, structure, and polarity of water.

Recall the discussion of intermolecular forces in Chapter 5.

6.6 ELECTROLYTES IN BLOOD

The concentration of positive and negative ions in biological fluids is of critical importance. Maintenance of a stable osmotic pressure in biological fluids is essential. The osmotic pressure of fluids is a colligative property; it is dependent on the total ion concentration in solution. Variation in the ionic concentration can destroy the fragile red blood cells as the resulting differential between the inside and outside pressure leads to crenation or hemolysis.

Even ions that do not undergo significant chemical reactions in solution, the sodium ion and the potassium ion, serve a variety of important functions. The potassium ion concentration within the cell is much greater (approximately ten times as great) than the sodium ion concentration. Outside of the cell the situation is reversed, and the sodium ion is the predominant ion. If osmosis were the only transport mechanism, these imbalances would not occur. One positive ion would be just as good as any other. However, the situation is more complex than this. Large protein molecules embedded in cell membranes actively pump sodium ions to the outside of the cell and potassium ions into the cell. This is termed *active transport* because cellular energy must be expended to transport those ions. Proper cell function in the regulation of muscles as well as the nervous system depends on the sodium/potassium ratio inside and outside of the cell.

Blood plays an important role in respiration, as a transporter of oxygen to the cells and waste carbon dioxide back to the lungs. Additionally, it is the medium for the exchange of nutrients and waste with tissues and cells. Nitrogen-containing waste products are continuously and efficiently removed from the blood by the kidneys.

A HUMAN PERSPECTIVE

An Extraordinary Molecule

Think for a moment. What is the only common molecule that exists in all three physical states of matter (solid, liquid, and gas) under natural conditions on earth? This molecule is absolutely essential for life; in fact, life probably arose in this substance. It is the most abundant molecule in the cells of living organisms (70–95%) and covers 75% of the earth's surface. Without it, cells quickly die, and without it the earth would not be a fit environment in which to live. By now you have guessed that we are talking about the water molecule. It is so abundant on earth that we take this deceptively simple molecule for granted.

What are some of the properties of water that cause it to be essential to life as we know it? Water has the ability to stabilize temperatures on the earth and in the body. This ability is due in part to the energy changes that occur when water changes physical state; but ultimately, this ability is due to the polar nature of the water molecule.

Life can exist only within a fairly narrow range of temperatures. Above or below that range, the chemical reactions necessary for life, and thus life itself, will cease. Water can moderate temperature fluctuation and maintain the range necessary for life, and one property that allows it to do so is its unusually high specific heat, 1 calorie/gram °C. This means that water can absorb or lose more heat energy than many other substances without a significant temperature change. This is because in the liquid state, every water molecule is hydrogen bonded to other water molecules. Since a temperature increase is really just a measure of increased (more rapid) molecular movement, we must get the water molecules moving more rapidly, independent of one another, to register a temperature increase. Before we can achieve this independent, increased activity, the hydrogen bonds between molecules must be broken. Much of the heat energy that water absorbs is involved in breaking hydrogen bonds and is *not* used to increase molecular movement. Thus a great deal of heat is needed to raise the temperature of water even a little bit.

Water also has a very high heat of vaporization. It takes 540 calories to change one gram of liquid water at 100°C to a gas and even more, 603 cal/g, when the water is at 37°C, human body temperature. That is about twice the heat of vaporization of alcohol. As water molecules evaporate, the surface of the liquid cools because only the highest-energy (or "hottest") molecules leave as a gas. Only the "hottest" molecules have enough energy to break the hydrogen bonds that bind them to other water molecules. Indeed, evaporation

of water molecules from the surfaces of lakes and oceans helps to maintain stable temperatures in those bodies of water. Similarly, evaporation of perspiration from body surfaces helps to prevent overheating on a hot day or during strenuous exercise.

Even the process of freezing helps stabilize and moderate temperatures; this is especially true in the fall. Water releases heat when hydrogen bonds are formed. This is an example of an exothermic process; thus when water freezes, solidifying into ice, additional hydrogen bonds are formed, and heat is released into the environment. As a result, the temperature change between summer and winter is more gradual, allowing organisms to adjust gradually to the change.

One last feature that we take for granted is the fact that when we put ice in our iced tea on a hot summer day, the ice will float. This means that the solid state of water is actually *less* dense than the liquid state! In fact, it is about 10% less dense, having an open lattice structure with each molecule hydrogen bonded to the maximum of four other water molecules. What would happen if ice did sink? All bodies of water, including the mighty oceans would eventually freeze solid, killing all aquatic and marine plant and animal life. Even in the heat of summer, only a few inches of ice at the surface would thaw. Instead, the ice forms at the surface and provides a layer of insulation that prevents the water below from freezing.

As we continue our study of chemistry, we will refer again and again to this amazing molecule. In other Human Perspective features we will examine other properties of water that make it essential to life.

In cases of loss of kidney function, mechanical devices—dialysis machines—mimic the action of the kidney. The blood is pumped through a long semipermeable membrane, the dialysis membrane. The dialysis process is similar to osmosis. However, in addition to water molecules, larger molecules (including the waste products in the blood) and ions can pass across the membrane from the blood into a dialyzing fluid. The dialyzing fluid is isotonic with normal blood; it also is similar in its concentration of all other essential blood components. The waste materials move across the dialysis membrane (from a higher to a lower concentration, as in osmosis). A successful dialysis procedure selectively removes the waste from the body without upsetting the critical electrolyte balance in the blood.

SUMMARY

A majority of chemical reactions, and virtually all important organic and biochemical reactions, take place not as a combination of two or more pure substances, but rather as reactants dissolved in solution, *solution reactions.*

6.1 Properties of Solutions

A *solution* is a homogeneous (or uniform) mixture of two or more substances. A solution is composed of one or more *solutes,* dissolved in a *solvent.* When the solvent is water, the solution is called an *aqueous solution.*

Liquid solutions are clear and transparent with no visible particles of solute. They may be colored or colorless, depending on the properties of the solute and solvent.

In *solutions of electrolytes* the solutes are ionic compounds that dissociate in solution to produce ions. They are good conductors of electricity. *Solutions of nonelectrolytes* are formed from nondissociating molecular solutes (nonelectrolytes), and their solutions are nonconducting.

The rule "like dissolves like" is the fundamental condition for solubility. Polar solutes are soluble in polar solvents, and nonpolar solutes are soluble in nonpolar solvents.

The degree of solubility depends on the difference between the polarity of solute and solvent, the temperature, and the pressure. Pressure considerations are significant only for solutions of gases.

When a solution contains all the solute that can be dissolved at a particular temperature, it is *saturated.* Excess solute falls to the bottom of the container as a *precipitate.* Occasionally, on cooling, the excess solute may remain in solution for a period of time before precipitation. Such a solution is a *supersaturated solution.* When excess solute, the precipitate, contacts solvent, the dissolution process reaches a state of dynamic equilibrium. *Colloidal suspensions* have particle sizes between those of true solutions and precipitates.

Henry's Law describes the solubility of gases in liquids. At a given temperature the solubility of a gas is proportional to the partial pressure of the gas.

6.2 Concentration of Solutions: Percentage

The amount of solute dissolved in a given amount of solution is the solution *concentration.* The more widely used percentage-based concentration units are *weight/volume percent, volume/ volume percent,* and *weight/weight percent.*

6.3 Concentration of Solutions: Moles and Equivalents

Molarity, symbolized M, is defined as the number of moles of solute per liter of solution.

Dilution is often used to prepare less concentrated solutions. The expression for this calculation is $(M_1)(V_1) = (M_2)(V_2)$. Knowing any three of these terms enables one to calculate the fourth. The concentration of ions in solution may be represented as moles per liter (molarity) or any other suitable concentration units. However, both concentrations must be in the same units.

Molarity emphasizes the number of individual ions. A 1 M solution of Na^+ contains Avogadro's number, 6.02×10^{23}, of sodium ions. In contrast, equivalents per liter emphasizes charge; a solution containing one equivalent of Na^+ per liter contains Avogadro's number of positive charge.

A mole is the number of grams of an atom, molecule, or ion corresponding to Avogadro's number of particles. One *equivalent* of an ion is the number of grams of the ion corresponding to Avogadro's number of electrical charges. Changing from moles per liter to equivalents per liter (or the reverse) is done using conversion factors.

6.4 Concentration-Dependent Solution Properties

Solution properties that depend on the concentration of solute particles, rather than the identity of the solute, are *colligative properties.*

There are three colligative properties of solutions, all of which depend on the concentration of *particles* in solution.

1. *Vapor pressure lowering. Raoult's Law* states that when a solute is added to a solvent, the vapor pressure of the solvent decreases in proportion to the concentration of the solute.

2. *Freezing point depression and boiling point elevation.* When a nonvolatile solid is added to a solvent, the freezing point of the resulting solution decreases, and the boiling point increases. The magnitudes of both the freezing point depression (ΔT_f) and the boiling point elevation (ΔT_b) are proportional to the solute concentration over a limited range of concentrations. The mole-based concentration unit, molality, is more commonly used in calculations involving colligative properties. This is due to the fact that molality is temperature independent. *Molality* (symbolized m) is defined as the number of moles of solute per kilogram of solvent in a solution.

3. *Osmosis and osmotic pressure. Osmosis* is the movement of solvent from a dilute solution to a more concentrated solution through a *semipermeable membrane.* The pressure that must be applied to the more concentrated solution to stop this flow is the *osmotic pressure.* The osmotic pressure, like the pressure exerted by a gas, may be treated quantitatively by using an equation similar in form to the ideal gas equation: $\pi = MRT$. By convention the molarity of particles in solution is termed *osmolarity (Osm)* for osmotic pressure calculations.

In biological systems, if the concentration of the fluid surrounding red blood cells is higher than that inside the cell (*a hypertonic* solution), water flows from the cell, causing it to collapse *(crenation).* Too low a concentration of this fluid relative to the solution within the cell (*a hypotonic* solution) will cause cell rupture *(hemolysis).*

Two solutions are *isotonic* if they have identical osmotic pressures. In that way the osmotic pressure differential across the cell is zero, and no cell disruption occurs.

6.5 Water as a Solvent

The role of water in the solution process deserves special attention; it is often referred to as the "universal solvent," and it is the principal biological solvent. These characteristics are a direct consequence of the molecular geometry and structure of water and its ability to undergo *hydrogen bonding.*

6.6 Electrolytes in Blood

The concentration of ions in biological fluids is important; proper cell behavior in the regulation of muscle function and the nervous system depends on the sodium/potassium ratio inside and outside of the cell.

KEY TERMS

aqueous solution (6.1)	osmotic pressure (6.4)
colligative properties (6.4)	precipitate (6.1)
colloidal suspension (6.1)	Raoult's Law (6.4)
concentration (6.2)	saturated solution (6.1)
crenation (6.4)	semipermeable membrane
electrolyte (6.1)	(6.4)
equivalent (6.3)	solubility (6.1)
hemolysis (6.4)	solute (6.1)
Henry's Law (6.1)	solution (6.1)
hydrogen bonding (6.5)	solvent (6.1)
hypertonic solution (6.4)	supersaturated solution (6.1)
hypotonic solution (6.4)	volume/volume percent
isotonic solution (6.4)	(% (V/V)) (6.2)
molality (6.4)	weight/volume percent
molarity (6.3)	(% (W/V)) (6.2)
nonelectrolyte (6.1)	weight/weight percent
osmolarity (6.4)	(% (W/W)) (6.2)
osmosis (6.4)	

QUESTIONS AND PROBLEMS

Concentration of Solutions: Percentage

6.17 Calculate the composition of each of the following solutions in weight/volume %:
  a. 20.0 g NaCl in 1.00 L solution
  b. 33.0 g sugar, $C_6H_{12}O_6$, in 5.00×10^2 mL solution

6.18 Calculate the composition of each of the following solutions in weight/volume %:
  a. 0.700 g KCl per 1.00 mL
  b. 1.00 moles $MgCl_2$ in 2.50×10^2 mL solution

6.19 Calculate the composition of each of the following solutions in volume/volume %:
  a. 50.0 mL ethyl alcohol dissolved in 1.00 L solution
  b. 50.0 mL ethyl alcohol dissolved in 5.00×10^2 mL solution

6.20 Calculate the composition of each of the following solutions in volume/volume %:
  a. 20.0 mL acetic acid dissolved in 2.50 L solution
  b. 20.0 g benzene ($d = 0.879$ g/mL) dissolved in 1.00×10^2 mL solution

6.21 Calculate the composition of each of the following solutions in weight/weight %:
  a. 21.0 g NaCl in 1.00×10^2 g solution
  b. 21.0 g NaCl in 5.00×10^2 mL solution ($d = 1.12$ g/mL)

6.22 Calculate the composition of each of the following solutions in weight/weight %:
  a. 1.00 g KCl in 1.00×10^2 g solution
  b. 50.0 g KCl in 5.00×10^2 g solution ($d = 1.14$ g/mL)

6.23 How many grams of solute are needed to prepare each of the following solutions?
  a. 2.50×10^2 g of 0.900% (W/W) NaCl
  b. 2.50×10^2 g of 1.25% (W/V) $NaC_2H_3O_2$ (sodium acetate)

6.24 How many grams of solute are needed to prepare each of the following solutions?
  a. 2.50×10^2 g of 5.00% (W/W) NH_4Cl (ammonium chloride)
  b. 2.50×10^2 g of 3.50% (W/V) Na_2CO_3

Concentration of Solutions: Moles and Equivalents

6.25 Calculate the molarity of each solution in Question 6.17.

6.26 Calculate the molarity of each solution in Question 6.18.

6.27 Calculate the number of grams of solute that would be needed to make each of the following solutions:
  a. 2.50×10^2 mL of 0.100 M NaCl
  b. 2.50×10^2 mL of 0.200 M $C_6H_{12}O_6$ (glucose)

6.28 Calculate the number of grams of solute that would be needed to make each of the following solutions:
  a. 2.50×10^2 mL of 0.100 M NaBr
  b. 2.50×10^2 mL of 0.200 M KOH

6.29 Calculate the molarity of a sucrose (table sugar, $C_{12}H_{22}O_{11}$) solution that contains 50.0 grams of sucrose per liter.

6.30 A saturated silver chloride solution is 1.58×10^{-4} g of silver chloride per 1.00×10^2 mL of solution. What is the molarity of this solution?

6.31 It is desired to prepare 0.500 L of a 0.100 M solution of NaCl from a 1.00 M stock solution. How many milliliters of the stock solution must be taken for the dilution?

6.32 50.0 mL of a 0.250 *M* sucrose solution was diluted to 5.00×10^2 mL. What is the molar concentration of the resulting solution?

6.33 A 50.0-mL portion of a stock solution was diluted to 500.0 mL. If the resulting solution was 2.00 *M*, what was the molarity of the original stock solution?

6.34 A 6.00-mL portion of an 8.00 *M* stock solution is to be diluted to 0.400 *M*. What will be the final volume after dilution?

Concentration-Dependent Solution Properties

6.35 What is meant by the term *colligative property?*

6.36 Name and describe four colligative solution properties.

6.37 Explain, in terms of solution properties, why salt is used to melt ice in the winter.

6.38 Explain, in terms of solution properties, why a wilted plant regains its ''health'' when watered.

Further Problems

6.39 If 40.0 g of NaOH are dissolved in 60.0 g of water, determine:
 a. Which is the solute and which is the solvent
 b. W/W%

6.40 If 40.0 g of ethanol are dissolved in 60.0 mL of water and the resulting solution has a volume of 1.10×10^2 mL, determine:
 a. W/V%
 b. molarity of the solute

6.41 Which of the following compounds would cause the greater freezing point depression, per mole, in H_2O: $C_6H_{12}O_6$ (glucose) or NaCl?

6.42 Which of the following compounds would cause the greater boiling point elevation, per mole, in H_2O: $MgCl_2$ or $HOCH_2CH_2OH$ (ethylene glycol, antifreeze)? (Hint: $MgCl_2$ is ionic; $HOCH_2CH_2OH$ is covalent.)

6.43 When roads are slippery because of snow or ice, the salt often used by road crews is $MgCl_2$ or $CaCl_2$. What advantage, if any, would the use of these salts have over the use of NaCl?

6.44 Overdevelopment of certain coastal areas in the United States has resulted in a lowering of the underground water table, which provides water for drinking and irrigation. As a result, ocean water is diffusing into the underground water supply to take the place of the water being consumed. Why is this a potential problem?

VOCABULARY QUIZ

6.1 _____ is the shrinkage of red blood cells due to water loss to the surrounding medium.

6.2 A(n) _____ is a substance that ionizes in water.

6.3 A(n) __solvent__ is the more concentrated solution of two separated by a semipermeable membrane.

6.4 A(n) __solute__ is the more dilute solution of two separated by a semipermeable membrane.

6.5 _____ is the number of moles of solute per liter of solution.

6.6 __Osmosis__ is the net flow of solvent through a semipermeable membrane.

6.7 __Osmotic pressure__ is the pressure required to stop net transfer of solvent across a semipermeable membrane.

6.8 A(n) _____ is a solution in which undissolved solute is in equilibrium with the solution.

6.9 The _____ is a component of a solution that is present in lesser quantity than the solvent.

6.10 A(n) _____ is a solution that is more concentrated than a saturated solution.

7

Chemical Reactions

LEARNING GOALS

◆ Be able to classify chemical reactions by type: combination, decomposition, or replacement.

◆ Be capable of recognizing acids and bases.

◆ Describe the role of the solvent in acid-base reactions, and explain the meaning of the term *pH*.

◆ Recognize the importance of pH in chemical and biochemical systems.

◆ Discuss the meaning and utility of neutralization reactions.

◆ State the meaning of the term *buffer* and describe the application of buffers to chemical and biochemical systems, particularly blood chemistry.

◆ Define *oxidation* and *reduction*, and describe some practical examples of redox processes.

◆ Calculate pH from concentration data.

◆ Calculate hydronium and/or hydroxide ion concentration from pH data.

Seeing a Thought

At one time, not very long ago, mental illness was believed to be caused by some failing of the human spirit. Thoughts are nonmaterial (you can't hold a thought in your hand), and the body is quite material. No clear relationship, other than the fact that thoughts somehow come from the brain, could be shown to link the body and the spirit.

A major revolution in the diagnosis and treatment of mental illness has taken place in the last two decades. Several forms of depression, paranoia, and schizophrenia have been shown to have chemical and genetic bases. Remarkable improvement in behavior often results from altering the chemistry of the brain by using chemical therapy. Similar progress may result from the use of gene therapy (discussed in Chapter 19).

Although a treatment of mental illness, as well as of memory and logic failures, may occasionally arise by chance, a cause-and-effect relationship, based on the use of scientific methodology, certainly increases the chances of developing successful treatment. If we understand the chemical reactions involved in the thought process, we can perhaps learn to "repair" them when, for whatever reason, they go astray.

Recently, scientists at Massachusetts General Hospital in Boston have developed sophisticated versions of magnetic resonance imaging devices (MRI, discussed in a "Clinical Perspective" in Chapter 4). MRI is normally used to locate brain tumors and cerebral damage in patients. The new generation of instruments is so sensitive that it is able to detect chemical change in the brain resulting from an external stimulus. A response to a question or the observation of a flash of light produces a measurable signal. This signal is enhanced with the aid of a powerful computer that enables the location of the signal to be determined with pinpoint accuracy. So there is evidence not only for the chemical basis of thought, but for its location in the brain as well.

In this chapter and throughout your study of chemistry you will be introduced to a wide variety of chemical reactions, some mundane, some quite interesting; all are founded on the same principles that power the thoughts and actions of all of us.

INTRODUCTION

A tremendous variety of chemical reactions occur in biological systems, in industry, and in the environment. Because of this it is useful to classify chemical reactions into a few general types, emphasizing similarities rather than differences. We classify reactions as involving either *combination* of reactants to produce product, *decomposition* of reactant into products, or *replacement* of one or more elements in a compound to yield a new product.

Reactions may also share similar characteristics because they involve the same process, such as combustion (burning), formation of a solid (precipitate) from a solution, or the transfer of a proton (H^+) or an electron.

Proton transfer reactions, known as *acid-base reactions,* and *electron transfer reactions,* also known as *oxidation-reduction reactions,* will be discussed in detail after we develop an understanding of the substances themselves (acids, bases, oxidizing and reducing agents) that undergo these reactions.

7.1 CLASSIFICATION OF CHEMICAL REACTIONS

Solutions of electrolytes are discussed in Section 6.1.

Spontaneous chemical reactions occur for a variety of reasons, all tending to achieve the lowest (most stable) electronic energy state. Strong electrolytes will react to form *weak* (less dissociated) *electrolytes,* if possible:

$$HCl(aq) + NaOH(aq) \longrightarrow NaCl(aq) + H_2O$$

The strong electrolytes HCl and NaOH react completely to produce H_2O, a weak electrolyte. In contrast, the reaction

$$NaCl(aq) + KNO_3(aq) \longrightarrow NaNO_3(aq) + KCl(aq)$$

does not occur; both reactants and products are soluble strong electrolytes. Such a mixture would produce an aqueous solution containing Na^+, K^+, Cl^-, and NO_3^- ions.

Reactions forming *gaseous products* occur; for example,

$$2HCl(aq) + Na_2S(aq) \longrightarrow H_2S(g) + 2NaCl(aq)$$

Reactions forming an *insoluble solid product* often take place:

$$AgNO_3(aq) + NaCl(aq) \longrightarrow AgCl(s) + NaNO_3(aq)$$

Solubility is discussed in Section 7.2.

There are thousands of different chemical reactions, and it is necessary and convenient to categorize these reactions into reaction types. One approach involves describing chemical reactions in terms of the reactants and the changes that the reactants undergo. Chemical reactions involve the *combination* of reactants to produce products, the *decomposition* of reactant(s) into products, or the *replacement* of one or more elements in a compound to yield products.

Combination reactions

Combination reactions involve the joining of two or more atoms or compounds, producing a product of different composition. The general form of a combination reaction is

$$A + B \longrightarrow AB$$

where A and B represent reactant elements or compounds and AB is the product.

Examples include:

1. the combination of a metal and a nonmetal to form a salt,

$$Ca(s) + Cl_2(g) \longrightarrow CaCl_2(s)$$

2. the combination of hydrogen and chlorine molecules to produce hydrogen chloride,

$$H_2(g) + Cl_2(g) \longrightarrow 2HCl(g)$$

3. formation of water from hydrogen and oxygen molecules,

$$2H_2(g) + O_2(g) \longrightarrow 2H_2O(g)$$

4. the reaction of magnesium oxide and carbon dioxide to produce magnesium carbonate,

$$MgO(s) + CO_2(g) \longrightarrow MgCO_3(s)$$

Decomposition reactions

Decomposition reactions produce two or more products from a single reactant. The general form of these reactions is the reverse of a combination reaction:

$$AB \longrightarrow A + B$$

Some examples are:

1. the heating of calcium carbonate to produce calcium oxide and carbon dioxide,

$$CaCO_3(s) \longrightarrow CaO(s) + CO_2(g)$$

2. the removal of water from a hydrated material (a **hydrate** is a substance that has water molecules incorporated in its structure),

$$CuSO_4 \cdot 5H_2O(s) \longrightarrow CuSO_4(s) + 5H_2O(g)$$

Replacement reactions

Replacement reactions include both *single-replacement* and *double-replacement*. In a **single-replacement reaction,** one atom replaces another in the compound, producing a new compound and the replaced atom:

$$A + BC \longrightarrow AC + B$$

Examples include:

1. the replacement of copper by zinc in copper sulfate,

$$Zn(s) + CuSO_4(aq) \longrightarrow ZnSO_4(aq) + Cu(s)$$

2. the replacement of aluminum by sodium in aluminum nitrate,

$$3Na(s) + Al(NO_3)_3(aq) \longrightarrow 3NaNO_3(aq) + Al(s)$$

Double-replacement reactions, on the other hand, involve *two compounds* undergoing a ''change of partners.'' Two compounds react by exchanging atoms to produce two new compounds:

$$AB + CD \longrightarrow AD + CB$$

For example,

1. the reaction of an acid (hydrochloric acid) and a base (sodium hydroxide) to produce water and salt, sodium chloride,

$$HCl(aq) + NaOH(aq) \longrightarrow H_2O(l) + NaCl(aq)$$

2. the formation of solid barium sulfate from barium chloride and potassium sulfate,

$$BaCl_2(aq) + K_2SO_4(aq) \longrightarrow BaSO_4(s) + 2KCl(aq)$$

QUESTION 7.1

Classify each of the following reactions as decomposition (D), combination (C), single-replacement (SR), or double-replacement (DR):

a. $HNO_3(aq) + KOH(aq) \longrightarrow KNO_3(aq) + H_2O(aq)$
b. $Al(s) + 3NiNO_3(aq) \longrightarrow Al(NO_3)_3(aq) + 3Ni(s)$
c. $KCN(aq) + HCl(aq) \longrightarrow HCN(aq) + KCl(aq)$
d. $MgCO_3(s) \longrightarrow MgO(s) + CO_2(g)$

QUESTION 7.2

Classify each of the following reactions as decomposition (D), combination (C), single-replacement (SR), or double-replacement (DR):

a. $2Al(OH)_3(s) \xrightarrow{\Delta} Al_2O_3(s) + 3H_2O(g)$

b. $Fe_2S_3(s) \xrightarrow{\Delta} 2Fe(s) + 3S(s)$

c. $Na_2CO_3(aq) + BaCl_2(aq) \longrightarrow BaCO_3(s) + 2NaCl(aq)$

d. $C(s) + O_2(g) \xrightarrow{\Delta} CO_2(g)$

7.2 TYPES OF CHEMICAL REACTIONS

Precipitation reactions

Precipitation reactions include any chemical change that results in one or more insoluble product(s) in solution. For aqueous solution reactions the product is insoluble in water.

An understanding of precipitation reactions is useful in many ways. They may explain natural phenomena, such as the formation of stalagmites and stalactites in caves; they are simply a precipitate in rocklike form. Kidney stones may result from the precipitation of calcium oxalate (CaC_2O_4). The routine act of preparing a solution requires that none of the solutes will react to form a precipitate.

How do you know whether a precipitate will form? Readily available solubility tables, such as Table 7.1, make prediction rather easy.

TABLE 7.1   Solubilities of Some Common Ionic Compounds

Sodium, potassium and ammonium compounds are generally *soluble*.

Nitrates and acetates are generally *soluble*.

Chlorides, bromides, and iodides (halides) are generally *soluble*. However, halide compounds containing lead(II), silver(I), and mercury(I) are *insoluble*.

Carbonates and phosphates are generally *insoluble*. Sodium, potassium, and ammonium carbonates and phosphates are, however, *soluble*.

Hydroxides and sulfides are generally *insoluble*. Sodium, potassium, calcium, and ammonium compounds are, however, *soluble*.

The following example illustrates the process.

EXAMPLE 7.1

Predicting Whether a Precipitation Will Occur

Will a precipitate form if two solutions of the soluble salts NaCl and $AgNO_3$ are mixed?

Solution

First, decide the probable reaction class. Two salts, if they react, will probably "exchange partners":

$$NaCl(aq) + AgNO_3(aq) \longrightarrow AgCl(?) + NaNO_3(?)$$

Next, refer to Table 7.1 to determine the solubility of AgCl and $NaNO_3$. From the table we predict that $NaNO_3$ is soluble and AgCl is not:

$$NaCl(aq) + AgNO_3(aq) \longrightarrow AgCl(s) + NaNO_3(aq)$$

The fact that the solid AgCl is predicted to form classifies this reaction as a precipitation reaction.

QUESTION 7.3

Predict whether the following reactants, when mixed in aqueous solution, undergo a precipitation reaction. Write a balanced equation for each precipitation reaction.

a.   potassium chloride and silver nitrate
b.   potassium acetate and silver nitrate

QUESTION 7.4

Predict whether the following reactants, when mixed in aqueous solution, undergo a precipitation reaction. Write a balanced equation for each precipitation reaction.

a.   sodium hydroxide and ammonium chloride
b.   sodium hydroxide and iron(II) chloride

Reactions with oxygen

Chapter 17

Many substances react with oxygen. These reactions are generally exothermic, releasing energy. The combustion of gasoline is used for transportation. Fossil fuel combustion is used to heat homes and provide energy for industry. Reactions involving oxygen provide energy for all sorts of biochemical processes.

When organic (carbon-containing) compounds react with the oxygen in air (burning), carbon dioxide is usually produced. If the compound contains hydrogen, water is the other product.

The reaction between oxygen and methane, CH_4, the major component of natural gas, is

$$CH_4(g) + 2O_2(g) \longrightarrow CO_2(g) + 2H_2O(g)$$

CO_2 and H_2O are waste products, and CO_2 may contribute to the greenhouse effect and global warming. The really important, unseen product is heat energy. That is why the reaction occurs in our furnace!

See An Environmental Perspective: The Greenhouse Effect and Global Warming.

Inorganic substances also react with oxygen and produce heat, but these reactions proceed more slowly. *Corrosion* (rusting iron) is a familiar example:

$$4Fe(s) + 3O_2(g) \longrightarrow 2Fe_2O_3(s)$$

(Rust)

Some reactions of metals with oxygen are very rapid. A dramatic example is the reaction of magnesium with oxygen, shown in Figure 7.1.

Another approach to the classification of chemical reactions is based on a consideration of charge transfer. **Acid-base reactions** involve the transfer of a *hydrogen ion,* H^+, from one reactant to another. Another important reaction type, **oxidation-reduction,** takes place because of the transfer of negative charge (one or more *electrons*) from one reactant to another.

Acid-base and oxidation-reduction reactions

The principles and applications of acid-base reactions will be discussed in Sections 7.3 through 7.5, and oxidation-reduction processes will be discussed in Section 7.6.

Acids and bases include some of the most important compounds in nature. Historically, it was recognized that certain compounds, acids, had a sour taste, were able to dissolve some metals, and caused vegetable dyes to change color. We now recognize that digestion of proteins is aided by stomach acid (hydrochloric acid) and that many biochemical processes such as enzyme catalysis are dependent on the proper level of acidity. Indeed, a wide variety of chemical reactions critically depend on the acid-base composition of the solution (see Figure 7.2). This is especially true of the biochemical reactions occurring in the cells of our bodies. For this reason the level of acidity must be very carefully regulated. This is done with substances called *buffers*.

7.3 ACIDS AND BASES

Section 15.9

Buffers are discussed in Section 7.5.

Bases have long been recognized by their bitter taste, slippery feel, and corrosive nature. Bases react strongly with acids and cause many metal ions in solution to form a solid precipitate.

FIGURE 7.1
The rapid oxidation-reduction reaction of magnesium metal and oxygen (in air) is a graphic example of a highly exothermic reaction.

FIGURE 7.2
The dependence of chemical species on the acidity of the solvent. Both aqueous solutions initially contained Na_2CrO_4 (sodium chromate). The solution on the left was made basic, and the yellow color of CrO_4^{2-} (chromate ion) is apparent. The solution on the right was made acidic, and the yellow CrO_4^{2-} (chromate ion) was converted to the reddish-brown $Cr_2O_7^{2-}$ (dichromate ion).

AN ENVIRONMENTAL PERSPECTIVE

The Greenhouse Effect and Global Warming

A greenhouse is a bright, warm, and humid environment for growing plants, vegetables, and flowers even during the cold winter months. It functions as a closed system where the concentration of water vapor is elevated and visible light streams through the windows; this creates an ideal climate for plant growth.

Some of the visible light is absorbed by plants and soil in the greenhouse and radiated as infrared radiation. This radiated energy is blocked by the glass or absorbed by water vapor and carbon dioxide (CO_2). This trapped energy warms the greenhouse and is a form of solar heating: light energy is converted to heat energy.

On a global scale, the same process takes place. Although more than half of the sunlight that strikes the earth's surface is reflected back into space, the fraction of light that is absorbed produces sufficient heat to sustain life. How does this happen? Greenhouse gases, such as CO_2 trap energy radiated from the earth's surface and store it in the atmosphere. This moderates our climate. The earth's surface would be much colder and more inhospitable if we were not

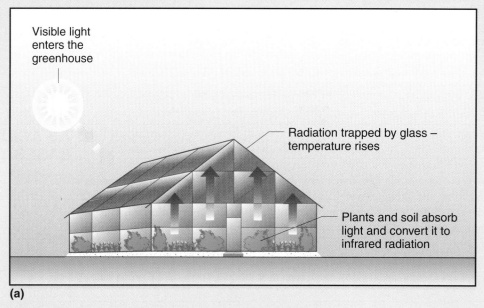

Visible light enters the greenhouse

Radiation trapped by glass – temperature rises

Plants and soil absorb light and convert it to infrared radiation

(a)

(a) A greenhouse traps solar radiation as heat. (b) Our atmosphere also acts as a solar collector. Carbon dioxide, like the windows of a greenhouse, allows the visible light to enter but traps the heat.

Learning the terminology

The properties of acids and bases are related to their chemical structure. All acids have certain common characteristics that enable them to increase the hydrogen ion concentration in water. All bases lower the hydrogen ion concentration in water.

Two theories, one following from the other, help us to understand the unique chemistry of acids and bases.

Arrhenius theory of acids and bases

The earliest definition of acids and bases is the **Arrhenius theory.** According to this theory an acid dissociates to form *hydrogen ions or protons* (H^+), and a base dissociates to form *hydroxide ions* (OH^-). For example, hydrochloric acid dissociates in solution according to the reaction

$$HCl \xrightarrow{H_2O} H^+ + Cl^-$$

Sodium hydroxide, a base, produces hydroxide ions in solution:

$$NaOH \xrightarrow{H_2O} Na^+ + OH^-$$

able to capture some reasonable amount of solar energy.

Can we have too much of a good thing? It appears so. Since 1900 the atmospheric concentration of CO_2 has increased from 296 parts per million (ppm) to over 350 ppm (approximately 17% increase). The energy demands of technological and population growth have caused massive increases in the combustion of organic matter and carbon-based fuels (coal, oil, and natural gas), adding over 50 billion tons of CO_2 to that already present in the atmosphere. Photosynthesis naturally removes CO_2 from the atmosphere.

However, the removal of forestland to create living space and cropland decreases the amount of vegetation available to consume atmospheric CO_2 through photosynthesis. The rapid destruction of the Amazon rainforest is just the latest of many examples.

If our greenhouse model is correct, an increase in CO_2 levels should produce global warming, perhaps changing our climate in unforseen and undesirable ways.

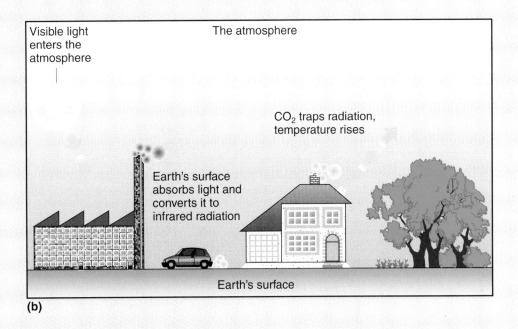

(b)

The Arrhenius theory satisfactorily explains the behavior of many acids and bases. However, a substance such as ammonia, NH_3, has basic properties but cannot be an Arrhenius base, since it contains no OH^-. The **Brönsted-Lowry theory** explains this mystery and gives us a broader view of acid-base theory by considering the role of the solvent in the dissociation process.

The Brönsted-Lowry theory defines an acid as a proton (H^+) donor and a base as a proton acceptor.

Brönsted-Lowry theory of acids and bases

Hydrochloric acid in solution *donates* a proton to the solvent water and behaves as a Brönsted-Lowry acid:

$$HCl + H_2O \longrightarrow H_3O^+ + Cl^-$$

H_3O^+ is referred to as the hydrated proton or **hydronium ion.**

The basic properties of ammonia are clearly accounted for by the Brönsted-Lowry theory. Ammonia *accepts* a proton from the solvent water, producing OH^-:

$$H-OH + NH_3 \longrightarrow NH_4^+ + OH^-$$

7.4 SOLUTIONS OF ACIDS AND BASES

When we use acids and bases in the laboratory, they are generally present as solutions of some specified concentration, not as pure substances. Acids and bases in foods, biological fluids, and industrial products are generally in solution as well. For this reason we will consider the properties and reactions of solutions of acids and bases in some detail.

In this section we develop an understanding of the *properties* of acids and bases as well as the ability to calculate the acid or base level of a solution, represented in terms of *pH*. We consider the reactions of acids with bases, *neutralization,* to produce a salt and water.

Strength of acids and bases

Sections 6.2 and 6.3

The concentration of an acid or base does affect the degree of dissociation. However, the major factor in determining the degree of dissociation is the strength of the acid or base.

The terms *acid or base strength* and *acid or base concentration* are easily confused. *Strength* is a measure of the *degree of dissociation* of an acid or base in solution, independent of its concentration. Concentration, as we have learned, refers to the amount of solute (in this case, the amount of acid or base) per quantity of solution.

The strength of acids and bases in water is dependent on the extent to which they react with the solvent, water. Acids and bases are classified as *strong* when the reaction with water is virtually 100% complete and as *weak* when the reaction with water is much less than 100% complete (perhaps as little as 2–3%).

Important strong acids include:

$$\text{Hydrochloric acid:} \qquad HCl + H_2O \longrightarrow H_3O^+ + Cl^-$$

$$\text{Nitric acid:} \qquad HNO_3 + H_2O \longrightarrow H_3O^+ + NO_3^-$$

$$\text{Sulfuric acid:} \qquad H_2SO_4 + H_2O \longrightarrow H_3O^+ + HSO_4^-$$

Section 5.4

Note that the equation for the dissociation of each of the above acids is written with a single arrow. This indicates that the reaction has little or no tendency to proceed in the reverse direction to establish equilibrium. All of the molecules of acid are converted to ions.

All strong bases are *metal hydroxides.* Strong bases completely dissociate, or ionize, in aqueous solution to produce hydroxide ions and metal cations. Of the common metal hydroxides, only NaOH and KOH are soluble in water and are the only readily usable strong bases:

$$\text{Sodium hydroxide:} \qquad NaOH \xrightarrow{H_2O} Na^+ + OH^-$$

$$\text{Potassium hydroxide:} \qquad KOH \xrightarrow{H_2O} K^+ + OH^-$$

The double arrow implies an equilibrium between dissociated and undissociated species.

Weak acids and weak bases dissolve in water principally in the molecular form. Only a small percent of the molecules dissociate to form the hydronium or hydroxide ion.

The most important weak acids are:

$$\text{Acetic acid:} \qquad CH_3COOH + H_2O \rightleftharpoons H_3O^+ + CH_3COO^-$$

$$\text{Carbonic acid:} \qquad H_2CO_3 + H_2O \rightleftharpoons H_3O^+ + HCO_3^-$$

We have already mentioned the most common weak base, ammonia. Many organic compounds function as weak bases. Several examples of weak bases follow:

$$\text{Pyridine:} \qquad C_5H_5N + H_2O \rightleftharpoons C_5H_5NH^+ + OH^-$$

$$\text{Aniline:} \qquad C_6H_5NH_2 + H_2O \rightleftharpoons C_6H_5NH_3^+ + OH^-$$

$$\text{Methylamine:} \qquad CH_3NH_2 + H_2O \rightleftharpoons CH_3NH_3^+ + OH^-$$

Many organic compounds have acid or base properties. The chemistry of organic acids and bases will be discussed in Chapters 12 (Carboxylic Acids and Carboxylic Acid Derivatives) and 14 (Amines and Amides).

The most fundamental chemical difference between strong and weak acids and bases is their equilibrium situation. A strong acid, such as HCl, does not, in aqueous solution, exist to any measurable degree in equilibrium with its ions, H_3O^+ and Cl^-. On the other hand, a weak acid, such as acetic acid, establishes a dynamic equilibrium with its ions, H_3O^+ and CH_3COO^-.

Energy-releasing reactions are discussed in Section 5.1.

Solutions of acids and bases used in the laboratory must be handled with care. Acids cause burns because of their exothermic reaction with water present in and on the skin. Bases react with proteins, principal components of the skin and eyes.

Such solutions are more hazardous if they are strong or concentrated. A strong acid or base produces more H_3O^+ or OH^- than do the corresponding weak substances. More concentrated acids or bases contain more H_3O^+ or OH^- than does a less concentrated solution of the same strength.

Aqueous solutions of acids and bases are electrolytes; the dissociation of the acid or base produces ions that can conduct an electrical current. As a result of the differences in the degree of dissociation, *strong acids and bases are strong electrolytes; weak acids and bases are weak electrolytes.* The conductivity of these solutions is principally due to the solute and not the solvent (water).

The dissociation of water

Solutions of electrolytes are discussed in Section 6.1.

Although pure water is virtually 100% molecular, a small number of water molecules do ionize. This process occurs by the transfer of a proton from one water molecule to another, producing a hydronium ion and a hydroxide ion:

$$H_2O + H_2O \rightleftharpoons H_3O^+ + OH^-$$

This process is the **autoionization,** or self-ionization, of water. Water is therefore a *very* weak electrolyte and a poor conductor of electricity. Water has *both* acid and base properties; the dissociation produces both the hydronium and hydroxide ion.

Pure water at room temperature has a hydronium ion concentration of $1.0 \times 10^{-7} M$. One hydroxide ion is produced for each hydronium ion; therefore the hydroxide ion concentration is also $1.0 \times 10^{-7} M$. Molar equilibrium concentration is conveniently indicated by brackets around the species whose concentration is represented:

$$[H_3O^+] = 1.0 \times 10^{-7}$$

$$[OH^-] = 1.0 \times 10^{-7}$$

The product of hydronium and hydroxide ion concentration in pure water is referred to as the **ion product for water.**

$$\text{ion product} = [H_3O^+][OH^-]$$

$$\text{ion product} = [1.0 \times 10^{-7}][1.0 \times 10^{-7}]$$

$$\text{ion product} = 1.0 \times 10^{-14}$$

The ion product is constant because its value does not depend on the nature or concentration of the solute, as long as the temperature does not change. The ion product is a temperature-dependent quantity.

The nature and concentration of the solutes added to water do alter the relative concentrations of H_3O^+ and OH^- present, but the product, $[H_3O^+][OH^-]$, always equals 1.0×10^{-14} at 25°C. This relationship is the basis for a scale that is useful in the measurement of the level of acidity or basicity of solutions. This scale, the pH scale, is discussed next.

The **pH scale** relates the hydronium ion concentration to a number, the pH, that serves as a useful indicator of the degree of acidity or basicity of a solution. The pH scale is somewhat analogous to the temperature scale used for assignment of relative levels of hot or cold. The temperature scale was developed to allow us to estimate how cold or how hot an object is. The pH scale specifies how acidic or how basic a solution is. The pH scale has values which range from zero (very acidic) to fourteen (very basic). A pH of seven, the middle of the scale, is neutral, neither acidic nor basic.

The pH scale

To help develop a concept of pH, consider the following:

◆ Addition of an acid (proton donor) to water *increases* the $[H_3O^+]$ and decreases the $[OH^-]$.

◆ Addition of a base (proton acceptor) to water *decreases* the $[H_3O^+]$ by increasing the $[OH^-]$.

◆ $[H_3O^+] = [OH^-]$ when *equal* amounts of acid and base are present.

◆ In all of the above cases, $[H_3O^+][OH^-] = 1.0 \times 10^{-14}$ = the ion product for water at 25°C.

(a)

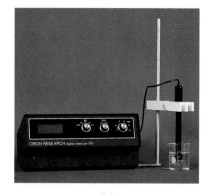

(b)

FIGURE 7.3
The measurement of pH. (a) A strip of test paper impregnated with indicator (a material that changes color as the acidity of the surroundings changes) is put in contact with the solution of interest. The resulting color is matched with a standard color chart (colors shown as a function of pH) to obtain the approximate pH. (b) A pH meter uses a sensor (a pH electrode) that develops an electrical potential that is proportional to the pH of the solution.

The pH of a solution can be calculated if the concentration of either H_3O^+ or OH^- is known. Alternatively, measurement of pH allows the calculation of H_3O^+ or OH^- concentration. The pH of aqueous solutions may be approximated by using indicating paper (pH paper) that develops a color related to the solution pH; alternatively, a pH meter can give us a much more exact pH measurement. A sensor measures an electrical property of a solution that is proportional to pH (Figure 7.3).

One of our objectives in this chapter is to calculate the pH of a solution when the hydronium or hydroxide ion concentration is known, as well as to calculate $[H_3O^+]$ or $[OH^-]$ from the pH. We will develop this skill using two different approaches, one requiring a working knowledge of logarithms, the other using decimal logic.

Approach I: Logarithm-based pH calculations

The pH of a solution is defined as the negative logarithm of the molar concentration of the hydronium ion:

$$pH = -\log [H_3O^+]$$

EXAMPLE 7.2

Calculating pH from Acid Molarity

Calculate the pH of a $1.0 \times 10^{-3} M$ solution of HCl.

Solution

HCl is a strong acid. If 1 mole of HCl dissociates, it produces 1 mole of H_3O^+. Therefore a $1.0 \times 10^{-3} M$ HCl solution has $[H_3O^+] = 1.0 \times 10^{-3} M$, and

$$pH = -\log [H_3O^+]$$
or, $$pH = -\log [1.0 \times 10^{-3}]$$

Consider the concentration term as composed of two parts, 1.0 and 10^{-3}. The logarithm of $1.0 = 0$, and the logarithm of 10^{-3} is simply the exponent, -3. Therefore

$$pH = -[\log 1.0 + \log 10^{-3}]$$

$$pH = -[0 - 3.00]$$

$$pH = -[-3.00] = 3.00$$

EXAMPLE 7.3

Calculating $[H_3O^+]$ from pH

Calculate the $[H_3O^+]$ of a solution of hydrochloric acid with pH = 4.00.

Solution

We use the pH expression:

$$pH = -\log [H_3O^+]$$

$$4.00 = -\log [H_3O^+]$$

Multiplying both sides of the equation by -1, we get

$$-4.00 = \log [H_3O^+]$$

Taking the antilogarithm of both sides (the reverse of a logarithm), we have

$$\text{antilog} -4.00 = [H_3O^+]$$

The antilog is the exponent of 10; therefore

$$1.0 \times 10^{-4} M = [H_3O^+]$$

EXAMPLE 7.4

Calculating the pH of a Base

Calculate the pH of a $1.0 \times 10^{-5} M$ solution of NaOH.

Solution

NaOH is a strong base. If 1 mole of NaOH dissociates, it produces 1 mole of OH^-. Therefore a $1.0 \times 10^{-5} M$ NaOH solution has $[OH^-] = 1.0 \times 10^{-5} M$. To calculate pH, we need $[H_3O^+]$. Recall that

$$[H_3O^+][OH^-] = 1.0 \times 10^{-14}$$

and

$$[H_3O^+] = \frac{1.0 \times 10^{-14}}{[OH^-]}$$

$$[H_3O^+] = \frac{1.0 \times 10^{-14}}{1.0 \times 10^{-5}}$$

$$[H_3O^+] = 1.0 \times 10^{-9} M$$

The solution is now similar to Example 7.2:

$$pH = -\log [H_3O^+]$$

$$pH = -\log [1.0 \times 10^{-9}]$$

$$pH = -(\log 1.0 + \log 10^{-9}) = -[0 + (-9.00)]$$

$$pH = 9.00$$

EXAMPLE 7.5

Calculating Both Hydronium and Hydroxide Ion Concentrations from pH

Calculate the $[H_3O^+]$ and $[OH^-]$ of a solution of a sodium hydroxide solution with a pH = 10.00.

Solution

First, calculate $[H_3O^+]$:

$$pH = -\log [H_3O^+]$$

$$10.00 = -\log [H_3O^+]$$

$$-10.00 = \log [H_3O^+]$$

$$\text{antilog} -10 = [H_3O^+]$$

$$1.0 \times 10^{-10} M = [H_3O^+]$$

To calculate the $[OH^-]$, we need to solve for $[OH^-]$, using the following expression:

$$[H_3O^+][OH^-] = 1.0 \times 10^{-14}$$

$$[OH^-] = \frac{1.0 \times 10^{-14}}{[H_3O^+]}$$

Substituting the $[H_3O^+]$ from the first part, we have

$$[OH^-] = \frac{1.0 \times 10^{-14}}{[1.0 \times 10^{-10}]}$$

$$[OH^-] = 1.0 \times 10^{-4} M$$

Often, the pH or $[H_3O^+]$ will not be a whole number (pH = 1.0, pH = 5.0, $[H_3O^+] = 1.0 \times 10^{-3}$ and so forth). With the advent of inexpensive and versatile calculators, calculations with noninteger numbers pose no great problems. Consider the following examples.

EXAMPLE 7.6

Calculating pH Using the Calculator

Calculate the pH of a sample of lakewater that has a $[H_3O^+] = 6.5 \times 10^{-5} M$.

Solution

$$pH = -\log [H_3O^+]$$

$$pH = -\log [6.50 \times 10^{-5}]$$

To perform the calculation on your calculator:

1. Enter 6.5×10^{-5} into your calculator. With most calculators the following protocol will work:

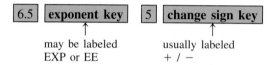

2. Press $\boxed{LOG}$ key. This should produce a value of -4.1871.
3. Since the pH is negative log, $\boxed{\text{change sign}}$, pH = 4.1871.
4. Round off to 4.19.

The pH, 4.19, is low enough to suspect acid rain. (See the Environmental Perspective in this chapter.)

EXAMPLE 7.7

Calculating $[H_3O^+]$ from pH

The measured pH of a sample of lakewater is 6.40. Calculate $[H_3O^+]$.

Solution

An alternative mathematical form of

$$pH = -\log [H_3O^+]$$

is the expression

$$[H_3O^+] = 10^{-pH}$$

which we will use when we must solve for $[H_3O^+]$.
To perform the calculation on your calculator:

1. Enter $\boxed{6.40}$.
2. Press $\boxed{\text{Change sign key, +/−}}$.
3. Press $\boxed{10^{\times}}$; the result is 3.98×10^{-7} or $4.0 \times 10^{-7} M = [H_3O^+]$.

The six examples above illustrate the most frequently used pH calculations. It is important to remember that in the case of a base you must convert the $[OH^-]$ to $[H_3O^+]$ using the expression for the ion product for the solvent, water.

Approach II: Decimal-based pH calculation

If you do not have facility with logarithms or a calculator available, it is still possible to approximate the pH of a solution of an acid or base as well as determine acid or base concentration from the pH. To do this, remember the following facts:

1. The pH of a 1 M solution of any strong acid is 0.
2. The pH of a 1 M solution of any strong base is 14.

3. Each tenfold change in concentration changes the pH by one unit. A tenfold change in concentration is equivalent to moving the decimal point one place.

4. A *decrease* in acid concentration *increases* the pH.

5. A *decrease* in base concentration *decreases* the pH.

For a strong acid:

HCl molarity	pH
1.0×10^{0}	0.00
1.0×10^{-1}	1.00
1.0×10^{-2}	2.00
1.0×10^{-3}	3.00
1.0×10^{-4}	4.00
1.0×10^{-5}	5.00
1.0×10^{-6}	6.00
1.0×10^{-7}	7.00

For a strong acid the exponent, with the sign changed, is the pH.

For a strong base,

NaOH molarity	pH
1.0×10^{0}	14.00
1.0×10^{-1}	13.00
1.0×10^{-2}	12.00
1.0×10^{-3}	11.00
1.0×10^{-4}	10.00
1.0×10^{-5}	9.00
1.0×10^{-6}	8.00
1.0×10^{-7}	7.00

For a strong base the exponent, algebraically added to 14, is the pH.

QUESTION 7.5

Solve the problems posed in Examples 7.2 and 7.3 using the decimal-based system developed above.

QUESTION 7.6

Solve the problems posed in Examples 7.4 and 7.5 using the decimal-based system developed above.

QUESTION 7.7

Calculate the pH corresponding to a solution of sodium hydroxide with a $[OH^-]$ of $1.0 \times 10^{-2}\ M$.

QUESTION 7.8

Calculate the pH corresponding to a solution of sodium hydroxide with a $[OH^-]$ of $1.0 \times 10^{-5}\ M$.

QUESTION 7.9

Calculate the $[H_3O^+]$ corresponding to pH = 8.50 using the most suitable method.

QUESTION 7.10

Calculate the $[H_3O^+]$ corresponding to pH = 4.50 using the most suitable method.

The importance of pH and pH control

Solution pH and pH control play a major role in many facets of our everyday lives. Consider a few examples:

◆ *Agriculture:* Crops grow best in a soil of proper pH. Proper fertilization involves the maintenance of a suitable pH.

◆ *Physiology:* If the pH of our blood were to shift by one unit, we would die. Many biochemical reactions in living organisms are extremely pH dependent.

◆ *Industry:* From manufacture of processed foods to the manufacture of automobiles, industrial processes often require rigorous pH control.

◆ *Municipal services:* Purification of drinking water and treatment of sewage must be carried out at their optimum pHs.

See "An Environmental Perspective: Acid Rain" in this chapter.

◆ *Acid rain:* Nitric acid and sulfuric acid, resulting largely from the reaction of components of vehicle emissions (nitrogen and sulfur oxides) with water, are carried down by precipitation and enter aquatic systems (lakes and streams), lowering the pH of the water. A less than optimum pH poses serious problems for native fish populations.

The list could continue on for many pages. However, in summary, any change that takes place in aqueous solution generally has at least some pH dependence.

Neutralization

The reaction of an acid with a base to produce a salt and water is referred to as **neutralization.** In the strictest sense, neutralization requires equal numbers of moles of H_3O^+ and OH^- to produce a neutral solution (no excess acid or base).

Consider the reaction of hydrochloric acid and sodium hydroxide:

$$HCl + NaOH \longrightarrow NaCl + H_2O$$

Acid   Base   Salt   Water

Chapter 4

Our objective is to make the balanced equation represent the process actually occurring. We recognize that HCl, NaOH, and NaCl are dissociated in solution:

$$H^+(aq) + Cl^-(aq) + Na^+(aq) + OH^-(aq) \longrightarrow Na^+(aq) + Cl^-(aq) + H_2O(l)$$

We further know that Na^+ and Cl^- are unchanged in the reaction. If we write only those components that actually change, we produce a *net, balanced ionic equation* as shown below:

$$H^+(aq) + OH^-(aq) \longrightarrow H_2O(l)$$

If we realize that the H^+ occurs in aqueous solution as the hydronium ion, H_3O^+, the most correct form of the net, balanced ionic equation is

$$H_3O^+(aq) + OH^-(aq) \longrightarrow 2H_2O(l)$$

The equation for any strong acid/strong base neutralization reaction is the same as the equation shown above.

A neutralization reaction may be used to determine the concentration of an unknown acid or base solution. The technique of **titration** involves the addition of measured amounts of a **standard solution** (one whose concentration is known with certainty) to neutralize the second, unknown solution. From the volumes of the two solutions and the concentration of the standard solution the concentration of the unknown solution may be determined. Consider the following application.

> *EXAMPLE 7.8*

Determine the Concentration of a Solution of Hydrochloric Acid

Step 1. A known volume (perhaps 25.00 mL) of the unknown acid is measured into a flask using a pipet.

Step 2. An **indicator,** a substance that changes color as the solution becomes neutral (see Figure 7.4), is added to the unknown solution.

Many indicators are naturally occurring substances.

Step 3. A solution of sodium hydroxide (perhaps 0.1000 M) is carefully added to the unknown solution using a **buret,** which is a long glass tube calibrated in milliliters. A stopcock at the bottom of the buret regulates the amount of liquid dispensed. The standard solution is added until the indicator changes color.

Step 4. At this point, the **equivalence point,** the number of moles of hydroxide ion added is equal to the number of moles of hydronium ion present in the unknown acid.

Step 5. The volume dispensed by the buret (perhaps 35.00 mL) is measured and used in the calculation of the unknown acid concentration.

Step 6. The calculation is as follows:

$$\text{moles}_{\text{acid}} = M_{\text{acid}} \times V_{\text{liters acid}}$$

$$\text{moles}_{\text{base}} = M_{\text{base}} \times V_{\text{liters base}}$$

At the equivalence point,

$$\text{moles}_{\text{acid}} = \text{moles}_{\text{base}}$$

and

$$M_{\text{acid}} \times V_{\text{liters acid}} = M_{\text{base}} \times V_{\text{liters base}}$$

or

$$M_{\text{acid}} = M_{\text{base}} \times \frac{V_{\text{liters base}}}{V_{\text{liters acid}}}$$

This is true only if the acid and base react in a 1:1 ratio (one mole of base and one mole of acid in the balanced equation). Situations involving other than 1:1 reactions will not be discussed here.

Since

$$M_{\text{base}} = 0.1000 \ M$$

$$V_{\text{liters acid}} = 25.00 \ \text{mL} \times \frac{1 \ \text{L}}{1000 \ \text{mL}} = 0.02500 \ \text{L}$$

$$V_{\text{liters base}} = 35.00 \ \text{mL} \times \frac{1 \ \text{L}}{1000 \ \text{mL}} = 0.03500 \ \text{L}$$

then

$$M_{\text{acid}} = 0.1000 \ M \times \frac{0.03500 \ \text{L}}{0.02500 \ \text{L}}$$

$$M_{\text{acid}} = 0.1400 \ M$$

The titration of an acid with a base is depicted in Figure 7.5.

FIGURE 7.4
The color of the petals of the hydrangea are formed by molecules that behave as acid-base indicators. The color is influenced by the pH of the soil in which the hydrangea is grown. Low pH causes the flowers to become pink.

QUESTION 7.11

Calculate the molar concentration of a sodium hydroxide solution if 40.00 mL of this solution were required to neutralize 20.00 mL of a 0.2000 M solution of hydrochloric acid.

QUESTION 7.12

Calculate the molar concentration of a sodium hydroxide solution if 36.00 mL of this solution were required to neutralize 25.00 mL of a 0.2000 M solution of hydrochloric acid.

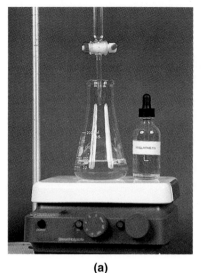 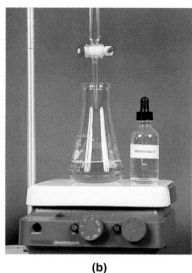

(a)   (b)

FIGURE 7.5
An acid-base titration. (a) An exact volume of a standard solution (in this example, a base) is added to a solution of unknown concentration (in this example, an acid). (b) From the volume (read from the buret) and concentration of the standard solution, coupled with the mass or volume of the unknown, the concentration of the unknown may be calculated.

7.5 ACID-BASE BUFFERS

A **buffer solution** contains components that enable the solution to resist large changes in pH when acids or bases are added. Buffer solutions may be prepared in the laboratory to maintain optimum conditions for a chemical reaction. Buffers are routinely used in commercial products to maintain optimum conditions for product behavior (see Figure 7.6).

Buffer solutions also occur naturally. Blood, for example, is a natural buffer maintaining a pH of approximately 7.4, optimum for oxygen transport. The buffering agent in blood is, in part, due to the unique interaction of carbonic acid (H_2CO_3) and bicarbonate ions (HCO_3^-).

The buffer process

The basis of buffer action is the establishment of an equilibrium between either a weak acid and its salt or a weak base and its salt.

Consider the case of a weak acid and its salt:

A common buffer solution may be prepared from acetic acid (CH_3COOH) and sodium acetate (CH_3COONa). An *equilibrium* is established in solution between the weak acid and the salt anion:

$$CH_3COOH + H_2O \rightleftharpoons H_3O^+ + CH_3COO^-$$

| Acetic acid (weak acid) | Water | Hydronium ion | Acetate ion (salt) |

Section 6.4

A buffer solution functions in accordance with LeChatelier's Principle, which states that an equilibrium system, when stressed, will shift its equilibrium to relieve that stress. This principle is illustrated by the following examples.

FIGURE 7.6
Commercial products that claim improved function due to their ability to control pH.

Addition of a basic substance to a buffer solution causes the following changes:

Addition of base (OH⁻) to a buffer solution

◆ OH^- from the base reacts with H_3O^+ producing water.

◆ Molecular acetic acid *dissociates* to replace the H_3O^+ used up by the base, maintaining the pH close to the initial level.

This is an example of LeChatelier's Principle, since the loss of H_3O^+ (the *stress*) is compensated by the dissociation of acetic acid to produce more H_3O^+.

Addition of an acidic solution to a buffer results in the following changes:

Addition of acid (H₃O⁺) to a buffer solution

◆ H_3O^+ from the acid increases the overall $[H_3O^+]$.

◆ The system reacts to this stress, in accordance with LeChatelier's Principle, to form more molecular acetic acid; the acetate ion combines with H_3O^+.

These effects may be summarized as follows:

$$CH_3COOH + H_2O \rightleftharpoons H_3O^+ + CH_3COO^-$$

$\xrightarrow{\text{OH}^- \text{ added, equilibrium shifts to the right}}$

$\xleftarrow{\text{H}_3\text{O}^+ \text{ added, equilibrium shifts to the left}}$

Note that buffering against base is a function of the concentration of the weak acid (in this case CH_3COOH). Buffering against acid is dependent on the concentration of the anion of the salt (CH_3COO^- in this example).

QUESTION 7.13

Explain how the molar concentration of H_2CO_3 in the blood would change if the partial pressure of CO_2 in the lungs were to increase. (Refer to "A Clinical Perspective: Control of Blood pH.")

QUESTION 7.14

Explain how the molar concentration of H_2CO_3 in the blood would change if the partial pressure of CO_2 in the lungs were to decrease. (Refer to "A Clinical Perspective: Control of Blood pH.")

QUESTION 7.15

Explain how the molar concentration of hydronium ion in the blood would change under each of the conditions described in Questions 7.13 and 7.14.

QUESTION 7.16

Explain how the pH of blood would change under each of the conditions described in Questions 7.13 and 7.14.

7.6 OXIDATION-REDUCTION PROCESSES

Oxidation-reduction processes are the basis for many types of chemical change. Corrosion, the operation of a battery, and biochemical energy-harvesting reactions are but a few examples. In this section we explore the basic concepts underlying this class of chemical reactions.

Oxidation and reduction

Oxidation is defined as a loss of electrons, loss of hydrogen atoms, or gain of oxygen atoms. *Sodium metal*, is, for example, oxidized to a *sodium ion*, losing one electron when it reacts with a nonmetal such as chlorine:

$$Na \longrightarrow Na^+ + e^-$$

AN ENVIRONMENTAL PERSPECTIVE

Acid Rain

Acid rain is a global environmental problem that has raised public awareness of the chemicals polluting the air through the activities of our industrial society. Normal rain has a pH of about 5.6 as a result of the chemical reaction between carbon dioxide gas and water in the atmosphere. The following equation shows this reaction:

$$CO_2(g) \quad + H_2O(l) \longrightarrow H_2CO_3(aq)$$

Carbon dioxide   Water   Carbonic acid

Acid rain refers to conditions that are much more acidic than this. In upstate New York the rain has as much as 25 times the acidity of normal rainfall. One rainstorm, recorded in West Virginia, produced rainfall that measured 1.5 on the pH scale. This is approximately the pH of stomach acid or about 10,000 times more acidic than "normal rain" (remember that the pH scale is logarithmic).

Acid rain is destroying life in streams and lakes. More than half the highland lakes in the western Adirondack Mountains have no native gamefish. In addition to these 300 lakes there are 140 lakes in Ontario that have suffered a similar fate. It is estimated that 48,000 other lakes in Ontario and countless others in the northeastern and central United States are threatened. Our forests are endangered as well. The acid rain decreases soil pH, which in turn alters the solubility of minerals needed by plants. Studies have shown that about 40% of the red spruce and maple trees in New England have died. Increased acidity of rainfall appears to be the major culprit.

What is the cause of this acid rain? The combustion of fossil fuels (gas, oil, and coal) by power plants produces oxides of sulfur and nitrogen. These react with water, as does the CO_2 in normal rain, but the products are strong acids: sulfuric and nitric acids. Let us look at the equations for these processes.

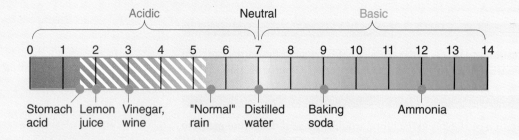

Indicates the range of pH values ascribed to acid rain

pH values for a variety of substances compared with the pH of acid rain.

Reduction is defined as a gain of electrons, gain of hydrogen atoms, or loss of oxygen atoms. A *chlorine atom* is reduced to a *chloride ion* by gaining one electron when it reacts with a metal such as sodium:

$$Cl + e^- \longrightarrow Cl^-$$

Oxidation and reduction are complementary processes. The *oxidation half-reaction* produces an electron that is the reactant for the *reduction half-reaction*. The combination of two half-reactions, one oxidation and one reduction, produces the complete reaction:

Oxidation half-reaction:	$Na \longrightarrow Na^+ + e^-$
Reduction half-reaction:	$Cl + e^- \longrightarrow Cl^-$
Complete reaction:	$Na + Cl \longrightarrow Na^+ + Cl^-$

Half-reactions, one oxidation and one reduction, are exactly that: one-half of a complete reaction. The two half-reactions combine to produce the complete reaction. Note that the electrons cancel; in the electron transfer process, no free electrons remain.

In the atmosphere, nitric oxide (NO) can react with oxygen to produce nitrogen dioxide as shown:

$$2NO(g) \; + \; O_2(g) \; \longrightarrow \; 2NO_2(g)$$

Nitric oxide   Oxygen   Nitrogen dioxide

Nitrogen dioxide (which causes the brown air color of smog) then reacts with water to form nitric acid:

$$3NO_2(g) + H_2O(l) \longrightarrow 2HNO_3(aq) + NO(g)$$

A similar chemistry is seen with the sulfur oxides. Coal may contain as much as 3% sulfur. When the coal is burned, the sulfur also burns; this produces the choking, acrid sulfur dioxide gas:

$$S(s) + O_2(g) \longrightarrow SO_2(g)$$

By itself, sulfur dioxide can cause serious respiratory problems for people with asthma or other lung diseases, but matters are worsened by the reaction of SO_2 with atmospheric oxygen:

$$2SO_2(g) + O_2(g) \longrightarrow 2SO_3(g)$$

Sulfur trioxide will react with water in the atmosphere:

$$SO_3(g) + H_2O(l) \longrightarrow H_2SO_4(aq)$$

The product, sulfuric acid, is even more irritating to the respiratory tract. When the acid rain created by the reactions shown above falls to earth, the impact is significant.

It is easy to balance these chemical equations, but it could require decades to balance the ecological systems that we have disrupted by our massive consumption of fossil fuels. A sudden decrease of even 25% in the use of fossil fuels would lead to worldwide financial chaos. Hopefully, development of alternative fuel sources, such as solar energy and safe nuclear power, will reduce our dependence on fossil fuels and help us to balance the global equation.

Damage caused by acid rain.

In the reaction described above, sodium metal is the **reducing agent;** it releases electrons for the reduction of chlorine. Chlorine is the **oxidizing agent;** it accepts electrons from the sodium, which is oxidized.

The reducing agent becomes oxidized and the oxidizing agent becomes reduced.

The characteristics of oxidizing and reducing agents are summarized below:

Oxidizing Agent	Reducing Agent
◆ Is reduced	◆ Is oxidized
◆ Gains electrons	◆ Loses electrons
◆ Causes oxidation	◆ Causes reduction

Oxidation-reduction processes are important in many areas as diverse as industrial manufacturing and biochemical processes.

Oxidation and reduction reactions

Corrosion of iron—rusting—is a commonplace example of an oxidation-reduction reaction (Figure 7.7). Millions of dollars are spent annually in an attempt to correct the damage resulting from corrosion. A current area of chemical research is concerned with the development of corrosion-inhibiting processes. In one type of corrosion, elemental iron is oxidized to iron(III)

A CLINICAL PERSPECTIVE

Control of Blood pH

A pH of 7.4 is maintained in blood partly by a carbonic acid–bicarbonate buffer system based on the following equilibrium:

$$H_2CO_3 + H_2O \rightleftharpoons H_3O^+ + HCO_3^-$$

Carbonic acid	Bicarbonate ion
(weak acid)	(salt)

The regulation process based on LeChatelier's Principle is similar to that of acetic acid–sodium acetate, which we have already discussed.

Red blood cells transport O_2, bound to hemoglobin, to the cells of body tissue. The metabolic waste product, CO_2, is picked up by the blood and delivered back to the lungs.

The CO_2 in the blood also participates in the carbonic acid/bicarbonate buffer equilibrium; carbon dioxide reacts with water in the blood to form carbonic acid:

$$CO_2 + H_2O \rightleftharpoons H_2CO_3$$

As a result the buffer equilibrium becomes more complex:

$$CO_2 + 2H_2O \rightleftharpoons H_2CO_3 + H_2O \rightleftharpoons H_3O^+ + HCO_3^-$$

Through this sequence of relationships the concentration of CO_2 in the blood affects the blood pH.

Higher than normal CO_2 levels shift the above equilibrium to the right (LeChatelier's Principle), increasing $[H_3O^+]$ and lowering the pH. The blood becomes too acidic, leading to numerous medical problems. A situation of high blood CO_2 levels and low pH is termed *acidosis*. Respiratory acidosis results from various diseases (emphysema, pneumonia) that restrict the breathing process, causing the buildup of waste CO_2 in the blood.

Lower than normal CO_2 levels, on the other hand, shift the equilibrium to the left, decreasing $[H_3O^+]$ and making the pH more basic; this condition is termed *alkalosis* (from "alkali," implying basic in nature). Hyperventilation, or rapid breathing, is a common cause of respiratory alkalosis.

At the same time, in this reaction, O_2 is being reduced to O^{2-} and is incorporated into the structure of iron(III) oxide. Electrons lost by iron reduce oxygen; this again shows that oxidation and reduction processes go hand in hand.

See Chapters 17 and 18 for a variety of examples.

oxide:

$$4Fe + 3O_2 \longrightarrow 2Fe_2O_3$$

There are many examples of biological oxidation-reduction reactions. For example, the electron-transport chain of aerobic respiration involves the reversible oxidation and reduction of iron atoms in cytochrome c,

$$\text{cytochrome } c \ (Fe^{3+}) + e^- \longrightarrow \text{cytochrome } c \ (Fe^{2+})$$

The reduced iron ion transfers an electron to an iron ion in another protein, called cytochrome c oxidase, according to the following reaction:

$$\text{cytochrome } c \ (Fe^{2+}) + \text{cytochrome } c \text{ oxidase } (Fe^{3+})$$

$$\text{cytochrome } c \ (Fe^{3+}) + \text{cytochrome } c \text{ oxidase } (Fe^{2+})$$

Cytochrome c oxidase eventually passes four electrons to O_2, the final electron acceptor of the chain:

$$O_2 + 4e^- + 2H^+ \longrightarrow 2H_2O$$

FIGURE 7.7
The rust (an oxide of iron) that diminishes structural strength and ruins the appearance of automobiles, bridges, and other iron-based objects is a common example of an oxidation-reduction reaction.

SUMMARY

7.1 Classification of Chemical Reactions

Spontaneous chemical reactions occur because of the tendency to achieve the lowest (most stable) electronic energy state. Strong electrolytes react to form weak (less dissociated) electrolytes, if possible. Reactions forming gaseous products and insoluble solid products are favored as well.

Chemical reactions involve the *combination* of reactants to produce products, the *decomposition* of reactant(s) into products, or the *replacement* of one or more elements in a compound to yield products. Replacement reactions are subclassified as either *single* or *double* replacement.

7.2 Types of Chemical Reactions

Reactions that produce products with similar characteristics are often classified as a single group. The formation of an insoluble solid, a precipitate, is very common. Such reactions are precipitation reactions.

Chemical reactions that have a common reactant may be grouped together. Reactions involving oxygen, *combustion reactions,* are such a class.

Another approach to the classification of chemical reactions is based on charge transfer. *Acid-base reactions* involve the transfer of a hydrogen ion, H^+, from one reactant to another. Another important reaction type, *oxidation-reduction,* takes place because of the transfer of negative charge, one or more electrons, from one reactant to another.

7.3 Acids and Bases

The earliest definition of acids and bases is the *Arrhenius theory.* According to this theory an acid dissociates to form hydrogen ions, H^+, and a base dissociates to form hydroxide ions, OH^-. The *Brönsted-Lowry theory* defines an acid as a proton (H^+) donor and a base as a proton acceptor.

7.4 Solutions of Acids and Bases

The strength of acids and bases in water depends on their degree of dissociation, the extent to which they react with the solvent, water. Acids and bases are strong when the reaction with water is virtually 100% complete and weak when the reaction with water is much less than 100% complete.

Weak acids and weak bases dissolve in water principally in the molecular form. Only a small percent of the molecules dissociate to form the *hydronium* ion or *hydroxide* ion.

Aqueous solutions of acids and bases are electrolytes; the dissociation of the acid or base produces ions, which conduct an electrical current. Strong acids and bases are strong electrolytes; weak acids and bases are weak electrolytes.

Although pure water is virtually 100% molecular, a small number of water molecules do ionize. This process occurs by the transfer of a proton from one water molecule to another, producing a hydronium ion and a hydroxide ion. This process is the *autoionization,* or self-ionization, of water.

Pure water at room temperature has a hydronium ion concentration of 1.0×10^{-7} M. One hydroxide ion is produced for each hydronium ion; therefore the hydroxide ion concentration is also 1.0×10^{-7} M. The product of hydronium and hydroxide ion concentration (1×10^{-14}) is the *ion product for water.*

The *pH scale* correlates the hydronium ion concentration with a number, the pH, that serves as a useful indicator of the degree of acidity or basicity of a solution. The pH of a solution is defined as the negative logarithm of the molar concentration of the hydronium ion (pH $= -\log [H_3O^+]$).

The reaction of an acid with a base to produce a salt and water is referred to as *neutralization.* Neutralization requires equal numbers of moles of H_3O^+ and OH^- to produce a neutral solution (no excess acid or base). A neutralization reaction may be used to determine the concentration of an unknown acid or base solution. The technique of *titration* involves the addition of measured amounts of a *standard solution* (one whose concentration is known) from a *buret* to neutralize the second, unknown solution. The *equivalence point* is signaled by an *indicator.*

7.5 Acid-Base Buffers

A *buffer solution* contains components that enable the solution to resist large changes in pH when acids or bases are added. The basis of buffer action is an equilibrium between either a weak acid and its salt or a weak base and its salt.

A buffer solution follows LeChatelier's Principle, which states that an equilibrium system, when stressed, will shift its equilibrium to alleviate that stress.

Buffering against base is a function of the concentration of the weak acid for an acidic buffer. Buffering against acid is dependent on the concentration of the anion of the salt.

7.6 Oxidation-Reduction Processes

Oxidation is defined as a loss of electrons, loss of hydrogen atoms, or gain of oxygen atoms. *Reduction* is defined as a gain of electrons, gain of hydrogen atoms, or loss of oxygen atoms.

Oxidation and reduction are complementary processes. The oxidation half-reaction produces an electron that is the reactant for the reduction half-reaction. The combination of two half-reactions, one oxidation and one reduction, produces the complete reaction.

The *reducing agent* releases electrons for the reduction to occur. The *oxidizing agent* accepts electrons, causing the oxidation to take place.

KEY TERMS

acid-base reaction (7.2)

Arrhenius theory (7.3)

autoionization (7.4)

Brönsted-Lowry theory (7.3)

buffer solution (7.5)

buret (7.4)

combination reaction (7.1)

decomposition reaction (7.1)

double-replacement reaction (7.1)

equivalence point (7.4)

hydrate (7.1)

hydronium ion (7.3)
indicator (7.4)
ion product for water (7.4)
neutralization (7.4)
oxidation (7.6)
oxidation-reduction reaction (7.2)
oxidizing agent (7.6)

pH scale (7.4)
reducing agent (7.6)
reduction (7.6)
single-replacement reaction (7.1)
standard solution (7.4)
titration (7.4)

QUESTIONS AND PROBLEMS

Chemical Reactions

7.17 Give an example of:
    a. a decomposition reaction
    b. a single-replacement reaction

7.18 Give an example of:
    a. a combination reaction
    b. a double-replacement reaction

7.19 Give an example of a precipitate-forming reaction.

7.20 Give an example of a reaction in which oxygen is a reactant.

7.21 Balance each of the following equations:
    a. $C_2H_6(g) + O_2(g) \rightarrow CO_2(g) + H_2O(g)$
    b. $K_2O(s) + P_4O_{10}(s) \rightarrow K_3PO_4(s)$
    c. $MgBr_2(aq) + H_2SO_4(aq) \rightarrow HBr(g) + MgSO_4(aq)$

7.22 Balance each of the following equations:
    a. $C_6H_{12}O_6(s) + O_2(g) \rightarrow CO_2(g) + H_2O(g)$
    b. $H_2O(l) + P_4O_{10}(s) \rightarrow H_3PO_4(aq)$
    c. $PCl_5(g) + H_2O(l) \rightarrow HCl(aq) + H_3PO_4(aq)$

7.23 Complete, then balance, each of the following equations:
    a. $Ca(s) + F_2(g) \rightarrow$
    b. $Mg(s) + O_2(g) \rightarrow$
    c. $H_2(g) + N_2(g) \rightarrow$

7.24 Complete, then balance, each of the following equations:
    a. $Li(s) + O_2(g) \rightarrow$
    b. $Ca(s) + N_2(g) \rightarrow$
    c. $Al(s) + S(s) \rightarrow$

Acids and Bases

7.25 **a.** Define an acid according to the Arrhenius theory.
    b. Define an acid according to the Brönsted-Lowry theory.

7.26 **a.** Define a base according to the Arrhenius theory.
    b. Define a base according to the Brönsted-Lowry theory.

Solutions of Acids and Bases

7.27 Calculate the $[H_3O^+]$ of an aqueous solution that is:
    a. $1.0 \times 10^{-7} M$ in OH^-
    b. $1.0 \times 10^{-3} M$ in OH^-

7.28 Calculate the $[H_3O^+]$ of an aqueous solution that is:
    a. $1.0 \times 10^{-9} M$ in OH^-
    b. $1.0 \times 10^{-5} M$ in OH^-

7.29 Label each solution in Problem 7.27 as acidic, basic, or neutral.

7.30 Label each solution in Problem 7.28 as acidic, basic, or neutral.

7.31 Calculate the pH of a solution that has
    a. $[H_3O^+] = 1.0 \times 10^{-7}$
    b. $[OH^-] = 1.0 \times 10^{-9}$

7.32 Calculate the pH of a solution that has:
    a. $[H_3O^+] = 1.0 \times 10^{-10}$
    b. $[OH^-] = 1.0 \times 10^{-5}$

7.33 Calculate *both* $[H_3O^+]$ and $[OH^-]$ for a solution that is:
    a. pH = 1.00
    b. pH = 9.00

7.34 Calculate *both* $[H_3O^+]$ and $[OH^-]$ for a solution that is:
    a. pH = 5.00
    b. pH = 7.20

7.35 Calculate *both* $[H_3O^+]$ and $[OH^-]$ for a solution that is:
    a. pH = 1.30
    b. pH = 9.70

7.36 Calculate *both* $[H_3O^+]$ and $[OH^-]$ for a solution that is:
    a. pH = 5.50
    b. pH = 7.00

7.37 What is a neutralization reaction?

7.38 Describe the purpose of a titration.

Buffer Solutions

7.39 Which of the following are capable of forming a buffer solution?
    a. NH_3 and NH_4Cl
    b. HNO_3 and KNO_3

7.40 Which of the following are capable of forming a buffer solution?
    a. HBr and $MgCl_2$
    b. H_2CO_3 and $NaHCO_3$

7.41 Define:
    a. buffer solution
    b. acidosis (refer to ''A Clinical Perspective: Control of Blood pH'')

7.42 Define:
    a. alkalosis (refer to ''A Clinical Perspective: Control of Blood pH'')
    b. standard solution

7.43 For the equilibrium situation involving acetic acid (CH_3COOH):

$$CH_3COOH + H_2O \rightleftharpoons CH_3COO^- + H_3O^+$$

explain the equilibrium shift occurring if:
    a. a strong acid is added to the solution
    b. the solution is diluted with water

7.44 For the equilibrium situation involving acetic acid (CH_3COOH):

$$CH_3COOH + H_2O \rightleftharpoons CH_3COO^- + H_3O^+$$

explain the equilibrium shift occurring if:
    a. a strong base is added to the solution
    b. more acetic acid is added to the solution

Oxidation-Reduction Reactions

7.45 Define:
    a. oxidation
    b. oxidizing agent

7.46 Define:
    a. reduction
    b. reducing agent

7.47 During an oxidation process in an oxidation-reduction reaction the species oxidized _____ electrons.

7.48 During an oxidation-reduction reaction the species _____ is the oxidizing agent.

7.49 During an oxidation-reduction reaction the species _____ is the reducing agent.

7.50 Metals tend to be good _____ agents.

Further Problems

7.51 For each of the following reactions, identify the type of reaction taking place. More than one classification may apply.
  a. $HNO_3 + KOH \rightarrow KNO_3 + H_2O$
  b. $Cu + 4HNO_3 \rightarrow Cu(NO_3)_2 + 2NO_2 + 2H_2O$

7.52 For each of the following reactions, identify the type of reaction taking place. More than one classification may apply.
  a. $AgNO_3 + KCl \rightarrow AgCl + KNO_3$
  b. $Mg + 2HCl \rightarrow MgCl_2 + H_2$

7.53 In the following reaction, identify the oxidized species, reduced species, oxidizing agent, and reducing agent:
$$Cl_2 + 2KI \longrightarrow 2KCl + I_2$$

7.54 In the following reaction, identify the oxidized species, reduced species, oxidizing agent, and reducing agent:
$$Zn + Cu^{2+} \longrightarrow Zn^{2+} + Cu$$

7.55 The pH of urine may vary between 4.5 and 8.2. Determine the H_3O^+ concentration and OH^- concentration if the measured pH is:
  a. 6.00
  b. 5.20
  c. 7.80

7.56 The hydronium ion concentration in blood of three different patients was:

Patient	$[H_3O^+]$
A	5.0×10^{-8}
B	3.1×10^{-8}
C	3.2×10^{-8}

What is their blood pH? If the normal range is 7.30–7.50, which, if any, of these patients have an abnormal blood pH?

7.57 Determine how many times more acidic a solution is at:
  a. pH 2 relative to pH 4
  b. pH 7 relative to pH 11
  c. pH 2 relative to pH 12

7.58 Determine how many times more basic a solution is at:
  a. pH 6 relative to pH 4
  b. pH 10 relative to pH 9
  c. pH 11 relative to pH 6

VOCABULARY QUIZ

7.1 The _____ theory describes the behavior of bases such as ammonia.

7.2 _____ is the reaction of a substance, such as water, with itself to produce a positive and a negative ion.

7.3 A(n) _____ contains an acid-base pair that is resistant to large changes in pH upon addition of strong acids or bases.

7.4 A(n) _____ reaction involves chemically separating two substances.

7.5 A(n) _____ reaction involves chemically joining two substances.

7.6 _____ is a loss of electrons.

7.7 A(n) _____ is a substance that oxidizes, or removes electrons from, another substance.

7.8 _____ is a numerical representation of acidity or basicity of a solution.

7.9 A(n) _____ solution is a solution whose concentration is accurately known.

7.10 _____ is the process of adding from a buret a solution to a sample until a reaction is complete, at which time the volume is accurately measured.

8

Radioactivity and Nuclear Medicine

LEARNING GOALS

◆ Know the characteristics of alpha, beta, and gamma radiation.

◆ Explain the difference between natural and artificial radioactivity.

◆ Be able to write balanced equations for common nuclear processes.

◆ Calculate the amount of radioactive substance remaining after a specified number of half-lives.

◆ Explain the process of radiocarbon dating.

◆ Cite several examples of the use of radioactive isotopes in medicine.

◆ Describe the use of ionizing radiation in cancer therapy.

◆ Discuss the preparation of radioisotopes for use in diagnostic imaging studies.

◆ Be familiar with common techniques for the detection of radioactivity, and know the common units in which radiation intensity is represented: the curie, roentgen, rad, and rem.

CHEMISTRY CONNECTION

An Extraordinary Woman in Science

The path to a successful career in science, or any other field for that matter, is seldom smooth or straight. This was certainly true for Madame Marie Sklodowska Curie. Her lifelong ambition was to raise a family and do something interesting for a career. This was a lofty goal for a nineteenth-century woman.

The political climate in Poland, coupled with the prevailing attitudes toward women and careers, especially careers in science, certainly did not make it any easier for Mme. Curie. To support herself and her sister, she toiled at menial jobs until moving to Paris to resume her studies.

It was in Paris that she met her future husband and fellow researcher, Pierre Curie. Working with crude equipment in a laboratory that was primitive, even by the standards of the time, she and Pierre made a most revolutionary discovery: Radioactivity, the emission of energy from certain substances, was released from *inside* of the atom and was independent of the molecular form of the substance. The absolute proof of this assertion came only after they processed over one *ton* of a material (pitchblende) to isolate less than a gram of pure radium. The difficult conditions under which this feat was accomplished are perhaps best stated by Sharon Bertsch McGrayne in her book *Nobel Prize Women in Science* (Birch Lane Press, New York, NY, p. 23):

The only space large enough at the school was an abandoned dissection shed. The shack was stifling hot in summer and freezing cold in winter. It had no ventilation system for removing poisonous fumes, and its roof leaked. A chemist accustomed to Germany's modern laboratories called it "a cross between a stable and a potato cellar and, if I had not seen the work table with the chemical apparatus, I would have thought it a practical joke." This ramshackle shed became the symbol of the Marie Curie legend.

The pale green glow emanating from the radium was beautiful to behold. Mme. Curie would go to the shed in the middle of the night to bask in the light of her accomplishment. She did not realize that this wonderful accomplishment would, in time, be responsible for her death.

Mme. Curie received not one, but two Nobel Prizes, one in physics and one in chemistry. She was the first woman in France to earn the rank of Professor.

As you study this chapter, the contributions of Mme. Curie, Pierre Curie, and the others of that time will become even more clear. Ironically, the field of medicine has been a major beneficiary of advances in nuclear and radiochemistry, despite the toxic properties of those same radioactive materials.

INTRODUCTION

Our discussion of the atom and atomic structure has revealed a nucleus containing protons and neutrons surrounded by electrons. Until now, we have treated the nucleus as simply a region of positive charge in the center of the atom. The focus of our interest has been the electrons and their arrangement around the nucleus; electron arrangement is an essential part of a discussion of bonding or chemical change.

Chapter 2

In this chapter we consider the nucleus and nuclear properties. The behavior of nuclei may have as great an effect on our everyday lives as any of the thousands of synthetic compounds developed over the past several decades; examples of nuclear technology range from everyday items (smoke detectors) to sophisticated instruments for medical diagnosis and treatment and electrical power generation (nuclear power plants).

Beginning in 1896 with Becquerel's discovery of radiation emitted from uranium ore, the technology arising from this and related findings has produced both risks and benefits. Although early discoveries of radioactivity and its properties expanded our fundamental knowledge and brought fame to the investigators, it was not accomplished without a price. Several early investigators died prematurely of cancer and other diseases caused by the radiation they studied.

Even today, the existence of nuclear energy and its associated technology are a mixed blessing. On one side, the horrors of Nagasaki and Hiroshima, the fear of nuclear war, and potential contamination of populated areas resulting from the peaceful application of nuclear energy are critical problems facing society. Conversely, thousands of lives have been saved because of the early detection of disease by X-ray diagnosis and the cure of cancer using cobalt-60 treatment. Furthermore, nuclear energy is an alternative energy source. It has provided an opportunity for us to compensate for the depletion of oil reserves.

8.1 NATURAL RADIOACTIVITY

Be careful not to confuse the mass number (neutrons and protons) with the atomic mass, which includes the contribution of electrons and is a true *mass* figure.

Radioactivity is the process by which atoms emit energetic particles or rays. These particles or rays are termed *radiation*. Nuclear radiation occurs as a result of an alteration in nuclear composition or structure; this process occurs in nature because the nucleus is unstable and hence radioactive. Radioactivity is a nuclear event; *matter and energy released during this process come from the nucleus.*

We shall designate the nucleus using *nuclear symbols,* analogous to the *atomic symbols* that were introduced in Section 2.2. The nuclear symbols consist of the *elemental symbol,* the *atomic number* (the number of protons in the nucleus), and the *mass number,* which is defined as the sum of neutrons and protons in the nucleus.

With the use of nuclear symbols the fluorine nucleus is represented as

$$\text{Mass number} \rightarrow \atop \text{Atomic number} \rightarrow \quad {}^{19}_{9}\text{F} \leftarrow \text{Atomic symbol}$$
$$\text{(or nuclear charge)}$$

This symbol is equivalent to writing "fluorine-19." This alternative representation is frequently used to denote specific isotopes of elements.

Isotopes are introduced in Section 2.2.

Not all nuclei are unstable; only unstable nuclei undergo change and produce radioactivity, the process of radioactive decay. Furthermore, not all atoms of a particular element undergo radioactive decay. Recall that different atoms of the same element having different masses exist as *isotopes.* One isotope of an element may be radioactive, while others of the same element may be quite stable.

Many elements in the periodic table occur in nature as mixtures of isotopes. Two common examples include carbon,

$${}^{12}_{6}\text{C} \qquad {}^{13}_{6}\text{C} \qquad {}^{14}_{6}\text{C}$$

Carbon-12   Carbon-13   Carbon-14

and hydrogen,

$${}^{1}_{1}\text{H} \qquad {}^{2}_{1}\text{H} \qquad {}^{3}_{1}\text{H}$$

Hydrogen-1   Hydrogen-2   Hydrogen-3

Protium   Deuterium   Tritium
           (symbol D)   (symbol T)

Section 8.3

Protium is a stable isotope and makes up more than 99.9% of naturally occurring hydrogen. Deuterium (D) can be isolated from hydrogen; it can form compounds such as "heavy water," D_2O. Heavy water is a potential source of deuterium for fusion processes. Tritium (T) is unstable, hence radioactive, and is a waste product of nuclear reactors.

In writing the symbols for a nuclear process, it is important to indicate the particular isotope involved. This is why the mass number and atomic number are used; these values tell us the number of neutrons in the species, hence the isotope's identity.

Three types of natural radiation emitted by unstable nuclei are *alpha particles, beta particles,* and *gamma rays.*

Alpha, beta, and gamma radiation have widespread use in the field of medicine. Other radiation particles, such as neutrinos and deuterons, will not be discussed here.

Alpha particles

Alpha particles (α) contain two protons and two neutrons. An alpha particle is identical to the nucleus of the helium atom (He) or a *helium ion* (He^{2+}), which also contains two protons (atomic number = 2) and two neutrons (mass number − atomic number = 2). Having no electrons to counterbalance the nuclear charge, the alpha particle may be symbolized as

$${}^{4}_{2}\text{He}^{2+} \qquad \text{or} \qquad {}^{4}_{2}\text{He} \qquad \text{or} \qquad \alpha$$

Alpha particles have a relatively large mass compared to other nuclear particles; consequently, alpha particles emitted by radioisotopes are relatively slow-moving particles (approximately 10% of the speed of light), and they are stopped by barriers as thin as a few pages of this book.

Beta particles

The **beta particle** (β), in contrast, is a fast-moving electron traveling at approximately 90% of the speed of light as it leaves the nucleus; it is formed in the nucleus by the conversion of a neutron into a proton. The beta particle is represented as

$$_{-1}^{0}e \quad \text{or} \quad _{-1}^{0}\beta \quad \text{or} \quad \beta$$

The subscript -1 is written in the same position as the atomic number and, like the atomic number (number of protons), indicates the charge of the particle.

Beta particles are smaller, faster, and more energetic than alpha particles. They are more penetrating and are stopped only by more dense materials such as wood, metal, or several layers of clothing.

Gamma rays (γ) are pure energy, resulting from nuclear processes; alpha radiation and beta radiation are matter. Since pure energy has no mass or charge, the symbol for a gamma ray is simply

$$\gamma$$

Gamma radiation is highly energetic and is the most penetrating form of nuclear radiation. Barriers of lead, concrete, or, more often, a combination of the two are required for protection from this type of radiation.

Gamma rays

Important properties of alpha, beta, and gamma radiation are summarized in Table 8.1.

The penetrating power of alpha radiation is very low. Damage to internal organs from this form of radiation is negligible except when an alpha particle emitter is actually ingested. Beta particles are higher in energy; still, they have limited penetrating power. They cause skin and eye damage and, to a lesser extent, damage to internal organs. Shielding is required in working with beta emitters; pregnant women must take special precautions.

The great penetrating power and high energy of gamma radiation make it particularly damaging to internal organs. However, one must take precautions when working with any type of radiation. Radiation safety is required, monitored, and enforced in the United States under provisions of the Occupational Safety and Health Act (OSHA).

Properties of alpha, beta, and gamma radiation

QUESTION 8.1

Gamma radiation is a form of *electromagnetic radiation*. Provide examples of other forms of electromagnetic radiation.

QUESTION 8.2

How does the energy of gamma radiation compare with that of other regions of the electromagnetic spectrum?

TABLE 8.1 A Summary of the Major Properties of Alpha, Beta, and Gamma Radiation

Name and Symbol	Identity	Charge	Mass (amu)	Velocity	Penetration
Alpha (α)	Helium nucleus	$+2$	4.0026	5–10% of the speed of light	Low
Beta (β)	Electron	-1	0.000549	Up to 90% of the speed of light	Medium
Gamma (γ)	Radiant energy	0	0	Speed of light	High

8.2 WRITING A BALANCED NUCLEAR EQUATION

Nuclear equations represent nuclear change in much the same way as chemical equations represent chemical change.

A **nuclear equation** represents the process of radioactive decay. In radioactive decay an isotope breaks down, producing a *new isotope, smaller particles, and/or energy*. The concept of mass balance, required when writing chemical equations, is also essential for nuclear equations. When writing a balanced equation, remember that:

◆ The total mass on each side of the reaction arrow must be identical.

◆ The sum of the charges of the reactant nuclei must equal the sum of the charges of the product nuclei.

Alpha decay

Consider the decay of one isotope of uranium, $^{238}_{92}U$, into thorium and an alpha particle. Because an alpha particle is lost in this process, this decay is called *alpha decay*.

Examine the balanced equation for this nuclear reaction:

$$^{238}_{92}U \longrightarrow {}^{234}_{90}Th + {}^{4}_{2}He$$

Uranium-238   Thorium-234   Helium-4

The mass on the right ($234 + 4 = 238$) is equal to the mass on the left. The number of protons on the right ($90 + 2 = 92$) is equal to the number of protons on the left.

Beta decay

Beta decay is illustrated by the decay of one of the less-abundant nitrogen isotopes, $^{16}_{7}N$. Nitrogen-16, upon decomposition, produces oxygen-16 and a beta particle. The reaction is represented as

$$^{16}_{7}N \longrightarrow {}^{16}_{8}O + {}^{0}_{-1}e$$

Note that the mass number of the beta particle is zero, since the electron includes no protons or neutrons. Sixteen amu are accounted for on both sides of the reaction arrow.

The total charge on the left ($+7$) is counterbalanced by $[8 + (-1)]$ or ($+7$) on the right. Therefore the equation is correctly balanced.

Gamma production

If *gamma radiation* were the only product of nuclear decay, there would be no change in the mass or identity of the radioactive nuclei. This is so because a gamma ray is pure energy, having no mass or charge. The gamma emitter has simply gone to a lower energy state. An example of an isotope that decays in this way is technetium-99m. Technetium-99m is described as a **metastable isotope,** meaning that it is unstable and increases its stability through gamma decay without change in the mass or charge of the isotope. The letter ''m'' is used to denote a metastable isotope. The decay equation for $^{99m}_{43}Tc$ is

$$^{99m}_{43}Tc \longrightarrow {}^{99}_{43}Tc + \gamma$$

More often, gamma radiation is produced along with other products. For example, iodine-131 decays as follows:

$$^{131}_{53}I \longrightarrow {}^{131}_{54}Xe + {}^{0}_{-1}\beta + \gamma$$

Iodine-131   Xenon-131   Beta   Gamma
                                particle   ray

An isotope of xenon, a beta particle, and gamma radiation are produced.

Predicting products of nuclear decay

It is possible to use a nuclear equation to predict one of the products of a nuclear reaction if the others are known. Consider the following example, in which we represent the unknown product as X:

$$^{40}_{19}K \longrightarrow X + {}^{0}_{-1}e$$

Step 1: The mass number of potassium is 40. Therefore the sum of the mass number of the products must also be 40. **X** must have a mass of 40 amu as well.

Step 2: Likewise, the charge on the left is $+19$, and the charge on the right must also be $+19$. The sum of the unknown nuclear charge plus the charge of the beta particle (-1) must equal 19.

Step 3: The unknown charge must be 20, since $[20 + (-1) = 19]$. The unknown is

$$^{40}_{20}X$$

If we consult the periodic table, the element that is atomic number 20 is calcium; therefore $X = ^{40}_{20}Ca$.

EXAMPLE 8.1

Predicting the Products of Radioactive Decay

Determine the identity of the unknown product of the alpha decay of californium-245:

$$^{245}_{96}Cm \longrightarrow ^{4}_{2}He + X$$

Solution

Step 1: The mass number of the californium isotope is 245. Therefore the sum of the mass number of the products must also be 245. **X** must have a mass of 241 amu.

Step 2: Likewise, the charge on the left is $+96$, and the charge on the right must also be $+96$. The sum of the unknown nuclear charge plus the charge of the alpha particle $(+2)$ must equal 96.

Step 3: The unknown charge must be 94, since $[94 + (+2) = 96]$. The unknown is

$$^{241}_{94}X$$

Referring to the periodic table, we find that the element that has atomic number 94 is plutonium; therefore $X = ^{241}_{94}Pu$.

QUESTION 8.3

Complete each of the following nuclear equations:

a. $^{85}_{36}Kr \longrightarrow X + ^{0}_{-1}e$

b. $X \longrightarrow ^{4}_{2}He + ^{222}_{86}Rn$

QUESTION 8.4

Complete each of the following nuclear equations:

a. $^{239}_{92}U \longrightarrow X + ^{0}_{-1}e$

b. $^{11}_{5}B \longrightarrow ^{7}_{3}Li + X$

Why are some isotopes radioactive while others are not? Do all radioactive isotopes decay at the same rate? Are all radioactive materials equally hazardous? We address these and other questions in this section.

The energy that holds the protons, neutrons, and other particles together in the nucleus is the **binding energy** of the nucleus. This binding energy must be quite large, since identically charged protons in the nucleus exert extreme repulsive forces on one another. These forces must be overcome if the nucleus is to be stable. When an isotope decays, some of this binding energy is released. This released energy is the source of the high-energy radiation emitted and the basis for all nuclear technology.

8.3 PROPERTIES OF RADIOISOTOPES

Nuclear structure and stability

Why are some isotopes more stable than others? The answer to this question is not completely clear. Evidence obtained so far points to several important factors that describe stable nuclei:

◆ Nuclear stability correlates with the ratio of neutrons to protons in the isotope. For example, for light atoms a neutron/proton ratio of 1 characterizes a stable atom.

◆ Nuclei with large numbers of protons (84 or more) tend to be unstable.

◆ Isotopes containing 2, 8, 20, 50, 82, or 126 protons or neutrons are stable. These *magic numbers* seem to indicate the presence of energy levels in the nucleus, analogous to electronic energy levels in the atom.

◆ Isotopes with even numbers of protons or neutrons are generally more stable than those with odd numbers of protons or neutrons.

Half-life

Refer to the discussion of radiation exposure and safety in Section 8.5.

Not all radioactive isotopes decay at the same rate. The rate of nuclear decay is generally represented in terms of the half-life of the isotope. The **half-life ($t_{1/2}$)** is the time required for one-half of a given quantity of a substance to undergo change. Each isotope has its own characteristic half-life that may be as short as a few millionths of a second or as long as a billion years. Half-lives of some naturally occurring isotopes are given in Table 8.2.

The stability of an isotope is indicated by the isotope's half-life. Isotopes with short half-lives decay rapidly; they are very unstable. This is not meant to imply that substances with long half-lives are less hazardous. Often, just the reverse is true.

Imagine that we begin with 100 mg of a radioactive isotope that has a half-life of 24 hours. After one half-life, or 24 hours, 1/2 of 100 mg will have decayed to other products, and 50 mg remain. After two half-lives (48 hours), 1/2 of the remaining material has decayed, leaving 25 mg, and so forth:

$$100 \text{ mg} \xrightarrow[\substack{\text{half-life} \\ (24 \text{ h})}]{\text{one}} 50 \text{ mg} \xrightarrow[\substack{\text{half-lives} \\ (48 \text{ h})}]{\text{two}} 25 \text{ mg} \longrightarrow \text{ etc.}$$

Decay of a radioisotope that has a reasonably short $t_{1/2}$ is experimentally determined by following its activity as a function of time. Graphing the results produces a radioactive decay curve as shown in Figure 8.1.

The mass of any radioactive substance remaining after a period of time may be calculated with a knowledge of the initial mass and the half-life of the isotope, following the scheme outlined above.

TABLE 8.2   Half-lives of Selected Radioisotopes

Name	Symbol	Half-life
Carbon-14	$^{14}_{6}C$	5730 years
Cobalt-60	$^{60}_{27}Co$	5.3 years
Hydrogen-3	$^{3}_{1}H$	12.3 years
Iodine-131	$^{131}_{53}I$	8.1 days
Iron-59	$^{59}_{26}Fe$	45 days
Molybdenum-99	$^{99}_{42}Mo$	67 hours
Sodium-24	$^{24}_{11}Na$	15 hours
Strontium-90	$^{90}_{38}Sr$	28 years
Technetium-99m	$^{99m}_{43}Tc$	6 hours
Uranium-235	$^{235}_{92}U$	710 million years

EXAMPLE 8.2

A 50.0-mg sample of iodine-131, used in hospitals in the treatment of hyperthyroidism, was saved for 32.4 days. If the half-life of iodine-131 is 8.1 days, how many milligrams remain?

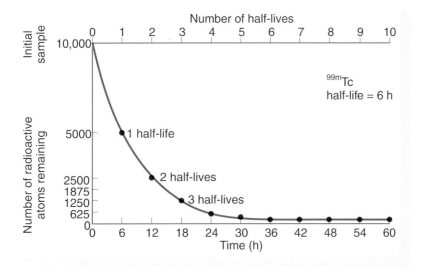

FIGURE 8.1
The decay curve for the medically useful radioisotope technetium-99m. Note that the number of radioactive atoms remaining—hence the radioactivity—approaches but never reaches zero. After ten half-lives (60 hours) the level of radiation is indistinguishable from background.

Solution

First calculate n, the number of half-lives elapsed using the half-life as a conversion factor:

$$n = 32.4 \text{ days} \times \frac{1 \text{ half-life}}{8.1 \text{ days}} = 4.0 \text{ half-lives}$$

Then calculate the amount remaining:

$$50.0 \text{ mg} \xrightarrow[\substack{\text{half-} \\ \text{life}}]{\text{first}} 25.0 \text{ mg} \xrightarrow[\substack{\text{half-} \\ \text{life}}]{\text{second}} 12.5 \text{ mg} \xrightarrow[\substack{\text{half-} \\ \text{life}}]{\text{third}} 6.25 \text{ mg} \xrightarrow[\substack{\text{half-} \\ \text{life}}]{\text{fourth}} 3.13 \text{ mg}$$

QUESTION 8.5

A 100.0-ng sample of sodium-24 was stored in a lead-lined cabinet for 2.5 days. How much sodium-24 remained? See Table 8.2 for the half-life of sodium-24.

QUESTION 8.6

If a patient is administered 10 ng of technetium-99m, how much will remain one day later, assuming that no technetium has been eliminated by any other process? See Table 8.2 for the half-life of technetium-99m.

Energy production

Einstein predicted that a small amount of nuclear mass corresponds to a very large amount of energy that is released when the nucleus breaks apart. Einstein's equation is

$$E = mc^2$$

where

$$E = \text{energy}$$

$$m = \text{mass}$$

$$c = \text{speed of light}$$

This heat energy, when rapidly released, is the basis for the greatest instruments of destruction: nuclear bombs. However, when heat energy is released in a controlled fashion, as in a nuclear power plant, the heat energy converts liquid water into steam. The steam, in turn, drives an electrical generator, producing electricity.

Three types of nuclear reactors can be used to generate electrical power. They are *fission, fusion,* and *breeder* reactors.

Fission (splitting) occurs when a heavy nucleus is split into smaller nuclei after being hit by a small nuclear particle such as a neutron. This splitting process releases large amounts of energy.

Fusion (meaning *to join together*) results from the combination of two small nuclei to form a larger nucleus with the concurrent release of large amounts of energy. The sun is a natural fusion reactor furnishing our solar system with light and heat. On the earth, despite research spanning decades, electric power from fusion is still an impractical alternative.

A **breeder reactor** literally manufactures its own fuel. A perceived shortage of fissionable isotopes makes the breeder an attractive alternative to fission reactors. A breeder reactor uses $^{238}_{92}U$, which is abundant but nonfissionable. In a series of steps the uranium-238 is converted to plutonium-239, which *is* fissionable and undergoes a fission chain reaction, producing energy.

Radiocarbon dating

Natural radioactivity is useful in establishing the approximate age of objects of archaeological, anthropological, or historical interest through **radiocarbon dating.**

Radiocarbon dating is based on the measurement of the relative amounts (or ratio) of $^{14}_{6}C$ and $^{12}_{6}C$ present in an object. $^{14}_{6}C$ is formed in the upper atmosphere by the bombardment of $^{14}_{7}N$ by high-speed neutrons from the sun:

$$^{14}_{7}N + {}^{1}_{0}n \longrightarrow {}^{14}_{6}C + {}^{1}_{1}H$$

The carbon-14, along with the more abundant carbon-12, is converted into living plant material by the process of photosynthesis. Carbon proceeds up the food chain as the plants are consumed by animals, including humans. When a plant or animal dies, the uptake of both carbon-14 and carbon-12 ceases. However, the amount of carbon-14 slowly decreases because carbon-14 is radioactive ($t_{1/2}$ = 5730 years).

When the artifact is found and studied, the relative amounts of carbon-14 and carbon-12 are determined; by using suitable equations involving the $t_{1/2}$ of carbon-14, it is possible to approximate the age of the artifact.

This technique has been widely used to increase our knowledge about the history of the earth, to establish the age of objects (Figure 8.2), and even to detect art forgeries. Early paintings were made with inks fabricated from vegetable dyes (plant material that, while alive, metabolized carbon).

FIGURE 8.2
Radiocarbon dating was used in the authentication study of the shroud of Turin. It is a nondestructive technique and is valuable in the estimation of the age of historical artifacts.

AN ENVIRONMENTAL PERSPECTIVE

Nuclear Waste Disposal

Nuclear waste arises from a variety of sources. A major source is the spent fuel from nuclear power plants. Medical laboratories generate large amounts of low-level waste from tracers and therapy. Even household items with limited lifetimes, such as certain types of smoke detectors, use a tiny amount of radioactive material.

Virtually everyone is aware, through television and newspapers, of the problems of solid waste (nonnuclear) disposal that our society faces. For the most part, this material will degrade in some reasonable amount of time. Still, we are disposing of trash and garbage at a rate that far exceeds nature's ability to recycle it.

Now imagine the problem with nuclear waste. We cannot alter the rate at which it decays. This is defined by the half-life. We can't heat it, stir it, or add a catalyst to speed up the process as we can with chemical reactions. Furthermore, the half-lives of many nuclear waste products are very long; plutonium, for example, has a half-life in excess of 24,000 years. Ten half-lives are required for the radioactivity of a substance to reach background levels. So we are talking about a *very* long storage time.

Where on earth can something so very hazardous be containerized and stored with reasonable assurance that it will lie undisturbed for a quarter of a million years? Perhaps this is a rhetorical question. Scientists, engineers, and politicians have debated this question for almost 50 years. As yet, no permanent disposal site has been agreed upon. Most agree that the best solution is burial in a stable rock formation, but there is no agreement on the location. Fear of earthquakes, which may release large quantities of radioactive materials into the underground water system, is the most serious consideration. Such a disaster could render large sections of the country unfit for habitation.

Many argue for the continuation of temporary storage sites with the hope that the progress of science and technology will, in the years ahead, provide a safer and more satisfactory long-term solution.

The nuclear waste problem, important for its own sake, also affects the development of future societal uses of nuclear chemistry. Before we can enjoy its benefits, we must learn to use and dispose of it safely.

A photograph of the earth, taken from the moon, clearly illustrates the limits of resources as well as the limits to waste disposal.

8.4 MEDICAL APPLICATIONS OF RADIOACTIVITY

The use of radiation in the treatment of various forms of cancer, as well as the newer area of **nuclear medicine,** the use of radioisotopes in diagnosis, has become widespread in the past quarter-century. Let's look at the properties of radiation that make it an indispensable tool in modern medical care.

Cancer therapy using radiation

When high-energy radiation, such as gamma radiation, passes through a cell, it may collide with one of the molecules in the cell and cause it to lose one or more electrons, producing an ion pair. For this reason, such radiation is termed **ionizing radiation.**

Ions produced in this way may damage biological molecules and cause changes in cellular biochemical processes. This may result in diminished or altered cell function or, in extreme cases, the death of the cell.

An organ that is cancerous is composed of both healthy cells and malignant cells. Tumor cells are more susceptible to the effects of gamma radiation than normal cells because they are undergoing cell division more frequently. Therefore exposure of the tumor area to carefully targeted and controlled dosages of high-energy gamma radiation from cobalt-60 (a high-energy gamma ray source) will kill a higher percentage of abnormal cells than normal cells. If the dosage is administered correctly, a sufficient number of malignant cells will die, destroying the tumor, and enough normal cells will survive to maintain the function of the affected organ.

Gamma radiation can cure cancer; paradoxically, the exposure of healthy cells to gamma radiation can actually cause cancer. For this reason, radiation therapy for cancer is a treatment that requires unusual care and sophistication.

Nuclear medicine

The diagnosis of a host of biochemical irregularities or diseases of the human body has been made routine through the use of radioactive tracers. **Tracers** are small amounts of radioactive substances used as probes to study internal organs. Medical techniques involving tracers are **nuclear imaging** procedures.

A small amount of the tracer, an isotope of an element that is known to be attracted to the organ of interest, is administered to the patient. For a variety of reasons, such as ease of administration of the isotope to the patient as well as targeting the organ of interest, the isotope is often a part of a larger molecule or ion. Because the isotope is radioactive, its path may be followed by using suitable detection devices. A "picture" of the organ is obtained, often far more detailed than is possible with conventional X-rays. Such techniques are noninvasive; that is, surgery is not required to investigate the condition of the internal organ, eliminating the risk associated with an operation.

The radioactive isotope of an element has exactly the same chemical behavior as any other isotope of the same element. For example, iodine-127, the most abundant nonradioactive isotope of iodine, tends to concentrate in the thyroid gland. Both radioactive iodine-131 and iodine-125 behave in the same way and are used to study the thyroid. The rate of uptake of the radioactive isotope gives valuable information regarding underactivity or overactivity (hypoactive or hyperactive thyroid).

Isotopes with short half-lives are preferred for tracer studies. These isotopes emit their radiation in a more concentrated burst (short-half-life materials have greater activity), facilitating their detection. If the radioactive decay is easily detected, the method is more sensitive and thus capable of providing more information. Furthermore, an isotope with a short half-life decays to background more rapidly; this is a mechanism for removal of the radioactivity from the body. If the radioactive element is also rapidly metabolized and excreted, this is obviously beneficial as well.

Examples of the use of imaging procedures for diagnosis of disease are briefly described below:

◆ *Bone disease and injury.* The most widely used isotope for bone studies is technetium-99m, which is incorporated into a variety of ions and molecules that direct the isotope to the tissue being investigated. Technetium compounds containing phosphate are preferentially adsorbed on the surface of bone. New bone formation (common to virtually all bone injuries) increases the incorporation of the technetium compound. As a result, an enhanced image appears at the site of the injury. Bone tumors behave in a similar fashion.

◆ *Cardiovascular diseases.* Thallium-201 is used in the diagnosis of coronary artery disease. The isotope is administered intravenously and delivered to the heart muscle in proportion to the blood flow. Areas of restricted flow are observed as having lower levels of radioactivity, indicating some type of blockage.

◆ *Pulmonary disease.* Xenon is one of the noble gases. Radioactive xenon-133 may be inhaled by the patient. The radioactive isotope will be transported from the lungs and distributed through the circulatory system. Monitoring the distribution, as well as the reverse process, the removal of the isotope from the body (exhalation), can provide evidence of obstructive pulmonary disease, such as cancer or emphysema.

Examples of useful isotopes and the organ(s) in which they tend to concentrate are summarized in Table 8.3.

For many years, imaging using radioactive tracers was used exclusively for diagnosis; recent applications have expanded to other areas of medicine as well. Imaging is now used extensively to guide surgery, assist in planning radiation therapy, and support the technique of angioplasty.

TABLE 8.3 Isotopes Commonly Used in Nuclear Medicine

Area of Body	Isotope	Use
Blood	Red blood cells tagged with chromium-51	Determine blood volume in body
Bone	Technetium-99m, barium-131	Allow early detection of the extent of bone tumors and active sites of rheumatoid arthritis
Brain	Technetium-99m	Detect and locate brain tumors and stroke
Coronary artery	Thallium-201	Determine the presence and location of obstructions in coronary arteries
Heart	Technetium-99m	Determine cardiac output, size, and shape
Kidney	Technetium-99m	Determine renal function and location of cysts; a common follow-up procedure for kidney transplant patients
Liver-spleen	Technetium-99m	Determine size and shape of liver and spleen; location of tumors
Lung	Xenon-133	Determine whether lung fills properly; locate region of reduced ventilation and tumors
Thyroid	Iodine-131	Determine rate of iodine uptake by thyroid

QUESTION 8.7

Technetium-99m is used in diagnostic imaging studies involving the brain. What fraction of the radioisotope remains after 12 hours have elapsed? See Table 8.2 for the half-life of technetium-99m.

QUESTION 8.8

Strontium-90 is a radioisotope used to study bone formation. A 21-year-old patient ingested strontium-90. How old will the patient be when 1/4 of the strontium-90 remains, assuming that none of the isotope is eliminated from the body through normal processes? See Table 8.2 for the half-life of strontium-90.

In the examples discussed thus far, all of the radioactive isotopes were naturally occurring. For this reason the radioactivity produced by these unstable isotopes is described as **natural radioactivity.** If, on the other hand, a normally stable, nonradioactive nucleus is made radioactive, the resulting radioactivity is termed **artificial radioactivity.** The stable nucleus is made unstable by the introduction of ''extra'' protons, neutrons, or both.

The process of forming radioactive substances is often accomplished in the core of a **nuclear reactor,** in which an abundance of small nuclear particles, particularly neutrons, is available. Alternatively, extremely high-velocity charged particles (such as alpha and beta particles) may be produced in **particle accelerators,** such as a cyclotron. Accelerators are extremely large and use magnetic and electric fields to ''push and pull'' charged particles toward their target at very high speeds. A portion of the accelerator at the Brookhaven National Laboratory is shown in Figure 8.3.

Making isotopes for medical applications

FIGURE 8.3
A portion of a linear accelerator located at Brookhaven National Laboratory in New York. Particles can be accelerated at velocities close to the speed of light and accurately strike small "target" nuclei. At such facilities, rare isotopes can be synthesized and their properties studied.

Many isotopes that are useful in medicine are produced by particle bombardment. A few examples are illustrated below:

◆ Gold-198, used as a tracer in the liver:

$$^{197}_{79}\text{Au} + {}^{1}_{0}\text{n} \longrightarrow {}^{198}_{79}\text{Au}$$

◆ Gallium-67, used in the diagnosis of Hodgkin's disease:

$$^{66}_{30}\text{Zn} + {}^{1}_{1}\text{p} \longrightarrow {}^{67}_{31}\text{Ga}$$

Some medically useful isotopes, with short half-lives, must be prepared near the site of the clinical test. Preparation and shipment from a reactor site would be time-consuming and result in an isotopic solution that had already undergone significant decay, resulting in diminished activity.

A common example is technetium-99m. It has a half-life of only 6 hours. It is prepared in a small generator, often housed in a hospital's radiology laboratory (Figure 8.4). The generator contains radioactive molybdate ion ($\text{MoO}_4{}^{2-}$). Molybdenum-99 is more stable than technetium-99m; it has a half-life of 67 hours.

The molybdate decays according to the following nuclear equation:

$$^{99}_{42}\text{Mo} \longrightarrow {}^{99\text{m}}_{43}\text{Tc} + {}^{0}_{-1}\text{e}$$

Chemically, radioactive molybdate converts to radioactive pertechnetate ion:

$$\text{MoO}_4{}^{2-} \longrightarrow \text{TcO}_4{}^{-}$$

The radioactive $\text{TcO}_4{}^{-}$ is removed from the generator when needed. It is administered to the patient as an aqueous salt solution that has an osmotic pressure identical to that of human blood.

8.5 BIOLOGICAL EFFECTS OF RADIATION

It is necessary to use suitable precautions in working with radioactive substances. The chosen protocol is based on an understanding of the effects of radiation, dosage levels and "tolerable levels," the way in which radiation is detected and measured, and the basic precepts of radiation safety.

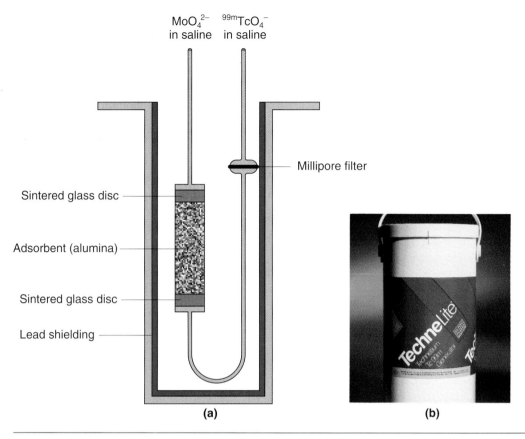

MoO_4^{2-} in saline $^{99m}TcO_4^-$ in saline

Millipore filter

Sintered glass disc

Adsorbent (alumina)

Sintered glass disc

Lead shielding

(a)

(b)

FIGURE 8.4
Preparation of Technetium-99m.
(a) A diagram depicting the conversion of $^{99}MoO_4^{2-}$ to $^{99m}TcO_4^-$ through radioactive decay. The radioactive pertechnetate ion is periodically removed from the generator in saline solution and used in tracer studies. (b) A photograph of a commercially available technetium-99m generator suitable for use in a hospital laboratory.

In working with radioactive materials, the following factors must be considered.

The magnitude of the half-life

Radiation exposure and safety

In considering safety, isotopes with short half-lives have, at the same time, one major disadvantage and one major advantage.

On one hand, short-half-life radioisotopes produce a larger amount of radioactivity per unit time than a long-half-life substance. For example, consider equal amounts of hypothetical isotopes that produce alpha particles. One has a half-life of 10 days; the other has a half-life of 100 days. After one half-life, each substance will produce exactly the same number of alpha particles. However, the first substance generates the alpha particles in only one-tenth of the time, hence emits ten times as much radiation per unit time.

On the other hand, materials with short half-lives (weeks, days, or less) may be safer to work with, especially if an accident occurs. A period of ten half-lives is sufficient for any isotope to decay to **background** levels. This is the level of radiation attributable to our surroundings on a day-to-day basis.

All matter is composed of both radioactive and nonradioactive isotopes. Small amounts of radioactive material in the air, water, soil, and so forth make up a part of the background levels. Cosmic rays from outer space continually bombard us with radiation, contributing to the total background. Owing to the inevitability of background radiation, there can be no such thing as ''zero'' radiation!

An isotope with a short half-life, for example 5.0 minutes, will decay to background in

$$10 \; \text{half-lives} \times \frac{5.0 \; \text{minutes}}{1 \; \text{half-life}} = 50 \; \text{minutes}$$

A spill of such material could be treated by waiting ten half-lives. Perhaps go to lunch. When you return to the laboratory, the material that was spilled will be no more radioactive than the floor itself. An accident with plutonium-239, which has a half-life of 24,000 years, would be quite a different matter! After 50 minutes, virtually all of the plutonium-239 would still remain.

FIGURE 8.5
Photograph of the construction of one-million-gallon capacity storage tanks for radioactive waste. Located in Hanford, Washington, they are now covered with 6–8 feet of earth.

See "An Environmental Perspective: Nuclear Waste Disposal."

Long-half-life isotopes, by-products of nuclear technology, pose the greatest problems for safe disposal. Finding a site that will remain undisturbed ''forever'' is quite a formidable task.

QUESTION 8.9

Describe the advantage of using isotopes with short half-lives for tracer applications in a medical laboratory.

QUESTION 8.10

Can you think of any disadvantage associated with the use of isotopes described in Question 8.9?

Shielding

Alpha and beta particles, being relatively low in energy, require low-level **shielding.** A lab coat and gloves are generally sufficient protection from this low-penetration radiation. On the other hand, shielding made of lead, concrete, or both is required for gamma rays (and X-rays, which are also high-energy radiation). Extensive manipulation of gamma emitters is often accomplished in laboratory and industrial settings by using robotic control: computer-controlled mechanical devices that can be programmed to perform virtually all manipulations normally carried out by humans.

Distance from the radioactive source

Radiation intensity varies *inversely* with the *square* of the distance from the source. Doubling the distance from the source *decreases* the intensity by a factor of 4 (2^2). Again, the use of robot manipulators is advantageous, allowing a greater distance between the operator and the radioactive source.

Time of exposure

The effects of radiation are cumulative. Generally, potential damage is directly proportional to the time of exposure. Workers exposed to moderately high levels of radiation on the job may be limited in the time that they can perform that task. For example, workers involved in the cleanup of the Three Mile Island nuclear plant, incapacitated in 1979, observed strict limits on the amount of time that they could be involved in the cleanup activities.

Types of radiation emitted

Alpha and beta emitters are generally less hazardous than gamma emitters, owing to differences in energy and penetrating power.

Virtually all applications of nuclear chemistry create radioactive waste and, along with it, the problems of safe handling and disposal. Most disposal sites, at present, are considered temporary, until a long-term safe solution can be found. Figure 8.5 conveys some feeling for the enormity of the problem.

8.6 DETECTION AND MEASUREMENT OF RADIATION

The changes that take place when radiation interacts with matter (such as photographic film) provide the basis of operation for various radiation detection devices.

The principal detection methods involve the use of either photographic film to create an image of the radioactive substance or a counter that allows the measurement of intensity of radiation emitted from some source by converting the radiation energy to an electrical signal.

Nuclear imaging

This approach is often used in nuclear medicine. An isotope is administered to a patient, perhaps iodine-131, which is used to study the thyroid gland, and the isotope begins to concentrate in the organ of interest. Nuclear images (photographs) of that region of the body are taken at periodic intervals using a special type of film. The emission of radiation from the radioactive substance creates the image, in much the same way as light causes the formation of images on conven-

AN ENVIRONMENTAL PERSPECTIVE

Radon and Indoor Air Pollution

Marie and Pierre Curie first discovered that air in contact with radium compounds became radioactive. Later experiments by Ernest Rutherford and others isolated the radioactive substance from the air. This substance was an isotope of the noble gas, radon (Rn).

We now know that radium (Ra) produces radon by spontaneous decay:

$$^{226}_{88}Ra \longrightarrow \, ^{4}_{2}He + \, ^{222}_{86}Rn$$

Radium in trace quantities is found in the soil and rock and is unequally distributed in the soil. The decay product, radon, is emitted from the soil to the surrounding atmosphere. (Radon is also found in higher concentrations when uranium is found in the soil; this is not surprising, since radium is formed as a part of the stepwise decay of uranium.)

If one constructs a building over soil or rock that has a high radium content (or uses stone with a high radium content to build the foundation!), the radon gas can percolate through the basement and accumulate in the house. Couple this with the need to build more energy-efficient, well-insulated dwellings, and the radon levels in buildings in some regions of the country can become quite high.

Radon itself is radioactive; however, its radiation is not the major problem. Since it is a gas and chemically inert, it is rapidly exhaled after breathing. However, radon decays to polonium:

$$^{222}_{86}Rn \longrightarrow \, ^{4}_{2}He + \, ^{218}_{84}Po$$

This polonium isotope is radioactive, has a long half-life, and is a nonvolatile heavy metal that can attach itself to bronchial or lung tissue and remain for a long time, emitting hazardous radiation.

In the United States, homes are now being tested and monitored for radon. Studies continue to attempt to find reasonable solutions to the problem. Current recommendations include sealing cracks and openings in basements, increasing ventilation, and evaluating sites prior to construction of buildings. Debate continues within the scientific community regarding a safe and attainable indoor air quality standard for radon.

---

tional film in a camera. Upon development of the series of photographs, a record of the organ's uptake of the isotope over time enables the radiologist to assess the condition of the organ.

Computer imaging

The coupling of rapid developments in the technology of television and computers, resulting in the marriage of these two devices, has brought about a versatile alternative to photographic imaging.

A specialized television camera, sensitive to emitted radiation from a radioactive substance administered to a patient, develops a continuous and instantaneous record of the voyage of the isotope throughout the body. The signal, transmitted to the computer, is stored, sorted, and portrayed on a cathode-ray screen. Advantages include increased sensitivity, allowing a lower dose of the isotope, speed through elimination of the developing step, and versatility of application, limited perhaps only by the creativity of the medical practitioners.

A particular type of computer imaging, useful in diagnostic medicine, is the CT scanner. The CT scanner gathers huge amounts of data and processes the data to produce detailed information, all in a relatively short time. Such a device may be less hazardous than conventional X-ray techniques because it generates more useful information per unit of radiation. It often produces a superior image. A photograph of a CT scanner is shown in Figure 8.6, and an image of a damaged spinal bone, taken by a CT scanner, is shown in Figure 8.7.

The Geiger counter

A Geiger counter is an instrument that detects ionizing radiation. Ions, produced by radiation passing through a tube filled with an ionizable gas, can conduct an electric current between two electrodes. This current flow can be measured and is proportional to the level of radiation (Figure 8.8). Such devices, which were routinely used in laboratory and industrial monitoring, have been largely replaced by more sophisticated devices, often used in conjunction with a computer.

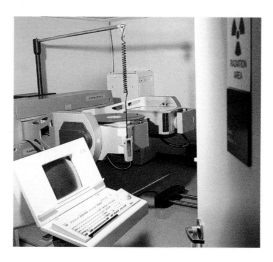

FIGURE 8.6
An imaging laboratory at the Greater Baltimore Medical Center.

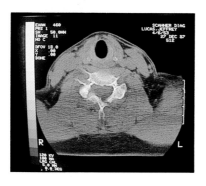

FIGURE 8.7
Damage observed in a spinal bone on a CT scan image.

Film badges

A common sight in any hospital or medical laboratory or any laboratory that routinely uses radioisotopes is the film badge worn by all staff members exposed in any way to low-level radioactivity.

A film badge is merely a piece of photographic film that is sensitive to energies corresponding to radioactive emissions. It is shielded from light, which would interfere, and mounted in a clip-on plastic holder that can be worn throughout the workday. The badges are periodically collected and developed; the degree of darkening is proportional to the amount of radiation to which the worker has been exposed, just as a conventional camera produces images on film in proportion to the amount of light that it sees.

FIGURE 8.8
The design of a Geiger counter used for the measurement of radioactivity.

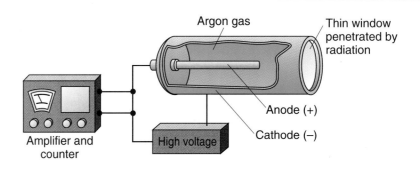

Proper record-keeping thus allows the laboratory using radioactive substances to maintain an ongoing record of each individual's exposure and, at the same time, promptly pinpoint any hazards that might otherwise go unnoticed.

8.7 UNITS OF RADIATION MEASUREMENT

The amount of radiation emitted by a source or received by an individual is reported in a variety of ways, using units that describe different aspects of radiation. The *curie* and the *roentgen* describe the intensity of the emitted radiation, while the *rad* and the *rem* describe the biological effects of radiation.

The curie

The **curie** is a measure of the amount of radioactivity in a radioactive source. The curie is independent of the nature of the radiation (alpha, beta, or gamma) as well as its effect on biological tissue. A curie is defined as the amount of radioactive material that produces 3.7×10^{10} atomic disintegrations per second.

The roentgen

The **roentgen** is a measure of ionizing radiation (X-ray and gamma ray) only. The roentgen is defined as the amount of radioactive isotope needed to produce 2×10^9 ion pairs when passing through 1 cubic centimeter of air at 0°C. The roentgen is a measure of radiation's interaction with air and gives no information about the effect on biological tissue.

The rad

The **rad, or radiation absorbed dosage,** provides more meaningful information than either of the previous units of measure. It takes into account the nature of the absorbing material. It is defined as the dosage of radiation able to transfer 2.4×10^{-3} calories of energy to 1 kilogram of matter.

The rem

The **rem, or roentgen equivalent for man,** describes the biological damage caused by the absorption of different kinds of radiation by the human body. The *rem* is obtained by multiplication of the *rad* by a factor called the *relative biological effect (RBE)*. The RBE is a function of the type of radiation (alpha, beta, or gamma). Although a beta particle is more energetic than an alpha particle, an alpha particle is approximately ten times more damaging to biological tissue. As a result, the RBE is 10 for alpha particles and 1 for beta particles. Relative yearly radiation dosages received by Americans are shown in Figure 8.9.

The **lethal dose (LD_{50})** of radiation is defined as the dosage of radiation that would be fatal for 50% of the exposed population. An estimated lethal dose is 500 rems. Some biological effect, however, may be detectable at a level as low as 25 rem.

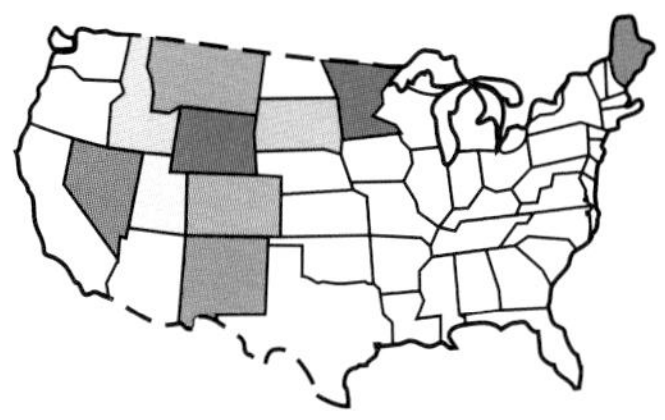

QUESTION 8.11

From a clinical standpoint, what advantages does expressing radiation in rems have over the use of other radiation units?

QUESTION 8.12

Is the roentgen unit used in the measurement of alpha radiation? Why or why not?

FIGURE 8.9
Relative yearly radiation dosages for individuals in the United States. The degree of shading is proportional to the magnitude of observed background radiation in the area.

SUMMARY

8.1 Natural Radioactivity

Radioactivity is the process by which atoms emit high-energy particles or rays. These particles or rays are termed radiation. Nuclear radiation occurs because the nucleus is unstable, hence radioactive. Nuclear symbols consist of the elemental symbol, the atomic number, and the mass number.

Not all nuclei are unstable; only unstable nuclei undergo change and produce radioactivity in the process of radioactive decay. Three types of natural radiation emitted by unstable nuclei are *alpha particles, beta particles,* and *gamma rays.*

8.2 Writing a Balanced Nuclear Equation

A *nuclear equation* represents a nuclear process such as radioactive decay. The total mass on each side of the reaction arrow must be identical, and the sum of the charges of the reactant nuclei must equal the sum of the charges of the product nuclei. Nuclear equations can be used to predict products of nuclear reactions.

8.3 Properties of Radioisotopes

The energy that holds nuclear particles together in the nucleus is the *binding energy* of the nucleus. When an isotope decays, some of this binding energy is released. Nuclear stability correlates with the ratio of neutrons to protons in the isotope. Nuclei with large numbers of protons tend to be unstable, and isotopes containing 2, 8, 20, 50, 82, or 126 protons or neutrons (magic numbers) are stable. Also, isotopes with even numbers of protons or neutrons are generally more stable than those with odd numbers of protons or neutrons.

The *half-life, $t_{1/2}$,* is the time required for one-half of a given quantity of a substance to undergo change. Each isotope has its own characteristic half-life. The degree of stability of an isotope is indicated by the isotope's half-life. Isotopes with short half-lives decay rapidly; they are very unstable.

Einstein predicted that a small amount of nuclear mass would convert to a very large amount of energy when the nucleus breaks apart. Electrical power generation using nuclear reactions may involve *fission, fusion,* or *breeder* reactors.

Radiocarbon dating is based on the measurement of the relative amounts of carbon-12 and carbon-14 present in an object and is useful in determining the age of objects containing carbon.

8.4 Medical Applications of Radioactivity

The use of radiation in the treatment of various forms of cancer, as well as the newer area of *nuclear medicine,* has become widespread in the past quarter-century.

Ionizing radiation, such as gamma radiation, causes changes in cellular biochemical processes that may damage or kill the cell. A cancerous organ is composed of both healthy and malignant cells. Exposure of the tumor area to controlled dosages of high-energy gamma radiation from cobalt-60 will kill a higher percentage of abnormal cells than normal cells and is a valuable cancer therapy.

The diagnosis of a host of biochemical irregularities or diseases of the human body has been made routine through the use of radioactive tracers. *Tracers* are small amounts of radioactive substances used as probes to study internal organs. Because the isotope is radioactive, its path may be followed by using suitable detection devices. A "picture" of the organ is obtained, often far more detailed than is possible with conventional X-rays.

The radioactivity produced by unstable isotopes is described as *natural radioactivity.* A normally stable, nonradioactive nucleus can be made radioactive, and this is termed *artificial radioactivity* (the process produces synthetic isotopes). Synthetic isotopes are often used in clinical situations. Isotopic synthesis may be carried out in the core of a *nuclear reactor* or in a *particle accelerator.* Short-lived isotopes, such as technetium-99m, are often produced directly at the site of the clinical testing.

8.5 Biological Effects of Radiation

Safety considerations are based on the magnitude of the *half-life, shielding,* distance from the radioactive source, time of exposure, as well as type of radiation emitted. We are never entirely free of the effects of radioactivity; *background radiation* is normal radiation attributable to our surroundings.

Virtually all applications of nuclear chemistry create radioactive waste and, along with it, the problems of safe handling and disposal. Most disposal sites are considered temporary, until a long-term safe solution can be found.

8.6 Detection and Measurement of Radiation

The changes that take place when radiation interacts with matter provide the basis for various radiation detection devices. Photographic imaging, computer imaging, the Geiger counter, and film badges represent the most frequently used devices for detecting and measuring radiation.

8.7 Units of Radiation Measurement

Commonly used radiation units include the *curie,* a measure of the amount of radioactivity in a radioactive source; the *roentgen,* a measure of ionizing radiation (X-ray and gamma ray); the *rad* (radiation absorbed dosage), which takes into account the nature of the absorbing material; and the *rem* (roentgen equivalent for man), which describes the biological damage caused by the absorption of different kinds of radiation by the human body. The *lethal dose of radiation,* LD_{50}, is defined as the dose that would be fatal for 50% of the exposed population within 30 days.

KEY TERMS

alpha particle (8.1)   beta particle (8.1)
artificial radioactivity (8.4)   binding energy (8.3)
background radiation (8.5)   breeder reactor (8.3)

curie (8.7)
fission process (8.3)
fusion process (8.3)
gamma ray (8.1)
half-life ($t_{1/2}$) (8.3)
ionizing radiation (8.4)
lethal dose (LD_{50}) (8.7)
metastable isotope (8.2)
natural radioactivity (8.4)
nuclear equation (8.2)
nuclear imaging (8.4)

nuclear medicine (8.4)
nuclear reactor (8.4)
particle accelerator (8.4)
rad (8.7)
radioactivity (8.1)
radiocarbon dating (8.3)
rem (8.7)
roentgen (8.7)
shielding (8.5)
tracer (8.4)

QUESTIONS AND PROBLEMS

Natural Radioactivity

8.13 Define or describe each of the following terms:
  a. natural radioactivity
  b. background radiation
  c. alpha particle
  d. alpha decay

8.14 Define or describe each of the following terms:
  a. beta particle
  b. gamma radiation
  c. beta decay
  d. artificial radioactivity

8.15 Write the nuclear symbol for each of the following:
  a. an alpha particle
  b. a beta particle
  c. a proton
  d. uranium-235

8.16 Write the nuclear symbol for each of the following:
  a. deuterium (hydrogen-2)
  b. tritium (hydrogen-3)
  c. nitrogen-15
  d. carbon-14

8.17 Compare and contrast the three major types of radiation produced by nuclear decay.

8.18 Rank the three major types of radiation in order of size, speed, and penetrating power.

Nuclear Reactions

8.19 Write a nuclear reaction to represent cobalt-60 decaying to nickel-60 plus a beta particle plus a gamma ray.

8.20 Write a nuclear reaction to represent radium-226 decaying to radon-222 plus an alpha particle.

8.21 Complete the following nuclear reaction:

$$^{23}_{11}\text{Na} + ^{2}_{1}\text{H} \longrightarrow \text{X} + ^{1}_{1}\text{H}$$

8.22 Complete the following nuclear reaction:

$$^{238}_{92}\text{U} + ^{14}_{7}\text{N} \longrightarrow \text{X} + 6^{1}_{0}\text{n}$$

Nuclear Stability

8.23 What is the difference between natural radioactivity and artificial radioactivity?

8.24 Is the fission of uranium-235 an example of natural or artificial radioactivity?

8.25 Summarize the major characteristics of nuclei for which we predict a high degree of stability.

8.26 Explain why the binding energy of a nucleus is expected to be large.

Half-Life and Energy

8.27 Which type of nuclear process splits nuclei to produce energy?

8.28 Which type of nuclear process combines small nuclei to produce energy?

8.29 Describe the process used to determine the age of the wooden coffin of King Tut.

8.30 What property of carbon enables one to assess the age of a painting?

8.31 If 3.2 mg of the radioisotope iodine-131 is administered to a patient, how much will remain in the body after 24 days, assuming that no iodine has been eliminated from the body by any other process? (See Table 8.2 for the half-life of iodine-131.)

8.32 A patient receives 10.0 ng of a radioisotope with a half-life of 12 hours. How much will remain in the body after 2.0 days, assuming that radioactive decay is the only path for removal of the isotope from the body?

8.33 A sample containing 1.00×10^2 mg of iron-59 is stored for 135 days. What mass of iron-59 will remain at the end of the storage period? (See Table 8.2 for the half-life of iron-59.)

8.34 An instrument for cancer treatment containing a cobalt-60 source was manufactured in 1968. In 1985 it was removed from service and, in error, was buried in a landfill with the source still in place. What percentage of its initial radioactivity will remain in the year 2000? (See Table 8.2 for the half-life of cobalt-60.)

Medical Applications of Radioactivity

8.35 The isotope indium-111 is used in medical laboratories as a label for blood platelets. To prepare indium-111, silver-108 is bombarded with an alpha particle, forming an intermediate isotope of indium. Write a nuclear equation for the process, and identify the intermediate isotope of indium.

8.36 Radioactive molybdenum-99 is used to produce the tracer isotope, technetium-99m. Write a nuclear equation for the formation of molybdenum-99 from stable molybdenum-98 bombarded with neutrons.

8.37 Describe an application of each of the following isotopes:
  a. technetium-99m
  b. xenon-133

8.38 Describe an application of each of the following isotopes:
  a. iodine-131
  b. thallium-201

Biological Effects of Radiation

8.39 What is the effect on one's level of radiation exposure resulting from:
  a. increasing one's distance from the source?
  b. wearing gloves?

8.40 What is the effect on one's level of radiation exposure resulting from:

  a. using concrete in lieu of wood paneling for the walls of a radiation laboratory?

  b. wearing a lab apron lined with thin sheets of lead?

8.41 What is the source of background radiation?

8.42 Why do high-altitude jet flights increase one's exposure to background radiation?

Detection and Measurement of Radiation

8.43 What is meant by the term *relative biological effect?*

8.44 What is meant by the term *lethal dose* of radiation?

8.45 Define each of the following units:

  a. curie

  b. roentgen

8.46 Define each of the following radiation units:

  a. rad

  b. rem

Further Problems

8.47 How many hours would a sample of radioactive material ($t_{1/2}$ = 75 minutes) require to reach background level?

8.48 How many milligrams of technetium-99m will remain after 30 hours if the initial sample weighed 1 gram?

8.49 Explain why cobalt-60 is useful in the treatment of cancer.

8.50 Isotopes used as radioactive tracers have chemical properties that are similar to those of a nonradioactive isotope of the same element. Explain why this is a critical consideration in their use.

8.51 X-ray technicians often wear badges containing photographic film. How is this film used to indicate exposure to X-rays?

8.52 Why would a Geiger counter be preferred to film for assessing the immediate danger resulting from a spill of some solution containing a radioisotope?

VOCABULARY QUIZ

8.1 The _____ consists of two protons and two neutrons, carries a +2 charge, and results from nuclear decay.

8.2 The _____ is an electron formed in the nucleus by the conversion of a neutron into a proton.

8.3 The energy required to break down the nucleus into its component parts is called the _____.

8.4 _____ is the name of the equation that represents the energy equivalent of mass being equal to the mass times the square of the speed of light.

8.5 _____ is the process of joining of light nuclei to form heavier nuclei accompanied by the release of large amounts of energy.

8.6 A form of electromagnetic radiation from nuclear processes is termed _____.

8.7 The length of time required for one-half of the initial mass of an isotope to decay to products is referred to as the _____.

8.8 _____ is radiation that is sufficiently high in energy to cause ion formation upon impact.

8.9 The _____ is the dosage of radiation that would be fatal to 50% of the exposed population.

8.10 A(n) _____ is a radioisotope that is selectively transmitted to the part of the body for which diagnosis is desired.

9

An Introduction to Organic Chemistry: The Hydrocarbons

LEARNING GOALS

◆ Explain the differences between organic and inorganic molecules.

◆ Learn the common functional groups.

◆ Write condensed and structural formulas for saturated and unsaturated hydrocarbons.

◆ Learn the basic rules of the I.U.P.A.C. Nomenclature System.

◆ Draw structural isomers of simple organic compounds.

◆ Write equations for combustion and halogenation reactions of alkanes.

◆ Write equations for addition reactions of alkenes, and apply Markovnikov's Rule.

The Origin of Organic Compounds

About 425 million years ago, mountain ranges rose, and enormous inland seas emptied, producing new and fertile lands. In the next 70 million years the simple aquatic plants evolved into land plants, and huge forests of ferns, trees, and shrubs flourished. Reptiles roamed the forests. During the period between 360 and 280 million years ago the seas rose and fell at least 50 times. During periods of flood, the forests were buried under sediments. When the seas fell again, the forests were reestablished. The cycle was repeated over and over. Each flood period deposited a new layer of peat—partially decayed, sodden, compressed plant matter. These layers of peat were compacted by the pressure of the new sediments forming above them. Much of the sulfur and hydrogen was literally squeezed out of the peat, increasing the percentage of carbon. Slowly, the peat was compacted into seams of coal, which is 55–95% carbon. Oil, consisting of a variety of hydrocarbons, formed on the bottoms of ancient oceans from the remains of marine plants and animals.

Together, coal and oil are the "fossil fuels" that we use to generate energy for transportation, industry, and our homes. In the last two centuries we have extracted many of the known coal reserves from the earth and have become ever more dependent on the world oil reserves. Coal and oil are products of the chemical reactions of photosynthesis that occurred over millions of years of the earth's history. Our society must recognize that they are nonrenewable resources. We must actively work to conserve the supply that remains and to develop alternative energy sources for the future.

In this chapter we take a closer look at the structure and properties of the hydrocarbons, such as those that make up oil. In this and later chapters we will study the amazing array of organic molecules (molecules made up of carbon, hydrogen, and a few other elements), many of which are essential to life. As we will see, all the structural and functional molecules of the cell, including the phospholipids that make up the cell membrane and the enzymes that speed up biological reactions, are organic molecules. Smaller organic molecules, such as the sugars glucose and fructose, are used as fuel by our cells, while others, such as penicillin and aspirin, are useful in the treatment of disease. All these organic compounds, and many more, are the subject of the remaining chapters of this text.

INTRODUCTION

Organic chemistry is the study of carbon-containing compounds. The term *organic* was coined in 1807 by the Swedish chemist Jöns Jakob Berzelius. At that time it was thought that all organic compounds, such as fats, sugars, coal, and petroleum, were formed by living or once living organisms. All early attempts to synthesize these compounds in the laboratory failed, and it was thought that a *vital force,* available only in living cells, was needed for their formation.

This idea began to change in 1828, when a 27-year-old German physician, whose first love was chemistry, synthesized the organic molecule urea from inorganic starting materials. This man was Friedrich Wöhler, the "father of organic chemistry."

As a child, Wöhler didn't do particularly well in school because he spent so much time doing chemistry experiments at home. Eventually, he did earn his medical degree, but he decided to study chemistry in the laboratory of Berzelius rather than practice medicine.

After a year he returned to Germany to teach and, as it turned out, to do the experiment that made him famous. The goal of the experiment was to prepare ammonium cyanate from a mixture of potassium cyanate and ammonium sulfate. He heated a solution of the two salts and crystallized the product. But the product didn't look like ammonium cyanate. It was white crystals that looked exactly like urea! Urea is a waste product of protein breakdown in the body and is excreted in the urine. Wöhler recognized urea crystals because he had previously purified them from the urine of dogs and humans. Excited about his accidental discovery, he wrote to his teacher and friend Berzelius, "I can make urea without the necessity of a kidney, or even an animal, whether man or dog."

$$NH_4^+O\!-\!C\!\equiv\!N^-$$

Ammonium cyanate
(inorganic salt)

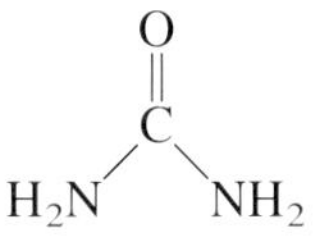

$$\underset{H_2N}{\overset{\displaystyle O}{\underset{\displaystyle}{\overset{\parallel}{C}}}}\!\!NH_2$$

Urea
(organic compound)

Ironically, Wöhler, the first man to synthesize an organic compound from inorganic substances, devoted the rest of his career to inorganic chemistry. However, other chemists continued this work, and as a result, the "vital force theory" was laid to rest, and modern organic chemistry was born.

9.1 THE CHEMISTRY OF CARBON

The number of possible carbon-containing compounds is almost limitless. The importance of these organic compounds is reflected in the fact that over half of this book is devoted to the study of molecules made with this single element.

Why are there so many organic compounds? There are several reasons. First, carbon can form *stable, covalent* bonds with other carbon atoms. Consider the following two forms of pure carbon, graphite and diamond:

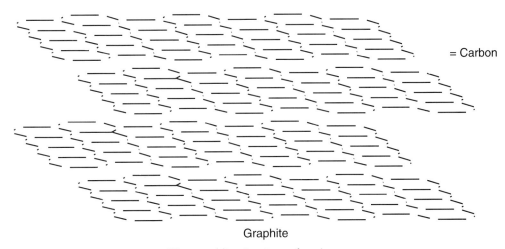

= Carbon

Graphite

The graphite structure of carbon

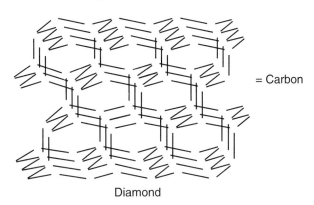

= Carbon

Diamond

The diamond structure of carbon

In future chapters we will discuss families of organic molecules containing oxygen atoms (alcohols, aldehydes, ketones, carboxylic acids, ethers, and esters), nitrogen atoms (amides and amines), sulfur atoms, and halogen atoms.

Graphite is planar and has many carbon-to-carbon bonds extending in two dimensions. Because the planar units can slide over one another, graphite is an excellent lubricant. Diamond is a large three-dimensional covalent structure. As a result it is extremely hard and stable.

A second reason for the vast number of organic compounds is that carbon atoms can form stable bonds with other elements. If a molecule is made only of carbon and hydrogen, it is a hydrocarbon. The hydrocarbons (alkanes, alkenes, alkynes, and aromatic hydrocarbons) are the subject of this chapter.

Third, carbon can form double or triple bonds with other carbon atoms to produce a variety of organic molecules with very different properties. Finally, the number of ways in which carbon and other atoms can be arranged is nearly limitless. Two organic compounds may have the same molecular formula (have the same number and kinds of atoms) but completely different structures and thus different properties. Molecules that have the same molecular formula but different structures are called *isomers*.

Important differences between organic and inorganic molecules

The bonds between two carbon atoms and between carbon and another atom are almost always *covalent bonds*, whereas the bonds found in many inorganic compounds are *ionic bonds*. Table 9.1 reviews the differences between an organic compound (methane, CH_4) and an inorganic compound (sodium chloride, NaCl).

In describing differences between organic and inorganic compounds it is useful to look at the differences between ionic and covalent bonds.

1. Ionic bonds result from the *transfer* of one or more electrons from one atom to another. Covalent bonds are formed by *sharing* one or more pairs of electrons.

2. The ionic bond is electrostatic, resulting from the attraction between the positive and negative ions formed by the electron transfer.

3. Ions form large, three-dimensional crystals made up of many positive and negative ions. Covalently bonded substances exist as discrete units called *molecules.*

4. Ionic compounds often dissociate in water. Water-soluble ionic compounds are electrolytes. Covalent molecules retain their identity in solution. They are nonelectrolytes.

As a result of these differences, ionic substances usually have much higher melting and boiling points than covalent compounds. The "like dissolves like" rule tells us that ionic compounds, if soluble at all, are more likely to dissolve in water than in a less polar solvent. Organic molecules are usually nonpolar or, at best, moderately polar. They are less soluble or insoluble in water.

Reactions involving inorganic compounds tend to be faster than those involving organic molecules. This is because the ionic bond is easily broken in water, leaving the ions free to react. On the other hand, energy is needed to break covalent bonds before a reaction can occur. This very high activation energy results in slower reactions.

TABLE 9.1   Comparison of the Major Properties of a Typical Organic and Inorganic Compound: Methane Versus Sodium Chloride

Organic (e.g., Methane)	Inorganic (e.g., Sodium Chloride)
Covalent bonding: CH_4	Ionic bonding: Na^+Cl^-
Low boiling point: $-164°C$	High boiling point: $1433°C$
Low melting point: $-182°C$	High melting point: $801°C$
Insoluble in water: trace	Soluble in water: 36 g/100 mL
Flammable	Nonflammable
Chemical reactivity: often slow	Chemical reactivity: often fast
Exists as a gas at room temperature and atmospheric pressure	Exists as a solid at room temperature and atmospheric pressure
Nonconductor of electricity in solution	Conductor of electricity in solution

The most general classification of organic compounds divides them into hydrocarbons and substituted hydrocarbons. **Hydrocarbon** molecules contain only carbon and hydrogen. A **substituted hydrocarbon** is one in which one or more hydrogen atoms is replaced by another atom or group of atoms.

The hydrocarbons can be further subdivided into aliphatic and aromatic hydrocarbons (Figure 9.1). The three families of **aliphatic hydrocarbons** are the alkanes, alkenes, and alkynes.

Alkanes are **saturated hydrocarbons** because they contain only carbon and hydrogen and have only carbon-to-hydrogen and carbon-to-carbon single bonds (Figure 9.2). The alkenes and alkynes are **unsaturated hydrocarbons** because they contain at least one carbon-to-carbon double or triple bond, respectively (Figure 9.3).

Some hydrocarbons are cyclic. Cycloalkanes consist of carbon atoms bonded to one another to produce a ring. **Aromatic hydrocarbons** contain a benzene ring or a derivative of the benzene ring (Figure 9.4).

Families of organic compounds

Alkanes contain only carbon-to-carbon single bonds (C—C); alkenes have at least one carbon-to-carbon double bond (C=C); and alkynes have at least one carbon-to-carbon triple bond (C≡C).

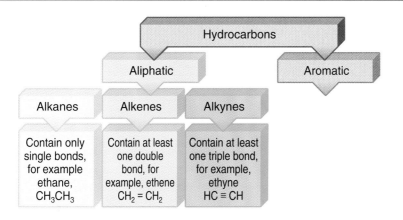

FIGURE 9.1
The family of hydrocarbons is divided into two major classes: aliphatic and aromatic. The aliphatic hydrocarbons are further subdivided into three major subclasses: alkanes, alkenes, and alkynes.

FIGURE 9.2
Molecular models of (left to right) methane (CH_4), ethane (C_2H_6), propane (C_3H_8), and butane (C_4H_{10}).

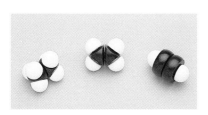

FIGURE 9.3
Molecular models of (left to right) an alkane, ethane, C_2H_6; an alkene, ethene, C_2H_4; and an alkyne, ethyne (commonly, acetylene) C_2H_2.

FIGURE 9.4
The aromatic compound benzene.

FIGURE 9.5
Five functional groups—from left to right, the carboxyl, carbonyl, hydroxyl, amino, and phosphate groups—alter the size, shape, and reactivity of the hydrocarbon methane in which they are substituted.

A substituted hydrocarbon is produced by replacing one or more hydrogen atoms with a functional group. A **functional group** is an atom or group of atoms arranged in a particular way that is primarily responsible for the chemical and physical properties of the molecule in which it is found (Figure 9.5). The importance of functional groups becomes more apparent when we consider that there is little chemical difference between a five-carbon and a six-carbon hydrocarbon. However, there is a great deal of difference between a five-carbon alcohol and a five-carbon alkane. Furthermore, hydrocarbons have little biological activity. However, the addition of a functional group confers unique and interesting properties on a molecule. Many times, these unique properties give the molecule important biological or medical properties.

All compounds that have a particular functional group are members of the same family. For instance, all compounds having the hydroxyl group (—OH) are classified as alcohols. The common functional groups are shown in Table 9.2.

The functional group is critical to the study of organic and biological chemistry. The chemistry of an organic compound is usually controlled by the functional group found in the molecule. While it would be impossible to learn the chemistry of each organic molecule, it is easy to learn the chemistry of each of the functional groups. In this way we can understand the chemistry of all members of a family of organic compounds just by learning the chemistry of its characteristic functional group.

TABLE 9.2   Common Functional Groups

Functional Group	Name	Family of Organic Compounds
$\begin{array}{c} H \quad\quad H \\ \diagdown C=C \diagup \\ H \diagup \quad\quad \diagdown H \end{array}$	Carbon-carbon double bond	Alkene
$H-C\equiv C-H$	Carbon-carbon triple bond	Alkyne
(benzene ring structure) (or) (benzene ring)	Benzene ring	Aromatic
$-\overset{\mid}{\underset{\mid}{C}}-X$ (X = F, Cl, Br, I)	Halogen atom	Alkyl halide
$-\overset{\mid}{\underset{\mid}{C}}-OH$	Hydroxyl group	Alcohol
$-\overset{\mid}{\underset{\mid}{C}}-O-R^*$	Alkoxy group	Ether
$\diagdown C=O \diagup$	Carbonyl group	Aldehyde or ketone
$-C=O$ $\overset{\mid}{OH}$	Carboxyl group	Carboxylic acid
$-C=O$ $\overset{\mid}{G}$ (G = Cl, OR*, and others)	Acyl group	Carboxylic acid derivatives
$-\overset{\mid}{\underset{\mid}{C}}-\overset{\mid}{N}-$	Amino group	Amine

*R is an abbreviation for any alkyl or aryl group; aryl is used for aromatic compounds in the same way that alkyl is used for aliphatic compounds (for example, methyl, ethyl, isopropyl). An aryl group is an aromatic compound with one hydrogen removed (for example, phenyl—the phenyl group is benzene with one hydrogen removed.)

There is an additional bonus to this approach. Each group of biological molecules (carbohydrates, lipids, proteins, and nucleic acids) is a family of large organic molecules characterized by one or more functional groups. Understanding the chemistry of the functional groups will allow you to understand small organic molecules, as well as the large biological molecules that allow life to exist.

This is analogous to the classification of the elements within the periodic table. See Chapter 2.

9.2 ALKANES

Structure and physical properties

Alkanes are saturated hydrocarbons; that is, alkanes contain only carbon and hydrogen bonded together through carbon-hydrogen and carbon-carbon single bonds. They have the general formula C_nH_{2n+2}.

Because alkanes and other hydrocarbons can reach very large sizes, a simple molecular formula often does not provide enough information about the structure of a molecule. For this reason there are several types of formulas used to describe organic molecules. The molecular formula, the structural formula, and the condensed formula have different uses in organic chemistry.

The **molecular formula** tells the kind and number of each type of atom in a molecule, but it doesn't show the bonding pattern. Organic molecules can exist as structural isomers. These are molecules that have the same molecular formula but different structures. Unfortunately, the molecular formula tells nothing about the structure of a molecule. Consider the molecular formulas for simple alkanes:

$$CH_4 \qquad C_2H_6 \qquad C_3H_8 \qquad C_4H_{10}$$

Methane   Ethane   Propane   Butane

Notice that the last molecular formula could represent two different molecules. How do we know which of the two is correct? The problem is solved by using the **structural formula,** which shows each atom and bond in a molecule. The advantage of the structural formula is that it shows the complete structure. The following are the structural formulas for the compounds shown above:

Recall that a covalent bond, representing a pair of shared electrons, can be drawn as a line between two atoms. For the structure to be correct, each carbon atom must show four pairs of shared electrons.

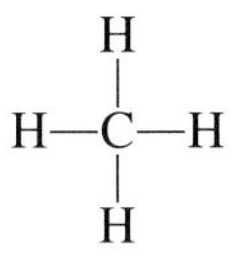

Methane 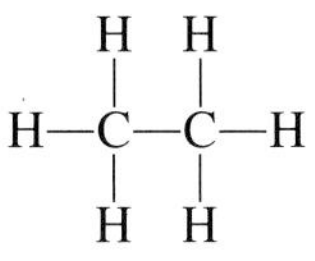   Ethane 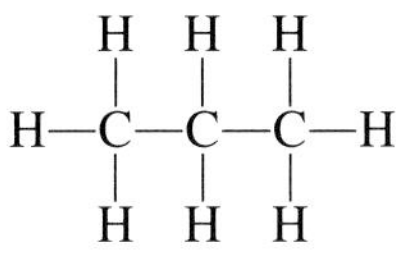   Propane

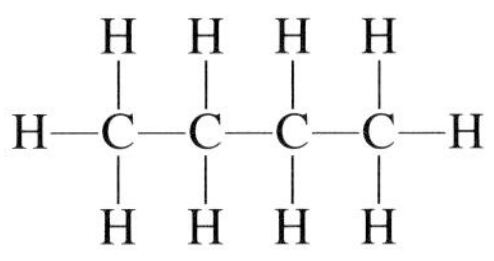

Butane 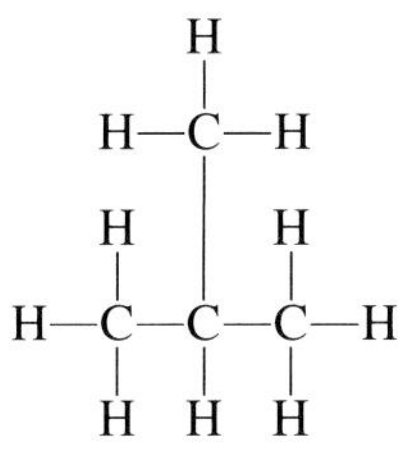   2-Methylpropane (*iso*-butane)

The structural formula shows the complete structure, but it is time-consuming to draw the structural formula for very large organic molecules. The compromise is the **condensed formula.** It shows all the atoms in a molecule and places them in a sequential order that indicates which atoms are bonded to which. The following are the condensed formulas for the five compounds above:

$$CH_4 \qquad CH_3CH_3 \qquad CH_3CH_2CH_3 \qquad CH_3CH_2CH_2CH_3 \qquad (CH_3)_3CH$$

Methane   Ethane   Propane   Butane   2-Methylpropane (*iso*-butane)

The names and formulas of the first ten straight-chain alkanes are shown in Table 9.3.

TABLE 9.3   Names and Formulas of the First Ten Straight-Chain Alkanes

Name	Molecular Formula	Condensed Formula
Alkanes	C_nH_{2n+2}	
Methane	CH_4	CH_4
Ethane	C_2H_6	CH_3CH_3
Propane	C_3H_8	$CH_3CH_2CH_3$
Butane	C_4H_{10}	$CH_3CH_2CH_2CH_3$ or $CH_3(CH_2)_2CH_3$
Pentane	C_5H_{12}	$CH_3CH_2CH_2CH_2CH_3$ or $CH_3(CH_2)_3CH_3$
Hexane	C_6H_{14}	$CH_3CH_2CH_2CH_2CH_2CH_3$ or $CH_3(CH_2)_4CH_3$
Heptane	C_7H_{16}	$CH_3CH_2CH_2CH_2CH_2CH_2CH_3$ or $CH_3(CH_2)_5CH_3$
Octane	C_8H_{18}	$CH_3CH_2CH_2CH_2CH_2CH_2CH_2CH_3$ or $CH_3(CH_2)_6CH_3$
Nonane	C_9H_{20}	$CH_3CH_2CH_2CH_2CH_2CH_2CH_2CH_2CH_3$ or $CH_3(CH_2)_7CH_3$
Decane	$C_{10}H_{22}$	$CH_3CH_2CH_2CH_2CH_2CH_2CH_2CH_2CH_2CH_3$ or $CH_3(CH_2)_8CH_3$

Section 3.4

Three-dimensional drawings of two simple members of this family are seen in Figure 9.6. Each carbon atom contains four single covalent bonds, while each hydrogen atom has only a single covalent bond. Although a carbon atom may be involved in single, double, or triple bonds, it always shares four pairs of electrons. When carbon is involved in four single bonds, the *bond angle,* the angle between two atoms or substituents attached to carbon, is 109.5°, as predicted by the valence shell electron pair repulsion theory. Thus alkanes contain carbon atoms that have tetrahedral geometry.

A tetrahedron is a geometric solid having the structure shown in Figure 9.7a. There are many different ways to draw the tetrahedral carbon (Figures 9.7b–9.7d). In Figure 9.7b, solid lines, dashes, and wedges are used to represent the structure of methane. Dashes go back into the page away from you; wedges come out of the page toward you; and solid lines are in the plane of the page. The structure in Figure 9.7c is the same as that in Figure 9.7b; it just leaves a lot more to the imagination. Figure 9.7d is a photograph of a ball and stick model of the methane molecule.

All hydrocarbons are composed of nonpolar molecules. As a result they are not water-soluble but are soluble in nonpolar organic solvents. Furthermore, they have relatively low melting points and boiling points and are generally less dense than water.

Nomenclature

Historically, organic compounds were named by the chemist who discovered them. Often the names reflected the source of the compound. For instance, the antibiotic penicillin is named for

FIGURE 9.6
(a) Photograph of a ball and stick model of ethane. All the carbon atoms have a tetrahedral arrangement, and all bond angles are approximately 109.5°.
(b) Drawing and (c) photograph of a ball and stick model of a more complex alkane, butane.

(a)   (b)   (c)

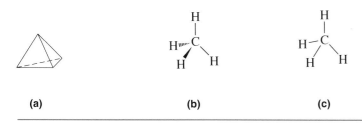

FIGURE 9.7
The tetrahedral carbon atom: (a) a tetrahedron; (b) the tetrahedral carbon drawn with dashes and wedges; (c) the stick drawing of the tetrahedral carbon atom; (d) photograph of a ball and stick model of methane.

the mold, *Penicillium notatum,* that produces it. The pain reliever aspirin was made by adding an acetate group to a compound purified from the bark of a willow tree, hence the name aspirin: *a-*(acetate) and *spirin* (genus of willow, *Spirea*).

These names are easy for us to remember because we come into contact with these compounds often. However, as the number of compounds increased, organic chemists realized that historical or trivial names were not adequate because they revealed nothing about the structure of a compound. Thousands of such compounds and their trivial names had to be memorized! What was needed was a set of nomenclature (naming) rules that would produce a unique name for every organic compound. Furthermore, the name should be so descriptive that, by knowing the name, a student or scientist could write the structure.

The International Union of Pure and Applied Chemistry (I.U.P.A.C.) is the organization responsible for establishing and maintaining a standard, universal system for naming organic compounds. The system of nomenclature developed by this group is called the **I.U.P.A.C. Nomenclature System.** The following rules are used for naming alkanes by the I.U.P.A.C. system:

Throughout this book we will primarily use the I.U.P.A.C. Nomenclature System. When common names are used, they will be shown in parentheses beneath the I.U.P.A.C. name.

1. Determine the name of the **parent compound.** This is the longest continuous carbon chain in the compound. Refer to Table 9.3 to determine these parent names. Parent chains are highlighted in yellow in the following examples:

$$\underset{\text{Br}}{\overset{1\quad2\quad3}{CH_3CHCH_3}} \qquad \underset{\text{CH}_3}{\overset{5\quad4\quad3\quad2\quad1}{CH_3CH_2CHCH_2CH_2}} \qquad \underset{\overset{CH_2CH_3}{\scriptstyle2\quad1}}{\overset{9\quad8\quad7\quad6\quad5\quad4\quad3}{CH_3CH_2CH_2CHCH_2CH_2CH_2CH_3}}$$

Parent name:
Propane   Pentane   Nonane

2. Name and number each atom or substituent attached to the parent compound. The number (see rule 3) tells us the position of the group on the main chain, and the name tells us what type of substituent is present at that position. For example:
   a. *The Halogens:* F—(fluoro), Cl—(chloro), Br—(bromo), and I—(iodo).
   b. *Alkyl Groups:* An **alkyl group** results when a hydrogen atom is removed from an alkane. The name of the alkyl group is derived from the name of the alkane, containing the same number of carbon atoms. The *-ane* is replaced by the *-yl* ending of an alkyl substituent. Thus CH_3— is a methyl group and CH_3CH_2— is an ethyl group. The first five continuous-chain alkyl groups are found in Table 9.4. Some branched-chain alkyl groups have special common names (Table 9.5).

3. Number the parent chain to give the lowest number to the first group encountered on the parent chain, regardless of the numbers that result for the other substituents. In the following examples the parent chain is highlighted in yellow:

$$\underset{\text{Br}}{\overset{1\quad2\quad3}{CH_3CHCH_3}} \qquad \underset{\overset{CH_2CH_3}{\scriptstyle4\quad5}}{\overset{3\quad2\quad1}{CH_3CHCH_2CH_3}} \qquad \underset{\overset{CH_2CH_2CH_2CH_3}{\scriptstyle5\quad6\quad7\quad8}}{\overset{1\quad2\quad3\quad4}{CH_3CH_2CH_2CHCH_2CH_3}}$$

Substituent:
2-Bromo   3-Methyl   4-Ethyl
2-Bromopropane   3-Methylpentane   4-Ethyloctane

TABLE 9.4 Names and Formulas of the First Five Continuous-Chain Alkyl Groups

Alkyl Group Structure	Name
CH_3—	Methyl
CH_3CH_2—	Ethyl
$CH_3CH_2CH_2$—	Propyl
$CH_3CH_2CH_2CH_2$—	Butyl
$CH_3CH_2CH_2CH_2CH_2$—	Pentyl

TABLE 9.5 Structures and Common Names of Some Branched-Chain Alkyl Groups

Structure	Common Name
CH₃CH— CH₃	Isopropyl*
CH₃ CH₃CHCH₂—	Isobutyl*
CH₃ CH₃CH₂CH—	sec-Butyl†
CH₃ CH₃C— CH₃	t-Butyl or tert-Butyl‡

*The prefix iso- (isomeric) is used when there is a methyl group at the end of the alkyl group.
†The prefix sec- (secondary) indicates that there are two carbons bonded to the "head" carbon, which is the carbon that attaches the alkyl group to the parent compound.
‡The prefix t- or tert- (tertiary) means that there are three carbons attached to the "head" carbon.

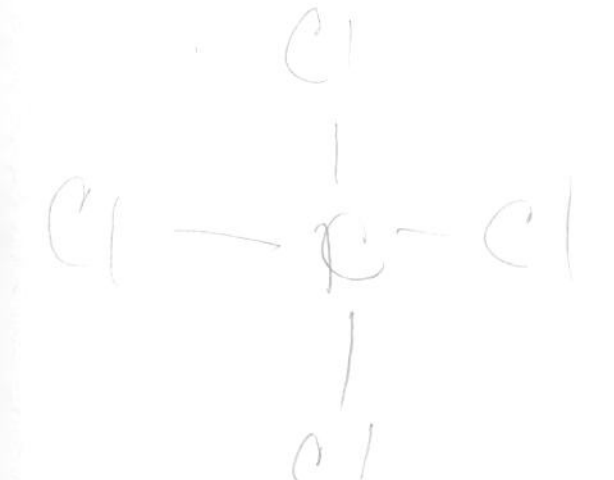

4. If the same substituent occurs more than once in the compound, a separate position number is given for each, and the prefixes di-, tri-, tetra-, penta-, and so forth are used, as shown in the following examples:

$$\underset{1}{CH_3}\underset{2}{CH}\underset{3}{CH_2}\underset{4}{CH_2}\underset{5}{CH}\underset{6}{CH_3}$$

with Br at positions 2 and 5

2,5-Dibromo
2,5-Dibromohexane

$$CH_3CH_2CHCH_2CHCH_2CHCH_2CH_2CH_3$$

with CH₃ substituents

1 2 3 4 5 6 7 8 9 10
10 9 8 7 6 5 4 3 2 1

3,5,7,-Trimethyl
NOT 4,6,8-trimethyl

5. Place the names of the substituents in alphabetical order before the name of the parent compound. Numbers are separated by commas, and numbers are separated from names by hyphens. By convention, halogen substituents are placed before alkyl substituents.

EXAMPLE 9.1

Naming Substituted Alkanes Using the I.U.P.A.C. System

Solution

$$\underset{6}{CH_3}\underset{5}{CH_2}\underset{4}{CH_2}\underset{3}{CH_2}\underset{2}{CH}\underset{1}{CH_3}$$
    Br

Parent chain: hexane
Substituent: 2-bromo (*not* 5-bromo)
Name: 2-bromohexane

$$\underset{5}{CH_3}\underset{4}{CH_2}—\underset{3}{CH}—\underset{2}{C}—\underset{1}{CH_3}$$
    with CH₃ groups

Parent chain: pentane
Substituents: 2,2,3-trimethyl (*not* 3,4,4-trimethyl)
Name: 2,2,3-trimethylpentane

$$\underset{1}{CH_3}\underset{2}{CH}\underset{3}{CH_2}\underset{4}{CH_2}\underset{5}{CH_2}\underset{6}{CH}\underset{7}{CH_2}\underset{8}{CH_2}\underset{9}{CH_3}$$
    Cl   CH₃

Parent name: nonane
Substituents: 2-chloro and 6-methyl
Name: 2-chloro-6-methylnonane

QUESTION 9.1

Name the following compounds, using the I.U.P.A.C. Nomenclature System:

a. CCl₄

b.
$$CH_3—\underset{}{\overset{CH_2CH_2CH_3}{C}}—CH_3$$
    CH₃

c.
$$CH_3—\underset{CH_3}{\overset{CH_3}{C}}—CH_3$$

d.
$$CH_2—CH—CH_2$$
 Br   Br   Br

QUESTION 9.2

Name the following compounds, using the I.U.P.A.C. Nomenclature System:

a. $CH_3CH_2CH_2CH_2CHCH_3$
                  |
                  CH_2CH_3

c. $CH_3CHCH_2CH_2CHCH_2$—Br
         | |
         I CH_3

      CH_2Br

b. CH_3—C═CH$_2$—Br
       |
      CH_3

           CH_2CH_3

d. $CH_3CHCHCH_2CH_2CH_2$—Cl
         |
         CH_3

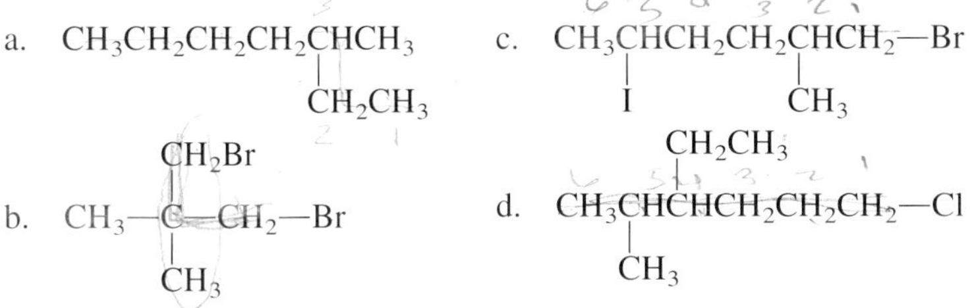

Having learned to name a compound using the I.U.P.A.C. Nomenclature System, it is easy to write the structural formula of a compound, given the name. First, draw the parent carbon chain. Be sure to indicate all four bonds for each carbon atom. For the compound *1-bromo-4-methylhexane,* draw a six-carbon (hexane) parent chain in the following way:

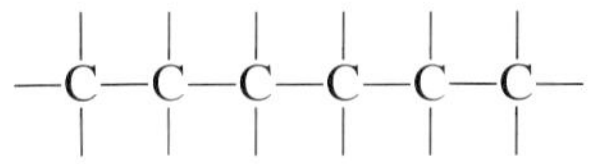

$$-\overset{|}{\underset{|}{C}}-\overset{|}{\underset{|}{C}}-\overset{|}{\underset{|}{C}}-\overset{|}{\underset{|}{C}}-\overset{|}{\underset{|}{C}}-\overset{|}{\underset{|}{C}}-$$

Next, number each carbon atom:

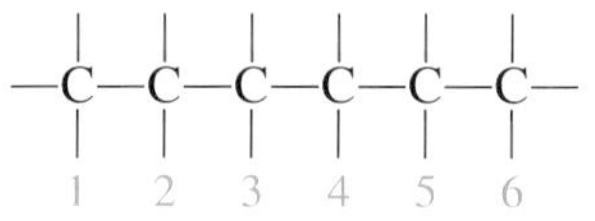

$$-\underset{1}{\overset{|}{\underset{|}{C}}}-\underset{2}{\overset{|}{\underset{|}{C}}}-\underset{3}{\overset{|}{\underset{|}{C}}}-\underset{4}{\overset{|}{\underset{|}{C}}}-\underset{5}{\overset{|}{\underset{|}{C}}}-\underset{6}{\overset{|}{\underset{|}{C}}}-$$

Now add the side groups. In this example a bromine atom is bonded to carbon-1, and a methyl group is bonded to carbon-4:

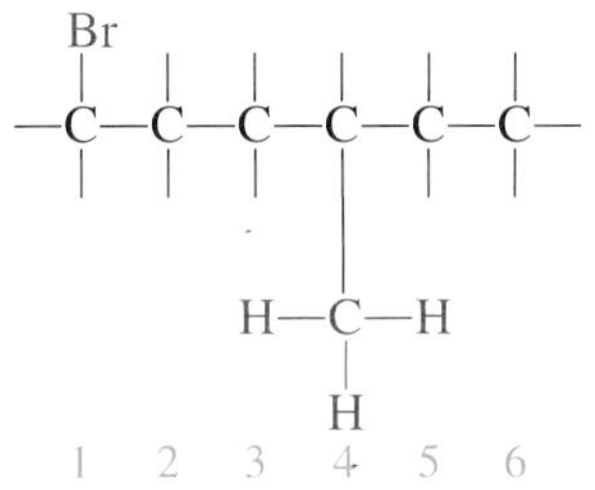

Finally, add the correct number of hydrogen atoms so that each carbon has four covalent bonds:

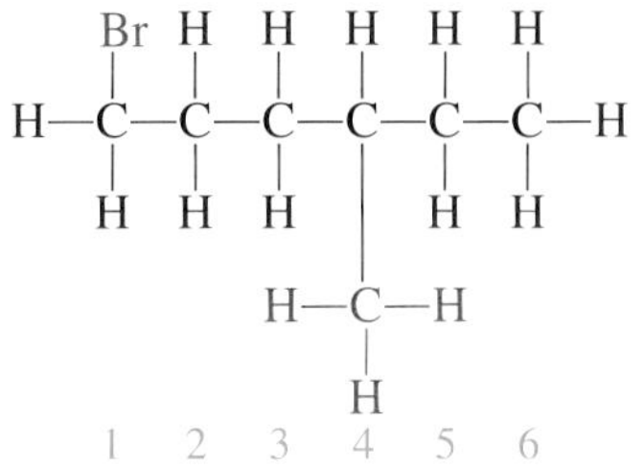

As a final check of your accuracy, name the compound that you have just drawn using the I.U.P.A.C. Nomenclature System, and compare the name with that in the original problem.

The condensed formula and molecular formulas can be written from the structural formula shown above. The condensed formula is $CH_2BrCH_2CH_2CHCH_2CH_3$, and the molecular formula is $C_7H_{15}Br$.
                                CH_3

Structural isomers

Molecules having the same molecular formula but different arrangements of atoms are called **structural isomers.** For instance, as we saw above, there are two structural isomers having the molecular formula C_4H_{10}: butane and 2-methylpropane. These isomers are unique compounds because of their structural differences, and they have different physical and chemical properties. Butane and 2-methylpropane both have molecular weights of 58.1 g/mol, but they differ slightly in their melting points and boiling points:

$$CH_3CH_2CH_2CH_3 \qquad CH_3\overset{\displaystyle CH_3}{\underset{|}{CH}}CH_3$$

Butane
b.p. = 0.5°C
m.p. = −138°C

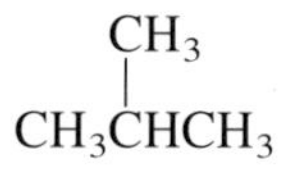

2-Methylpropane
b.p. = −12°C
m.p. = −145°C

EXAMPLE 9.2

Drawing Structural Isomers of Alkanes

Write all the structural isomers having the molecular formula C_6H_{14}.

Solution

1. Begin with the continuous six-carbon chain structure:

$$CH_3{-}CH_2{-}CH_2{-}CH_2{-}CH_2{-}CH_3$$

Isomer A

2. Now try five-carbon chain structures with a methyl group attached to one of the internal carbon atoms of the chain:

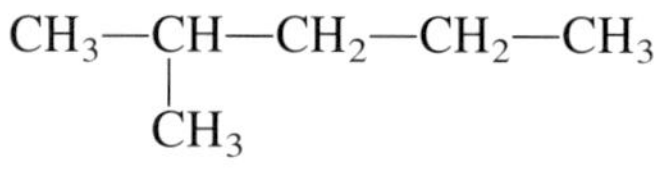

$$CH_3{-}\underset{\underset{\displaystyle CH_3}{|}}{CH}{-}CH_2{-}CH_2{-}CH_3 \qquad \text{and} \qquad CH_3{-}CH_2{-}\underset{\underset{\displaystyle CH_3}{|}}{CH}{-}CH_2{-}CH_3$$

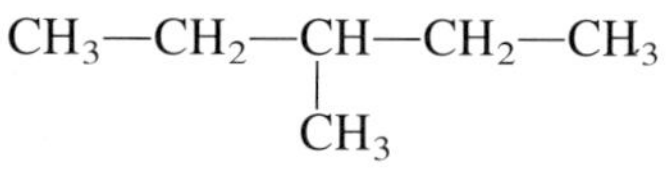

Isomer B Isomer C

3. Next consider the possibilities for a four-carbon structure to which two methyl groups (—CH_3) may be attached:

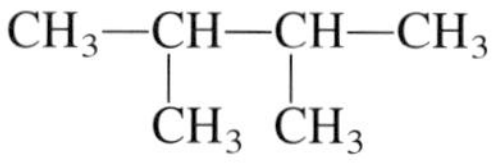

$$CH_3{-}\underset{\underset{\displaystyle CH_3}{|}}{CH}{-}\underset{\underset{\displaystyle CH_3}{|}}{CH}{-}CH_3 \qquad \text{and} \qquad CH_3{-}\overset{\overset{\displaystyle CH_3}{|}}{\underset{\underset{\displaystyle CH_3}{|}}{C}}{-}CH_2{-}CH_3$$

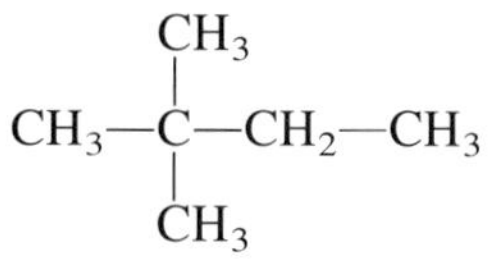

Isomer D Isomer E

These are the five possible structural isomers of C_6H_{14}. At first it may seem that other isomers are also possible. But careful comparison will show that they are duplicates of those already constructed. For example, rather than add two methyl groups, a single ethyl group (—CH_2CH_3) could be added to the four-carbon chain, as seen here:

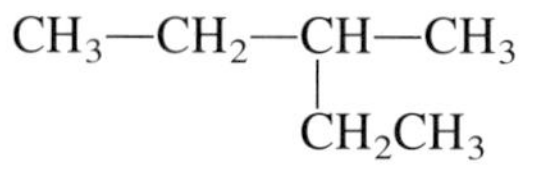

$$CH_3{-}CH_2{-}\underset{\underset{\displaystyle CH_2CH_3}{|}}{CH}{-}CH_3$$

But close examination will show that this is identical to isomer C above. Perhaps we could add one ethyl group and one methyl group to a three-carbon parent chain, with the following results:

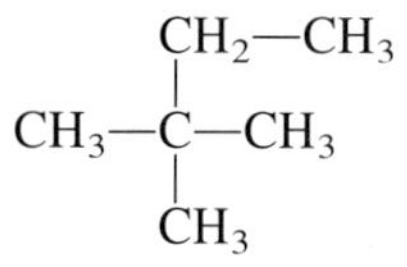

$$CH_3{-}\overset{\overset{\displaystyle CH_2{-}CH_3}{|}}{\underset{\underset{\displaystyle CH_3}{|}}{C}}{-}CH_3$$

Again we find that this structure is the same as one of the isomers we have already identified, isomer E.

AN ENVIRONMENTAL PERSPECTIVE

Oil-Eating Bacteria

Our highly industrialized society has come to rely more and more on petroleum as a source of energy as well as a raw material source for the manufacture of plastics, drugs, and a host of other consumables. Over 50% of the petroleum consumed in the United States is imported, and the major carrier is the supertanker.

Well-publicized oil spills, such as that from the *Exxon Valdez* (in Alaska in 1989) have fueled research to develop cleanup methods that will help to preserve the fragile aquatic environment.

It has been known for some time that there are strains of bacteria that will accelerate the oxidation of many of the compounds present in unrefined petroleum. These bacteria have been termed "oil-eating bacteria."

Recently, oceanographers at the University of Texas have developed strains of bacteria that will actually "eat" a wide variety of crude oils. At the same time these bacteria have a very short lifetime. It appears that they die shortly after they have operated on an oil slick.

This latter characteristic, a short lifetime in water, is particularly appealing to scientists, who fear that the introduction of nonindigenous (nonnative) bacteria into natural water systems may disrupt the ecology of the water.

Some also fear that the products of these reactions, in which some of the oil is converted to fatty acids, may disperse in water and cause more problems than the original oil spill.

Obviously, a great deal of research involving biodegradation remains to be done. Such technologies offer hope for alleviating many land-based solid waste disposal problems, in addition to petroleum spills.

To check whether you have accidentally made duplicate isomers, name them using the I.U.P.A.C. Nomenclature System. All isomers must have different I.U.P.A.C. names. So if two names are identical, the structures are also identical. Use the I.U.P.A.C. Nomenclature System to name the isomers in this example, and prove to yourself that the last two structures are simply duplicates of two of the original five isomers.

QUESTION 9.3

Draw a complete structural formula for each of the linear isomers of the following alkanes:

a. C_4H_9Br b. $C_4H_8Br_2$ c. $C_5H_{11}I$

QUESTION 9.4

Name all of the isomers that you obtained in Question 9.3.

The **cycloalkanes** are a family having C—C single bonds in a ring structure. They have the general molecular formula C_nH_{2n} and thus have two fewer hydrogen atoms than the corresponding alkane (C_nH_{2n+2}). The relationship that exists between an alkane and a cycloalkane is shown below for hexane and cyclohexane:

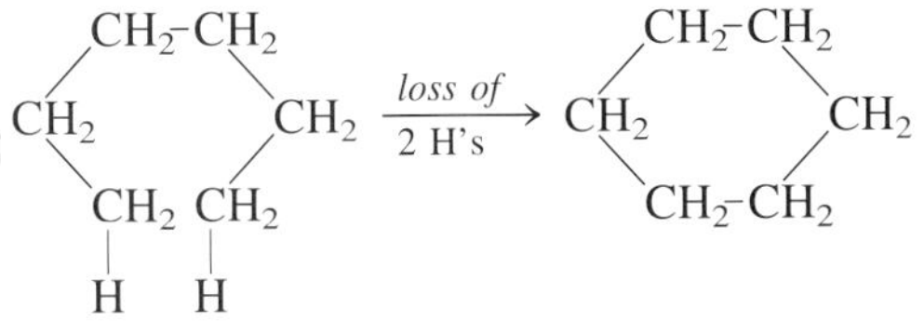

Cycloalkanes

$$
\begin{array}{ccc}
CH_2-CH_2 & & CH_2-CH_2 \\
CH_2 \qquad CH_2 & \xrightarrow[\text{2 H's}]{\text{loss of}} & CH_2 \qquad CH_2 \\
CH_2 \quad CH_2 & & CH_2-CH_2 \\
H \quad\; H & &
\end{array}
$$

Hexane   Cyclohexane

Alkane   *Cycloalkane*

C_nH_{2n+2} C_nH_{2n}

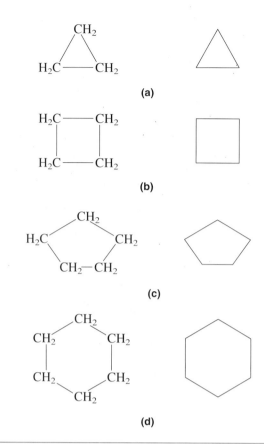

FIGURE 9.8
Cycloalkanes: (a) cyclopropane;
(b) cyclobutane; (c) cyclopentane;
(d) cyclohexane. All of the
cycloalkanes are shown in their
condensed structural forms (left
column) and abbreviated planar
structures (right column).

The structures and names of some simple cycloalkanes are seen in Figure 9.8.

In the I.U.P.A.C. Nomenclature System the cycloalkanes are named by applying the following simple rules:

◆ Determine the name of the alkane with the same number of carbon atoms and add the prefix
cyclo-. For example, cyclopentane is the cyclic alkane that has five carbon atoms.

◆ If the cycloalkane is substituted, place the names of the groups in alphabetical order before
the name of the cycloalkane. No number is needed if there is only one substituent. As with
alkanes, halogen substituents are placed before alkyl substituents.

◆ If more than one group is present, use numbers that result in the *lowest possible position
numbers*.

EXAMPLE 9.3

Naming a Substituted Cycloalkane Using the I.U.P.A.C. Nomenclature System

Solution

Parent Chain: cyclopentane
Substituent: 1,2-dibromo
Name: 1,2-dibromocyclopentane

Parent Chain: cyclohexane
Substituent: 1,3-dimethyl
Name: 1,3-dimethylcyclohexane

QUESTION 9.5

Name each of the following substituted cycloalkanes using the I.U.P.A.C. Nomenclature System:

a.

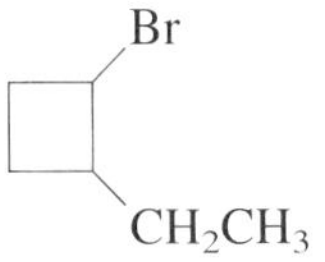

b.

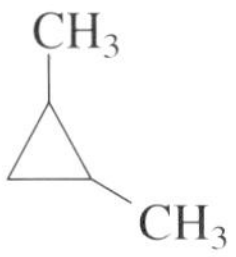

c.

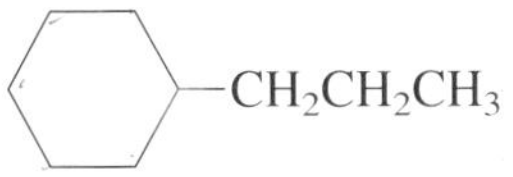

QUESTION 9.6

Name each of the following substituted cycloalkanes using the I.U.P.A.C. Nomenclature System:

a.

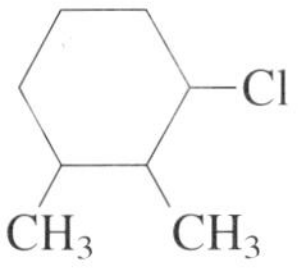

b.

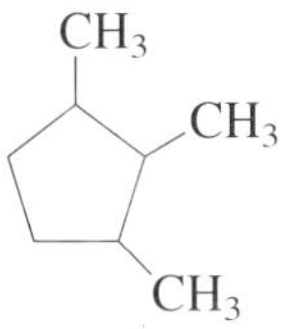

c.

Combustion

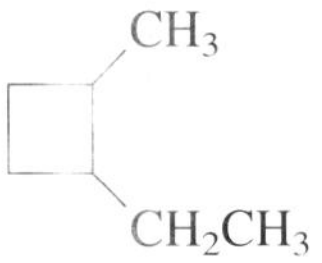

Reactions of alkanes and cycloalkanes

Alkanes, cycloalkanes, and other hydrocarbons can be oxidized (by burning) in the presence of excess molecular oxygen. In this reaction, called **combustion,** they burn at high temperatures, producing carbon dioxide and water and releasing large amounts of energy as heat.

$$C_nH_{2n+2} + O_2 \longrightarrow CO_2 + H_2O + \text{heat energy}$$

Alkane $\quad$ Oxygen $\longrightarrow$ Carbon dioxide $\quad$ Water $\quad$ Heat energy

The following examples show a combustion reaction for a simple alkane and a simple cycloalkane:

Section 7.2

$$CH_4 + 2O_2 \longrightarrow CO_2 + 2H_2O + \text{heat energy}$$
Methane

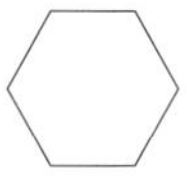

$+ 9O_2 \longrightarrow 6CO_2 + 6H_2O + \text{heat energy}$

Cyclohexane

A MEDICAL PERSPECTIVE

Polyhalogenated Hydrocarbons Used as Anesthetics

Polyhalogenated hydrocarbons are hydrocarbons containing two or more halogen atoms. Some polyhalogenated compounds are notorious for the problems they have caused humankind. For instance, some of the early insecticides such as DDT, chlordane, kepone, and lindane do not break down rapidly in the environment. As a result, these toxic compounds accumulate in biological tissue of a variety of animals, including humans, and may cause neurological damage, birth defects, or even death.

Other halogenated hydrocarbons are very useful in medicine. They were among the first anesthetics (pain relievers) used routinely in medical practice. These chemicals played a central role as the studies of medicine and dentistry advanced into modern times:

$$CH_3CH_2-Cl \qquad CH_3-Cl$$

Chloroethane   Chloromethane
(ethyl chloride)   (methyl chloride)

Chloroethane and chloromethane are local anesthetics. A local anesthetic deadens the feeling in a portion of the body. Applied topically (on the skin), chloroethane and chloromethane numb the area. Rapid evaporation of these anesthetics lowers the temperature, deadening the local nerve endings. They act rapidly, but the effect is brief, and feeling is restored quickly.

$$CHCl_3$$

Trichloroethane
(chloroform)

In the past, chloroform was used as both a general and a local anesthetic. When administered through inhalation, it rapidly causes loss of consciousness. However, the effects of this powerful anesthetic are of short duration. Chloroform is no longer used because it was shown to be carcinogenic.

$$CH_3-\underset{\underset{\displaystyle Cl}{|}}{CH}-Br$$

1-Bromo-1-chloroethane
(Halothane)

Halothane is a general anesthetic that is administered by inhalation. It is considered to be a very safe anesthetic and is widely used.

See "An Environmental Perspective: The Greenhouse Effect and Global Warming" in Chapter 7.

The energy released, along with their availability and relatively low cost, makes hydrocarbons very useful as fuels. In fact, combustion is essential to our very existence. It is the process by which we heat our homes, run our cars, and generate electricity. While combustion of fossil fuels is vital to our industry and society, it also represents a threat to our environment. The buildup of CO_2 may contribute to global warming and change the face of the earth in future generations.

Other pollutants are formed as a result of incomplete combustion. If not enough oxygen is present, partial combustion produces compounds such as carbon monoxide, formaldehyde, and acetic acid. The following equations show some incomplete combustion reactions that contribute to air pollution:

$$2CH_4 + 3O_2 \longrightarrow 2CO + 4H_2O$$

Methane   Carbon monoxide

$$CH_4 + O_2 \longrightarrow H-\overset{\overset{\displaystyle O}{\|}}{C}-H + H_2O$$

Methane   Methanal
                      (formaldehyde)

$$2C_2H_6 + 3O_2 \longrightarrow 2CH_3COOH + 2H_2O$$

Ethane   Ethanoic acid
                 (acetic acid)

AN ENVIRONMENTAL PERSPECTIVE

DDT and Biological Magnification

We have heard the warnings for years: Stop using nonbiodegradable insecticides because they are killing many animals other than their intended victims! Are these chemicals not specifically targeted to poison insects? How then can they be considered a threat to humans and other animals?

DDT, a polyhalogenated hydrocarbon, was discovered in the early 1940s by Paul Müller, a Swiss chemist. Müller showed that DDT is a nerve poison that causes convulsions, paralysis, and eventually death in insects. From the 1940s until 1972, when it was banned in the United States, DDT was sprayed on crops to kill insect pests, sprayed on people as a delousing agent, and sprayed in and on homes to destroy mosquitoes carrying malaria. At first, DDT appeared to be a miraculous chemical, saving literally millions of lives and millions of dollars in crops. However, as time went by, more and more evidence of a dark side of DDT use accumulated. Over time, the chemical had to be sprayed in greater and greater doses as the insect populations evolved to become more and more resistant to it. In 1962, Rachel Carson published her classic work, *The Silent Spring,* which revealed that DDT was accumulating in the environment. In particular, high levels of DDT in birds interfered with their calcium metabolism. As a result, the egg shells produced by the birds were too thin to support development of the chick within. In spring, when the air should have been filled with bird song, there was silence. This is the "silent spring" referred to in the title of Carson's book.

DDT is not biodegradable; furthermore, it is not water-soluble, but it is soluble in nonpolar solvents. Thus if DDT is ingested by an animal, it will dissolve in fat tissue and accumulate there, rather than being excreted in the urine. When DDT is introduced into the food chain, which is inevitable when it is sprayed over vast areas of the country, the result is *biological magnification.* This stepwise process begins when DDT applied to crops is ingested by insects. The insects, in turn, are eaten by birds, and the birds are eaten by a hawk. We can imagine another food chain: Perhaps the insects are eaten by mice, which are in turn eaten by a fox, which is then eaten by an owl. Or to make it more personal, perhaps the grass is eaten by a cow, which then becomes your dinner. With each step up one of these food chains, the concentration of DDT in the tissues becomes higher and higher because it is not degraded, it is simply stored. Eventually, the concentration may reach toxic levels in some of the animals in the food chain.

DDT : *Dichlorodiphenyltrichloroethane*

Consider for a moment the series of events that occurred in Borneo in 1955. The World Health Organization elected to spray DDT in Borneo because 90% of the inhabitants were infected with malaria. As a result of massive spraying, the mosquitoes bearing the malaria parasite were killed. If this sounds like the proverbial happy ending, read on. This is just the beginning of the story. In addition to the mosquitoes, millions of other household insects were killed. In tropical areas it is common for small lizards to live in the homes, eating insects found there. The lizards ate the dead and dying DDT-contaminated insects and were killed by the neurotoxic effects of DDT. The house cats ate the lizards, and they, too, died. The number of rats increased dramatically because there were no cats to control the population. The rats and their fleas carried sylvatic plague, a form of bubonic plague. With more rats in contact with the humans came the threat of a bubonic plague epidemic. Happily, cats were parachuted into the affected areas of Borneo, and the epidemic was avoided.

The story has one further twist. Many of the islanders lived in homes with thatched roofs. The vegetation used to make these roofs was the preferred food source for a caterpillar that was not affected by DDT. Normally, the wasp population preyed on these caterpillars and kept the population under control. Unfortunately, the wasps were killed by the DDT. The caterpillars prospered, devouring the thatched roofs, which collapsed on the inhabitants.

Every good story has a moral, and this one is not difficult to decipher. The introduction of large amounts of any chemical into the environment, even to eradicate disease, has the potential for long-term and far-reaching effects that may be very difficult to predict. We must be cautious with our fragile environment. Our well-intentioned intervention all too often upsets the critical balance of nature, and in the end we inadvertently do more harm than good.

Halogenation

Alkanes and cycloalkanes can also react with a halogen (usually chlorine or bromine) in a reaction called **halogenation.** Halogenation is a **substitution reaction,** that is, a reaction that results in the replacement of one group for another. In this reaction a halogen atom is substituted for one of the hydrogen atoms in the alkane. The products of this reaction are an **alkyl halide** or *haloalkane* and a hydrogen halide. This substitution reaction can occur only in the presence of heat and/or light, as indicated by the reaction conditions noted over the arrows. The general equation for the halogenation of an alkane is presented below. The R in the general structure for the alkane is an abbreviation for any alkyl group.

$$
R-\underset{\underset{H}{|}}{\overset{\overset{H}{|}}{C}}-H \;+\; X_2 \;\xrightarrow{\text{light or heat}}\; R-\underset{\underset{H}{|}}{\overset{\overset{H}{|}}{C}}-X \;+\; H-X
$$

Alkane   Halogen $\xrightarrow{\text{light or heat}}$ Alkyl halide   Hydrogen halide

$$
H-\underset{\underset{H}{|}}{\overset{\overset{H}{|}}{C}}-H \;+\; Br_2 \;\xrightarrow{\text{light or heat}}\; H-\underset{\underset{H}{|}}{\overset{\overset{H}{|}}{C}}-Br \;+\; H-Br
$$

Methane   Bromine $\longrightarrow$ Bromomethane   Hydrogen bromide

$$
CH_3CH_3 \;+\; Cl_2 \;\xrightarrow{\text{light}}\; CH_3CH_2-Cl \;+\; H-Cl
$$

Ethane   Chlorine $\longrightarrow$ Chloroethane   Hydrogen chloride

Cyclohexane + Chlorine $\longrightarrow$ Chlorocyclohexane + Hydrogen chloride

If the halogenation reaction is allowed to continue, the alkyl halide formed may react with other halogen atoms. When this happens, a mixture of products may be formed. For instance, bromination of methane will produce bromomethane (CH_3Br), dibromomethane (CH_2Br_2), tri-bromomethane ($CHBr_3$), and tetrabromomethane (CBr_4).

In more complex alkanes, halogenation can occur to some extent at all positions to give a mixture of monosubstituted products. For example, bromination of propane produces a mixture of 1-bromopropane and 2-bromopropane.

9.3 ALKENES AND ALKYNES

Structure and physical properties

Alkenes and **alkynes** are unsaturated hydrocarbons. The characteristic functional group of an alkene is the carbon-carbon double bond. The functional group that characterizes the alkynes is the carbon-carbon triple bond. The following general formulas compare the structures of alkanes, alkenes, and alkynes.

	Alkane	Alkene	Alkyne
General Formulas:	C_nH_{2n+2}	C_nH_{2n}	C_nH_{2n-2}
Structural Formulas:	$H-\underset{\underset{H}{\mid}}{\overset{\overset{H}{\mid}}{C}}-\underset{\underset{H}{\mid}}{\overset{\overset{H}{\mid}}{C}}-H$	$\underset{H}{\overset{H}{>}}C{=}C\underset{H}{\overset{H}{<}}$	$H-C{\equiv}C-H$
	Ethane (Ethane)	Ethene (Ethylene)	Ethyne (Acetylene)
Molecular Formulas:	C_2H_6	C_2H_4	C_2H_2
Condensed formulas:	CH_3CH_3	$H_2C{=}CH_2$	$HC{\equiv}CH$

These compounds have the same number of carbon atoms but differ in the number of hydrogen atoms, a feature of all alkanes, alkenes, and alkynes that contain the same number of carbon atoms. Alkenes contain two fewer hydrogens than the corresponding alkane, and alkynes contain two fewer hydrogens than the corresponding alkene.

In alkanes the four bonds to the central carbon have tetrahedral geometry. When carbon is bonded by one double bond and two single bonds, as in ethene (an alkene), the molecule is *planar,* because all atoms lie in a single plane. Each bond angle is approximately 120°. When two carbon atoms are bonded by a triple bond, as in ethyne (an alkyne), the molecule is linear, and all atoms are positioned in a straight line (Figure 9.9).

Section 3.4

Alkenes and alkynes are nonpolar. As a result of the "like dissolves like" rule, they are not soluble in water but are very soluble in nonpolar solvents such as other hydrocarbons. They also have relatively low boiling points and melting points.

Tetrahedral   **Planar**   **Linear**

FIGURE 9.9
(a) Three-dimensional drawings and ball and stick models of ethane, ethene, and ethyne.
(b) Examples of typical long-chain hydrocarbons.

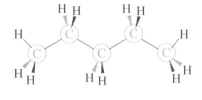

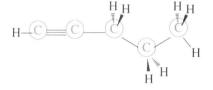

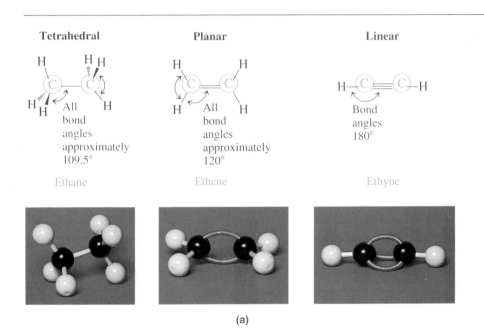

(a)

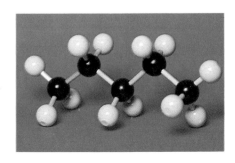
A long-chain alkane
(pentane)

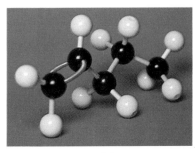
A long-chain alkene
(1-pentene)

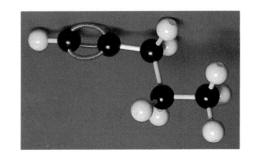
A long-chain alkyne
(1-pentyne)

(b)

Nomenclature

To determine the name of an alkene or alkyne using the I.U.P.A.C. Nomenclature System, the following simple rules are used:

◆ Name the parent compound using the longest continuous carbon chain containing the double bond (alkenes) or triple bond (alkynes).

◆ Replace the -*ane* ending of the alkane with the -*ene* ending for an alkene or the -*yne* ending for an alkyne. For example:

$$CH_3—CH_3 \qquad CH_2{=}CH_2 \qquad CH{\equiv}CH$$

Eth**ane**   Eth**ene**   Eth**yne**

$$CH_3—CH_2—CH_3 \qquad CH_2{=}CH—CH_3 \qquad CH{\equiv}C—CH_3$$

Prop**ane**   Prop**ene**   Prop**yne**

◆ Number the chain to give the lowest number for the first of the two carbons containing the double bond or triple bond. For example:

$$\overset{4}{C}H_3\overset{3}{C}H_2\overset{2}{C}H{=}\overset{1}{C}H_2 \qquad\qquad \overset{1}{C}H{\equiv}\overset{2}{C}—\overset{3}{C}H_2\overset{4}{C}H_2\overset{5}{C}H_3$$

1-Butene   1-Pentyne
(*not* 3-butene)   (*not* 4-pentyne)

◆ Name and number all groups bonded to the parent alkene or alkyne, and place the name and number in front of the name of the parent compound, as shown in the following examples:

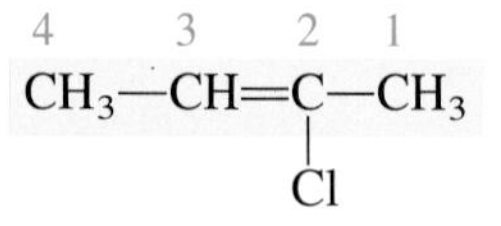

$$\overset{4}{C}H_3—\overset{3}{C}H{=}\overset{2}{\underset{\underset{Cl}{|}}{C}}—\overset{1}{C}H_3 \qquad\qquad \overset{1}{C}H_3\overset{2}{\underset{\underset{Br}{|}}{C}}H—\overset{3}{C}{\equiv}\overset{4}{C}—\overset{5}{C}H_2\overset{6}{C}H_3$$

2-Chloro-2-butene 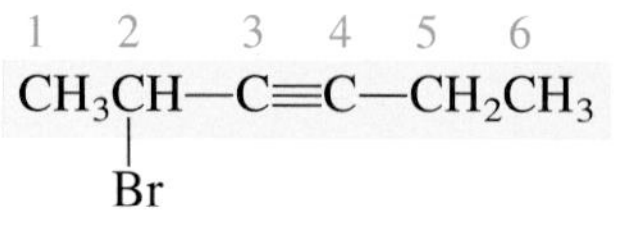   2-Bromo-3-hexyne

---

EXAMPLE 9.4

Naming Alkenes and Alkynes Using the I.U.P.A.C. Nomenclature System

Solution

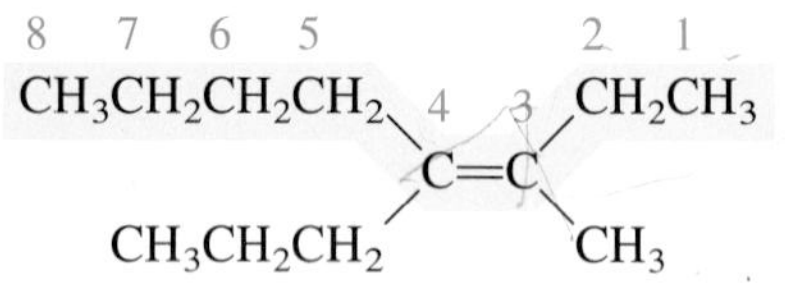

$$\overset{8}{C}H_3\overset{7}{C}H_2\overset{6}{C}H_2\overset{5}{C}H_2 \underset{CH_3CH_2CH_2}{\overset{}{\diagdown}}\overset{4}{C}{=}\overset{3}{C}\underset{CH_3}{\overset{\overset{2}{C}H_2\overset{1}{C}H_3}{\diagup}}$$

Longest chain containing the double bond: octene
Position of double bond: 3-octene (*not* 5-octene)
Substituents: 3-methyl and 4-propyl
Name: 3-methyl-4-propyl-3-octene

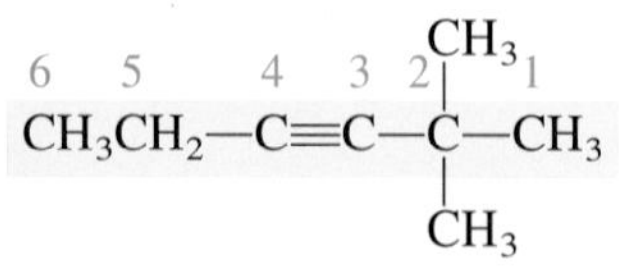

$$\overset{6}{C}H_3\overset{5}{C}H_2—\overset{4}{C}{\equiv}\overset{3}{C}—\overset{2}{\underset{\underset{CH_3}{|}}{\overset{\overset{CH_3}{|}}{C}}}—\overset{1}{C}H_3$$

Longest chain containing the triple bond: hexyne
Position of triple bond: 3-hexyne (must be!)
Substituents: 2,2-dimethyl
Name: 2,2-dimethyl-3-hexyne

QUESTION 9.7

Draw a complete structural formula for each of the following compounds:

a. 1-Bromo-3-hexyne   c. Dichloroethyne

b. 2-Butyne   d. 9-Iodo-1-nonyne

QUESTION 9.8

Name the following compounds using the I.U.P.A.C. Nomenclature System:

a. $CH_3-C\equiv C-CH_2CH_3$

b. 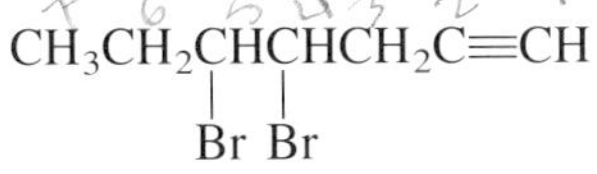 $CH_3CH_2CHCHCH_2C\equiv CH$
$\quad\quad\quad\ \ \overset{|}{Br}\ \overset{|}{Br}$

c. 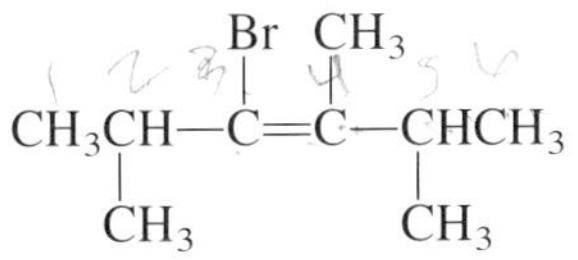 $CH_3CH-\overset{\overset{Br}{|}}{C}=\overset{\overset{CH_3}{|}}{C}-CHCH_3$
$\quad\quad\ \ \overset{|}{CH_3}\quad\quad\ \overset{|}{CH_3}$

d. 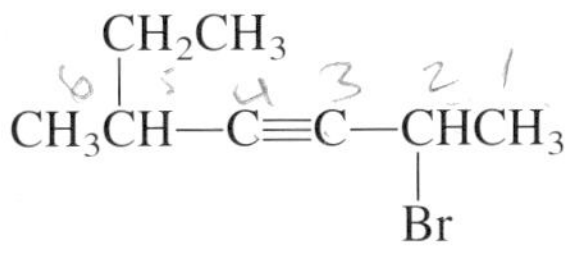 $\quad\quad\ \overset{CH_2CH_3}{|}$
$CH_3CH-C\equiv C-CHCH_3$
$\quad\quad\quad\quad\quad\ \overset{|}{Br}$

The carbon-carbon double bond is rigid. As a result, rotation around the double bond is not possible. In contrast, carbon-carbon single bonds do exhibit free rotation. When there are two different groups on each of the carbon atoms attached in the double bond, the rigidity of the double bond produces another class of isomers: **geometric isomers.** Geometric isomers differ from one another by groups being on the same or opposite sides of the rigid double bond.

Geometric isomers are also called *cis-* and *trans-* isomers. The *cis-* and *trans-* prefixes provide an easy method for naming two geometric isomers. Examples are provided here.

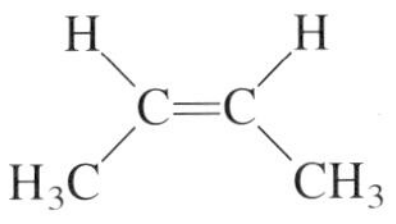

Geometric isomers: a consequence of unsaturation

cis-2-Butene 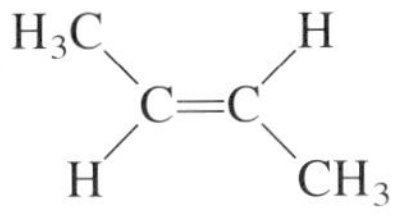   *trans*-2-Butene

The prefixes *cis-* and *trans-* refer to the placement of the substituents attached to the carbon-carbon double bond (in this example the H's and CH_3's). When groups are on the same side of the double bond, as in the structure on the left, the prefix *cis-* is used. When groups are on opposite sides of the double bond, as in the structure on the right, *trans-* is the appropriate prefix.

Geometric isomers are also possible in certain cycloalkanes. Two substituents on the same side of the plane of the ring give the *cis*-isomer, and two substituents on opposite sides of the plane of the ring give the *trans*-isomer:

cis-1,2-Dibromocyclopentane (both groups on the same side of the plane of the ring—*cis*.)

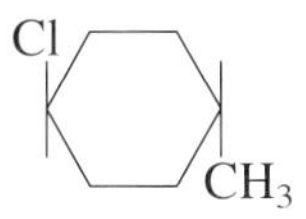

trans-1-Chloro-4-methylcyclohexane (two groups on opposite sides of the plane of the ring—*trans*.)

QUESTION 9.9

Draw condensed formulas for each of the following compounds:

a. *cis*-3-Octene   b. *trans*-5-Chloro-2-hexene   c. *trans*-2,3-Dichloro-2-butene

Name each of the following compounds, using the I.U.P.A.C. System. Be sure to indicate *cis-* or *trans-* where applicable.

a.

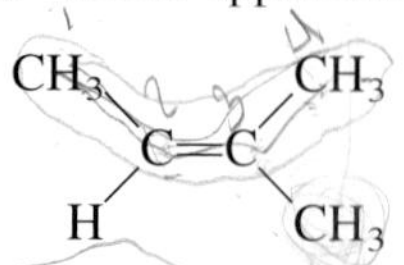

b.

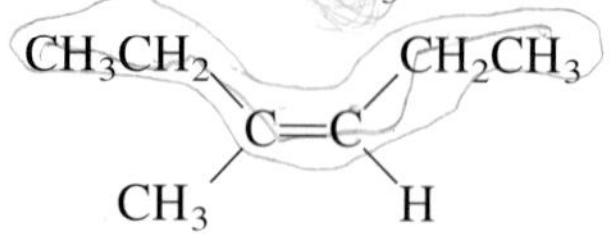

c.

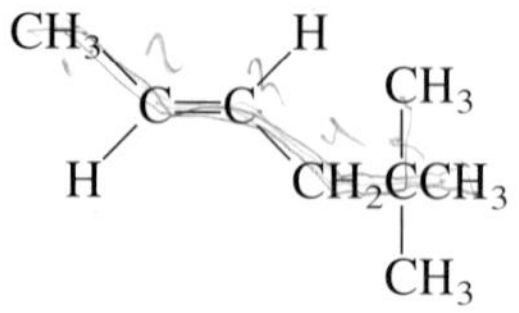

Reactions involving alkenes

Reactions of alkenes involve the carbon-carbon double bond. The key reaction of the double bond is the **addition reaction.** This involves the addition of two atoms or groups of atoms to a double bond. The major alkene addition reactions include addition of hydrogen (H_2), halogens (Cl_2 or Br_2), water (HOH), or hydrogen halides (HBr or HCl). A generalized addition reaction is shown below:

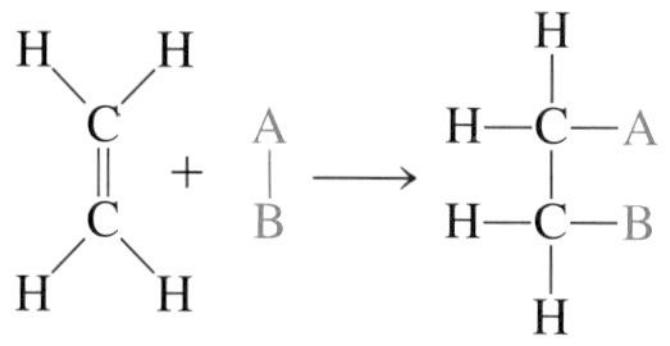

The product of this reaction is either an alkane or a substituted alkane.

Hydrogenation: addition of H_2 to an alkene

Hydrogenation is the addition of a molecule of hydrogen (H_2) to a carbon-carbon double bond to give an alkane. In this reaction the double bond is broken, and two new C—H single bonds result.

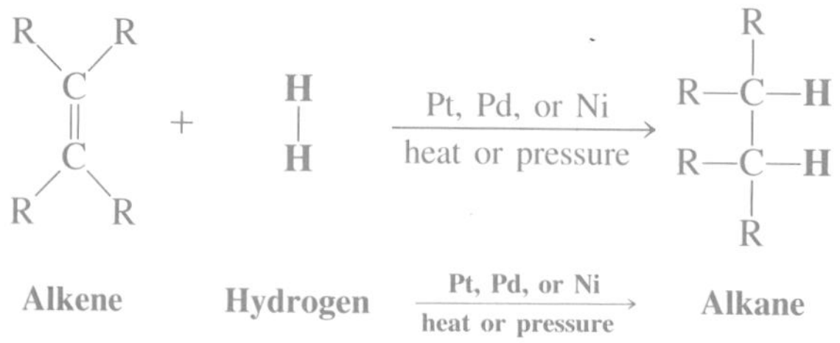

Several hydrogenation reactions are shown below:

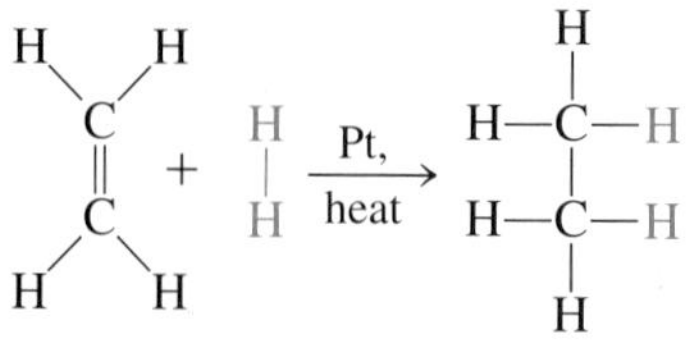

Ethene   Ethane

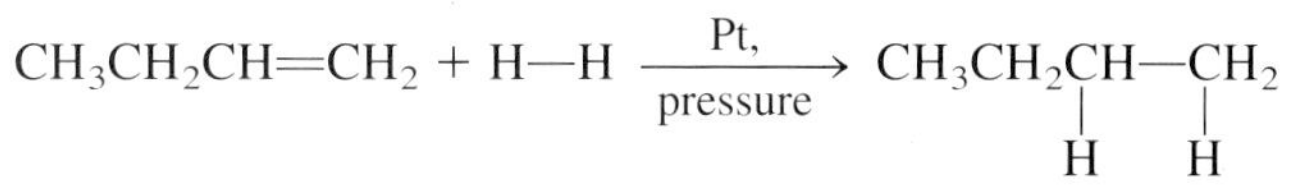

$$CH_3CH_2CH{=}CH_2 + H{-}H \xrightarrow[\text{pressure}]{Pt,} CH_3CH_2CH{-}CH_2$$
$$\underset{\text{H}}{|} \quad \underset{\text{H}}{|}$$

1-Butene   Butane

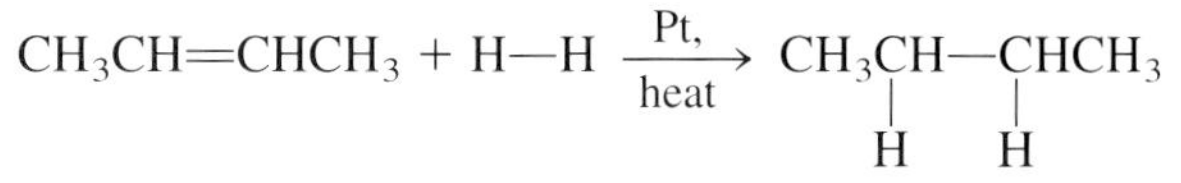

$$CH_3CH{=}CHCH_3 + H{-}H \xrightarrow[\text{heat}]{Pt,} CH_3CH{-}CHCH_3$$
$$\underset{\text{H}}{|} \quad \underset{\text{H}}{|}$$

2-Butene   Butane

Platinum, palladium, or nickel is needed as a catalyst to speed up the reaction. Heat and/or pressure may also be required.

Hydrogenation is used in the food industry to produce margarine, which is a mixture of hydrogenated vegetable oils (Figure 9.10). Vegetable oils are unsaturated, that is, they contain many double bonds and as a result have low melting points and are liquid at room temperature. The hydrogenation of these double bonds to single bonds increases the melting point of these oils and results in a fat, such as Crisco, that remains solid at room temperature. Through further processing they may be converted to margarine, such as corn oil or sunflower oil margarines.

Recall that a catalyst itself undergoes no change in the course of a chemical reaction (see Section 5.3).

Section 13.2

Halogenation: addition of X_2 to an alkene

Chlorine (Cl_2) or bromine (Br_2) can be added to a double bond. This reaction, called **halogenation,** proceeds readily and does not require a catalyst:

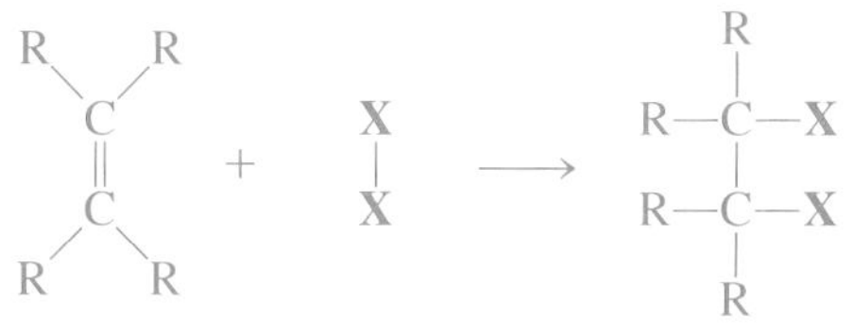

Alkene   Halogen $\longrightarrow$ Alkyl dihalide

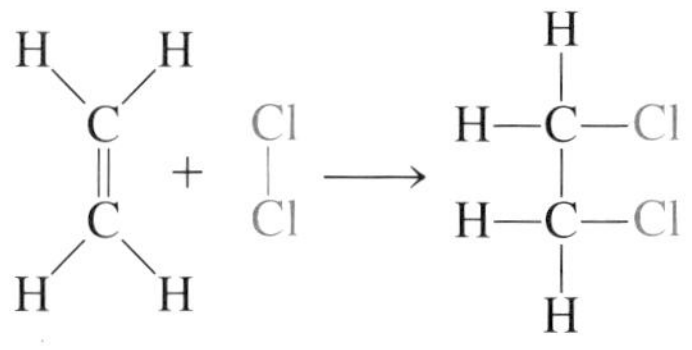

Ethene   Chlorine $\longrightarrow$ 1,2-dichloroethane

FIGURE 9.10
The conversion of a typical oil to a fat involves hydrogenation. In this example, triolein (an oil) is converted to tristearin (a fat).

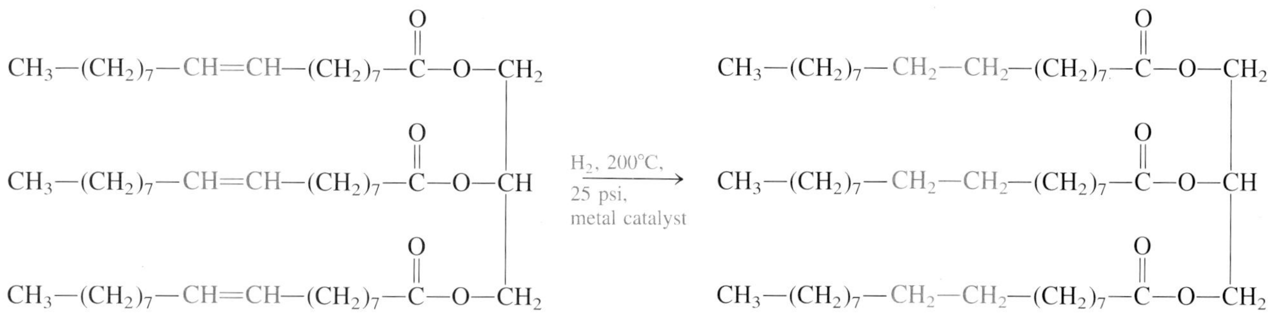

An *oil*   A *fat*

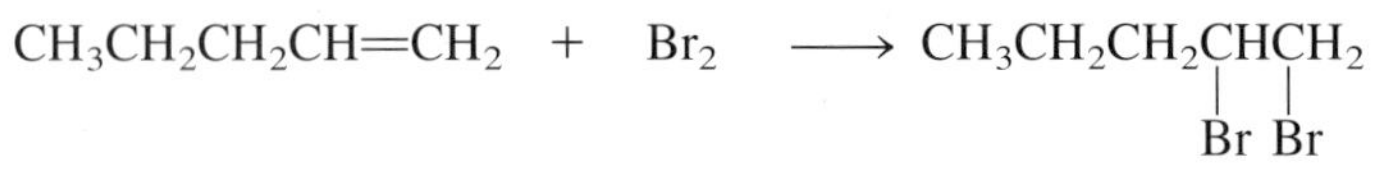

$$CH_3CH_2CH_2CH{=}CH_2 \ + \ Br_2 \ \longrightarrow \ CH_3CH_2CH_2\underset{\displaystyle \overset{|}{Br}}{C}H\underset{\displaystyle \overset{|}{Br}}{C}H_2$$

1-Pentene	Bromine	1,2-Dibromopentane
(colorless)	(red)	(colorless)

This bromination reaction can be used to show the presence of double bonds in an organic compound. The reaction mixture is red because of the presence of dissolved bromine. If the red color is lost, the bromine has been consumed. Thus bromination has occurred, and the compound must have had a carbon-carbon double bond. The greater the amount of bromine that must be added to the reaction, the more unsaturated the compound is, that is, the greater the number of carbon-to-carbon double bonds.

Hydration: addition of H_2O to an alkene

A water molecule can be added to an alkene. This reaction, termed **hydration,** requires a trace of acid (H^+) as a catalyst. The product is an alcohol, as shown in the following reaction:

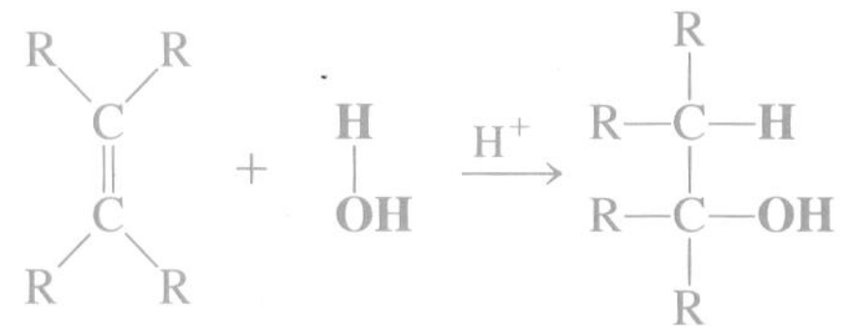

Alkene   Water $\xrightarrow{H^+}$ Alcohol

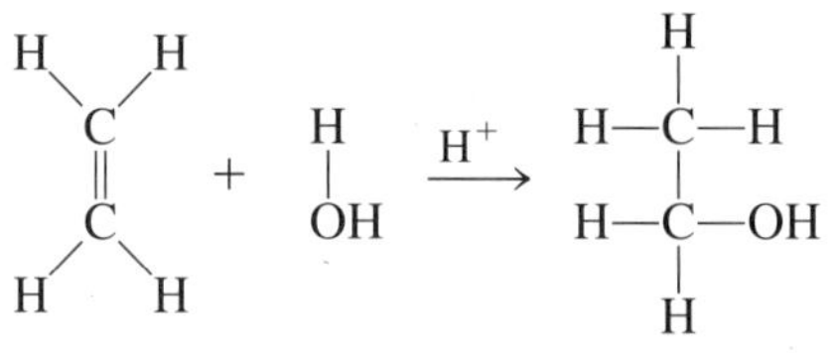

Ethene   Water $\longrightarrow$ Ethanol
(ethyl alcohol)

With alkenes in which the groups attached to the two carbons of the double bond are different (unsymmetrical alkenes), two products are possible. For example:

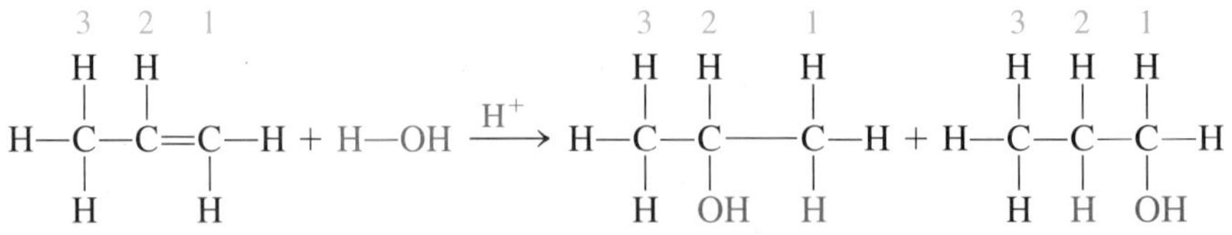

Propene	Major Product	Minor Product
(propylene)	2-Propanol	1-Propanol
	(isopropyl alcohol)	(propyl alcohol)

As you can see, hydration of an unsymmetrical alkene, such as propene, favors one product (2-propanol) over the other. The Russian chemist Vladimir Markovnikov studied many such reactions and came up with a rule that can be used to predict the major product of such a reaction. **Markovnikov's Rule** tells us that the carbon of the carbon-carbon double bond that has more hydrogen atoms originally receives the hydrogen atom being added to the double bond. The remaining carbon forms a bond with the —OH. Simply stated, ''the rich get richer''— the carbon with the most hydrogens gets the new one as well. In the example above, carbon-1 has two C—H bonds originally, and carbon-2 has only one. The product, 2-propanol, results from the new C—H bond forming on carbon-1 and the new C—OH bond on carbon-2.

Hydrohalogenation: addition of HX to an alkene

A hydrogen halide (HBr, HCl, or HI) also can be added to an alkene. The product of this reaction, called **hydrohalogenation,** is an alkyl halide:

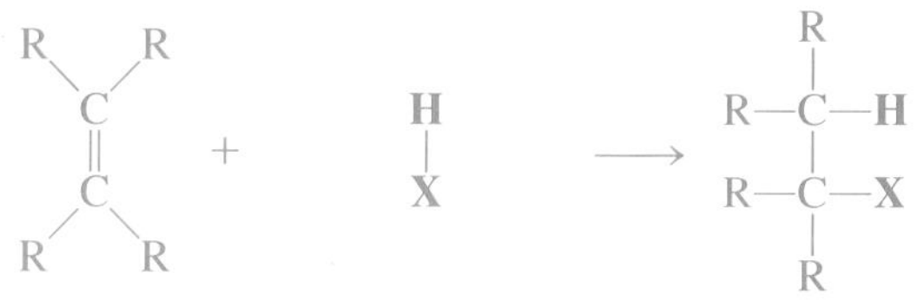

Alkene   Hydrogen halide $\longrightarrow$ Alkyl halide

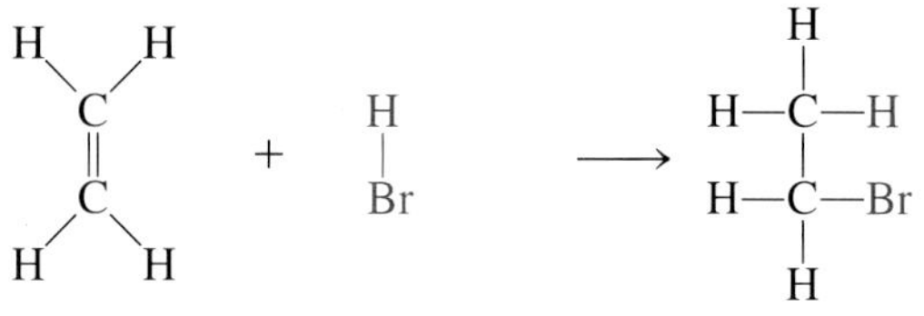

Ethene   Hydrogen bromide   Bromoethane

This reaction also follows Markovnikov's Rule. That is, if HX is added to an unsymmetrical alkene, the hydrogen atom will be added preferentially to the carbon atom that originally had the most hydrogen atoms. Consider the following example:

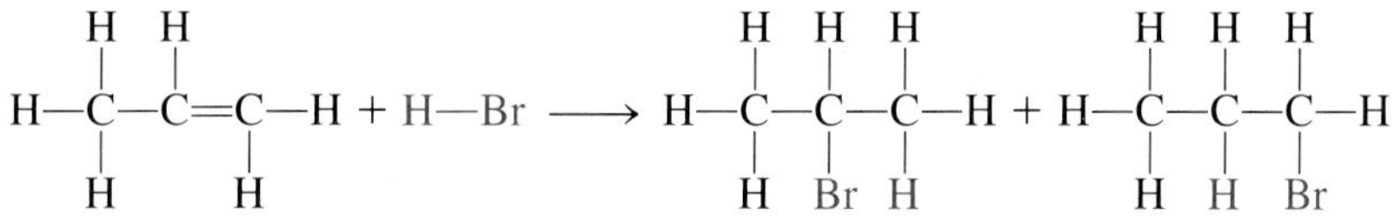

Propene   2-Bromopropane   1-Bromopropane
                           Major product   **Minor product**

QUESTION 9.11

Predict the major product in each of the following reactions. Name the alkene reactant and the product using I.U.P.A.C. Nomenclature.

a.

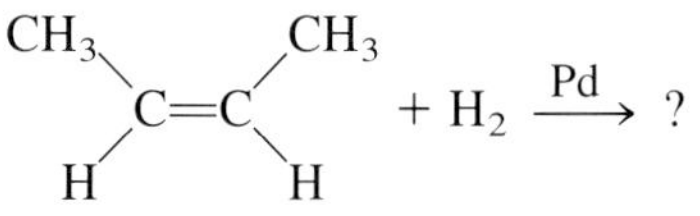

b. $CH_3CH_2CH{=}CH_2 + H_2O \xrightarrow{H^+}$?

c. $CH_3CH{=}CHCH_3 + Cl_2 \longrightarrow$?

d. $CH_3CH_2CH_2CH{=}CH_2 + HBr \longrightarrow$?

QUESTION 9.12

Predict the major product in each of the following reactions. Name the alkene reactant and the product using I.U.P.A.C. Nomenclature.

a.

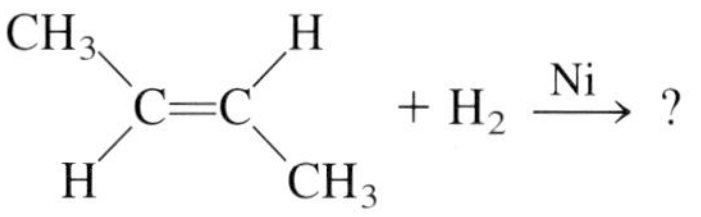

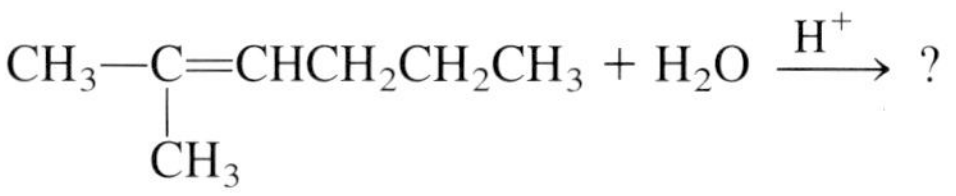

c. 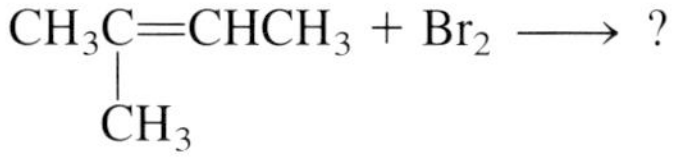 $CH_3C{=}CHCH_3 + Br_2 \longrightarrow$?
    with CH_3 substituent

b. $CH_3-C{=}CHCH_2CH_2CH_3 + H_2O \xrightarrow{H^+}$? with CH_3 substituent

d. 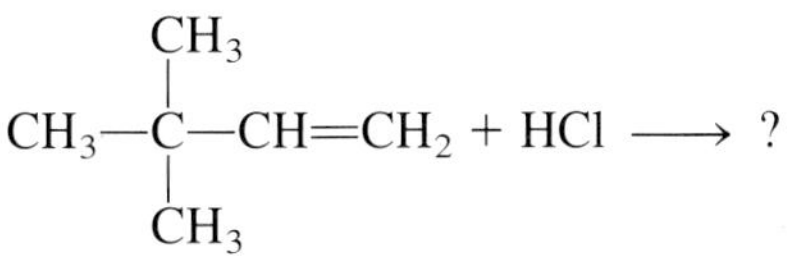 $CH_3-\underset{CH_3}{\overset{CH_3}{C}}-CH{=}CH_2 + HCl \longrightarrow$?

9.4 AROMATIC HYDROCARBONS

Structure and physical properties

Aromatic hydrocarbons were originally named for their pleasant aromas, but not all aromatic compounds have pleasant fragrances. Structurally, we find that each member of this family contains an *aromatic ring*. The most common aromatic ring is benzene, whose structure is shown in Figure 9.11.

The benzene ring consists of six carbon atoms joined in a hexagonal arrangement. A simplistic, though not completely correct, model (Figure 9.11a) depicts the carbon atoms joined by alternating single and double bonds. In reality (Figures 9.11b–9.11d) six of the twelve electrons of the three double bonds are shared equally among the six carbon atoms. The most common representation of the benzene ring is seen in Figure 9.11d. The equal sharing of the six electrons of the double bonds results in a rigid, flat, ring structure, in contrast to the relatively flexible, nonaromatic cyclohexane ring.

Aromatic hydrocarbons originate from natural sources, as do the other hydrocarbons. For instance, petroleum and coal both contain numerous aromatic hydrocarbons in varying amounts.

Aromatic compounds tend to be less reactive than alkenes and alkynes. For example, no reaction occurs between benzene and Br_2 in the presence of heat or light.

Nomenclature

Most simple aromatic compounds are named as derivatives of benzene. Thus benzene is the parent compound, and the name of any atom or group bonded to benzene is used as a prefix, as seen in the following examples:

NO_2 CH_2CH_3 Br

Nitrobenzene Ethylbenzene Bromobenzene

Other members of this family have unique names based on history rather than logic:

CH_3 OH NH_2 OCH_3

Toluene Phenol Aniline Anisole

FIGURE 9.11
Four ways to represent the benzene molecule: (a) classical planar view; (b) orbital view; (c) planar representation using a circle to represent six of the twelve electrons that make up the double bonds seen in part (a); and (d) most commonly used representation.

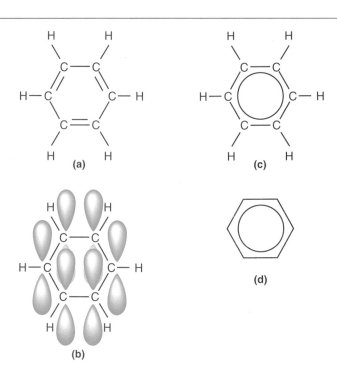

A HUMAN PERSPECTIVE

Aromatic Compounds and Carcinogenesis

We come into contact with many naturally occurring aromatic compounds each day. Originally, the name "aromatic" was given to these compounds because of the pleasant aromas of some members of this family. Indeed, many food flavorings and fragrances that we enjoy contain aromatic rings. Examples of other aromatic compounds include preservatives (such as BHT, butylated hydroxytoluene), insecticides (such as DDT), pharmaceutical drugs (such as aspirin), and toiletries.

The *polynuclear aromatic hydrocarbons* (PAH) are an important family of aromatic hydrocarbons that generally have toxic effects. They have also been shown to be carcinogenic, that is, they cause cancer. PAH are formed from the joining of the rings so that they share a common bond (edge). Several common examples are shown below:

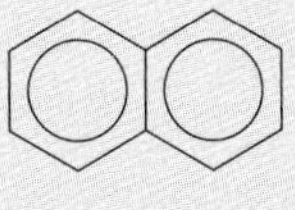

Naphthalene

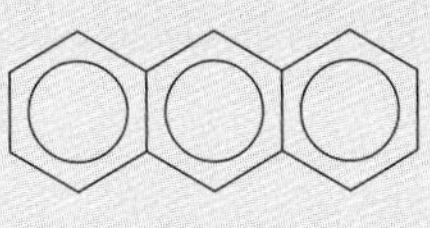

Anthracene

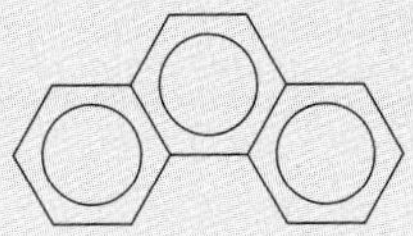

Phenanthrene

The more complex members of this family (typically consisting of five or six rings at a minimum) are among the most potent carcinogens known. It has been shown that the carcinogenic nature of these chemicals results from their ability to bind to the nucleic acid (DNA) in cells. As we will see in Chapter 19, the ability of the DNA to guide the cell faithfully from generation to generation is dependent on the proper expression of the genetic information, a process called *transcription,* and the accurate copying or replication of the DNA. Accurate DNA replication is essential so that every new cell inherits a complete copy of all the genetic information that is identical to that of the original parent cell. If a mistake is made in the DNA replication process, the result is an error, or mutation, in the new DNA molecule. Some of these errors in the DNA may cause the new cell to grow out of control, resulting in cancer.

Polynuclear aromatic hydrocarbons are thought to cause cancer by covalently binding to the DNA in cells and interfering with the correct replication of the DNA. Some of the mutations that result may cause a cell to begin to divide in an uncontrolled fashion, giving rise to a cancerous tumor.

Benzopyrene, shown below, is found in tobacco smoke, smokestack effluents, charcoal-broiled meat, and automobile exhaust. It is one of the strongest carcinogens known. It is estimated that the wide variety of all cancers are caused by chemical carcinogens, such as PAH, in the environment.

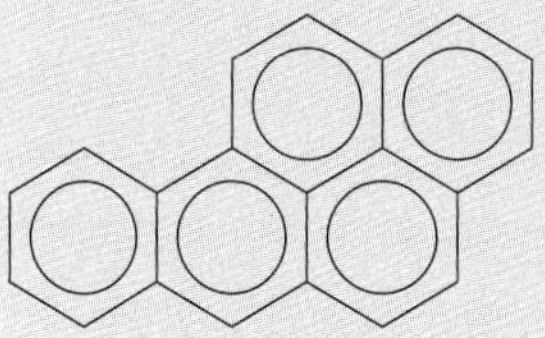

Benzopyrene

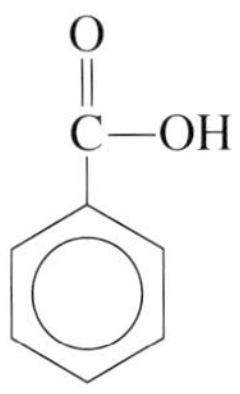

Benzoic acid

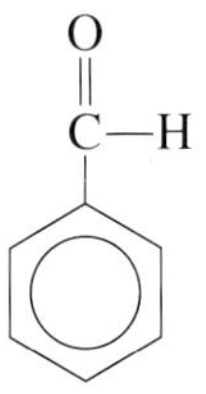

Benzaldehyde

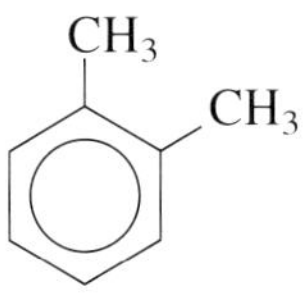

ortho-Xylene

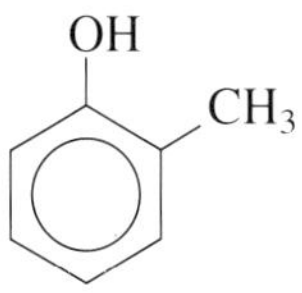

ortho-Cresol

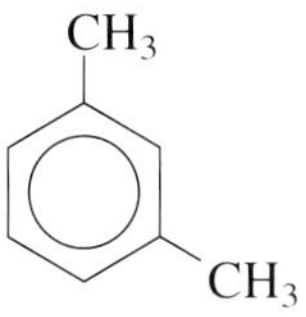

meta-Xylene

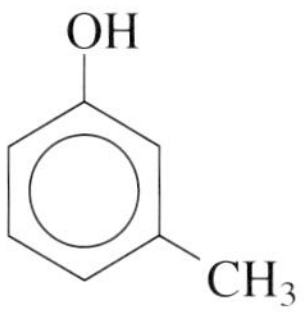

meta-Cresol

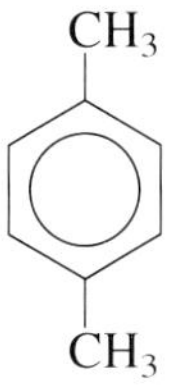

para-Xylene

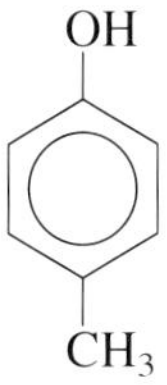

para-Cresol

When two groups are present on the ring, three possible orientations exist, and they may be named by either the I.U.P.A.C. Nomenclature System or the **common system of nomenclature.** If the groups or atoms are located on two adjacent carbons, they are referred to as *ortho (o)* in the common system or with the prefix 1,2- in the I.U.P.A.C. System. If they are on carbons separated by one carbon atom, they are termed *meta (m)* in the common system or 1,3- in the I.U.P.A.C. System. Finally, if the substituents are on carbons separated by two carbon atoms, they are said to be *para (p)* in the common system or 1,4- in the I.U.P.A.C. System. The following examples demonstrate both of these systems:

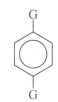

Two groups 1,2 or *ortho*   Two groups 1,3 or *meta*   Two groups 1,4 or *para*

G = Any group

If there are three or more groups attached to the benzene ring, numbers must be used to describe their location. The names of the substituents are given in alphabetical order.

QUESTION 9.13

Draw each of the following compounds:

a. 1,3,5-Trichlorobenzene
b. *ortho*-Cresol
c. 2,5-Dibromophenol
d. *para*-Dinitrobenzene
e. 2-Nitroaniline
f. *meta*-Nitrotoluene

QUESTION 9.14

Draw each of the following compounds:

a. 2,3-Dichlorotoluene
b. 3-Bromoaniline
c. 1-Bromo-3-ethylbenzene
d. *o*-Nitrotoluene
e. *p*-Xylene
f. *o*-Dibromobenzene

SUMMARY OF REACTIONS

Reactions of alkanes

Combustion:

$$C_nH_{2n+2} + O_2 \longrightarrow CO_2 + H_2O + \text{heat energy}$$

Alkane Oxygen $\longrightarrow$ **Carbon dioxide Water   Heat energy**

Halogenation:

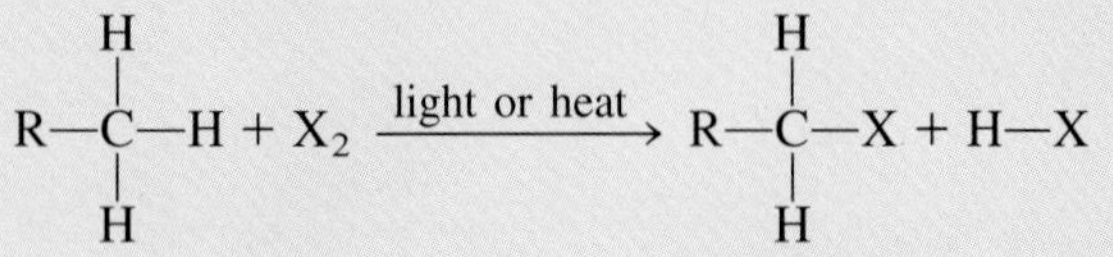

$$R{-}\underset{\underset{H}{|}}{\overset{\overset{H}{|}}{C}}{-}H + X_2 \xrightarrow{\text{light or heat}} R{-}\underset{\underset{H}{|}}{\overset{\overset{H}{|}}{C}}{-}X + H{-}X$$

Alkane Halogen $\xrightarrow{\text{light or heat}}$ **Alkyl halide Hydrogen halide**

Addition reactions of alkenes

Hydrogenation:

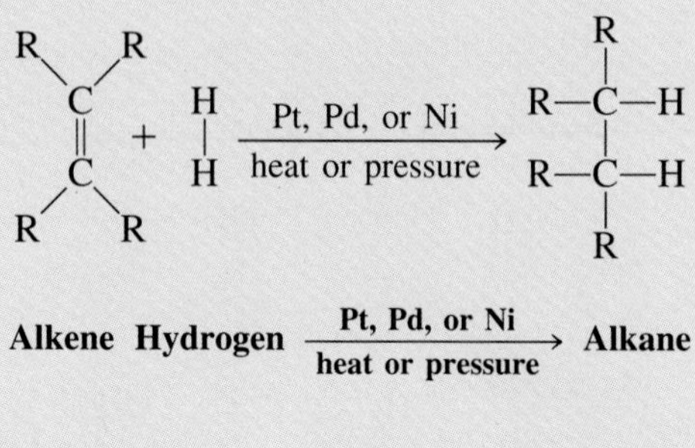

$$\underset{R}{\overset{R}{\diagdown}}C{=}\underset{R}{\overset{R}{\diagup}}C + \underset{H}{\overset{H}{\underset{|}{|}}} \xrightarrow[\text{heat or pressure}]{\text{Pt, Pd, or Ni}} \begin{array}{c} R \\ R{-}C{-}H \\ R{-}C{-}H \\ R \end{array}$$

Alkene Hydrogen $\xrightarrow[\text{heat or pressure}]{\text{Pt, Pd, or Ni}}$ **Alkane**

Halogenation:

Alkene   Halogen $\longrightarrow$ Alkyl dihalide

Hydration:

Alkene   Water $\xrightarrow{H^+}$ Alcohol

Hydrohalogenation:

Alkene   Hydrogen halide $\longrightarrow$ Alkyl halide

and boiling points. In the *I.U.P.A.C. Nomenclature System* the alkanes are named by determining the number of carbon atoms in the parent compound and numbering the carbon chain to provide the lowest possible number for all substituents. The substituent names and numbers are used as prefixes before the name of the parent compound.

Structural isomers are molecules that have the same molecular formula but different structures. They have different physical and chemical properties because the atoms are bonded to one another in different patterns.

Alkanes can participate in *combustion* reactions. In complete combustion reactions they are oxidized to produce carbon dioxide, water, and heat energy. They can also undergo *halogenation* reactions to produce alkyl halides.

9.3 Alkenes and Alkynes

Alkenes and *alkynes* are *unsaturated hydrocarbons.* Alkenes are characterized by the presence of at least one carbon-carbon double bond and have the general molecular formula C_nH_{2n}. Alkynes are characterized by the presence of at least one carbon-carbon triple bond and have the general molecular formula C_nH_{2n-2}. The physical properties of the alkenes and alkynes are similar to those of alkanes, but their chemical properties are quite different. While alkanes undergo *substitution reactions,* alkenes and alkynes undergo *addition reactions.* The principal addition reactions of the unsaturated hydrocarbons are *halogenation, hydration, hydrohalogenation,* and *hydrogenation.*

9.4 Aromatic Hydrocarbons

The *aromatic hydrocarbons* contain a benzene ring. They are named as derivatives of benzene. Several members of this family have historical common names that are used, such as aniline, phenol, and toluene. Aromatic compounds tend to be less reactive than alkenes or alkynes.

SUMMARY

9.1 The Chemistry of Carbon

The modern science of organic chemistry began with Wöhler's synthesis of urea in 1828. At that time, people believed that it was impossible to synthesize an organic molecule outside of a living system. We now define organic chemistry as the study of carbon-containing compounds. The differences between the ionic bond, which is characteristic of inorganic substances, and the covalent bond in organic compounds are responsible for the great contrast in properties and reactivity between organic and inorganic compounds. All organic compounds are classified as either *hydrocarbons* or *substituted hydrocarbons.* A *functional group* is an atom or group of atoms arranged in a particular way that imparts specific chemical or physical properties to a molecule. The major families of organic molecules are defined by the specific functional groups that they contain.

9.2 Alkanes

The *alkanes* are *saturated hydrocarbons,* that is, hydrocarbons that have only carbon and hydrogen atoms that are bonded together by carbon-carbon and carbon-hydrogen single bonds. They have the general molecular formula C_nH_{2n+2} and are generally nonpolar, water-insoluble compounds with low melting

KEY TERMS

addition reaction (9.3)	hydration (9.3)
aliphatic hydrocarbon (9.1)	hydrocarbon (9.1)
alkane (9.2)	hydrogenation (9.3)
alkene (9.3)	hydrohalogenation (9.3)
alkyl group (9.2)	I.U.P.A.C. Nomenclature
alkyl halide (9.2)	System (9.2)
alkyne (9.3)	Markovnikov's Rule (9.3)
aromatic hydrocarbon (9.1)	molecular formula (9.2)
combustion (9.2)	parent compound (9.2)
common system of	saturated hydrocarbon (9.1)
nomenclature (9.4)	structural formula (9.2)
condensed formula (9.2)	structural isomers (9.2)
cycloalkane (9.2)	substituted hydrocarbon (9.1)
functional group (9.1)	substitution reaction (9.2)
geometric isomer (9.3)	unsaturated hydrocarbon (9.1)
halogenation (9.2, 9.3)	

QUESTIONS AND PROBLEMS

The Chemistry of Carbon

9.15 Consider the differences between organic and inorganic compounds as you answer each of the following questions:
  a. Which compounds make good electrolytes?
  b. Which compounds exhibit ionic bonding?
  c. Which compounds have lower melting points?
  d. Which compounds are more likely to be soluble in water?
  e. Which compounds are flammable?

9.16 Describe the major differences between ionic and covalent bonds.

9.17 Give the structural formula for each of the following:

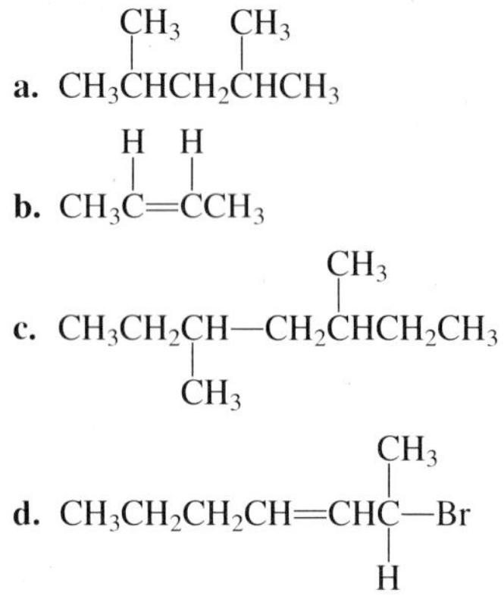

a. $CH_3CHCH_2CHCH_3$ with CH_3 groups above second and fourth carbons

b. $CH_3C=CCH_3$ with H H above the two central carbons

c. $CH_3CH_2CH—CH_2CHCH_2CH_3$ with CH_3 groups

d. $CH_3CH_2CH_2CH=CHC—Br$ with CH_3 above and H below

9.18 Condense each of the following structural formulas:

a. H—C—C—C—C—H (with H's and a H—C—H branch)

b. H—C—C—C—C—C—C—C—H (with branches)

c. H—C—C—C—C—C—H (with branches)

d. H—C—C—C—H (with branches)

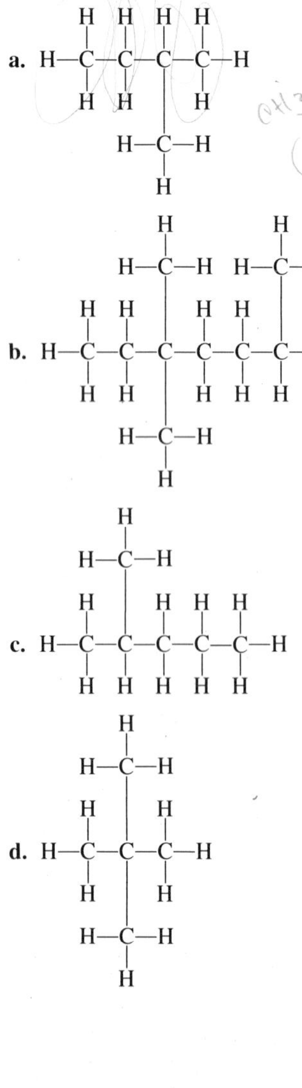

9.19 Which of the following structures are not possible? State your reasons.

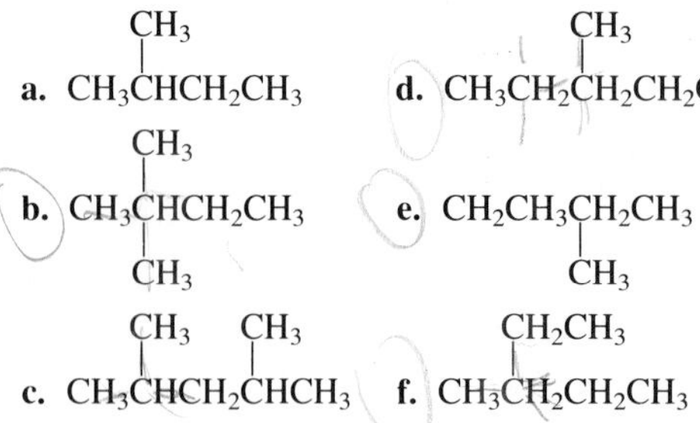

a. $CH_3CHCH_2CH_3$ with CH_3 above

b. $CH_3CHCH_2CH_3$ with CH_3 above and CH_3 below

c. $CH_3CHCH_2CHCH_3$ with CH_3, CH_3 above

d. $CH_3CH_2CH_2CH_2CH_3$ with CH_3 above

e. $CH_2CH_3CH_2CH_3$ with CH_3 above and CH_3 below

f. $CH_3CH_2CH_2CH_3$ with CH_2CH_3 above

9.20 Using the octet rule, explain why carbon forms four bonds in a stable compound.

9.21 Using structural formulas, draw a typical alcohol, aldehyde, ketone, carboxylic acid, ester, and amine. (*Hint:* Refer to Table 9.2.)

9.22 Name the functional group in each of the following molecules:

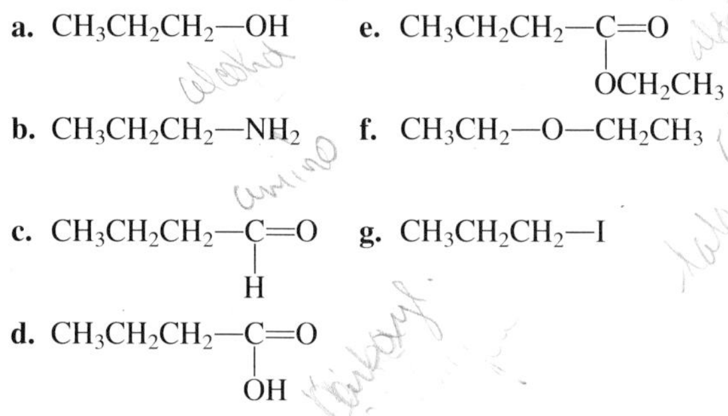

a. $CH_3CH_2CH_2—OH$

b. $CH_3CH_2CH_2—NH_2$

c. $CH_3CH_2CH_2—C=O$ with H below

d. $CH_3CH_2CH_2—C=O$ with OH below

e. $CH_3CH_2CH_2—C=O$ with OCH_2CH_3 below

f. $CH_3CH_2—O—CH_2CH_3$

g. $CH_3CH_2CH_2—I$

Alkanes

9.23 Draw each of the following:
  a. 2-Bromobutane
  b. 2-Chloro-2-methylpropane
  c. 2,2-Dimethylhexane
  d. Dichlorodiiodomethane
  e. 1,4-Diethylcyclohexane
  f. 2-Iodo-2,4,4-trimethylpentane

9.24 Draw each of the following compounds using complete structural formulas:
  a. 2,2-Dibromobutane
  b. 2-Iododecane
  c. 1,2-Dichloropentane
  d. 1-Bromo-2-methylcyclopentane
  e. 1,1,1-Trichlorodecane
  f. 1,2-Dibromo-1,1,2-trifluoroethane
  g. 3,3,5-Trimethylheptane
  h. 1,3,5-Trifluoropentane

9.25 Name each of the following using the I.U.P.A.C. Nomenclature System:

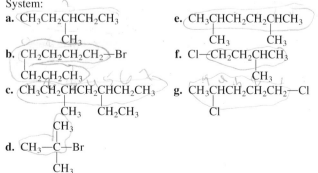

a. $CH_3CH_2CHCH_2CH_3$ with CH_3 below

b. $CH_2CH_2CH_2CH_2—Br$ with $CH_2CH_2CH_3$ below

c. $CH_3CH_2CHCH_2CHCH_2CH_3$ with CH_3 and CH_2CH_3 below

d. $CH_3—C—Br$ with CH_3 above and CH_3 below

e. $CH_3CHCH_2CH_2CHCH_3$ with CH_3 and CH_3 below

f. $Cl—CH_2CH_2CHCH_3$ with CH_3 below

g. $CH_3CHCH_2CH_2CH_2—Cl$ with Cl below

9.26 Give the common name and the I.U.P.A.C. name for each of the following:

a.
$$CH_3$$
$$CH_3CHCl$$

b.
$$CH_3CHCH_2CH_3$$
$$|$$
(Br)

c.
$$Br$$
$$|$$
$$CH_3—C—Br$$
$$|$$
$$CH_3$$

d.
$$CH_3$$
$$CH_3CHCH_2—Cl$$

e.
$$CH_3$$
$$|$$
$$CH_3—C—CH_3$$
$$|$$
$$I$$

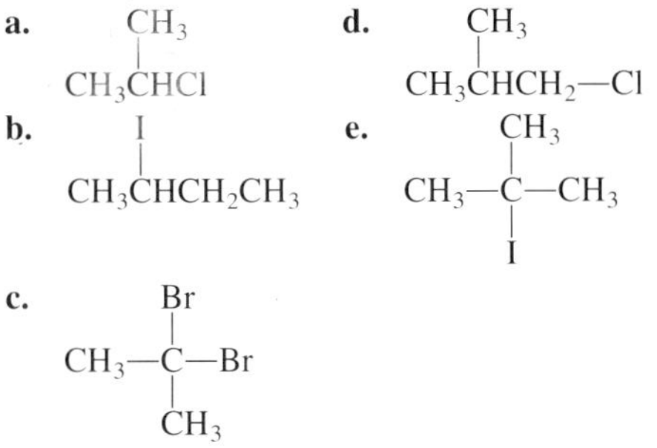

9.27 Name each of the following cycloalkanes using the I.U.P.A.C. Nomenclature System:

a.
$$CH_3$$
$$CH_3$$
$$CH_3$$

b. (triangle)
$$CH_3$$
$$CH_3$$

c.
$$CH_3$$
$$CH_3$$
$$CH_3$$
$$CH_3$$

d.
$$Cl$$
$$Cl \quad\quad Cl$$
$$Cl \quad\quad Cl$$

e.
$$CH_2CH_3$$
(cyclopentane)

f.
$$CH_3$$
$$CH_2CH_2CH_3$$
(cyclobutane)

g.
$$Cl$$
$$Cl$$
(cyclohexane)

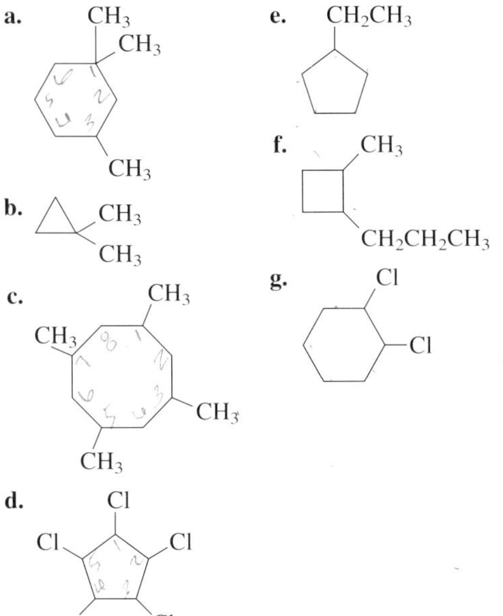

9.28 Draw the structure of each of the following cycloalkanes:
a. 1-Bromo-2-methylcyclobutane
b. Iodocyclopropane
c. 1-Bromo-3-chlorocyclopentane
d. 1,2-Dibromo-3-methylcyclohexane

9.29 Which of the following pairs of compounds are identical? Which are isomers? Which are completely unrelated?

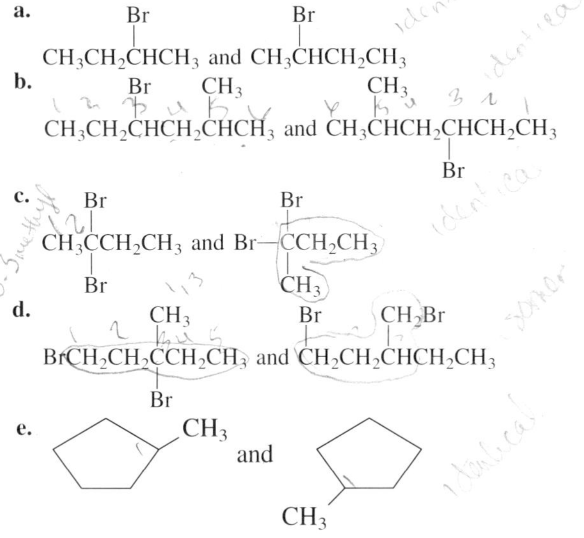

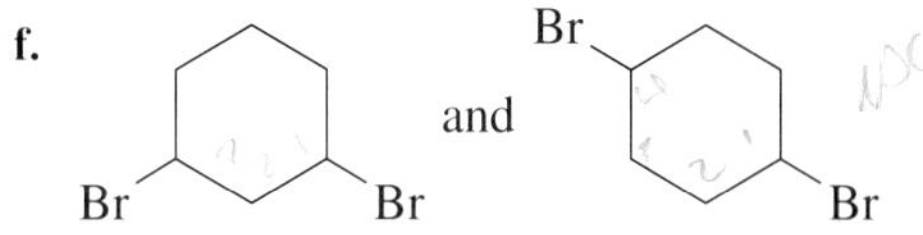

a.
$$Br \quad\quad\quad Br$$
$$| \quad\quad\quad\quad |$$
$$CH_3CH_2CHCH_3 \text{ and } CH_3CHCH_2CH_3$$

b.
$$Br \quad CH_3 \quad\quad\quad CH_3$$
$$| \quad | \quad\quad\quad\quad |$$
$$CH_3CH_2CHCH_2CHCH_3 \text{ and } CH_3CHCH_2CHCH_2CH_3$$
$$\quad\quad\quad\quad\quad\quad\quad\quad\quad\quad\quad\quad |$$
$$\quad\quad\quad\quad\quad\quad\quad\quad\quad\quad\quad\quad Br$$

c.
$$Br \quad\quad\quad\quad Br$$
$$| \quad\quad\quad\quad\quad |$$
$$CH_3CCH_2CH_3 \text{ and } Br—CCH_2CH_3$$
$$| \quad\quad\quad\quad\quad\quad |$$
$$Br \quad\quad\quad\quad\quad CH_3$$

d.
$$CH_3 \quad\quad\quad\quad Br \quad CH_2Br$$
$$| \quad\quad\quad\quad\quad | \quad |$$
$$BrCH_2CH_2CCH_2CH_3 \text{ and } CH_2CH_2CHCH_2CH_3$$
$$| $$
$$Br$$

e.
(cyclopentane with CH_3) and (cyclopentane with CH_3)

f.
(cyclohexane with two Br) and (cyclohexane with two Br)

9.30 Which of the following pairs of molecules are identical compounds? Which are structural isomers?

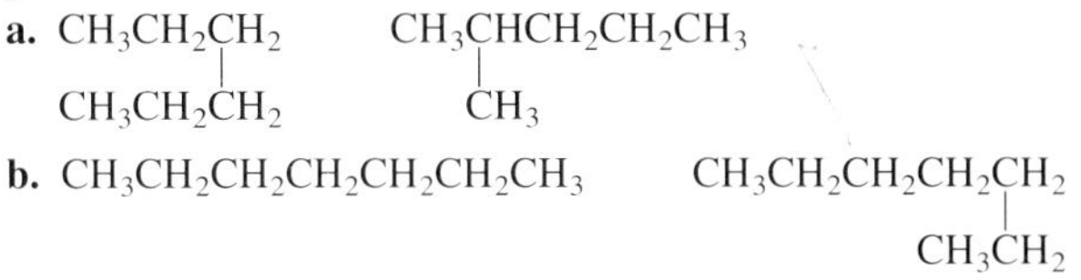

a.
$$CH_3CH_2CH_2 \quad\quad CH_3CHCH_2CH_2CH_3$$
$$CH_3CH_2CH_2 \quad\quad\quad CH_3$$

b.
$$CH_3CH_2CH_2CH_2CH_2CH_2CH_3 \quad\quad CH_3CH_2CH_2CH_2CH_2$$
$$\quad\quad\quad\quad\quad\quad\quad\quad\quad\quad\quad\quad\quad CH_3CH_2$$

9.31 Complete each of the following reactions by supplying the missing reactant or product as indicated by a question mark:

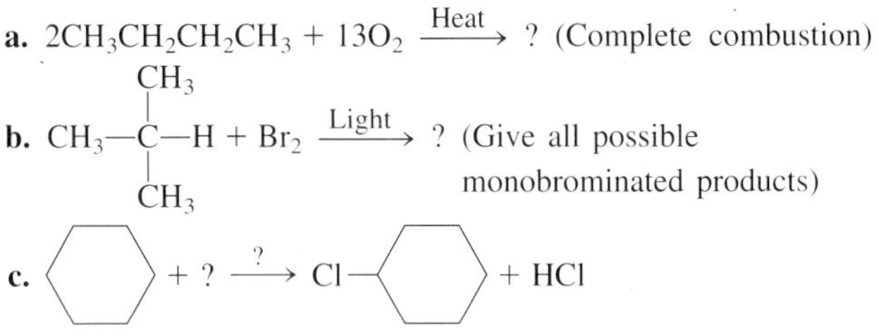

a. $2CH_3CH_2CH_2CH_3 + 13O_2 \xrightarrow{\text{Heat}} ?$ (Complete combustion)

b.
$$CH_3$$
$$|$$
$$CH_3—C—H + Br_2 \xrightarrow{\text{Light}} ?$$ (Give all possible
$$|$$
$$CH_3$$
    monobrominated products)

c. (cyclohexane) $+ ? \xrightarrow{?} Cl—$(cyclohexane)$ + HCl$

9.32 Give all the possible monochlorinated products for the following reaction:

$$CH_3$$
$$|$$
$$CH_3CHCH_2CH_3 + Cl_2 \xrightarrow{\text{Light}} ?$$

Name the products using I.U.P.A.C. nomenclature.

9.33 Draw the structural isomers of molecular formula C_6H_{14} and name each using the I.U.P.A.C. Nomenclature System:
a. Which one gives two and only two monobromo derivatives when it reacts with Br_2 and light? Name the products using the I.U.P.A.C. Nomenclature System.
b. Which give three and only three monobromo products? Name the products using the I.U.P.A.C. Nomenclature System.
c. Which give four and only four monobromo products? Name the products using the I.U.P.A.C. Nomenclature System.

9.34 a. Draw and name all of the isomeric products one would obtain from the bromination of propane with Br_2/light. If halogenation were a completely random reaction and had an equal probability of occurring at any of the C—H bonds in a molecule, what percentage of each of these monobromo products would be expected?
b. Answer part (a) using 2-methylpropane as the starting material.

Alkenes and Alkynes

9.35 Draw a condensed formula for each of the following compounds:
a. 2-Methyl-2-hexene
b. *trans*-3-Heptene
c. *cis*-1-Chloro-2-pentene
d. *cis*-2-Chloro-2-methyl-3-heptene
e. *trans*-5-Bromo-2,6-dimethyl-3-octene

9.36 Draw a condensed formula for each of the following compounds:
a. 2-Hexyne
b. 4-Methyl-1-pentyne
c. 1-Chloro-4,4,5-trimethyl-2-heptyne
d. 2-Bromo-3-chloro-7,8-dimethyl-4-decyne

9.37 How could you distinguish between a sample of cyclohexane and a sample of hexene (both C_6H_{12}) using a simple chemical test? (*Hint:* Refer to the subsection entitled "Halogenation: Addition of X_2 to an alkene.")

9.38 Quantitatively, one mole of Br_2 is consumed per mole of alkene, and two moles of Br_2 are consumed per mole of alkyne. How many moles of Br_2 would be consumed for one mole of each of the following:
  a. 2-Hexyne
  b. Cyclohexene
  c.

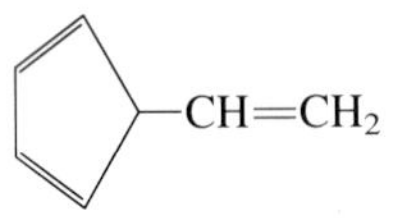

$—CH{=}CH_2$

  d.

$—C{\equiv}C—CH_3$

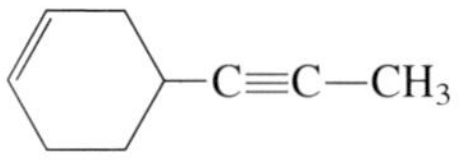

9.39 Complete each of the following reactions by supplying the missing reactant or product(s) as indicated by a question mark:
  a. $CH_3CH_2CH{=}CHCH_2CH_3 + ? \longrightarrow CH_3CH_2CH_2CH_2CH_2CH_3$

  b.
$$CH_3{-}\underset{\underset{CH_2}{\|}}{C}{-}CH_3 + ? \longrightarrow CH_3\underset{\underset{CH_3}{|}}{C}{-}OH$$

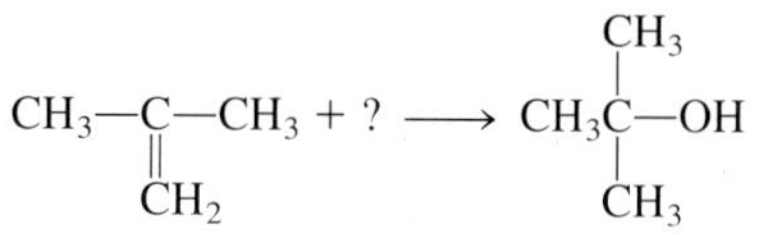

  c. ? + (cyclohexene) $\longrightarrow$ (cyclohexane with Br and H)

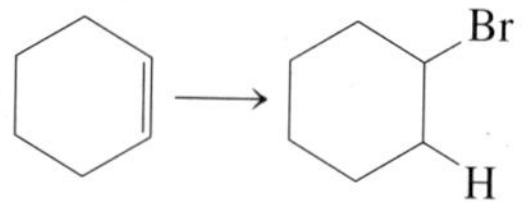

  d. $2CH_3CH_2CH_2CH_2CH_2CH_3 + ?O_2 \xrightarrow{\text{Heat}} ?$ (Complete combustion)

  e. ? + (cyclohexane) $\longrightarrow$ $Cl{-}$(cyclohexane) $+ HCl$

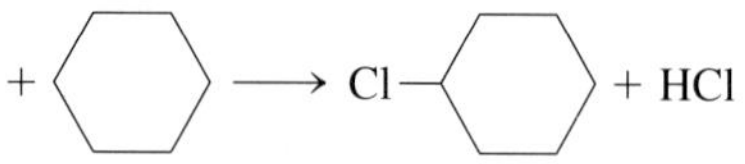

  f. ? $\xrightarrow{H_2O,\ H^+}$ (cyclopentane with OH)

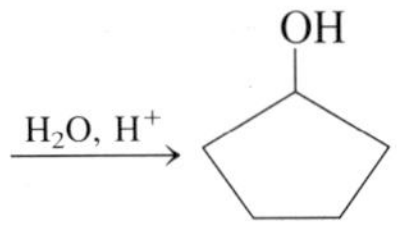

9.40 Draw and name the product in each of the following reactions:
  a. Cyclopentene + H_2O (H^+)
  b. Cyclopentene + HCl
  c. Cyclopentene + H_2
  d. Cyclopentene + HI

9.41 How does a substitution reaction differ from an addition reaction?

9.42 Give an example of a substitution reaction and of an addition reaction.

9.43 Name each of the following using the I.U.P.A.C. Nomenclature System:
  a. $CH_3CH_2\underset{\underset{CH_3}{|}}{C}HCH{=}CH_2$
  b. $CH_2CH_2CH_2CH_2{-}Br$ with $CH_2CH{=}CH_2$ substituent
  c. $CH_3CH_2CH{=}CH\underset{\underset{Br}{|}}{C}HCH_2CH_3$
  d. $CH_3{-}\underset{\overset{\overset{CH_3}{|}}{\underset{\underset{CH_3}{|}}{C}}}{}{-}$(cyclohexene ring)$-CH_3$
  e. $CH_3\underset{\underset{CH_3}{|}}{C}HCH_2CH{=}\underset{\underset{CH_3}{|}}{C}CH_3$
  f. $Cl{-}CH_2\underset{\underset{CH_3}{|}}{C}HC{\equiv}C{-}H$
  g. $CH_3\underset{\underset{Cl}{|}}{C}HCH_2CH_2CH_2{-}C{\equiv}C{-}H$
  h. Br (cyclopentane ring) Cl

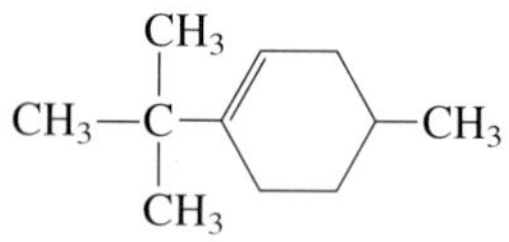

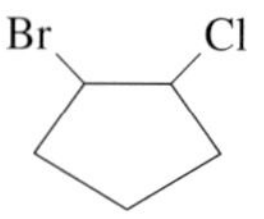

9.44 Of the following compounds, which can exist in either the *cis-* or *trans-* isomeric form? Draw the two geometric isomers.
  a. 2,3-Dibromobutane
  b. 2-Heptene
  c. 2,3-Dibromo-2-butene
  d. Propene
  e. 1-Bromo-1-chloro-2-methylpropene
  f. 1,1-Dichloroethene
  g. 1,2-Dibromoethene
  h. 3-Ethyl-2-methyl-2-hexene

Aromatic Hydrocarbons

9.45 Draw the structure for each of the following compounds:
  a. 2,4-Dibromotoluene
  b. 1,2,4-Triethylbenzene
  c. Isopropylbenzene
  d. 2-Bromo-5-chlorotoluene

9.46 Name each of the following compounds using the I.U.P.A.C. System.

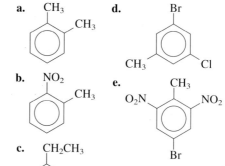

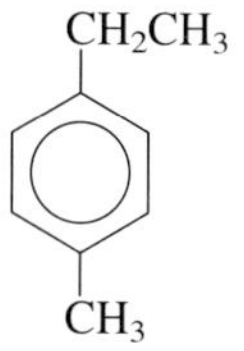

Further Problems

9.47 Give the general formula for each of the following:
  a. An alkane
  b. An alkyne
  c. An alkene
  d. A cycloalkane
  e. A cycloalkene

9.48 Of the compounds listed in Problem 9.47, which are saturated? Which are unsaturated?

9.49 What major structural feature distinguishes the alkanes, alkenes, and alkynes? Give examples.

9.50 What is the major structural feature that distinguishes between saturated and unsaturated hydrocarbons?

9.51 Give an example, using structural formulas, of each of the following families of organic compounds. Each of your examples should contain a minimum of three carbons. (*Hint:* Refer to Table 9.2.)
  a. A ketone
  b. An aldehyde
  c. A carboxylic acid
  d. An amide
  e. An amine
  f. An alcohol
  g. An ester
  h. An ether

9.52 Folic acid is a vitamin required by the body for nucleic acid synthesis. The structure of folic acid is given below. Circle and identify as many functional groups as possible.

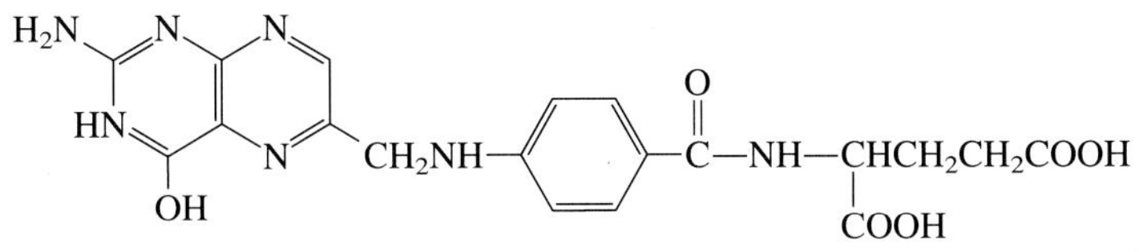

Folic acid

9.53 A hydrocarbon with a formula C_5H_{10} decolorized Br_2 and consumed one mole of hydrogen upon hydrogenation. Draw all the possible isomers of C_5H_{10} that are possible based on the above information.

9.54 Which of the following alkenes would not exhibit *cis-/trans-* geometric isomerism?

a.

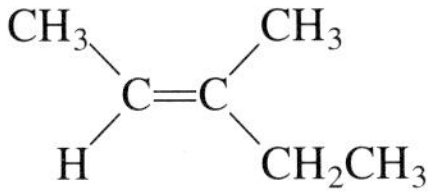

b.

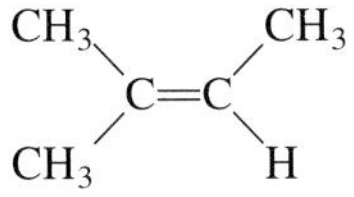

c.

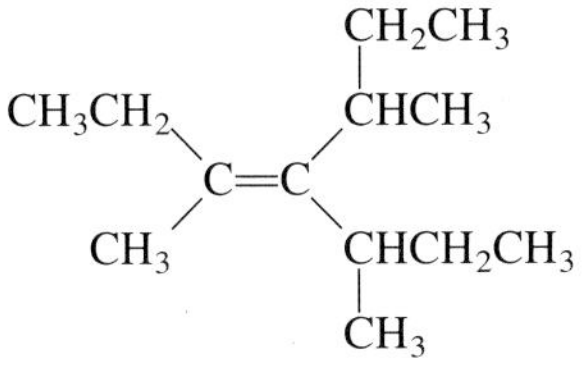

d.

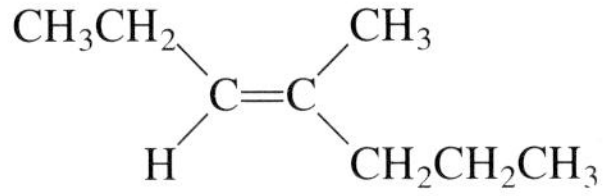

e.

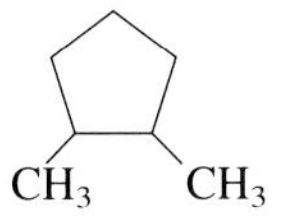

9.55 Draw each of the following compounds using condensed formulas:
 a. 1,3,5-Trifluoropentane
 b. *cis*-2-Octene

c. Dipropylacetylene
d. 3,3,5-Trimethyl-1-hexene
e. 1-Bromo-3-chloro-1-heptyne

9.56 Draw each of the following compounds using condensed formulas:
 a. *meta*-Cresol
 b. 1-Octyne
 c. Propylbenzene
 d. 1,3,5-Trinitrobenzene
 e. *cis*-1,2-Dichloro-1-fluoroethene

VOCABULARY QUIZ

9.1 A(n) _alkane_ is a hydrocarbon that contains only carbon and hydrogen bonded together through carbon-hydrogen and carbon-carbon single bonds. They are saturated hydrocarbons that have the general molecular formula C_nH_{2n+2}.

9.2 Two molecules having the same molecular formulas but different chemical structures are called _isomers_.

9.3 _____ are isomers (which by definition have the same molecular formula) that differ from one another because of the placement of substituents on a double bond or a ring.

9.4 A(n) _____ is a simple hydrocarbon group that results from the removal of one hydrogen from the original hydrocarbon (e.g., methyl, CH_3—; ethyl, CH_3CH_2—).

9.5 In the I.U.P.A.C. Nomenclature System the _parent chain_ is the longest chain containing the principal functional group (e.g., the hydroxyl group) in the molecule that is being named.

9.6 A(n) _alkyne_ is any hydrocarbon that contains one or more carbon-carbon double or triple bonds.

9.7 A(n) _alkene_ is any hydrocarbon that contains one or more carbon-carbon double bonds. They are also described as unsaturated hydrocarbons with the general formula C_nH_{2n}.

9.8 A(n) _hydrocarbon_ is a compound containing only hydrogen and carbon.

9.9 An atom or group of atoms that imparts specific chemical and physical properties to a molecule is called a(n) _____.

9.10 A(n) _____ is a reaction that results in the replacement of one group for another.

10

Oxygen- and Sulfur- Containing Organic Compounds

CHEMISTRY CONNECTION

Fetal Alcohol Syndrome

The first months of pregnancy are a time of great joy and anticipation but are not without moments of anxiety. On her first visit to the obstetrician the mother-to-be is tested for previous exposure to a number of infectious diseases that could damage the fetus. She is provided with information about diet, weight gain, and drugs that could harm the baby. Among the drugs that should be avoided are alcoholic beverages.

The use of alcoholic beverages by a pregnant woman can cause *fetal alcohol syndrome (FAS)*. A *syndrome* is a set of symptoms that occur together and are characteristic of a particular disease. In this case, physicians noticed that infants born to women with chronic alcoholism showed a reproducible set of abnormalities including mental retardation, poor growth before and after birth, and facial malformations.

Mothers who report only social drinking may have children with *fetal alcohol effects,* a less severe form of fetal alcohol syndrome. This milder form is characterized by a reduced birth weight, some learning disabilities, and behavioral problems.

How does alcohol consumption cause these varied symptoms? No one is exactly sure, but it is well known that the alcohol consumed by the mother crosses the placenta and enters the bloodstream of the fetus. Within about 15 minutes the concentration of alcohol in the blood of the fetus is as high as that of the mother! However, the mother has enzymes to detoxify the alcohol in her blood; the fetus does not. Now consider that alcohol can cause cell division to stop or be radically altered. It is thought that even a single night on the town could be enough to cause FAS by blocking cell division during a critical developmental period.

This raises the question "How much alcohol can a pregnant woman safely drink?" As we have seen, the severity of the symptoms seems to increase with the amount of alcohol consumed by the mother. However, it is virtually impossible to do the scientific studies that would conclusively determine the risk to the fetus caused by different amounts of alcohol. There is some evidence that suggests that there is a risk associated with drinking even 1 ounce of absolute (100%) alcohol each day. Because of these facts and uncertainties, the American Medical Association and the U.S. Surgeon General recommend that pregnant women completely abstain from alcohol.

In this chapter we will study the alcohols, along with several other families of organic compounds that are important to biological systems. In addition to the structure, properties, and reactions of these compounds, we will consider the biological significance and medical application of these molecules.

INTRODUCTION

The characteristic functional group of the *alcohols* and *phenols* is the *hydroxyl group* (—OH). Alcohols have the general structure R—OH, where R is any alkyl group. Phenols are similar in structure but contain an aryl group in place of the alkyl group. Both can be viewed as substituted water molecules in which one of the hydrogen atoms has been replaced by an alkyl or aryl group.

An aryl group is a benzene ring with one hydrogen atom removed.

General Formula:

$$\underset{\text{R}\qquad\text{H}}{\overset{\text{O}}{\diagup\diagdown}} \qquad \underset{\text{Ar}\qquad\text{H}}{\overset{\text{O}}{\diagup\diagdown}}$$

Alcohol · · · · Phenol

Example:

$$\underset{CH_3\qquad OH}{\overset{\text{O}}{\diagup\diagdown}}$$

Methanol
(methyl alcohol)

Ethers have two alkyl or aryl groups attached to the oxygen atom and may be thought of as substituted alcohols. The functional group characteristic of an ether is R—O—R. *Thiols* are a family of compounds that contain the sulfhydryl group (—SH). They, too, have a structure similar to that of alcohols.

$$\underset{\text{R}\qquad\text{R}'}{\overset{\text{O}}{\diagup\diagdown}} \qquad\qquad \underset{CH_3\qquad CH_3}{\overset{\text{O}}{\diagup\diagdown}} \qquad\qquad R—SH \qquad\qquad CH_3—SH$$

Ethers
(R and R′ = R or Ar)

Methoxymethane
(dimethyl ether)

Thiol
(R = R or Ar)

Methanethiol

Aldehydes and *ketones* are two of the families of organic compounds characterized by the *carbonyl group,* a carbon atom and oxygen atom joined by a double bond. Ketones and aldehydes differ in the type of atoms attached to the carbonyl group. In ketones, two carbon-containing groups are attached to the carbonyl carbon, while in aldehydes the carbonyl carbon is bonded to at least one hydrogen. The second group may be a carbon-containing group or another hydrogen.

O   O

‖   ‖

C   C

R   H   CH$_3$ H

Aldehyde   Ethanal

(R = H, R, or Ar)   (acetaldehyde)

O   O

‖   ‖

C   C

R   R′   CH$_3$ CH$_3$

Ketone   Propanone

(R and R′ = R or Ar)   (acetone)

As we will see in upcoming chapters, many important biological molecules, including sugars, fats, and proteins, contain hydroxyl groups. All sugars are either aldehydes or ketones, and the thiol group is found in the structure of some amino acids and is essential for keeping proteins in the proper three-dimensional shape required for their biological function. Thus these functional groups play a central role in the structures and chemistry of biological molecules.

Section 11.2

10.1 ALCOHOLS

Structure and physical properties

An **alcohol** is an organic compound that contains a **hydroxyl group** (—OH) attached to an alkyl group. The R—O—H portion of an alcohol is similar to the structure of water. The oxygen and the two atoms bonded to it lie in the same plane, and the R—O—H bond angle is approximately 104°.

The hydroxyl groups of alcohols, and thus alcohol molecules themselves, are very polar because the oxygen and hydrogen atoms have different electronegativities. Because the two atoms involved in this polar bond are oxygen and hydrogen, hydrogen bonds can form between alcohol molecules (Figure 10.1).

FIGURE 10.1
(a) Hydrogen bonding between alcohol molecules. (b) Hydrogen bonding between alcohol molecules and water molecules.

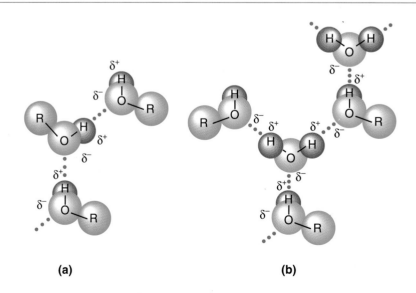

(a)   (b)

As a result of this intermolecular hydrogen bonding, alcohols boil at much higher temperatures than hydrocarbons of similar molecular weight. These higher boiling points are caused by the large amount of heat needed to break the hydrogen bonds that attract the alcohol molecules to one another. Compare the boiling points of butane and propanol, which have similar molecular weights:

$$CH_3CH_2CH_2CH_3 \qquad CH_3CH_2CH_2OH$$

Butane	1-Propanol
M.W. = 58	M.W. = 60
b.p. = −0.5°C	b.p. = 97.2°C

Alcohols with fewer than four or five carbon atoms are very soluble in water, and those with five to eight carbons are moderately soluble in water. This is due to the ability of the alcohol to form intermolecular hydrogen bonds with water molecules (see Figure 10.1b). As the carbon chain length of an alcohol increases, the nonpolar hydrocarbon part of the molecule increases. Thus the hydroxyl group has a smaller effect. As a result, large alcohols are nearly insoluble in water.

The presence of polar hydroxyl groups in large biological molecules—for instance, proteins and nucleic acids—allows intramolecular hydrogen bonding that keeps these molecules in the shapes needed for biological function.

Intermolecular hydrogen bonds are attractive forces between two molecules. *Intramolecular* hydrogen bonds are attractive forces between polar groups within the same molecule.

In the I.U.P.A.C. Nomenclature System, alcohols are named according to the following steps:

Nomenclature

The way to determine the parent compound was described in Section 9.2.

◆ Determine the name of the *parent compound,* the longest continuous carbon chain containing the —OH group.

◆ Replace the −*e* ending of the alkane chain with the *-ol* ending of the alcohol. Following this pattern, an alkane becomes an alkanol. For instance, ethan*e* becomes ethan*ol,* and propan*e* becomes propan*ol.*

◆ Number the parent chain to give the carbon bearing the hydroxyl group the lowest possible number.

◆ Name and number all substituents, and add them as prefixes to the "alkanol" name.

◆ Alcohols containing two hydroxyl groups are named *-diols.* Those bearing three hydroxyl groups are called *-triols.* A number giving the position of each of the hydroxyl groups is needed in these cases.

EXAMPLE 10.1

Naming an Alcohol Using I.U.P.A.C. Nomenclature

Solution

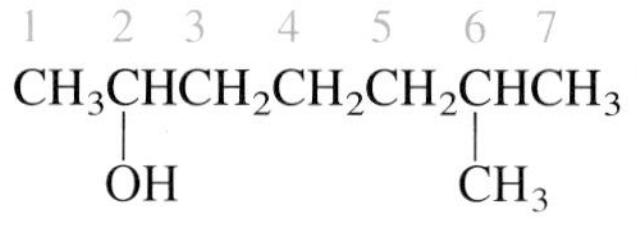

$$\overset{1}{C}H_3\overset{2}{C}H\overset{3}{C}H_2\overset{4}{C}H_2\overset{5}{C}H_2\overset{6}{C}H\overset{7}{C}H_3$$

with OH on carbon-2 and CH₃ on carbon-6

Parent compound: heptane (becomes heptanol)
Position of —OH: carbon-2 (*not* carbon-6)
Substituents: 6-methyl
Name: 6-methyl-2-heptanol

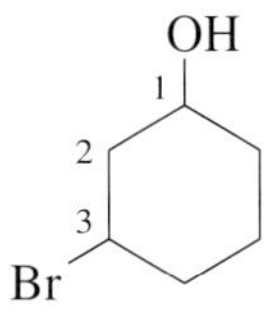

Parent compound: cyclohexane (becomes cyclohexanol)
Position of —OH: carbon-1 (*not* carbon-3)
Substituents: 3-bromo (*not* 5-bromo)
Name: 3-bromocyclohexanol (it is assumed that the
 —OH is on carbon 1 in cyclic structures)

See Section 9.2 for the names of the common alkyl groups.

The common names for alcohols are derived from the alkyl group corresponding to the parent compound. The name of the alkyl group is followed by the word "alcohol." For some alcohols, such as ethylene glycol and glycerol, historical names are used and must simply be memorized. The examples below provide the I.U.P.A.C. and common names of several alcohols:

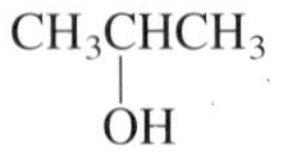

$$CH_3CHCH_3 \qquad HOCH_2CH_2OH \qquad CH_3CH_2OH$$
$$|$$
$$OH$$

2-Propanol   1,2-Ethanediol   Ethanol
(isopropyl   (ethylene glycol)   (ethyl alcohol)
alcohol)

QUESTION 10.1

Name each of the following compounds, using the I.U.P.A.C. Nomenclature System.

a. 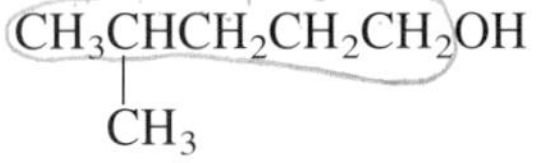 $CH_3CHCH_2CH_2CH_2OH$
$\qquad |$
$\qquad CH_3$

c. 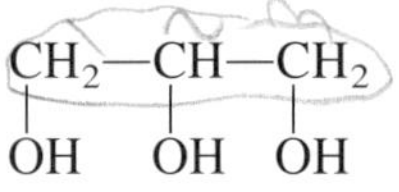 $CH_2{-}CH{-}CH_2$
$\qquad |\qquad |\qquad |$
$\qquad OH \quad OH \quad OH$

(Common name: Glycerol)

b. 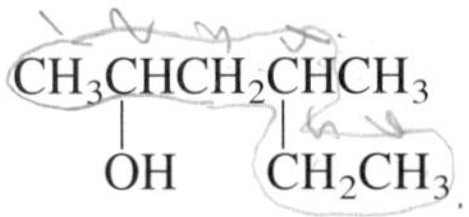 $CH_3CHCH_2CHCH_3$
$\qquad |\qquad\qquad |$
$\qquad OH \qquad CH_2CH_3$

d. 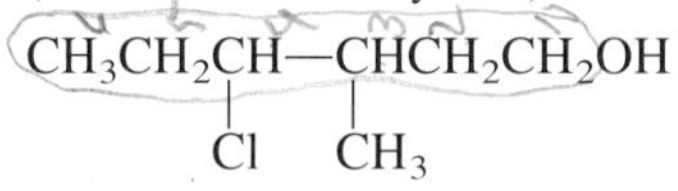 $CH_3CH_2CH{-}CHCH_2CH_2OH$
$\qquad\qquad\qquad |\qquad |$
$\qquad\qquad\qquad Cl \quad CH_3$

QUESTION 10.2

Give the common name and the I.U.P.A.C. name for each of the following compounds.

a. $CH_3CH_2CH_2CH_2CH_2CH_2CH_2OH$

b. 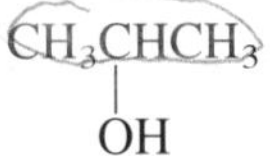 CH_3CHCH_3
$\qquad |$
$\qquad OH$

c. 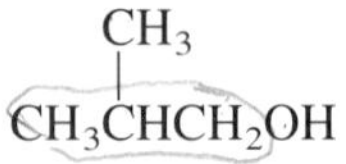 $\qquad CH_3$
$\qquad\quad |$
$\quad CH_3CHCH_2OH$

Medically important alcohols

Section 10.5

See "A Clinical Perspective: Aldehydes in Medicine" later in this chapter.

Methanol

Methanol (methyl alcohol), CH_3OH, is a colorless and odorless liquid that is used as a solvent and as the starting material for the synthesis of methanal (formaldehyde). Methanol is often called "wood alcohol" because it can be made by heating wood in the absence of air. Methanol is toxic and can cause blindness and perhaps death if ingested.

Ethanol

Ethanol (ethyl alcohol), CH_3CH_2OH, is a colorless and odorless liquid and is the alcohol in alcoholic beverages. It is also widely used as a solvent and as a raw material for the preparation of other organic chemicals.

Fermentation reactions are described in detail in Section 16.4 and in "A Human Perspective: Fermentations: The Good, the Bad, and the Ugly."

The ethanol used in alcoholic beverages comes from the **fermentation** of carbohydrates (sugars and starches). The beverage produced depends on the starting material and the fermentation process: scotch (grain), bourbon (corn), burgundy wine (grapes and grape skins), and chablis wine (grapes without red skins). The fermentation process is illustrated below:

$$C_6H_{12}O_6 \xrightarrow[\text{enzyme action}]{\substack{\text{Several steps} \\ \text{involving}}} 2CH_3CH_2OH + 2CO_2$$

Sugar   Ethanol
(glucose)   (ethyl alcohol)

The alcoholic beverages listed above have quite different alcohol concentrations. Wines are generally 12–13% alcohol because the yeasts that produce the ethanol are killed by ethanol concentrations of 12–13%. (Wine producers are always trying to find strains of yeast with greater ethanol tolerance.) To produce bourbon or scotch with an alcohol concentration of 40–45% ethanol (80 or 90 proof), the original fermentation products must be distilled.

The sale and use of pure ethanol (100% ethanol) are regulated by the federal government. To prevent illegal use of pure ethanol, it is *denatured* by the addition of a denaturing agent (benzene or methanol is often used), which makes it unfit to drink.

2-Propanol

2-Propanol (isopropyl alcohol),

$$\underset{\underset{\displaystyle OH}{|}}{CH_3CHCH_3}$$

is commonly called "rubbing alcohol" because patients with high fevers are often given alcohol baths to reduce the body temperature. Rapid evaporation of the alcohol results in skin cooling.

Section 5.7

It is also used as a disinfectant, an astringent (skin-drying agent), an industrial solvent, and a raw material in the synthesis of organic chemicals. It is colorless, has a very slight odor, and is toxic when ingested.

1,2-Ethanediol

1,2-Ethanediol (ethylene glycol),

$$\underset{\underset{\displaystyle OH}{|}}{CH_2}\!-\!\underset{\underset{\displaystyle OH}{|}}{CH_2}$$

is used as automobile antifreeze. When added to water in the radiator, the ethylene glycol solute lowers the freezing point and raises the boiling point of the water. Ethylene glycol has a sweet taste but is extremely poisonous. For this reason, color additives are used in antifreeze to ensure that it is properly identified.

Section 6.4

1,2,3-Propanetriol

1,2,3-Propanetriol (glycerol),

$$\underset{\underset{\displaystyle OH}{|}}{CH_2}\!-\!\underset{\underset{\displaystyle OH}{|}}{CH}\!-\!\underset{\underset{\displaystyle OH}{|}}{CH_2}$$

is a viscous, sweet-tasting, nontoxic liquid. It is very soluble in water and is used in cosmetics, pharmaceuticals, and lubricants. Glycerol is obtained as a by-product of the hydrolysis of fats.

Section 13.2

Classification of alcohols

Alcohols are classified as **primary (1°), secondary (2°), or tertiary (3°)** depending on the number of alkyl groups attached to the carbon bearing the hydroxyl (—OH) group. If no alkyl groups are attached, the alcohol is methyl alcohol; if there is a single alkyl group, the alcohol is a primary alcohol; an alcohol with two alkyl groups bonded to the carbon bearing the hydroxyl group is a secondary alcohol, and if three alkyl groups are attached, the alcohol is a tertiary alcohol.

$$\underset{\underset{\displaystyle OH}{|}}{\overset{\overset{\displaystyle H}{|}}{H\!-\!C\!-\!H}} \qquad \underset{\underset{\displaystyle OH}{|}}{\overset{\overset{\displaystyle H}{|}}{R\!-\!C\!-\!H}} \qquad \underset{\underset{\displaystyle OH}{|}}{\overset{\overset{\displaystyle H}{|}}{R\!-\!C\!-\!R}} \qquad \underset{\underset{\displaystyle OH}{|}}{\overset{\overset{\displaystyle R}{|}}{R\!-\!C\!-\!R}}$$

Methyl alcohol   1° Alcohol   2° Alcohol   3° Alcohol

QUESTION 10.3

Classify each of the following alcohols as 1°, 2°, 3°, or aromatic (phenol):

a. $CH_3CH_2CH_2CH_2OH$

b. 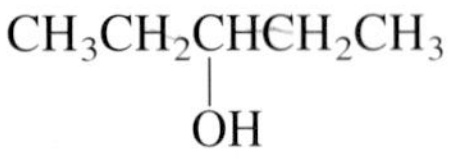 $CH_3CH_2CHCH_2CH_3$
       |
       OH

c.

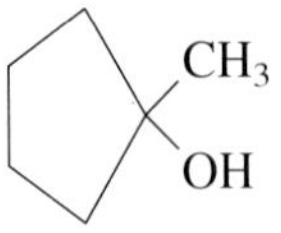

    CH_3
    OH

d.

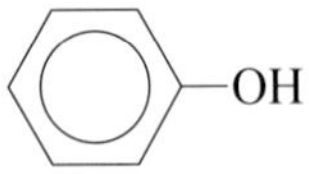

    OH

e.

HO

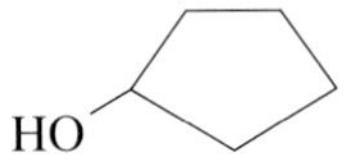

QUESTION 10.4

Classify each of the following alcohols as 1°, 2°, or 3°:

a. 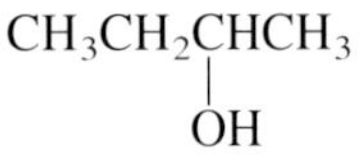 $CH_3CH_2CHCH_3$
       |
       OH

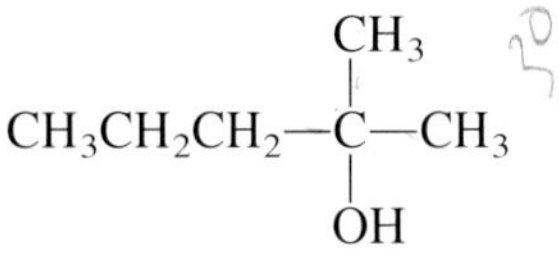

c. CH_3CH_2—OH

b.
    CH_3
    |
    $CH_3CH_2CH_2$—C—CH_3
    |
    OH

d. 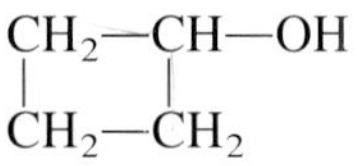 CH_2—CH—OH
    | |
    CH_2—CH_2

Reactions involving alcohols

Section 9.3

Preparation of alcohols

Alcohols can be prepared by the **hydration** of alkenes:

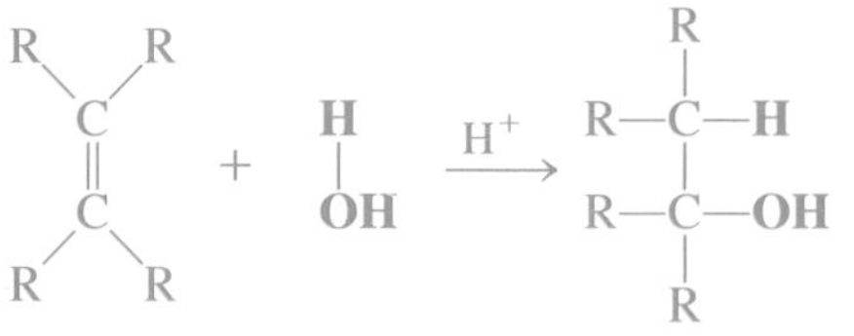

Alkene   Water   Alcohol

They may also be prepared via the reduction of aldehydes and ketones. This reaction, summarized below, is discussed in Section 10.5.

Aldehyde   Hydrogen   Alcohol
or
Ketone

Dehydration of alcohols

Alcohols undergo **dehydration** (lose water) when heated with concentrated sulfuric acid (H_2SO_4) or phosphoric acid (H_3PO_4). We have just seen that alkenes can be hydrated to give alcohols. Dehydration is simply the reverse process: the conversion of an alcohol back to an alkene. This is seen in the following general reaction and the examples that follow:

$$R-\underset{\underset{H}{|}}{\overset{\overset{H}{|}}{C}}-\underset{\underset{OH}{|}}{\overset{\overset{H}{|}}{C}}-H \xrightarrow{H^+,\ heat} R-CH{=}CH_2 + \mathbf{H-OH}$$

Alcohol   Alkene   Water

$$H-\underset{\underset{H}{|}}{\overset{\overset{H}{|}}{C}}-\underset{\underset{OH}{|}}{\overset{\overset{H}{|}}{C}}-H \xrightarrow{H^+,\ heat} CH_2{=}CH_2 + H-OH$$

Ethanol   Ethene
(ethyl alcohol)   (ethylene)

$$CH_3CH_2CH_2OH \xrightarrow{H^+,\ heat} CH_3CH{=}CH_2 + H_2O$$

1-Propanol   Propene
(propyl alcohol)   (propylene)

In some cases, dehydration of alcohols produces a mixture of products, as seen in the following example:

$$CH_3CH_2-\underset{\underset{OH}{|}}{CH}-CH_3 \xrightarrow[heat]{H^+} CH_3CH_2-CH{=}CH_2 + CH_3-CH{=}CH-CH_3 + H_2O$$

2-Butanol   1-Butene   2-Butene

QUESTION 10.5

Predict the products obtained on reacting each of the following alkenes with water and a trace of acid:

a. Ethene   b. Propene   c. 1-Butene

d. 2-Butene   e. 2-Methylpropene

QUESTION 10.6

Draw the alkene products that would be produced on dehydration of each of the following alcohols:

a. $CH_3\underset{\underset{OH}{|}}{CH}CH_3$

b. $CH_3CH_2\underset{\underset{OH}{|}}{CH}CH_3$

c. $CH_3-\underset{\underset{OH}{|}}{\overset{\overset{CH_3}{|}}{C}}-CH_2CH_3$

d. $CH_3-\underset{\underset{OH}{|}}{\overset{\overset{CH_3}{|}}{C}}-CH_3$

An *oxidation* reaction involves a gain of oxygen or the loss of hydrogen. A *reduction* reaction involves the loss of oxygen or gain of hydrogen. If both hydrogen and oxygen are gained or lost, the reaction is neither an oxidation nor a reduction.

Oxidation reactions

Alcohols are oxidized, by using a variety of oxidizing agents, to aldehydes, ketones, and carboxylic acids. The most commonly used oxidizing agents are basic potassium permanganate ($KMnO_4/OH^-$) and chromic acid (H_2CrO_4). The symbol [O] over the reaction arrow is used throughout this book to designate any general oxidizing agent, as we see in the following reactions:

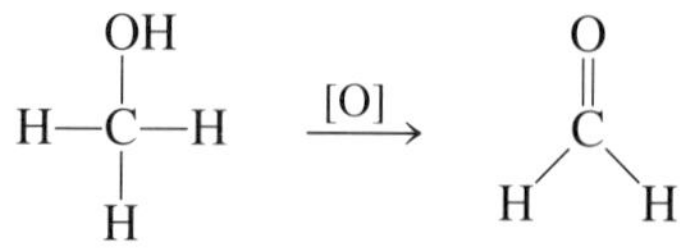

$$H-\overset{\displaystyle OH}{\underset{\displaystyle H}{C}}-H \xrightarrow{[O]} \overset{\displaystyle O}{\underset{H \quad H}{C}}$$

Methanol
(methyl alcohol)
An alcohol

Methanal
(formaldehyde)
An aldehyde

Oxidation of a primary alcohol:

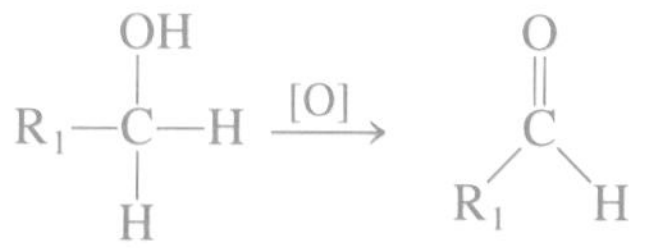

$$R_1-\overset{\displaystyle OH}{\underset{\displaystyle H}{C}}-H \xrightarrow{[O]} \overset{\displaystyle O}{\underset{R_1 \quad H}{C}}$$

1° Alcohol   An aldehyde

Oxidation of a secondary alcohol:

$$R_1-\overset{\displaystyle OH}{\underset{\displaystyle H}{C}}-R_2 \xrightarrow{[O]} \overset{\displaystyle O}{\underset{R_1 \quad R_2}{C}}$$

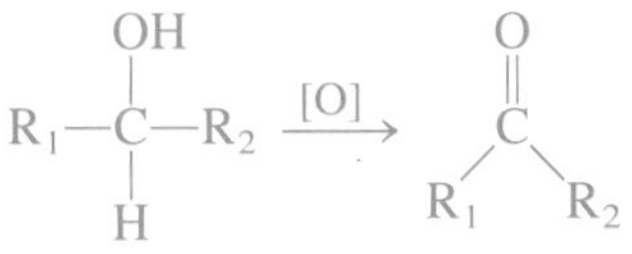

2° Alcohol   A ketone

Oxidation of a tertiary alcohol:

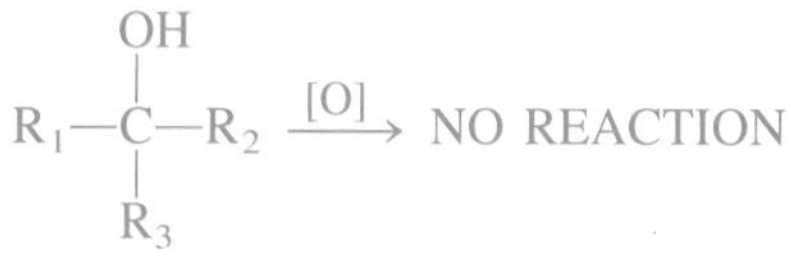

$$R_1-\overset{\displaystyle OH}{\underset{\displaystyle R_3}{C}}-R_2 \xrightarrow{[O]} \text{NO REACTION}$$

3° Alcohol

The above equations show that oxidation of methanol or a primary alcohol produces an aldehyde. Oxidation of a secondary alcohol produces a ketone. Tertiary alcohols cannot be oxidized. For the oxidation reaction to occur, the carbon bearing the hydroxyl group must contain at least one C—H bond. Since tertiary alcohols contain three C—C bonds to the carbon bearing the hydroxyl group, they cannot undergo oxidation. As we will see later in this chapter, aldehydes can undergo further oxidation to give carboxylic acids.

When ethanol is metabolized in the liver, it is oxidized to ethanal (acetaldehyde). If too much ethanol is present in the body, an overabundance of ethanal is formed, which causes many of the adverse effects of the "morning-after hangover." Continued oxidation of ethanal produces ethanoic acid (acetic acid), which is used in energy generating reactions in the cell and eventually oxidized to CO_2 and H_2O. These reactions, summarized below, are catalyzed by liver enzymes.

Chapter 12

$$CH_3CH_2-OH \longrightarrow CH_3\overset{\displaystyle O}{\overset{\|}{C}}-H \longrightarrow CH_3\overset{\displaystyle O}{\overset{\|}{C}}-OH \longrightarrow CO_2 + H_2O$$

Ethanol
(ethyl alcohol)

Ethanal
(acetaldehyde)

Ethanoic
acid (acetic acid)

10.2 PHENOLS

Phenols are compounds in which the hydroxyl group is attached to benzene. Like alcohols, they are polar compounds because of the polar hydroxyl group. Thus the simpler phenols are some-

A HUMAN PERSPECTIVE

Alcohol Consumption and the Breathalyzer Test

Ethanol has been used widely as a beverage, a medicinal, and a solvent in numerous pharmaceutical preparations. Such common usage often overshadows the fact that ethanol is a toxic substance. Ethanol consumption is associated with a variety of long-term effects, including cirrhosis of the liver, death of brain cells, and alcoholism. Alcohol consumed by the mother can even affect the normal development of her unborn child and result in fetal alcohol syndrome. For these reasons, over-the-counter cough and cold medications that used to be prepared in ethanol are now manufactured in alcohol-free form.

Short-term effects, linked to the social use of ethanol, center on its effects on behavior, reflexes, and coordination. Blood alcohol levels of 0.05 to 0.15% seriously inhibit coordination. Blood levels in excess of 0.10% are considered evidence of intoxication in most states. Blood alcohol levels in the range of 0.30% to 0.50% produce unconsciousness and the risk of death.

The loss of some coordination and reflex action is particularly serious when the affected individual attempts to operate a motor vehicle. Law enforcement has come to rely on the "breathalyzer" test to screen for individuals suspected of driving while intoxicated. Those with a positive breathalyzer test are then given a more accurate blood test to establish their guilt or innocence.

The suspect is required to exhale into a solution that will react with the unmetabolized alcohol in the breath. The partial pressure of the alcohol in the exhaled air has been demonstrated to be proportional to the blood alcohol level. The solution is an acidic solution of dichromate ion, which is yellow-orange. The alcohol reduces the chromium in the dichromate ion from +6 to +3, the Cr^{3+} ion, which is green. The intensity of the green color is measured, and it is proportional to the amount of ethanol that was oxidized. The reaction follows:

$$16H^+ + 2Cr_2O_7^{2-} + 3CH_3CH_2OH \longrightarrow$$

Yellow-orange

$$3CH_3COOH + 4Cr^{3+} + 11H_2O$$

Green

The breathalyzer test is a technological development based on a scientific understanding of the chemical reactions that ethanol may undergo—a further example of the dependence of technology on science.

---

what soluble in water. They are found in flavorings and fragrances (mint and savory) and are used as preservatives (butylated hydroxytoluene, BHT).

Thymol (mint)

Carvacrol (savory)

Butylated hydroxy toluene, BHT (food preservative)

Phenols are also widely used in health care as germicides. In fact, carbolic acid, a dilute solution of phenol, was used as an antiseptic and disinfectant by Joseph Lister in his early work to decrease postsurgical infections. He used carbolic acid to bathe surgical wounds and to "sterilize" his instruments. Other derivatives of phenol that are used as antiseptics and disinfectants include hexachlorophene, hexylresorcinol, and *o*-phenylphenol.

A dilute solution of phenol must be used because concentrated phenol causes severe burns and because phenol is not highly soluble in water.

Phenol (carbolic acid; phenol dissolved in water; antiseptic)

Hexachlorophene (antiseptic)

Hexylresorcinol (antiseptic)

o-Phenylphenol (antiseptic)

10.3 ETHERS

Ethers are structurally related to alcohols. The C—O bonds of ethers are polar, and thus ether molecules are polar. However, ethers do not form hydrogen bonds to one another because there is no —OH group. Therefore they have much lower boiling points than alcohols of similar molecular weights but higher boiling points than alkanes of similar molecular weight. Compare the following examples:

$$CH_3CH_2CH_2CH_3 \qquad CH_3-O-CH_2CH_3 \qquad CH_3CH_2CH_2OH$$

Butane	Methoxyethane	1-Propanol
(butane)	(ethyl methyl ether)	(propyl alcohol)
M.W. = 58	M.W. = 60	M.W. = 60
b.p. = −0.5°C	b.p. = 7.9°C	b.p. = 97.2°C

An alkoxy group is an alkyl group bonded to an oxygen atom (—OR).

In the I.U.P.A.C. system of naming ethers the —OR substituent is named as an alkoxy group. This is analogous to the name *hydroxy* for the —OH group. Thus, CH_3-O- is methoxy, CH_3CH_2-O- is ethoxy, and so on.

EXAMPLE 10.2

Naming an Ether Using I.U.P.A.C. Nomenclature

Solution

$$\overset{\displaystyle O-CH_3}{\underset{1 \quad 2 \quad 3 \quad 4 \quad 5 \quad 6 \quad 7 \quad 8 \quad 9}{CH_3CH_2CHCH_2CH_2CH_2CH_2CH_2CH_3}}$$

Parent compound: nonane
Position of alkoxy group: carbon-3 (*not* carbon-7)
Substituents: 3-methoxy
Name: 3-methoxynonane

In the common system of nomenclature, ethers are named by placing the names of the two alkyl groups attached to the ether oxygen as prefixes in front of the word ether. The names of the two groups can be placed either alphabetically or by size (smaller to larger), as seen in the following examples:

$$CH_3-O-CH_3 \qquad CH_3-O-CH_2CH_3 \qquad CH_3CH_2-O-CH(CH_3)_2$$

Dimethyl ether	Ethyl methyl ether	Ethyl isopropyl
or	or	ether
methyl ether	methyl ethyl ether	

Ethers are moderately chemically inert. They do not react with reducing agents or bases under normal conditions. However, they are extremely volatile and highly flammable and hence must always be treated with great care.

Diethyl ether was the first general anesthetic used. The dentist Dr. William Morton is credited with its introduction in the late 1800s. Diethyl ether functions as an anesthetic by interacting with the central nervous system. It appears that diethyl ether (and many other general anesthetics) function by accumulating in the lipid material of the nerve cells, thereby interfering with nerve impulse transmission. This results in analgesia, a lessened perception of pain.

Halogenated ethers are also routinely used as general anesthetics. They are less flammable than diethyl ether and are therefore safer to store and work with. *Penthrane* and *enthrane* (trade names) are two of the more commonly used members of this family:

Penthrane   Enthrane

Compounds that contain the sulfhydryl group (—SH) are called **thiols.** They are similar to alcohols in structure, but the sulfur atom replaces the oxygen atom.

Thiols and many other sulfur compounds have nauseating aromas. They are found in substances as different as the defensive spray of the North American striped skunk, onions, and garlic.

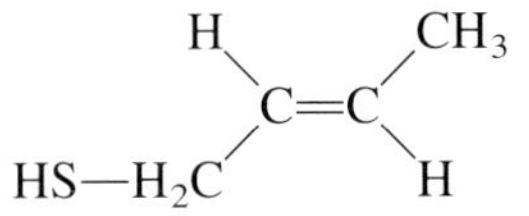

$$H \quad\quad CH_3$$
$$C=C$$
$$HS—H_2C \quad\quad H$$

trans-2-butene-1-thiol
North American skunk
defense spray

Thiols are involved in protein structure and conformation. It is the ability of two thiol groups to easily undergo oxidation to a **disulfide** bond (—S—S—) that is responsible for this involvement. *Cysteine* is an amino acid that contains a sulfhydryl group. Cysteine is found in many proteins and plays a pivotal role in the conformation of the protein by forming disulfide bonds with other cysteine molecules within the protein. In this way, two distant parts of the protein become linked to one another. Similarly, two different protein molecules may be joined to one another by disulfide bonds, as seen in the structure of human insulin (Figure 10.2). The structure of cysteine is shown below:

Section 15.2

Amino acids are the subunits from which the proteins are made. A protein is a long polymer, or chain, of many amino acids bonded to one another.

$$H \quad O$$
$$^+NH_3—C—C—O^-$$
$$CH_2—SH$$

Cysteine

The oxidation of two cysteine molecules to produce a disulfide bond is seen in Figure 15.11.

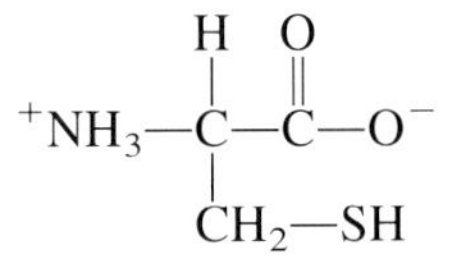

Many other thiols play important roles in biological systems. For example, *BAL (British Anti-Lewisite)* is used as an antidote for mercury poisoning. The two thiol groups of BAL complex with mercury and remove it from the system before it can do any damage.

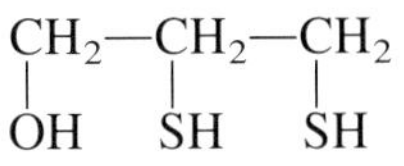

$$CH_2—CH_2—CH_2$$
$$OH \quad SH \quad SH$$

BAL

Coenzyme A is a thiol that serves as a "carrier" of acetyl groups (CH_3CO_2—) in biochemical reactions. It plays a central role in metabolism by shuttling acetyl groups from one reaction to another. Coenzyme A is made up of the nucleotide ADP, the vitamin pantothenic acid, and the amino acid cysteine. When the two-carbon acetate group is attached to coenzyme A, the product is acetyl coenzyme A (acetyl CoA). The bond between coenzyme A and the acetyl group is a high-energy *thioester bond.* This "energizes" the acetyl group so that it can participate in other biochemical reactions.

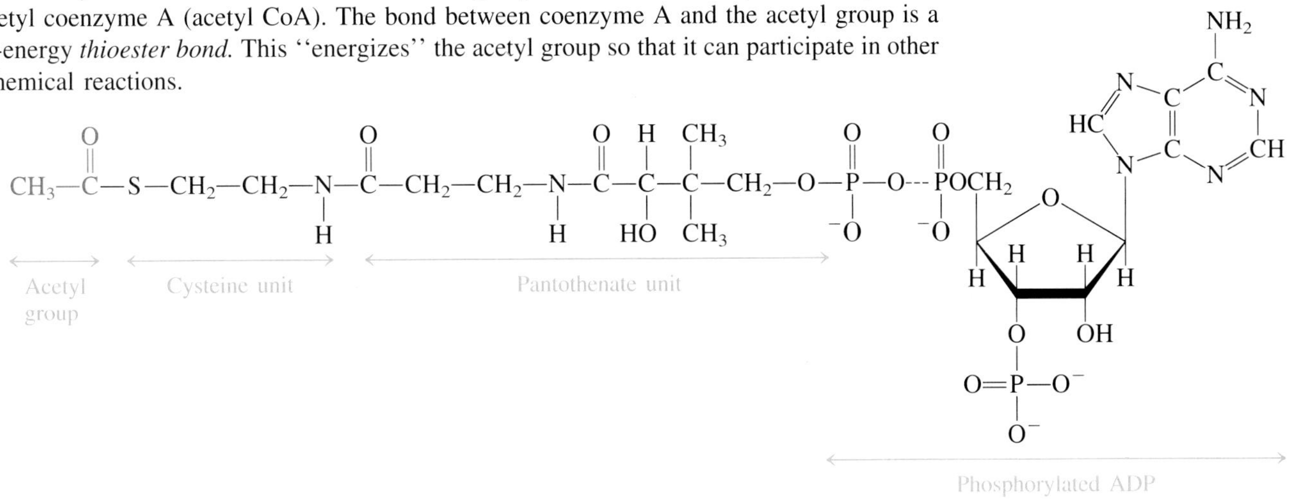

Acetyl coenzyme A
(acetyl CoA)

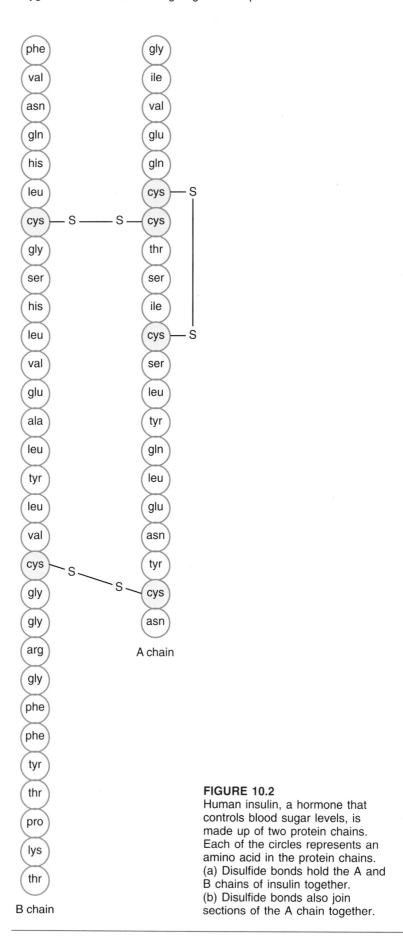

FIGURE 10.2
Human insulin, a hormone that controls blood sugar levels, is made up of two protein chains. Each of the circles represents an amino acid in the protein chains. (a) Disulfide bonds hold the A and B chains of insulin together. (b) Disulfide bonds also join sections of the A chain together.

Acetyl CoA is made and used in the energy-producing reactions that provide most of the energy for life processes. It is also required for the biosynthesis of many biological molecules.

The reactions involving coenzyme A are discussed in detail in Chapters 16, 17, and 18.

Aldehydes and **ketones** are polar compounds because of the polar **carbonyl group.** Thus they have higher boiling points than nonpolar hydrocarbons. Because they cannot form intermolecular hydrogen bonds, their boiling points are lower than those of alcohols of comparable molecular weight.

Aldehydes and ketones can form intermolecular hydrogen bonds with water (Figure 10.3). As a result, the smaller members of the two families (five or fewer carbon atoms) are reasonably soluble in water. However, as the carbon chain length increases, the compounds become less polar and more hydrocarbonlike. These larger compounds are soluble in nonpolar organic solvents.

10.5 ALDEHYDES AND KETONES

Structure and physical properties

Aldehydes

In the I.U.P.A.C. System, aldehydes are named according to the following set of rules:

Nomenclature

◆ Determine the parent compound, that is, the longest continuous carbon chain containing the carbonyl group.

◆ Replace the final -*e* of the parent alkane with -*al*.

◆ Number the chain beginning with the carbonyl carbon (or aldehyde group) as carbon-1.

◆ Number and name all substituents as usual.

Several examples are provided here with common names given in parentheses:

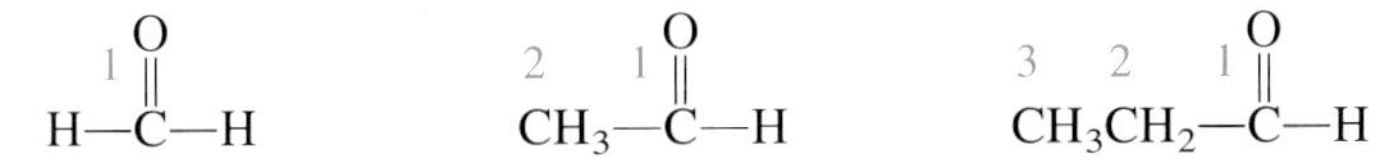

Methanal
(formaldehyde)

Ethanal
(acetaldehyde)

Propanal
(propionaldehyde)

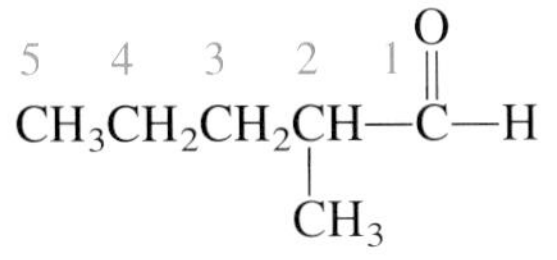

2-Methylpentanal

The common names of the aldehydes are derived from the same Latin roots as the corresponding carboxylic acids. The common names of the first five aldehydes are seen in Table 10.1.

Section 12.1

FIGURE 10.3
(a) Hydrogen bonding between the carbonyl group of an aldehyde and water. (b) Polar interactions between carbonyl groups of ketones.

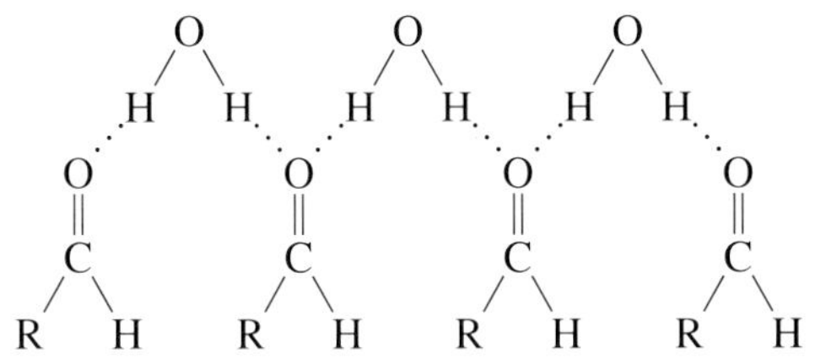

(a) 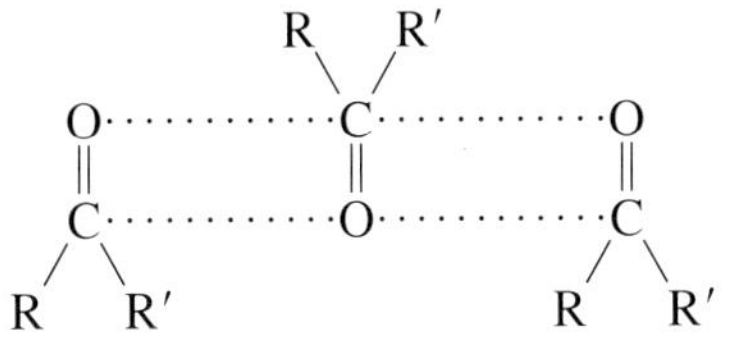   (b)

TABLE 10.1 Common Names and Formulas for the Aldehydes

Name	Formula
Formaldehyde	$H-\overset{\overset{\displaystyle O}{\|\|}}{C}-H$
Acetaldehyde	$CH_3-\overset{\overset{\displaystyle O}{\|\|}}{C}-H$
Propionaldehyde	$CH_3CH_2-\overset{\overset{\displaystyle O}{\|\|}}{C}-H$
Butyraldehyde	$CH_3CH_2CH_2-\overset{\overset{\displaystyle O}{\|\|}}{C}-H$
Valeraldehyde	$CH_3CH_2CH_2CH_2-\overset{\overset{\displaystyle O}{\|\|}}{C}-H$

In the common system of nomenclature, substituted aldehydes are named as derivatives of the straight-chain parent compound (Table 10.1). Greek letters are used to indicate the position of the substituents. The carbon atom bonded to the carbonyl group is the α-carbon, the next is the β-carbon, and so on.

$$\overset{\delta}{C}-\overset{\gamma}{C}-\overset{\beta}{C}-\overset{\alpha}{C}-\overset{\overset{\displaystyle O}{\|\|}}{C}-H$$

Consider the following examples:

$$CH_3CH_2CH_2\underset{\underset{\displaystyle CH_3}{\|}}{CH}-\overset{\overset{\displaystyle O}{\|\|}}{C}-H \qquad CH_3CH_2\underset{\underset{\displaystyle CH_3}{\|}}{CH}CH_2-\overset{\overset{\displaystyle O}{\|\|}}{C}-H$$

2-Methylpentanal   3-Methylpentanal
(α-methylvaleraldehyde)   (β-methylvaleraldehyde)

Ketones

The rules for naming ketones are directly analogous to those for naming aldehydes. In ketones, however, the *-e* ending of the parent alkane is replaced with the *-one* suffix of the ketone family, and the location of the carbonyl carbon is indicated with a number. The longest carbon chain is numbered to give the carbonyl carbon the lowest possible number. For example,

$$\overset{1}{C}H_3-\overset{\overset{\displaystyle O}{\|\|}}{\underset{2}{C}}-\overset{3}{C}H_3 \qquad \overset{4}{C}H_3\overset{3}{C}H_2-\overset{\overset{\displaystyle O}{\|\|}}{\underset{2}{C}}-\overset{1}{C}H_3 \qquad \overset{8}{C}H_3\overset{7}{C}H_2\overset{6}{C}H_2\overset{5}{C}H_2-\overset{\overset{\displaystyle O}{\|\|}}{\underset{4}{C}}-\overset{3}{C}H_2\overset{2}{C}H_2\overset{1}{C}H_3$$

Propanone   2-Butanone   4-Octanone
(No number necessary)   (methyl ethyl ketone)   (*not* 5-octanone)
(acetone)   (butyl propyl ketone)

The common names of ketones are derived by naming the alkyl groups that are bonded to the carbonyl carbon. These are used as prefixes followed by the word "ketone." The alkyl groups may be arranged alphabetically or by size (smaller to larger).

EXAMPLE 10.3

Naming Aldehydes and Ketones Using the I.U.P.A.C. Nomenclature System

Solution

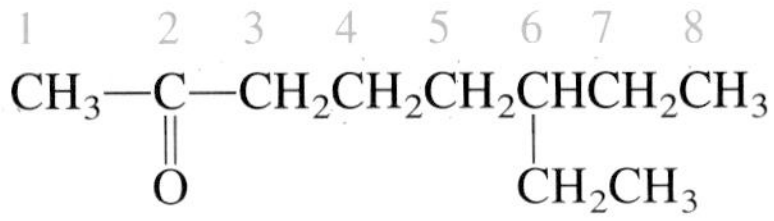

$$\overset{1}{CH_3}-\overset{2}{\underset{\underset{O}{\|}}{C}}-\overset{3}{CH_2}\overset{4}{CH_2}\overset{5}{CH_2}\overset{6}{\underset{\underset{CH_2CH_3}{|}}{CH}}\overset{7}{CH_2}\overset{8}{CH_3}$$

Parent compound: octane (becomes octanone)
Position of carbonyl group: carbon-2 (*not* carbon-7)
Substituents: 6-ethyl (*not* 3-ethyl)
Name: 6-ethyl-2-octanone

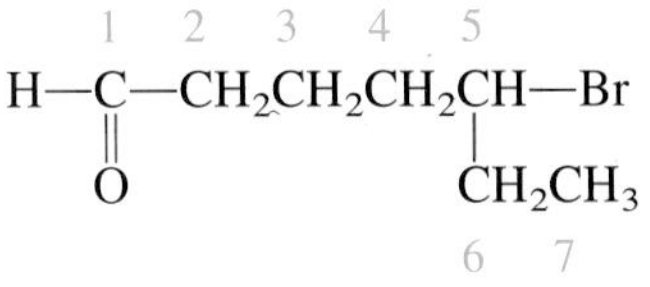

$$\overset{1}{H}-\overset{2}{\underset{\underset{O}{\|}}{C}}-\overset{3}{CH_2}\overset{}{CH_2}\overset{4}{CH_2}\overset{5}{\underset{\underset{\underset{6\quad7}{CH_2CH_3}}{|}}{CH}}-Br$$

Parent compound: heptane (becomes heptanal)
Position of carbonyl group: carbon-1 (*not* carbon-7)
Substituents: 5-bromo (*not* 3-bromo)
Name: 5-bromoheptanal (*not* -1-heptanal)

QUESTION 10.7

Name each of the following compounds, using the I.U.P.A.C. Nomenclature System:

a. 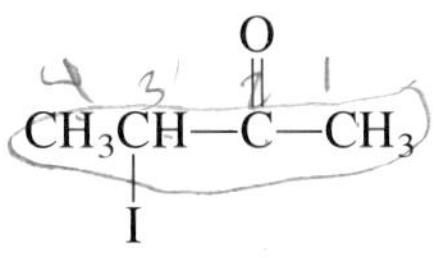 $CH_3CH-\overset{\overset{O}{\|}}{C}-CH_3$
     $\underset{I}{|}$

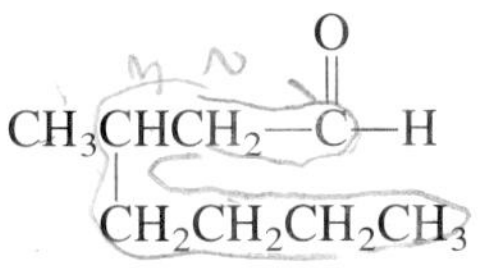

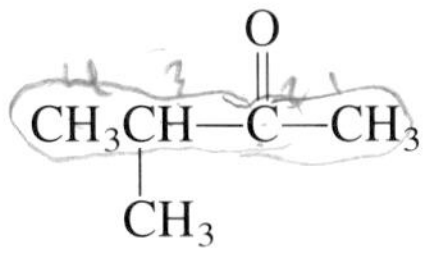

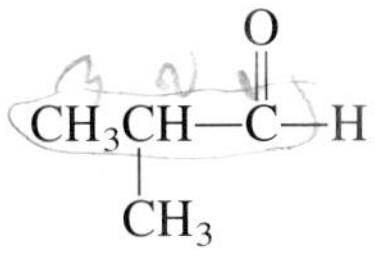

d. $CH_3CHCH_2-\overset{\overset{O}{\|}}{C}-H$
     $\underset{CH_2CH_2CH_2CH_3}{|}$

b. $CH_3CH-\overset{\overset{O}{\|}}{C}-CH_3$
     $\underset{CH_3}{|}$

e. $CH_3CH-\overset{\overset{O}{\|}}{C}-H$
     $\underset{CH_3}{|}$

c. $CH_3CH-\overset{\overset{O}{\|}}{C}-CH_2CH_3$
     $\underset{F}{|}$

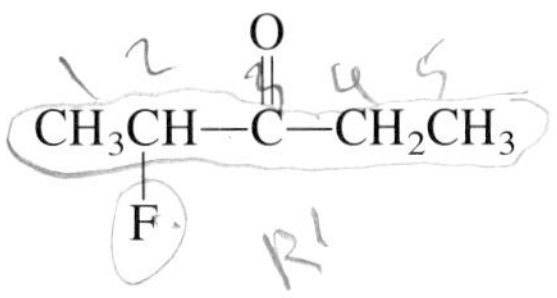

QUESTION 10.8

Write the condensed formula for each of the following compounds:

a. Methyl isopropyl ketone (What is the I.U.P.A.C. name for this compound?)

b. 4-Heptanone

c. Nonanal

d. 7-Bromoheptanal

e. 2-Fluorocyclohexanone

f. Hexachloroacetone (What is the I.U.P.A.C. name of this compound?)

Methanal (formaldehyde) is a gas (b.p. −21°). It is available commercially as an aqueous solution called *formalin*. Formalin is used as a preservative for tissues and as an embalming fluid. For other uses of formaldehyde, see ''A Clinical Perspective: Aldehydes in Medicine.''

Important aldehydes and ketones

A CLINICAL PERSPECTIVE

Aldehydes in Medicine

Most aldehydes have irritating, unpleasant odors. Formalin, a 40% solution of formaldehyde, has often been used to preserve biological tissues and for embalming. It has also been used to disinfect environmental surfaces, body fluids, and feces. Under no circumstances is it used as an antiseptic on human tissue because of its noxious fumes and the skin irritation that it causes.

Formaldehyde is useful in the production of killed virus vaccines. A deadly virus, such as polio virus, can be treated with heat and formaldehyde. Formaldehyde reacts with the genetic information (RNA) of the virus, damaging it irreparably. It also reacts with the virus proteins but does not change their shape. Thus when you are injected with the Salk killed polio vaccine, the dead virus can't replicate and harm you. However, it will be recognized by your immune system, which will produce antibodies that will protect you against polio virus infection.

Formaldehyde can also be produced in the body! Drinking wood alcohol (methanol) causes blindness, respiratory failure, convulsions, and death. The liver enzyme *alcohol dehydrogenase,* whose function it is to detoxify alcohols, catalyzes the conversion of methanol to formaldehyde (methanal). The

formaldehyde produced reacts with cellular proteins, causing the range of symptoms listed above.

Acetaldehyde (ethanal) is produced from ethanol by the liver enzymes and is largely responsible for the symptoms of hangover experienced after a night of too much partying. This aldehyde is useful in treating alcoholics because of the unpleasant symptoms that it causes. When taken orally, in combination with alcohol, acetaldehyde quickly produces symptoms of a violent hangover with none of the *perceived* benefits of drinking alcohol.

The liver enzymes that oxidize ethanol to acetaldehyde are the same as those that oxidize methanol to formaldehyde. Physicians take advantage of this in the treatment of wood alcohol poisoning by trying to keep those enzymes busy with a reaction that produces a *less* toxic (not nontoxic) by-product. In cases of methanol poisoning, the patient receives ethanol intravenously. The ethanol should then be in greater concentration than methanol and should compete successfully for the liver enzymes and be converted to acetaldehyde. This gives the body time to excrete the methanol before it is oxidized to the potentially deadly formaldehyde.

Ethanal (acetaldehyde) is produced from ethanol in the liver and is responsible for the symptoms of a hangover.

Propanone (acetone), the simplest ketone, is an important and versatile solvent for organic compounds. It has the ability to dissolve organic compounds while being miscible with water. As a result, it has a number of industrial applications and is used as a solvent in adhesives, paints, cleaning solvents, nail polish, and nail polish remover. Propanone is flammable and should therefore be treated with appropriate care.

Many aldehydes and ketones are produced industrially as food and fragrance chemicals, medicinals, and agricultural chemicals. They are particularly important to the food industry, in which they are used as artificial and/or natural additives to food. Vanillin, a principal component of natural vanilla, is shown in Figure 10.4. Artificial vanilla flavoring is a dilute solution of synthetic vanillin dissolved in ethanol. See Figure 10.4 for additional examples of important aldehydes and ketones.

Reactions involving aldehydes and ketones

Preparation of aldehydes and ketones

Because many alcohols are commercially available, they provide excellent starting materials for the synthesis of many aldehydes and ketones. In the laboratory, aldehydes and ketones are prepared primarily by the *oxidation* of the corresponding alcohol. As we saw in Section 10.2, the oxidation of methyl alcohol gives methanal (formaldehyde). The oxidation of a primary alcohol produces an aldehyde, and the oxidation of a secondary alcohol yields a ketone. Tertiary alcohols do not undergo oxidation.

EXAMPLE 10.4

Differences in the Oxidation of Primary, Secondary, and Tertiary Alcohols

Using specific examples, show the oxidation of a primary, secondary, and tertiary alcohol.

Solution

The oxidation of a primary alcohol to an aldehyde:

$$CH_3CH_2CH_2{-}\overset{\displaystyle H}{\underset{\displaystyle H}{\overset{|}{\underset{|}{C}}}}{-}OH \xrightarrow{H_2CrO_4} CH_3CH_2CH_2{-}\overset{\displaystyle O}{\overset{\|}{C}}{-}H$$

1-Butanol (butyl alcohol) — Butanal (butyraldehyde)

FIGURE 10.4
Industrially important aldehydes and ketones.

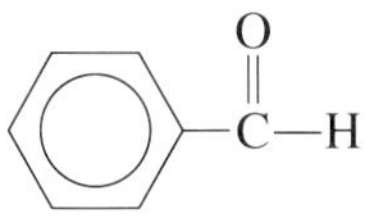
Benzaldehyde—oil of almonds

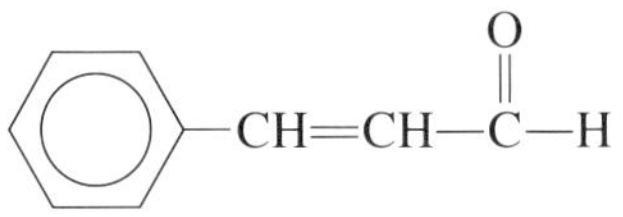
Cinnamaldehyde—oil of cinnamon

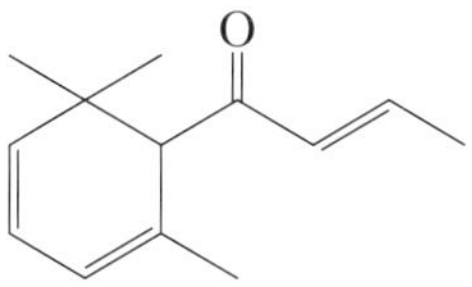
α-Demascone—berry flavoring

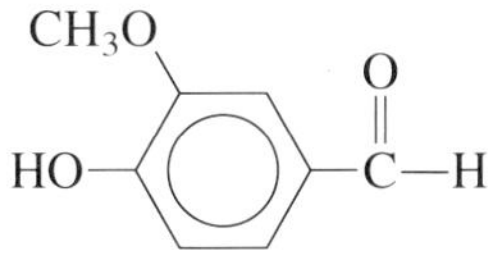
Vanillin—oil of vanilla beans

$CH_3CH_2CH_2CH_2CH_2CH_2{-}\overset{O}{\overset{\|}{C}}{-}CH_3$ 2-Octanone—mushroom flavoring

$CH_3{-}\overset{CH_3}{\overset{|}{C}}{=}CH{-}CH_2{-}CH_2{-}\overset{CH_3}{\overset{|}{C}}{=}CH{-}\overset{O}{\overset{\|}{C}}{-}H$ Citral—oil of lemongrass

$H{-}\overset{O}{\overset{\|}{C}}{-}H$ Methanal—common name formaldehyde—a gas at room temperature; *Formalin* is a 40% solution of methanal in water; it is used to preserve biological specimens and as an embalming fluid.

$CH_3{-}\overset{O}{\overset{\|}{C}}{-}H$ Ethanal—common name acetaldehyde—industrial starting material for acetic acid *(vinegar);* causes symptoms of a hangover.

$CH_3{-}\overset{O}{\overset{\|}{C}}{-}CH_3$ Propanone—common name acetone—an important industrial solvent.

$CH_3CH_2{-}\overset{O}{\overset{\|}{C}}{-}CH_3$ Butanone—common name methyl ethyl ketone—an important industrial solvent.

The oxidation of a secondary alcohol to a ketone:

$$CH_3CH_2CH_2CH_2-\underset{\underset{H}{|}}{\overset{\overset{CH_3}{|}}{C}}-OH \xrightarrow[H_2O]{KMnO_4,\ OH^-,} CH_3CH_2CH_2CH_2-\overset{\overset{O}{\|}}{C}-CH_3$$

2-Hexanol   2-Hexanone

The oxidation of a cyclic secondary alcohol to a ketone:

Cyclohexanol   Cyclohexanone

Tertiary alcohols cannot undergo oxidation:

$$CH_3CH_2CH_2-\underset{\underset{CH_3}{|}}{\overset{\overset{CH_3}{|}}{C}}-OH \xrightarrow{H_2CrO_4} NO\ REACTION$$

2-Methyl-2-pentanol

Oxidation reactions

Aldehydes are easily oxidized further to carboxylic acids, while ketones do not generally undergo further oxidation. The reason for this is that a carbon-hydrogen bond, present in the aldehyde but not in the ketone, is needed for the reaction to occur. In fact, aldehydes are so easily oxidized that it is often very difficult to prepare them because they continue to react to give the carboxylic acid rather than the desired aldehyde. Aldehydes are susceptible to air oxidation, even at room temperature, and cannot be stored for long periods of time. The following example shows a general equation for the oxidation of an aldehyde to a carboxylic acid:

$$R-\overset{\overset{O}{\|}}{C}-H \xrightarrow{[O]} R-\overset{\overset{O}{\|}}{C}-OH$$

Aldehyde   **Carboxylic acid**

Many oxidizing agents can be used. As we saw for the oxidation of alcohols, both basic potassium permanganate and chromic acid are good oxidizing agents, as the following specific example shows:

$$CH_3-\overset{\overset{O}{\|}}{C}-H \xrightarrow[H_2O,\ OH^-]{KMnO_4,} CH_3-\overset{\overset{O}{\|}}{C}-OH$$

Ethanal   Ethanoic acid
(acetaldehyde)   (acetic acid)

The reaction of benzaldehyde to benzoic acid is an example of the conversion of an *aromatic* aldehyde to the corresponding aromatic carboxylic acid:

Benzaldehyde   Benzoic acid

Aldehydes and ketones can be distinguished on the basis of differences in their reactivity. The most common laboratory test for this is the **Tollens' Test.** When exposed to the Tollens' reagent, a basic solution of $Ag(NH_3)_2^+$, an aldehyde undergoes oxidation. The silver ion (Ag^+) is reduced to silver metal (Ag^0) as the aldehyde is oxidized to a carboxylic acid.

$$\underset{\text{Aldehyde}}{R-\overset{\overset{\displaystyle O}{\|}}{C}-H} \; + \; \underset{\substack{\text{Silver} \\ \text{ammonia complex---} \\ \text{Tollens' reagent}}}{Ag(NH_3)_2^+} \longrightarrow \underset{\substack{\text{Carboxylic} \\ \text{acid}}}{R-\overset{\overset{\displaystyle O}{\|}}{C}-OH} \; + \; \underset{\substack{\text{Silver} \\ \text{metal} \\ \text{mirror}}}{Ag^0}$$

Silver metal precipitates from solution and coats the test tube, producing a smooth silver mirror. The test is therefore often called the Tollens' Silver Mirror Test. The commercial manufacture of silver mirrors uses a similar process. Ketones cannot be oxidized to carboxylic acids and do not react with the Tollens' reagent.

EXAMPLE 10.5

Writing the Equation for the Reaction of an Aldehyde and a Ketone with Tollen's Reagent

Write equations for the reaction of propanal and 2-pentanone with Tollens' reagent.

Solution

$$\underset{\text{Propanal}}{CH_3CH_2-\overset{\overset{\displaystyle O}{\|}}{C}-H} + Ag(NH_3)_2^+ \longrightarrow \underset{\text{Propanoic acid}}{CH_3CH_2-\overset{\overset{\displaystyle O}{\|}}{C}-OH} + Ag^0$$

$$\underset{\text{2-Pentanone}}{CH_3CH_2CH_2-\overset{\overset{\displaystyle O}{\|}}{C}-CH_3} + Ag(NH_3)_2^+ \longrightarrow \text{NO REACTION}$$

Another test that is used to distinguish between aldehydes and ketones is **Benedict's Test.** Here, a buffered aqueous solution of copper(II) hydroxide and sodium citrate reacts to oxidize aldehydes but does not generally react with ketones. Cu^{2+} is reduced to Cu^+ in the process. Cu^{2+} is soluble and gives a blue solution, while the Cu^+ precipitates as the red solid copper(I) oxide, Cu_2O.

All simple sugars (monosaccharides) are either aldehydes or ketones. Glucose is an aldehyde sugar that is commonly called *blood sugar* because it is the sugar found transported in the blood and used for energy by many cells. In uncontrolled diabetes, glucose may be found in the urine. One convenient means of determining the amount of glucose in the urine is to use the Benedict's Test and look for the color change. The reaction of glucose with the Benedict's reagent is represented in the following equation:

$$\underset{\text{Glucose}}{\begin{array}{c} O \diagdown \; \diagup H \\ C \\ | \\ H-C-OH \\ | \\ HO-C-H \\ | \\ H-C-OH \\ | \\ H-C-OH \\ | \\ CH_2OH \end{array}} + 2Cu^{2+} + OH^- \longrightarrow \begin{array}{c} O \diagdown \; \diagup OH \\ C \\ | \\ H-C-OH \\ | \\ HO-C-H \\ | \\ H-C-OH \\ | \\ H-C-OH \\ | \\ CH_2OH \end{array} + Cu_2O$$

Reduction reactions

Aldehydes and ketones are both readily reduced to the corresponding alcohol by a large number of different reducing agents. Throughout the text the symbol [H] over the reaction arrow represents a reducing agent.

The classical method of ketone reduction is **hydrogenation.** The carbonyl compound is reacted with hydrogen gas and a catalyst (nickel, platinum, or palladium metal) in a pressurized reaction vessel. Heating may also be necessary. The carbon-oxygen double bond (the carbonyl group) is reduced to a carbon-oxygen single bond. This is similar to the reduction of an alkene to an alkane (the reduction of a carbon-carbon double bond to a carbon-carbon single bond). The addition of hydrogen to a carbon-carbon double bond is shown in the following example:

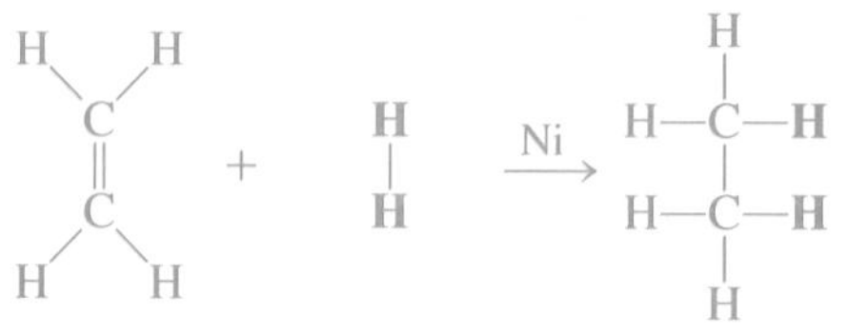

$$
\underset{\text{Alkene}}{\overset{\text{H}\quad\text{H}}{\underset{\text{H}\quad\text{H}}{\text{C}=\text{C}}}} + \underset{\text{Hydrogen}}{\overset{\text{H}}{\underset{\text{H}}{|}}} \xrightarrow{\text{Ni}} \underset{\text{Alkane}}{\overset{\text{H}}{\underset{\text{H}}{\overset{|}{\text{H}-\text{C}-\text{H}}\atop\text{H}-\text{C}-\text{H}}}}
$$

Compare this reaction to the addition of hydrogen to a carbon-oxygen double bond seen below:

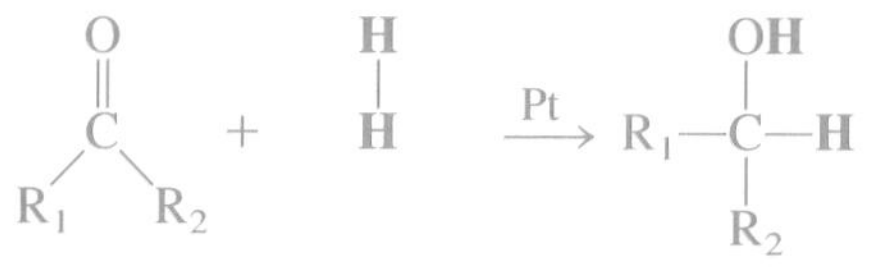

$$
\underset{\substack{\text{Aldehyde}\\\text{or ketone}}}{\overset{\text{O}}{\underset{R_1\quad R_2}{\text{C}}}} + \underset{\text{Hydrogen}}{\overset{\text{H}}{\underset{\text{H}}{|}}} \xrightarrow{\text{Pt}} \underset{\text{Alcohol}}{\overset{\text{OH}}{\underset{R_2}{R_1-\text{C}-\text{H}}}}
$$

EXAMPLE 10.6

Writing an Equation Representing the Hydrogenation of a Ketone

Write an equation showing the hydrogenation of 3-pentanone.

Solution

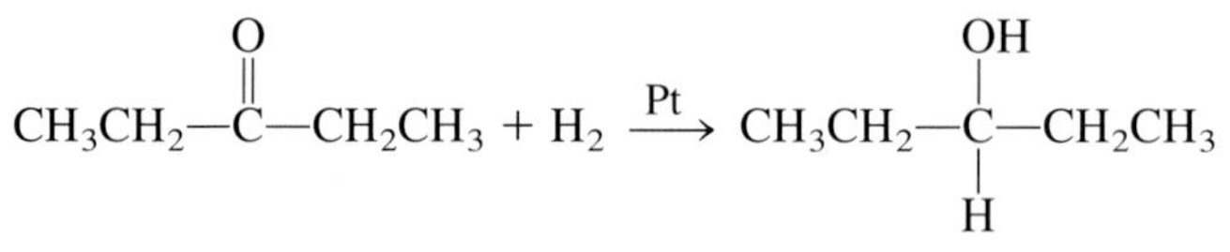

$$
\underset{\text{3-Pentanone}}{\overset{\text{O}}{\text{CH}_3\text{CH}_2-\text{C}-\text{CH}_2\text{CH}_3}} + \text{H}_2 \xrightarrow{\text{Pt}} \underset{\text{3-Pentanol}}{\overset{\text{OH}}{\underset{\text{H}}{\text{CH}_3\text{CH}_2-\text{C}-\text{CH}_2\text{CH}_3}}}
$$

QUESTION 10.9

Label each of the following as an oxidation or a reduction reaction:

a.   Ethanal to ethanol

b.   Benzoic acid to benzaldehyde

c.   Cyclohexanone to cyclohexanol

d.   2-Propanol to propanone

e.   2,3-Butanedione (found in butter) to 2,3-butanediol

QUESTION 10.10

Write an equation for each of the reactions in Question 10.9.

Addition reactions

The principal reaction of the carbonyl group is **addition** across the highly polar carbon-oxygen double bond. These reactions require that a catalytic amount of acid be present in the solution, as shown by H^+ over the arrow for the reactions shown below.

In an addition reaction between an alcohol and an aldehyde or ketone, the hydrogen of the alcohol adds to the carbonyl oxygen. The alkoxyl group of the alcohol (—OR) adds to the carbonyl carbon. The product is either a **hemiacetal** (addition to an aldehyde) or a **hemiketal** (addition to a ketone). The addition of an alcohol to an aldehyde and to a ketone are seen in the following equations:

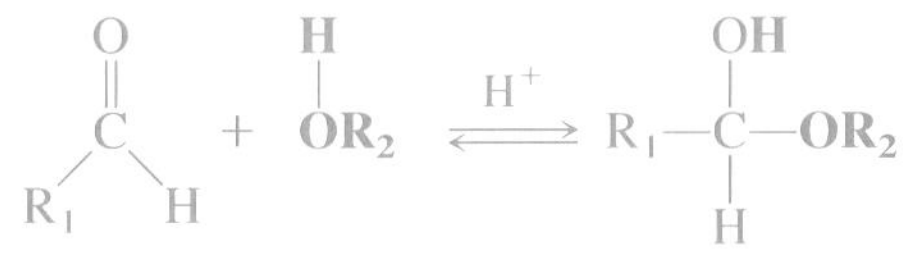

$$\underset{\text{Aldehyde}}{\underset{R_1}{\overset{O}{\underset{H}{\overset{\|}{C}}}}} + \underset{\text{Alcohol}}{\overset{H}{\underset{OR_2}{|}}} \underset{}{\overset{H^+}{\rightleftharpoons}} \underset{\text{Hemiacetal}}{R_1-\underset{H}{\overset{OH}{\underset{|}{\overset{|}{C}}}}-OR_2}$$

$$\underset{\text{Ketone}}{\underset{R_1}{\overset{O}{\underset{R_2}{\overset{\|}{C}}}}} + \underset{\text{Alcohol}}{\overset{H}{\underset{OR_3}{|}}} \underset{}{\overset{H^+}{\rightleftharpoons}} \underset{\text{Hemiketal}}{R_1-\underset{CH_3}{\overset{OH}{\underset{|}{\overset{|}{C}}}}-OR_3}$$

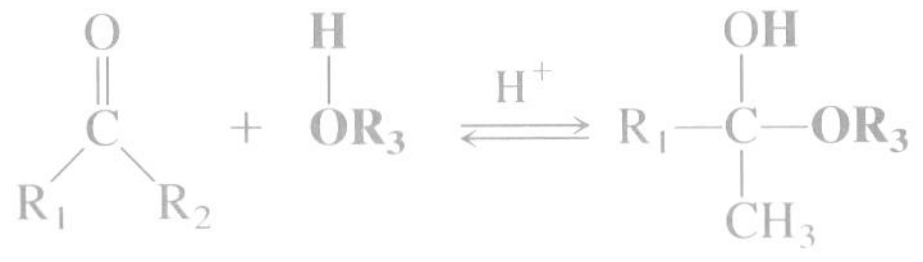

Notice that both hemiacetals and hemiketals have a hydroxyl group (—OH) and an alkoxyl group (—OR) attached to the same carbon atom. The difference between the two is that a hemiacetal has a hydrogen and an alkyl group bonded to the carbon that bears the —OH and —OR, while the hemiketal has two alkyl groups.

EXAMPLE 10.7

Writing an Equation Representing the Reaction of a Ketone with an Alcohol to Produce a Hemiketal

Write an equation showing the reaction of propanone with methanol to produce propanone methyl hemiketal.

Solution

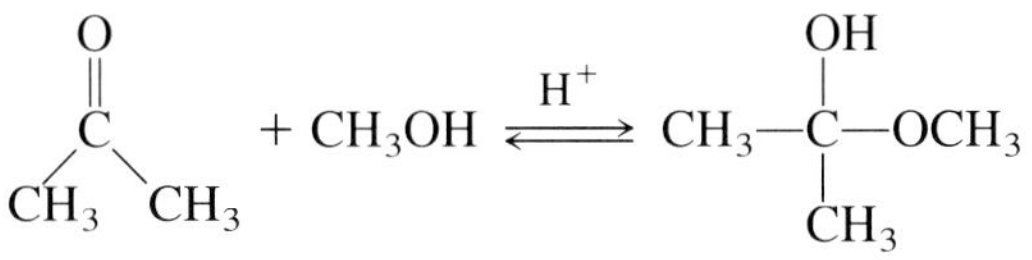

$$\underset{\text{Propanone}}{\underset{CH_3}{\overset{O}{\underset{CH_3}{\overset{\|}{C}}}}} + CH_3OH \overset{H^+}{\rightleftharpoons} \underset{\substack{\text{Propanone methyl}\\\text{hemiketal}\\\text{(common name)}}}{CH_3-\underset{CH_3}{\overset{OH}{\underset{|}{\overset{|}{C}}}}-OCH_3}$$

Hemiacetals and hemiketals are readily formed in carbohydrates. Monosaccharides contain several hydroxyl groups and one carbonyl group. The linear form of a monosaccharide quickly undergoes an intramolecular reaction in solution to give a cyclic hemiacetal or hemiketal. This internal reaction is shown in Figure 10.5 and discussed in detail in Section 11.2.

Hemiacetals and hemiketals are very reactive. If excess alcohol is present in the reaction mixture, they will undergo a substitution reaction in which the —OH group is exchanged for another —OR group. The products of these reactions are **acetals** and **ketals,** as seen in the

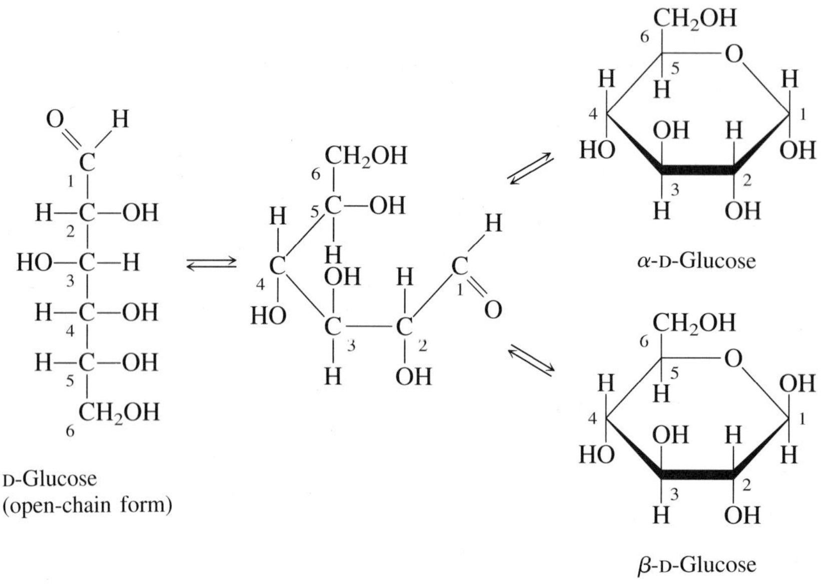

FIGURE 10.5
Hemiacetal formation in sugars, shown for the intramolecular reaction of D-glucose.

following reactions:

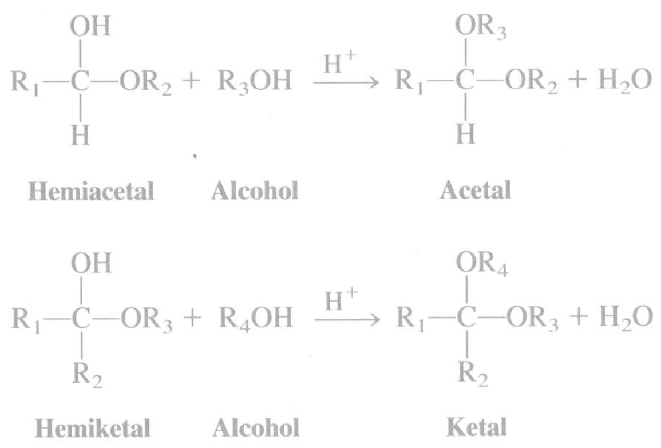

When the hemiacetal or hemiketal of one monosaccharide reacts with a hydroxyl group of another monosaccharide, the product is an acetal or a ketal. A sugar molecule made up of two monosaccharides is called a *disaccharide*. The C—O—C bond between the two monosaccharides is called a *glycosidic bond* (Figure 10.6).

FIGURE 10.6
Acetal formation, demonstrated in the formation of the disaccharide sucrose, common table sugar. The reaction between the hydroxyl groups of the monosaccharides glucose and fructose produces the acetal sucrose. The bond between the two sugars is a glycosidic bond.

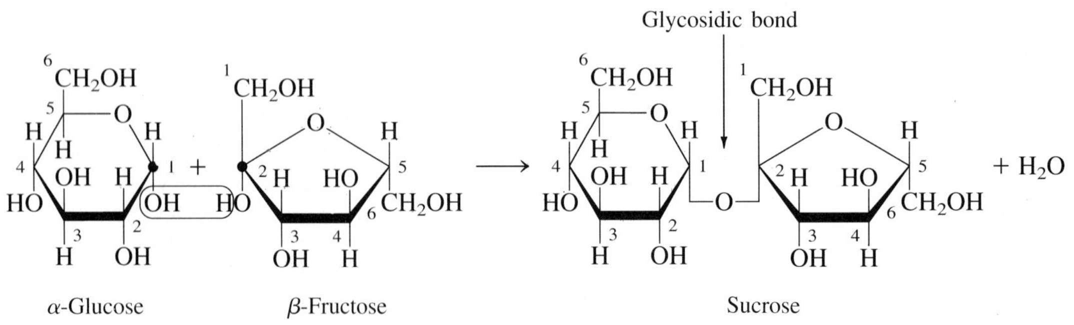

A HUMAN PERSPECTIVE

The Chemistry of Vision

β-Carotene is found in many yellow vegetables, as well as in tomatoes and spinach. When β-carotene is cleaved, two molecules of vitamin A are produced. In the body, vitamin A is converted to 11-*cis*-retinal, an unsaturated aldehyde that is a vital component in the photochemical transformations that make up the vision process.

The retina of the eye contains two types of cells that are responsible for vision: *rods* and *cones.* Rods are primarily responsible for vision in dim light. Cones are responsible for vision in bright light and for the detection of color.

In the retina a protein called *opsin* combines with 11-*cis*-retinal to form a modified protein, *rhodopsin.* The 11-*cis*-retinal portion of rhodopsin is a prosthetic group (a nonprotein portion of a protein that is necessary for its action).

When light strikes the rods, the light energy is absorbed by the 11-*cis*-retinal, which is photochemically converted to 11-*trans*-retinal. This causes a change in the shape of rhodopsin itself, producing *metarhodopsin.* In the next step, 11-*trans*-retinal dissociates from opsin to begin the visual process. This dissociation causes ions to flow more freely into the rod cells. The influx of ions, in turn, stimulates nerve cells that send signals to the brain. Interpretation of those signals produces the visual image.

Following the initial light stimulus, retinal returns to the *cis*-isomer and reassociates with opsin. The system is then ready for the next impulse of light. However, some retinal is lost in the process and must be replaced by conversion of dietary vitamin A to retinal. As you might expect, a deficiency of vitamin A can have terrible consequences. In children, lack of vitamin A causes *xerophthalmia,* an eye disease that results first in night blindness and eventually in total blindness. This can be prevented by an adequate dietary supply of this vitamin.

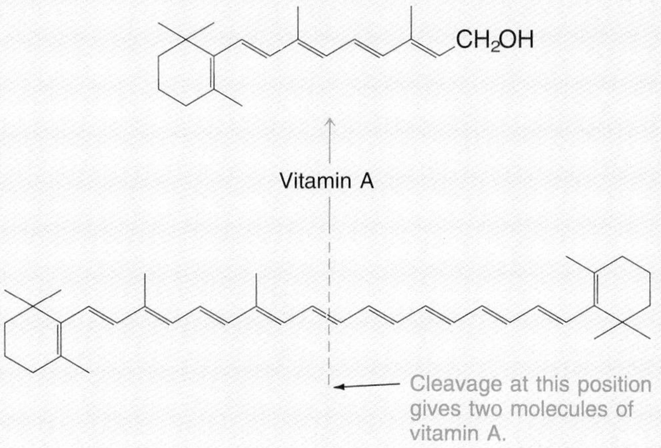

Vitamin A

Cleavage at this position gives two molecules of vitamin A.

β-Carotene

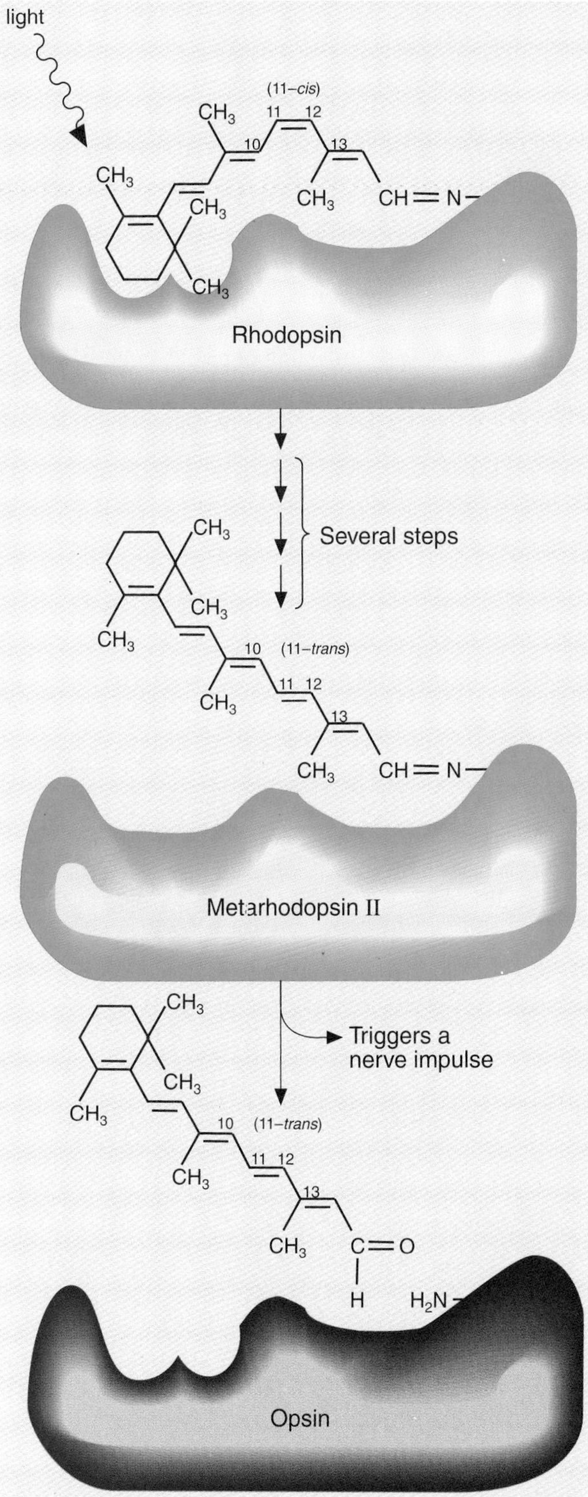

light

Rhodopsin

Several steps

Metarhodopsin II

Triggers a nerve impulse

Opsin

The chemistry of vision: Light is absorbed by rhodopsin, *cis-trans*-isomerization of the 11-*cis*-retinal to 11-*trans*-retinal results. The metarhodopsin formed is converted through one or more pathways, to opsin and a nerve impulse is sent to the brain. Opsin is converted to rhodopsin to begin the cycle again.

SUMMARY OF REACTIONS

Alcohols

Preparation of alcohols by hydration of alkenes:

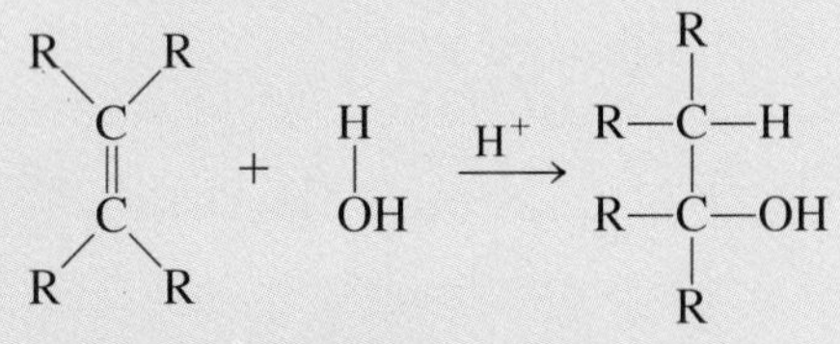

$$\text{Alkene} + \text{Water} \xrightarrow{H^+} \text{Alcohol}$$

Alkene   Water   Alcohol

Preparation of alcohols by reduction of an aldehyde or ketone:

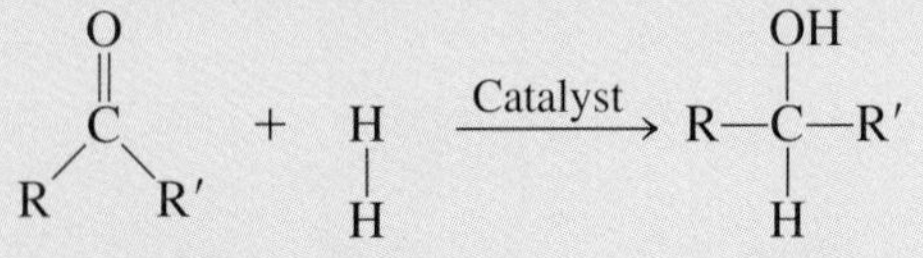

$$\text{Aldehyde or ketone} + \text{H}_2\text{O} \xrightarrow{\text{Catalyst}} \text{Alcohol}$$

Aldehyde or   Water   Alcohol
ketone

Dehydration of alcohols:

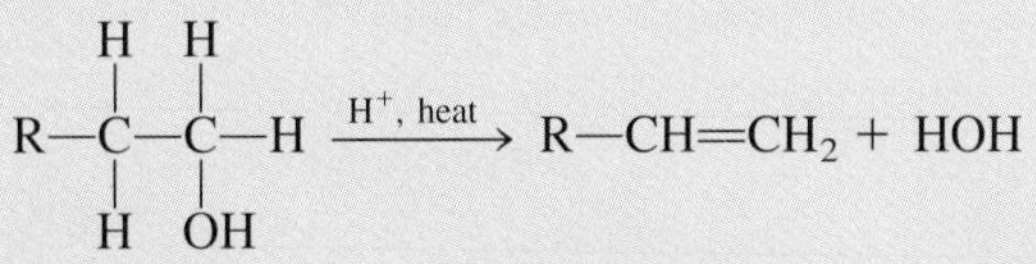

$$R-\overset{H}{\underset{H}{C}}-\overset{H}{\underset{OH}{C}}-H \xrightarrow{H^+,\ heat} R-CH=CH_2 + HOH$$

Alcohol   Alkene   Water

Oxidation of a primary alcohol:

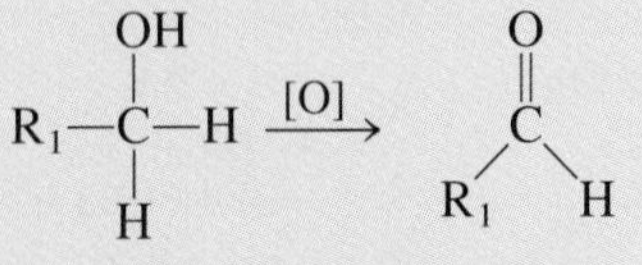

$$R_1-\overset{OH}{\underset{H}{C}}-H \xrightarrow{[O]} \overset{O}{\underset{R_1\quad H}{C}}$$

1° Alcohol   An aldehyde

Oxidation of a secondary alcohol:

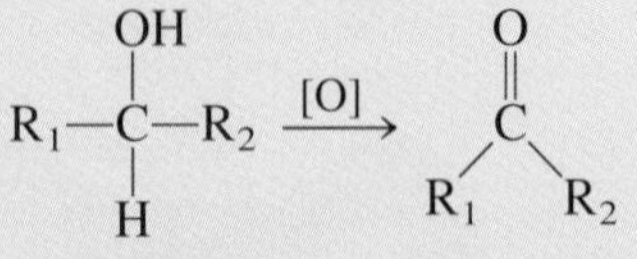

$$R_1-\overset{OH}{\underset{H}{C}}-R_2 \xrightarrow{[O]} \overset{O}{\underset{R_1\quad R_2}{C}}$$

2° Alcohol   A ketone

Oxidation of a tertiary alcohol:

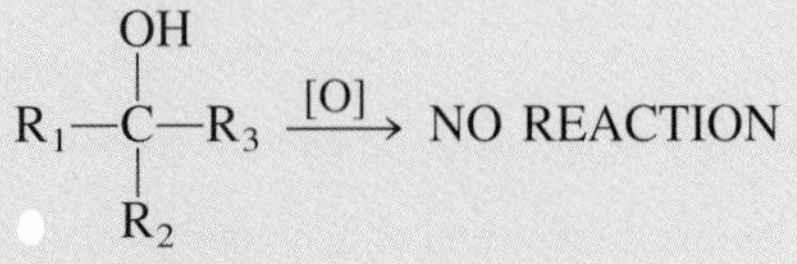

$$R_1-\overset{OH}{\underset{R_2}{C}}-R_3 \xrightarrow{[O]} \text{NO REACTION}$$

3° Alcohol

Aldehydes and Ketones

Oxidation of an aldehyde:

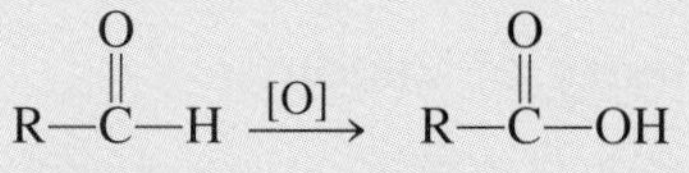

$$\overset{O}{\underset{}{R-C-H}} \xrightarrow{[O]} \overset{O}{\underset{}{R-C-OH}}$$

Aldehyde   Carboxylic acid

Reduction of aldehydes and ketones:

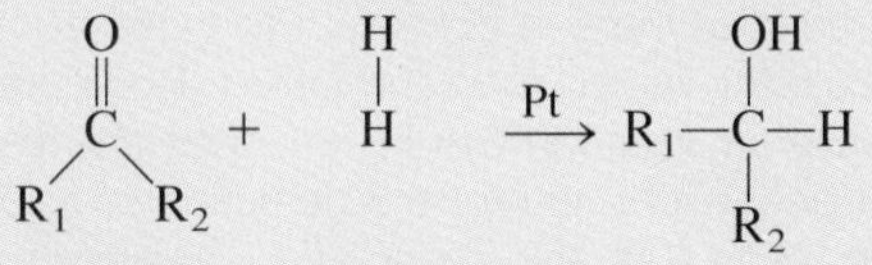

$$\overset{O}{\underset{R_1\quad R_2}{C}} + \overset{H}{\underset{H}{}} \xrightarrow{Pt} R_1-\overset{OH}{\underset{R_2}{C}}-H$$

Aldehyde   Hydrogen   Alcohol
or ketone

Addition of an alcohol to an aldehyde—hemiacetal formation:

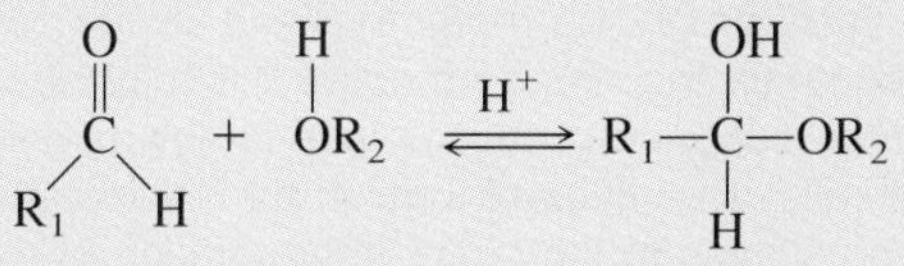

$$\overset{O}{\underset{R_1\quad H}{C}} + \overset{H}{\underset{}{OR_2}} \xrightleftharpoons{H^+} R_1-\overset{OH}{\underset{H}{C}}-OR_2$$

Aldehyde   Alcohol   Hemiacetal

Addition of an alcohol to a ketone—hemiketal formation:

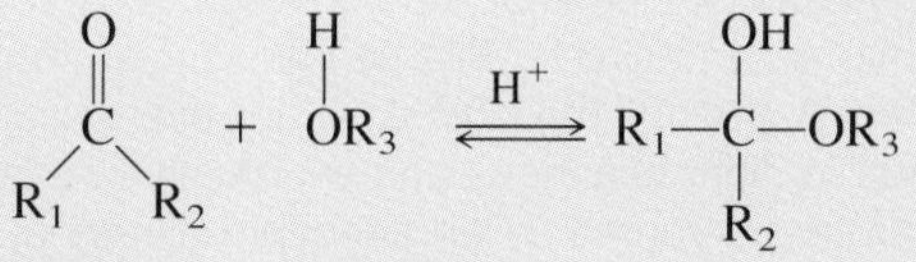

$$\overset{O}{\underset{R_1\quad R_2}{C}} + \overset{H}{\underset{}{OR_3}} \xrightleftharpoons{H^+} R_1-\overset{OH}{\underset{R_2}{C}}-OR_3$$

Ketone   Alcohol   Hemiketal

Acetal formation:

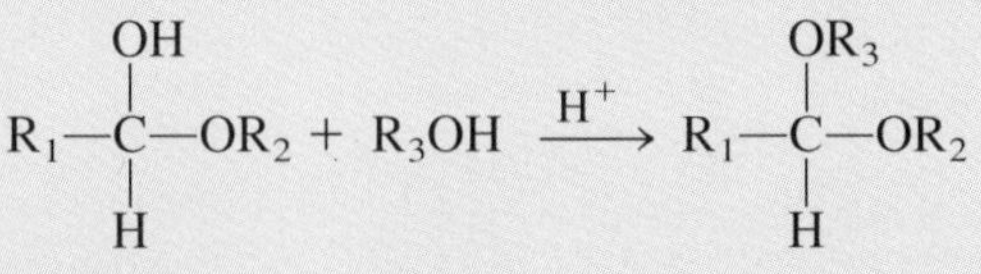

$$R_1-\overset{OH}{\underset{H}{C}}-OR_2 + R_3OH \xrightarrow{H^+} R_1-\overset{OR_3}{\underset{H}{C}}-OR_2$$

Hemiacetal   Alcohol   Acetal

Ketal formation:

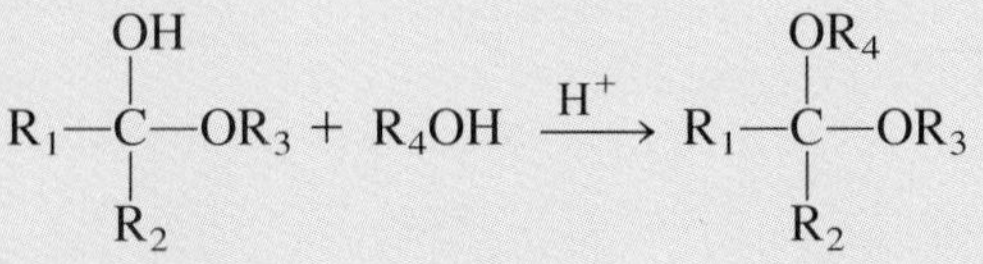

$$R_1-\overset{OH}{\underset{R_2}{C}}-OR_3 + R_4OH \xrightarrow{H^+} R_1-\overset{OR_4}{\underset{R_2}{C}}-OR_3$$

Hemiketal   Alcohol   Ketal

SUMMARY

10.1 Alcohols

Alcohols are characterized by the *hydroxyl group (—OH)* and have the general formula R—OH. They are very polar, owing to the polar hydroxyl group, and are able to form intermolecular hydrogen bonds. Because of hydrogen bonding between alcohol molecules, they have higher boiling points than hydrocarbons of comparable molecular weight. The smaller alcohols are very water-soluble. Alcohols are named by determining the parent compound and replacing the *-e* ending with *-ol*. The chain is numbered to give the hydroxyl group the lowest possible number. Alcohols may be classified as *primary, secondary,* or *tertiary,* depending on the number of alkyl groups attached to the carbon bearing the hydroxyl group. Alcohols can be prepared by the *hydration* of alkenes. Alcohols can undergo *dehydration* to yield alkenes. Primary and secondary alcohols undergo oxidation reactions to yield aldehydes and ketones, respectively. Tertiary alcohols do not undergo oxidation.

10.2 Phenols

Phenols are alcohol-like compounds in which the hydroxyl group is attached to a benzene ring; they have the general formula Ar—OH. Many phenols are important as antiseptics and disinfectants.

10.3 Ethers

Ethers are characterized by the R—O—R functional group. Ethers are generally nonreactive but are extremely flammable. Diethyl ether was the first general anesthetic used in medical practice. It has since been replaced by penthrane and enthrane, which are less flammable.

10.4 Thiols

Thiols are characterized by the sulfhydryl group (—SH). The amino acid cysteine is a thiol that is extremely important for maintaining the correct shapes of proteins. Coenzyme A is a thiol that serves as a ''carrier'' of acetyl groups in biochemical reactions.

10.5 Aldehydes and Ketones

The *carbonyl group* (〉C=O) is characteristic of the *aldehydes* and *ketones.* The carbonyl group and the two groups attached to it are coplanar. In ketones the carbonyl carbon is attached to two carbon-containing groups, while in aldehydes the carbonyl carbon is attached to at least one hydrogen; the second group attached to the carbonyl carbon in aldehydes may be another hydrogen or a carbon atom. Owing to the polar carbonyl group, aldehydes and ketones are polar compounds. Their boiling points are higher than those of comparable hydrocarbons but lower than those of comparable alcohols. Small aldehydes and ketones are reasonably soluble in water because of the hydrogen bonding between the carbonyl group and water molecules. Larger carbonyl-containing compounds are less polar and thus are more soluble in nonpolar organic solvents.

In the I.U.P.A.C. Nomenclature System, aldehydes are named by determining the parent compound and replacing the final *-e* of the parent alkane with *-al*. The chain is numbered beginning with the carbonyl carbon as carbon-1. Ketones are named by determining the parent compound and replacing the *-e* ending of the parent alkane with the *-one* suffix of the ketone family. The longest carbon chain is numbered to give the carbonyl carbon the lowest possible number. Many members of these families are important as food and fragrance chemicals, medicinals, and agricultural chemicals. In the laboratory, aldehydes and ketones are prepared by the oxidation of alcohols. Oxidation of a primary alcohol produces an aldehyde; oxidation of a secondary alcohol yields a ketone. Tertiary alcohols do not react under these conditions. Aldehydes and ketones can be distinguished from one another on the basis of the ability to undergo oxidation reactions. The *Tollens' Test* and *Benedict's Test* are the most common such tests. Aldehydes are easily oxidized to carboxylic acids. Ketones do not undergo further oxidation reactions. Aldehydes and ketones are readily reduced to alcohols by *hydrogenation*. The most common reaction of the carbonyl group is *addition* across the highly polar carbon-oxygen double bond. The addition of an alcohol to an aldehyde produces a *hemiacetal*. A hemiacetal may react with a second alcohol molecule to form an *acetal*. The reaction of a ketone with an alcohol produces a *hemiketal*. A hemiketal may react with a second alcohol molecule to form a *ketal*. Hemiacetals and hemiketals are readily formed in carbohydrates.

KEY TERMS

acetal (10.5)
addition reaction (10.5)
alcohol (10.1)
aldehyde (10.5)
Benedict's Test (10.5)
carbonyl group (10.5)
dehydration (10.1)
disulfide (10.4)
ether (10.3)
fermentation (10.1)
hemiacetal (10.5)
hemiketal (10.5)

hydration (10.1)
hydrogenation (10.5)
hydroxyl group (10.1)
ketal (10.5)
ketone (10.5)
phenol (10.2)
primary (1°) alcohol (10.1)
secondary (2°) alcohol (10.1)
tertiary (3°) alcohol (10.1)
thiol (10.4)
Tollens' Test (10.5)

QUESTIONS AND PROBLEMS

Structure and Physical Properties

10.11 Arrange the following compounds in order of increasing boiling point, beginning with the lowest:

    a. $CH_3CH_2CH_2CH_2CH_3$ **b.** $CH_3—\underset{\underset{O}{\|}}{C}—CH_2CH_2CH_3$

c. $CH_3CHCH_2CH_2CH_3$ d. $CH_3CH_2CH_2—O—CH_2CH_3$
      |
     OH

10.12 Why do alcohols have higher boiling points than alkanes? Why are small alcohols readily soluble in water?

10.13 Which member of each of the following pairs is more soluble in water?

  a. CH_3CH_2OH or $CH_3CH_2CH_2CH_2OH$

  b. CH_2CH_2 or CH_3CH_2OH
     | |
    OH OH

  c. $CH_3CH_2CH_2CH_2CH_3$ or $CH_3CH_2CH_2CH_2—OH$

  d.   OH   or CH_3CHCH_3
                  |
                   OH

10.14 Arrange the three alcohols in each of the following sets in order of increasing solubility in water:

  a. $CH_3CH_2CH_2OH$ CH_2CHCH_2 $CH_2CH_2CH_2$
                       | | | | |
                     OH OHOH   OH   OH

  b. Pentyl alcohol   1-Hexanol   Ethylene glycol

Nomenclature

10.15 Give the I.U.P.A.C. name for each of the following compounds:

  a. $CH_3CH_2CH_2CH_2CH_2CH_2CH_2OH$

  b. CH_3CHCH_3
        |
     OH

  c. CH_3
            |
    $CH_3—C—CH_3$
            |
         CH_2OH

          Br
          |
  d. $CH_3CH_2CHCH_2CH_2CH_2OH$
              CH_3

  e. $CH_3CH—CCH_2CH_2CH_3$
        | |
     OH   CH_3

  f. $CH_2CH_2CH_2CH_3$
               |
   $CH_3CH_2CCH_2CH_3$
            |
          OH

10.16 Draw each of the following, using complete structural formulas:

  a. 3-Hexanol
  b. 1,2,3-Pentanetriol
  c. 2-Methyl-2-pentanol
  d. Cyclohexanol
  e. 3,4-Dimethyl-3-heptanol

Medically Important Alcohols

10.17 What is denatured alcohol? Why is alcohol denatured?

10.18 What are the principal uses of methanol, ethanol, and isopropyl alcohol?

Classification of Alcohols

10.19 Classify each of the following as either 1°, 2°, or 3° alcohols:

  a. 3-Methyl-1-butanol
  b. 2-Methylcyclopentanol

  c. *t*-Butyl alcohol
  d. 1-Methylcyclopentanol
  e. 2-Methyl-2-pentanol

10.20 Classify each of the following as either 1°, 2°, or 3° alcohols:

  a. $CH_3CH_2CH_2CH_2CH_2CH_2CH_2OH$

  b. CH_3CHCH_3
        |
     OH

  c. CH_3
           |
   $CH_3—C—CH_3$
          |
        CH_2OH

        Br
        |
  d. $CH_3CH_2CHCH_2CH_2CH_2OH$
             CH_3

  e. $CH_3CH—CCH_2CH_2CH_3$
       | |
    OH   CH_3

Reactions Involving Alcohols

10.21 Predict the products formed by the hydration of the following alkenes:

  a. 1-Pentene
  b. 2-Pentene
  c. 3-Methyl-1-butene
  d. 3,3-Dimethyl-1-butene

10.22 Draw the alkene products of the dehydration of the following alcohols:

  a. 2-Pentanol
  b. 3-Methyl-1-pentanol
  c. 2-Butanol
  d. 4-Chloro-2-pentanol
  e. 1-Propanol

10.23 What would be the product(s) resulting from the oxidation of each of the following alcohols with, for example, potassium permanganate? If no reaction occurs, write N.R.

  a. 2-Butanol
  b. 2-Methyl-2-hexanol
  c. Cyclohexanol
  d. 1-Methyl-1-cyclopentanol

10.24 We have seen that ethanol is metabolized to ethanal (acetaldehyde) in the liver. What would be the product formed, under the same conditions, from each of the following alcohols:

  a. CH_3OH
  b. $CH_3CH_2CH_2OH$
  c. $CH_3CH_2CH_2CH_2OH$

10.25 Give the oxidation products of the following alcohols. If no reaction occurs, write N.R.

        OH
        |
  a. $CH_3CH_2CHCH_2CH_3$ e. ⬡—$CH_2CH_2CH_2OH$

  b. $CH_3CH_2CH_2OH$

        OH   CH_3
        | |
  c. $CH_3CHCH_2CHCH_3$

        OH
        |
  d. $CH_3—C—CH_2CH_3$
          |
        CH_3

10.26 Write an equation, using complete structural formulas, demonstrating each of the following chemical transformations:
  a. Oxidation of an alcohol to an aldehyde
  b. Oxidation of an alcohol to a ketone
  c. Dehydration of a cyclic alcohol to a cycloalkene
  d. Hydrogenation of an alkene to an alkane

Phenols

10.27 2,4,6-Trinitrophenol is known by the common name *picric acid*. Picric acid is a solid but is readily soluble in water. In solution it is used as a biological tissue stain. As a solid, it is also known to be unstable and may explode. In this way it is similar to 2,4,6-trinitrotoluene (TNT). Draw the structures of picric acid and TNT. Why is picric acid readily soluble in water while TNT is not?

10.28 Name the following aromatic compounds, using the I.U.P.A.C. System:

a.

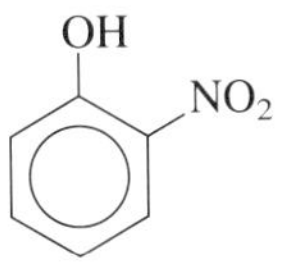

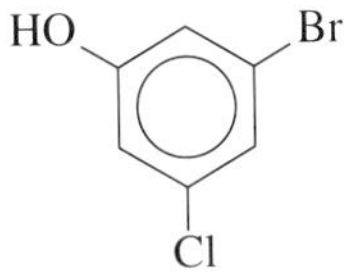

b. 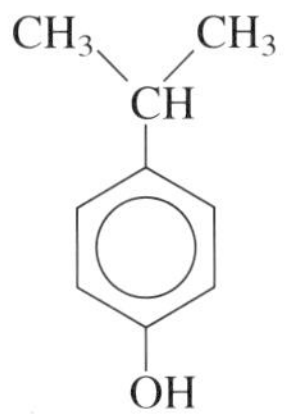 CH_3 CH_3

c. HO   Br   Cl

d. 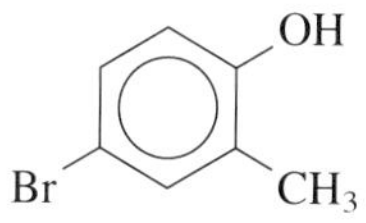 OH   Br CH_3

10.29 List some phenol compounds that are commonly used as antiseptics or disinfectants.

10.30 Why must a dilute solution of phenol be used for disinfecting environmental surfaces?

Ethers

10.31 Draw all of the alcohols and ethers of molecular formula $C_4H_{10}O$.

10.32 Name each of the isomers drawn for Problem 10.31.

10.33 Give the I.U.P.A.C. names for penthrane and enthrane.

10.34 Why have penthrane and enthrane replaced diethyl ether as a generalized anesthetic?

Nomenclature of Aldehydes and Ketones

10.35 Draw each of the following using complete structural formulas:
  a. Methanal
  b. 7,8-Dibromooctanal
  c. Acetone
  d. Hydroxyethanal
  e. 3-Chloro-2-pentanone
  f. Benzaldehyde
  g. 4-Bromo-3-hexanone

10.36 Name each of the following using the I.U.P.A.C. Nomenclature System:

a. 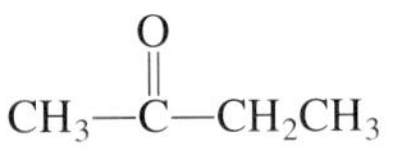 $CH_3-\overset{\displaystyle O}{\overset{\|}{C}}-CH_2CH_3$

b. 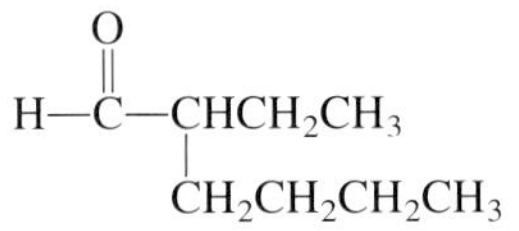 $H-\overset{\displaystyle O}{\overset{\|}{C}}-\underset{\underset{\displaystyle CH_2CH_2CH_2CH_3}{|}}{CH}CH_2CH_3$

c. $Cl-\overset{\overset{\displaystyle Cl}{|}}{\underset{\underset{\displaystyle Cl}{|}}{C}}-\overset{\displaystyle O}{\overset{\|}{C}}-CH_3$

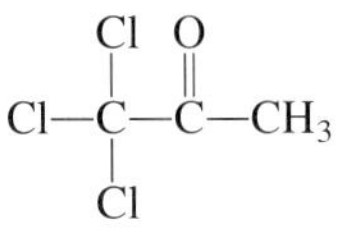

d.

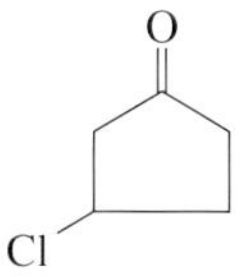

e. 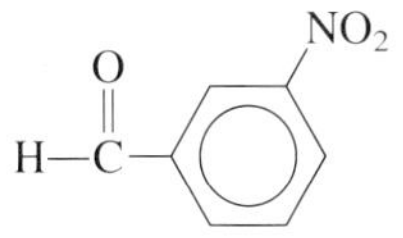 $H-\overset{\displaystyle O}{\overset{\|}{C}}$ NO_2

f. 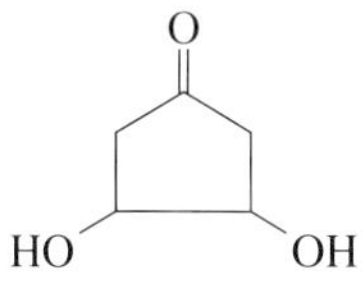 HO   OH

Thiols

10.37 Cystine is an amino acid formed from the oxidation of two cysteine molecules to form a disulfide bond. The molecular formula of cystine is $C_6H_{12}O_4N_2S_2$. Draw the structural formula of cystine. [Hint: For the structure of cysteine, see Figure 15.3.]

10.38 Explain the way in which British Anti-Lewisite acts as an antidote for mercury poisoning.

Reactions Involving Aldehydes and Ketones

10.39 Draw the structures of each of the following compounds, and draw and name the product that you would expect to produce by oxidizing each of the following alcohols:
  a. 2-Butanol
  b. 2-Methyl-1-propanol
  c. Cyclopentanol
  d. 2-Methyl-2-propanol
  e. 2-Nonanol
  f. 1-Decanol

10.40 Draw the generalized equation for the oxidation of primary and secondary alcohols.

10.41 Draw the structures of the reactants and products for each of the following reactions. Label each as an oxidation or a reduction reaction:
  a. Ethanal to ethanol
  b. Cyclohexanone to cyclohexanol
  c. 2-Propanol to propanone

10.42 An unknown has been determined to be one of the following three compounds:

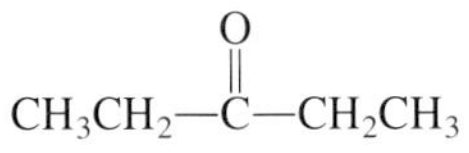

$CH_3CH_2-\overset{\displaystyle O}{\overset{\|}{C}}-CH_2CH_3$ $CH_3CH_2CH_2CH_2-\overset{\displaystyle O}{\overset{\|}{C}}-H$

3-Pentanone    Pentanal

$CH_3CH_2CH_2CH_2CH_3$

Pentane

The unknown is fairly soluble in water and produces a silver mirror when treated with the silver ammonia complex. A red precipitate appears when it is treated with the Benedict's reagent. Which of the compounds above is the correct structure for the unknown? Explain your reasoning.

10.43 Which of the following compounds would be expected to give a positive Tollens' Test?
  a. 3-Pentanone
  b. Cyclohexanone
  c. 3-Methylbutanal
  d. Cyclopentanol
  e. 2,2-Dimethyl-1-pentanol
  f. Acetaldehyde

10.44 Write an equation representing the reaction of glucose with the Benedict's reagent. How is this test used in medicine?

10.45 Write an equation for the addition of one ethanol molecule to each of the following aldehydes and ketones:

a. $CH_3-\overset{\overset{\displaystyle O}{\|}}{C}-CH_3$

b. $CH_3CH_2-\overset{\overset{\displaystyle O}{\|}}{C}-H$

c. $CH_3-\overset{\overset{\displaystyle O}{\|}}{C}-H$

d. $CH_3-\overset{\overset{\displaystyle O}{\|}}{C}-CH_2CH_2CH_3$

10.46 What is the general name for the product that is formed when an aldehyde reacts with one molecule of alcohol? What is the general name of the product that is formed when a ketone reacts with one molecule of alcohol?

10.47 What is the general name for the product that is formed when an aldehyde reacts with two molecules of alcohol? What is the general name of the product that is formed when a ketone reacts with two molecules of alcohol?

10.48 Write an equation for the addition of two methanol molecules to each of the following aldehydes and ketones:

a. $CH_3-\overset{\overset{\displaystyle O}{\|}}{C}-CH_3$

b. $CH_3CH_2-\overset{\overset{\displaystyle O}{\|}}{C}-H$

c. $CH_3-\overset{\overset{\displaystyle O}{\|}}{C}-H$

d. $CH_3-\overset{\overset{\displaystyle O}{\|}}{C}-CH_2CH_2CH_3$

Further Problems

10.49 Write an equation for the preparation of 2-butanol from 1-butene. What type of reaction is involved?

10.50 Write a general equation for the preparation of an alcohol from an aldehyde or ketone. What type of reaction is involved?

10.51 An alcohol can be oxidized to produce an aldehyde or a ketone. What aldehyde or ketone is produced by the oxidation of each of the following alcohols?
  a. Methanol
  b. 1-Propanol
  c. 3-Pentanol
  d. 2-Methyl-2-butanol

10.52 An aldehyde can be oxidized to produce a carboxylic acid. Draw the carboxylic acid that would be produced by the oxidation of each of the following aldehydes.
  a. Methanal
  b. Ethanal
  c. Propanal
  d. Butanal

10.53 Indicate whether each of the following statements is true or false.
  a. Aldehydes and ketones can be oxidized to produce carboxylic acids.
  b. Oxidation of a primary alcohol produces an aldehyde.
  c. Oxidation of a tertiary alcohol produces a ketone.
  d. Alcohols can be produced by the oxidation of an aldehyde or ketone.

10.54 Indicate whether each of the following statements is true or false.
  a. Ketones, but not aldehydes, react in the Tollens' silver mirror test.
  b. Addition of one alcohol molecule to an aldehyde results in formation of a hemiacetal.
  c. The cyclic forms of monosaccharides are intramolecular hemiacetals or intramolecular hemiketals.
  d. Disaccharides (sugars composed of two covalently joined monosaccharides) are either acetals or ketals.

10.55 Write the reaction, occurring in the liver, that causes the oxidation of ethanol. What is the product of this reaction and what symptoms are caused by the product?

10.56 Write the reaction, occurring in the liver, that causes the oxidation of methanol. What is the product of this reaction and what is the possible result of the accumulation of the product in the body?

VOCABULARY QUIZ

10.1 Organic compounds that contain hydroxyl groups attached to alkyl groups are _____.

10.2 A family of organic compounds that contain a sulfhydryl group is the _____.

10.3 _____ is a reaction that involves the loss of a water molecule.

10.4 The functional group that consists of a carbon double bonded to an oxygen is _____.

10.5 A test for the presence of aldehydes that uses a buffered solution of Cu(II) and that can be used to test for the presence of glucose in the blood is _____.

10.6 The product of the reaction between an aldehyde and an alcohol is called a(n) _____.

10.7 A(n) _____ is the product of the reaction between a hemiketal and an alcohol.

10.8 Hydrogenation is the reaction in which _____ is added to a double or triple bond.

10.9 In inorganic chemistry, _____ is the loss of electrons accompanied by a change in charge. In organic chemistry this is more generally seen as a gain of oxygen or a loss of hydrogen.

10.10 An alcohol with three alkyl groups bonded to the carbon bearing the hydroxyl group is a(n) _____ alcohol.

11

Carbohydrates

LEARNING GOALS

◆ Understand the concepts of chirality, enantiomers, stereoisomers, and D- and L-families

◆ Recognize whether a sugar is a reducing or a nonreducing sugar

◆ Draw and name the common, simple carbohydrates using structural formulas and Fischer projection formulas

◆ Given the Fischer projection of a monosaccharide, be able to draw the Haworth projection of its α- and β-cyclic forms and vice versa

◆ Discuss the structural, chemical, and biochemical properties of the monosaccharides, oligosaccharides, and polysaccharides

◆ Know the difference between galactosemia and lactose intolerance

◆ Know the difference between complex and simple carbohydrates and the amounts of each recommended in the daily diet

◆ Discuss the use of the Benedict's reagent to measure the level of glucose in urine

CHEMISTRY CONNECTION

Chemistry Through the Looking Glass

In his children's story *Through the Looking Glass,* Lewis Carroll's heroine Alice wonders whether "looking-glass milk" would be good to drink. As we will see in this chapter, many biological molecules, such as the sugars, exist as two isomers, *stereoisomers,* that are mirror images of one another. Since two mirror-image forms occur, it is rather remarkable that in our bodies, and in most of the biological world, only one of the two is found. For instance, the common sugars are members of the D-family, while all the common amino acids that make up our proteins are members of the L-family. It is not too surprising, then, that the enzymes in our bodies that break down the sugars and proteins we eat are *stereospecific,* that is, they recognize only one mirror-image isomer. Knowing this, we can make an educated guess that "looking-glass milk" could not be digested by our enzymes and therefore would not be a good source of food for us. It is even possible that it might be toxic to us!

Pharmaceutical chemists are becoming more and more concerned with the stereochemical purity of the drugs that we take. Consider a few examples. In 1960 the drug thalidomide was commonly prescribed in Europe as a sedative. However, during that year, hundreds of women who took thalidomide during pregnancy gave birth to babies with severe birth defects. Thalidomide, it turned out, was a mixture of two stereoisomers. One is a sedative; the other is a teratogen, a chemical that causes birth defects.

One of the common side-effects of taking antihistamines

for colds or allergies is drowsiness. Again, this is the result of the fact that antihistamines are mixtures of stereoisomers. One causes drowsiness; the other is a good decongestant.

One stereoisomer of the compound carvone is associated with the smell of spearmint; the other produces the aroma of caraway seeds or dill. One mirror-image form of limonene smells like lemons; the other has the aroma of oranges.

The pain reliever ibuprofen is currently sold as a mixture of stereoisomers, but one is a much more effective analgesic than the other.

Taste, smell, and the biological effects of drugs in the body all depend on the stereochemical form of compounds and their interactions with cellular enzymes or receptors. As a result, chemists are actively working to devise methods of separating the isomers in pure form. Alternatively, methods of conducting stereospecific syntheses that produce only one stereoisomer are being sought. By preparing pure stereoisomers, the biological activity of a compound can be much more carefully controlled. This will lead to safer medications.

In this chapter we will begin our study of stereochemistry, the spatial arrangement of atoms in molecules, with the carbohydrates. Later, we will examine the stereochemistry of the amino acids that make up our proteins and consider the stereochemical specificity of the metabolic reactions that are essential to life. A more complete treatment of stereochemistry is found in Appendix C: "Stereochemistry and Stereoisomers Revisited."

INTRODUCTION

Carbohydrates are produced in plants by photosynthesis (Figure 11.1). Natural carbohydrate sources such as grains and cereals, breads, sugar cane, fruits, milk, and honey are an important source of energy for animals. Carbohydrates, especially glucose, are the primary energy source for the brain and nervous system and can be used by many other tissues. When "burned" by cells for energy, each gram of carbohydrate releases 4 kilocalories of energy.

A kilocalorie is the same as the Calorie referred to in the "count-your-calories" books.

Section 11.4

Sections 11.2 and 11.3

See "A Human Perspective: Tooth Decay and Simple Sugars"

A healthy diet should contain both complex carbohydrates, such as starches and cellulose, and simple sugars, such as fructose and sucrose. However, the quantity of simple sugars, especially sucrose, should be minimized because large quantities of sucrose in the diet promote obesity and tooth decay.

Complex carbohydrates are better for us than the simple sugars. Starch, found in rice, potatoes, breads, and cereals, is an excellent energy source. In addition, the complex carbohydrates, such as cellulose, provide us with an important supply of dietary fiber.

It is hard to determine exactly what percentage of the daily diet *should* consist of carbohydrates. The *actual* percentage varies widely throughout the world, from 80% in the Far East, where rice is the main component of the diet, to 40–50% in the United States. Currently, it is recommended that about 58% of the calories in the diet should come from carbohydrates and that no more than 10% of the daily caloric intake should be sucrose. In 1992 the U.S. Department of Agriculture adopted a food pyramid to show the recommended amounts of various foods in the diet (Figure 11.2). The foods at the bottom of the pyramid, grains (breads, cereals, rice, pasta), and at the next level, fruits and vegetables, should be the most abundant in our diet. These food groups are our major sources of dietary carbohydrates.

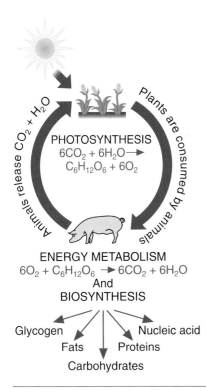

FIGURE 11.1
Carbohydrates are produced by the process of photosynthesis, which uses the energy of sunlight to produce hexoses from CO_2 and H_2O. The plants use these hexoses to generate energy for cellular function and to produce macromolecules, including starch, cellulose, fats, nucleic acids, and proteins. Animals depend on plants as a source of organic carbon. The hexoses are metabolized to generate energy and are used as precursors for the biosynthesis of glycogen, fats, proteins, and nucleic acids.

QUESTION 11.1

What is the current recommendation for the amount of carbohydrates that should be included in the diet? Of the daily intake of carbohydrates, what percentage should be simple sugar?

QUESTION 11.2

Distinguish between simple and complex sugars. What are some sources of complex carbohydrates?

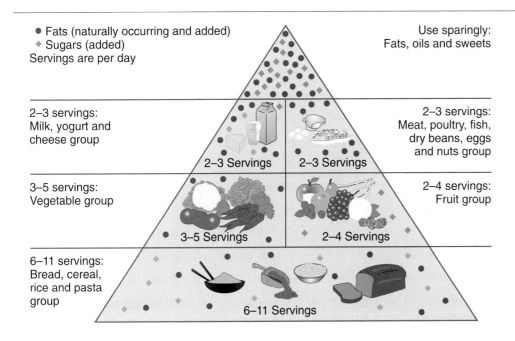

FIGURE 11.2
The U.S. Department of Agriculture has adopted a food pyramid to explain that carbohydrates in the form of cereals, grains, fruits, and vegetables should make up the majority of our diet. Fats and sweets should be consumed sparingly. Source: U.S. Department of Agriculture.

11.1 TYPES OF CARBOHYDRATES

One way of classifying carbohydrates is by size. **Monosaccharides** are the simplest carbohydrates because they contain a single (mono-) sugar (**saccharide**) unit. Intermediate in size are the **oligosaccharides,** consisting of two to ten monosaccharide units joined by bonds through bridging oxygen atoms. Such a bond is called a **glycosidic bond. Disaccharides,** consisting of two monosaccharides, are the most common of these. The largest and most complex carbohydrates are the **polysaccharides;** they are long chains of many monosaccharides.

11.2 MONOSACCHARIDES

Section 16.3
Section 11.2

Monosaccharides are composed of carbon, hydrogen, and oxygen, and most are characterized by the general formula $(CH_2O)_n$, where n is any integer from 3 to 7. As we will see, this general formula is an oversimplification because several biologically important monosaccharides do not conform to the general formula. For instance, several blood group antigen and bacterial cell wall monosaccharides are substituted with amino groups. Many of the intermediates in carbohydrate metabolism carry phosphate groups. Deoxyribose, the monosaccharide found in DNA, has one fewer oxygen atom than the formula would predict.

Nomenclature

Monosaccharides can be named on the basis of the functional groups they contain. A monosaccharide with a ketone (carbonyl) group is a **ketose.** If an aldehyde (carbonyl) group is present, it is called an **aldose.** Because monosaccharides also contain many hydroxyl groups, they are sometimes called *polyhydroxyaldehydes* or *polyhydroxyketones.*

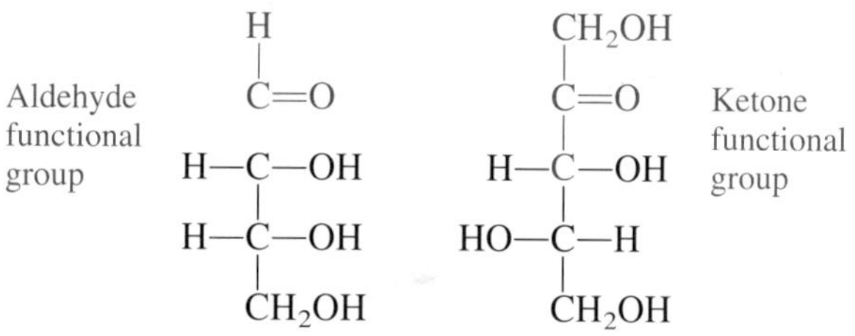

An aldose   A ketose

Another system of nomenclature tells us the number of carbon atoms in the main skeleton. A three-carbon skeleton monosaccharide is a **triose,** a four-carbon sugar is a **tetrose,** a five-carbon sugar is a **pentose,** a six-carbon sugar is a **hexose,** and so on. Combining the two naming systems gives even more information about the structure and composition of a sugar. For example, an aldotetrose is a four-carbon sugar that is also an aldehyde.

In addition to these general names, each monosaccharide has a unique name. These names are shown in blue in the structures below. Because the monosaccharides can exist in several different isomeric forms, it is important to provide the complete name. Thus the complete names of the structures below are D-glyceraldehyde, D-glucose, and D-fructose. These names tell us that the structure represents one particular sugar and also identifies the sugar as one of two possible isomeric forms (D- or L-).

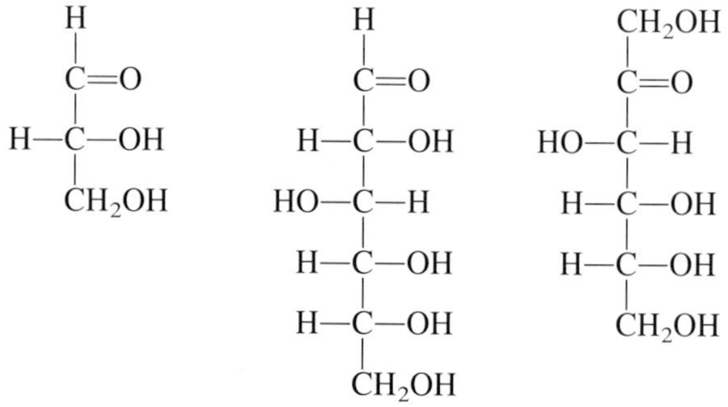

Aldose	Aldose	Ketose
Triose	Hexose	Hexose
Aldotriose	Aldohexose	Ketohexose
D-Glyceraldehyde	D-Glucose	D-Fructose

QUESTION 11.3

What is the structural difference between an aldose and a ketose?

QUESTION 11.4

Explain the difference between:

a. a ketohexose and an aldohexose

b. a triose and a pentose

Structure

The prefixes D- and L- found in the complete name of a monosaccharide are used to identify one of two possible isomeric forms called **stereoisomers.** By definition, each member of a pair of stereoisomers must have the same molecular formula. How then do isomers of the D-family differ from those of the L-family? D- and L-isomers differ in the spatial arrangement of atoms in the molecule.

Stereochemistry is the study of the different spatial arrangements of atoms. In each member of a pair of stereoisomers, all of the atoms are bonded together using exactly the same bonding pattern; they differ only in the arrangements of their atoms in space. A general example of a pair of stereoisomers is shown in Figure 11.3. In this example the general molecule Cabcd is formed from the bonding of a central carbon to four different groups: a, b, c, and d. This results in two molecules rather than one. Each isomer is bonded together through the exact *same* bonding pattern, yet they are *not* identical. If they were identical, they would be superimposable one upon the other; *they are not.* They are therefore stereoisomers. These two stereoisomers have a mirror-image relationship that is analogous to the mirror-image relationship of the left and right hands (see Figure 11.3b). Two stereoisomers that are nonsuperimposable mirror im-

Stereoisomers

For a more detailed discussion of stereochemistry, see Appendix C, "Stereochemistry and Stereoisomers Revisited."

Build models of these compounds using toothpicks and gumdrops of five different colors to prove this to yourself.

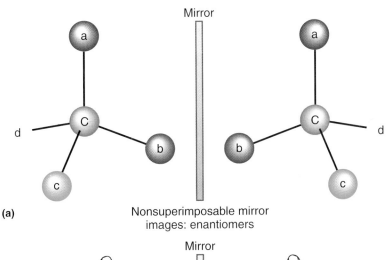

(a) Nonsuperimposable mirror images: enantiomers

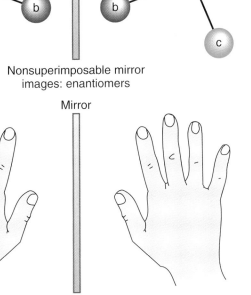

(b)

FIGURE 11.3
(a) A pair of enantiomers for the general molecule Cabcd. (b) Mirror-image right and left hands.

ages of one another are called a pair of **enantiomers.** One is a member of the D-family, and the other is a member of the L-family.

Molecules that are capable of existing in nonsuperimposable mirror image, enantiomeric forms are called **chiral.** The term simply means that as a result of different three-dimensional arrangements of atoms, the molecule can exist in two mirror-image forms. For any pair of nonsuperimposable mirror-image forms (enantiomers), one is always designated D- and the other L-.

A carbon atom that has four different groups bonded to it is called an **asymmetric** or **chiral carbon** atom. Any molecule containing a chiral carbon can exist as a pair of enantiomers. Consider the simplest carbohydrate, glyceraldehyde, which is shown in Figure 11.4. Notice that the second carbon is bonded to four different groups. It is therefore the chiral carbon. As a result, we can draw two enantiomers of glyceraldehyde that are nonsuperimposable mirror images of one another.

In Figure 11.4a the stereoisomers of glyceraldehyde are presented in the two-dimensional **Fischer projection.** A Fischer projection formula is used to designate a specific three-dimensional arrangement of atoms in space using a two-dimensional drawing (compare Figures 11.4a and 11.4b). The Fischer projection is drawn as a cross with the chiral carbon at the center of the cross, the intersection of the horizontal and vertical lines. The vertical line of the drawing represents two bonds to the chiral carbon going away from us, behind the paper. The horizontal lines represent two bonds coming toward us, in front of the paper. In the drawing below, the Fischer projection is compared with a three-dimensional drawing and a ball and stick drawing for 1-bromo-1-chloroethane:

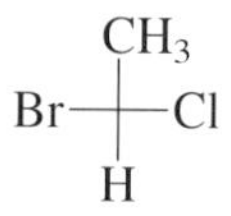

$$Br{-}\overset{\displaystyle CH_3}{\underset{\displaystyle H}{|}}{-}Cl \quad = \quad Br{-}\overset{\displaystyle CH_3}{\underset{\displaystyle H}{C}}{-}Cl \quad = \quad$$

Fischer projection 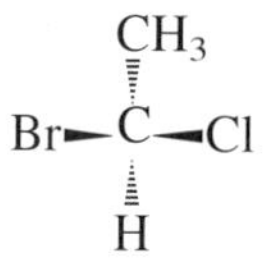   3-D drawing

The structures and designations of D- and L-glyceraldehyde are defined by convention. In fact, the D- and L- terminology is generally applied only to carbohydrates. For organic molecules the D- and L- convention has been replaced by a new system that provides the absolute configuration of a chiral carbon. This system, called the (R) and (S) system, is described in Appendix C, ''Stereochemistry and Stereoisomers Revisited.''

When we examine the Fischer projection for D-glyceraldehyde, we see that the hydroxyl group is drawn to the right of the chiral carbon, whereas the hydroxyl group of L-glyceraldehyde is drawn to the left of the chiral carbon. Notice that the positions of the groups bonded to carbons 1 and 3 do not matter because they are not chiral carbon atoms. In other words, any arrangement of atoms or groups attached to these carbon atoms is the same as any other arrangement.

Some important monosaccharides

D-Glyceraldehyde

The simplest carbohydrate is the three-carbon sugar **D-glyceraldehyde** (Figure 11.4). D-glyceraldehyde is a triose (three-carbon) and an aldose (aldehyde group at the top); therefore it is an aldotriose. First, note that this structure is drawn with the most oxidized carbon, the aldehyde, at the ''top.'' The most oxidized carbon is always placed at the top when the structures of open-chain carbohydrates are written; this carbon is numbered C-1. C-2 of D-glyceraldehyde is covalently bonded to four different groups. As we have just discussed, such a carbon is chiral. Reflection of D-glyceraldehyde in a mirror gives L-glyceraldehyde.

By convention it is the position of the hydroxyl group on the chiral carbon farthest from the carbonyl group (farthest from the oxidized end) that determines whether a monosaccharide is in the D- or L- configuration. If the —OH group is on the right (reader's right), the molecule is in its D-configuration. If the —OH group is on the left, the molecule is in its L-configuration. Almost all carbohydrates in living systems are members of the D-family.

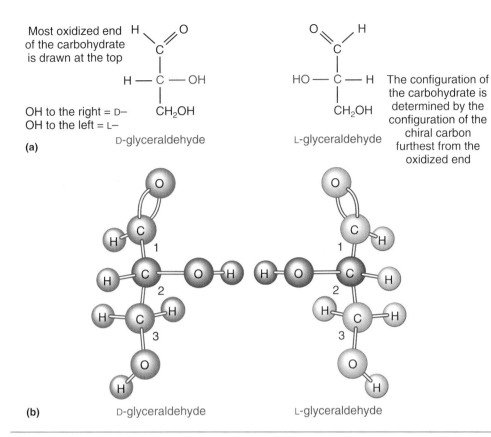

Most oxidized end of the carbohydrate is drawn at the top

OH to the right = D–
OH to the left = L–

(a)

D-glyceraldehyde   L-glyceraldehyde

The configuration of the carbohydrate is determined by the configuration of the chiral carbon furthest from the oxidized end

(b)   D-glyceraldehyde   L-glyceraldehyde

FIGURE 11.4
(a) Fischer Projection of D- and L-glyceraldehyde. (b) A three-dimensional representation of D- and L-glyceraldehyde.

D-Glyceraldehyde   D-Glucose   D-Fructose

QUESTION 11.5

Indicate whether each of the following molecules is an aldose or a ketose:

a. ketose

$$CH_3$$
$$C=O$$
$$H-C-OH$$
$$CH_2OH$$

D-

b. aldose

$$H$$
$$C=O$$
$$H-C-OH$$
$$H-C-OH$$
$$HO-C-H$$
$$CH_2OH$$

L-

c. ketose

$$CH_2OH$$
$$C=O$$
$$HO-C-H$$
$$H-C-OH$$
$$H-C-OH$$
$$CH_2OH$$

D-

d. aldose

$$H$$
$$C=O$$
$$H-C-OH$$
$$CH_2OH$$

D-

e. ketose

$$CH_3$$
$$C=O$$
$$H-C-OH$$
$$H-C-OH$$
$$H-C-OH$$
$$CH_2OH$$

D-

f. aldose

$$H$$
$$C=O$$
$$HO-C-H$$
$$H-C-OH$$
$$HO-C-H$$
$$CH_2OH$$

L-

QUESTION 11.6

Determine the configuration (D- or L-) for each of the molecules in Question 11.5.

Glucose

Glucose is the most important sugar in the human body. It is found in numerous foods and has several common names, including dextrose, grape sugar, and blood sugar.

The amount of glucose in the blood is critical to normal body function. As a result, the concentration is carefully controlled by the hormones insulin and glucagon. Normal blood glucose levels are 100–120 mg/100 mL, with the highest concentrations appearing after a meal. Insulin stimulates the uptake of the excess glucose by most cells of the body, and after 1–2 hr, levels return to normal. If blood glucose concentrations drop too low, the individual feels lightheaded and shaky. When this happens, glucagon stimulates the liver to release glucose into the blood, reestablishing normal levels. We will take a closer look at this delicate balancing act in Section 18.6.

The molecular formula of glucose, an aldohexose, is $C_6H_{12}O_6$. The Fischer projection structure of glucose is seen in Figure 11.5, and the method used to draw this structure is described in the following example.

EXAMPLE 11.1

Drawing the Fisher Projection Structure of a Monosaccharide

Draw the Fisher projection structure for D-glucose.

Solution

Glucose is an aldohexose.

Step 1: Draw six carbons in a straight vertical line; each carbon is separated from the ones above and below it by a bond:

$$
\begin{array}{c}
1\ C \\
| \\
2\ C \\
| \\
3\ C \\
| \\
4\ C \\
| \\
5\ C \\
| \\
6\ C
\end{array}
$$

FIGURE 11.5
Cyclization of glucose to give α- and β-D-glucose. Note that the carbonyl carbon (C-1) becomes chiral in this process, yielding the two forms of glucose named above.

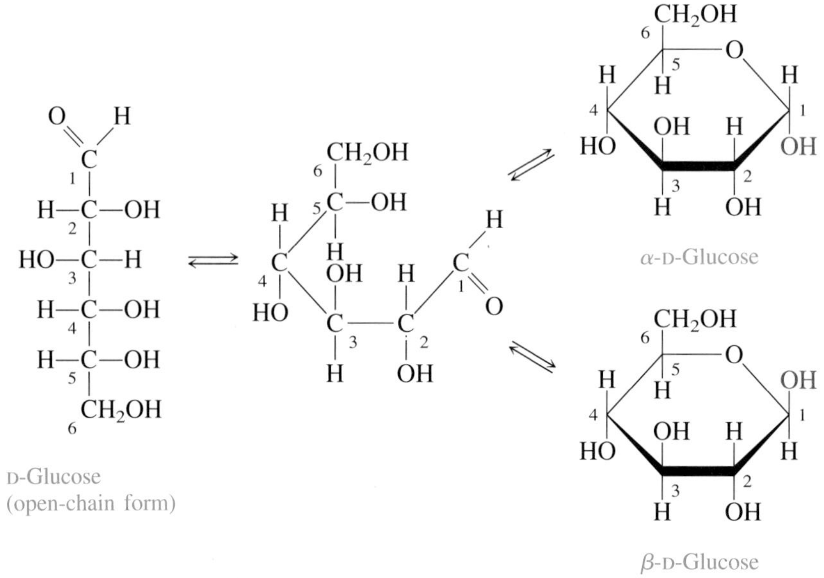

D-Glucose
(open-chain form)

α-D-Glucose

β-D-Glucose

Step 2: The most highly oxidized carbon is, by convention, drawn on the uppermost carbon (carbon 1). In this case, carbon 1 is an aldehyde carbon:

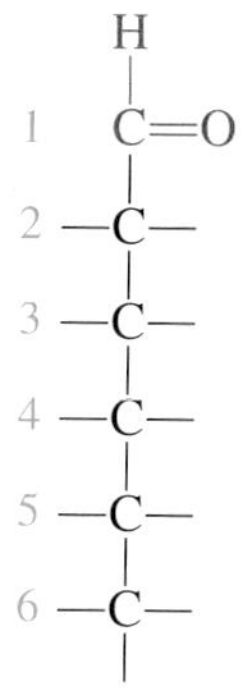

$$
\begin{array}{cl}
& H \\
& | \\
1 & C{=}O \quad \text{Most oxidized end of} \\
& | \qquad\quad \text{carbon chain; aldehyde} \\
2 & -C- \\
& | \\
3 & -C- \\
& | \\
4 & -C- \\
& | \\
5 & -C- \\
& | \\
6 & -C- \\
& |
\end{array}
$$

Step 3: The atoms are added to the next to the last carbon atom, at the bottom of the chain, to give either the D- or L-configuration as desired. Remember, when the —OH group is to the right, you have D-glucose, and when it is to the left, you have L-glucose. When in doubt, compare your structure to D-glyceraldehyde!

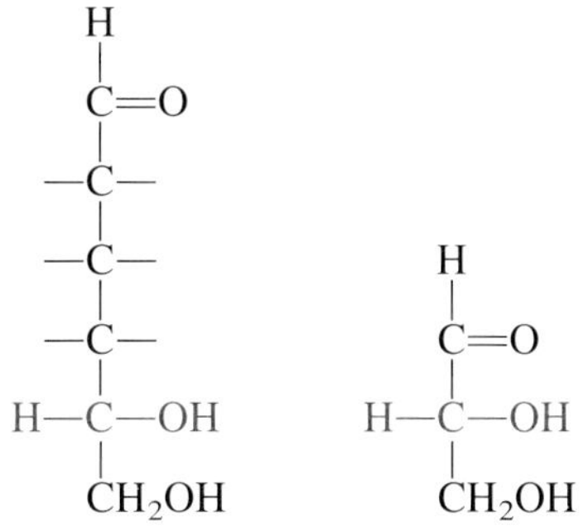

$$
\begin{array}{cc}
H & \\
| & \\
C{=}O & \\
| & H \\
-C- & | \\
| & C{=}O \\
-C- & | \\
| & H-C-OH \\
-C- & | \\
| & CH_2OH \\
H-C-OH & \\
| & \\
CH_2OH &
\end{array}
$$

Compare chiral carbons farthest from the carbonyl group

D-Isomer   D-Glyceraldehyde

Step 4: All the remaining atoms are then added to give the desired carbohydrate. For example, one would draw the following structure for D-glucose:

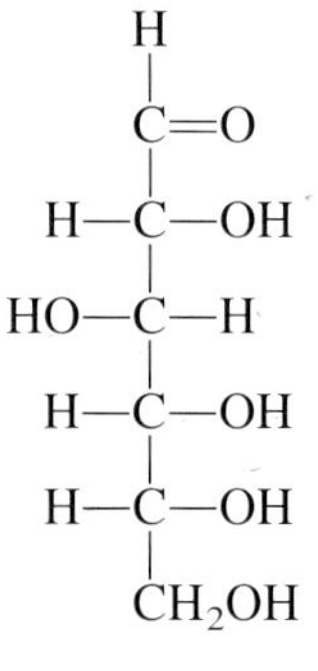

$$
\begin{array}{c}
H \\
| \\
C{=}O \\
| \\
H-C-OH \\
| \\
HO-C-H \\
| \\
H-C-OH \\
| \\
H-C-OH \\
| \\
CH_2OH
\end{array}
$$

D-Glucose

The positions for the hydrogen atoms and the hydroxyl groups on the remaining carbons must be looked up. For instance, the complete structures of D-fructose and D-galactose are seen in Figures 11.7 and 11.8.

In actuality the open-chain form of glucose is present in very small concentrations in cells. It exists in cyclic form under physiological conditions because the carbonyl group at C-1 of glucose reacts with the hydroxyl group at C-5 to give a six-membered ring. In the discussion of

Section 10.5

The term *intramolecular* tells us that the reacting carbonyl and hydroxyl groups are part of the same molecule.

aldehydes, we noted that the reaction between an aldehyde and an alcohol yields a **hemiacetal.** When the aldehyde portion of the glucose molecule reacts with the C-5 hydroxyl group, the product is a cyclic *intramolecular hemiacetal.* For D-glucose, two isomers can be formed in this reaction (Figure 11.5). These isomers are called α- and β-D-glucose. Two isomers are formed because the cyclization reaction creates a new chiral carbon, in this case C-1. In the α isomers the C-1 hydroxyl group is below the ring, and in the β isomers the C-1 hydroxyl group is above the ring.

In Figure 11.5 a new type of structural formula, called a **Haworth projection,** is presented. Although on first inspection it appears complicated, it is quite simple to derive a Haworth projection from a Fischer projection, as the following example shows.

EXAMPLE 11.2

Drawing the Haworth Projections of Monosaccharides from the Fisher Projections

Draw the Haworth projections of α- and β-D-glucose from the Fisher projections.

Solution

1. Before attempting to draw a Haworth projection, look at the cyclic structures in Figure 11.5. Try to imagine that you are seeing the ring in three dimensions. Some of the substituent groups on the molecule are above the ring, and some are beneath it. The question then becomes: How do we determine which groups to place above the ring and which to place beneath the ring?

2. Look at the two-dimensional Fischer structure. Note the groups (drawn in blue) to the left of the carbon chain. These are placed above the ring in the Haworth projection.

```
      H—C—OH                      HO—C—H
       | 1                          | 1
      H—C—OH                      H—C—OH
       | 2                          | 2
     HO—C—H        O             HO—C—H        O
       | 3                          | 3
      H—C—OH                      H—C—OH
       | 4                          | 4
  HO—CH₂—C—H                  HO—CH₂—C—H
      6   | 5                     6   | 5

   α-D-Glucose                   β-D-Glucose
```

3. Now note the groups (drawn in red) to the right of the carbon chain. These will be located beneath the carbon ring in the Haworth projection.

```
      H—C—OH                      HO—C—H
       | 1                          | 1
      H—C—OH                      H—C—OH
       | 2                          | 2
     HO—C—H        O             HO—C—H        O
       | 3                          | 3
      H—C—OH                      H—C—OH
       | 4                          | 4
  HO—CH₂—C—H                  HO—CH₂—C—H
      6   | 5                     6   | 5

   α-D-Glucose                   β-D-Glucose
```

There is a simple trick for remembering the difference between α- and β-cyclic sugars. By rearranging the letters of beta we get β = "beat (beta) up." If the group is "up" in the β-form, it must be "down" in the α-form.

4. Thus in the Haworth projection of the cyclic form of any D-sugar the —CH₂OH group is always "up." When the —OH group at C-1 is also "up," *cis* to the —CH₂OH group, the sugar is β-D-glucose. When the —OH group at C-1 is "down," *trans* to the —CH₂OH group, the sugar is α-D-glucose.

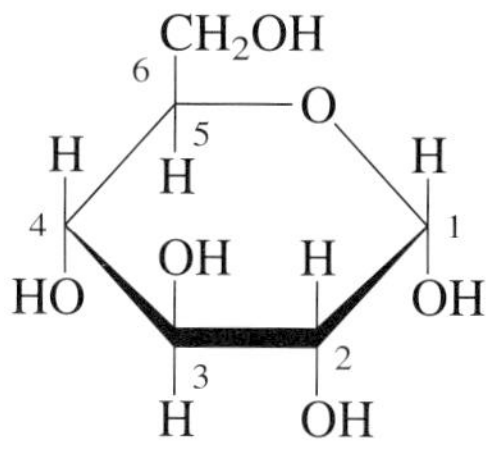

α-D-Glucose 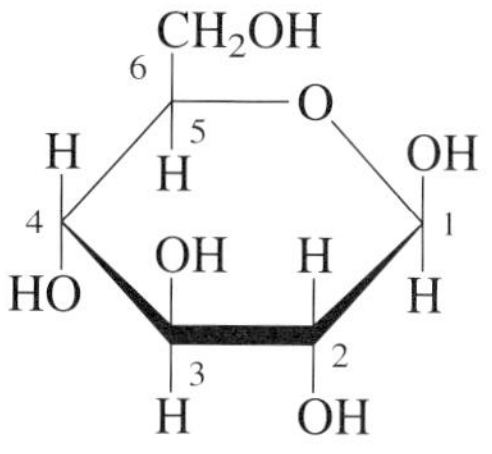   β-D-Glucose

---

QUESTION 11.7

Refer to the linear Fisher structure of D-galactose in Figure 11.7. Draw the Haworth projections of α- and β-D-galactose.

QUESTION 11.8

Refer to the linear Fisher structure of D-ribose in Figure 11.8. Draw the Haworth projections of α- and β-D-ribose.

D-Fructose

Fructose

Fructose, also called levulose and fruit sugar, is the sweetest of all sugars. It is found in large amounts in honey, corn syrup, and sweet fruits. The structure of fructose is similar to that of glucose. When there is a —CH$_2$OH group instead of a —CHO group at carbon-1 and a —C=O group instead of CHOH at carbon-2, the sugar is a ketose. In this case it is D-fructose.

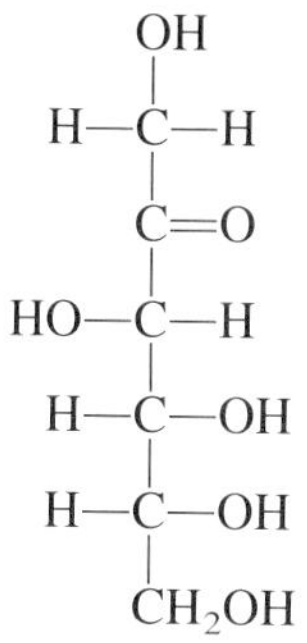

Cyclization of fructose produces α- and β-D-fructose (Figure 11.6). Fructose is a ketose, or ketone sugar. Recall that the reaction between an alcohol and a ketone yields a **hemiketal.** Thus the reaction between the C-2 keto group and the C-5 hydroxyl group in the fructose molecule produces an *intramolecular hemiketal.* Fructose forms a five-membered ring structure.

Section 10.5

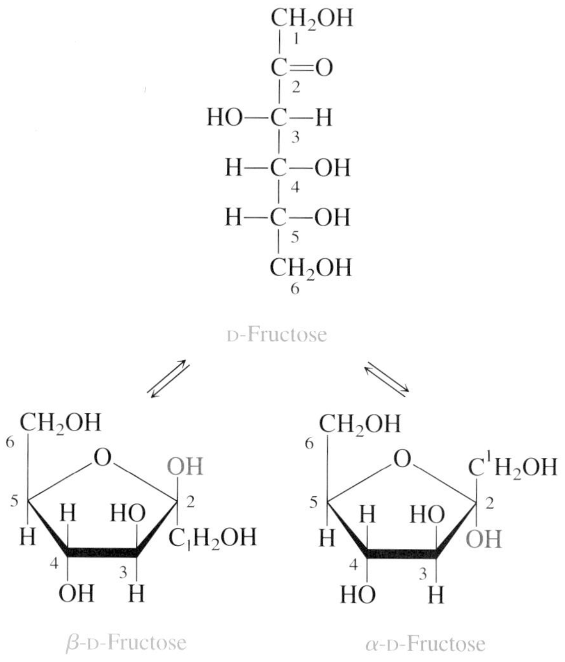

D-Fructose

β-D-Fructose   α-D-Fructose

FIGURE 11.6
Cyclization of D-fructose to give α- and β-D-fructose.

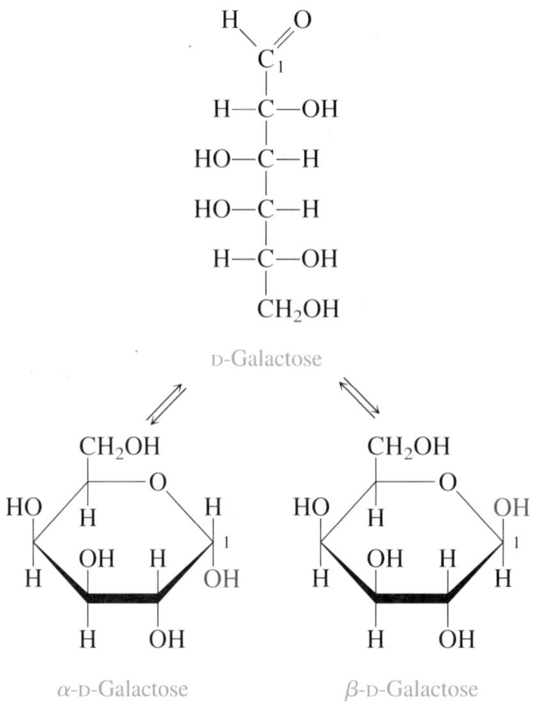

FIGURE 11.7
Cyclization of D-galactose to
α- and β-D-galactose.

Section 11.3

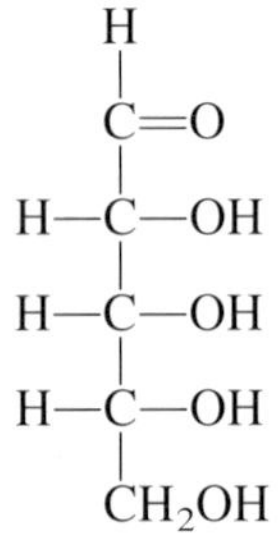

D-Ribose

Reducing sugars

Galactose

Another important hexose is **galactose.** The Fisher structure of D-galactose and the Haworth projections of α-D-galactose and β-D-galactose are shown in Figure 11.7. Galactose is found in biological systems as a component of the disaccharide lactose, or milk sugar. This is the principal sugar found in the milk of all mammals. β-D-Galactose and a modified form, N-acetyl-β-D-galactosamine, are also components of the blood group antigens.

Ribose and deoxyribose, five-carbon sugars

Ribose is a component of many biologically important molecules, including RNA, and various coenzymes, a group of compounds required by many of the enzymes that carry out biochemical reactions in the body. The structure of the five-carbon sugar D-ribose is shown in its open-chain form here and in the α- and β-cyclic isomer forms in Figure 11.8.

DNA, the molecule that carries the genetic information of the cell, contains 2-deoxyribose (Figure 11.9). In this molecule the —OH group at C-2 has been replaced by a hydrogen, hence the designation "2-deoxy."

The aldehyde group of aldoses is readily oxidized by the Benedict's reagent. Recall that the **Benedict's reagent** is a basic buffer solution that contains Cu^{2+} ions. The Cu^{2+} ions are reduced to Cu^{+} ions, which, in basic solution, precipitate as brick-red Cu_2O. The aldehyde of the aldose is converted to a carboxylate anion:

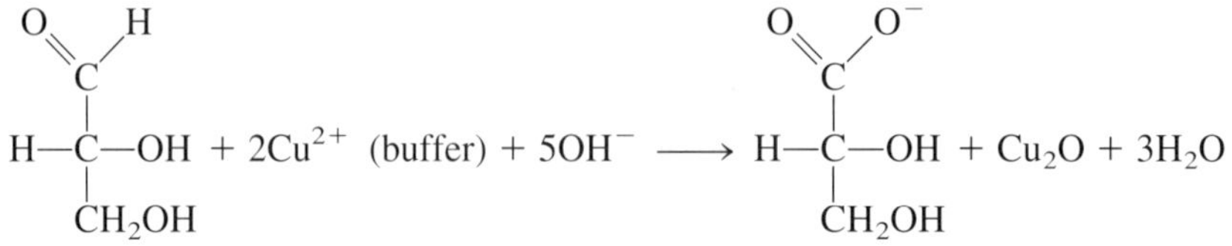

Although most ketones are not easily oxidized, ketoses are an exception to that rule. Because of the —OH groups on the carbon next to the carbonyl group, ketoses can be converted to aldoses and thus are also **reducing sugars.** In fact, all monosaccharides and all the common disaccharides, except sucrose, are reducing sugars.

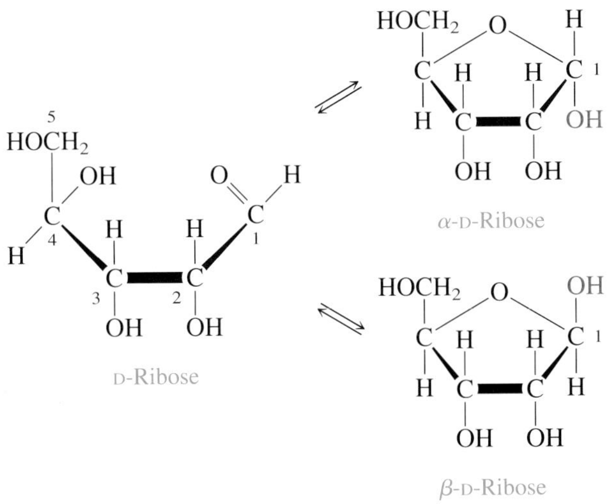

FIGURE 11.8
Cyclization of D-ribose to α- and β-D-ribose.

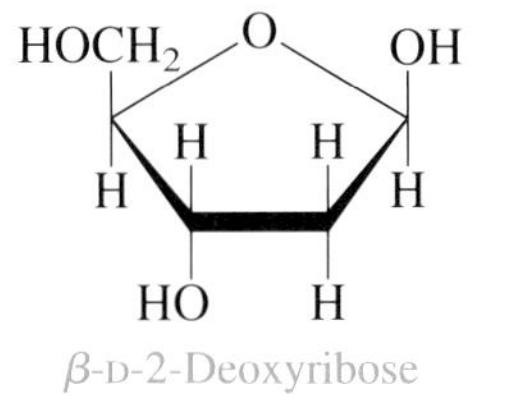

FIGURE 11.9
Structure of β-D-2-deoxyribose.

The Benedict's reagent is used to test for *glucosuria,* the presence of excess glucose in the urine. Individuals suffering from *Type I insulin-dependent diabetes mellitus* do not produce the hormone insulin, which controls the uptake of glucose from the blood. When the blood glucose level rises above 160 mg/100 mL, the kidney is unable to reabsorb the excess, and glucose is found in the urine. Although the level of blood glucose can be controlled by the injection of insulin, urine glucose levels must be monitored to ensure that the amount of insulin injected is correct. The Benedict's reagent is a useful tool because the amount of Cu_2O formed, and hence the degree of color change in the reaction, is directly proportional to the amount of reducing sugar in the urine. A brick-red color indicates a very high concentration of glucose in the urine. Yellow, green, and blue-green solutions indicate decreasing amounts of glucose in the urine, and a blue solution indicates an insignificant concentration.

See "A Clinical Perspective: Diabetes Mellitus and Ketone Bodies" in Chapter 18.

11.3 OLIGOSACCHARIDES

Recall that **oligosaccharides** are formed by joining two to ten monosaccharides. The most common oligosaccharides are **disaccharides,** which consist of two monosaccharides joined by bonds through an "oxygen bridge." Examples of these bonds, called glycosidic bonds, are seen in Figures 11.10 (maltose), 11.12 (lactose), and 11.13 (sucrose).

A glycosidic bond is formed in the reaction between the C-1 hydroxyl group of one cyclic monosaccharide and any hydroxyl group of another sugar. We have seen that these cyclic sugars are actually hemiacetals or hemiketals. Recall that when a hemiacetal reacts with an alcohol, the product is an *acetal,* and when a hemiketal reacts with an alcohol, the product is a *ketal.* In the case of disaccharides the alcohol comes from a second monosaccharide. The acetals or ketals formed are given the general name *glycosides,* and the carbon-oxygen bonds are called **glycosidic bonds.**

Section 10.5

If an α-D-glucose and a second glucose are linked, as shown in Figure 11.10, the disaccharide is **maltose,** or malt sugar. This is one of the intermediates in the hydrolysis of starch. Since the C-1 hydroxyl group of α-D-glucose is attached to C-4 of another glucose molecule, the disaccharide is linked by an $\alpha(1 \rightarrow 4)$ glycosidic bond.

Maltose is a reducing sugar. Any disaccharide that has a hemiacetal hydroxyl group (a free —OH group at C-1) is a reducing sugar. This is because the cyclic structure can open at this position to form a free aldehyde. Disaccharides that do not contain a hemiacetal group on C-1 do not react with the Benedict's reagent and are called **nonreducing sugars.**

Maltose
Section 11.4

Milk sugar, or **lactose,** is a disaccharide made up of one molecule of β-D-galactose and one of either α- or β-D-glucose. Galactose differs from glucose only in the configuration of the hydroxyl group at C-4 (Figure 11.11). In the cyclic form of glucose the C-4 hydroxyl group is

Lactose

A HUMAN PERSPECTIVE

Blood Transfusions and the Blood Group Antigens

The first blood transfusions were tried in the seventeenth century, when physicians used animal blood to replace human blood lost by hemorrhages. Unfortunately, many people died as a result of this attempted cure, and transfusions were banned in much of Europe. Transfusions from human donors were somewhat less lethal, but violent reactions often led to the death of the recipient, and by the nineteenth century, transfusions had been abandoned as a medical failure.

In 1904, Dr. Karl Landsteiner performed a series of experiments on the blood of workers in his laboratory. His results explained the mysterious transfusion fatalities, and blood transfusions were reinstated as a life-saving clinical tool. Landsteiner took blood samples from his co-workers. He separated the blood cells from the serum, the liquid component of the blood, and mixed these samples in test tubes. When he mixed serum from one individual with blood cells of another, Landsteiner observed that, in some instances, the serum samples caused clumping, or *agglutination,* of red blood cells (RBC). The agglutination reaction always indicated that the two bloods were incompatible and transfusion could lead to life-threatening reactions. As a result of many such experiments, Landsteiner showed that there are four human blood groups, designated A, B, AB, and O.

We now know that differences among blood groups reflect differences among oligosaccharides attached to the proteins and lipids of the RBC membranes. The oligosaccharides on the RBC surface have a common core, as shown in the accompanying figure, consisting of N-acetylglucosamine, galactose, N-acetylneuraminic acid (sialic acid), and L-fucose. It is the terminal monosaccharide of this oligosaccharide that distinguishes the cells of different blood types and governs the compatibility of the blood types.

The A blood group antigen has β-D-N-acetylgalactosamine

at its end, whereas the B blood group antigen has α-D-galactose. In type O blood, neither of these sugars is found on the cell surface; only the core oligosaccharide is present. Some of the oligosaccharides on type AB blood cells have a terminal β-D-N-acetylgalactosamine, while others have a terminal α-D-galactose.

Why does agglutination occur? The clumping reaction that occurs when incompatible bloods are mixed is an antigen-antibody reaction. Antigens are large molecules, often portions of bacteria or viruses, that stimulate the immune defenses of the body to produce protective antibodies. Antibodies bind to the foreign antigens and help to destroy them.

People with type A blood also have antibodies against type B blood (anti-B antibodies) in the blood serum. If the person with type A blood receives a transfusion of type B blood, the anti-B antibodies bind to the type B blood cells, causing clumping and destruction of those cells that can result in death. Individuals with type B blood also produce anti-A antibodies and therefore cannot receive a transfusion from a type A individual. Those with type AB blood are considered to be *universal recipients* because they have neither anti-A nor anti-B antibodies in their blood. (If they did, they would destroy their own red blood cells!) Thus in emergency situations a patient with type AB blood can receive blood from an individual of any blood type without serious transfusion reactions. Type O blood has no A or B antigens on the RBC but has both anti-A and anti-B antibodies. Because of the presence of both types of antibodies, type O individuals can receive transfusions only from a person who is also type O. On the other hand, the absence of A and B antigens on the red blood cell surface means that type O blood can be safely transfused into patients of any blood type. Hence type O individuals are *universal donors.*

"down," and in galactose it is "up." In lactose the C-1 hydroxyl group of β-D-galactose is bonded to the C-4 hydroxyl group of β-D-glucose. The bond between the two monosaccharides is therefore a $\beta(1 \rightarrow 4)$ glycosidic bond (Figure 11.12).

Lactose is the principal sugar in mammalian milk. To be used by the body as an energy source, lactose must be hydrolyzed to produce glucose and galactose. Note that this is simply the

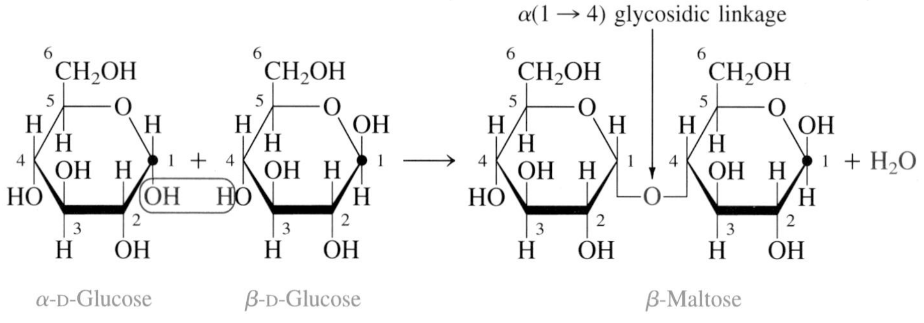

FIGURE 11.10

Glycosidic bond formed between the C-1 hydroxyl group of α-D-glucose and the C-4 hydroxyl group of β-D-glucose. The disaccharide is called β-maltose because the hydroxyl group at the reducing end of the disaccharide has the β-configuration.

α-D-Glucose   β-D-Glucose   β-Maltose

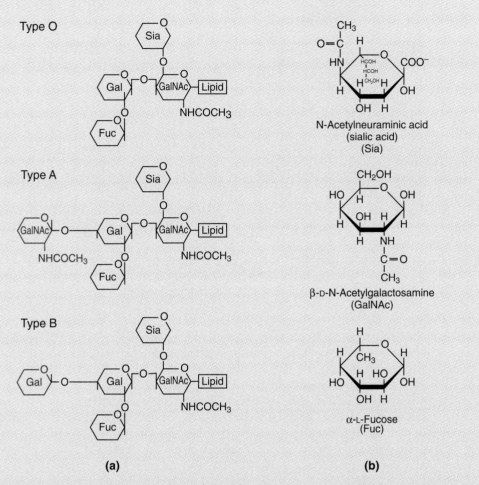

(a)   **(b)**

Schematic diagram of the blood group oligosaccharides. (a) Only the core oligosaccharide is found on the surface of type O red blood cells. On type A red blood cells, β-D-N-acetylgalactosamine is linked to the galactose (Gal) moiety of the core oligosaccharide. On type B red blood cells, a galactose molecule is found attached to the galactose of the core oligosaccharide. (b) The structures of some of the unusual monosaccharides found in the blood group oligosaccharides.

reverse of the reaction shown in Figure 11.12. Glucose liberated by the hydrolysis of galactose is used directly in the energy-harvesting reactions of glycolysis. However, a series of reactions is necessary to convert galactose into a phosphorylated form of glucose that can be used in cellular metabolic reactions. In humans the genetic disease **galactosemia** is caused by the absence of one or more of the enzymes needed for this conversion. A toxic compound formed from galactose accumulates in people who suffer from galactosemia. If the condition is not treated, galactose-

Chapter 16

β-D-Glucose   β-D-Galactose

FIGURE 11.11
Comparison of the cyclic forms of glucose and galactose. Note that galactose is identical to glucose except in the position of the C-4 hydroxyl group.

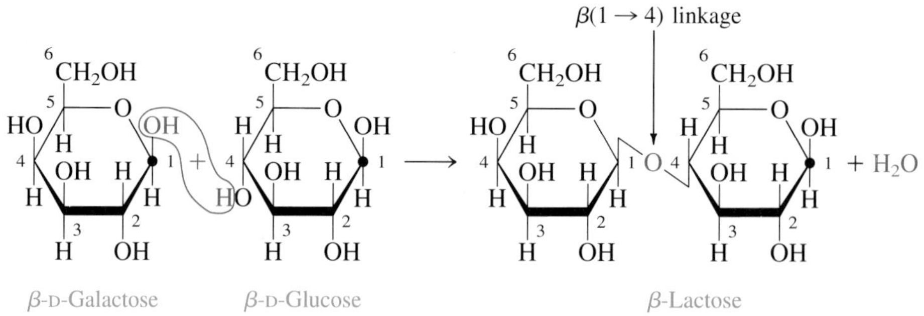

FIGURE 11.12
Glycosidic bond formed between the C-1 hydroxyl group of β-D-galactose and the C-4 hydroxyl group of β-D-glucose. The disaccharide is called β-lactose because the hydroxyl group at the reducing end of the disaccharide has the β-configuration.

β-D-Galactose β-D-Glucose β-Lactose

mia leads to severe mental retardation, cataracts, and early death. However, the effects of this disease can be avoided entirely by providing galactosemic infants with a diet that does not contain galactose. Such a diet, of course, cannot contain lactose and therefore must contain no milk or milk products.

Many adults, and some children, are unable to hydrolyze lactose because they do not make the enzyme *lactase*. This condition is known as **lactose intolerance.** Undigested lactose remains in the intestinal tract and causes cramping and diarrhea that can eventually lead to dehydration. Some of the lactose is metabolized by intestinal bacteria that release organic acids and CO_2 gas into the intestines, causing further discomfort. Lactose intolerance is unpleasant, but its effects can be avoided by a diet that excludes milk and milk products.

Sucrose

Many sugars are not sweet, but **sucrose,** also called cane sugar or beet sugar, is a conspicuous and important exception. Sucrose is an important carbohydrate in plants. It is water-soluble and can easily be transported through the circulatory system of the plant. It cannot be synthesized by animals. High concentrations of sucrose inhibit the growth of microorganisms, so it is used as a preservative. Of course, it is also widely used as a sweetener. In fact, it is estimated that the average American consumes 86 pounds of sucrose each year. It has been suggested that sucrose in the diet is undesirable because it represents a source of empty calories, that is, it contains no vitamins or minerals. However, the only negative association that has been scientifically verified is the link between sucrose in the diet and dental caries, or cavities (see ''A Human Perspective: Tooth Decay and Simple Sugars.'')

Sucrose is a disaccharide of α-D-glucose joined to β-D-fructose (Figure 11.13). The glycosidic linkage between α-D-glucose and β-D-fructose is quite different from those that we have examined for lactose and maltose. Both of the carbons that were previously part of a hemiacetal or a hemiketal have reacted to form this linkage. Such a bond is called an α,β glycosidic linkage, in this case involving the C-1 of glucose and the C-2 of fructose (noted in red in Figure 11.13). As a result, the ring structure cannot open up, and no aldehyde or ketone group can be formed. Therefore sucrose will not react with the Benedict's reagent and is not a reducing sugar.

FIGURE 11.13
Glycosidic bond formed between the C-1 hydroxyl of α-D-glucose and the C-2 hydroxyl of β-D-fructose. This bond is called an α,β glycosidic linkage. The disaccharide formed in this reaction is sucrose.

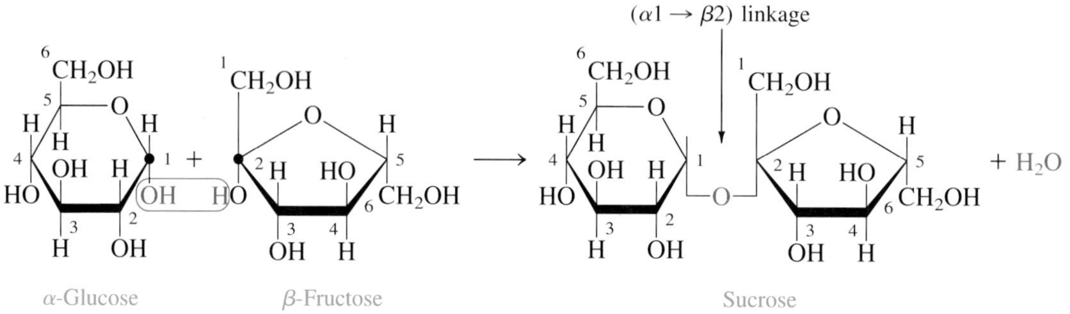

α-Glucose β-Fructose Sucrose

Most carbohydrates that are found in nature are large polymers of glucose. Thus a polysaccharide is a large molecule composed of many monosaccharide units (the monomers) joined in one or more chains.

As seen in Figure 11.1, plants have the ability to use the energy of sunlight to produce monosaccharides, principally glucose, from CO_2 and H_2O. Although sucrose is the major transport form of sugar in the plant, starch (a polysaccharide) is the principal storage form in most plants. These plants store glucose in starch granules. Nearly all plant cells contain some starch granules, but in some seeds, such as corn, as much as 80% of the cell's dry weight is starch.

Starch is a heterogeneous material composed of the glucose polymers **amylose** and **amylopectin.** Amylose, which accounts for about 80% of the starch of a plant cell, is a linear polymer of α-D-glucose molecules connected by glycosidic bonds between C-1 and C-4. Thus, the glucose units in amylose are joined by $\alpha(1 \rightarrow 4)$ glycosidic bonds. A single chain can contain up to 4000 glucose units. Amylose coils up into a helix that repeats every six glucose units. The structure of amylose is found in Figure 11.14.

Amylose is degraded by two types of enzymes. These are produced in the pancreas, from which they are secreted into the small intestines, and the salivary glands, from which they are secreted into the saliva. α-*Amylase* cleaves the glycosidic bonds of amylose chains at random along the chain, producing shorter polysaccharide chains. The enzyme β-*amylase* sequentially cleaves dimers of glucose, maltose, from the reducing end of the amylose chain. The maltose is hydrolyzed into glucose by the enzyme *maltase*. The glucose is quickly absorbed by intestinal cells and used by the cells of the body as a source of energy.

Amylopectin is a highly branched amylose in which the branches are attached to the C-6 hydroxyl groups by $\alpha(1 \rightarrow 6)$ glycosidic bonds (see Figure 11.15). The main chain consists of $\alpha(1 \rightarrow 4)$ glycosidic bonds. Each branch contains 20–25 glucose units, and there are so many branches that the main chain can scarcely be distinguished.

11.4 POLYSACCHARIDES

Starch

A polymer is a large molecule made up of many small units, the monomers, held together by chemical bonds. See A Human Perspective: Carboxylic Acid Derivatives of Special Interest in Chapter 12.

Enzymes are proteins that serve as biological catalysts. They speed up biochemical reactions so that life processes can function.

Section 11.3

FIGURE 11.14
Structure of amylose. (a) A linear chain of α-D-glucose joined in $\alpha(1 \rightarrow 4)$ glycosidic linkage makes up the primary structure of amylose. (b) Owing to hydrogen bonding, the amylose chain forms a left-handed helix that contains six glucose units per turn.

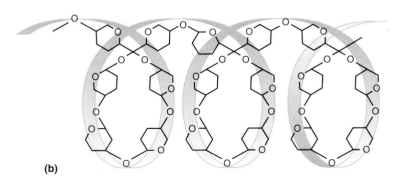

A HUMAN PERSPECTIVE

Tooth Decay and Simple Sugars

How many times have you heard the lecture from parents or your dentist about brushing your teeth after a sugary snack? Annoying as this lecture might be, it is based on sound scientific data that demonstrate that the cause of tooth decay is plaque and acid formed by the bacterium *Streptococcus mutans* using sucrose as its substrate.

Saliva is teeming with bacteria in concentrations up to one hundred million (10^8) per milliliter of saliva! Within minutes after you brush your teeth, sticky glycoproteins in the saliva adhere to tooth surfaces. Then millions of oral bacteria immediately bind to this surface.

Although all oral bacteria adhere to the tooth surface, only *S. mutans* causes dental caries, or cavities. Why does this bacterium cause cavities when all the others do not? The answer lies in a special enzyme called *glucosyl transferase* that is found on the surface of *S. mutans* cells.

Glucosyl transferase is a very specific enzyme. It can act only on the disaccharide sucrose, which it breaks down into glucose and fructose. As the accompanying diagram shows, the enzyme then adds the glucose to a growing polysaccharide chain called *dextran* that adheres tightly to both the tooth enamel and the bacteria. *Plaque* is made up of huge masses of bacteria, embedded in dextran, adhering to the tooth surface.

This is just the first stage of cavity formation. Note in the accompanying figure that the second sugar released by the cleavage of sucrose is fructose. The bacteria utilize the fructose in the energy-harvesting pathways of glycolysis and lactic acid fermentation. Production of lactic acid decreases the pH on the tooth surface and begins to dissolve calcium from the tooth enamel.

Why is the acid not washed away from the tooth surface? After all, we produce about one liter of saliva each day, which should dilute the acid and remove it from the tooth surface. The problem is the dextran plaque; it is not permeable to saliva, and thus plaque keeps the bacteria and the lactic acid localized on the enamel.

What measures can we take to prevent tooth decay? Practice good oral hygiene; brushing after each meal and flossing regularly reduces plaque buildup. Eat a diet rich in calcium; this helps to build strong tooth enamel. Include many complex carbohydrates in the diet; these cannot be used by glucosyl transferase and will not lead to the formation of acid. Further, the complex carbohydrates from fruits and vegetables help prevent decay by mechanically removing plaque from tooth surfaces. Avoid sucrose-containing snacks between meals. Studies have shown that the consumption of a sucrose-rich dessert with a meal, followed by brushing, does not produce many cavities. However, even small amounts of sugar ingested between meals are very cariogenic.

Researchers have developed a vaccine that prevents tooth decay in rats. Such a vaccine may one day be available for human beings.

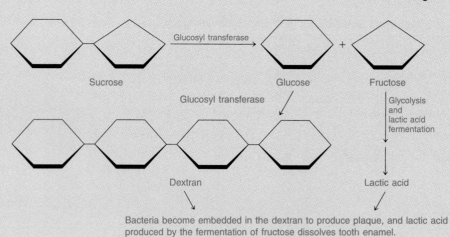

Bacteria become embedded in the dextran to produce plaque, and lactic acid produced by the fermentation of fructose dissolves tooth enamel.

Action of the glucosyl transferase of *Streptococcus mutans*, which is responsible for tooth decay.

Glycogen

Glycogen is the major glucose storage molecule of animals. The structure of glycogen is similar to that of amylopectin. The ''main chain'' is linked by $\alpha(1 \rightarrow 4)$ glycosidic bonds, and it has numerous $\alpha(1 \rightarrow 6)$ glycosidic bonds, which provide many branch points along the chain. Glycogen differs from amylopectin only by having more and shorter branches. Otherwise, the two molecules are virtually identical. The structure of glycogen is shown in Figure 11.16.

Glycogen is stored in the liver and skeletal muscle. Glycogen synthesis and degradation in the liver are carefully regulated. As we will see in Section 18.6, these two processes are intimately involved in keeping blood glucose levels constant.

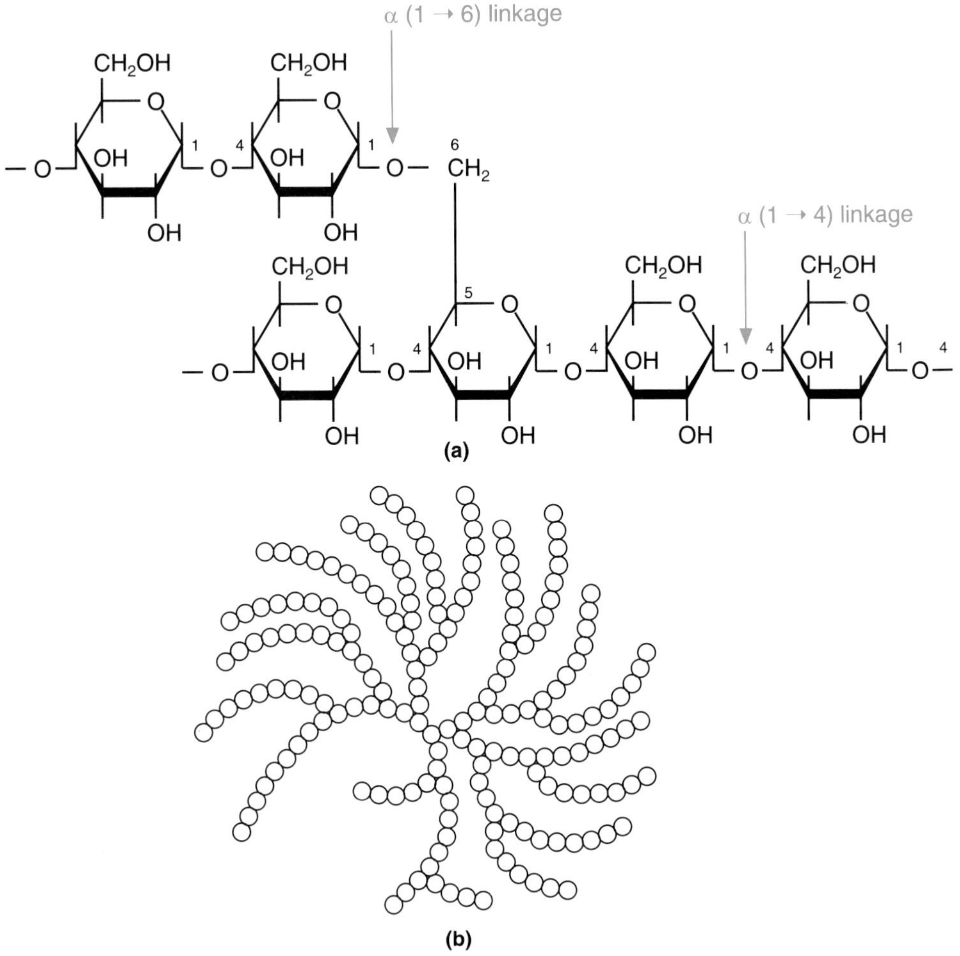

(a)

(b)

FIGURE 11.15
Structure of amylopectin.
(a) Amylopectin consists of branched chains of amylose. Branching in amylopectin occurs by $\alpha(1 \rightarrow 6)$ glycosidic bonds between glucose units. The main chain is bonded $\alpha(1 \rightarrow 4)$. (b) A representation of the branched-chain structure of amylopectin. Each circle represents a glucose molecule.

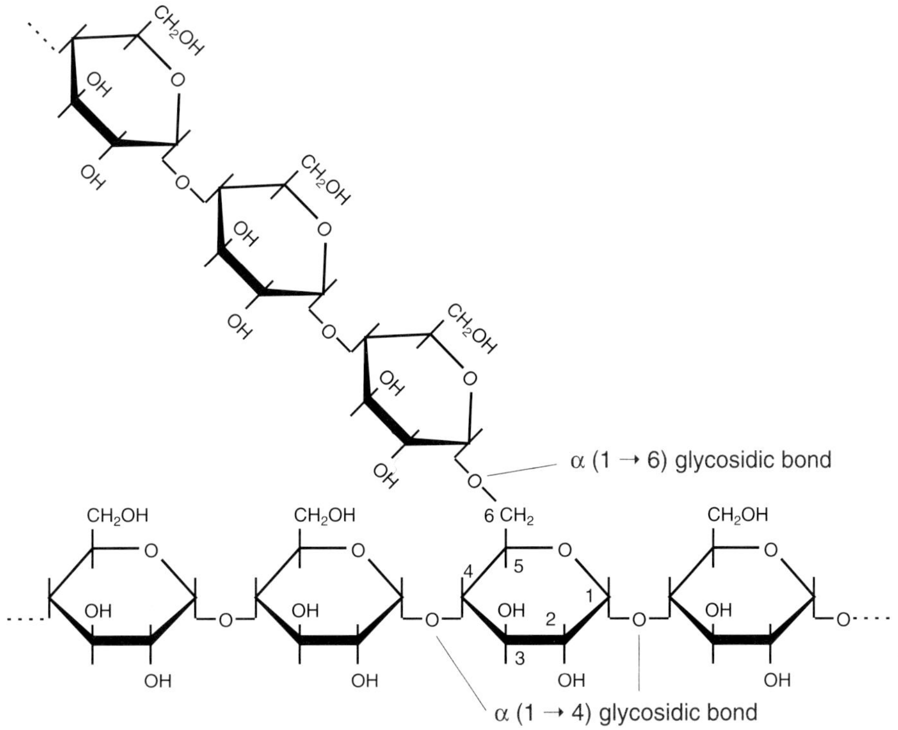

FIGURE 11.16
The structure of glycogen.

A CLINICAL PERSPECTIVE

The Bacterial Cell Wall

The major component of bacterial cell walls is a complex polysaccharide known as a *peptidoglycan*. The name tells us that this structure consists of sugar molecules (-glycan) and peptides (peptido-; short polymers of amino acids).

As the accompanying structure shows, the carbohydrate portion of the peptidoglycan is a polymer of alternating units of two modified glucose molecules called *N-acetylglucosamine* and *N-acetylmuramic acid*. These two unusual monosaccharides are joined by a $\beta(1 \rightarrow 4)$ glycosidic bond. In addition, each N-acetylmuramic acid is bonded to a tetrapeptide, a chain of four amino acids.

The structural strength of the cell wall is a result of penta-

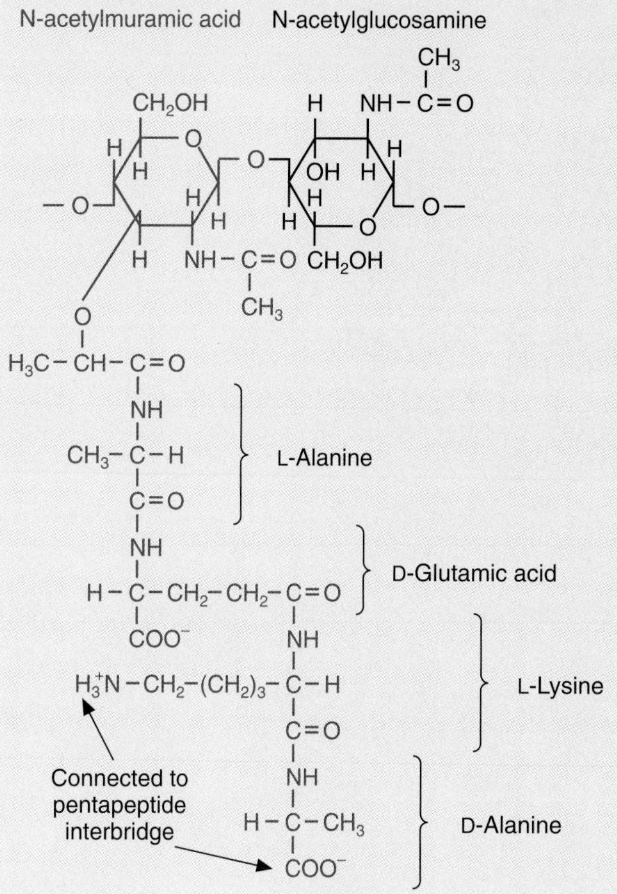

N-acetylmuramic acid   N-acetylglucosamine

(c)

Structures of N-acetylglucosamine and N-acetylmuramic acid in $\beta(1 \rightarrow 4)$ glycosidic linkage. Note the tetrapeptide bridge linked to the N-acetylmuramic acid.

Cellulose

The most abundant polysaccharide, indeed the most abundant organic molecule in the world, is **cellulose,** a polymer of β-D-glucose units linked by $\beta(1 \rightarrow 4)$ glycosidic bonds (Figure 11.17). A molecule of cellulose typically contains about 3000 glucose units, but the largest known cellulose, produced by the alga *Valonia*, contains 26,000 glucose molecules.

Cellulose is a structural component of the plant cell wall. The unbranched structure of the cellulose polymer and the $\beta(1 \rightarrow 4)$ glycosidic linkages allow cellulose molecules to form long, straight chains of parallel cellulose molecules called *fibrils*. These fibrils are quite rigid; thus it is not surprising that cellulose is a cell wall structural element.

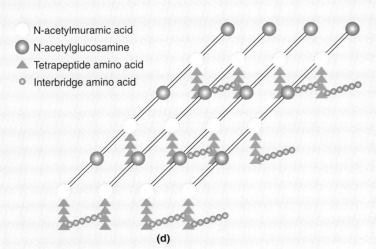

- ○ N-acetylmuramic acid
- ◉ N-acetylglucosamine
- ▲ Tetrapeptide amino acid
- ◎ Interbridge amino acid

(d)

The three-dimensional structure of one layer of peptidoglycan.

peptide cross-bridges that link the repeat units to one another (see the figure below). Millions of such cross-linkages produce an enormous peptidoglycan molecule, dozens of layers thick, around the bacterium. This thick wall is very rigid. It allows the bacterium to maintain its shape and protects it from bursting if the salt concentration of the environment is too low (hypotonic conditions).

Our bodies are constantly being assaulted by a variety of bacteria, and as you might expect, we have evolved protective mechanisms to minimize the damage. For instance, the enzyme *lysozyme,* found in tears and saliva, catalyzes the hydrolysis of the $\beta(1 \rightarrow 4)$ glycosidic bonds of peptidoglycan. As the accompanying figure shows, the enzyme has a deep groove on the surface (the active site) that a six-sugar unit of the cell wall can slip into like a bank card into the slot of an automatic teller machine. Lysozyme then catalyzes bond breakage and destroys the cell wall of the bacterium.

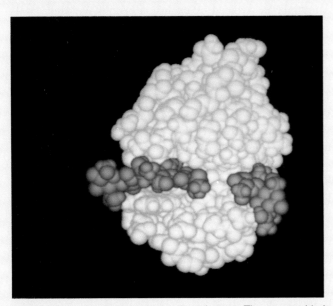

Conformation of lysozyme bound to its substrate. The enzyme binds with a six-sugar portion of the bacterial cell wall and cleaves it. The substrate fits into a deep crevice on the surface of the enzyme.

Penicillin G

The penicillins are antibiotics that interfere with bacterial cell wall synthesis. The human body has no structures similar to the bacterial cell wall, so treatment with penicillins selectively destroys the bacteria, causing no harm to the patient. In practice, however, it must always be remembered that some individuals may develop an allergy to penicillins.

The penicillins inhibit the enzyme that catalyzes the formation of the cross-linkage between the tetrapeptides. The antibiotic binds irreversibly to the active site of that enzyme so that it cannot bind to the tetrapeptide tail. Thus no cross-linkage can be made. Without the rigid, highly cross-linked peptidoglycan, the bacterial cells rupture and die.

FIGURE 11.17
The structure of cellulose.

In contrast to glycogen, amylose, and amylopectin, cellulose *cannot* be digested by humans. The reason for this is that we cannot synthesize the enzyme *cellulase,* which can hydrolyze the $\beta(1 \rightarrow 4)$ glycosidic linkages of the cellulose polymer. Indeed, only a few animals, such as termites, cows, and goats, are able to digest cellulose. These animals have, within their digestive tracts, microorganisms that produce the enzyme cellulase. The sugars released by this microbial digestion can then be absorbed and used by these animals.

QUESTION 11.9

What chemical reactions are catalyzed by α-amylase and β-amylase?

QUESTION 11.10

Why are humans unable to digest cellulose?

SUMMARY

Carbohydrates are found in a wide variety of naturally occurring substances and serve as principal energy sources for the body. Dietary carbohydrates include complex carbohydrates, such as starch in potatoes, and simple carbohydrates, such as sucrose.

Types of Carbohydrates

Carbohydrates are classified as *monosaccharides* (one sugar unit), *oligosaccharides* (two to ten sugar units), or *polysaccharides* (many sugar units).

Monosaccharides

Monosaccharides that have an aldehyde as their most oxidized functional group are *aldoses,* and those having a ketone group as their most oxidized functional group are *ketoses.* They may be classified as *trioses, tetroses, pentoses,* and so forth, depending on the number of carbon atoms in the carbohydrate.

Stereoisomers of monosaccharides exist, because of the presence of *chiral* carbon atoms. They are classified as D- or L- depending on the arrangement of the atoms on the chiral carbon farthest from the aldehyde or ketone group. In the *Fischer projections,* if the —OH on this carbon is to the right, the stereoisomer is of the D-family. If the —OH group is to the left, the stereoisomer is of the L-family.

Important monosaccharides include *glyceraldehyde, glucose, fructose,* and *ribose.* Monosaccharides containing five- or six-carbon atoms can exist as five-membered or six-membered rings. Formation of a ring produces a new chiral carbon at the original carbonyl carbon, which is designated either α or β depending on the orientation of the groups. The cyclization of an aldose produces an intramolecular *hemiacetal,* and the cyclization of a ketose yields an intramolecular *hemiketal.*

Reducing sugars are oxidized by the *Benedict's reagent.* All monosaccharides and all common disaccharides, except sucrose, are reducing sugars. The Benedict's reagent can be used to determine the concentration of glucose in urine.

Oligosaccharides

Important oligosaccharides include *lactose* and *sucrose.* Lactose is a disaccharide of β-D-galactose bonded $(1 \rightarrow 4)$ with D-glucose. In *galactosemia,* defective metabolism of galactose leads to accumulation of a toxic by-product. The ill effects of galactosemia are avoided by exclusion of milk and milk products from the diet of affected infants. Sucrose is a dimer of α-D-glucose bonded $(1 \rightarrow 2)$ with β-D-fructose.

Polysaccharides

Starch, the storage polysaccharides of plant cells, is composed of approximately 80% amylose and 20% amylopectin. *Amylose* is a polymer of α-D-glucose residues bonded $\alpha(1 \rightarrow 4)$. Amylose forms a helix. *Amylopectin* has many branches. Its main chain consists of α-D-glucose units bonded $(1 \rightarrow 4)$. The branches are connected by $\alpha(1 \rightarrow 6)$ glycosidic bonds.

Glycogen, the major storage polysaccharide of animal cells, resembles amylopectin, but it has more, shorter branches. The liver reserve of glycogen is used to regulate blood glucose levels.

Cellulose is the major structural molecule of plants. It is a $\beta(1 \rightarrow 4)$ polymer of D-glucose that can contain thousands of glucose monomers. Cellulose cannot be digested by animals because they do not produce an enzyme capable of cleaving the $\beta(1 \rightarrow 4)$ glycosidic linkage.

KEY TERMS

aldose (11.2)	fructose (11.2)
amylopectin (11.4)	galactose (11.2)
amylose (11.4)	galactosemia (11.3)
asymmetric carbon (11.2)	glucose (11.2)
Benedict's reagent (11.2)	glyceraldehyde (11.2)
cellulose (11.4)	glycogen (11.4)
chiral (11.2)	glycosidic bond (11.1, 11.3)
disaccharide (11.1, 11.3)	Haworth projections (11.2)
enantiomers (11.2)	hemiacetal (11.2)
Fischer projection (11.2)	hemiketal (11.2)

hexose (11.2)
ketose (11.2)
lactose (11.3)
lactose intolerance (11.3)
maltose (11.3)
monosaccharide (11.1, 11.2)
nonreducing sugar (11.3)
oligosaccharide (11.1, 11.3)
pentose (11.2)

polysaccharide (11.1, 11.4)
reducing sugar (11.2)
ribose (11.2)
saccharide (11.1)
stereochemistry (11.2)
stereoisomers (11.2)
sucrose (11.3)
tetrose (11.2)
triose (11.2)

QUESTIONS AND PROBLEMS

Types of Carbohydrates

11.11 What is the difference between a monosaccharide and a disaccharide?

11.12 What is a polysaccharide?

Monosaccharides

11.13 Identify each of the following sugars, and label each as either a hemiacetal or a hemiketal.

a.

c.

b.

11.14 Draw the open-chain form of the sugars in Problem 11.13.

11.15 Draw all of the different possible aldotrioses of molecular formula $C_3H_6O_3$.

11.16 Draw all of the different possible aldotetroses of molecular formula $C_4H_8O_4$.

11.17 Is there any difference between dextrose and D-glucose?

11.18 The structure of D-glucose is provided below. Draw its mirror image.

```
        H
        |
        C=O
        |
   H—C—OH
        |
  HO—C—H
        |
   H—C—OH
        |
   H—C—OH
        |
      CH2OH
```

11.19 How are D- and L-glyceraldehyde related?

11.20 Determine whether each of the following is a D- or L-sugar:

a.
```
        O
        ‖
        CH
        |
   H——OH
        |
   H——OH
        |
      CH2OH
```

b.
```
        O
        ‖
        CH
        |
   H——OH
        |
   H——OH
        |
  HO——H
        |
      CH2OH
```

c.
```
        O
        ‖
        CH
        |
  HO——H
        |
   H——OH
        |
  HO——H
        |
      CH2OH
```

d.
```
        O
        ‖
        CH
        |
   H——OH
        |
  HO——H
        |
   H——OH
        |
      CH2OH
```

11.21 Why does cyclization of D-glucose give two isomers, α- and β-D-glucose?

11.22 Draw the structure of the open chain form of D-fructose, and show how it cyclizes to form α- and β-D-fructose.

11.23 Which of the following would give a positive Benedict's Test?
  a. Sucrose
  b. Glycogen
  c. β-Maltose
  d. α-Lactose

11.24 Why is the Benedict's reagent useful for determining the amount of glucose in the urine?

Oligosaccharides

11.25 Maltose is a disaccharide isolated from amylose that consists of two glucose units linked α(1 → 4). Draw the structure of this molecule.

11.26 Sucrose is a disaccharide formed by linking α-D-glucose and β-D-fructose by a 1 → 2 bond. Draw the structure of this disaccharide. (*Hint:* Refer to Figure 11.13.)

11.27 What is the major biological source of lactose?

11.28 What metabolic defect causes galactosemia?

11.29 What simple treatment prevents most of the ill effects of galactosemia?

11.30 What are the major physiological effects of galactosemia?

Polysaccharides

11.31 What is the difference between the structure of cellulose and the structure of amylose?

11.32 How does the structure of amylose differ from that of amylopectin and glycogen?

11.33 What is the major physiological purpose of glycogen?

11.34 Where in the body do you find glycogen stores?

Further Problems

11.35 Read the labels on some of the foods in your kitchen, and see how many products you can find that list one or more carbohydrates among the ingredients in the package. Make a list of these compounds, and attempt to classify them according to parent structure (for example, monosaccharides, oligosaccharides, polysaccharides).

11.36 Some oligosaccharides are often referred to by their common names. What are the chemical names of (a) milk sugar, (b) beet sugar, and (c) cane sugar?

11.37 How many kilocalories of energy are released when one gram of carbohydrate is "burned" or oxidized?

11.38 List some natural sources of carbohydrates.

11.39 Draw and provide the names of an aldohexose and a ketohexose.

11.40 Draw and provide the name of an aldotriose.

11.41 Describe what is meant by a pair of enantiomers. Draw an example of a pair of enantiomers.

11.42 What is a chiral carbon atom?

11.43 Where are α-amylase and β-amylase produced?

11.44 Where do α-amylase and β-amylase carry out their enzymatic functions?

11.45 When discussing sugars, what is meant by an intramolecular hemiacetal?

11.46 When discussing sugars, what is meant by an intramolecular hemiketal?

11.47 What is lactose intolerance?

11.48 What is the difference between lactose intolerance and galactosemia?

VOCABULARY QUIZ

11.1 _____ is a human genetic disease caused by the inability to convert galactose into a phosphorylated form of glucose that can be used in cellular metabolic reactions.

11.2 A two-dimensional formula used to represent the three-dimensional structure of a molecule is a(n) _____.

11.3 A carbon atom bonded to four different chemical groups is called a(n) _____ or a(n) _____ carbon.

11.4 Two stereoisomers that are nonsuperimposable mirror images are called _____.

11.5 _____ is the glucose storage polymer found in the liver and muscle of animals.

11.6 The condition of _____ is characterized by higher than normal blood glucose levels.

11.7 _____ are a means of representing the orientation of substituent groups around a cyclic sugar molecule.

11.8 A sugar that can be oxidized by the Benedict's reagent is a(n) _____.

11.9 The study of the spatial arrangement of atoms in a molecule is _____.

11.10 The general term for a five-carbon sugar that is an aldehyde is _____.

12

Carboxylic Acids and Carboxylic Acid Derivatives

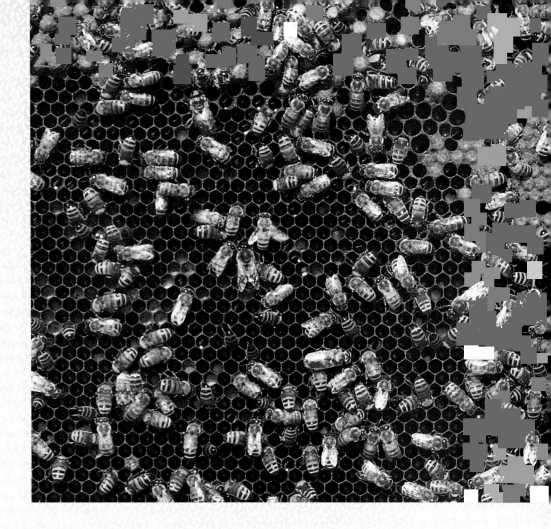

LEARNING GOALS

◆ Know the carboxylic acids and esters that are of natural, medical, or environmental importance

◆ Draw and name the common carboxylic acids and esters

◆ Write equations for the hydrolysis of esters

◆ Write equations for the synthesis of a carboxylic acid by the oxidation of primary alcohols or aldehydes

◆ Write equations for the synthesis of esters from carboxylic acids and alcohols

◆ Define the term *saponification* and know how a soap works in the emulsification of grease and oils

◆ Understand the significance of thioesters and phosphoesters in biological systems

CHEMISTRY CONNECTION

Wake Up, Sleeping Gene

A common carboxylic acid, butyric acid, holds the promise of being an effective treatment for two age-old human genetic diseases. Sickle cell anemia and β-thalassemia are human genetic diseases of the β-globin portion of hemoglobin, the protein that carries oxygen from the lungs to tissues throughout the body. Normal hemoglobin consists of two α-globin proteins, two β-globin proteins, and four heme groups. In sickle cell anemia the faulty β-globin gene calls for the synthesis of a sticky form of hemoglobin that forms long polymers. This distorts the red blood cells into elongated, sickled shapes that get stuck in capillaries and can't provide the oxygen needed by the tissues. In β-thalassemia there may be no β-globin produced at all. This results in short-lived red blood cells and severe anemia.

These two genetic diseases do not affect the fetus because before birth and for several weeks after birth, a fetal globin is made, rather than the adult β-globin. Fetal hemoglobin has a stronger affinity for oxygen than the adult form, ensuring that the fetus gets enough oxygen from the mother's blood through the placenta.

Two observations have led to a possible treatment of these diseases. First, physicians found some sickle cell anemia patients who suffered only mild symptoms because they continued to make high levels of fetal hemoglobin. Second was the observation that some babies born to diabetic mothers continued to produce fetal hemoglobin for an unusually long time after birth. Coincidentally, there was an unexpectedly high concentration of aminobutyric acid, a modified carboxylic acid, in the blood of these infants.

Susan Perrine of the Children's Hospital Oakland Research Center decided to try to reawaken the dormant fetal globin gene. She and her colleagues injected a sodium butyrate solution (the sodium salt of butyric acid) into three sickle cell patients and three β-thalassemia patients. As a result of the 2- to 3-week treatment, fetal hemoglobin production was boosted as much as 45% in these individuals. One β-thalassemia patient even experienced a complete reversal of the symptoms. Moreover, this treatment had few adverse side-effects.

Longer studies with larger numbers of patients will be needed before this treatment can be declared a total success. However, Perrine's results hold the promise of a full and active life for individuals who were previously limited in activity and expected a short life span.

In this chapter we study the properties and reactions of the carboxylic acids; their salts, such as the sodium butyrate used to treat hemoglobin disorders; and their derivatives, the esters. We will focus on the importance of these molecules in biological systems, medicine, and the food industry.

INTRODUCTION

Carboxylic acids have the following general structure:

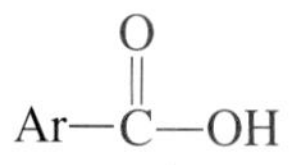

Aromatic carboxylic acid 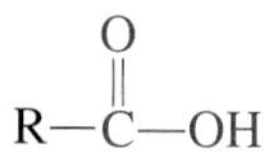 | Aliphatic carboxylic acid

They are characterized by the carboxyl group, shown in red in the structure above. It may also be written in condensed form as —COOH or —CO₂H. The name "carboxylic acid" describes this family of compounds quite well. The term "carboxylic" is taken from the terms "carbonyl" and "hydroxyl," the two structural units that make up the carboxyl group. The word "acid" in the name tells us one of the more important properties of these molecules: They dissociate in water to release protons. Thus they are acids.

In this chapter we will also study the esters, which have the following general structure:

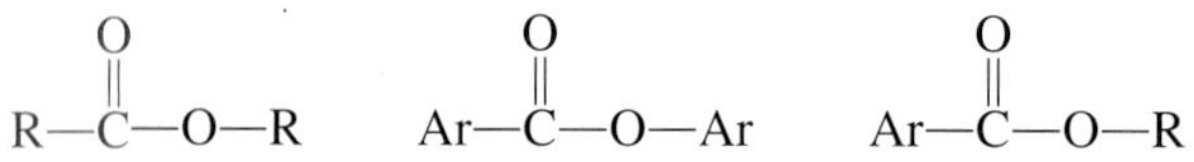

Examples of aliphatic and aromatic esters

The group shown in red in the structures above is called the **acyl group.** The acyl group is part of the functional group of the carboxylic acid derivatives, including the esters and amides.

Chapter 14

The **carboxyl group** consists of two very polar functional groups, the carbonyl group and the hydroxyl group. Thus **carboxylic acids** are very polar compounds. In addition, they can hydrogen bond to one another and to molecules of a polar solvent such as water. As a result of intermolecular hydrogen bonding, they boil at higher temperatures than aldehydes, ketones, or alcohols of comparable molecular weight.

As with alcohols, the smaller carboxylic acids are soluble in water (see Figure 12.1). However, solubility falls off dramatically as the carbon content of the carboxylic acid increases because the molecules become more hydrocarbonlike and less polar. For example, acetic acid (the carboxylic acid found in vinegar) is completely soluble in water, while hexadecanoic acid (a 16-carbon carboxylic acid found in palm oil) is insoluble in water.

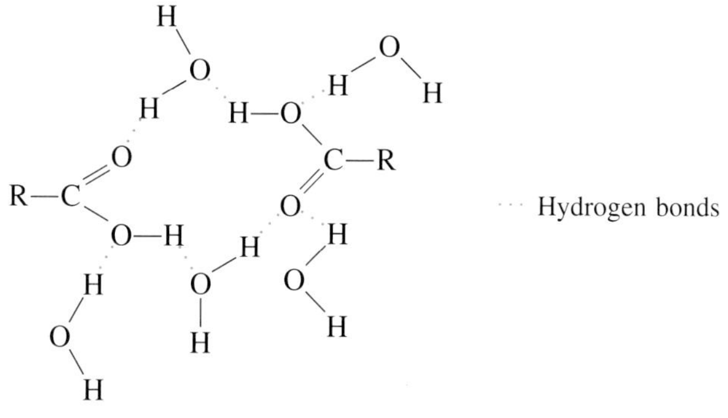

The lower-molecular-weight carboxylic acids have sharp, sour tastes and unpleasant aromas. Formic acid, HCOOH, is used as a chemical defense by ants and causes the burning sensation of the ant bite. Acetic acid, CH_3COOH, is found in vinegar; propionic acid, CH_3CH_2COOH, is responsible for the tangy flavor of Swiss cheese; and butyric acid, $CH_3CH_2CH_2COOH$, causes the stench associated with rancid butter and gas gangrene.

The longer-chain carboxylic acids are generally called **fatty acids** and are important components of biological membranes and triglycerides, the major lipid storage form in the body.

12.1 CARBOXYLIC ACIDS

Structure and physical properties

Long-chain carboxylic acids, such as hexadecanoic acid (palmitic acid), are generally called *fatty acids*. They are found in fats and oils of both plant and animal origin. These will be discussed in Chapter 13.

QUESTION 12.1

Which member of each of the following pairs has the lower boiling point?

a. Hexanoic acid or 3-hexanone

b. 3-Hexanone or 3-hexanol

c. 3-Hexanol or hexane

d. Dipropyl ether or hexanal

e. Hexanal or hexanoic acid

QUESTION 12.2

The functional group is largely responsible for the physical and chemical properties of the various chemical families. Why would one predict that a carboxylic acid would be more polar and have a higher boiling point than an alcohol of comparable molecular weight?

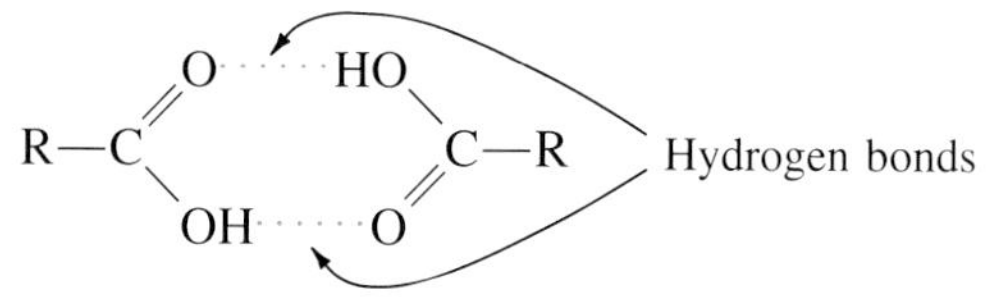

FIGURE 12.1
Hydrogen bonding (a) in carboxylic acids and (b) between carboxylic acids and water.

Nomenclature

In the I.U.P.A.C. System, carboxylic acids are named according to the following set of rules:

◆ Determine the parent compound, the longest continuous carbon chain bearing the carboxyl group.

◆ Replace the *-e* ending of the parent alkane with the suffix *-oic acid*. If there are two carboxyl groups, the suffix *-dioic acid* is used.

◆ Number the chain so that the carboxyl carbon is carbon-1.

◆ Name and number substituents in the usual way.

The following examples illustrate the naming of carboxylic acids:

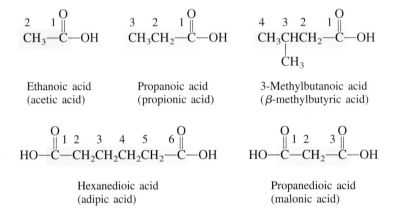

Ethanoic acid (acetic acid)	Propanoic acid (propionic acid)	3-Methylbutanoic acid (β-methylbutyric acid)

Hexanedioic acid
(adipic acid)

Propanedioic acid
(malonic acid)

EXAMPLE 12.1

Naming a Carboxylic Acid Using the I.U.P.A.C. Nomenclature System

Solution

$$\overset{\displaystyle O}{\underset{}{HO-\overset{1}{C}}}-\overset{2}{C}H\overset{3}{C}H_2\overset{4}{C}H\overset{5}{C}H_3$$
Br   CH₃

Parent compound: pentane (becomes pentanoic acid)
Position of —COOH: carbon-1 (Must be!)
Substituents: 2-bromo and 4-methyl
Name: 2-bromo-4-methylpentanoic acid

$$\overset{8}{C}H_3\overset{7}{C}H\overset{6}{C}H_2\overset{5}{C}H\overset{4}{C}H_2\overset{3}{C}H\overset{2}{C}H_2-\overset{1}{C}-OH$$
Br   Br   Br

Parent compound: octane (becomes octanoic acid)
Position of —COOH: carbon-1 (Must be!)
Substituents: 3,5,7-tribromo
Name: 3,5,7-tribromooctanoic acid

The carboxylic acid derivatives of cycloalkanes are named by adding the suffix *carboxylic acid* to the name of the cycloalkane or substituted cycloalkane. The carboxyl group is always on carbon-1 and other substituents are named and numbered as usual.

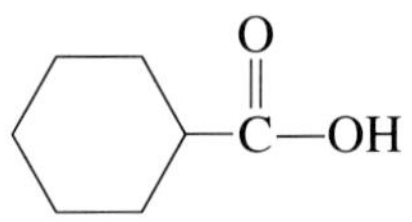

Cyclohexanecarboxylic
acid

QUESTION 12.3

Determine the I.U.P.A.C. name for each of the following structures:

a. 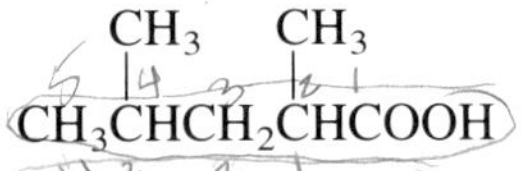 CH$_3$CHCH$_2$CHCOOH   *2,4-dimethylpentanoic acid*
   with CH$_3$, CH$_3$ groups

b. 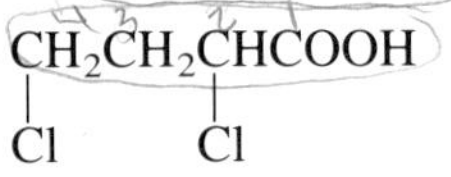 CH$_2$CH$_2$CHCOOH   *2,4-dichlorobutanoic acid*
   with Cl, Cl

c. 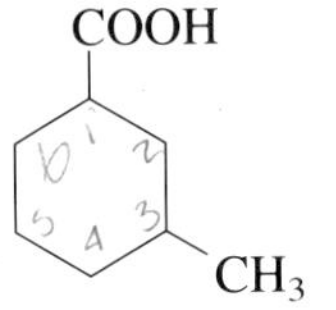 COOH ... CH$_3$ *3-methylcyclohexanecarboxylic acid*

d. 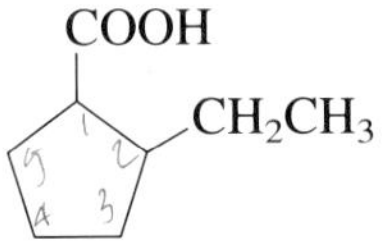 COOH ... CH$_2$CH$_3$ *2-ethylcyclopentanecarboxylic acid*

QUESTION 12.4

Write the structure for each of the following carboxylic acids:

a. 2,3-Dihydroxybutanoic acid
b. 2-Bromo-3-chloro-4-methylhexanoic acid
c. 1,4-Cyclohexanedicarboxylic acid
d. 4-Hydroxycyclohexanecarboxylic acid

As we have seen so often, the use of common names, rather than systematic names, still persists. Often these names have evolved from the source of a given compound. This is certainly true of the carboxylic acids. Table 12.1 shows the I.U.P.A.C. and common names of several carboxylic acids, as well as their sources and the Latin or Greek words that gave rise to the common names.

In the common system of nomenclature, substituted carboxylic acids are named as derivatives of the parent compound (Table 12.1). Greek letters are used to indicate the position of the substituent. The carbon atom bonded to the carboxyl group is the α-carbon, the next is the β-carbon, and so on.

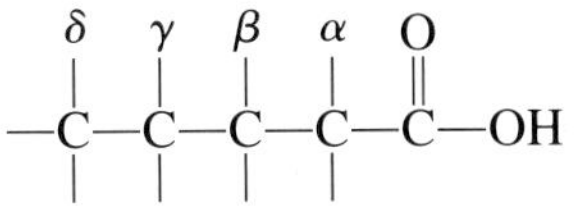

$$\overset{\delta}{-C}-\overset{\gamma}{C}-\overset{\beta}{C}-\overset{\alpha}{C}-\overset{O}{C}-OH$$

Some examples of common names are:

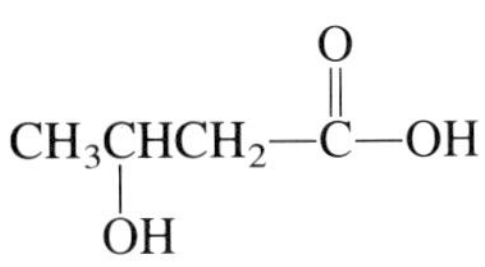

CH$_3$CHCH$_2$—C(=O)—OH   (OH)   CH$_3$CH—C(=O)—OH   (OH)

β-Hydroxybutryic acid 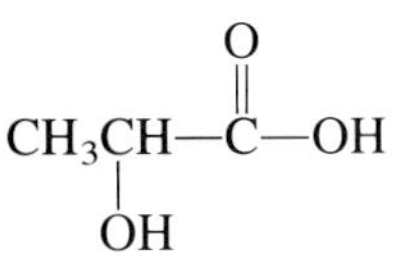 α-Hydroxypropionic acid

The aromatic carboxylic acids are usually named, in either system, as derivatives of benzoic acid. Generally, the -oic acid or -ic acid suffix is attached to the appropriate prefix. However, "common names" of substituted benzoic acids (for example, toluic acid and phthalic acid) are frequently used.

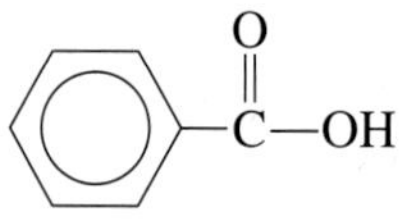

Benzoic acid 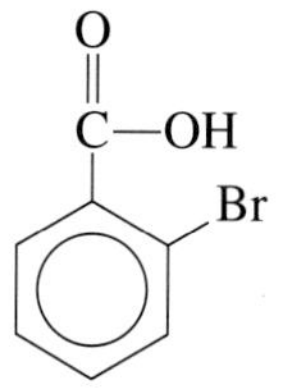   *o*-Bromobenzoic acid

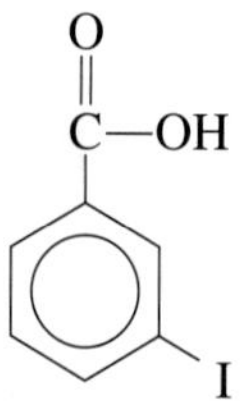

m-Iodobenzoic acid 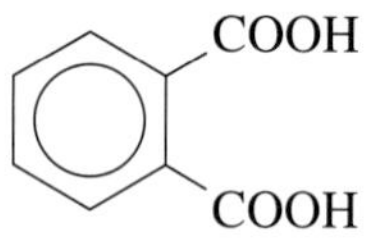   Phthalic acid

The phenyl group is benzene with one hydrogen removed.

Often the phenyl group is treated as a substituent, and the name is derived from the appropriate alkanoic acid parent chain. For example:

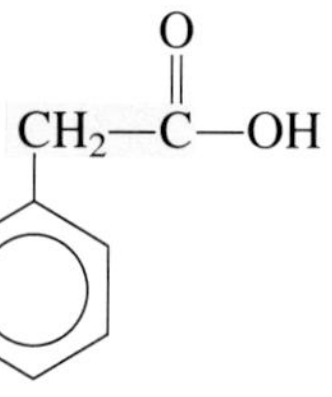

2-Phenylethanoic acid
(α-phenylacetic acid)

3-Phenylpropanoic acid 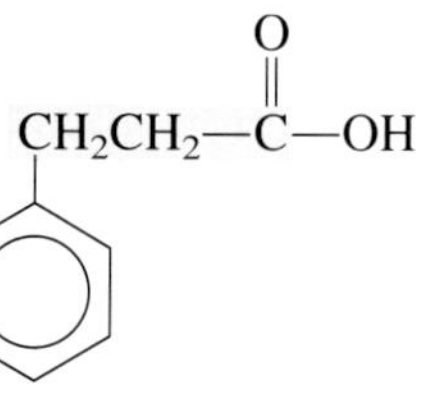
(β-phenylpropionic acid)

TABLE 12.1   Names and Sources of Some Common Carboxylic Acids

Name	Structure	Source	Root
Formic acid (methanoic acid)	HCOOH	Ants	L: *formica,* ant
Acetic acid (ethanoic acid)	CH_3COOH	Vinegar	L: *acetum,* vinegar
Propionic acid (propanoic acid)	CH_3CH_2COOH	Swiss cheese	Gk: *protos,* first *pion,* fat
Butyric acid (butanoic acid)	$CH_3(CH_2)_2COOH$	Rancid butter	L: *butyrum,* butter
Valeric acid (pentanoic acid)	$CH_3(CH_2)_3COOH$	Valerian root	
Caproic acid (hexanoic acid)	$CH_3(CH_2)_4COOH$	Goat fat	L: *caper,* goat
Caprylic acid (octanoic acid)	$CH_3(CH_2)_6COOH$	Goat fat	L: *caper,* goat
Capric acid (decanoic acid)	$CH_3(CH_2)_8COOH$	Goat fat	L: *caper,* goat
Palmitic acid (hexadecanoic acid)	$CH_3(CH_2)_{14}COOH$	Palm oil	
Stearic acid (octadecanoic acid)	$CH_3(CH_2)_{16}COOH$	Tallow (beef fat)	Gk: *stear,* tallow

QUESTION 12.5

Draw each of the following:

a. *o*-Toluic acid

b. 2,4,6-Tribromobenzoic acid

c. 2,2,2-Triphenylethanoic acid

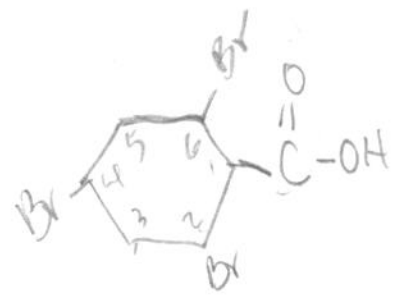

QUESTION 12.6

Draw each of the following:

a. *p*-Toluic acid

b. 3-Phenylhexanoic acid

c. 3-Phenylcyclohexanecarboxylic acid

Some important carboxylic acids

As seen in Table 12.1, many carboxylic acids occur in nature. Fatty acids can be isolated from a variety of sources including palm oil, coconut oil, butter, milk, lard, and tallow (beef fat). More complex carboxylic acids are also found in a variety of foodstuffs. For example, citric acid is found in citrus fruits and is often used to give the sharp taste to sour candies. It is also added to foods as a preservative and antioxidant. Adipic acid (hexanedioic acid) gives tartness to soft drinks and helps to retard spoilage.

Bacteria in milk produce lactic acid as a product of fermentation of sugars. Lactic acid contributes a tangy flavor to yogurt and buttermilk. It is also used as a food preservative to lower the pH to a level that retards microbial growth that causes food spoilage. Lactic acid is also produced in muscle cells when an individual is exercising strenuously. If the level of lactic acid in the muscle and bloodstream becomes high enough, the muscle can't continue to work.

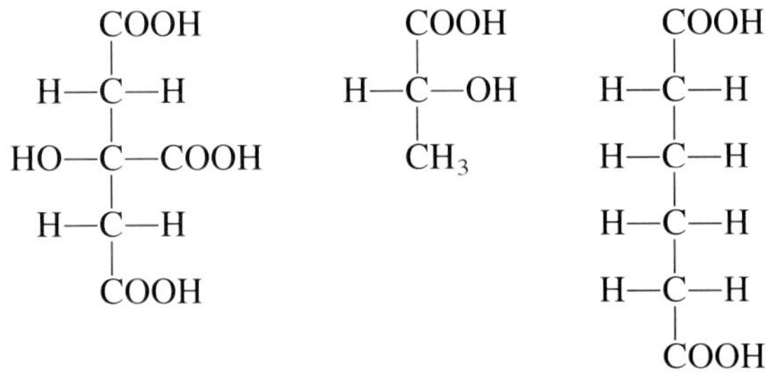

Citric acid
(*citrus fruit*)

Lactic acid
(*yogurt*)

Adipic acid
(*beet juice*)

Reactions involving carboxylic acids

Preparation of carboxylic acids

Many of the small carboxylic acids are prepared on a commercial scale. For example, ethanoic (acetic) acid, found in vinegar, is produced commercially by the **oxidation** of either ethanol or ethanal as shown here:

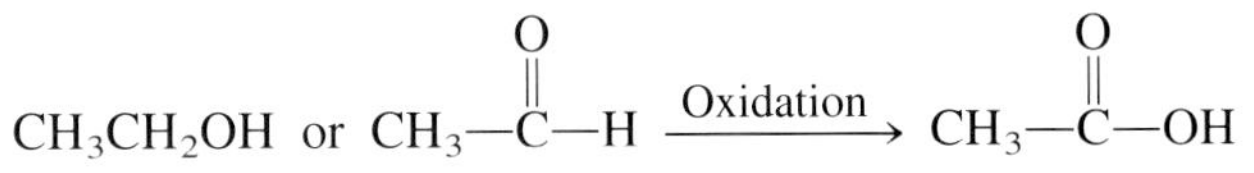

CH₃CH₂OH or CH₃—C—H $\xrightarrow{\text{Oxidation}}$ CH₃—C—OH

Ethanol   Ethanal   Ethanoic acid

A variety of oxidizing agents, including oxygen, can be used, and catalysts are often required to provide acceptable yields. Other simple carboxylic acids can be made by oxidation of the appropriate alcohol or aldehyde.

AN ENVIRONMENTAL PERSPECTIVE

Garbage Bags from Potato Peels

One of the problems facing society is our enormous accumulation of trash. This has prompted intense efforts to recycle aluminum, paper, and plastics. But one of the problems that remains is the plastic trash bag. When garbage in plastic bags is buried in landfills, the soil bacteria are unable to degrade the plastic and thus can't get to the biodegradable materials inside. Imagine a twenty-fourth century archeologist excavating one of these monuments to our society!

Intensive research is underway to invent a truly biodegradable trash bag. One of the more creative methods is to make plastic sheets from lactic acid. Lactic acid is a natural carboxylic acid produced by fermentation of sugars, particularly in milk and working muscle. Many soil bacteria can degrade polymers of lactic acid. Thus these trash bags would be easily broken down in landfill soil.

To make plastics from lactic acid requires a large supply of this carboxylic acid. As it turns out, this supply can be obtained from garbage!

About 10 billion pounds of potato waste are created each year from the process of making french fries. In fact, nearly half the mass of the potato is wasted. Several billion liters of whey, a carbohydrate-rich liquid left over from cheese making, are also dumped down the drain. Both of these waste products can be easily converted to glucose, which can be converted into lactic acid. Lactic acid molecules are then converted into long polymers. These polymers are used to make sheets that can be fashioned into trash bags.

Because the lactic acid polymers are biocompatible, they

Scientists are making biodegradable plastic from garbage. Lactic acid can be prepared from potato peels or whey. The lactic acid can then be polymerized to produce the plastic polylactic acid, which can be broken down by microorganisms.

have already been applied to medical practice. For instance, some sutures are made from lactic acid plastics.

Several problems remain to be solved before these trash bags appear in the market. The chief problem is that the end product (polylactic acid) is currently too expensive for commercial production. However, future research and development promise to produce an "environmentally friendly" garbage bag.

These reactions were discussed in Sections 10.1 and 10.5.

In the laboratory, carboxylic acids are prepared by the oxidation of aldehydes or primary alcohols. Most common oxidizing agents, such as chromic acid, can be used. The general reaction is

$$R-CH_2OH \xrightarrow{[O]} R-\overset{\displaystyle O}{\underset{\displaystyle \|}{C}}-H \xrightarrow{[O]} R-\overset{\displaystyle O}{\underset{\displaystyle \|}{C}}-OH$$

Primary alcohol   **Aldehyde**   **Carboxylic acid**

EXAMPLE 12.2

Writing Equations for the Oxidation of a Primary Alcohol to a Carboxylic Acid

Write equations showing the oxidation of 1-propanol to propanoic acid.

Solution

$$CH_3CH_2-\overset{\displaystyle H}{\underset{\displaystyle H}{C}}-OH \xrightarrow{H_2CrO_4} CH_3CH_2-\overset{\displaystyle O}{\underset{\displaystyle \|}{C}}-H \xrightarrow[\text{oxidation}]{\text{continued}} CH_3CH_2-\overset{\displaystyle O}{\underset{\displaystyle \|}{C}}-OH$$

1-Propanol   Propanal   Propanoic acid
(propyl alcohol)   (propionaldehyde)   (propionic acid)

Acid-base reactions

The carboxylic acids behave as acids because they are proton donors. They are weak acids   *Sections 7.3 and 7.4*
that dissociate to form a carboxylate ion and a hydrogen ion, as seen in the following example:

$$R-\overset{\overset{\displaystyle O}{\|}}{C}-OH \rightleftharpoons R-\overset{\overset{\displaystyle O}{\|}}{C}-O^- + H^+$$

Carboxylic	Carboxylate	Hydrogen
acid	anion	ion

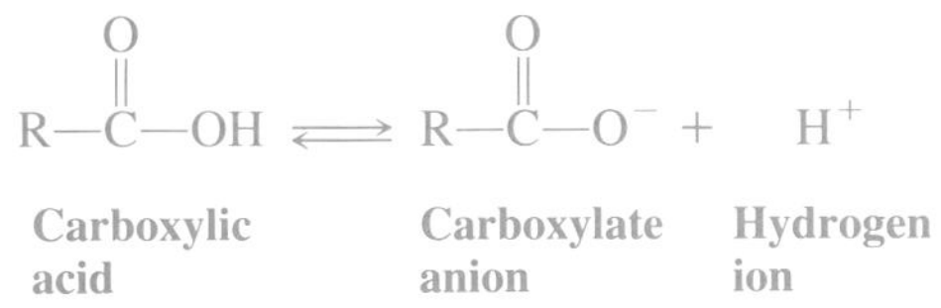

Since carboxylic acids are weak acids, they dissociate only slightly in solution. The majority of
the acid remains in solution in the undissociated form. Typically, less than 5% of the acid is
ionized (approximately 5 carboxylate ions to every 95 carboxylic acid molecules).

When strong bases are added to a carboxylic acid, neutralization occurs. The acid protons
are removed by the OH$^-$ to form water and the carboxylate ion. The equilibrium shown above is   *Section 5.4*
shifted to the right, owing to removal of H$^+$. This is an illustration of LeChatelier's Principle.

The carboxylate anion and the cation of the base form the carboxylic acid salt.

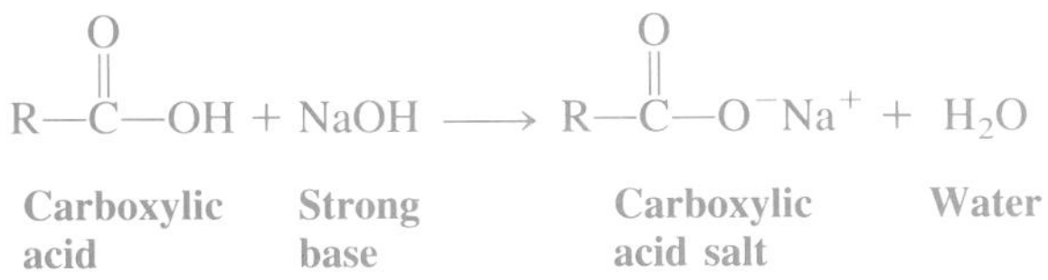

$$R-\overset{\overset{\displaystyle O}{\|}}{C}-OH + NaOH \longrightarrow R-\overset{\overset{\displaystyle O}{\|}}{C}-O^-Na^+ + H_2O$$

Carboxylic	Strong	Carboxylic	Water
acid	base	acid salt	

The following examples show the neutralization of acetic acid and benzoic in solutions of
the strong base NaOH.

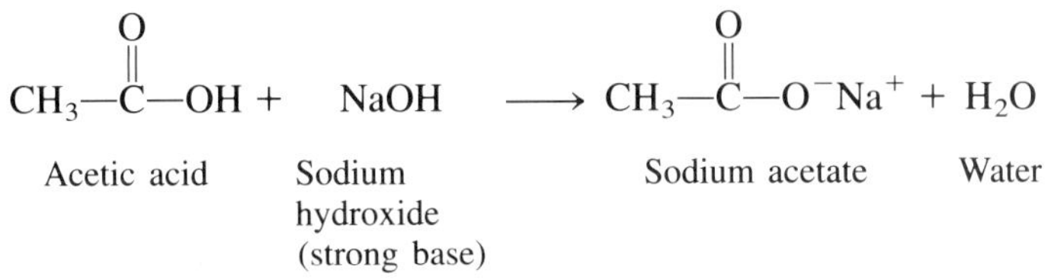

$$CH_3-\overset{\overset{\displaystyle O}{\|}}{C}-OH + NaOH \longrightarrow CH_3-\overset{\overset{\displaystyle O}{\|}}{C}-O^-Na^+ + H_2O$$

Acetic acid	Sodium hydroxide (strong base)	Sodium acetate	Water

Sodium benzoate is commonly used as a food preservative.

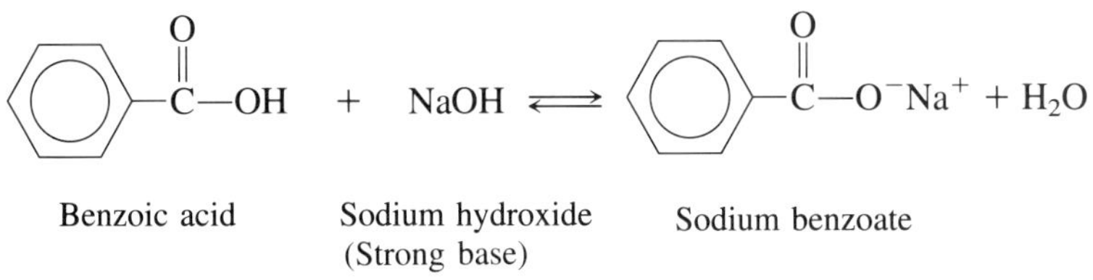

Benzoic acid	Sodium hydroxide (Strong base)	Sodium benzoate

Notice that the salt of a carboxylic acid is named by replacing the *-ic acid* suffix with *-ate*.
Thus acetic acid becomes acetate, and benzoic acid becomes benzoate. This name is preceded by
the name of the appropriate cation, sodium in the examples above.

The salts are ionic substances and hence quite soluble in water. The long-chain carboxylic
acid salts (fatty acid salts) are good **soaps.** According to Roman legend, soap was discovered by
washerwomen following a heavy rain on Mons Sapo ("Mount Soap"). An important sacrificial
altar was located on the mountain. The rain mixed with the remains of previous animal sacri-
fices—wood ash and animal fat—at the base of the altar. Thus the three substances required to
make soap accidentally came together—water, fat, and alkali (potassium carbonate and potassium hydroxide, called potash, leached from the wood ash). The soap mixture flowed down the
mountain and into the Tiber River, where the washerwomen quickly realized its value.

We still make soap using the old Roman recipe, from water, a strong base, and natural fats
and oils obtained from animals or plants. The carbon content of the fatty acid salts governs the
solubility of a soap. The lower-molecular-weight acid salts (up to 12 carbon) have greater
solubility in water and give a lather containing large bubbles. The higher-molecular-weight acid
salts (14–20 carbons) are much less soluble in water and produce a lather with fine bubbles. The

nature of the cation also affects the solubility of the soap. In general, the potassium salts of the acids are more soluble in water than the sodium salts. The synthesis of a soap is summarized below:

$$
\begin{array}{c}
\text{CH}_2\text{—O—}\overset{\overset{\displaystyle O}{\|}}{\text{C}}\text{—R} \\[2mm]
\text{CH—O—}\overset{\overset{\displaystyle O}{\|}}{\text{C}}\text{—R}' \\[2mm]
\text{CH}_2\text{—O—}\overset{\overset{\displaystyle O}{\|}}{\text{C}}\text{—R}''
\end{array}
\xrightarrow[\substack{\text{H}_2\text{O,} \\ \text{heat}}]{\text{M}^+\text{OH}^-}
\begin{array}{c}
\text{CH}_2\text{—OH} \\[2mm]
\text{CH—OH} \\[2mm]
\text{CH}_2\text{—OH}
\end{array}
+ \; \text{R—}\overset{\overset{\displaystyle O}{\|}}{\text{C}}\text{—O}^-\,\text{M}^+ + \text{R}'\text{—}\overset{\overset{\displaystyle O}{\|}}{\text{C}}\text{—O}^-\,\text{M}^+ + \text{R}''\text{—}\overset{\overset{\displaystyle O}{\|}}{\text{C}}\text{—O}^-\,\text{M}^+
$$

Fat or oil   Glycerol   Soap
(triglyceride)   (Mixture of carboxylic
                                                  acid salts)

where $\text{M}^{\oplus} = \text{Na}^{\oplus}$ or $\text{K}^{\oplus}$

The role of soap in the removal of soil and grease is best understood by considering the functional groups in soap molecules and studying the way in which they interact with oil and water. The long, continuous side chains of carbon atoms in a soap molecule resemble an alkane, and they dissolve other nonpolar compounds such as oils and greases ("like dissolves like"). The large nonpolar hydrocarbon part of the molecule is described as *hydrophobic*, which means "water-fearing." This part of the molecule is repelled by water. The highly polar carboxylate end of the molecule is called *hydrophilic*, which means "water-loving."

When soap is dissolved in water, the carboxylate end actually dissolves. The hydrocarbon part is repelled by the water molecules so that a thin film of soap is formed on the surface of the water with the hydrocarbon chains protruding outward. This greatly lowers the surface tension of the water. When soap solution comes in contact with oil or grease, the hydrocarbon part dissolves in the oil or grease, but the polar carboxylate group remains dissolved in water. When particles of oil or grease are surrounded by soap molecules, the resulting "units" formed are called *micelles*. A simplified view of this phenomenon is shown in Figure 12.2.

Micelles repel one another because they are surrounded on the surface by the negatively charged carboxylate ions. Mechanical action (for example, scrubbing or tumbling in a washing machine) causes oil or grease to be surrounded by soap molecules and broken into small droplets so that relatively small micelles are formed. These small micelles are then washed away. Careful examination of this solution shows that it is an *emulsion* containing suspended micelles.

Surface tension is a property of liquids in which the exposed surface tends to contract to the smallest possible area. The high surface tension of water is caused by intermolecular hydrogen bonding.

A more detailed diagram of a micelle is found in Figure 18.1.

An emulsion is a suspension of very fine droplets of an oil in water.

FIGURE 12.2
Simplified view of the action of a soap. The wiggly lines represent the long, continuous carbon chains of each soap molecule. (a) The thin film of soap molecules that forms at the water surface reduces surface tension. (b) Particles of oil and grease are surrounded by soap molecules to form a micelle.

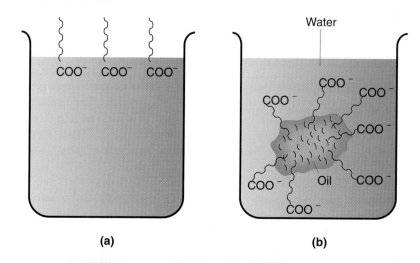

(a)   (b)

QUESTION 12.7

Write the formula of the organic product obtained through each of the following reactions:

a. $CH_3CH_2CH_2OH \xrightarrow{H_2CrO_4}$?   *[handwritten:]* $CH_3CH_2-\overset{O}{\overset{\|}{C}}-H \rightarrow CH_3CH_2-\overset{O}{\overset{\|}{C}}-OH$

b. $H\overset{O}{\overset{\|}{C}}CH_2CH_2CH_2CH_3 \xrightarrow{H_2CrO_4}$?   *[handwritten:]* $HO-\overset{O}{\overset{\|}{C}}-CH_2CH_2CH_2CH_3$

c. $CH_3CH_2COOH + KOH \longrightarrow$?   *[handwritten:]* $CH_3CH_2-\overset{O}{\overset{\|}{C}}-O^-K^+$

d. $CH_3CH_2CH_2COOH + Ba(OH)_2 \longrightarrow$?   *[handwritten:]* $[CH_3CH_2CH_2-COO]_2^-\ Ba^{2+}$

QUESTION 12.8

Complete each of the following reactions by supplying the missing product(s):

a. $CH_3CH_2OH \xrightarrow{H_2CrO_4}$?   *[handwritten:]* $CH_3-\overset{O}{\overset{\|}{C}}-H \rightarrow CH_3\overset{O}{\overset{\|}{C}}-OH$

b. $H\overset{O}{\overset{\|}{C}}CH_2CH_2\overset{O}{\overset{\|}{C}}H \xrightarrow{H_2CrO_4}$?

c. $CH_3CH_2CH_2CH_2CH_2COOH + KOH \longrightarrow$?

d. Benzoic acid + sodium hydroxide $\longrightarrow$?

Esterification

Carboxylic acids react with alcohols to form esters and water according to the following general reaction:

$$R_1-\overset{O}{\overset{\|}{C}}-OH + R_2OH \xrightarrow{Acid} R_1-\overset{O}{\overset{\|}{C}}-OR_2 + H_2O$$

Carboxylic acid   Alcohol   Ester   Water

The details of these reactions will be examined in detail in the next section.

Esters are also mildly polar and have pleasant aromas. Many esters are found in natural foodstuffs; banana oil (2-methylbutyl ethanoate; common name, isoamyl acetate), pineapples (ethyl butanoate; common name, ethyl butyrate), and raspberries (isobutyl methanoate; common name, isobutyl formate) are but a few examples.

Esters boil at approximately the same temperature as aldehydes or ketones of comparable molecular weight. The simpler ones are somewhat soluble in water.

Esters are **carboxylic acid derivatives,** organic compounds derived from carboxylic acids. They are formed from the reaction of a carboxylic acid with an alcohol, and both of these families are reflected in the naming of the ester. They are named according to the following set of rules:

◆ Use the *alkyl* or *aryl* portion of the alcohol name as the first name.

◆ The *-ic acid* ending of the name of the carboxylic acid is replaced with *-ate* and follows the first name.

For example, in the following reaction, ethanoic acid reacts with methanol to produce methyl ethanoate:

$$CH_3-\overset{O}{\overset{\|}{C}}-OH + CH_3OH \xrightarrow{H^+,\ heat} CH_3-\overset{O}{\overset{\|}{C}}-OCH_3 + H_2O$$

Ethan*oic acid*   *Methanol*   *Methyl* ethan*oate*
(acetic acid)   (methyl alcohol)   (methyl acetate)

12.2 ESTERS

Structure and physical properties

Nomenclature

See "A Human Perspective: Carboxylic Acid Derivatives of Special Interest."

Similarly, acet*ic acid* and *ethanol* react to produce *ethyl* acet*ate*, and the product of the reaction between benzo*ic acid* and *isopropyl* alcohol is *isopropyl* benzo*ate*.

Reactions involving esters

Preparation of esters

The conversion of a carboxylic acid to an ester requires heat and is catalyzed by a trace of acid (H^+). When esters are prepared directly from a carboxylic acid and an alcohol, a water molecule is lost, as seen in the following reaction:

$$R_1-\overset{\overset{\displaystyle O}{\|}}{C}-OH + R_2OH \xrightarrow{H^+, \text{ heat}} R_1-\overset{\overset{\displaystyle O}{\|}}{C}-OR_2 + H_2O$$

Carboxylic   Alcohol   Ester   Water
acid

$$CH_3CH_2-\overset{\overset{\displaystyle O}{\|}}{C}-OH + \quad CH_3OH \xrightarrow{H^+, \text{ heat}} CH_3CH_2-\overset{\overset{\displaystyle O}{\|}}{C}-OCH_3 + H_2O$$

Propanoic acid   Methanol   Methyl propanoate
(propionic acid)   (methyl alcohol)   (methyl propionate)

Hydrolysis of esters

Esters undergo **hydrolysis** reactions in water, as shown in the following general reaction:

$$R_1-\overset{\overset{\displaystyle O}{\|}}{C}-OR_2 + H_2O \xrightarrow{H^+, \text{ heat}} R_1-\overset{\overset{\displaystyle O}{\|}}{C}-OH + R_2OH$$

Ester   Water   Carboxylic   Alcohol
acid

This reaction requires heat. A small amount of acid (H^+) or base (OH^-) must be added to catalyze the reaction, as seen in the following examples:

$$CH_3CH_2-\overset{\overset{\displaystyle O}{\|}}{C}-OCH_2CH_2CH_3 + H_2O \xrightarrow{H^+, \text{ heat}} CH_3CH_2-\overset{\overset{\displaystyle O}{\|}}{C}-OH + CH_3CH_2CH_2OH$$

Propyl propanoate   Propanoic acid   1-Propanol
(propyl propionate)   (propionic acid)   (propanol)

The base-catalyzed hydrolysis of an ester is called **saponification.**

$$R_1-\overset{\overset{\displaystyle O}{\|}}{C}-OR_2 + H_2O \xrightarrow{NaOH, \text{ heat}} R_1-\overset{\overset{\displaystyle O}{\|}}{C}-O^-Na^+ + R_2OH$$

Ester   Water   Carboxylic   Alcohol
acid salt

Under basic conditions the sodium salt of the carboxylic acid is actually produced.

$$CH_3-\overset{\overset{\displaystyle O}{\|}}{C}-OCH_2CH_2CH_2CH_3 \xrightarrow{NaOH, \text{ heat}} CH_3-\overset{\overset{\displaystyle O}{\|}}{C}-O^-Na^+ + CH_3CH_2CH_2CH_2OH$$

Butyl ethanoate   Sodium ethanoate   1-Butanol
(butyl acetate)   (sodium acetate)   (butyl alcohol)

The carboxylic acid is formed when the reaction mixture is neutralized with an acid such as HCl.

$$CH_3-\overset{\overset{\displaystyle O}{\|}}{C}-O^-Na^+ + HCl \longrightarrow CH_3-\overset{\overset{\displaystyle O}{\|}}{C}-OH + NaCl$$

Sodium ethanoate   Ethanoic acid
(sodium acetate)   (acetic acid

Saponification is used to hydrolyze fats and oils, triesters of glycerol, to the salts of long chain fatty acids, *soaps.*

QUESTION 12.9

Complete each of the following reactions by supplying the missing products. Draw the structure and name the product using the I.U.P.A.C. Nomenclature System.

a. $CH_3-\overset{\overset{\displaystyle O}{\|}}{C}-OCH_2CH_2CH_3 + H_2O \xrightarrow{H^+,\ heat}$?

b. $CH_3CH_2CH_2CH_2CH_2-\overset{\overset{\displaystyle O}{\|}}{C}-OCH_2CH_2CH_2CH_3 + H_2O \xrightarrow{KOH,\ heat}$?

c. $CH_3CH_2CH_2CH_2-\overset{\overset{\displaystyle O}{\|}}{C}-OCH_3 + H_2O \xrightarrow{NaOH,\ heat}$?

d. $CH_3CH_2CH_2CH_2CH_2-\overset{\overset{\displaystyle O}{\|}}{C}-\underset{\underset{\displaystyle CH_3}{|}}{O}CHCH_2CH_2CH_3 + H_2O \xrightarrow{H^+,\ heat}$?

QUESTION 12.10

Draw the products that result from the saponification of methyl benzoate with sodium hydroxide followed by neutralization with hydrochloric acid.

An alcohol can react with phosphoric acid to produce a phosphate ester, or **phosphoester,** as seen in the following example:

12.3 NATURE'S HIGH-ENERGY COMPOUNDS: PHOSPHOESTERS AND THIOESTERS

Phosphate ester bond

$$ROH + HO-\overset{\overset{\displaystyle O}{\|}}{\underset{\underset{\displaystyle OH}{|}}{P}}-OH \longrightarrow R-O-\overset{\overset{\displaystyle O}{\|}}{\underset{\underset{\displaystyle OH}{|}}{P}}-OH + H_2O$$

Alcohol   Phosphoric acid   Phosphate ester   Water

The phosphate ester functional group is noted in the equation above. Phosphate esters of monosaccharides are very important in energy-harvesting reactions in the cell. For instance, the first step in glycolysis is the phosphorylation of glucose to produce glucose-6-phosphate:

The many phosphorylated intermediates in the metabolism of sugars will be discussed in Chapter 16.

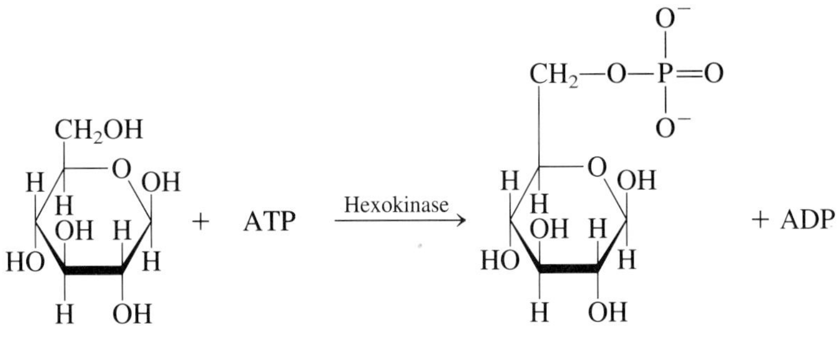

β-D-Glucose β-D-Glucose 6-phosphate

In this reaction the source of the phosphoryl group is **adenosine triphosphate (ATP),** which is the universal energy currency for all living organisms. As such, ATP is used to store energy released in cellular metabolic reactions and provides the energy required for most of the

A HUMAN PERSPECTIVE

Carboxylic Acid Derivatives of Special Interest

Polymers

Polymers are *macromolecules*—very large molecules. They result from the combination of many smaller molecules, usually in a repeating pattern, to give molecules whose molecular weight may be 10,000 g/mol or greater. The small molecules that make up the polymer are called *monomers*.

A polymer may be made from a single type of monomer. Such polymers would have the following general structure:

chain continues ~ —A—A—A—A—A—A—~ chain continues

Alternatively, two different monomers can be copolymerized, producing the following kind of polymer:

chain continues ~ —A—B—A—B—A—B—~ chain continues

One important class of polymers is the polyesters. Polyesters are synthesized by reacting a dicarboxylic acid and a dialcohol (diol). Each of the combining molecules has two reactive functional groups. As seen in the accompanying figure, the polymer chain grows when the "head" of one chain combines with the "tail" of a second chain. Each time a pair of molecules reacts, using one functional group from each, a new molecule is formed that still contains two reactive functional groups. In theory the process could continue indefinitely. However, depending on conditions, side reactions, called termination reactions, occur to halt the process.

Polyesters have grown into an an extremely profitable field with the birth of "doubleknit" (polyester) fabrics.

There are several classes of naturally occurring polymers of great biochemical importance. Polysaccharides (polycarbohydrates) are essential forms of energy storage in both plant and animal cells. The polymer cellulose also forms a tough, rigid cell wall that protects plant cells and gives them shape. Proteins (polyamino acids) are essential cellular components that perform many functions in the body. Many are enzymes, biological catalysts that speed up chemical reactions in the cell. Others are structural components in the body, such as the proteins that make up hair and fingernails. Still others serve transport functions. For instance, the protein hemoglobin carries oxygen from the lungs to the tissues of the body. Proteins are also responsible for movement of muscle.

The genetic information of the cell is stored in nucleic acids (DNA polynucleotides), and the genetic message is carried and expressed by other nucleic acids (RNA).

$$n\,CH_3CH_2O-\overset{O}{\underset{\|}{C}}-\langle\bigcirc\rangle-\overset{O}{\underset{\|}{C}}-OCH_2CH_3 + n\,HOCH_2CH_2OH \underset{}{\overset{HOCH_2CH_2\ddot{O}:^\ominus\,Na^\oplus\ or\ H^\oplus}{\rightleftharpoons}}$$

Diethyl terephthalate   Ethylene glycol
(excess)

$$\text{\textasciitilde}CH_2CH_2-O-\left[\overset{O}{\underset{\|}{C}}-\langle\bigcirc\rangle-\overset{O}{\underset{\|}{C}}-OCH_2CH_2O\right]_n-\overset{O}{\underset{\|}{C}}-\langle\bigcirc\rangle-\overset{O}{\underset{\|}{C}}-OCH_2CH_2\text{\textasciitilde} + 2n\,CH_3CH_2OH$$

Dacron
(polymeric ester)
The polymerization process for difunctional compounds (shown for Dacron).

Analgesics (pain killers) and antipyretics (fever reducers)

Aspirin (acetylsalicylic acid) is the most widely used drug in the world. Hundreds of millions of dollars are spent annually on this compound. It is used primarily as a pain reliever (analgesic) and in the reduction of fever (antipyretic). Aspirin's side effects are a problem for some individuals. Because aspirin inhibits clotting, it is not recommended during pregnancy, nor should it be used by individuals with ulcers. In those instances *acetaminophen,* found in the over-the-counter pain-reliever, Tylenol, is often prescribed.

Acetylsalicylic acid
(*aspirin*)   Phenacetin
(*APC tablets*)   Acetaminophen
(*tylenol*)

Some common analgesics.

Pheromones

Pheromones, chemicals secreted by animals, influence the behavior of other members of the same species. They often represent the major means of communication among simpler animals. The term "pheromone" literally means "to carry" and "to excite" (Greek, *pherein,* to carry; Greek, *horman,* to excite). They are chemicals carried or shed by one member of the species and used to alert other members of the species.

Pheromones may be involved in sexual attraction, trail marking, aggregation or recruitment, territorial marking, or signaling alarm. Others may be involved in defense or in species socialization—for example, designating various classes within the species as a whole. Among all of the pheromones, insect pheromones have been the most intensely studied. Many of the insect pheromones are carboxylic acids or acid derivatives. Examples of members of this class of chemicals are provided in the accompanying figure along with the principal function of each compound.

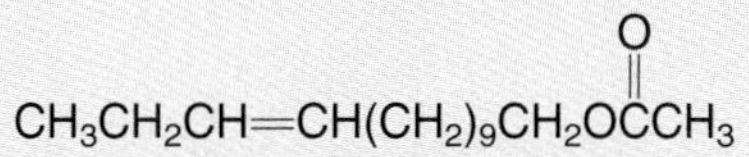

$$CH_3CH_2CH{=}CH(CH_2)_9CH_2OCCH_3$$

Tetracecenyl acetate
(European corn borer sex pheromone)

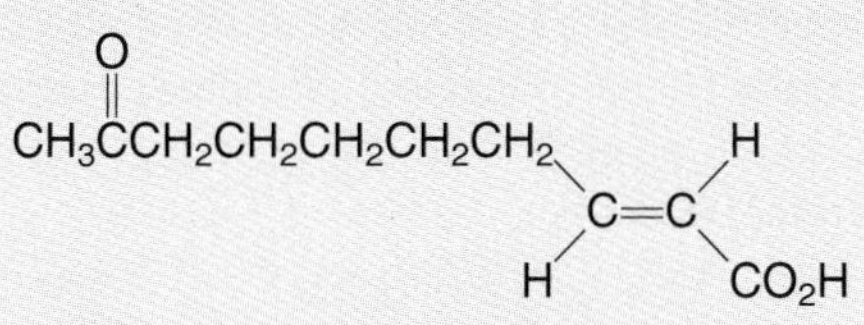

9-Keto-*trans*-2-decenoic acid
(queen bee socializing/royalty pheromone)

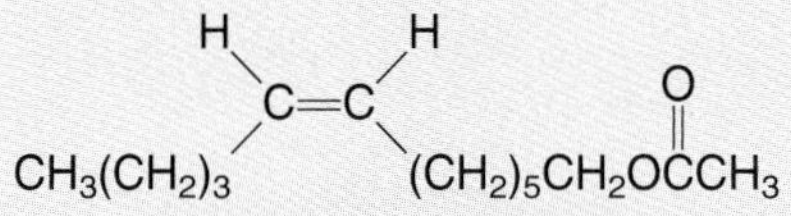

cis-7-Dodecenyl acetate
(cabbage looper sex pheromone)

Sex pheromones.

Flavor and fragrance chemicals

Volatile esters are often pleasant in both aroma and flavor. Natural fruit flavors are complex mixtures of many esters and other organic compounds. Chemists can isolate these mixtures and identify the chemical components. With this information they are able to synthesize artificial fruit flavors, using just a few of the esters found in the natural fruit. As a result, the artificial flavors rarely have the full-bodied flavor of nature's original blend.

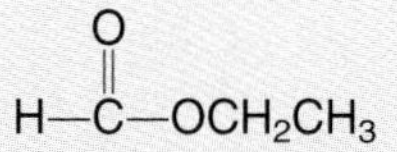

$$H{-}\overset{\displaystyle O}{\overset{\|}{C}}{-}OCH_2CH_3 \qquad \text{Rum}$$

Ethyl methanoate
(ethyl formate)

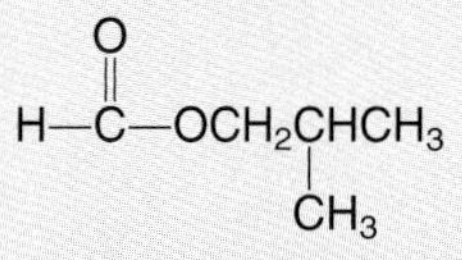

$$H{-}\overset{\displaystyle O}{\overset{\|}{C}}{-}OCH_2CHCH_3 \qquad \text{Raspberries}$$

Isobutyl methanoate
(isobutyl formate)

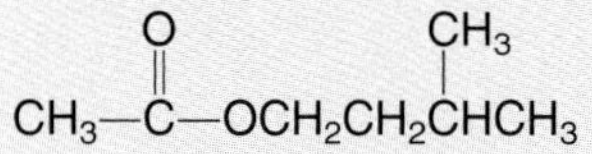

$$CH_3{-}\overset{\displaystyle O}{\overset{\|}{C}}{-}OCH_2CH_2CHCH_3 \qquad \text{Bananas}$$

3-Methylbutyl ethanoate
(isoamyl acetate)

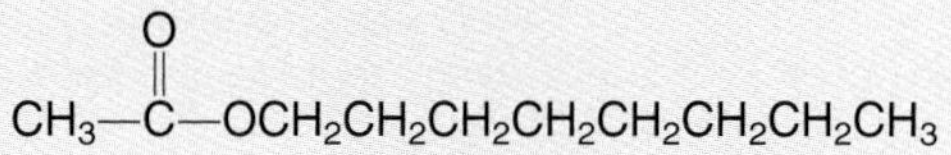

$$CH_3{-}\overset{\displaystyle O}{\overset{\|}{C}}{-}OCH_2CH_2CH_2CH_2CH_2CH_2CH_2CH_3 \qquad \text{Oranges}$$

Octyl ethanoate
(octyl acetate)

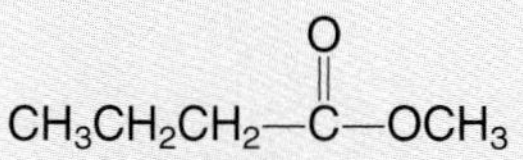

$$CH_3CH_2CH_2{-}\overset{\displaystyle O}{\overset{\|}{C}}{-}OCH_3 \qquad \text{Apples}$$

Methyl butanoate
(methyl butyrate)

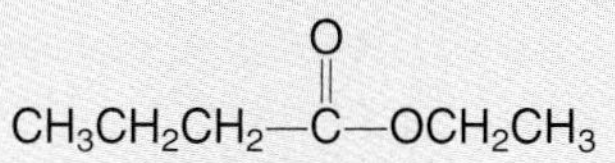

$$CH_3CH_2CH_2{-}\overset{\displaystyle O}{\overset{\|}{C}}{-}OCH_2CH_3 \qquad \text{Pineapples}$$

Ethyl butanoate
(amyl butyrate)

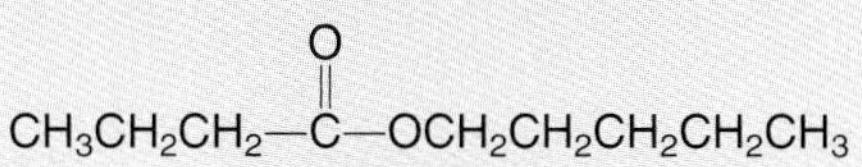

$$CH_3CH_2CH_2{-}\overset{\displaystyle O}{\overset{\|}{C}}{-}OCH_2CH_2CH_2CH_2CH_3 \qquad \text{Apricots}$$

Pentyl butanoate
(pentyl butyrate)

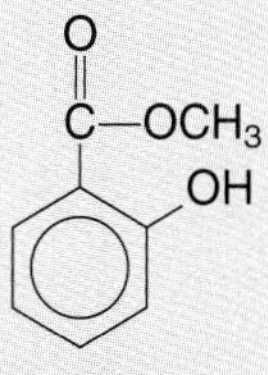

Methyl salicylate   Oil of wintergreen

$$CH_3CH_2CH_2{-}\overset{\displaystyle O}{\overset{\|}{C}}{-}SCH_3 \qquad \text{Strawberries}$$

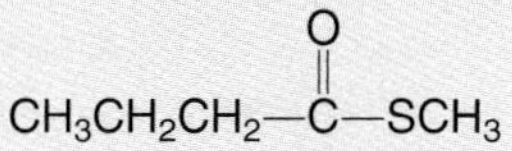

Methyl thiobutanoate
(methyl thiobutyrate)

(a thioester in which sulfur replaces oxygen)
Some interesting flavor and fragrance compounds.

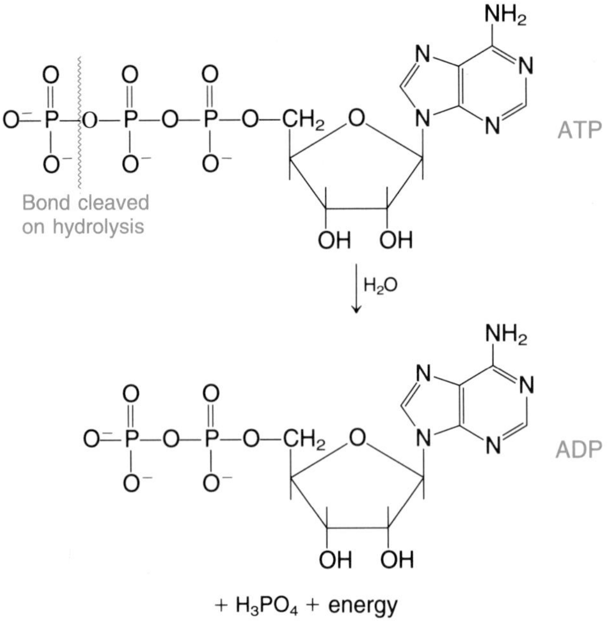

FIGURE 12.3
The hydrolysis of the phosphoric anhydride bond of ATP is accompanied by the release of energy that is used for biochemical reactions in the cell.

Phosphoryl is the term used to describe the functional group derived from phosphoric acid that is part of another molecule.

Section 19.1

reactions that occur in the cell. The transfer of a phosphoryl group from ATP to glucose "energizes" the glucose molecule in preparation for other reactions of the pathway.

ATP consists of a nitrogenous base (adenine) and a phosphate ester of the sugar ribose (Figure 12.3). The triphosphate group attached to ribose is made up of three phosphate groups bonded to one another by phosphoric anhydride bonds. When two phosphate groups react with one another, a water molecule is lost. Because water is lost, the resulting bond is called a **phosphoric anhydride,** or phosphoanhydride, bond.

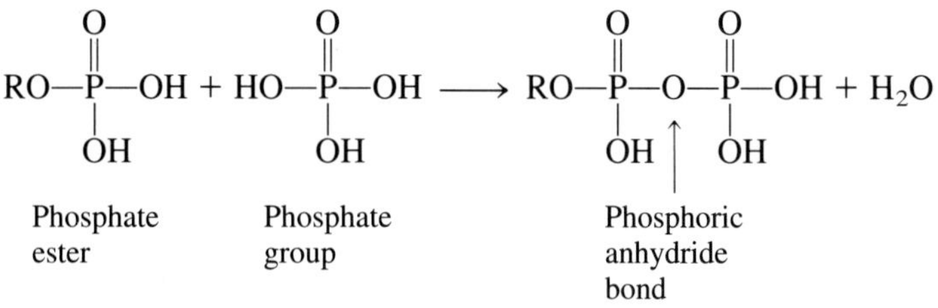

The functions and properties of ATP in energy metabolism are discussed in Section 16.1. The nucleotide triphosphates involved in the synthesis of DNA are considered in Chapter 19.

Section 10.4

The energy of ATP is made available through hydrolysis of either of the two phosphoric anhydride bonds, as seen in Figure 12.3. This is an exothermic process; that is, energy is given off. When the phosphoryl group is transferred to another molecule—for instance, glucose—some of that energy resides in the phosphorylated sugar, thereby "energizing" it. The importance of ATP as an energy source becomes apparent when we realize that we synthesize and break down an amount of ATP equivalent to our body weight each day.

Cellular enzymes can carry out a reaction between a thiol and a carboxylic acid to produce a **thioester:**

$$R_1-S-\overset{\overset{\displaystyle O}{\|}}{C}-R_2$$

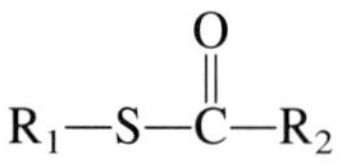

Thioester

The reactions that produce thioesters are essential in energy-harvesting pathways as a means of "activating" acyl groups for subsequent breakdown reactions. The complex thiol coenzyme A is the most important acyl group activator in the cell. The detailed structure of coenzyme A appears in Section 10.4, but it is generally abbreviated CoA—SH to emphasize the importance of the sulfhydryl group. The most common thioester is the acetyl ester, called **acetyl coenzyme A** (acetyl CoA).

Acetyl CoA acts as an acyl group transfer agent by carrying the acetyl group from glycolysis or β-oxidation of a fatty acid to an intermediate of the citric acid cycle. This reaction is shown in the following equation:

CoA—S—C—CH₃ + ... → ... + CoA—SH

| Acetyl CoA | Oxaloacetate | Citrate | Coenzyme A |

As we will see in Chapter 17, the citric acid cycle completely oxidizes the acetyl group to two CO_2 molecules. The electrons that are harvested in the process are used to produce large amounts of ATP. Coenzyme A also serves to activate the acyl group of fatty acids during β-oxidation, the pathway by which fatty acids are oxidized to produce ATP.

The acyl group of a carboxylic acid is named by replacing the *-oic acid* or *-ic* suffix with *-yl*. For instance, the acyl group of acetic acid is the acetyl group.

CoA—S—C—CH₃

Acetyl coenzyme A
(acetyl CoA)

Glycolysis, β-oxidation, and the citric acid cycle are cellular energy-harvesting pathways that we will study in Chapters 16, 17, and 18.

Chapter 18

SUMMARY OF REACTIONS

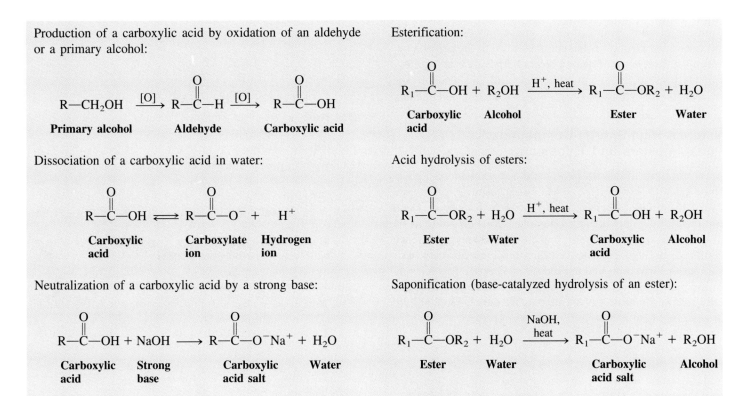

Production of a carboxylic acid by oxidation of an aldehyde or a primary alcohol:

R—CH₂OH $\xrightarrow{[O]}$ R—C—H $\xrightarrow{[O]}$ R—C—OH

Primary alcohol   **Aldehyde**   **Carboxylic acid**

Dissociation of a carboxylic acid in water:

R—C—OH $\rightleftharpoons$ R—C—O⁻ + H⁺

Carboxylic acid   **Carboxylate ion**   **Hydrogen ion**

Neutralization of a carboxylic acid by a strong base:

R—C—OH + NaOH $\longrightarrow$ R—C—O⁻Na⁺ + H₂O

Carboxylic acid   **Strong base**   **Carboxylic acid salt**   **Water**

Esterification:

R₁—C—OH + R₂OH $\xrightarrow{H^+, \text{ heat}}$ R₁—C—OR₂ + H₂O

Carboxylic acid   **Alcohol**   **Ester**   **Water**

Acid hydrolysis of esters:

R₁—C—OR₂ + H₂O $\xrightarrow{H^+, \text{ heat}}$ R₁—C—OH + R₂OH

Ester   **Water**   **Carboxylic acid**   **Alcohol**

Saponification (base-catalyzed hydrolysis of an ester):

R₁—C—OR₂ + H₂O $\xrightarrow{\text{NaOH, heat}}$ R₁—C—O⁻Na⁺ + R₂OH

Ester   **Water**   **Carboxylic acid salt**   **Alcohol**

Formation of a phosphoester bond:

$$ROH + HO—\overset{\overset{\displaystyle O}{\|}}{\underset{\underset{\displaystyle OH}{|}}{P}}—OH \longrightarrow RO—\overset{\overset{\displaystyle O}{\|}}{\underset{\underset{\displaystyle OH}{|}}{P}}—OH + H_2O$$

Alcohol   Phosphoric acid   Phosphate ester   Water

SUMMARY

Carboxylic Acids

The functional group of the *carboxylic acids* is the *carboxyl group* (—COOH). Because the carboxyl group is extremely polar and carboxylic acids can form intermolecular hydrogen bonds, they have higher boiling points and melting points than alcohols. The lower-molecular-weight carboxylic acids are water-soluble and tend to taste sour and have upleasant aromas. The longer-chain carboxylic acids are called *fatty acids*. Carboxylic acids are named (I.U.P.A.C.) by replacing the *-e* ending of the parent compound with *-oic acid*. Common names are often derived from the source of the carboxylic acid. They are synthesized by the oxidation of primary alcohols or aldehydes. Carboxylic acids are weak acids. They are neutralized by strong bases to form salts. *Soaps* are salts of long-chain carboxylic acids (fatty acids).

Esters

Esters are mildly polar and have pleasant aromas. The boiling points and melting points of esters are comparable to those of aldehydes and ketones. Esters are formed from the reaction between a carboxylic acid and an alcohol. They can undergo hydrolysis back to the parent carboxylic acid and alcohol. The base-catalyzed hydrolysis of an ester is called *saponification*.

Nature's High-Energy Compounds: Phosphoesters and Thioesters

An alcohol can react with phosphoric acid to produce a phosphate ester *(phosphoester)*. When two phosphate groups are joined, the resulting bond is a *phosphoric anhydride* bond. These two functional groups are important to the structure and function of *adenosine triphosphate (ATP)*, the universal energy currency of all cells. Cellular enzymes can carry out a reaction between a thiol and a carboxylic acid to produce a *thioester*. This reaction is essential for the activation of acyl groups in carbohydrate and fatty acid metabolism. Coenzyme A is the most important thiol involved in these pathways.

KEY TERMS

acetyl coenzyme A (12.3)
acyl group (Introduction)

adenosine triphosphate (ATP)
(12.3)

carboxyl group (12.1)
carboxylic acid (12.1)
carboxylic acid derivative
 (12.2)
ester (12.2)
fatty acid (12.1)
hydrolysis (12.2)

oxidation (12.1)
phosphoester (12.3)
phosphoric anhydride (12.3)
saponification (12.2)
soap (12.1)
thioester (12.3)

QUESTIONS AND PROBLEMS

Structure and Nomenclature of Carboxylic Acids

12.11 Write the complete structural formulas for each of the following carboxylic acids:
 a. 2-Bromopentanoic acid
 b. 2-Bromo-3-methylbutanoic acid
 c. 2-Bromocyclohexanecarboxylic acid
 d. 2,6-Dichlorocyclohexanecarboxylic acid
 e. 2,4,6-Timethylstearic acid
 f. Propenoic acid

12.12 Name each of the following carboxylic acids using both the common and the I.U.P.A.C. Nomenclature System:
 a.
 $$H—\overset{\overset{\displaystyle O}{\|}}{C}—OH$$
 b.
 $$CH_3CH\underset{\underset{\displaystyle CH_3}{|}}{}CH_2—\overset{\overset{\displaystyle O}{\|}}{C}—OH$$
 c.
 $$\overset{\overset{\displaystyle O}{\|}}{C}—OH$$ (cyclopentane)
 d. $$CH_3CH_2\underset{\underset{\displaystyle Br}{|}}{C}HCH_2—\overset{\overset{\displaystyle O}{\|}}{C}—OH$$ with CH_3
 e. $$CH_3CH_2\underset{\underset{\displaystyle CH_2CH_3}{|}}{C}HCH_2CH_2—\overset{\overset{\displaystyle O}{\|}}{C}—OH$$

12.13 Write a complete structural formula and determine the I.U.P.A.C. name for each of the carboxylic acids of molecular formula $C_4H_8O_2$.

12.14 Write the general structure of an aldehyde, a ketone, a carboxylic acid, and an ester. What similarities exist among these structures?

12.15 Write the condensed structure of each of the following carboxylic acids:
 a. 4,4-Dimethylhexanoic acid
 b. 3-Bromo-4-methylpentanoic acid
 c. 2,3-Dinitrobenzoic acid
 d. 3-Methylcyclohexanecarboxylic acid

12.16 Write the names for each of the following carboxylic acids using I.U.P.A.C. nomenclature.
 a. (benzene ring with $\overset{\overset{O}{\|}}{C}—OH$ and NO_2)
 b. (benzene ring with $\overset{\overset{O}{\|}}{C}—OH$ and CH_2CH_3)
 c. (cyclopentane with $\overset{\overset{O}{\|}}{C}—OH$)

Structure and Properties of Carboxylic Acids and Esters

12.17 Which member in each of the following pairs has the higher boiling point?
  a. Heptanoic acid or 1-heptanol
  b. Propanal or 1-propanol
  c. Methyl pentanoate or pentanoic acid
  d. 1-Butanol or butanoic acid

12.18 Which member in each of the following pairs is more soluble in water?

  a. $CH_3CH_2CH_2CH_2CH_2-\overset{\overset{\displaystyle O}{\|}}{C}-OH$ or

  $CH_3CH_2CH_2CH_2CH_2-\overset{\overset{\displaystyle O}{\|}}{C}-O^-Na^+$

  b. $CH_3CH_2CH_2CH_2CH_2CH_2CH_2CH_2CH_3$ or
  $CH_3CH_2CH_2CH_2CH_2CH_2CH_2CH_2OH$

  c. $CH_3CH_2-O-CH_2CH_3$ or $CH_3CH_2-\overset{\overset{\displaystyle O}{\|}}{C}-OCH_3$
  d. $CH_3CH_2-O-CH_2CH_3$ or $CH_3CH_2CH_2CH_2CH_3$
  e. Decanoic acid or ethanoic acid
  f.
  $CH_3CH_2CH_2-\overset{\overset{\displaystyle O}{\|}}{C}-OH$ or $CH_3CH_2-\overset{\overset{\displaystyle O}{\|}}{C}-OCH_3$

Reactions Involving Carboxylic Acids

12.19 Complete each of the following reactions by supplying the missing portion indicated by a question mark:

  a. $CH_3-\overset{\overset{\displaystyle O}{\|}}{C}-H \xrightarrow{H_2CrO_4}$?   *[handwritten: $CH_3-\overset{O}{\overset{\|}{C}}-OH$]*

  b. $CH_3CH_2CH_2-\overset{\overset{\displaystyle O}{\|}}{C}-OH + CH_3OH \underset{}{\overset{H^+,\ heat}{\rightleftharpoons}}$?   *[handwritten: $CH_3-\overset{O}{\overset{\|}{C}}-O$]*

  c. $\overset{\overset{\displaystyle O}{\|}}{\langle\!\!\!\square\rangle-C-OH} \xrightarrow{?} \langle\!\!\!\square\rangle-\overset{\overset{\displaystyle O}{\|}}{C}-OCH_3$ *[handwritten: $R-OH$ / CH_3OH; carbox / ester]*

12.20 Complete each of the following reactions by supplying the missing part(s) indicated by the question mark(s):

  a. $CH_3CH_2CH_2OH \xrightarrow{?(1)} CH_3CH_2-\overset{\overset{\displaystyle O}{\|}}{C}-OH \underset{?(3)}{\overset{NaOH}{\rightleftharpoons}}$?(4)

  $\downarrow ?(2)$

  $CH_3CH_2-\overset{\overset{\displaystyle O}{\|}}{C}-O\underset{\underset{\displaystyle CH_3}{|}}{CH}CH_3$

  b. $CH_3COOH + NaOH \longrightarrow$?
  c. $CH_3CH_2CH_2CH_2CH_2COOH + NaOH \longrightarrow$?
  d.
  $? + CH_3CH_2\overset{\underset{\displaystyle CH_3}{|}}{CH}OH \xrightarrow{H^+} CH_3-\overset{\overset{\displaystyle O}{\|}}{C}-O\overset{\underset{\displaystyle CH_3}{|}}{CH}CH_2CH_3$

12.21 How might $CH_3CH_2CH_2CH_2CH_2OH$ be converted to each of the following products?
  a. $CH_3CH_2CH_2CH_2CHO$
  b. $CH_3CH_2CH_2CH_2COOH$

12.22 Which of the following alcohols can be oxidized to a carboxylic acid? Name the carboxylic acid produced. For those alcohols that cannot be oxidized to a carboxylic acid, name the final product.
  a. Ethanol
  b. 2-Propanol
  c. 1-Propanol
  d. 3-Pentanol

Structure and Nomenclature of Esters

12.23 Write each of the following, using condensed formulas:
  a. Methyl benzoate
  b. Butyl decanoate
  c. Methyl propionate
  d. Ethyl propionate
  e. Ethyl *m*-nitrobenzoate
  f. Isopropyl acetate
  g. Methyl butyrate

12.24 Name each of the following esters using the I.U.P.A.C. Nomenclature System:

  a. $CH_3-\overset{\overset{\displaystyle O}{\|}}{C}-OCH_2CH_3$

  b. $CH_3CH_2-\overset{\overset{\displaystyle O}{\|}}{C}-OCH_3$

  c. $CH_3\overset{\underset{\displaystyle CH_3}{|}}{C}HCH_2-\overset{\overset{\displaystyle O}{\|}}{C}-OCH_3$

  d. $\langle\!\!\!\bigcirc\!\!\!\rangle-\overset{\overset{\displaystyle O}{\|}}{C}-O-\langle\!\!\!\bigcirc\!\!\!\rangle$

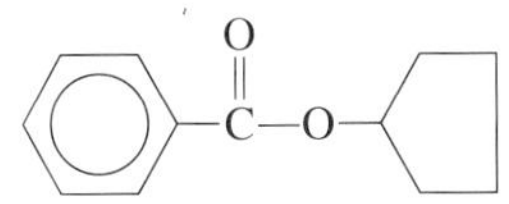

  e. $\langle\!\!\!\bigcirc\!\!\!\rangle-\overset{\overset{\displaystyle O}{\|}}{C}-OCH_2CH_2CH_3$

  f. $\overset{\overset{\displaystyle O}{\|}}{C}-OCH_3$ on benzene ring

  g. $CH_2\overset{}{C}HCH_2CH_2-\overset{\overset{\displaystyle O}{\|}}{C}-OCH_2CH_3$ with Br on C1 and C2 ($\underset{\underset{\displaystyle Br}{|}}{}\ \underset{\underset{\displaystyle Br}{|}}{}$)

Reactions Involving Esters

12.25 Complete each of the following reactions by supplying the missing portion indicated with a question mark:

  a. $CH_3CH_2CH_2-\overset{\overset{\displaystyle O}{\|}}{C}-OH + CH_3CH_2OH \xrightarrow{H^+,\ heat}$?   *[handwritten: ester $CH_3CH_2CH_2\overset{O}{\overset{\|}{C}}-O-CH_2CH_3$; carboxylic acid / alcohol]*

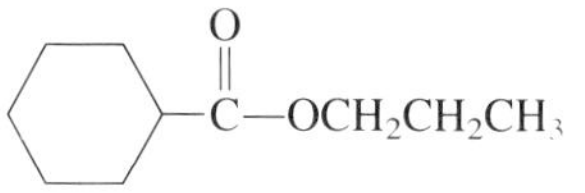

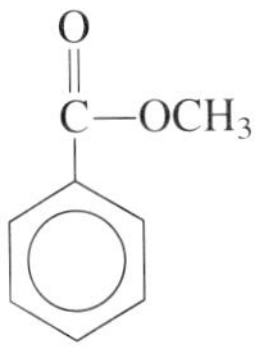

  b.
  $CH_3CH_2-\overset{\overset{\displaystyle O}{\|}}{C}-OCH_2CH_3 + H_2O \xrightarrow{H^+,\ heat}$?   *[handwritten: ester; $CH_3CH_2-\overset{O}{\overset{\|}{C}}-OH + CH_2CH_2OH$]*

  c. $CH_3\overset{\underset{\displaystyle CH_3}{|}}{C}HCH_2CH_2-\overset{\overset{\displaystyle O}{\|}}{C}-OH + ? \xrightarrow{H^+,\ heat}$ *[handwritten: carbox; $CH_3CH_2CH_2OH$]*
  $CH_3\overset{\underset{\displaystyle CH_3}{|}}{C}HCH_2CH_2-\overset{\overset{\displaystyle O}{\|}}{C}-OCH_2CH_2CH_3$ *[handwritten: ester]*

  d. $CH_3CH_2\overset{\underset{\displaystyle Br}{|}}{C}HCH_2-\overset{\overset{\displaystyle O}{\|}}{C}-OCH_2CH_3 + H_2O \xrightarrow{OH^-,\ heat}$?   *[handwritten: ester]*

  [handwritten at bottom: $CH_3CH_2CHCH_2-\overset{O}{\overset{\|}{C}}-O^- + CH_2CH_3OH$ with Br]

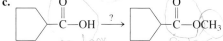

12.26 Complete each of the following reactions by supplying the missing portion indicated with a question mark:

a. 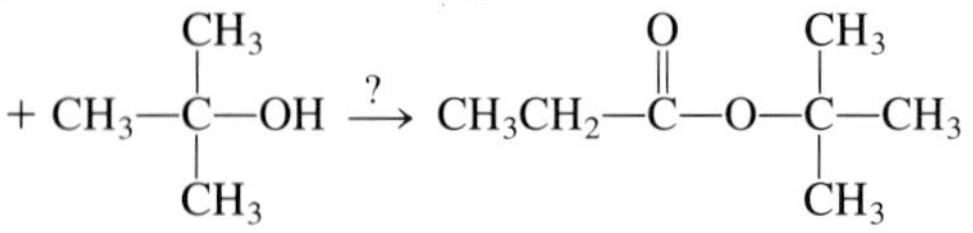 $? + CH_3-\overset{\overset{\displaystyle CH_3}{|}}{\underset{\underset{\displaystyle CH_3}{|}}{C}}-OH \xrightarrow{?} CH_3CH_2-\overset{\displaystyle O}{\overset{||}{C}}-O-\overset{\overset{\displaystyle CH_3}{|}}{\underset{\underset{\displaystyle CH_3}{|}}{C}}-CH_3$

b. $CH_3CH_2CH_2CH_2COOH + CH_3CH_2CH_2CH_2OH \xrightarrow{H^+, \text{ heat}} ?$

c. 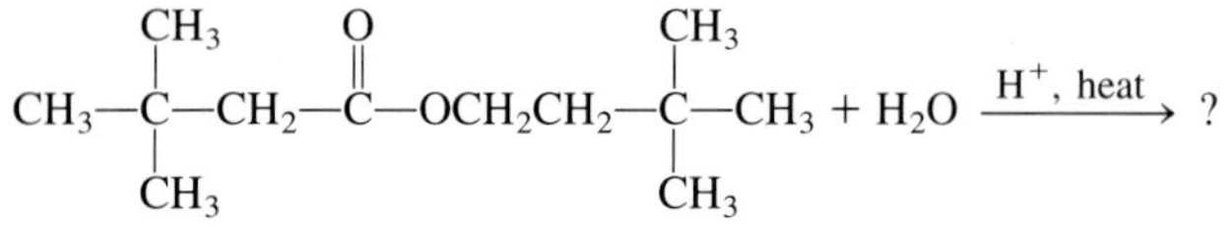 $CH_3-\overset{\overset{\displaystyle CH_3}{|}}{\underset{\underset{\displaystyle CH_3}{|}}{C}}-CH_2-\overset{\displaystyle O}{\overset{||}{C}}-OCH_2CH_2-\overset{\overset{\displaystyle CH_3}{|}}{\underset{\underset{\displaystyle CH_3}{|}}{C}}-CH_3 + H_2O \xrightarrow{H^+, \text{ heat}} ?$

d. 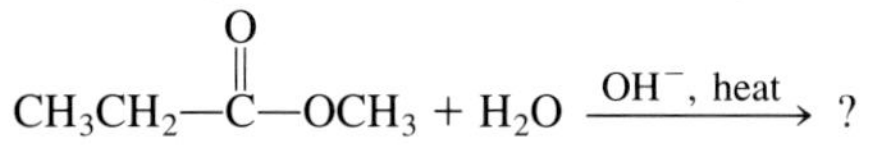 $CH_3CH_2-\overset{\displaystyle O}{\overset{||}{C}}-OCH_3 + H_2O \xrightarrow{OH^-, \text{ heat}} ?$

12.27 What is saponification? Give an example using actual molecules.

12.28 When the methyl ester of hexanoic acid is hydrolyzed in aqueous sodium hydroxide in the presence of heat, a homogeneous solution results. When the solution is acidified with dilute aqueous hydrochloric acid, a new product forms. What is the new product? Draw its structure.

12.29 The structure of salicylic acid is shown below. If this acid reacts with methanol, the product is an ester, methyl salicylate. Methyl salicylate is known as oil of wintergreen and is often used as a flavoring agent. Draw the structure of the product of this reaction.

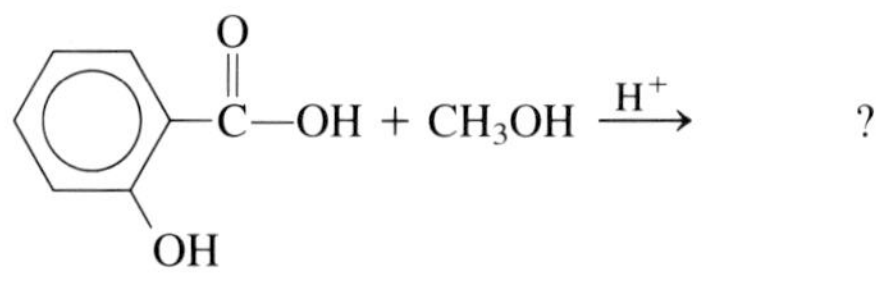

Salicylic acid   Methyl salicylate,
                               oil of wintergreen

12.30 When salicylic acid reacts with acetic anhydride, one of the products is an ester, acetylsalicylic acid. Acid anhydrides like acetic anhydride are formed by the reaction between two carboxylic acids with the loss of water. This is very similar to phosphoric anhydride formation. Acetylsalicylic acid is the active ingredient in aspirin. Draw the structure of acetylsalicylic acid. (*Hint:* Acid anhydrides are hydrolyzed by water.)

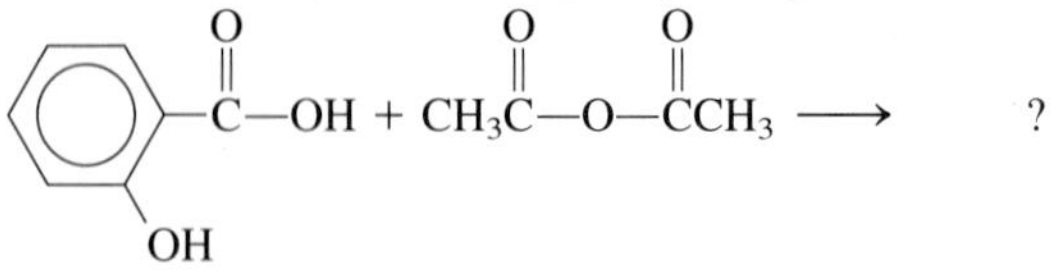

Salicylic acid   Acetylsalicylic
                               acid

12.31 Compound A ($C_6H_{12}O_2$) reacts with water, acid, and heat to yield compound B ($C_5H_{10}O_2$) and compound C (CH_4O). Compound B is acidic. Both compounds A and B contain a tetrahedral carbon atom. Deduce possible structures of compounds A, B, and C.

12.32 What products are formed when methyl *o*-bromobenzoate reacts with each of the following?
a. Aqueous acid and heat
b. Aqueous base and heat

Phosphoesters and Thioesters

12.33 By reacting phosphoric acid with an excess of ethanol, it is possible to obtain the mono-, di-, and triesters of phosphoric acid.

Draw all three of these products.

12.34 What is meant by a phosphoric anhydride bond?

12.35 We have described the molecule ATP as the body's energy storehouse. What do we mean by this designation? How does ATP actually store energy and provide it to the body as needed?

12.36 Write an equation for each of the following reactions:
a. Ribose + phosphoric acid
b. Methanol + phosphoric acid
c. Adenosine diphosphate + phosphoric acid

12.37 Draw the thioester bond between the acetyl group and coenzyme A.

12.38 Explain the significance of thioester formation in the metabolic pathways involved in fatty acid and carbohydrate breakdown.

12.39 It is also possible to form esters of other inorganic acids such as sulfuric acid and nitric acid. One particularly noteworthy product is nitroglycerine, which is both highly unstable (explosive) and widely used in the treatment of the heart condition known as angina, a constricting pain in the chest usually resulting from coronary heart disease. In the latter case its function is to alleviate the pain associated with angina. Nitroglycerine may be administered as a tablet (usually placed just beneath the tongue when needed) or as a salve or paste that can be applied to and absorbed through the skin. Nitroglycerine is the trinitroester of glycerol. Draw the structure of nitroglycerine, using the structure of glycerol provided below.

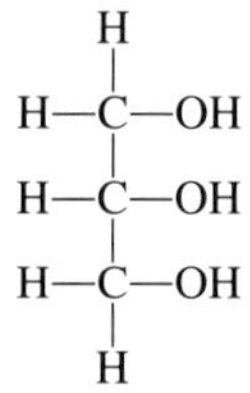

Glycerol

12.40 Show the structure of the thioester that would be formed between coenzyme A and stearic acid.

Further Problems

12.41 Provide the common and I.U.P.A.C. names for each of the following compounds:

a. 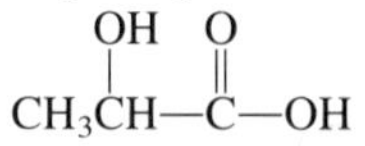 $CH_3\overset{\overset{\displaystyle OH}{|}}{CH}-\overset{\displaystyle O}{\overset{||}{C}}-OH$

b. $CH_3\overset{\overset{\displaystyle OH}{|}}{CH}CH_2-\overset{\displaystyle O}{\overset{||}{C}}-OH$

c. $CH_3\overset{\overset{\displaystyle CH_3}{|}}{\underset{\underset{\displaystyle CH_3}{|}}{C}}CH_2CH_2-\overset{\displaystyle O}{\overset{||}{C}}-OH$

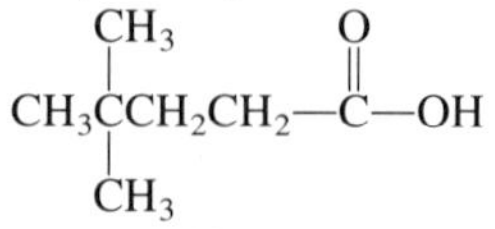

d. 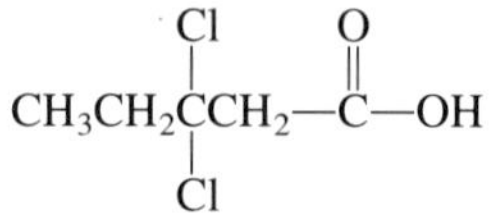 $CH_3CH_2\overset{\overset{\displaystyle Cl}{|}}{\underset{\underset{\displaystyle Cl}{|}}{C}}CH_2-\overset{\displaystyle O}{\overset{||}{C}}-OH$

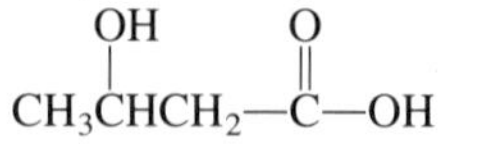

12.42 Draw the structure of each of the following carboxylic acids:
a. β-Chlorobutyric acid
b. α,β-Dibromovaleric acid
c. β,γ-Dihydroxybutyric acid
d. δ-Bromo-γ-chloro-β-methylcaproic acid

12.43 Describe the properties of low molecular weight carboxylic acids.

12.44 What are some of the biological functions of fatty acids, long chain carboxylic acids?

12.45 Why are citric acid and adipic acid added to some food products?

12.46 What is the function of lactic acid in food products? Of what significance is lactic acid in muscle metabolism?

12.47 How are carboxylic acids produced commercially?

12.48 Carboxylic acids are described as weak acids. What is meant by that description?

12.49 How is a soap prepared?

12.50 How do soaps assist the removal of oil and grease from clothing?

VOCABULARY QUIZ

12.1 The universal energy currency for all cells is _____.

12.2 A chemical reaction in which a bond is broken and a water molecule is released is called _____.

12.3 _____ is the hydrolysis of an ester by an aqueous base.

12.4 The long-chain carboxylic acids are called _____.

12.5 The conversion of an alcohol to a carboxylic acid is an example of a(n) _____ reaction.

12.6 _____ is the product of the reaction between a thiol and a carboxylic acid.

12.7 The characteristic functional group of the carboxylic acid derivatives is the _____.

12.8 The characteristic functional group of the carboxylic acids is the _____.

12.9 The product of the reaction between phosphoric acid and an alcohol is a(n) _____.

12.10 The alkali metal salt of a fatty acid is a(n) _____.

13

Lipids

LEARNING GOALS

◆ Be familiar with the physical and chemical properties and biological function of each of the families of lipids.

◆ Know the structure and functions of cell membranes.

◆ Write the structures of simple examples of each of the classes of lipids.

◆ Name the common lipids.

◆ Know the method of synthesizing glycerides and the reactions of glycerides: esterification, hydrolysis, saponification, and hydrogenation.

◆ Understand the functions of prostaglandins in physiological processes.

◆ Know how aspirin reduces pain.

◆ Be familiar with the steroid hormones.

◆ Understand the role of the lipoproteins in triglyceride and cholesterol transport in the body.

◆ Appreciate the roles of HDL, LDL, and cholesterol in heart disease.

Life-Saving Lipids

In the intensive-care nursery the premature infant struggles for life. Born three and a half months early, the baby weighs only 1.6 pounds, and the lungs labor to provide enough oxygen to keep the tiny body alive. Premature infants often have respiratory difficulties because they have not yet begun to produce *pulmonary surfactant.*

Pulmonary surfactant is a combination of phospholipids and proteins that reduces surface tension in the alveoli of the lungs. (Alveoli are the small, thin-walled air sacs in the lungs.) This allows efficient gas exchange across the membranes of the alveolar cells; oxygen can more easily diffuse from the air into the tissues and carbon dioxide can easily diffuse from the tissues into the air.

Without pulmonary surfactant, gas exchange in the lungs is very poor. Pulmonary surfactant is not produced until early in the sixth month of pregnancy. Premature babies born before they have begun secretion of natural surfactant suffer from *respiratory distress syndrome (RDS),* which is caused by the severe difficulty they have obtaining enough oxygen from the air that they breathe.

Until recently, RDS was a major cause of death among premature infants, but now a life-saving treatment is available. A fine aerosol of an artificial surfactant is administered directly into the trachea. The Burroughs Wellcome Company product EXOSURF® Neonatal™ contains the phospholipid lecithin to reduce surface tension; 1-hexadecanol, which spreads the lecithin; and a polymer called tyloxapol, which disperses both the lecithin and the 1-hexadecanol.

Artificial pulmonary surfactant therapy has dramatically reduced premature infant death caused by RDS and appears to have reduced overall mortality for all babies born weighing less than 700 g (about 1.5 pounds). Advances such as this have come about as a result of research on the makeup of body tissues and secretions in both healthy and diseased individuals. Often, such basic research provides the information needed to develop effective therapies.

In this chapter we will study the chemistry of lipids with a wide variety of structures and biological functions. Among these are the triglycerides that stock our adipose tissue, pain-producing prostaglandins, and steroids that determine our secondary sexual characteristics.

INTRODUCTION

Lipids seem to be the most controversial group of biological molecules, particularly in the fields of medicine and nutrition. One concern is the use of anabolic steroids by athletes. While these hormones increase muscle mass and enhance performance, we are just beginning to understand the damage they cause to the body.

We are concerned about what types of dietary fat we should consume. We hear frequent news about the amounts of saturated fats and cholesterol in our diets because a strong correlation has been found between these lipids and heart disease. Large quantities of dietary saturated fats may also predispose an individual to colon, esophageal, stomach, and breast cancers. Such results suggest that we should reduce our intake of cholesterol and saturated fats.

Standards of fat intake have not been experimentally determined. However, the most recent U.S. Dietary Guidelines recommend that dietary fat not exceed 30% of the daily caloric intake, and no more than 10% should be saturated fats.

The term **lipids** actually refers to a collection of organic molecules of varying chemical composition. They are grouped together on the basis of their solubility in nonpolar solvents. Lipids are commonly subdivided into four main groups:

1. *Fatty acids* (saturated and unsaturated)
2. *Glycerides* (glycerol-containing lipids)
3. *Nonglyceride lipids* (sphingolipids, steroids, waxes)
4. *Complex lipids* (lipoproteins and glycolipids)

13.1 BIOLOGICAL FUNCTIONS OF LIPIDS

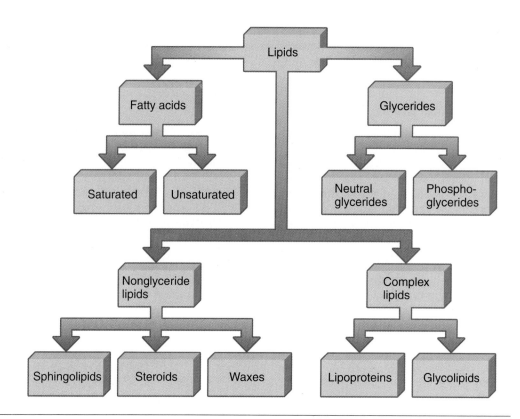

FIGURE 13.1
The classification of lipids.

In this chapter we examine the structure, properties, chemical reactions, and biological functions of each of the lipid groups shown in Figure 13.1.

As a result of differences in their structures, lipids serve many different functions in the human body. The following brief list will give you an idea of the importance of lipids in biological processes:

◆ *Energy source.* Like carbohydrates, lipids are an excellent source of energy for the body. When oxidized, each gram of fat releases 9 kilocalories of energy, more than twice the energy released by oxidation of a gram of carbohydrate.

◆ *Energy storage.* Most of the energy stored in the body is in the form of lipids (triglycerides). Stored in fat cells called *adipocytes,* these fats are a particularly rich source of energy for the body.

◆ *Cell membrane structural components.* Phospholipids make up the basic structure of all cell membranes. These membranes control the flow of molecules into and out of cells and allow cell-to-cell communication.

◆ *Hormones.* The steroid hormones are critical chemical messengers that allow tissues of the body to communicate with one another. The prostaglandins exert strong biological effects on both the cells that produce them and other cells of the body.

◆ *Vitamins.* The lipid-soluble vitamins, A, D, E, and K, play a major role in the regulation of several critical biological processes, including blood clotting and vision.

◆ *Vitamin absorption.* Dietary fat serves as a carrier of the lipid-soluble vitamins. All are transported into cells of the small intestine in association with fat molecules. Therefore a diet that is too low in fat can result in a deficiency of these four vitamins.

◆ *Protection.* Fats serve as a shock absorber, or protective layer, for the vital organs. About 4% of the total body fat is reserved for this critical function.

◆ *Insulation.* Fat stored beneath the skin (subcutaneous fat) serves to insulate the body from extremes of cold temperatures.

Fatty acids are long-chain monocarboxylic acids. As a consequence of their biosynthesis, fatty acids generally contain an *even number* of carbon atoms. The general formula for a **saturated fatty acid** is $CH_3(CH_2)_nCOOH$, where n is an even integer between 10 and 22. If $n = 16$, the result is an 18-carbon saturated fatty acid, stearic acid, having the following structural formula:

13.2 FATTY ACIDS

Structure and properties

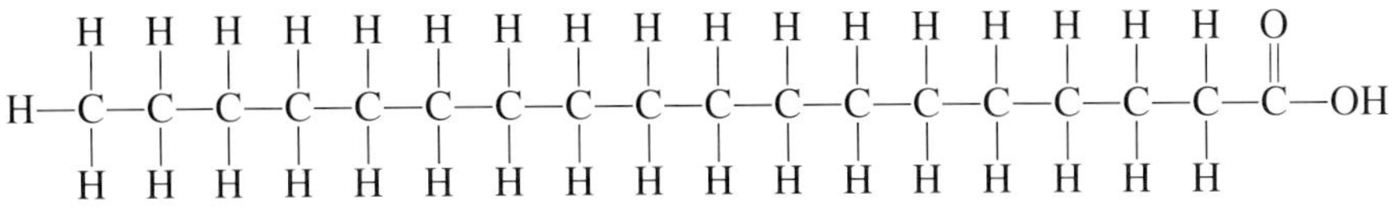

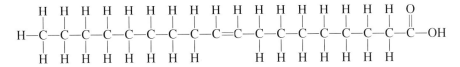

Notice that each of the carbons in the chain is bonded to the maximum number of hydrogen atoms. To help remember the structure of a saturated fatty acid, you might think of each carbon in the chain being "saturated" with hydrogen atoms. Examples of common saturated fatty acids are given in Table 13.1. An example of an **unsaturated fatty acid** is the 18-carbon unsaturated fatty acid oleic acid, which has the following structural formula:

The saturated fatty acids may be thought of as derivatives of alkanes, the saturated hydrocarbons described in Chapter 9.

In the case of unsaturated fatty acids there is at least one carbon-to-carbon double bond. Because of the double bonds, the carbon atoms involved in these bonds are not "saturated" with hydrogen atoms. Examples of common unsaturated fatty acids are also given in Table 13.1.

The unsaturated fatty acids may be thought of as derivatives of the alkenes, the unsaturated hydrocarbons discussed in Chapter 9.

TABLE 13.1 Common Saturated and Unsaturated Fatty Acids

Common Saturated Fatty Acids

Common Name	I.U.P.A.C. Name	Melting Point (°C)	RCOOH Formula	Condensed Formula
Capric	Decanoic	32	$C_9H_{19}COOH$	$CH_3(CH_2)_8COOH$
Lauric	Dodecanoic	44	$C_{11}H_{23}COOH$	$CH_3(CH_2)_{10}COOH$
Myristic	Tetradecanoic	54	$C_{13}H_{27}COOH$	$CH_3(CH_2)_{12}COOH$
Palmitic	Hexadecanoic	63	$C_{15}H_{31}COOH$	$CH_3(CH_2)_{14}COOH$
Stearic	Octadecanoic	70	$C_{17}H_{35}COOH$	$CH_3(CH_2)_{16}COOH$
Arachidic	Eicosanoic	77	$C_{19}H_{39}COOH$	$CH_3(CH_2)_{18}COOH$

Common Unsaturated Fatty Acids

Common Name	I.U.P.A.C. Name	Melting Point (°C)	RCOOH Formula	Number of Double Bonds	Position of Double Bonds
Palmitoleic	*cis*-9-Hexadecenoic	0	$C_{15}H_{29}COOH$	1	9
Oleic	*cis*-9-Octadecenoic	16	$C_{17}H_{33}COOH$	1	9
Linoleic	*cis,cis*-9,12-Octadecadienoic	5	$C_{17}H_{31}COOH$	2	9, 12
Linolenic	All *cis*-9,12,15-Octadecatrienoic	−11	$C_{17}H_{29}COOH$	3	9, 12, 15
Arachidonic	All *cis*-5,8,11,14-Eicosatetraenoic	−50	$C_{19}H_{31}COOH$	4	5, 8, 11, 14

Condensed Formula

Palmitoleic	$CH_3(CH_2)_5CH{=}CH(CH_2)_7COOH$
Oleic	$CH_3(CH_2)_7CH{=}CH(CH_2)_7COOH$
Linoleic	$CH_3(CH_2)_4CH{=}CH{-}CH_2{-}CH{=}CH(CH_2)_7COOH$
Linolenic	$CH_3CH_2CH{=}CH{-}CH_2{-}CH{=}CH{-}CH_2{-}CH{=}CH(CH_2)_7COOH$
Arachidonic	$CH_3(CH_2)_4CH{=}CH{-}CH_2{-}CH{=}CH{-}CH_2{-}CH{=}CH{-}CH_2{-}CH{=}CH{-}(CH_2)_3COOH$

EXAMPLE 13.1

Writing the Structural Formula of an Unsaturated Fatty Acid

Draw the structural formula for palmitoleic acid

Solution

The I.U.P.A.C. name of palmitoleic acid is *cis*-9-hexadecenoic acid. The name tells us that this is a sixteen-carbon fatty acid having a carbon-to-carbon double bond between carbons 9 and 10. The name also reveals that this is the *cis* isomer.

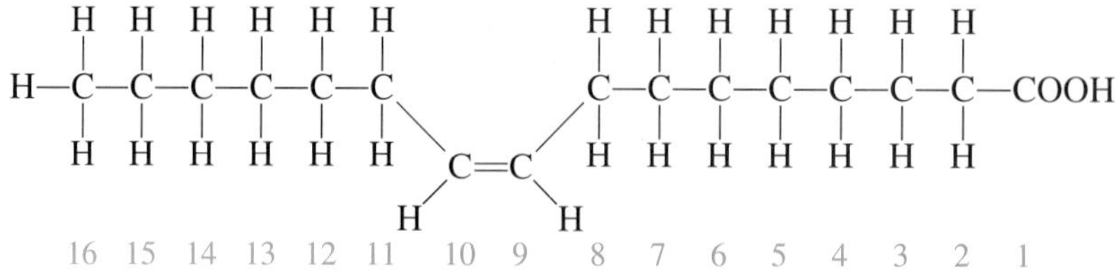

Section 9.2

The melting points of saturated fatty acids increase with increasing carbon number, as is the case with alkanes. Saturated fatty acids containing ten or more carbons are solids at room temperature. The same effect is seen with unsaturated fatty acids. However, the melting points also decrease markedly as the number of C=C units increases (Table 13.1).

QUESTION 13.1

Draw formulas for each of the following fatty acids:

a. Oleic acid $(C_{17}H_{33}COOH)$

b. Lauric acid

c. Linoleic acid

d. Stearic acid $C_{17}H_{35}COOH$

QUESTION 13.2

What is the I.U.P.A.C. name for each of the fatty acids in Question 13.1? (*Hint:* Review the naming of carboxylic acids in Section 12.1)

Chemical reactions of fatty acids

The reactions of fatty acids are identical to those of short-chain carboxylic acids. The major reactions that they undergo include esterification, hydrolysis, acid-base reactions, and addition at the double bond.

Esterification

Sections 12.1 and 12.2

In **esterification,** fatty acids react with alcohols to form esters and water according to the following general reaction:

$$R_1-\overset{\overset{\displaystyle O}{\|}}{C}-OH + HOR_2 \longrightarrow R_1-\overset{\overset{\displaystyle O}{\|}}{C}-OR_2 + H_2O$$

Acid   Alcohol   Ester   Water

Acid hydrolysis

Section 12.2

Recall that **hydrolysis** is the reverse of esterification, producing fatty acids from esters:

$$R_1-\overset{\overset{\displaystyle O}{\|}}{C}-OR_2 + HO-H \xrightarrow{\text{H}^+} R_1-\overset{\overset{\displaystyle O}{\|}}{C}-OH + R_2OH$$

Ester   Water   Acid   Alcohol

Saponification

Saponification is the base-catalyzed hydrolysis of an ester:

Sections 12.1 and 12.2

$$R_1\!-\!\overset{\displaystyle O}{\overset{\|}{C}}\!-\!OR_2 + NaOH \longrightarrow R_1\!-\!\overset{\displaystyle O}{\overset{\|}{C}}\!-\!O^-Na^+ + R_2OH$$

Ester　　　　Base　　　　　　　　Salt　　　　　　Alcohol

The product of this reaction, an ionized salt, is, a soap. Because soaps have a long uncharged hydrocarbon tail and a negatively charged terminus, they form micelles that dissolve oil and dirt particles. Thus the dirt is emulsified and broken into small particles and can be rinsed away.

Reaction at the double bond (unsaturated fatty acids)

Hydrogenation is an example of an addition reaction. The following is a typical example of the addition of hydrogen to a double bond of a fatty acid:

Section 9.3

$$CH_3(CH_2)_4CH\!=\!CHCH_2CH\!=\!CH(CH_2)_7COOH \xrightarrow{\ 2H_2,\ Ni\ } CH_3(CH_2)_{16}COOH$$

Linoleic acid　　　　　　　　　　　　　　　　　Stearic acid

Hydrogenation is used in the food industry to convert polyunsaturated vegetable oils into saturated solid fats. Margarine would be liquid at room temperature, but hydrogenation converts it to a spreadable solid with properties similar to those of butter. Artificial coloring is added to margarine to give it the same color as butter.

QUESTION 13.3

Write out the complete equation for each of the following reactions:

a.　Esterification of lauric acid and ethanol

b.　Reaction of oleic acid with NaOH

c.　Hydrogenation of arachidonic acid

QUESTION 13.4

Write out the complete equation for each of the following reactions:

a.　Esterification of capric acid and 2-pentanol

b.　Reaction of lauric acid with KOH

c.　Hydrogenation of palmitoleic acid

Some of the unsaturated fatty acids containing more than one double bond cannot be synthesized by the body. For instance, linolenic acid and linoleic acid (see Table 13.1) are called **essential fatty acids** because they must be supplied in the diet. Linoleic acid is required for the biosynthesis of **arachidonic acid,** the precursor of a class of hormonelike molecules known as the **prostaglandins.**

Prostaglandins are extremely potent biological molecules with hormonelike activity. They received the name "prostaglandins" because they were originally isolated from seminal fluid produced in the prostate gland, but more recently they also have been isolated from most animal tissues. Prostaglandins are unsaturated carboxylic acids consisting of a twenty-carbon skeleton that contains a five-carbon ring. Several general classes of prostaglandins are grouped under the designations A, B, E, and F, among others. The examples in Figure 13.2 illustrate the general structure of prostaglandins and the current nomenclature system.

Prostaglandins are made in all tissues, and they exert their biological effects on the cells that produce them and on other cells in the immediate vicinity. Because the prostaglandins affect so

Prostaglandins

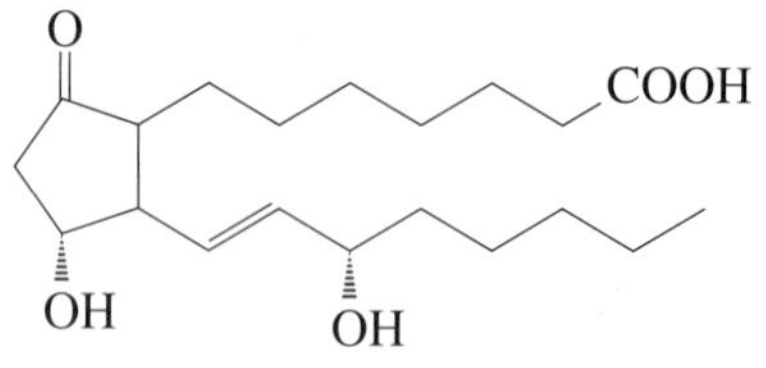

Prostaglandin E$_1$

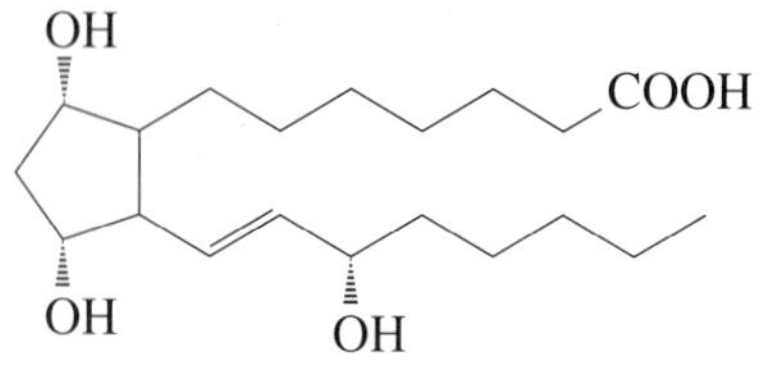

Prostaglandin F$_1$

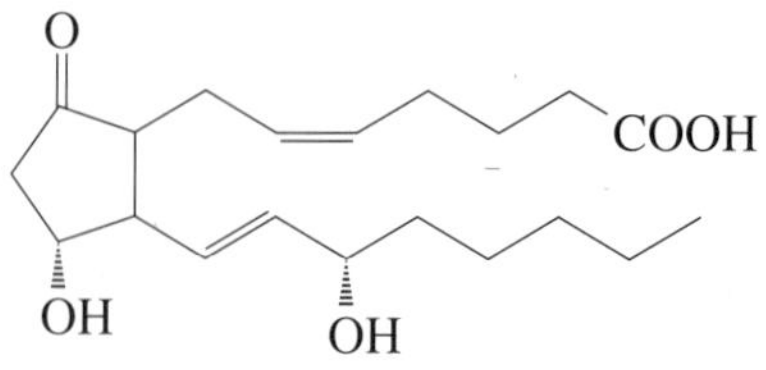

Prostaglandin E$_2$

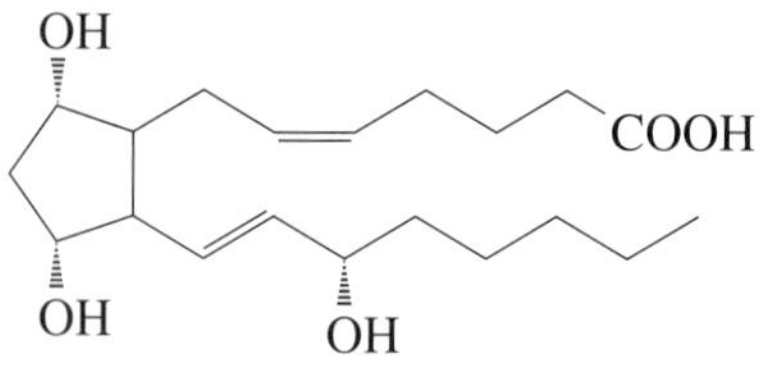

Prostaglandin F$_2$

FIGURE 13.2
The structures of four prostaglandins.

many body processes and often cause opposing effects in different tissues, it can be difficult to keep track of their many regulatory functions. The following is a brief summary of some of the biological processes that are thought to be regulated by these hormonelike molecules.

- *Blood clotting.* Blood clots form when a blood vessel is damaged, yet such clotting along the walls of undamaged vessels could result in heart attack or stroke. The prostaglandinlike molecule thromboxane A$_2$, secreted by platelets, stimulates the clotting process. Conversely, PGI$_2$ (prostacyclin), produced in the cells lining the blood vessel, inhibits clot formation and thus prevents the untimely production of blood clots.

- *The inflammatory response.* The inflammatory response is a protective mechanism that is initiated when tissue is damaged by mechanical injury, burns, or invasion by microorganisms. This causes the swelling, redness, fever, and pain associated with such injuries. Prostaglandins promote the pain and fever caused by the inflammatory response. Drugs such as aspirin block prostaglandin synthesis and help relieve the symptoms.

- *Reproductive system.* PGE$_2$ stimulates smooth muscle contraction, particularly uterine contractions during labor. There is strong evidence that dysmenorrhea (painful menstruation) suffered by many women may be the result of an excess of two prostaglandins. Drugs that inhibit prostaglandin synthesis are found to provide virtually complete relief from these symptoms.

- *Gastrointestinal tract.* Prostaglandins both inhibit the secretion of acid and increase the secretion of a protective mucous layer into the stomach. In this way they help protect the stomach lining. Prolonged use of aspirin, which inhibits prostaglandin synthesis, may lead to ulceration of the stomach lining.

- *Respiratory tract.* Prostaglandinlike molecules called *leukotrienes* promote the constriction of the bronchi associated with asthma. Other prostaglandins promote bronchodilation.

As mentioned above, prostaglandins stimulate the inflammatory response and, as a result, are partially responsible for the cascade of events that causes pain. Aspirin has long been known to alleviate such pain, and we now know that it does so by inhibiting the synthesis of prostaglandins.

The first step of prostaglandin synthesis (Figure 13.3) is the conversion of arachidonic acid to PGH$_2$ by the enzyme *cyclooxygenase.* This reaction occurs in all tissues that are able to produce prostaglandins. The conversion of PGH$_2$ into the other biologically active forms requires the appropriate enzymes, which are found only in certain tissues.

Aspirin works by inhibiting cyclooxygenase, which catalyzes the first step in prostaglandin synthesis. The acetyl group from aspirin becomes covalently linked to the enzyme, causing it to be inactivated (Figure 13.4). Because cyclooxygenase is one of the steps that occurs in all cells, aspirin effectively inhibits synthesis of all the prostaglandins.

13.3 GLYCERIDES

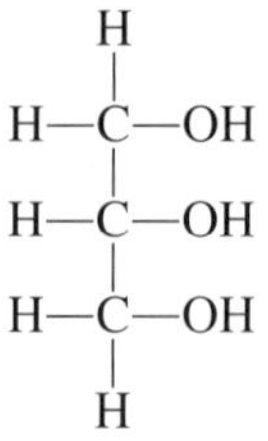

Glycerol

Glycerides are lipids that contain the glycerol molecule. They may be subdivided into two classes: neutral glycerides and phosphoglycerides. Neutral glycerides are nonionic and nonpolar. Phosphoglyceride molecules have a polar region, the phosphoryl group, in addition to the nonpolar fatty acid tails. The structures of each of these types of glycerides are critical to their function.

Neutral glycerides

The esterification of glycerol with a fatty acid produces a **neutral glyceride.** Esterification may occur at one, two, or all three positions, producing **monoglycerides, diglycerides,** or **triglycerides.** You will also see these referred to as mono-, di-, or triacylglycerols.

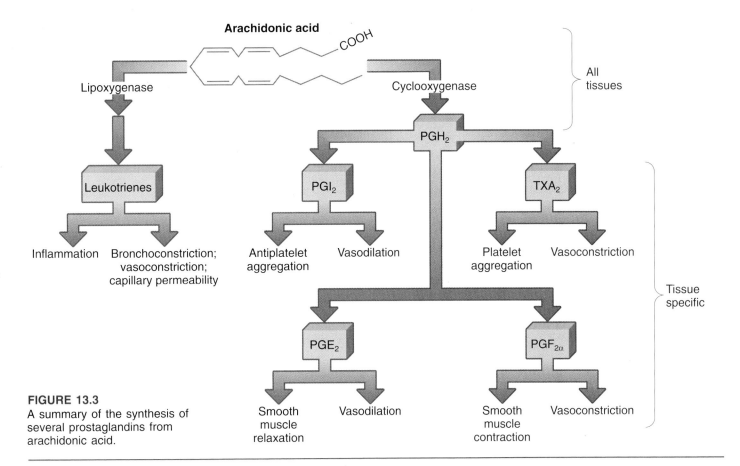

FIGURE 13.3
A summary of the synthesis of several prostaglandins from arachidonic acid.

Writing an Equation for the Synthesis of a Monoglyceride

Solution

$$
\begin{array}{cccc}
\text{H} & & \text{H} \quad \text{O} & \\
| & & | \quad \| & \\
\text{H—C—OH} & \text{O} & \text{H—C—O—C—R} & \\
| & \| & | & \\
\text{H—C—OH} + \text{R—C—OH} \rightleftharpoons & \text{H—C—OH} & + \text{H}_2\text{O} \\
| & & | & \\
\text{H—C—OH} & & \text{H—C—OH} & \\
| & & | & \\
\text{H} & & \text{H} &
\end{array}
$$

Glycerol   Fatty acid   Monoglyceride   Water

Aspirin
(acetylsalicylate)
+
Enzyme—NH₂

Inactive enzyme
+
Salicylate

FIGURE 13.4
Aspirin inhibits the synthesis of prostaglandins by acetylating the enzyme cyclooxygenase. The acetylated enzyme is no longer functional.

Although monoglycerides and diglycerides are present in nature, the most important neutral glycerides are the triglycerides, the major component of fat cells. The triglyceride consists of a glycerol backbone (shown in black below) joined to three fatty acid units through ester bonds (shown in red below). The formation of a triglyceride is shown in the following reaction:

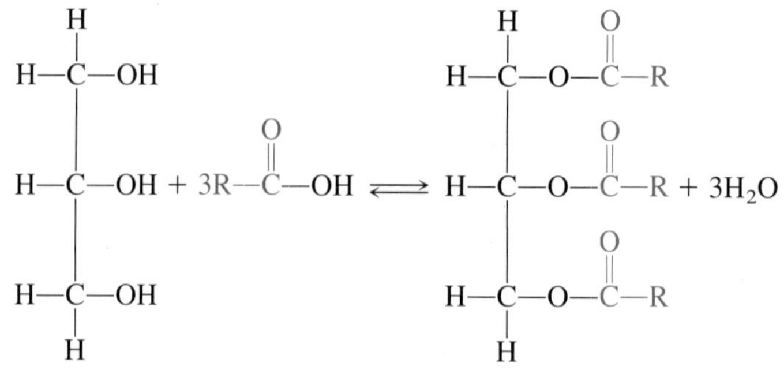

Glycerol   Fatty acids   Triglyceride   Water

A common example of a triglyceride is glyceryl tristearate:

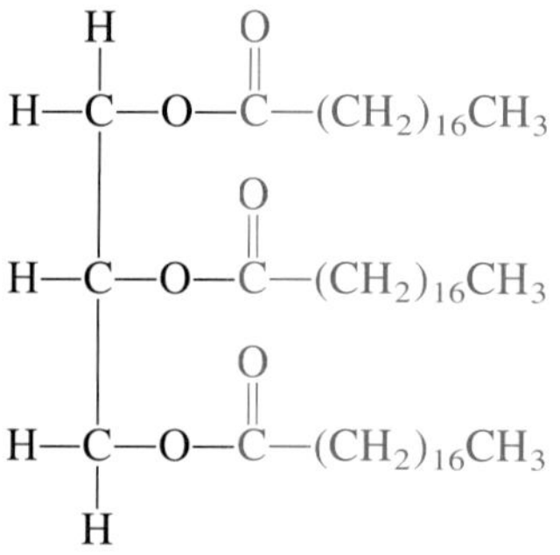

Glyceryl tristearate (tristearin)

A triglyceride is named by combining the ''backbone'' name, glyceryl (from glycerol), with the fatty acid name. The prefix tri- is used because three stearic acid units are attached to the glycerol backbone. Triglycerides may also have two or three different fatty acyl groups.

Neutral glycerides are neutral because bonding throughout the molecule is covalent. These long molecules readily stack with one another and constitute the majority of the lipids stored in the body's fat cells.

The principal function of triglycerides in biochemical systems is the storage of energy. If more energy-rich nutrients are consumed than are required for metabolic processes, much of the excess is converted to neutral glycerides and stored as triglycerides in fat cells of *adipose tissue.* When energy is needed, the triglycerides are metabolized by the body, and energy is released. For this reason, exercise, along with moderate reduction in caloric intake, is recommended for overweight individuals. Exercise, an energy-demanding process, increases the rate of metabolism of fats and results in weight loss.

Section 18.1

See also ''A Human Perspective: Losing Those Unwanted Pounds of Adipose Tissue'' in Chapter 18.

Phosphoglycerides

Phospholipids are a group of lipids containing a phosphoryl group (PO_4^{3-}). The presence of the phosphoryl group results in a molecule with a polar head (the phosphoryl group) and a nonpolar tail (the alkyl chain of the fatty acid). Because the phosphoryl group ionizes in solution, a charged lipid results.

The most abundant membrane lipids are derived from glycerol-3-phosphate and are known as **phosphoglycerides.** Phosphoglycerides contain acyl groups derived from long-chain fatty acids at C-1 and C-2 of glycerol-3-phosphate. At C-3 the phosphoryl group is joined to glycerol by a phosphoester bond. The simplest phosphoglyceride contains a free phosphoryl group and is known as a **phosphatidate** (Figure 13.5). When the phosphoryl group is attached to another hydrophilic molecule, a more complex phosphoglyceride is formed. For example, *phosphatidylcholine (lecithin)* and *phosphatidylethanolamine (cephalin)* are found in the membranes of most cells (Figure 13.5).

Section 12.3

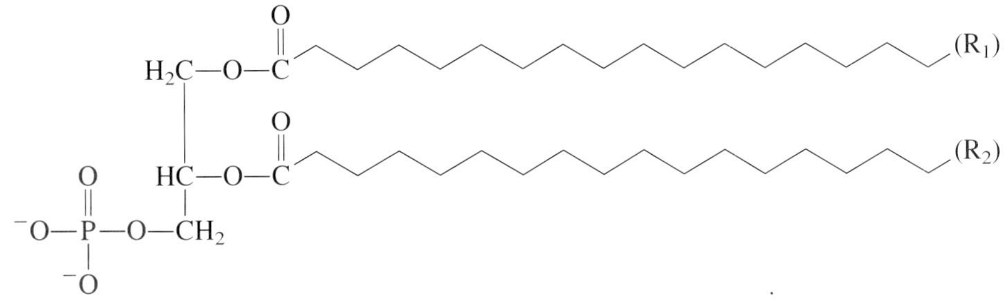

Phosphatidate
(a)

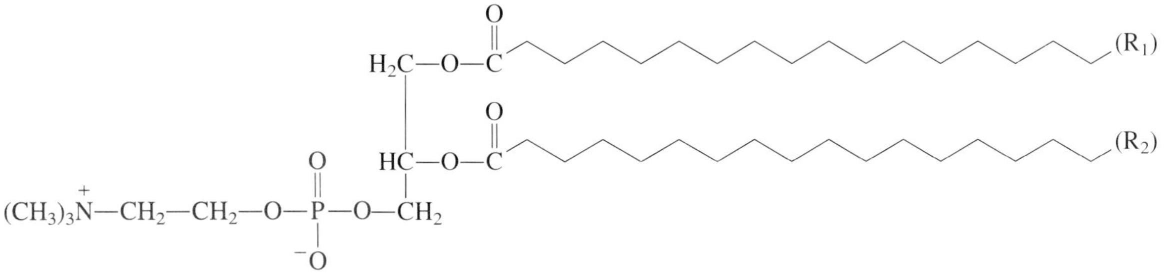

Phosphatidylcholine (lecithin)
(b)

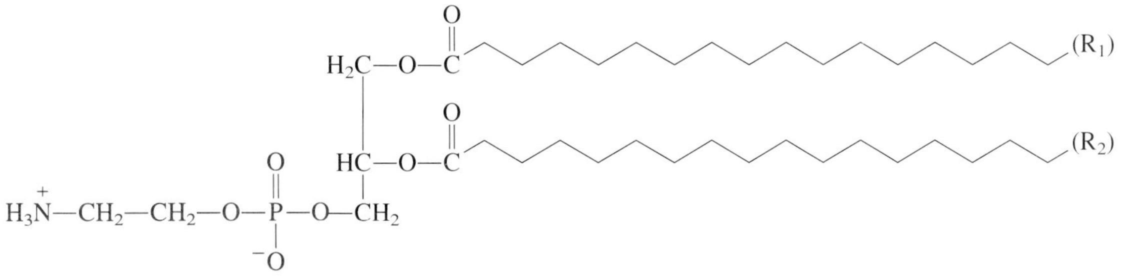

Phosphatidylethanolamine (cephalin)
(c)

FIGURE 13.5
The structures of (a) phosphatidate and the common membrane phospholipids, (b) phosphatidylcholine (lecithin), and (c) phosphatidylethanolamine (cephalin).

Lecithin possesses a polar "head" and a nonpolar "tail." This structure is similar to that of soap and detergent molecules, discussed earlier. The ionic "head" is hydrophilic and interacts with water molecules, while the nonpolar "tail" is hydrophobic and interacts with nonpolar molecules. This bipolar nature is central to the structure and function of cell membranes.

In addition to being a component of cell membranes, lecithin is the major phospholipid in pulmonary surfactant. It is also found in egg yolks and soybeans and is used as an emulsifying agent in ice cream. An **emulsifying agent** aids in the suspension of fats in water. The bipolar lecithin serves as a bridge, holding together two noncompatible substances.

See "Life-Saving Lipids," the Chemistry Connection at the beginning of this chapter.

Cephalin is similar in general structure to lecithin; the amino alcohol group bonded to the phosphoryl group is the only difference.

QUESTION 13.5

Using condensed formulas, draw the mono-, di-, and triglycerides that would result from the esterification of glycerol with each of the following acids:

a. Oleic acid
b. Capric acid
c. Palmitic acid
d. Lauric acid

Name the triglycerides that are produced in the reactions discussed in Question 13.5.

The structure of biological membranes

Biological membranes are *lipid bilayers* of phospholipids in which the hydrophobic hydrocarbon tails are packed in the center of the bilayer and the ionic head groups are exposed on the surface (Figure 13.6). Lipid bilayers form because the hydrocarbon tails of the phospholipids need to escape from water. The hydrocarbon tails of membrane phospholipids provide a thin shell of nonpolar material that prevents mixing of molecules on either side of the membrane. The nonpolar tails of membrane phospholipids thus provide a barrier between the cell and its surroundings. The polar heads of phospholipids are exposed to water and are highly solvated.

The fluid mosaic structure of biological membranes

Membranes are not static; they are composed of molecules in motion. The fluidity of biological membranes is determined by the proportion of saturated and unsaturated fatty acids in the membrane phospholipids. About half of the fatty acids isolated from membrane lipids are unsaturated. We also find that the percentage of unsaturated fatty acid groups in membrane lipids is inversely proportional to the temperature of the environment. Bacteria, for example, have different ratios of saturated and unsaturated fatty acids in their membrane lipids depending on the temperatures of their surroundings. The membranes of bacteria that grow in the Arctic Ocean have high levels of unsaturated fatty acids so that their membranes remain fluid even at these frigid temperatures. On the other hand, the organisms that live in the hot springs of Yellowstone National Park, with temperatures near the boiling point of water, have membranes with high levels of saturated fatty acids. This flexibility in fatty acid content enables the bacteria to maintain the same membrane fluidity over a temperature range of almost 100°C.

An inverse relationship between two variables simply means that one variable increases in magnitude as the other decreases (Appendix A).

FIGURE 13.6
(a) Schematic diagram of a phospholipid bilayer. (b) Space-filling model of a membrane phospholipid.

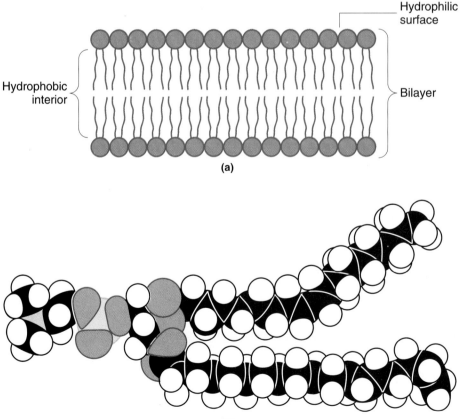

Hydrophilic surface

Hydrophobic interior

Bilayer

(a)

(b)

Generally, the body temperatures of mammals are quite constant, and the fatty acid composition of their membrane lipids is usually very uniform. One interesting exception is the reindeer. Much of the year, reindeer must travel through ice and snow. Therefore their hooves and lower legs must continue to function at much colder temperatures than the rest of the body experiences. Because of this, the percentage of unsaturation in the membranes varies along the length of the reindeer's leg, so the proportion of unsaturated fatty acid groups is greater closer to the hoof. The lower melting points and greater fluidity of lipids that contain a high proportion of unsaturated fatty acid groups permit the membranes to function in the low temperatures of ice and snow to which the hoof is exposed.

Thus membranes are fluid, regardless of the environmental temperature conditions. In fact, it is believed that they have the consistency of olive oil.

Embedded within the phospholipid bilayer are many proteins and glycoproteins. When viewed by electron microscopy, the membrane appears to be a *mosaic,* studded with proteins. Because of the fluidity of membranes and the physical appearance, our concept of membrane structure is called the **fluid mosaic model** (Figure 13.7).

Some of the proteins are called **peripheral proteins** because they are bound to only one of the surfaces of the membrane. Other membrane proteins, termed **transmembrane proteins,** are embedded within the membrane and extend completely through it, being exposed both inside and outside the cell. These membrane proteins and glycoproteins carry out many vital functions for the cell. Some of them serve as receptors for hormones, and many are involved in cell-to-cell recognition and communication. Others are channels or gates through which required nutrients and ions enter or leave the cell.

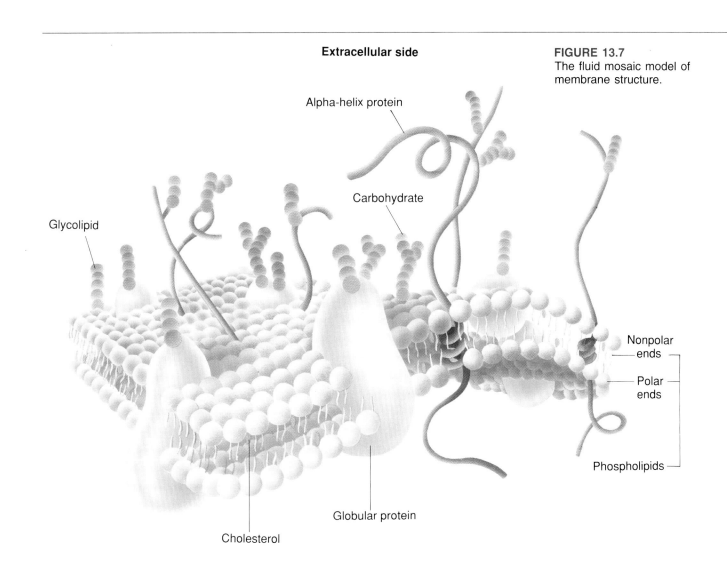

Extracellular side

FIGURE 13.7
The fluid mosaic model of membrane structure.

Alpha-helix protein

Carbohydrate

Glycolipid

Nonpolar ends

Polar ends

Phospholipids

Globular protein

Cholesterol

A CLINICAL PERSPECTIVE

Antibiotics That Destroy Membranes

The "age of antibiotics" began in 1927 when Alexander Fleming discovered, quite by accident, that a product of the mold *Penicillium* can kill susceptible bacteria. We now know that penicillin inhibits bacterial growth by interfering with cell wall synthesis. Since Fleming's time, hundreds of antibiotics, which are microbial products that either kill or inhibit the growth of susceptible bacteria or fungi, have been discovered. The key to antibiotic therapy is to find a "target" in the microbe, a metabolic process or structure that the human does not have. In this way the antibiotic will selectively inhibit the disease-causing organism without harming the patient.

Many antibiotics disrupt cell membranes. The cell membrane is not an ideal target for antibiotic therapy because all cells, human and bacterial, have membranes. Therefore both types of cells would be damaged. Because these antibiotics exhibit a wide range of toxic side-effects when ingested, they are usually used to combat infections topically (on body surfaces). In this way, damage to the host is minimized but the inhibitory effect on the microbe is maximized.

Polymyxins are antibiotics produced by the bacterium *Bacillus polymyxa.* They are protein derivatives having one end that is highly hydrophobic because of an attached fatty acid. The opposite end is highly hydrophilic. Because of these properties, the polymyxins bind to membranes with the hydrophobic end embedded within the membrane, while the hydrophilic end remains outside the cell. As a result, the integrity of the membrane is disrupted, and leakage of cellular constituents occurs, causing cell death.

Although the polymyxins have been found to be useful in treating some urinary tract infections, pneumonias, and infections of burn patients, other antibiotics are now favored because of the toxic effects of the polymyxins on the kidney and central nervous system. Polymyxin B is still used topically and is available as an over-the-counter ointment in combination with two other antibiotics, neomycin and bacitracin.

Amphotericin B

Nystatin

The structures of amphotericin B and nystatin, two antifungal antibiotics.

Two other antibiotics that destroy membranes, amphotericin B and nystatin, are large ring structures that are used in treating serious systemic fungal infections. These antibiotics form complexes with cholesterol in the fungal cell membrane, and they disrupt the membrane permeability and cause leakage of cellular constituents. Neither is useful in treating bacterial infections because most bacteria have no cholesterol in their membranes. Both amphotericin B and nystatin are extremely toxic and cause symptoms that include nausea and vomiting, fever and chills, anemia, and renal failure. It is easy to understand why the use of these drugs is restricted to treatment of life-threatening fungal diseases.

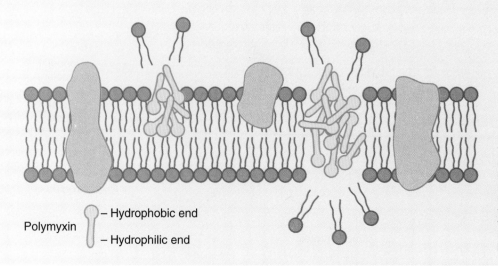

Polymyxin — Hydrophobic end / — Hydrophilic end

The mechanism of action of polymyxins. The hydrophilic end of these peptide derivatives remains outside the cell, while the hydrophobic end is embedded within the membrane. In this way it acts like a detergent, disrupting membrane integrity and killing the cell.

Since the lipid bilayer is fluid, these membrane proteins can float freely within the membrane. Thus we can think of the fluid mosaic membrane as being analogous to an ocean filled with mobile, floating icebergs.

Sphingolipids are lipids that are not derived from glycerol. They are phospholipids, because they contain a phosphoryl group, and are derived from sphingosine, a nitrogen-containing (amino) alcohol:

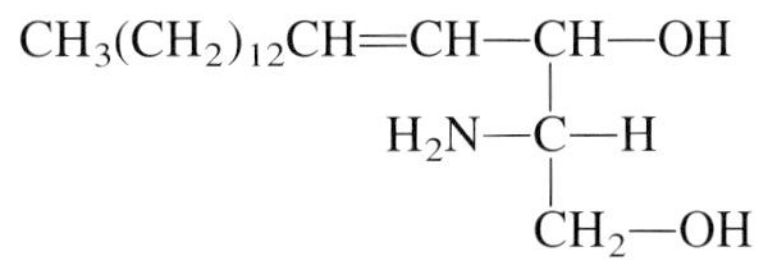

13.4 NONGLYCERIDE LIPIDS

Sphingolipids

$$CH_3(CH_2)_{12}CH{=}CH{-}CH{-}OH$$
$$H_2N{-}C{-}H$$
$$CH_2{-}OH$$

Sphingosine

The **sphingomyelins** are an important class of sphingolipids:

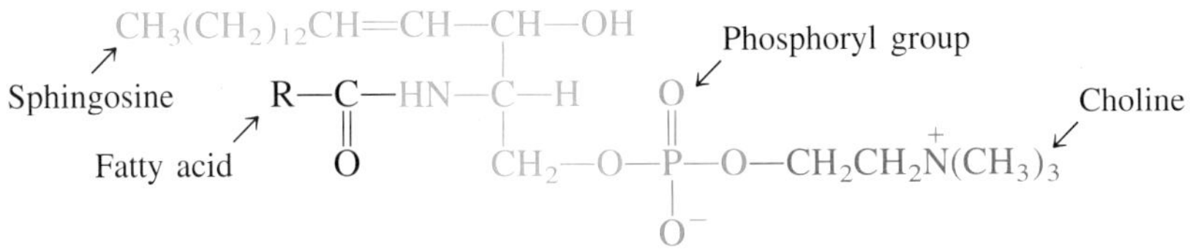

Sphingomyelin

Sphingomyelins are located throughout the body but function principally in brain and nerve tissue. They are found in abundance in the myelin sheath that surrounds and insulates cells of the central nervous system. In humans, about 25% of the lipids of the myelin sheath are sphingomyelins. Their role is essential to proper cerebral function and nerve transmission.

Steroids are a naturally occurring family of organic molecules of biochemical and medical interest. A great deal of controversy has surrounded various steroids. We worry about the amount of cholesterol in the diet and the possible health effects. We are concerned about the use of anabolic steroids by athletes wishing to build muscle mass and improve their performance. However, members of this family of molecules derived from cholesterol have many important functions in the body. The bile salts that aid in the emulsification and digestion of lipids are steroid molecules, as are the sex hormones testosterone and estrone.

The steroids are members of a large, diverse collection of lipids called the *isoprenoids*. All of these compounds are built from one or more five-carbon units called *isoprene*.

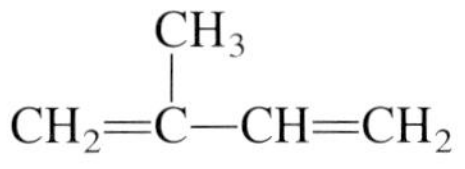

Terpene is the general term for lipids that are synthesized from isoprene units. Thus the steroids and bile salts, the lipid-soluble vitamins, chlorophyll, and certain plant hormones are all terpenes.

All steroids contain the steroid nucleus (steroid carbon skeleton) as shown here:

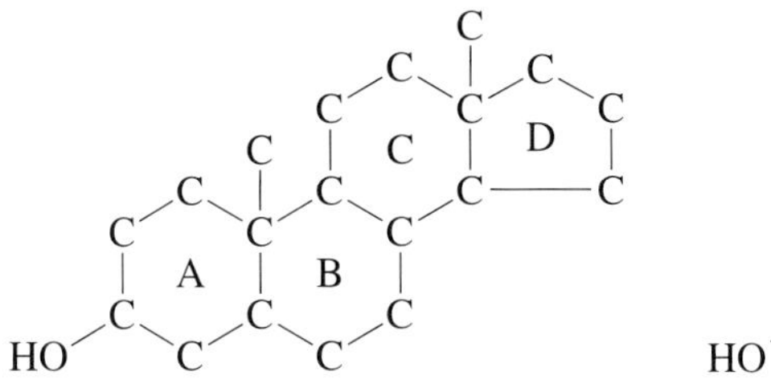

Steroids

Section 18.1

$$CH_2{=}\underset{\underset{CH_3}{|}}{C}{-}CH{=}CH_2$$

Isoprene

The structure and function of the lipid-soluble vitamins are found in Appendix D, "The Lipid-Soluble Vitamins."

Carbon skeleton of
the steroid nucleus

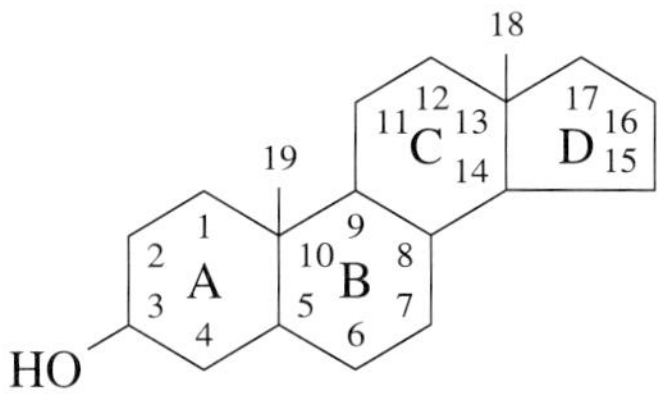

Steroid nucleus

A HUMAN PERSPECTIVE

Anabolic Steroids and Athletics

In the 1988 Summer Olympics, Ben Johnson of Canada ran the fastest 100-meter race in history, 9.79 seconds, and was awarded the Gold Medal. Little more than two days later, Michele Verdier of the International Olympic Committee stood at a press conference and read the following statement: "The urine sample of Ben Johnson, Canada, Athletics, 100 meters, collected Saturday, 24th September 1988, was found to contain metabolites of a banned substance, namely stanozolol, an anabolic steroid." Johnson was disqualified, and Carl Lewis of the United States became the Olympic Gold Medalist in the 100-meter race.

Why do athletes competing in power sports take anabolic steroids? Use of anabolic steroids has a number of desirable effects for the athlete. First, they help build the muscle mass needed to succeed in sprints or weight lifting. They hasten the healing of muscle damage caused by the intense training of the competitive athlete. Finally, anabolic steroids may help the athlete maintain an aggressive attitude, not just during the competition but also throughout training.

If these hormones have such beneficial effects, why not allow all athletes to use them? Unfortunately, the beneficial effects are far outweighed by the negative side-effects.

Stanozolol

These include kidney and liver damage, stroke, impotence and infertility, an increase in cardiovascular disease, and extremely aggressive behavior.

Even though these life-threatening side-effects are well known, athletes continue to use anabolic steroids. The temptation must have been too great for Ben Johnson. After a period of suspension from amateur athletics, Johnson again entered competition. In March 1993, testing before a track meet revealed that he had used anabolic steroids to enhance his performance. As a result, he was forever banned from amateur competition.

The steroid carbon skeleton consists of four fused rings. Each ring pair has two carbons in common. Thus two fused rings share one or more common bonds as part of their ring backbones. For example, rings A and B, B and C, and C and D are all fused in the preceding structure. Many steroids commonly contain two methyl groups, carbons 18 and 19, as part of their carbon skeleton.

Section 13.5

Cholesterol, a common steroid, is found in the membranes of most animal cells. It is readily soluble in the hydrophobic region of membranes and is involved in regulation of the fluidity of the membrane. There is a strong correlation between the concentration of cholesterol found in the blood plasma and heart disease, particularly **atherosclerosis** (hardening of the arteries). Cholesterol, in combination with other substances, appears to coat the arteries, causing a narrowing of the passageway. As narrowing increases, more pressure is necessary to ensure adequate blood flow, and high blood pressure *(hypertension)* develops. Hypertension is also linked to heart disease.

Cholesterol

Egg yolks contain a high concentration of cholesterol, as do many other dairy products and animal fats, so it has been recommended that the amounts of these products in the diet be regulated to moderate the dietary intake of cholesterol.

Steroids play a role in the reproductive cycle. In a series of chemical reactions, cholesterol is converted to the steroid *progesterone,* the most important hormone associated with pregnancy. Produced in the ovaries and in the placenta, progesterone is responsible for both the successful initiation and the successful completion of pregnancy. It prepares the lining of the uterus to accept the fertilized egg. Once the egg is attached, progesterone is involved in the development of the fetus and plays a role in the suppression of further ovulation during pregnancy.

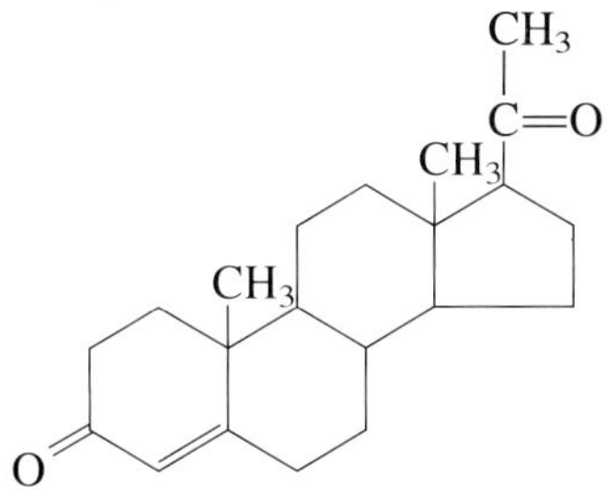

Progesterone

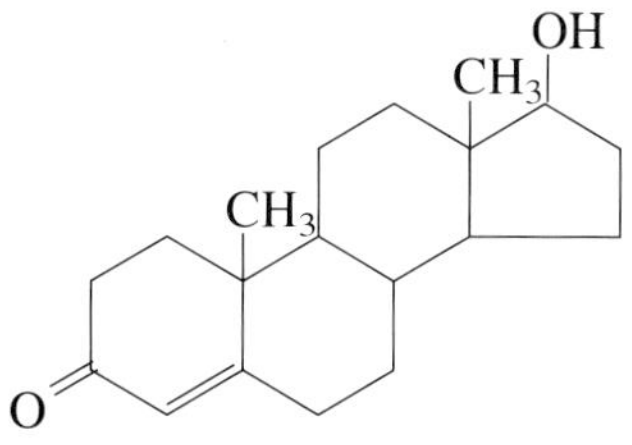

Testosterone

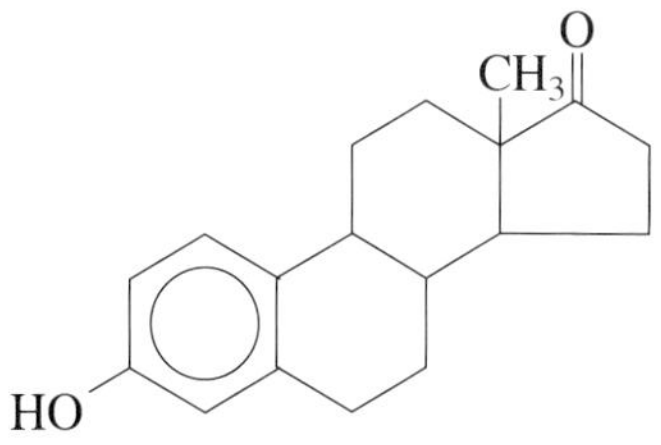

Estrone

Testosterone, a male sex hormone found in the testes, and *estrone,* a female sex hormone, are both produced by the chemical modification of progesterone. These hormones are involved in the development of the traditional male and female sex characteristics.

Many steroids, including progesterone, have played important roles in the development of birth control agents. 19-Norprogesterone was one of the first synthetic birth control agents. It is approximately ten times as effective as progesterone in providing birth control. However, its utility was severely limited because this compound could not be administered orally and had to be taken by injection. A related compound, norlutin (chemical name: 17-α-ethynyl-19-nortestosterone), was found to provide both the strength and the effectiveness of 19-norprogesterone and could be taken orally. A number of oral birth control agents have been marketed that are similar to norlutin in structure. All of these compounds act by inducing a false pregnancy in the female, which prevents the ovulation process. Though there have been problems associated with "the pill," it appears to be an effective and safe method of family planning for the majority of the population.

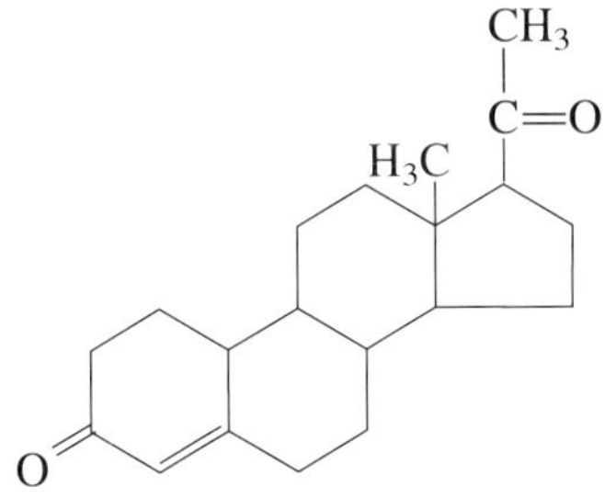

Cortisone is also important to the proper regulation of a number of biochemical processes. For example, it is involved in the metabolism of carbohydrates. Cortisone is also a very important medicinal agent used in the treatment of rheumatoid arthritis, asthma, gastrointestinal disorders, many skin conditions, and a variety of other diseases. However, treatment with cortisone is not without risk. Some of the possible side-effects of cortisone therapy include fluid retention, sodium retention, and potassium loss that can lead to congestive heart failure. Other side-effects include muscle weakness, osteoporosis, gastrointestinal upsets including peptic ulcers, and neurological symptoms including vertigo, headaches, and convulsions.

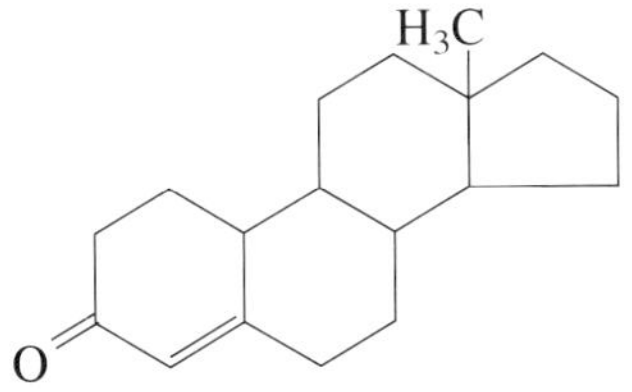

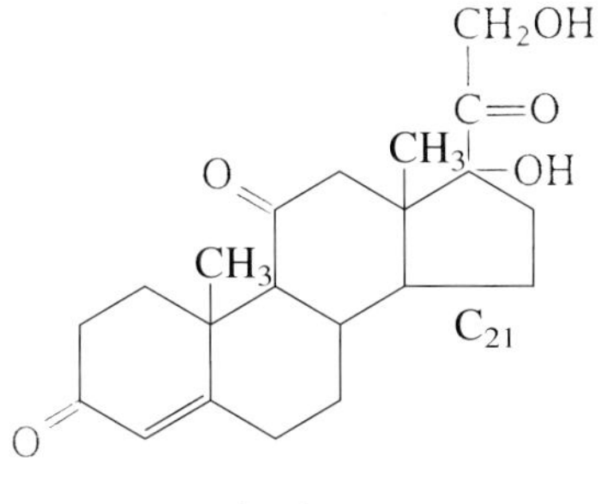

19-Norprogesterone

Norlutin

Cortisone

QUESTION 13.7

Draw the structure of the steroid nucleus. Note the locations of the A, B, C, and D steroid rings.

QUESTION 13.8

What is meant by the term *fused ring?*

A CLINICAL PERSPECTIVE

Steroids and the Treatment of Heart Disease

The foxglove plant *(Digitalis purpurea)* is an herb that produces one of the most powerful known stimulants of heart muscle. The active ingredients of the foxglove plant (digitalis) are the so-called cardiac glycosides or *cardiotonic steroids,* which include digitoxin, digosin, and gitalin.

Digitoxin

The structure of digitoxin, one of the cardiotonic steroids produced by the foxglove plant.

Digitalis purpurea, the foxglove plant.

These drugs are used clinically in the treatment of congestive heart failure, which results when the heart is not beating with strong, efficient strokes. When the blood is not propelled through the cardiovascular system efficiently, fluid builds up in the lungs and lower extremities (edema). The major symptoms of congestive heart failure are an enlarged heart, weakness, edema, shortness of breath, and fluid accumulation in the lungs.

This condition was originally described in 1785 by a physician, William Withering, who found a peasant woman whose folk medicine was famous as a treatment for chronic heart problems. Her potion contained a mixture of more than 20 herbs, but Dr. Withering, a botanist as well as physician, quickly discovered that foxglove was the active ingredient in the mixture. Withering used *Digitalis purpurea* successfully to treat congestive heart failure and even described some cautions in its use.

The cardiotonic steroids are extremely strong heart stimu-

lants. A dose as low as 1 mg increases the stroke volume of the heart (volume of blood per contraction), increases the strength of the contraction, and reduces the heart rate. When the heart is pumping more efficiently because of stimulation by digitalis, the edema disappears.

Digitalis can be used to control congestive heart failure, but the dose must be carefully determined and monitored because the therapeutic dose is close to the dose that causes toxicity. The symptoms that result from high body levels of cardiotonic steroids include vomiting, blurred vision and lightheadedness, increased water loss, convulsions, and death. Only a physician can determine the initial dose and maintenance schedule for an individual to control congestive heart failure and yet avoid the toxic side-effects.

Waxes

$$CH_3(CH_2)_{14} - \overset{O}{\overset{\|}{C}} - O - (CH_2)_{29}CH_3$$

Myricyl palmitate
(beeswax)

$$CH_3(CH_2)_{14} - \overset{O}{\overset{\|}{C}} - O - (CH_2)_{15}CH_3$$

Cetyl palmitate
(whale oil)

Waxes are derived from many different sources and have a variety of chemical compositions, depending on the source. Paraffin wax, for example, is composed of a mixture of solid hydrocarbons (usually straight-chain compounds). Carbowax, in contrast, is a polyether that is prepared synthetically. The natural waxes generally are composed of a long-chain fatty acid esterified to a long-chain alcohol. Because the long hydrocarbon tails are extremely hydrophobic, waxes are completely insoluble in water. Waxes are also solid at room temperature, owing to their high molecular weights. Two examples of waxes are myricyl palmitate, a major component of beeswax, and whale oil (spermaceti wax), from the head of the sperm whale, which is composed of cetyl palmitate.

Naturally occurring waxes have a variety of uses. Lanolin, which serves as a protective coating for hair and skin, is used in skin creams and ointments. Carnauba wax is used in automobile polish. Whale oil was once used as a fuel, in ointments, and in candles. However, synthetic waxes have replaced whale oil to a large extent, because of efforts to ban the hunting of whales.

Complex lipids are lipids that are bonded to other types of molecules. The most common and important complex lipids are plasma lipoproteins, which are responsible for the transport of other lipids in the body.

Lipids are only sparingly soluble in water, and the movement of lipids from one organ to another through the bloodstream requires a transport system that uses **plasma lipoproteins.** Lipoprotein particles consist of a core of hydrophobic lipids and proteins (Figure 13.8).

There are four major classes of human plasma lipoproteins:

◆ **Chylomicrons** carry dietary triglycerides from the intestine to other tissues. The remaining lipoproteins are classified by their densities.

◆ **Very low density lipoproteins (VLDL)** bind triglycerides synthesized in the liver and carry them to adipose and other tissues for storage.

◆ **Low-density lipoproteins (LDL)** carry cholesterol to peripheral tissues and help regulate cholesterol levels in those tissues. These are richest in cholesterol, frequently carrying 40% of the plasma cholesterol.

◆ **High-density lipoproteins (HDL)** are bound to plasma cholesterol; however, they transport cholesterol from peripheral tissues to the liver.

A summary of the composition of each of the plasma lipoproteins is presented in Figure 13.9.

A general scheme for transport of lipids in lipoprotein complexes between tissues is summarized in Figure 13.10.

Chylomicrons are aggregates of triglycerides and protein that transport dietary triglycerides to cells throughout the body. Not all lipids in the blood are derived directly from the diet. Triglycerides and cholesterol are also synthesized in the liver and also are transported through the blood in lipoprotein packages. Triglycerides are assembled into VLDL particles that carry the energy-rich lipid molecules either to tissues requiring an energy source or to adipose tissue for storage. Similarly, cholesterol is assembled into LDL particles for transport from the liver to peripheral tissues.

13.5 COMPLEX LIPIDS

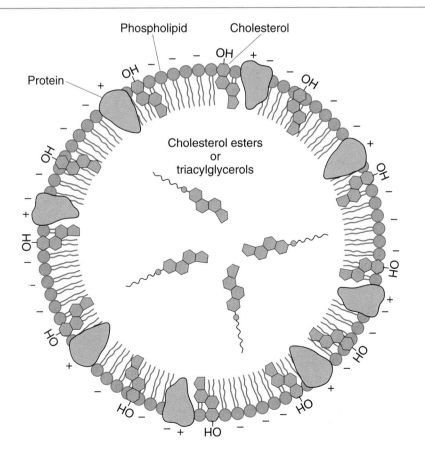

FIGURE 13.8
A model for the structure of a plasma lipoprotein. The various lipoproteins are composed of a shell of protein, cholesterol, and phospholipids surrounding more hydrophobic molecules such as triglycerides or cholesterol esters (cholesterol esterified to fatty acids).

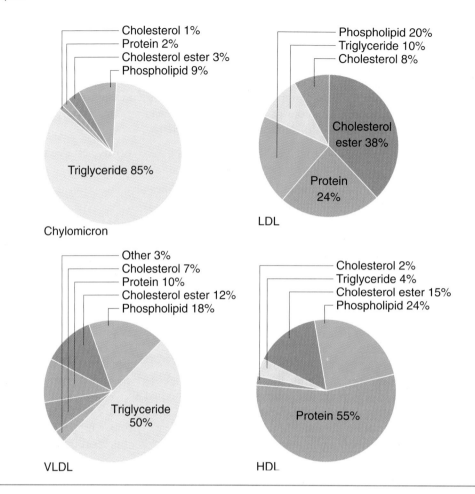

Cholesterol 1%
Protein 2%
Cholesterol ester 3%
Phospholipid 9%

Triglyceride 85%

Chylomicron

Phospholipid 20%
Triglyceride 10%
Cholesterol 8%

Cholesterol ester 38%

Protein 24%

LDL

Other 3%
Cholesterol 7%
Protein 10%
Cholesterol ester 12%
Phospholipid 18%

Triglyceride 50%

VLDL

Cholesterol 2%
Triglyceride 4%
Cholesterol ester 15%
Phospholipid 24%

Protein 55%

HDL

FIGURE 13.9
A summary of the relative amounts of cholesterol, phospholipid, protein, triglycerides, and cholesterol esters in the four classes of lipoproteins.

FIGURE 13.10
General scheme for the transport of lipoproteins between tissues in the human body.

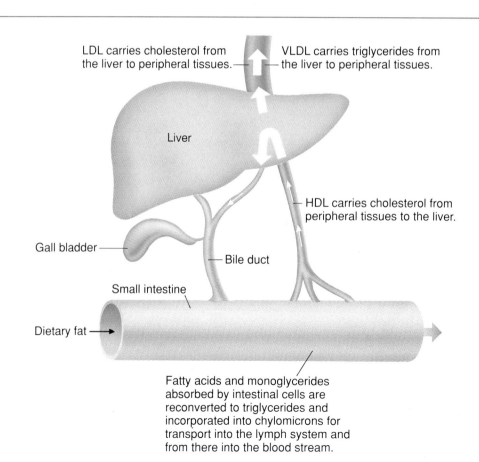

LDL carries cholesterol from the liver to peripheral tissues.

VLDL carries triglycerides from the liver to peripheral tissues.

Liver

HDL carries cholesterol from peripheral tissues to the liver.

Gall bladder

Bile duct

Small intestine

Dietary fat

Fatty acids and monoglycerides absorbed by intestinal cells are reconverted to triglycerides and incorporated into chylomicrons for transport into the lymph system and from there into the blood stream.

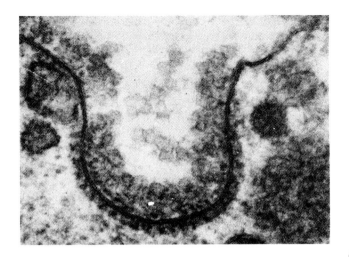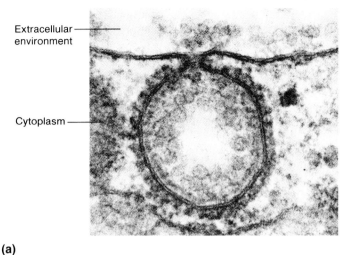

(a)

(b)

FIGURE 13.11
Receptor-mediated endocytosis.
(a) Electron micrographs of the process of receptor-mediated endocytosis. (b) Summary of the events of receptor-mediated endocytosis of LDL and the fate of the cholesterol brought into the cell.

Entry of LDL particles into the cell is dependent on a specific recognition event and binding between the LDL particle and a protein receptor embedded within the membrane. Low-density lipoprotein receptors (LDL receptors) are found in the membranes of cells outside the liver and are responsible for the uptake of cholesterol by the cells of various tissues. LDL (lipoprotein bound to cholesterol) binds specifically to the LDL receptor, and the complex is taken into the cell by a process called *receptor-mediated endocytosis* (Figure 13.11). The membrane begins to invaginate; in other words, it is pulled into the cell at the site of the LDL receptor complexes. This draws the entire LDL particle into the cell. Eventually, the invagination becomes very deep, and the portion of the membrane surrounding the LDL particles pinches away from the cell membrane and forms a membrane around the LDL particles. As we saw in Section 13.3, membranes are fluid and readily flow. Thus they can form a vesicle or endosome containing the LDL particles.

Cellular digestive organelles known as *lysosomes* fuse with the endosomes. This fusion is accomplished when the membranes of the endosome and the lysosome flow together to create one larger membrane-bound body or vesicle. Hydrolytic enzymes from the lysosome then digest the entire complex to release cholesterol into the cytoplasm of the cell. There, cholesterol inhibits its own biosynthesis and activates an enzyme that stores cholesterol in cholesterol ester droplets. Cholesterol also inhibits the synthesis of LDL receptors to ensure that the cell will not take up too much cholesterol. People who have a genetic defect in the gene coding for the LDL receptor accumulate LDL cholesterol in the plasma. This excess plasma cholesterol is then deposited on the artery walls, causing atherosclerosis.

Liver lipoprotein receptors enable large amounts of cholesterol to be removed from the blood, thus ensuring low concentrations of cholesterol in the blood plasma. Other factors being equal, the person with the most lipoprotein receptors will be the least vulnerable to a high-cholesterol diet and have the least likelihood of developing atherosclerosis.

There is also evidence that high levels of HDL in the blood help reduce the incidence of atherosclerosis, perhaps because HDL carries cholesterol from the peripheral tissues back to the liver. In the liver, some of the cholesterol is used for bile synthesis and secreted into the intestines, from which it is excreted.

A final correlation has been made between diet and atherosclerosis. People whose diet is high in saturated fats tend to have high levels of cholesterol in the blood. Although the relationship between saturated fatty acids and cholesterol metabolism is unclear, it is known that a diet rich in unsaturated fats results in decreased cholesterol levels. In fact, the use of unsaturated fat in the diet results in a decrease in the level of LDL and an increase in the level of HDL. With the positive correlation between heart disease and high cholesterol levels, the current dietary recommendations include a diet that is low in fat and the substitution of unsaturated fats (vegetable oils) for saturated fats (animal fats).

SUMMARY

13.1 Biological Functions of Lipids

Lipids are organic molecules characterized by their solubility in nonpolar solvents. Lipids are subdivided into classes based on structural characteristics: *fatty acids, glycerides,* nonglycerides, and *complex lipids.* Lipids serve many functions in the body, including energy storage, protection of organs, insulation, and absorption of vitamins. Other lipids are energy sources, hormones, or vitamins. Cells store chemical energy in the form of lipids, and the cell membrane is a lipid bilayer.

13.2 Fatty Acids

Fatty acids are *saturated* and *unsaturated* carboxylic acids containing between 12 and 24 carbon atoms. Fatty acids with even numbers of carbon atoms occur most frequently in nature.

13.3 Glycerides

Glycerides are the most abundant lipids. The triesters of glycerol *(triglycerides)* are of greatest importance. Neutral triglycerides are important because of their ability to store energy. The ionic *phospholipids* are important components of all biological membranes. The *fluid mosaic model* of membrane structure pictures biological membranes that are composed of lipid bilayers in which proteins are embedded. Membrane lipids contain polar head groups and nonpolar hydrocarbon tails. The hydrocarbon tails of phospholipids are derived from saturated and unsaturated long-chain fatty acids containing an even number of carbon atoms.

13.4 Nonglyceride Lipids

Nonglyceride lipids consist of *sphingolipids, steroids,* and *waxes. Sphingomyelin* is a component of the myelin sheath around cells of the central nervous system. The *steroids* are important for many biochemical functions: *Cholesterol* is a membrane component; testosterone, progesterone, and estrone are sex hormones; and cortisone is an anti-inflammatory steroid that is important in the regulation of many biochemical pathways.

13.5 Complex Lipids

Plasma lipoproteins are complex lipids that transport other lipids through the bloodstream. *Chylomicrons* carry dietary triglycerides from the intestine to other tissues. *Very low density lipoproteins* carry triglycerides synthesized in the liver to other tissues for storage. *Low-density lipoproteins* carry cholesterol to peripheral tissues and help regulate blood cholesterol levels. *High-density lipoproteins* transport cholesterol from peripheral tissues to the liver.

KEY TERMS

arachidonic acid (13.2)
atherosclerosis (13.4)
cholesterol (13.4)
chylomicron (13.5)
complex lipid (13.5)
diglyceride (13.3)
emulsifying agent (13.3)
essential fatty acid (13.2)
esterification (13.2)
fatty acid (13.2)
fluid mosaic model (13.3)
glyceride (13.3)
high-density lipoprotein (HDL) (13.5)
hydrogenation (13.2)
hydrolysis (of triglycerides) (13.2)
lipid (13.1)
low-density lipoprotein (LDL) (13.5)

monoglyceride (13.3)
neutral glyceride (13.3)
peripheral protein (13.3)
phosphatidate (13.3)
phosphoglyceride (13.3)
phospholipid (13.3)
plasma lipoprotein (13.5)
prostaglandins (13.2)
saponification (13.2)
saturated fatty acid (13.2)
sphingolipid (13.4)
sphingomyelin (13.4)
steroid (13.4)
terpene (13.4)
transmembrane protein (13.3)
triglyceride (13.3)
unsaturated fatty acid (13.2)
very low density lipoprotein (VLDL) (13.5)
wax (13.4)

QUESTIONS AND PROBLEMS

Biological Functions of Lipids

13.9 List the four main groups of lipids.

13.10 List the biological functions of lipids.

Fatty Acids: Structure, Properties, and Chemical Reactions

13.11 What is the difference between a saturated and an unsaturated fatty acid?

13.12 Write the structure for a saturated and an unsaturated fatty acid.

13.13 As the length of the hydrocarbon chain of saturated fatty acids increases, what is the effect on the melting points?

13.14 As the number of carbon-to-carbon double bonds in fatty acids increases, what is the effect on the melting points?

13.15 Draw the structures of each of the following fatty acids:
  a. Decanoic acid
  b. Stearic acid
  c. *trans*-5-Decenoic acid
  d. *cis*-5-Decenoic acid

13.16 What are the common and I.U.P.A.C. names of each of the following fatty acids?
  a. $C_{15}H_{31}COOH$
  b. $C_{11}H_{23}COOH$
  c. $CH_3(CH_2)_5CH{=}CH(CH_2)_7COOH$
  d. $CH_3(CH_2)_7CH{=}CH(CH_2)_7COOH$

13.17 Write an equation for each of the following reactions:
  a. Esterification of glycerol with three molecules of myristic acid
  b. Acid hydrolysis of glyceryl tristearate
  c. Reaction of decanoic acid with KOH
  d. Hydrogenation of linoleic acid

13.18 Write an equation for each of the following reactions:
  a. Esterification of glycerol with three molecules of palmitic acid
  b. Acid hydrolysis of glyceryl trioleate
  c. Reaction of stearic acid with KOH
  d. Hydrogenation of oleic acid

Fatty Acids: Prostaglandins

13.19 What is the function of the essential fatty acids?

13.20 What molecules are formed from arachidonic acid?

13.21 What is the biochemical basis for the effectiveness of aspirin in decreasing the inflammatory response?

13.22 What is the role of prostaglandins in the inflammatory response?

13.23 List four effects of prostaglandins.

13.24 What are the functions of thromboxane A_2 and leukotrienes?

Glycerides: Neutral Glycerides and Phosphoglycerides

13.25 Draw the structure of the triglyceride molecule formed by esterification at C-1, C-2, and C-3 with hexadecanoic acid, *trans*-9-hexadecenoic acid, and *cis*-9-hexadecenoic acid, respectively.

13.26 Draw one possible structure of a triglyceride that contains the three fatty acids stearic acid, palmitic acid, and oleic acid.

13.27 Draw the structure of the phosphatidate formed between glycerol-3-phosphate that is esterified at C-1 and C-2 with capric and lauric acids, respectively.

13.28 Draw the structure of a lecithin molecule in which the fatty acyl groups are derived from stearic acid.

13.29 How will the properties of a biological membrane change if the fatty acyl tails of the phospholipids are converted from saturated to unsaturated chains?

13.30 What is the function of unsaturation in the hydrocarbon tails of membrane lipids?

13.31 What is the basic structure of a biological membrane?

13.32 Describe the fluid mosaic model of membrane structure.

Nonglyceride Lipids

13.33 What is a sphingolipid?

13.34 What is the function of sphingomyelin?

13.35 What is the role of cholesterol in biological membranes?

13.36 How does cholesterol contribute to atherosclerosis?

13.37 What are the biological functions of progesterone, testosterone, and estrone?

13.38 How has our understanding of the steroid sex hormones contributed to the development of oral contraceptives?

13.39 What is the medical application of cortisone?

13.40 What are the possible side-effects of cortisone treatment?

13.41 A wax found in beeswax is myricyl palmitate. What fatty acid and what alcohol are used to form this compound?

13.42 A wax found in the head of sperm whales is cetyl palmitate. What fatty acid and what alcohol are used to form this compound?

Complex Lipids

13.43 What are the four major types of plasma lipoproteins?

13.44 What is the function of each of the four types of plasma lipoproteins?

Further Problems

13.45 Describe peripheral membrane proteins.

13.46 Describe transmembrane proteins and list some of their functions.

13.47 What are isoprenoids?

13.48 What is a terpene?

13.49 List some important biological molecules that are terpenes.

13.50 Draw the five-carbon isoprene unit.

13.51 What is the relationship between atherosclerosis and high blood pressure?

13.52 How is LDL taken into cells?

13.53 How does a genetic defect in the LDL receptor contribute to atherosclerosis?

13.54 What is the correlation between saturated fats in the diet and atherosclerosis?

VOCABULARY QUIZ

13.1 The 27-carbon steroid ring molecule that is the precursor for the sex hormones, is required for the regulation of membrane fluidity, and has been implicated in atherosclerosis and high blood pressure is _____.

13.2 The current model of the structure of biological membranes is called the _____.

13.3 The most common lipids found in biological membranes that consist of two fatty acids esterified at the C-1 and C-2 positions of glycerol, a phosphoryl group esterified at the C-3 position, and another hydrophilic molecule attached to the phosphoryl group are called _____.

13.4 The most common lipid storage form in the body that consists of three fatty acids esterified to a glycerol molecule is called a(n) _____.

13.5 A(n) _____ is a long-chain monocarboxylic acid.

13.6 The sphingolipid found in abundance in the sheath that surrounds and insulates cells of the central nervous system is _____.

13.7 The plasma lipoprotein that carries triglycerides from the intestine to various tissues throughout the body is the _____.

13.8 A fatty acid that cannot be synthesized by the body and must be obtained in the diet is called a(n) _____.

13.9 _____ is the plasma lipoprotein that carries cholesterol to peripheral tissues and helps to regulate cholesterol levels in those tissues.

13.10 A bipolar molecule that aids in the suspension of fats in water is called a(n) _____.

14

Amines and Amides

LEARNING GOALS

◆ Draw and name simple amines and
amides.

◆ Classify amines as primary,
secondary, or tertiary.

◆ Draw and discuss the structure of the
amide bond.

◆ Write equations showing the basicity
and neutralization of amines.

◆ Write equations for the preparation
and hydrolysis of amides.

◆ Know that amphetamines,
barbiturates, analgesics, anesthetics,
decongestants, and antibiotics are
among the medically important
amines and amides.

◆ Recognize that many carcinogens are
amines or amine derivatives.

CHEMISTRY CONNECTION

The Nicotine Patch

Smoking cigarettes is one of the most difficult habits to break—so difficult, in fact, that physicians now suspect that smoking is more than a habit: It's an addiction. The addictive drug in tobacco is *nicotine.*

Nicotine, one of the *heterocyclic amines* that we will study in this chapter (Figure 14.3), is a highly toxic compound. In fact, it has been used as an insecticide! Small doses from cigarette smoking initially stimulate the autonomic (involuntary) nervous system. However, repeated small doses of nicotine obtained by smokers eventually depress the involuntary nervous system. As a result, the smoker *needs* another cigarette.

Some people have been able to quit smoking through behavioral modification programs, hypnosis, or sheer willpower. Others quit only after smoking has contributed to life-threatening illness, such as emphysema or a heart attack. Yet there are people who cannot quit even after a diagnosis of lung cancer.

One promising advance to help people quit smoking is the nicotine patch. The patch is applied to the smoker's skin, and

nicotine from the patch slowly diffuses through the skin and into the bloodstream. Because the body receives a constant small dose of nicotine, the smoker no longer craves a cigarette. Of course, the long-range goal is to completely cure the addiction to nicotine. This is done by decreasing doses of nicotine in the patches as the treatment period continues. Eventually, after a period of about three months, the former smoker no longer needs the patches.

There are those who criticize this therapy because nicotine is a toxic chemical. However, the benefits seem to outweigh any negative aspects. A smoker inhales not only nicotine, but also dozens of other substances that have been shown to cause cancer. When someone successfully quits smoking, the body no longer suffers the risks associated with the substances in cigarette smoke.

In this chapter we study the structure and properties of amines and their derivatives, the amides. We will see that several are important pain killers, decongestants, and antibiotics, while others are addictive drugs and carcinogens.

INTRODUCTION

Amines are organic molecules characterized by the presence of an *amino group* ($—NH_2$) or a substituted amino group (an amino group in which one or more of the hydrogen atoms are replaced by an organic group).

Amides are the products of a reaction between a carboxylic acid and ammonia or an amine. It is important to understand the structure and chemistry of amines and amides because the amino and amide functional groups are key components of the *amino acids* and *proteins.* These proteins carry out all of the work required for life processes. Each amino acid is characterized by the presence of an amino group and a carboxyl group. When amino acids are bonded to one another to produce proteins, it is the amino group of one amino acid that reacts with the carboxyl group of a second amino acid. The resulting *amide bond* is called a *peptide bond.* In this chapter and the next we will investigate amines, amides, and amino acids and the role that they play in protein structure and function.

Chapter 15

14.1 AMINES

Structure and physical properties

Amines are organic derivatives of ammonia and, like ammonia, they are basic. In fact, amines are the most important type of organic base found in nature. We can think of them as substituted ammonia molecules in which one, two, or three of the ammonia hydrogens have been replaced by an organic group:

$$H—\underset{\underset{H}{|}}{N}—H \quad \xrightarrow[\text{for H}]{\text{R substitutes}} \quad H—\underset{\underset{H}{|}}{N}—H$$

Ammonia   An amine

Section 3.4

Like ammonia, amines are pyramidal. The nitrogen atom has three groups attached and a nonbonding pair of electrons (Figure 14.1).

Amines are classified according to the number of alkyl or aryl groups attached to the nitrogen. In a **primary amine,** one of the hydrogens is replaced by an organic group. In a **secondary amine,** two hydrogens are replaced. In a **tertiary amine,** three organic groups replace the hydrogens:

$$
\begin{array}{cccc}
& H & H & R \\
& | & | & | \\
H-N-H & R-N-H & R-N-R & R-N-R \\[4pt]
\text{Ammonia} & 1° \text{ amine} & 2° \text{ amine} & 3° \text{ amine} \\
& \text{(primary amine)} & \text{(secondary amine)} & \text{(tertiary amine)}
\end{array}
$$

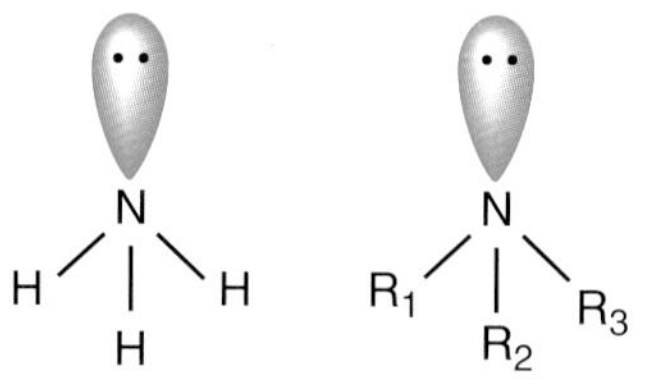

FIGURE 14.1
The pyramidal structure of amines. Note the similarities in structure between an amine and the ammonia molecule.

EXAMPLE 14.1

Classifying Amines as Primary, Secondary, or Tertiary

Solution

Compare the structure of the amine with that of ammonia.

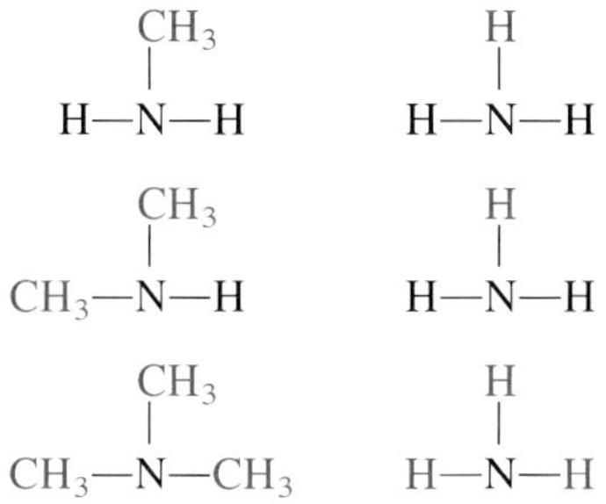

$$
\begin{array}{cc}
CH_3 & H \\
| & | \\
H-N-H & H-N-H
\end{array}
$$
1° amine: one hydrogen replaced

$$
\begin{array}{cc}
CH_3 & H \\
| & | \\
CH_3-N-H & H-N-H
\end{array}
$$
2° amine: two hydrogens replaced

$$
\begin{array}{cc}
CH_3 & H \\
| & | \\
CH_3-N-CH_3 & H-N-H
\end{array}
$$
3° amine: three hydrogens replaced

QUESTION 14.1

Determine whether each of the following amines is primary, secondary, or tertiary:

a.
$$
\begin{array}{c}
CH_2CH_3 \\
| \\
CH_3CH_2-N-CH_3
\end{array}
$$
3tiary

b. $CH_3CH_2CH_2-NH_2$ *1mary*

c.
$$
\begin{array}{c}
H \\
| \\
CH_3-N-CH_3
\end{array}
$$
secondary

QUESTION 14.2

Classify each of the following amines as primary, secondary, or tertiary:

a. CH_3-NH_2 *primary*

b.
$$
\begin{array}{c}
CH_3 \\
| \\
CH_3CH_2CH_2CH_2-N-CH_2CH_3
\end{array}
$$
tertiary

c.
$$
\begin{array}{c}
CH_2CH_2CH_3 \\
| \\
H-N-CH_3
\end{array}
$$
secondary

The nitrogen atom is more electronegative than the hydrogen atoms in amines. As a result, the N—H bond is polar, and hydrogen bonding between amine molecules or between amine molecules and water can occur (Figure 14.2).

Section 5.7

QUESTION 14.3

Refer to Figure 14.2, and draw a similar figure showing the hydrogen bonding that results between water and a 2° amine.

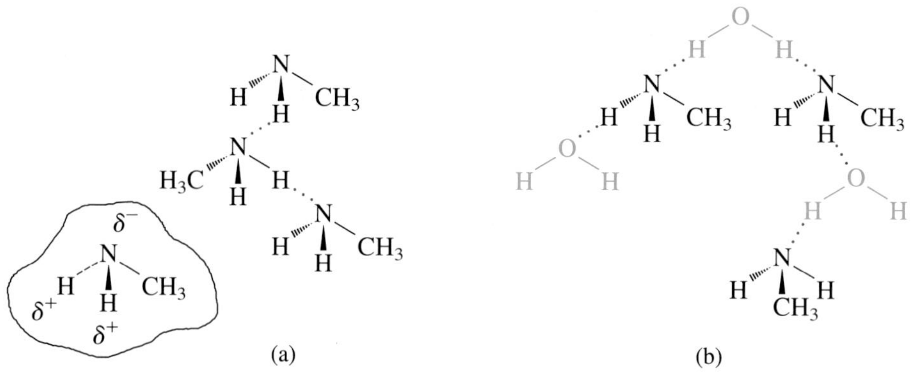

FIGURE 14.2
Hydrogen bonding (a) in methylamine and (b) between methylamine and water. Dotted lines represent hydrogen bonds.

QUESTION 14.4

Refer to Figure 14.2, and draw hydrogen bonding between two primary amines.

Nomenclature

Several systems for naming amines have evolved, including, of course, the I.U.P.A.C. Nomenclature System. However, the I.U.P.A.C. names are not the most commonly used names and will not be presented in this text.

The nomenclature system that has gained great popularity is known as the *Chemical Abstracts* or CA system. This system is approved for use by I.U.P.A.C. and will be presented here because it is logical and easy to use. In the CA system the final *-e* of the name of the parent compound is dropped, and the suffix *-amine* is added. For instance,

$$CH_3-NH_2 \qquad CH_3CH_2CH_2-NH_2 \qquad CH_3CH_2CH_2CHCH_3$$
$$\overset{|}{NH_2}$$

Methanamine   Propanamine   2-Pentanamine

For secondary or tertiary amines the prefix *N-alkyl* is added to the name of the parent compound. For example,

$$CH_3-NH-CH_2CH_3 \qquad\qquad CH_3-\overset{\overset{\displaystyle CH_3}{|}}{N}-CH_3$$

N-methylethanamine   *N,N*-dimethylmethanamine

Several aromatic amines have special names that are also approved for use in the I.U.P.A.C. System. For example, the amine of benzene is given the name *aniline*. In the CA system, aniline is named *benzenamine*. In either case, if there are additional groups attached to the nitrogen, they are indicated with the letter *N-* followed by the name of the alkyl group.

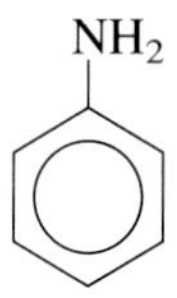

Aniline or benzenamine 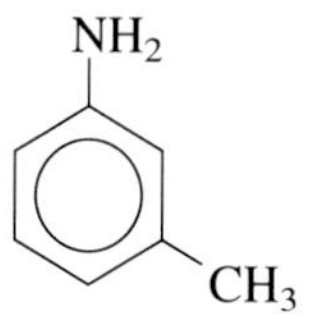   *m*-Toluidine or *meta*-toluidine 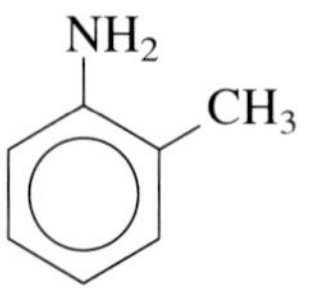   *o*-Toluidine or *ortho*-toluidine 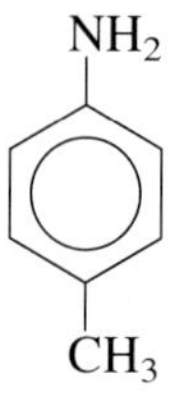   *p*-Toluidine or *para*-toluidine

A CLINICAL PERSPECTIVE

Medically Important Amines

Although amines play many different roles in our day-to-day lives, one important use is in medicine. A host of drugs derived from amines are responsible for improving the quality of life, while others, such as cocaine and heroin, are highly addictive.

Amphetamines, such as benzedrine and methedrine, stimulate the central nervous system. They elevate blood pressure and pulse rate and are often used to decrease fatigue. Medically, they have been used to treat depression and epilepsy. Amphetamines have also been prescribed as diet pills because they decrease the appetite. Their use is controlled by federal law because excess use of amphetamines can cause paranoia and mental illness.

Many of the medicinal amines are *analgesics* (pain relievers) or *anesthetics* (pain blockers). Novocaine and related compounds, for example, are used as local anesthetics. Demerol is a very strong pain reliever.

Ephedrine and neosynephrine are used as *decongestants* in cough syrups and nasal sprays. They cause shrinking of the membranes that line the nasal passages. These compounds are related to two chemicals that are important to the functioning of the central nervous system, dopa and dopa-

mine, which are described in the "A Human Perspective: Amines and the Central Nervous System."

The *sulfa drugs,* the first chemicals used to fight bacterial infections, are synthesized from amines.

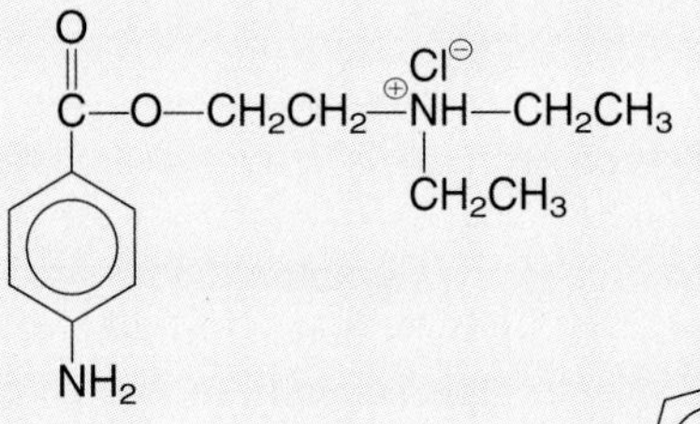

Novocaine

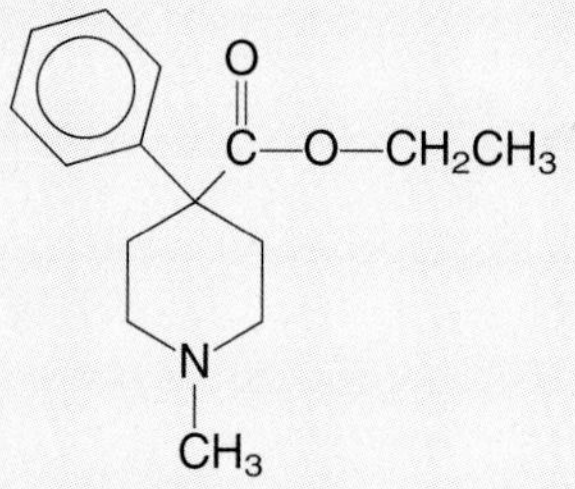

Demerol

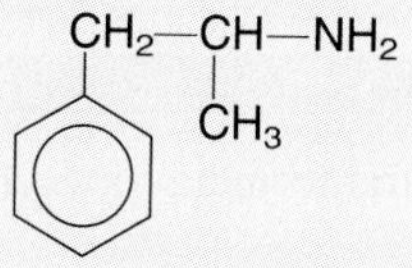

2-Amino-1-phenylpropane
(Amphetamine)

Benzedrine

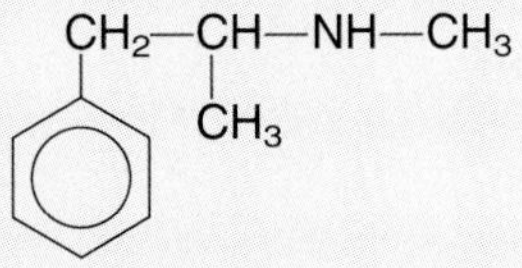

2-Methylamino-1-phenylpropane
(Methamphetamine)

Methedrine

Decongestants

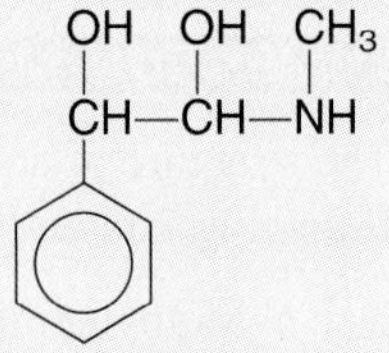

Ephedrine

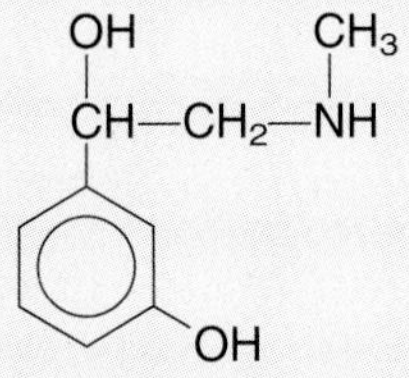

Neosynephrine

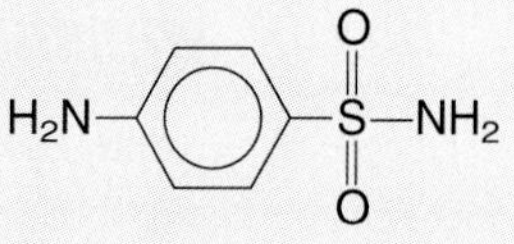

Sulfanilamide—a sulfa drug

EXAMPLE 14.2

Naming Amines Using the Chemical Abstracts System

Solution

$$\overset{3}{C}H_3\overset{2}{C}H_2\overset{1}{C}H_2—NH—CH_3$$

N-methylpropamine

Parent compound: propane (becomes propanamine)
Additional group on N: methyl (becomes *N*-methyl)
Name: *N*-methylpropanamine

TABLE 14.1 Common and *Chemical Abstracts* Names of Amines

Compound	CA Name	Common Name
$R-NH_2$	Alkan*amine*	Alkyl*amine*
CH_3-NH_2	Methanamine	Methylamine
$CH_3CH_2-NH_2$	Ethanamine	Ethylamine
$CH_3CH_2CH_2-NH_2$	Propanamine	Propylamine
$CH_3-NH-CH_3$	N-Methylmethanamine	Dimethylamine
$CH_3-NH-CH_2CH_3$	N-Methylethanamine	Ethylmethylamine
$CH_3-\overset{\displaystyle CH_3}{\overset{\displaystyle \vert}{N}}-CH_3$	N,N-Dimethylmethanamine	Trimethylamine

Common names are often used for the simple amines. The common names of the alkyl groups bonded to the amine nitrogen are followed by the ending *-amine*. Each group is listed alphabetically in one continuous word followed by the suffix *-amine*:

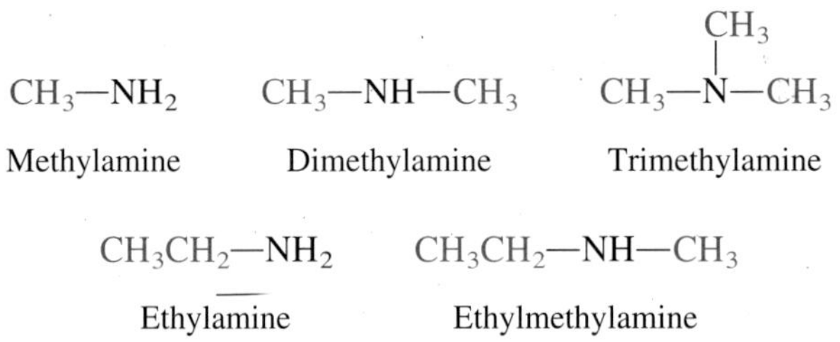

$$CH_3-NH_2 \qquad CH_3-NH-CH_3 \qquad CH_3-\overset{\displaystyle CH_3}{\overset{\displaystyle \vert}{N}}-CH_3$$

Methylamine   Dimethylamine   Trimethylamine

$$CH_3CH_2-NH_2 \qquad CH_3CH_2-NH-CH_3$$

Ethylamine   Ethylmethylamine

Table 14.1 compares these systems of nomenclature for a number of simple amines.

QUESTION 14.5

The structure of aniline is provided above. Draw the complete structural formula for each of the following amines:

a. N-Methylaniline

b. N,N-Dimethylaniline

c. N-Ethylaniline

d. N-Isopropylaniline

QUESTION 14.6

Name each of the following amines using the CA and common nomenclature systems:

a. 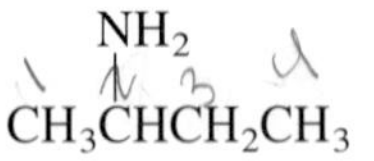 $\overset{\displaystyle NH_2}{\overset{\displaystyle \vert}{CH_3CHCH_2CH_3}}$ *2 - butamine*

b. 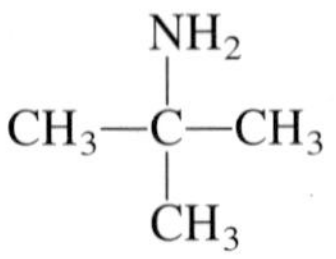 $CH_3-\overset{\displaystyle NH_2}{\underset{\displaystyle CH_3}{\overset{\displaystyle \vert}{\underset{\displaystyle \vert}{C}}}}-CH_3$

c. $\overset{\displaystyle CH_3}{\overset{\displaystyle \vert}{\overset{\displaystyle NH}{\overset{\displaystyle \vert}{CH_3CHCH_2CH_3}}}}$ *N —*

d. 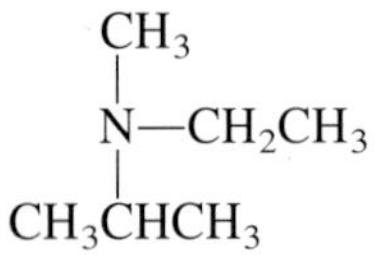 $\overset{\displaystyle CH_3}{\overset{\displaystyle \vert}{\overset{\displaystyle N-CH_2CH_3}{\overset{\displaystyle \vert}{CH_3CHCH_3}}}}$ *N,N —*

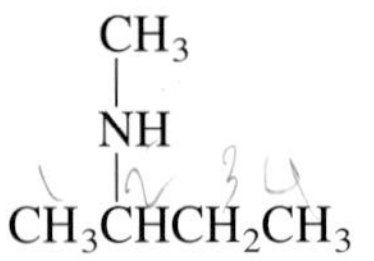

QUESTION 14.7

Draw the complete structural formula for each of the following compounds:

a. 2-Propanamine

b. 3-Octanamine

c. *N*-Ethyl-2-heptanamine

d. 2-Methyl-2-pentanamine

e. 4-Chloro-5-iodo-1-nonanamine

f. *N,N*-Diethyl-1-pentanamine

QUESTION 14.8

Draw the condensed formula for each of the following compounds:

a. Diethylmethylamine

b. 4-Methylpentylamine

c. *N*-Methylaniline

d. Triisopropylamine

e. Methyl-*t*-butylamine

f. Ethylhexylamine

Basicity of amines

Amines behave as weak bases when dissolved in water. The nonbonding pair (lone pair) of electrons of the nitrogen atom can be shared with a proton (H^+) from a water molecule, producing an **alkylammonium ion.** Hydroxide ions are also formed, and so the resulting solution is basic.

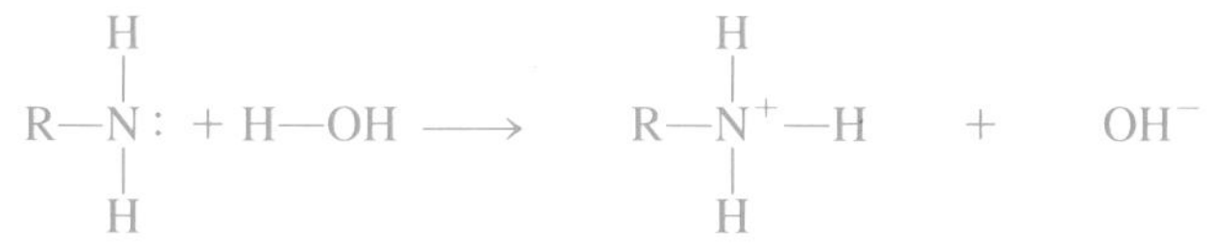

Reactions involving amines

$$
\begin{array}{cccc}
\text{H} & & \text{H} & \\
| & & | & \\
\text{R}-\text{N}: & + \text{H}-\text{OH} \longrightarrow & \text{R}-\text{N}^+-\text{H} & + \quad \text{OH}^- \\
| & & | & \\
\text{H} & & \text{H} &
\end{array}
$$

Amine   Water   Alkylammonium ion   Hydroxide ion

$$
\begin{array}{cccc}
\text{H} & & \text{H} & \\
| & & | & \\
\text{CH}_3-\text{N}: & + \text{H}-\text{OH} \rightleftharpoons & \text{CH}_3-\text{N}^+-\text{H} & + \quad \text{OH}^- \\
| & & | & \\
& & \text{H} &
\end{array}
$$

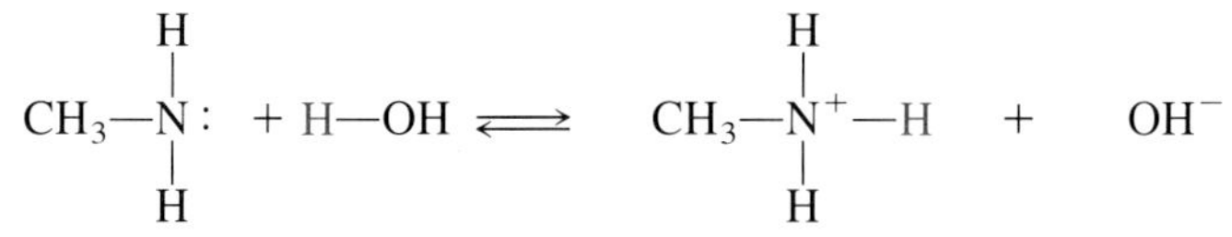

Methylamine   Water   Methylammonium ion   Hydroxide ion

Neutralization of amines

Because amines are bases, they react with acids to form alkylammonium salts. The reaction of methylamine with hydrochloric acid, shown below, is typical of these reactions.

Recall that the reaction of an acid and a base gives a salt (Section 7.4).

$$
\begin{array}{ccc}
\text{H} & & \text{H} \\
| & & | \\
\text{R}-\text{N}: & + \text{HCl} \longrightarrow & \text{R}-\text{N}^+-\text{H} \ \text{Cl}^- \\
| & & | \\
\text{H} & & \text{H}
\end{array}
$$

Amine   Acid   Alkylammonium salt

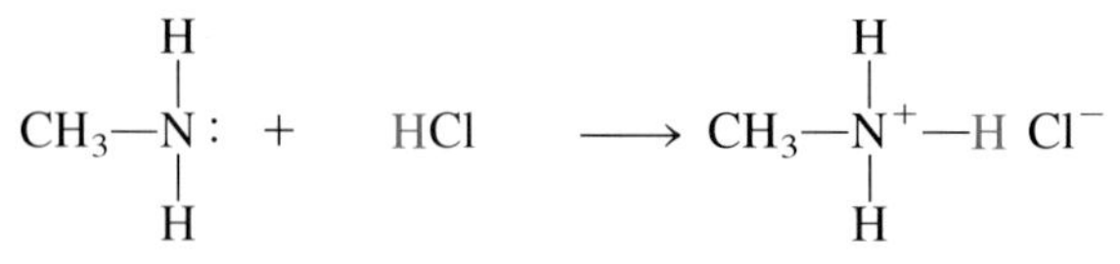

$$CH_3-\overset{\overset{\displaystyle H}{|}}{\underset{\underset{\displaystyle H}{|}}{N}}: \ + \ HCl \ \longrightarrow \ CH_3-\overset{\overset{\displaystyle H}{|}}{\underset{\underset{\displaystyle H}{|}}{N^+}}-H \ Cl^-$$

| Methylamine | Hydrochloric acid | Methylammonium chloride |

Alkylammonium salts are named by replacing the suffix *-amine* with *ammonium*. This is then followed by the name of the anion. The salts are ionic and hence are quite soluble in water.

A variety of important drugs are amines. They are usually administered as alkylammonium salts because the salts are much more soluble in aqueous solutions and in body fluids.

QUESTION 14.9

Complete each of the following reactions by supplying the missing product(s):

a. 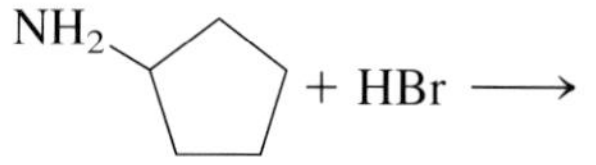 NH_2⟨cyclopentane⟩ + HBr $\longrightarrow$

b. $CH_3CH_2-NH-CH_3 + H_2O \longrightarrow$?

c. $CH_3-NH_2 + H_2O \longrightarrow$?

QUESTION 14.10

Complete each of the following reactions by supplying the missing product(s):

a. $CH_3-NH_2 + HI$ b. $CH_3CH_2-NH_2 + HBr$ c. $(CH_3CH_2)_2NH + HCl$

Quaternary ammonium salts

Quaternary ammonium salts are ammonium salts that have four organic groups bonded to the nitrogen. They have the following general structure:

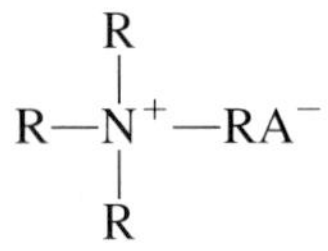

$$R-\overset{\overset{\displaystyle R}{|}}{\underset{\underset{\displaystyle R}{|}}{N^+}}-R \ A^-$$

Quaternary ammonium salts that have a very long carbon chain, sometimes called "quats," are used as disinfectants and antiseptics because they have detergent activity. Two popular quats are benzalkonium chloride (Zephiran™) and cetylpyridinium chloride, found in the mouthwash Cepacol®.

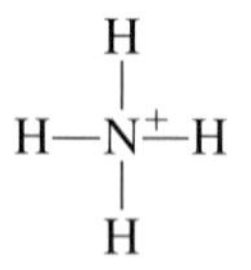

$$H-\overset{\overset{\displaystyle H}{|}}{\underset{\underset{\displaystyle H}{|}}{N^+}}-H$$

$$\left[\langle\!\!\bigcirc\!\!\rangle-CH_2-\overset{\overset{\displaystyle CH_3}{|}}{\underset{\underset{\displaystyle CH_3}{|}}{N^+}}-C_{18}H_{37} \right] Cl^-$$

| Ammonium ion | Benzalkonium chloride |

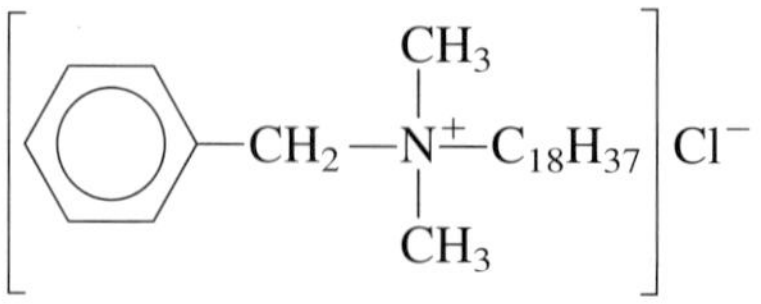

Section 13.3

See "A Human Perspective: Amines and the Central Nervous System."

Choline is an important quaternary ammonium salt in the body. It is part of the hydrophilic "head" of the membrane phospholipid lecithin. Choline is also a precursor for the synthesis of the neurotransmitter acetylcholine.

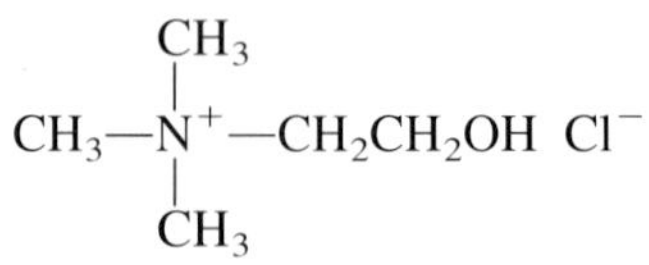

$$CH_3-\overset{\overset{\displaystyle CH_3}{|}}{\underset{\underset{\displaystyle CH_3}{|}}{N^+}}-CH_2CH_2OH \ Cl^-$$

Choline

A MEDICAL PERSPECTIVE

Secondary Amines and Cancer

Many of the amines and amine derivatives have been linked to cancer in animals and, in several cases, humans. Little is known about the mode of action of many of these compounds, and a great deal of research is underway to determine how they are involved in the development of cancer. It appears that these *carcinogens* (cancer-causing chemicals) damage the DNA, causing mutations in genes that control cell division. This damage results in the formation of "outlaw" cancer cells. These compounds damage the DNA by alkylating (adding an alkyl group to) the DNA chain.

It is known that secondary amines can react with substances such as nitrous acid (HNO_2) to form nitrosoamines. Nitrosoamines, in turn, can react further to give diazocompounds. Diazocompounds act as the alkylating agents to alkylate the DNA. The reaction, in part, is as follows:

Many of the medicines and foods that we consume contain secondary amines. In addition, the nitrite ion is widely used as a preservative for bacon, ham, sausage, and other meat products. Nitrites give the meat a pleasant pink color and keep it from turning grey. They also inhibit the growth of some harmful bacteria. It is possible that nitrites in foods could react with the acid found in the saliva and stomach juices to form nitrous acid. This might, in turn, undergo the reactions shown below. Fortunately, the concentration of nitrite in foods is very low. However, research continues in an effort to determine whether the nitrites and secondary amines in the food we eat play a role in colon cancers.

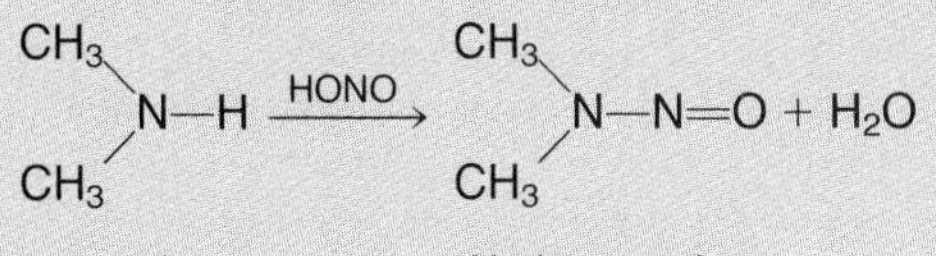

$$\underset{\text{2° amine}}{\underset{CH_3}{\overset{CH_3}{\diagdown}}N-H} \xrightarrow{HONO} \underset{\text{N-nitrosoamine}}{\underset{CH_3}{\overset{CH_3}{\diagdown}}N-N=O} + H_2O$$

$$\underset{\text{Alkylated—DNA}}{CH_3-\textbf{DNA}} + N_2 + H_2O \overset{\textbf{DNA}}{\longleftarrow} \underset{\text{Diazocompound}}{CH_3-N=N-OH}$$

14.2 HETEROCYCLIC AMINES

Heterocyclic amines are cyclic compounds that have at least one nitrogen atom in the ring structure. The structures and common names of several heterocyclic amines important in nature are seen below:

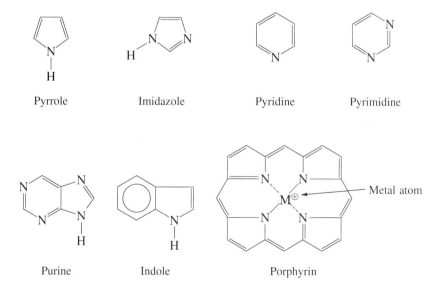

Pyrrole Imidazole Pyridine Pyrimidine

Purine Indole Porphyrin

— Metal atom

The pyrimidine and purine rings are found in DNA and RNA. The porphyrin ring structure is found in hemoglobin (an oxygen-carrying blood protein), myoglobin (an oxygen-carrying protein found in muscle tissue), and chlorophyll (a photosynthetic plant pigment). The indole and pyridine rings are found in many **alkaloids,** which are naturally occurring compounds with one or more nitrogen-containing heterocyclic rings. The alkaloids include cocaine, nicotine, quinine, morphine, heroin, and LSD (Figure 14.3).

Section 19.1

Chapter 18

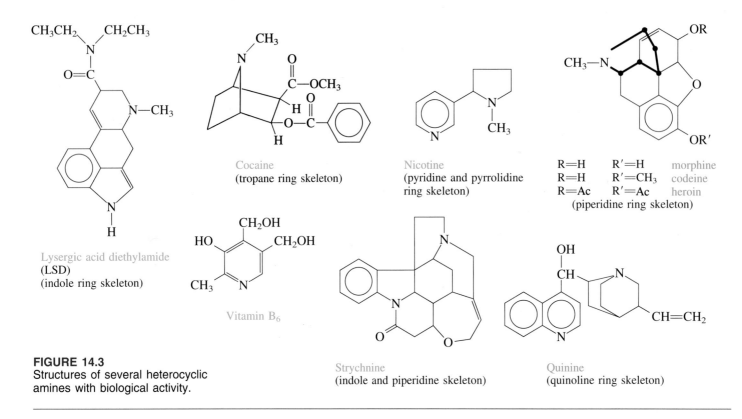

FIGURE 14.3
Structures of several heterocyclic amines with biological activity.

Lysergic acid diethylamide (LSD) is a hallucinogenic compound that may cause severe mental disorders. Cocaine is produced by the coca plant. In small doses it is used as an anesthetic for the sinuses and eyes. An **anesthetic** is a drug that causes a lack of sensation in any part of the body (local anesthetic) or causes unconsiousness (general anesthetic). In higher doses, cocaine causes an intense feeling of euphoria followed by a deep depression. Cocaine is addictive because the user needs larger and larger amounts to overcome the depression. Nicotine is one of the simplest heterocyclic amines and appears to be the addictive component of cigarette smoke.

Morphine was the first alkaloid to be isolated from the sap of the opium poppy. Morphine is a strong **analgesic,** a drug that acts as a pain killer. However, it is a powerful and addictive narcotic. Codeine, also produced by the opium poppy, is a less powerful analgesic than morphine, but it is one of the most effective cough suppressants known. Heroin is produced in the laboratory by adding two acetyl groups to morphine. It was initially made in the hopes of producing a compound with the benefits of morphine but lacking the addictive qualities. However, heroin is even more addictive than morphine.

Strychnine is found in the seeds of an Asiatic tree. It is extremely toxic and was commonly used as a rat poison at one time. Quinine, isolated from the bark of South American trees, was the first effective treatment for malaria. Vitamin B_6 is one of the water-soluble vitamins required by the body.

The water-soluble vitamins are discussed in Appendix E.

14.3 AMIDES

Amides are an important class of nitrogen-containing organic compounds containing the **amide group** shown here:

A HUMAN PERSPECTIVE

Amines and the Central Nervous System

The *central nervous system* (CNS) consists of the brain, the spinal cord, and all of the nerves that radiate from the spinal cord. The molecules that are principally responsible for transmitting messages—signals—between the various nerve cells are called *neurotransmitters*. Serotonin, a heterocyclic amine, and acetylcholine, a quaternary ammonium ion, are two of the most important neurotransmitters in the body. Serotonin appears to mediate certain types of behavior. A deficiency in serotonin, for example, has been linked to mental depression, a disease that some believe is becoming a national epidemic. Acetylcholine, in contrast, is involved in the transmission of nerve impulses that control the contraction of muscles.

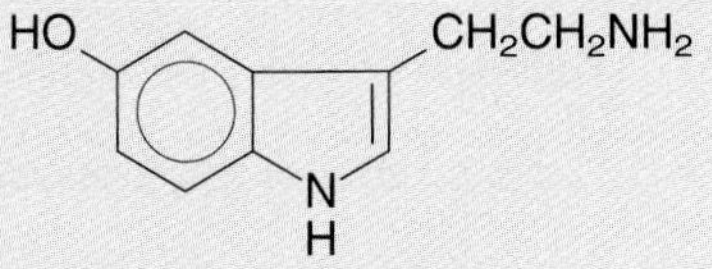

HO—[ring]—CH₂CH₂NH₂

Serotonin

CH₃—N⁺—CH₂CH₂—O—C—CH₃ (with CH₃ groups and carbonyl O)

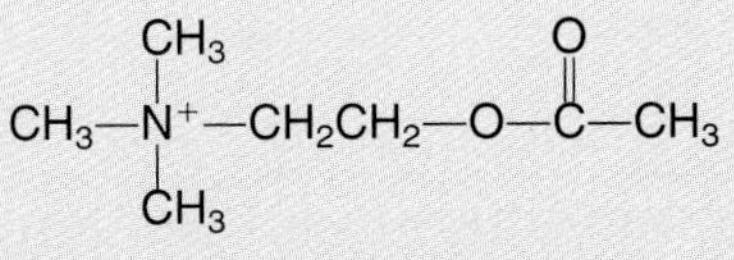

Acetylcholine

    L-Dopa and dopamine are also critical to good health. A deficiency in the neurotransmitter dopamine, for example, results in Parkinson's disease, a disorder characterized by tremors, quiet monotonous speech, loss of memory and problem-solving ability, and loss of motor function. In the brain, dopamine is synthesized from L-dopa. It would seem logical to treat Parkinson's disease with dopamine. However, dopamine cannot cross the blood-brain barrier to enter brain cells. Therefore L-dopa is used to treat this disorder.

    Both epinephrine (adrenaline) and norepinephrine are hormones that are involved in the "fight or flight" response. Epinephrine stimulates the breakdown of glycogen to produce glucose. The glucose is metabolized to produce energy for the body. Norepinephrine is involved with the CNS in the stimulation of other glands and the constriction of blood ves-

sels. L-Dopa, dopamine, epinephrine, and norepinephrine are all produced in the same biochemical pathway that begins with the amino acid tyrosine.

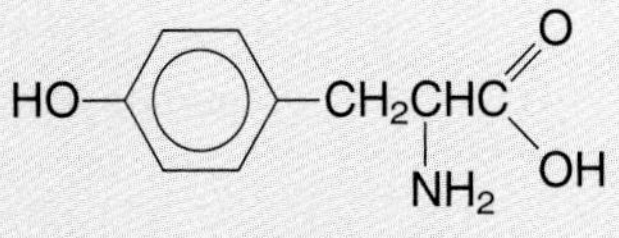

Tyrosine

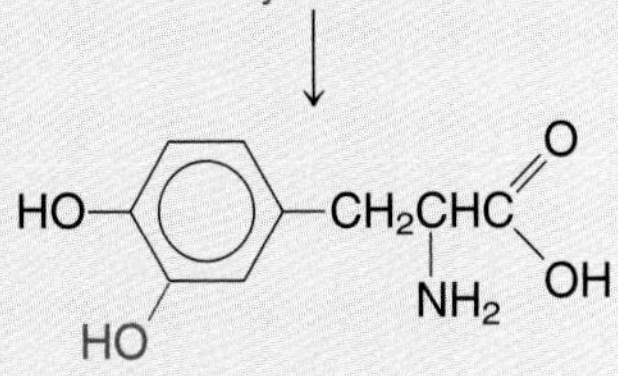

L-Dopa

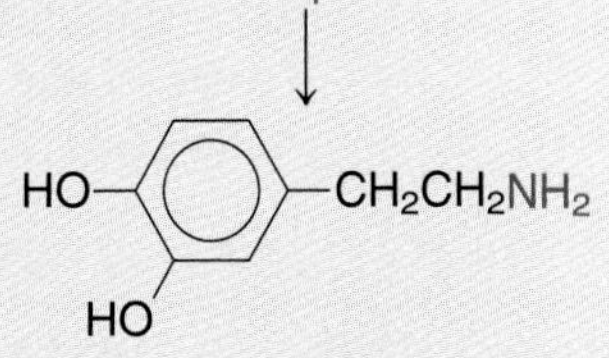

Dopamine

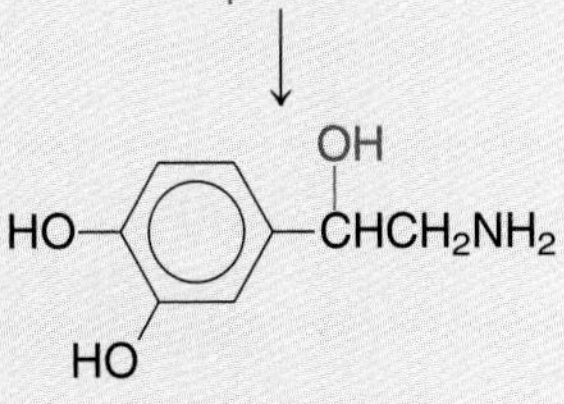

Norepinephrine

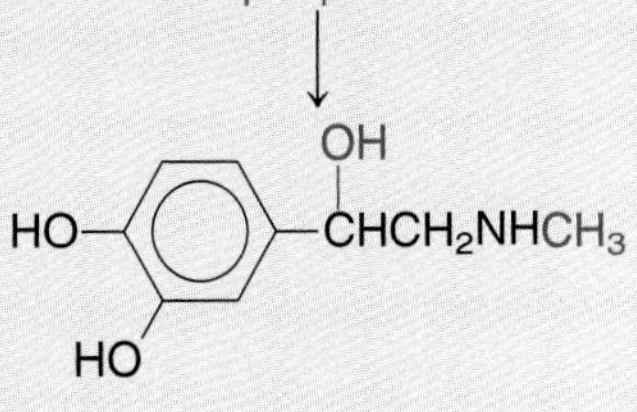

Epinephrine (adrenaline)

Amides are the product of the reaction between a carboxylic acid and ammonia or an amine. As a result, the amide group is composed of two portions: the carbonyl group from a carboxylic acid and the amino group from ammonia or an amine.

Most amides are solids at room temperature. They have very high boiling points, and the simpler ones are quite soluble in water. Both of these properties are a result of strong intermolecular

Structure and physical properties

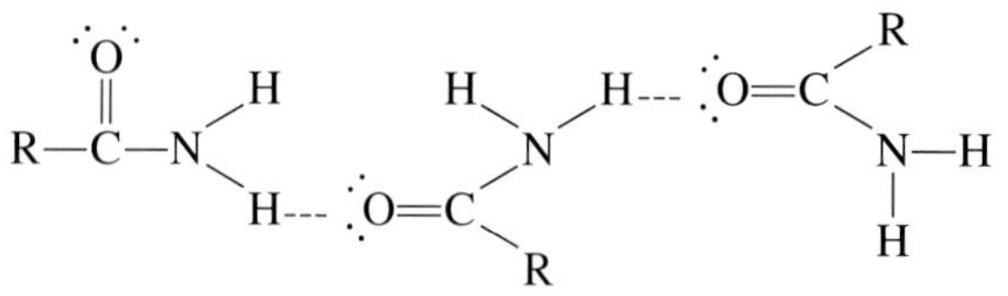

FIGURE 14.4
Hydrogen bonding in amides.

hydrogen bonding between the N—H bond of one amide and the C═O group of a second amide. This is shown in Figure 14.4.

Nomenclature

Section 12.1

The common and I.U.P.A.C. names of the amides are derived from the common and I.U.P.A.C. names of the carboxylic acids from which they were made. Remove the *-ic acid* ending of the common name or the *-oic acid* ending of the I.U.P.A.C. name of the carboxylic acid, and replace it with the ending *-amide*. Several examples of the common and I.U.P.A.C. nomenclature are provided in Table 14.2 and in the structures below:

$$CH_3—\overset{O}{\overset{\|}{C}}—NH_2 \qquad\qquad CH_3CH_2—\overset{O}{\overset{\|}{C}}—NH_2$$

Ethan*oic acid* → Ethan*amide*
OR
Acet*ic acid* → Acet*amide*

Propan*oic acid* → Propan*amide*
OR
Propion*ic acid* → Propion*amide*

Substituents on the nitrogen are placed as prefixes and are indicated by *N*- followed by the name of the substituent. There are no spaces between the prefix and the amide name. For example:

$$CH_3CH_2—\overset{O}{\overset{\|}{C}}—NH—CH_3$$

N-methylpropanamide

$$CH_3CH_2CH_2CH_2CH_2—\overset{O}{\overset{\|}{C}}—NH—CH_2CH_2CH_3$$

N-propylhexanamide

TABLE 14.2 I.U.P.A.C. and Common Names of Simple Amides

Compound	I.U.P.A.C. Name	Common Name
$R—\overset{O}{\overset{\|}{C}}—NH_2$	Alkan*amide* (*-amide* replaces the *-oic acid* ending of the I.U.P.A.C. name of carboxylic acid)	Alkan*amide* (*-amide* replaces the *-ic acid* ending of the common name of carboxylic acid)
$H—\overset{O}{\overset{\|}{C}}—NH_2$	Methanamide	Formamide
$CH_3—\overset{O}{\overset{\|}{C}}—NH_2$	Ethanamide	Acetamide
$CH_3CH_2—\overset{O}{\overset{\|}{C}}—NH_2$	Propanamide	Propionamide
$H—\overset{O}{\overset{\|}{C}}—NHCH_3$	*N*-methylmethanamide	*N*-methylformamide
$CH_3—\overset{O}{\overset{\|}{C}}—NHCH_3$	*N*-methylethanamide	*N*-methylacetamide

A CLINICAL PERSPECTIVE

Medically Important Amides

Barbiturates are often referred to as "downers." Barbiturates are derived from amides and are used as sedatives. They are also used as anticonvulsants for epileptics and for people suffering from a variety of brain disorders that manifest themselves in neurosis, anxiety, and tension.

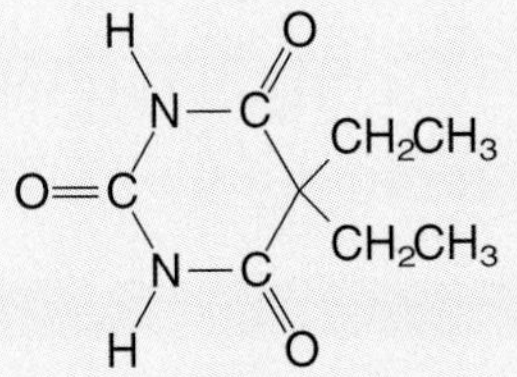

Barbital—a barbiturate

Phenacetin and acetaminophen are also amides. Acetaminophen is an aromatic amide that is commonly used in place of aspirin, particularly by people who are allergic to aspirin or who suffer stomach bleeding from the use of aspi-

rin. It was first synthesized in 1893 and is the active ingredient in Tylenol® and Datril®. Like aspirin, acetaminophen relieves pain and reduces fever. However, unlike aspirin, it is not an anti-inflammatory drug.

Phenacetin was synthesized in 1887 and used as an analgesic for almost a century. Its structure and properties are similar to those of acetaminophen. However, it was banned by the U.S. Food and Drug Administration in 1983 because of the kidney damage and blood disorders that it causes.

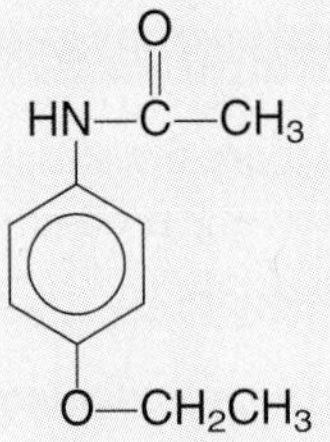

Phenacetin

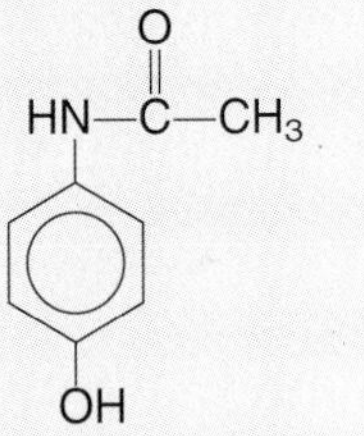

Acetaminophen

Preparation of amides

Amides are prepared directly from the carboxylic acid. This reaction, called **amidation,** is performed by heating a mixture of the carboxylic acid with either ammonia or an amine. The products are an amide and water. The bond between the carbonyl carbon and the amino nitrogen is called the **amide bond.**

$$R\overset{\overset{\text{O}}{\|}}{-}C-OH + NH_3 \xrightarrow{\text{Heat}} R\overset{\overset{\text{O}}{\|}}{-}C-NH_2 + H_2O$$

| Carboxylic acid | Ammonia or an amine | Amide | Water |

Reactions involving amides

Three specific examples follow:

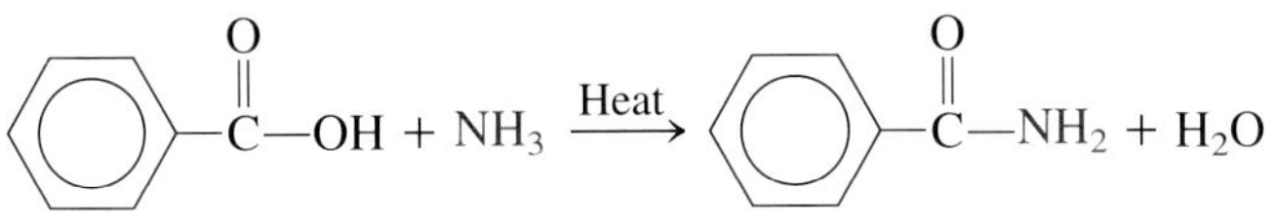

Benzoic acid → Benzamide

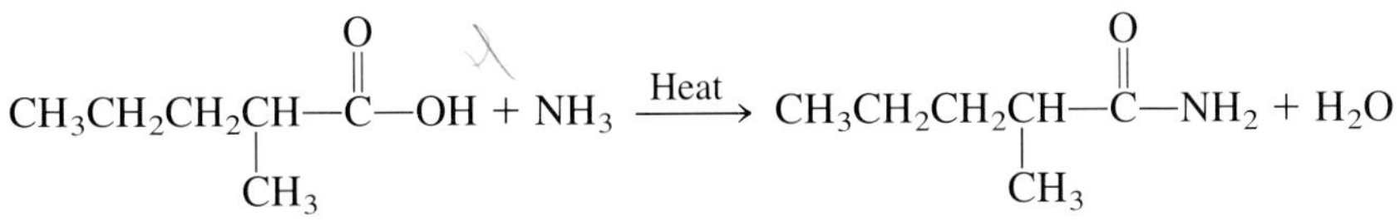

$$CH_3CH_2CH_2CH\overset{\overset{\text{O}}{\|}}{-}C-OH + NH_3 \xrightarrow{\text{Heat}} CH_3CH_2CH_2CH\overset{\overset{\text{O}}{\|}}{-}C-NH_2 + H_2O$$
$$\quad\quad\quad\quad\underset{|}{CH_3} \quad\quad\quad\quad\quad\quad\quad\quad\quad \underset{|}{CH_3}$$

2-Methylpentanoic acid

2-Methylpentanamide

$$CH_3CH_2CH_2CH_2-\overset{\overset{\displaystyle O}{\|}}{C}-OH + NH_2CH_3 \xrightarrow{\text{Heat}} CH_3CH_2CH_2CH_2-\overset{\overset{\displaystyle O}{\|}}{C}-NHCH_3 + H_2O$$

Pentanoic acid   Methanamine   *N*-Methylpentanamide

QUESTION 14.11

What is the structure of the amine that, on reaction with the carboxylic acids shown, will give each of the following products?

a. $CH_3-\overset{\overset{\displaystyle O}{\|}}{C}-OH \longrightarrow CH_3-\overset{\overset{\displaystyle O}{\|}}{C}-NHCH_3 + H_2O$

b. $CH_3CH_2CH_2CH_2\underset{\underset{\displaystyle CH_3CH_2}{|}}{CH}-\overset{\overset{\displaystyle O}{\|}}{C}-OH \longrightarrow (CH_3)_2N-\overset{\overset{\displaystyle O}{\|}}{C}-\underset{\underset{\displaystyle CH_3CH_2}{|}}{C}HCH_2CH_2CH_2CH_3 + H_2O$

QUESTION 14.12

What are the structures of the carboxylic acids and the amines that will react to give each of the following products?

a.   *N*-ethylhexanamide

b.   *N*-propylbutanamide

Hydrolysis of amides

Hydrolysis of an amide results in breaking the amide bond to produce a carboxylic acid and ammonia or an amine. It is very difficult to hydrolyze the amide bond. In fact, the reaction requires heating the amide in the presence of a strong acid or base.

$$R-\overset{\overset{\displaystyle O}{\|}}{C}-NH-R' + H_3O^+ \longrightarrow R-\overset{\overset{\displaystyle O}{\|}}{C}-OH + R'-\overset{+}{N}H_3$$

Amide   Strong   Carboxylic   Alkylammonium
               acid   acid   ion
                                                   or
                                                   ammonium ion

$$CH_3CH_2CH_2-\overset{\overset{\displaystyle O}{\|}}{C}-NH_2 + H_3O^+ \longrightarrow CH_3CH_2CH_2-\overset{\overset{\displaystyle O}{\|}}{C}-OH + \overset{+}{N}H_4$$

Butanamide   Butanoic acid
(butyramide)   (butyric acid)

If a strong base is used, the products are the amine and the salt of the carboxylic acid, as demonstrated below:

$$R-\overset{\overset{\displaystyle O}{\|}}{C}-NH-R' + NaOH \longrightarrow R-\overset{\overset{\displaystyle O}{\|}}{C}-O^- Na^+ + R'-NH_2$$

Amide   Strong   Carboxylic   Amine
               base   acid salt   or
                                                   ammonia

$$CH_3CH_2-\overset{\overset{\displaystyle O}{\|}}{C}-NHCH_3 + NaOH \longrightarrow CH_3CH_2-\overset{\overset{\displaystyle O}{\|}}{C}-O^- Na^+ + CH_3NH_2$$

N-methylpropanamide   Sodium propanoate   Methanamine
(*N*-methylpropionamide)   (sodium propionate)   (methylamine)

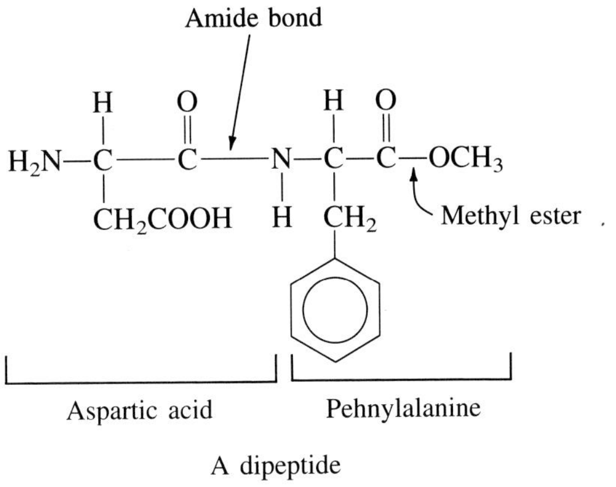

FIGURE 14.5
The amide bond. NutraSweet®, the dipeptide aspartame, is a molecule composed of two amino acids joined by an amide (peptide) bond.

The amide bond is the central feature in the structure of proteins. Proteins are polymers of amino acids. Each amino acid has both a carboxyl group and an amino group. The amide bond that forms between the carboxyl group of one amino acid and the amino group of another is called the **peptide bond.** By joining the amino acids together by amide bonds, small *peptides* and larger *proteins* are produced. Because protein structure and function are essential for life processes, it is fortunate indeed that the amide bonds that hold them together are not easily hydrolyzed at physiological pH and temperature.

Peptides, proteins, and enzymes are discussed in Chapter 15.

The artificial sweetener, NutraSweet®, is not a sugar at all. Rather it is a dipeptide composed of two amino acids, aspartic acid and the methyl ester of phenylalanine, which are joined by an amide bond (Figure 14.5).

SUMMARY OF REACTIONS

Basicity of Amines

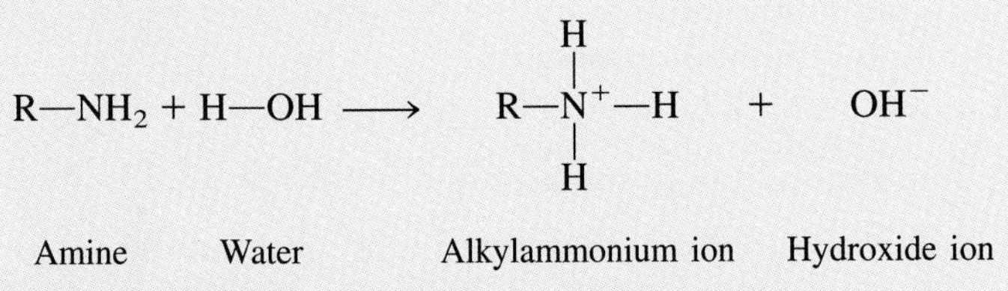

$$R-NH_2 + H-OH \longrightarrow R-\overset{\overset{H}{|}}{\underset{\underset{H}{|}}{N^+}}-H \ + \ OH^-$$

Amine   Water   Alkylammonium ion   Hydroxide ion

Neutralization of Amines

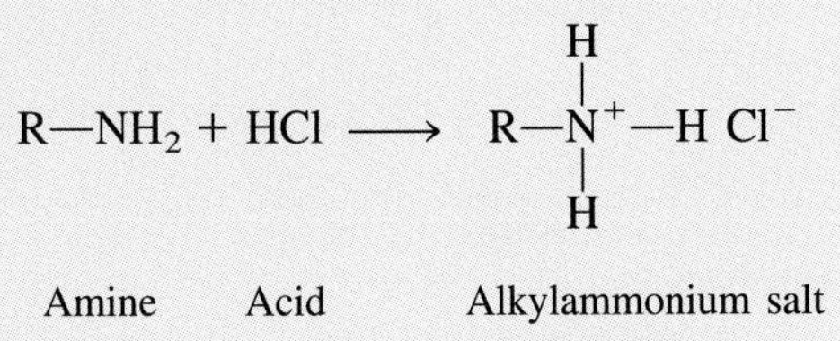

$$R-NH_2 + HCl \longrightarrow R-\overset{\overset{H}{|}}{\underset{\underset{H}{|}}{N^+}}-H \ Cl^-$$

Amine   Acid   Alkylammonium salt

Amidation

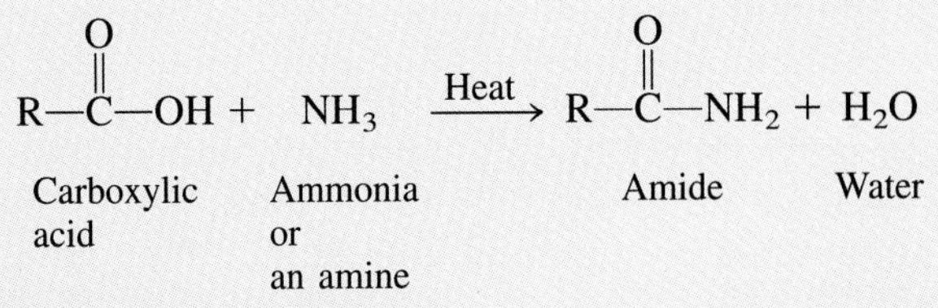

$$R-\overset{\overset{O}{||}}{C}-OH + NH_3 \xrightarrow{Heat} R-\overset{\overset{O}{||}}{C}-NH_2 + H_2O$$

Carboxylic   Ammonia   Amide   Water
acid   or
         an amine

Hydrolysis of Amides

$$R-\overset{\overset{O}{||}}{C}-NH-R' + H_3O^+ \longrightarrow R-\overset{\overset{O}{||}}{C}-OH + R'-\overset{+}{N}H_3$$

Amide   Strong   Carboxylic   Alkyl-
       acid   acid   ammonium
                               ion

$$R-\overset{\overset{O}{||}}{C}-NH-R' + NaOH \longrightarrow R-\overset{\overset{O}{||}}{C}-O^-Na^+ + R'-NH_2$$

Amide   Strong   Carboxylic   Amine
       base   acid salt   or
                                   ammonia

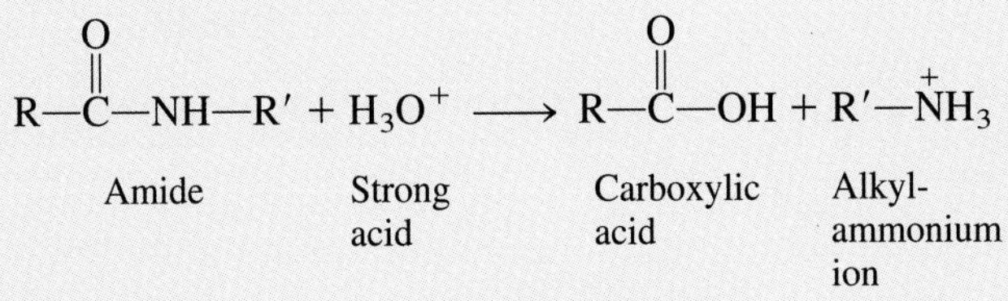

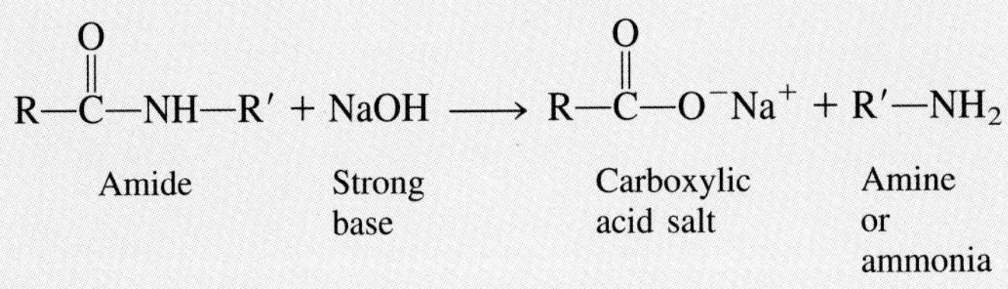

SUMMARY

14.1 Amines

Amines are a family of organic compounds that contain an amino group or substituted amino group. A *primary amine* has the general formula RNH_2; a *secondary amine* has the general formula R_2NH; and a *tertiary amine* has the general formula R_3N. In the *Chemical Abstracts* nomenclature system, amines are named as *alkanamines*. In the common system they are named as *alkylamines*. Amines behave as weak bases, forming *alkylammonium ions* in water and alkylammonium salts when they react with acids. *Quaternary ammonium salts* are ammonium salts that have four organic groups bonded to the nitrogen atom.

14.2 Heterocyclic Amines

Heterocyclic amines are cyclic compounds having at least one nitrogen atom in the ring structure. *Alkaloids* are natural plant products that contain at least one heterocyclic ring. Many alkaloids have powerful biological effects.

14.3 Amides

Amides are formed in a reaction between a carboxylic acid and an amine (or ammonia). The *amide bond* is the bond between the carbonyl carbon of the carboxylic acid and the nitrogen of the amine. In the I.U.P.A.C. Nomenclature System they are named by replacing the *-oic acid* ending of the carboxylic acid with the *-amide* ending. In the common system of nomenclature the *-ic acid* ending of the carboxylic acid is replaced by the *-amide* ending. Hydrolysis of an amide produces a carboxylic acid and an amine (or ammonia). The amide bond between two amino acids is called a *peptide bond*.

KEY TERMS

alkaloid (14.2)	anesthetic (14.2)
alkylammonium ion (14.1)	heterocyclic amines (14.2)
amidation (14.3)	peptide bond (14.3)
amide bond (14.3)	primary (1°) amine (14.1)
amide group (14.3)	quaternary ammonium salt
amides (14.3)	(14.1)
amines (14.1)	secondary (2°) amine (14.1)
analgesic (14.2)	tertiary (3°) amine (14.1)

QUESTIONS AND PROBLEMS

Amines

14.13 Name each of the following amines using the *Chemical Abstracts* system of nomenclature:

a. $CH_3CH_2CH—NH_2$ *2-butamine* (handwritten)
           |
         CH_3

b. $CH_3CH_2CH_2CHCH_2CH_3$ *3-hexamine* (handwritten)
                |
              NH_2

c.

—NH_2 *cyclopentamine* (handwritten)

d. $(CH_3)_3C—NH_2$ *2-methyl-2-propamine* (handwritten)

14.14 Name each of the following amines using the CA and common nomenclature systems:

a. $CH_3CH_2CH_2CH_2CH_2CH_2CH_2CH_2—NH_2$ *octamine* (handwritten)

b.
Cl—⬡—NH_2

c. $CH_3CHCH_2CH_3$
     |
    NH_2

          CH_3
          |
d. $CH_3—N—CH_2CH_3$

14.15 Draw the structure of each of the following compounds:
a. Diethylamine
b. Butylamine
c. 3-Decanamine
d. 3-Bromo-2-pentanamine
e. Triphenylamine

14.16 Draw the structure of each of the following compounds:
a. *N,N*-Dipropylaniline
b. Cyclohexanamine
c. 2-Bromocyclopentanamine
d. Tetraethylammonium iodide
e. 3-Bromobenzenamine

14.17 Draw each of the following compounds using condensed formulas:
a. 2-Pentanamine
b. 2-Bromo-1-butanamine
c. Ethylisopropylamine
d. Cyclopentanamine

14.18 Draw each of the following compounds using condensed structural formulas:
a. Dipentylamine
b. 3,4-Dinitroaniline
c. 4-Methyl-3-heptanamine
d. *t*-Butylpentylamine
e. 3-Methyl-3-hexanamine
f. Trimethylammonium iodide

14.19 Draw structural formulas for the eight isomeric amines that have the molecular formula $C_4H_{11}N$. Name each of the isomers using the CA system, and determine whether each isomer is a 1°, 2°, or 3° amine.

14.20 Draw all of the amines of molecular formula C_3H_9N. Name each of the isomers using the CA system, and determine whether each isomer is a primary, secondary, or tertiary amine.

14.21 Classify each of the following amines as 1°, 2°, or 3°:
a. Cyclohexanamine
b. Dibutylamine
c. 2-Methyl-2-heptanamine
d. Tripentylamine

14.22 Classify each of the following amines as either primary, secondary, or tertiary:
a. Benzenamine
b. *N*-Ethyl-2-pentanamine
c. Methylethylamine

d. Tripropylamine

e. *m*-Chloroaniline

14.23 Complete each of the following reactions by supplying the missing reactant or product indicated by a question mark:

a. 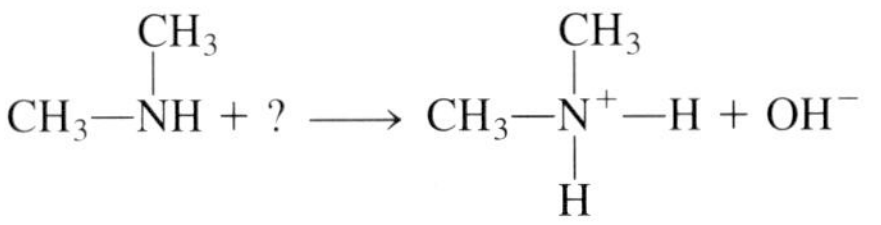 $CH_3-\overset{\overset{\displaystyle CH_3}{|}}{N}H + ? \longrightarrow CH_3-\overset{\overset{\displaystyle CH_3}{|}}{\underset{\underset{\displaystyle H}{|}}{N^+}}-H + OH^-$

b. 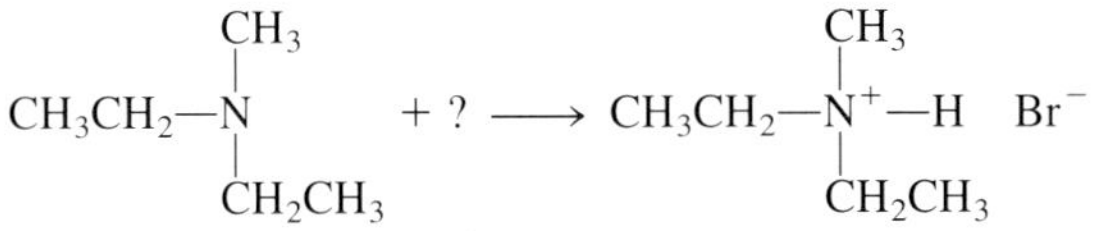 $CH_3CH_2-\overset{\overset{\displaystyle CH_3}{|}}{\underset{\underset{\displaystyle CH_2CH_3}{|}}{N}} + ? \longrightarrow CH_3CH_2-\overset{\overset{\displaystyle CH_3}{|}}{\underset{\underset{\displaystyle CH_2CH_3}{|}}{N^+}}-H \quad Br^-$

c. $CH_3CH_2CH_2-NH_2 + H_2O \longrightarrow ? + OH^-$

d. 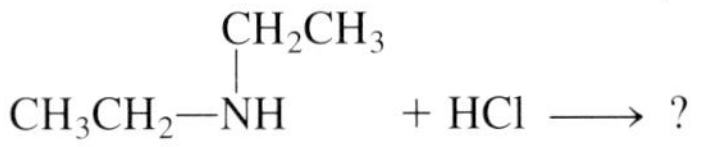 $CH_3CH_2-\overset{\overset{\displaystyle CH_2CH_3}{|}}{N}H + HCl \longrightarrow ?$

14.24 Complete each of the following reactions by supplying the missing reactant or product indicated by a question mark:

a. $CH_3CH_2-NH_2 + H_2O \longrightarrow ? + OH^-$

b. 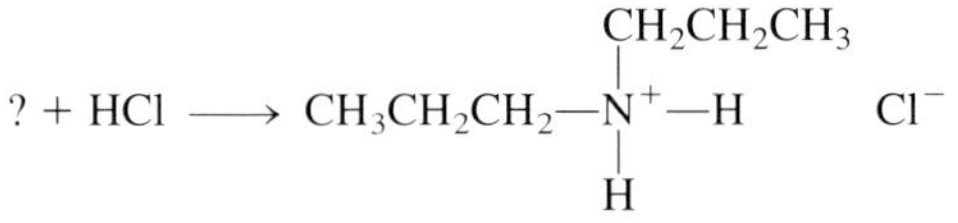 $? + HCl \longrightarrow CH_3CH_2CH_2-\overset{\overset{\displaystyle CH_2CH_2CH_3}{|}}{\underset{\underset{\displaystyle H}{|}}{N^+}}-H \quad Cl^-$

c. 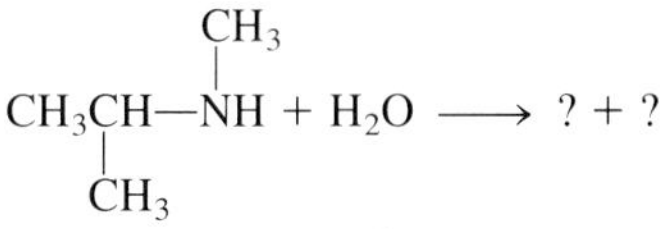 $CH_3\overset{\overset{\displaystyle CH_3}{|}}{CH}-\overset{}{N}H + H_2O \longrightarrow ? + ?$
(CH_3 below)

d. $NH_3 + HBr \longrightarrow ?$

Heterocyclic Amines

14.25 Indole and pyridine rings are found in alkaloids.
   a. Sketch each ring.
   b. Name one compound containing each of the ring structures described above, and indicate its use.

14.26 What is an alkaloid?

14.27 List some heterocyclic amines that are used in medicine.

14.28 Distinguish between the terms *analgesic* and *anesthetic.*

Amides

14.29 Name the following amides using the I.U.P.A.C. and common systems of nomenclature:
   a. 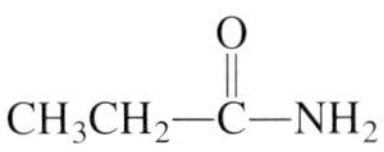 $CH_3CH_2-\overset{\overset{\displaystyle O}{||}}{C}-NH_2$ *Propanamide*
   b. $CH_3CH_2CH_2CH_2-\overset{\overset{\displaystyle O}{||}}{C}-NH_2$ *Pentanamide*
   c. $CH_3-\overset{\overset{\displaystyle O}{||}}{C}-N(CH_3)_2$

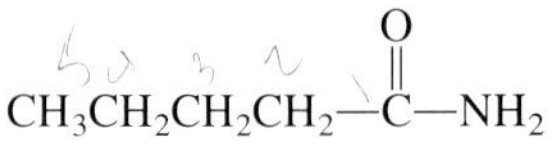

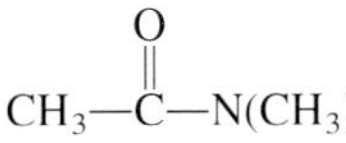

14.30 Name each of the following amides using the I.U.P.A.C. Nomenclature System:
   a. 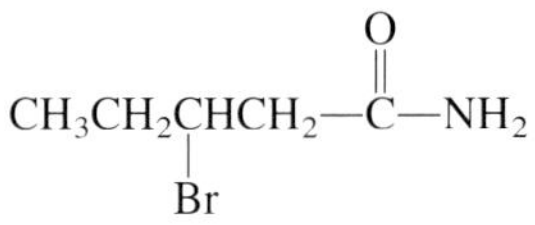 $CH_3CH_2\overset{}{\underset{\underset{\displaystyle Br}{|}}{CH}}CH_2-\overset{\overset{\displaystyle O}{||}}{C}-NH_2$

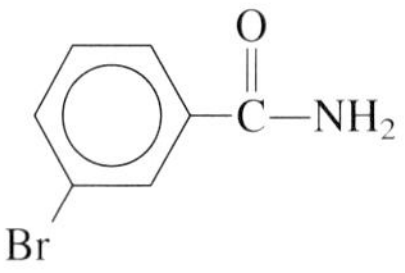

b. (structure: benzene ring with Br substituent and $-\overset{\overset{\displaystyle O}{||}}{C}-NH_2$ group)

c. $CH_3\overset{}{\underset{\underset{\displaystyle CH_3}{|}}{CH}}-\overset{\overset{\displaystyle O}{||}}{C}-NH_2$

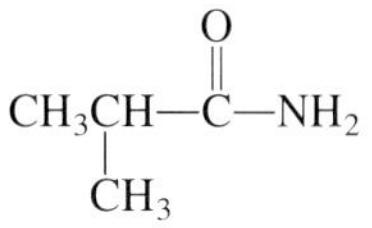

14.31 Draw the condensed structural formula of each of the following amides:
   a. Ethanamide
   b. *N*-Methylpropanamide
   c. *N,N*-Diethylbenzamide
   d. 3-Bromo-4-methylhexanamide
   e. *N,N*-Dimethylacetamide

14.32 Draw the condensed formula of each of the following amides:
   a. Acetamide
   b. 4-Methylpentanamide
   c. *N,N*-Dimethylpropanamide
   d. Formamide
   e. *N*-Ethylpropionamide

14.33 The active ingredient in many insect repellents is *N,N*-diethyl-*m*-toluamide. Draw the structure of this compound. Which carboxylic acid and amine could be reacted to give this compound?

14.34 When carboxylic acids and amines are combined, an amide is formed. This procedure may be used to synthesize acetaminophen, the active ingredient in Tylenol®. Complete the following reaction:

$CH_3\overset{\overset{\displaystyle O}{||}}{C}-OH + H_2N-\text{(benzene ring)}-OH \longrightarrow ? + H_2O$

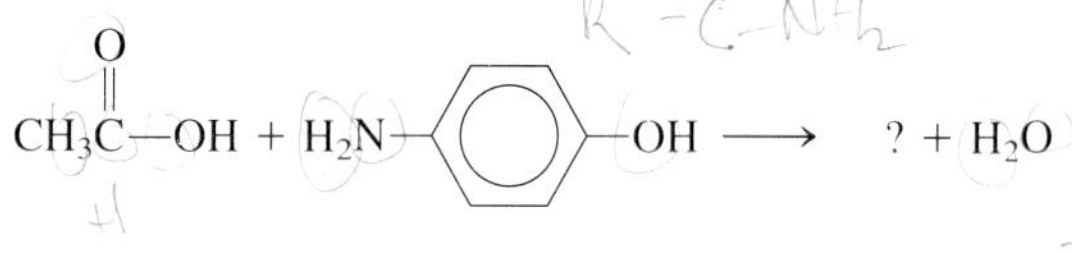

Acetaminophen

14.35 Complete each of the following reactions by supplying the missing reactant(s) or product(s) indicated by a question mark. Provide the systematic name for all the reactants and products.
   a. $? + CH_3CH_2CH_2-NH_2 \longrightarrow$
   $CH_3CH_2CH_2-NH-\overset{\overset{\displaystyle O}{||}}{C}-CH_2CH_3 + H_2O$
   b. $CH_3CH_2-\overset{\overset{\displaystyle O}{||}}{C}-OH + NH_3 \longrightarrow ? + H_2O$
   c. $? + ? \longrightarrow CH_3CH_2CH_2-\overset{\overset{\displaystyle O}{||}}{C}-NH-CH_2CH_3 + H_2O$

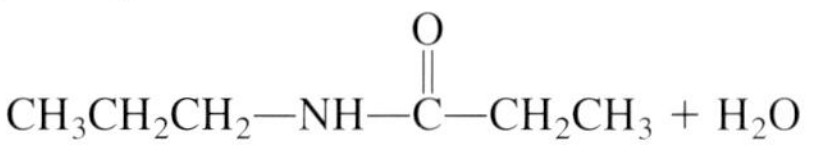

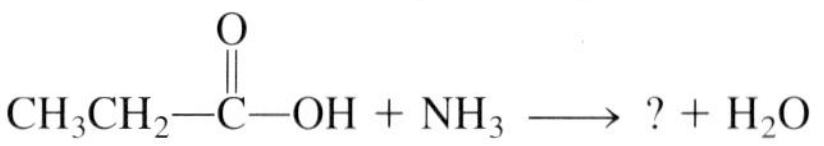

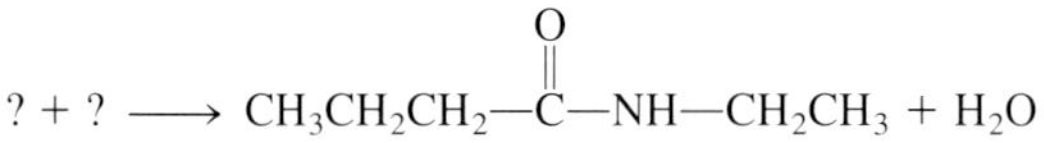

14.36 Complete the following by supplying the missing reagents indicated by a question mark. Draw the structures of each of the reactants and products.
   a. Ethanoic acid + ? $\longrightarrow$ ethanamide
   b. Propanamine + ? $\longrightarrow$ *N*-propylpentanamide
   c. Propionic acid + ? $\longrightarrow$ propionamide

14.37 Complete each of the following reactions by supplying the missing reactant(s) or product(s) indicated by a question mark. Provide the systematic name for all the reactants and products.
   a. 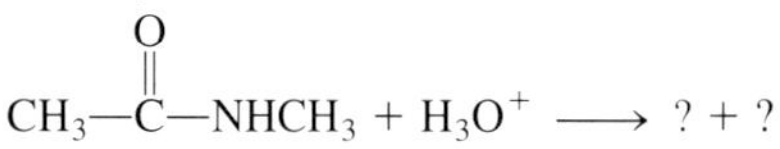 $CH_3-\overset{\overset{\displaystyle O}{||}}{C}-NHCH_3 + H_3O^+ \longrightarrow ? + ?$

b. $? + H_3O^+ \longrightarrow CH_3CH_2CH_2-\overset{\overset{\displaystyle O}{\|}}{C}-OH + CH_3NH_2$

c. $CH_3\overset{\overset{\displaystyle}{|}}{\underset{\underset{\displaystyle CH_3}{|}}{C}HCH_2}-\overset{\overset{\displaystyle O}{\|}}{C}-NHCH_2CH_3 + ? \longrightarrow$

$CH_3\underset{\underset{\displaystyle CH_3}{|}}{C}HCH_2-\overset{\overset{\displaystyle O}{\|}}{C}-OH + ?$

14.38 Complete each of the following by supplying the missing reagents. Draw the structures of each of the reactants and products.
 a. *N*-Methylpropionamide + ? $\longrightarrow$ methanamine + ?
 b. *N,N*-Dimethylacetamide + strong acid $\longrightarrow$? + ?
 c. Formamide + strong acid $\longrightarrow$? + ?

Further Problems

14.39 Lidocaine is often used as a local anesthetic. For medicinal purposes it is often used in the form of its hydrochloride salt because the salt is water-soluble. The structure of lidocaine hydrochloride is provided below. Locate the amide functional group.

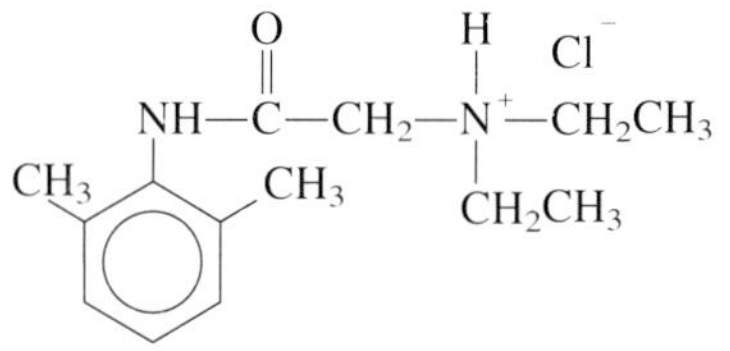

Lidocaine hydrochloride

14.40 Putrescine and cadaverine are two odoriferous amines that are produced by decaying flesh. Putrescine is 1,4-diaminobutane, and cadaverine is 1,5-diaminopentane. Draw the structures of these two compounds.

14.41 The antibiotic penicillin BT contains functional groups discussed in this chapter. The structure of penicillin BT is provided below. Locate and name as many functional groups as you can.

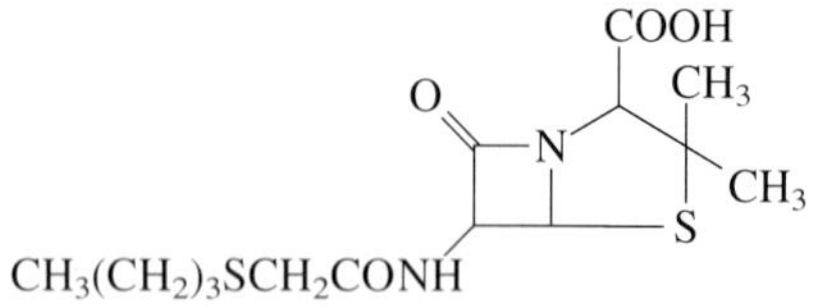

Penicillin BT

14.42 Saccharin, an artificial sweetener, is shown below. Circle the amide group in saccharin.

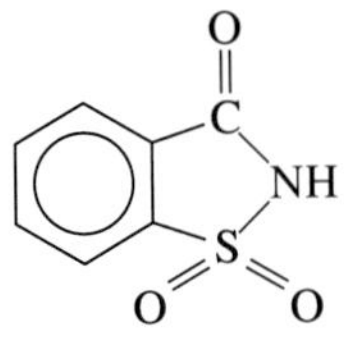

Saccharin

14.43 Briefly explain why the lower-molecular-weight amines (fewer than five carbons) exhibit appreciable solubility in water.

14.44 Why is the salt of an amine appreciably more soluble in water than the amine from which it was formed?

14.45 Most drugs containing amine groups are not administered as the amine but rather as the ammonium salt. Can you suggest a reason why?

14.46 Why does aspirin upset the stomach while acetaminophen (Tylenol®) does not?

VOCABULARY QUIZ

14.1 The amide bond joining two amino acids is a(n) _____.

14.2 An amine having the general formula RNH_2 is a(n) _____.

14.3 The functional group that is produced by a reaction between a carboxylic acid and an amine is the _____.

14.4 A(n) _____ is an amine with three alkyl groups attached to the nitrogen atom.

14.5 A(n) _____ is a ring structure that has a nitrogen atom as one of the ring atoms.

14.6 A drug that can act as a pain killer is a(n) _____.

14.7 The _____ are naturally occurring compounds that contain one or more nitrogen heterocyclic rings. These compounds often have powerful effects on the human body and mind.

14.8 A(n) _____ is the cation formed when the nonbonding electron pair of an amine nitrogen is shared with a proton.

14.9 A(n) _____ has the general formula $R_4N^+A^-$.

14.10 The collection of organic molecules with the general formulas RNH_2, R_2NH, and R_3N is the _____ family.

15

Protein Structure and Enzymes

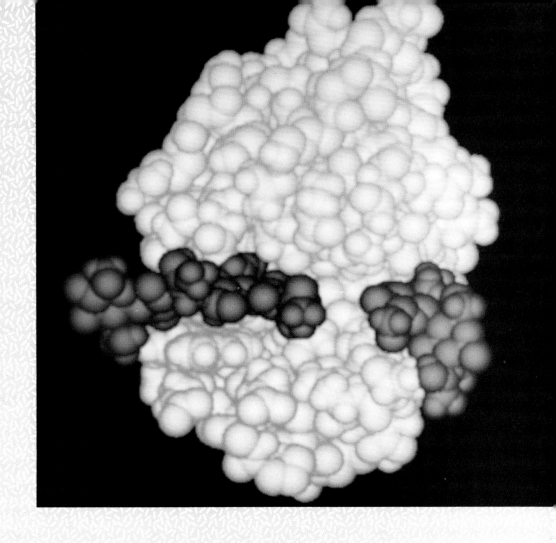

345

Can Radioactive Antibodies Cure Cancer?

Each year, we spend billions of dollars on cancer diagnosis, treatment, and research. Yet each year, tens of thousands of Americans die of this deadly disease. Recently, Dr. Mark Kaminski of the University of Michigan described a new treatment for a cancer of the immune system called B-cell lymphoma. This treatment combines two powerful tools in the battle against cancer.

B-cell lymphoma is a cancer of the B-cells that produce antibodies in the normal immune system. There are about 32,000 cases of this type of cancer each year, and, unfortunately, it is a very difficult cancer to treat.

Antibodies are proteins produced by the body, usually in response to infection by bacteria and viruses. They specifically recognize the invader and help to destroy it or remove it from the body. Although they usually fight infections, antibodies can be made to recognize other types of targets, for instance, particular "cancer antigens" on the surface of cancer cells. Kaminski is using antibodies that recognize these cancer antigens. To these antibodies he has covalently attached a radioactive isotope of iodine.

The idea behind the treatment is that the antibodies will bind to the cancer cells and the radioactivity will kill the surrounding tumor cells. In addition, the antibodies themselves attract other cells of the immune system, called T-cells. These T-cells will also contribute to cell death in the tumor.

So far, Kaminski and his co-workers have treated nine patients, none of whom had responded to standard chemotherapy. In four patients the cancer disappeared. Two of these patients have remained cancer-free for over one year. In two others the cancer was reduced but did not disappear. Three others were not helped by the radioactive antibody treatment.

Although the results are by no means conclusive, Kaminski has demonstrated a promising new method of cancer treatment. Cleverly, this treatment involves the use of the body's own protective antibodies.

In this chapter we will be studying proteins. In addition to serving as antibodies, we will see that the proteins carry out most of the work of the cell by acting as enzymes and transport proteins. They also make up the majority of the structural material in the cell and serve as the body's defense system against bacterial and viral disease.

INTRODUCTION

In the 1800s, Johannes Mulder came up with the name **protein,** a term derived from a Greek word that means "of first importance." Indeed, proteins are a very important class of food molecules because they provide an organism not only with carbon and hydrogen, but also with nitrogen and sulfur. These latter two elements are unavailable from fats and carbohydrates, the other major classes of food molecules.

In addition to their dietary importance, the proteins carry out most of the work in a cell. Protection of the body from infection, mechanical support and strength, and metabolic reactions—all are functions of proteins that are essential to life.

15.1 CELLULAR FUNCTIONS OF PROTEINS

Proteins have many biological functions, as the following short list suggests.

In the broadest sense, an antigen is any substance that stimulates an immune response.

◆ **Enzymes,** biological catalysts, are proteins. Reactions that would take days or weeks or require extremely high temperatures without enzymes are completed in an instant. Without these remarkable enzymes, life would not be possible.

◆ **Antibodies** (also called *immunoglobulins*) are specific protein molecules produced by specialized cells of the immune system in response to foreign **antigens.** These foreign invaders include bacteria and viruses that infect the body. Each antibody is custom-made to a single foreign antigen and helps to end the infection by binding to the antigen and helping to destroy it or remove it from the body.

◆ **Transport proteins** carry materials from one place to another in the body. The protein *transferrin* transports iron from the liver to the bone marrow, where it is used to synthesize the heme group for hemoglobin. The proteins *hemoglobin* and *myoglobin* are responsible for transport and storage of oxygen in higher organisms.

◆ **Regulatory proteins** control many aspects of cell function, including metabolism and reproduction. We can function only within a limited set of conditions. For life to exist, body temperature, the pH of the blood, and blood glucose levels must be carefully regulated. Many of the hormones that regulate body function, such as *insulin* and *glucagon,* are proteins.

◆ **Structural proteins** provide mechanical support to large animals and provide them with their outer coverings. Our hair and fingernails are largely composed of the protein *keratin.* Other proteins provide mechanical strength for our bones, tendons, and skin. Without such support, large, multicellular organisms like ourselves could not exist.

◆ Proteins are necessary for all forms of movement. Our muscles, including that most important muscle, the heart, contract and expand through the interaction of actin and myosin proteins. Sperm can swim because they have long flagella made up of proteins.

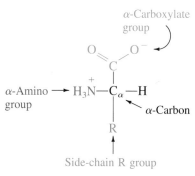

FIGURE 15.1
General structure of an α-amino acid. All amino acids isolated from proteins, except proline, have this general structure.

The proteins of the body are made up of 20 subunits called **α-amino acids.** The general structure of an α-amino acid is seen in Figure 15.1. We find that 19 of the 20 amino acids that are commonly isolated from proteins have this same general structure.

The α-carbon in the general structure is attached to a carboxylate group (a carboxyl group that has lost a proton, $-COO^-$), a protonated amino group (an amino group that has gained a proton, NH_3^+), a hydrogen, and a side chain or R group. These are important structural features of α-amino acids because the carboxylate group of one amino acid reacts with the protonated amino group of another, forming an amide bond called the *peptide bond.* Thus these two functional groups are necessary for the covalent binding of amino acids to one another to form a protein. Furthermore, the R groups cause the proteins to fold into precise, three-dimensional shapes that will determine their ultimate function.

The α-carbon is attached to four different groups in all amino acids except glycine. The α-carbon of α-amino acids is therefore chiral. That is, an α-amino acid isolated from a protein cannot be superimposed on its mirror image.

The configuration of α-amino acids isolated from proteins is L-. This is based on comparison of amino acids with D-glyceraldehyde (Figure 15.2). The configuration of α-amino acids isolated from proteins is opposite to that of D-glyceraldehyde; that is, the orientation of the four groups around L-alanine resembles the orientation of the four substituents around the chiral carbon of L-glyceraldehyde.

15.2 THE COMPLEX DESIGN OF PROTEINS

α-Amino acids

Section 11.2

The pH within the cell must be about 7 for life functions to occur. At this pH the carboxylic acid exists as a carboxylate anion, $-COO^-$, and the amino group is protonated, $-N^+H_3$. The molecular species in which the carboxylate group is protonated, $-COOH$, and the amino group unprotonated, NH_2, does not exist in aqueous solution because the acidic carboxyl group ionizes, and the basic amino group picks up the proton that is released. As a result, amino acids in water exist as dipolar ions called *zwitterions.*

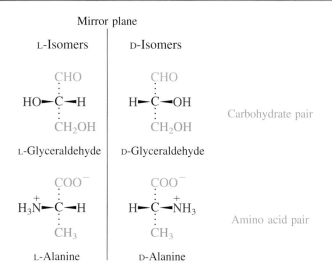

FIGURE 15.2
Structure of D- and L-glyceraldehyde and their relationship to D- and L-alanine. (The student should build models of these compounds, from which it will be immediately apparent that the members of each pair are nonsuperimposable mirror images.)

A HUMAN PERSPECTIVE

The Opium Poppy and Peptide Synthesis in the Brain

The seeds of the oriental poppy contain morphine. *Morphine* is a narcotic that has a variety of effects on the body and the brain, including drowsiness, euphoria, mental confusion, and chronic constipation. Although morphine was first isolated in 1805, not until the 1850s and the advent of the hypodermic was it effectively used as a pain killer. During the American Civil War, morphine was used extensively to relieve the pain of wounds and amputations. It was at this time that the addictive properties were noticed. By the end of the Civil War, over 100,000 soldiers were addicted to morphine.

As a result of the Harrison Act (1914), morphine came under government control and was made available only by prescription. Although morphine is addictive, *heroin,* a derivative of morphine, is much more addictive and induces a greater sense of euphoria that lasts for a longer time.

Why do heroin and morphine have such powerful effects on the brain? Both drugs have been found to bind to *receptors* on the surface of the cells of the brain. The function of

these receptors is to bind specific chemical signals and to direct the brain cells to respond. Yet it seemed odd that the cells of our brain should have receptors for a plant chemical. This mystery was solved in 1975, when John Hughes discovered that the brain itself synthesizes small peptide hormones with a morphinelike structure. Two of these opiate peptides are called *methionine enkephalin,* or met-enkephalin, and *leucine enkephalin,* or leu-enkephalin.

These neuropeptide hormones have a variety of effects. They inhibit intestinal motility and blood flow to the gastrointestinal tract. This explains the chronic constipation of morphine users. In addition, it is thought that these *enkephalins* play a role in pain perception, perhaps serving as a pain blockade. This is supported by the observation that they are found in higher concentrations in the bloodstream following painful stimulation. It is further suspected that they may play a role in mood and mental health. The so-called "runner's high" is thought to be a euphoria brought about by an excessively long or strenuous run!

Unlike morphine, the action of enkephalins is short-lived. They bind to the cellular receptor and thereby induce the cells to respond. Then they are quickly destroyed by enzymes in the brain that hydrolyze the peptide bonds of the enkephalin. Once destroyed, they are no longer able to elicit a cellular response. Morphine and heroin bind to these same receptors and induce the cells to respond. However, these drugs are not destroyed and therefore persist in the brain for long periods of time at concentrations high enough to continue to cause biological effects.

Many researchers are working to understand why drugs like morphine and heroin are addictive. Studies with cells in culture have suggested one mechanism for morphine tolerance and addiction. Normally, when the cell receptors bind to enkephalins, this signals the cell to decrease the production of a chemical messenger called *cyclic AMP,* or simply cAMP. (This compound is very closely related to the nucleotide adenosine-5'-monophosphate.) The decrease in cAMP level helps to block pain and elevate one's mood. When morphine is applied to these cells, they become desensitized; that is, they do not decrease cAMP production and thus behave as

Heroin

Morphine

The structures of heroin and morphine.

The hydrophobic interaction between nonpolar R groups is one of the forces that helps maintain the proper three-dimensional shape of a protein.

Proline (Pro)

Because all of the amino acids have a carboxyl group and an amino group, all differences between amino acids depend upon their side-chain R groups. The amino acids are grouped in Figure 15.3 according to the polarity of their side chains.

The side chains of some amino acids are nonpolar. They prefer contact with one another to contact with water and are said to be **hydrophobic** ("water-fearing"). These amino acids are generally found buried in the interior of proteins, where they can associate with one another and remain isolated from water. Ten amino acids fall into this category: alanine, valine, leucine, isoleucine, proline, glycine, cysteine, methionine, phenylalanine, and tryptophan. The R group of proline is unique; it is actually tied to the α-amino group.

The side chains of the remaining amino acids are polar. They are attracted to water, **hydrophilic** ("water-loving"). The hydrophilic side chains are often found on the surfaces of proteins. The polar amino acids can be subdivided into three classes.

Tyr-Gly-Gly-Phe-Met
Methionine enkephalin

Tyr-Gly-Gly-Phe-Leu
Leucine enkephalin

Structures of the peptide opiates leucine enkephalin and methionine enkephalin. These are the body's own opiates.

though no morphine were present. However, a greater amount of morphine will once again cause the decrease in cAMP levels. Thus addiction and the progressive need for more of the drug seem to result from biochemical reactions in the cells.

This logic can be extended to understand withdrawal symptoms. When an addict stops using the drug, he or she exhibits withdrawal symptoms that include excessive sweating, anxiety, and tremors. The cause of this may be that the high levels of morphine were keeping the cAMP levels low, thus reducing pain and causing euphoria. When morphine is removed completely, the cells overreact and produce huge quantities of cAMP. The result of this is all of the unpleasant symptoms known collectively as the withdrawal syndrome.

Clearly, morphine and heroin have demonstrated the potential for misuse and are a problem for society in several respects. Often, the money needed to support a drug habit is acquired by illegal means such as robbery, theft, and prostitution. More recently, it has become apparent that the use of shared needles for the injection of drugs is resulting in the alarming spread of the virus responsible for Acquired Immune Deficiency Syndrome (AIDS). Nonetheless, morphine remains one of the most effective pain killers known. Certainly, for people suffering from cancer, painful burns, or serious injuries the risk of addiction is far outweighed by the benefits of relief from excruciating pain.

◆ *Polar, neutral amino acids* have R groups that have a high affinity for water but that are not ionic. Serine, threonine, tyrosine, asparagine, and glutamine fall into this category. These amino acids can associate with one another by hydrogen bonding.

◆ *Negatively charged amino acids* have ionized carboxyl groups in their side chains. At pH 7 these amino acids have a net charge of -1. Aspartate and glutamate are the two amino acids in this category. They are acidic amino acids because ionization of the carboxylic acid releases a proton.

◆ *Positively charged amino acids.* At pH 7, lysine, arginine, and histidine have a net positive charge because their side chains contain positive groups. These amino acids are basic because the side chain reacts with water, picking up a proton and releasing a hydroxide anion.

Section 5.7

Hydrogen bonding is another weak interaction that helps maintain the proper three-dimensional structure of a protein.

The positively and negatively charged amino acids within a protein can interact with one another to form ionic bridges. This is yet another attractive force that helps to keep the protein chain folded in a precise way.

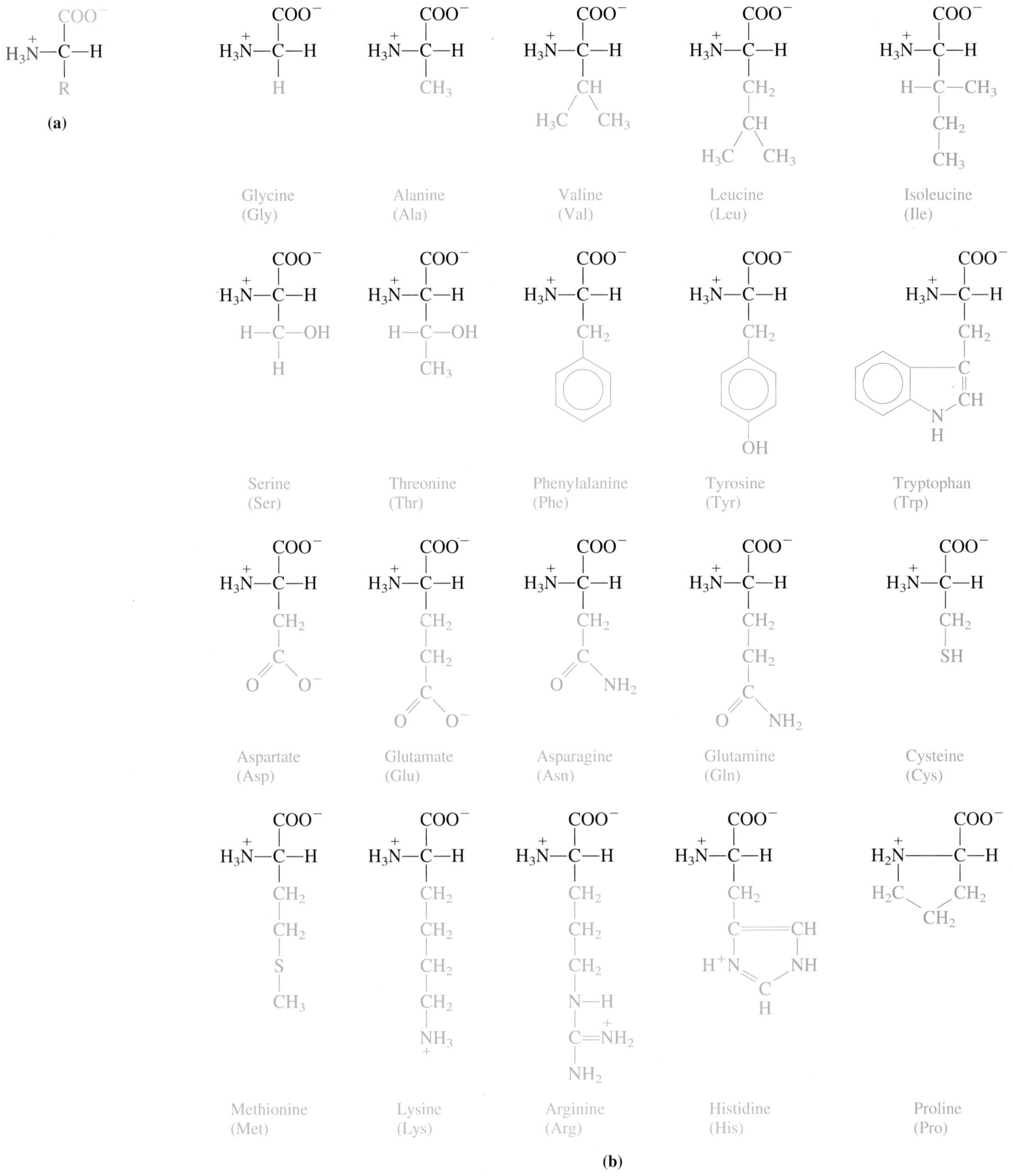

(a)

Glycine
(Gly)

Alanine
(Ala)

Valine
(Val)

Leucine
(Leu)

Isoleucine
(Ile)

Serine
(Ser)

Threonine
(Thr)

Phenylalanine
(Phe)

Tyrosine
(Tyr)

Tryptophan
(Trp)

Aspartate
(Asp)

Glutamate
(Glu)

Asparagine
(Asn)

Glutamine
(Gln)

Cysteine
(Cys)

Methionine
(Met)

Lysine
(Lys)

Arginine
(Arg)

Histidine
(His)

Proline
(Pro)

(b)

FIGURE 15.3
Structures of the amino acids. (a) The general structure of an amino acid. (b) Structures of the 20 α-amino acids isolated from proteins. The side chains are classified by their polarity.

The names of the amino acids are abbreviated by their first three letters. These abbreviations are shown in Table 15.1.

Write the three-letter abbreviation and draw the structure of each of the following amino acids:

a. Glycine Gly   d. Aspartate asp

b. Proline pro   e. Lysine Lys

c. Threonine thr

Indicate whether each of the amino acids listed in Question 15.1 is polar, nonpolar, basic, or acidic.

Proteins are polymers of L-α-amino acids. The carboxyl group of one amino acid is linked to the amino group of another amino acid. This reaction is identical to amidation, and the amide bond formed in the reaction is called a **peptide bond** (Figure 15.4).

The peptide bond

The molecule formed by condensing two amino acids is called a *dipeptide*. The amino acid with a free α-N$^+$H$_3$ group is known as the amino terminal, or simply the **N-terminal amino acid** (glycine in Figure 15.4), and the amino acid with a free —COO$^-$ group is known as the carboxyl, or **C-terminal amino acid** (alanine in Figure 15.4). Structures of proteins are conventionally written with their N-terminal amino acid on the left.

FIGURE 15.4

(a) Condensation of two α-amino acids to give a dipeptide. The two amino acids shown are glycine and alanine. (b) Structure of a pentapeptide. Amino acid residues are enclosed in boxes. Glycine is the amino-terminal amino acid, and alanine is the carboxy-terminal amino acid.

TABLE 15.1 Names and Three-Letter Abbreviations of the α-Amino Acids

Amino Acid	Three-Letter Abbreviation
Alanine	ala
Arginine	arg
Asparagine	asn
Aspartic acid	asp
Cysteine	cys
Glutamine	gln
Glutamic acid	glu
Glycine	gly
Histidine	his
Isoleucine	ile
Leucine	leu
Lysine	lys
Methionine	met
Phenylalanine	phe
Proline	pro
Serine	ser
Threonine	thr
Tryptophan	trp
Tyrosine	tyr
Valine	val

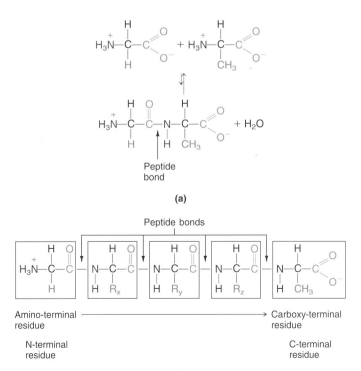

To understand why the N-terminal amino acid is placed first and the C-terminal amino acid is placed last, we need to look at the process of protein synthesis. As we will see in Section 19.6, the N-terminal amino acid is the first amino acid of the protein. It forms a peptide bond involving its carboxyl group and the amino group of the second amino acid in the protein. Thus there is a free amino group literally projecting from the left end of the protein. Similarly, the C-terminal amino acid is the last amino acid added to the protein during protein synthesis. Since the peptide bond is formed between the amino group of this amino acid and the carboxyl group of the previous amino acid, there is a free carboxyl group projecting from the right end of the protein chain.

The number of amino acids in small peptides is indicated by the prefixes di- (two units), tri- (three units), tetra- (four units), and so forth. Peptides are named as derivatives of the C-terminal amino acid, which receives its entire name. For all other amino acids the ending -ine is changed to -yl. Thus the dipeptide alanyl-glycine has glycine as its C-terminal amino acid residue, as indicated by its full name, "glycine":

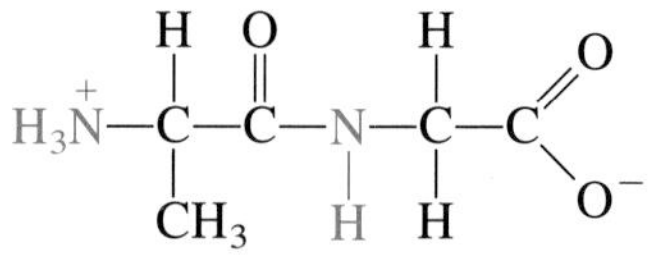

Alanyl-glycine
(ala-gly)

The dipeptide formed from alanine and glycine that has alanine as its C-terminal amino acid is glycyl-alanine:

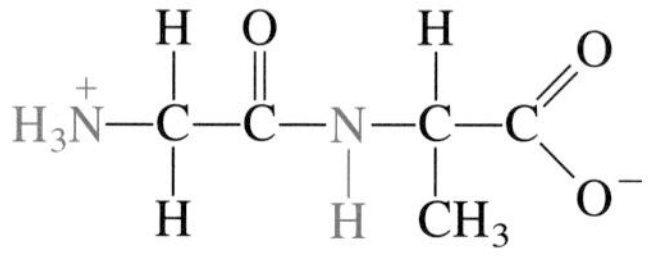

Glycyl-alanine
(gly-ala)

The structures of small peptides can easily be drawn with practice if certain rules are followed. First note that the backbone of the peptide contains the repeating sequence

$$N-C-C-N-C-C-N-C-C$$
$$1 \quad 2 \qquad 1 \quad 2 \qquad 1 \quad 2$$

where N is the α-amino group, *carbon-1* is the α-carbon, and *carbon-2* is the carboxyl group. *Carbon-1* is always bonded to a hydrogen atom and to the R group side chain that is unique to each amino acid. Continue drawing as outlined in the following example.

EXAMPLE 15.1

Writing the Structure of the Tripeptide Alanyl-glycyl-valine

Solution

Step 1: Write out the backbone for a tripeptide. It will contain three sets of three atoms, nine atoms in all. Remember that the N-terminal amino acid is written to the left.

$$N-C-C \qquad N-C-C \qquad N-C-C$$
Set 1 \qquad Set 2 \qquad Set 3

Step 2: Add oxygens to the carboxyl carbons and hydrogens to the amino nitrogens:

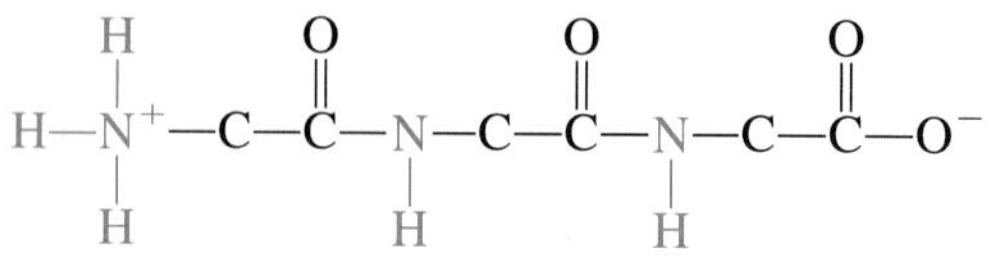

Step 3: Add hydrogens to the α-carbons:

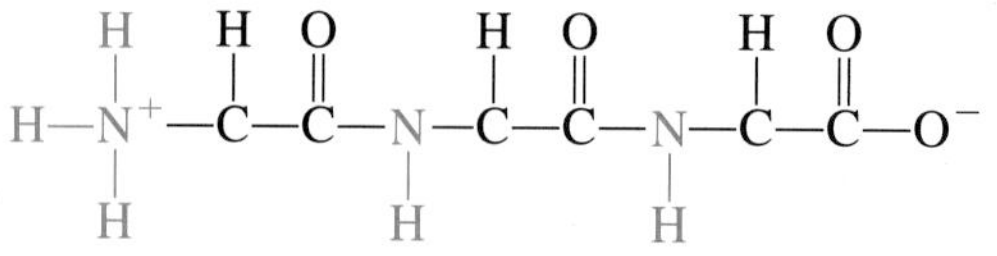

Step 4: Add the side chains. In this example (ala-gly-val) they are, from left to right, —CH$_3$, H, and —CH(CH$_3$)$_2$:

$$
H-N^+-\overset{\overset{\displaystyle H}{|}}{\underset{\underset{\displaystyle H}{|}}{C}}-\overset{\overset{\displaystyle H}{|}}{\underset{\underset{\displaystyle CH_3}{|}}{C}}-\overset{\overset{\displaystyle O}{\|}}{C}-N-\overset{\overset{\displaystyle H}{|}}{\underset{\underset{\displaystyle H}{|}}{C}}-\overset{\overset{\displaystyle O}{\|}}{C}-N-\overset{\overset{\displaystyle H}{|}}{\underset{\underset{\displaystyle CH}{|}}{C}}-\overset{\overset{\displaystyle O}{\|}}{C}-O^-
$$

QUESTION 15.3

Write the structure of each of the following peptides:

a. Alanyl-phenylalanine

b. Lysyl-alanine

c. Phenylalanyl-tyrosyl-leucine

QUESTION 15.4

Write the structure of each of the following peptides:

a. Glycyl-valyl-serine

b. Threonyl-cysteine

c. Isoleucyl-methionyl-aspartate

The peptide bond is planar, and the two adjacent α-carbons lie *trans* to it (Figure 15.5). The hydrogen of the amide nitrogen is also *trans* to the oxygen of the carbonyl group. Almost all of the peptide bonds in proteins are planar and have a *trans* configuration. This is quite important physiologically because it makes protein structures relatively rigid. If they could not hold their shapes, they could not function.

The **primary structure** of a protein is the amino acid sequence of the protein chain. It results from the covalent bonding between the amino acids in the chain (peptide bonds). The primary structures of proteins are translations of information contained in genes. Each protein has a different primary structure with different amino acids in different places along the chain.

Primary structure of proteins
Chapter 19

The primary sequence of a protein, the chain of covalently linked amino acids, folds into regularly repeating structures that resemble designs in a tapestry. These repeating structures define the **secondary structure** of the protein. The secondary structure is the result of hydrogen

Secondary structure of proteins

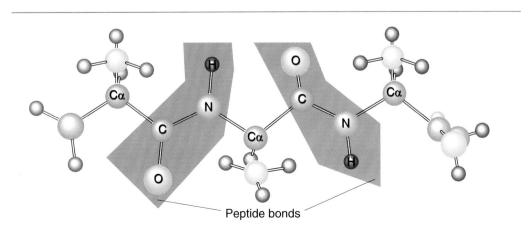

Peptide bonds

FIGURE 15.5
Conformation of peptide bond is planar. The C=O and N—H groups of the peptide bond are *trans* to one another. These groups are in boxes in the structure.

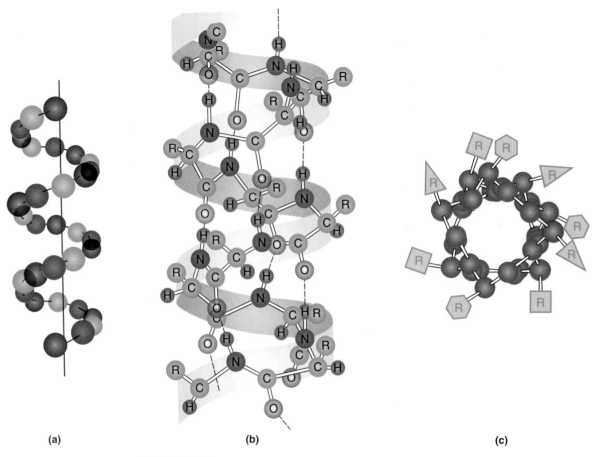

(a)   (b)   (c)

FIGURE 15.6
The α-helix. (a) Schematic diagram showing only the helical backbone. (b) Molecular model representation. Note that all of the hydrogen bonds between C=O and N—H groups are parallel to the long axis of the helix. The pitch of the helix is 5.4 Å (0.54 nm), and there are 3.6 amino acid residues per turn. (c) Top view of an α-helix. The side chains of the helix point away from the long axis of the helix. The view is into the barrel of the helix.

bonding between the amide hydrogens and carbonyl oxygens of the peptide bonds. Many hydrogen bonds are needed to maintain the secondary structure and thereby the overall structure of the protein. Different regions of a protein chain may have different types of secondary structure. The two most common types are the α-helix and the β-pleated sheet.

α-Helix

The most common type of secondary structure is a coiled, helical conformation known as the **α-helix** (Figure 15.6). The α-helix has several important features:

◆ Every amide hydrogen and carbonyl oxygen is involved in a hydrogen bond when the chain coils into an α-helix. These hydrogen bonds lock the α-helix into place.

◆ Every carbonyl oxygen is hydrogen bonded to an amide hydrogen four residues away in the chain.

◆ The polypeptide chain in an α-helix is right-handed.

Fibrous proteins are proteins arranged in fibers or sheets. The **α-keratins** are fibrous proteins that form the covering (hair, wool, and fur) of most land animals. Human hair provides a typical example of the structure of the α-keratins. The proteins of hair consist almost exclusively of polypeptide chains coiled up into α-helices. A single α-helix is coiled in a bundle with two other helices to give a three-stranded *protofibril* that is part of an array known as a *microfibril* (Figure 15.7). These structures, which resemble "molecular pigtails," possess great mechanical strength, and they are virtually insoluble in water.

The fibrous proteins of muscle are also composed of proteins that contain considerable numbers of α-helices. **Myosin,** one of the major proteins of muscle, for example, is a rodlike structure in which two α-helices form a coiled coil (Figure 15.8).

The major structural property of a coiled coil of α-helices is its great mechanical strength. This property is applied very efficiently in both the fibrous proteins of skin and those of muscle. As you can imagine, these proteins must be very strong to carry out their functions of mechanical support and muscle contraction.

β-Pleated sheet

The second common secondary structure in proteins resembles the pleated folds of drapery and is known as **β-pleated sheet** (Figure 15.9). All of the carbonyl oxygens and amide hydrogens in a β-pleated sheet are involved in hydrogen bonds, and the polypeptide chain is nearly

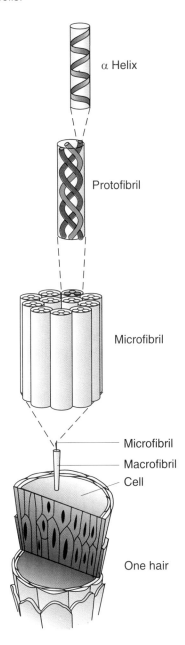

FIGURE 15.7
Structure of the α-keratins. These proteins are assemblies of triple-helical protofibrils that are assembled in an array known as a microfibril. These in turn are assembled into macrofibrils. Hair is a collection of macrofibrils and hair cells.

α Helix

Protofibril

Microfibril

Microfibril
Macrofibril
Cell

One hair

FIGURE 15.8
Schematic diagram of the structure of myosin. This muscle protein consists of a rodlike coil of α-helices with two globular heads, also composed of protein, attached to myosin at its C-terminus. In muscle, myosin molecules are assembled into thick filaments that alternate with thin filaments composed of the proteins actin, troponin, and tropomyosin. Working together, these filaments allow muscles to contract and relax.

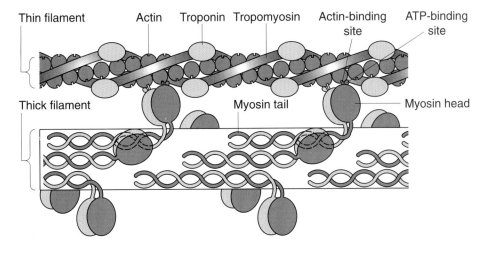

FIGURE 15.9
Structure of the β-pleated sheet. The polypeptide chains are nearly completely extended, and hydrogen bonds (red) between C=O and N—H groups are at right angles to the long axis of the polypeptide chains.

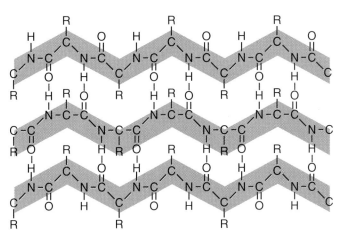

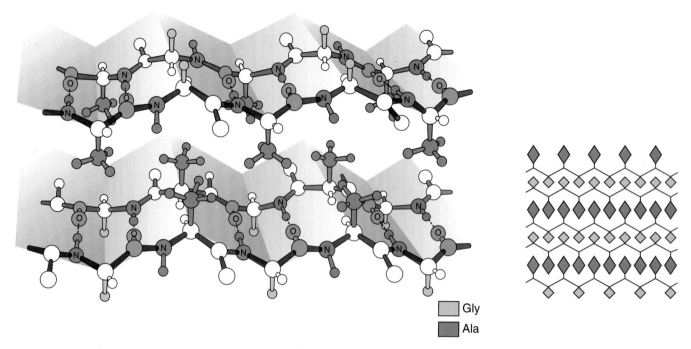

Gly

Ala

FIGURE 15.10
The structure of silk fibroin is almost entirely antiparallel β-pleated sheet. (a) The molecular structure of a portion of the silk fibroin protein. (b) A schematic representation of the antiparallel β-pleated sheet with the nestled R groups.

completely extended. The polypeptide chains in a β-pleated sheet can have two orientations. If the N-termini are head to head, the structure is known as a *parallel* β-pleated sheet. And if the N-terminus of one chain is aligned with the C-terminus of a second chain (head to tail), the structure is known as an *antiparallel* β-pleated sheet.

Some fibrous proteins are composed of β-pleated sheets. For example, the silkworm produces *silk fibroin,* a protein whose structure is an antiparallel β-pleated sheet (Figure 15.10). The polypeptide chains of a β-pleated sheet are almost completely extended, and silk does not stretch easily. Glycine accounts for nearly half of the amino acid residues of silk fibroin. Alanine and serine account for most of the others. The methyl groups of alanine residues and the hydroxymethyl groups of serine residues lie on opposite sides of the sheet. Thus the stacked sheets nestle comfortably, like sheets of corrugated cardboard.

Tertiary structure of proteins

The majority of cellular proteins are soluble in the cell cytoplasm. These soluble proteins are usually **globular.** This compact, spherical structure is called the **tertiary structure** of the protein. The peptide chain with its regions of secondary structure, α-helix and β-pleated sheet, further folds on itself to achieve the tertiary structure.

The globular tertiary structure forms spontaneously and is maintained as a result of interactions among the R groups of the amino acids. The structure is maintained by the following molecular interactions:

◆ Hydrophobic attractions between the R groups of nonpolar amino acids.

◆ Hydrogen bonds between the polar R groups of the polar amino acids.

◆ Ionic bonds between the R groups of oppositely charged amino acids.

◆ Covalent bonds between thiol-containing amino acids. Two cysteine residues can be oxidized to a dimeric amino acid called cystine (Figure 15.11). The disulfide bond of cystine can be a cross-link between different proteins, or it can tie two segments within a protein together.

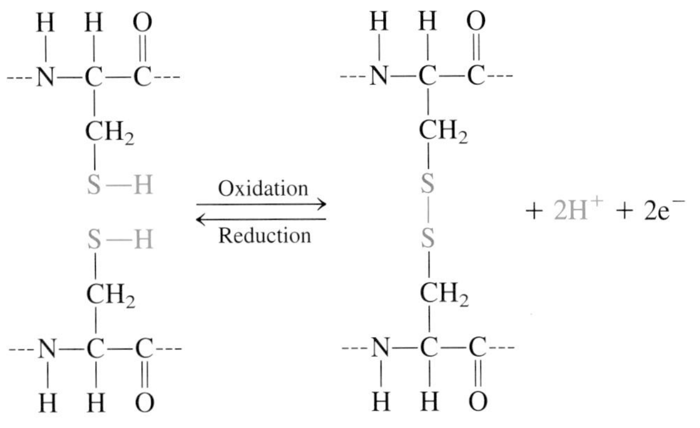

$$\text{Cysteine} \underset{\text{Reduction}}{\overset{\text{Oxidation}}{\rightleftharpoons}} \text{Cystine} + 2H^+ + 2e^-$$

FIGURE 15.11
Oxidation of two cysteines to give the dimer cystine. This reaction occurs in cells and is readily reversible.

The bonds that maintain the tertiary structure of proteins are shown in Figure 15.12. The importance of these bonds becomes clear when we realize that it is the tertiary structure of the protein that determines its biological function. Most of the time, nonpolar amino acid residues are buried, closely packed, in the interior of a globular protein, out of contact with water. Polar and charged amino acid residues lie on the surfaces of globular proteins. The structure of the globular protein myoglobin is seen in Figure 15.13.

For many proteins the functional form is not composed of a single peptide but is rather an aggregate of smaller globular peptides. For instance, the protein hemoglobin is composed of four individual globular peptide subunits: two identical α-subunits and two identical β-subunits.

Quaternary structure of proteins

FIGURE 15.12
Summary of the weak interactions that help maintain the tertiary structure of a protein.

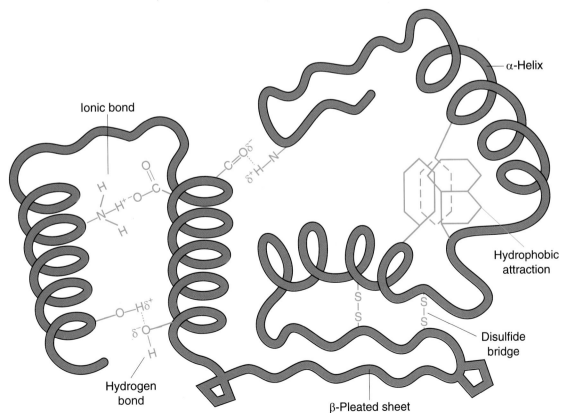

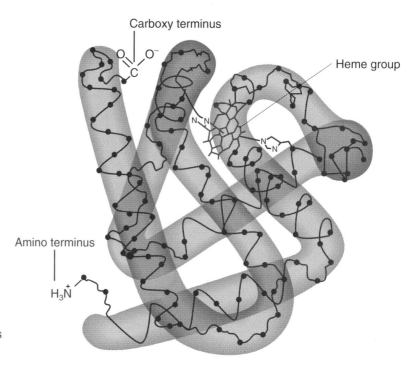

Carboxy terminus

Heme group

Amino terminus

FIGURE 15.13
Myoglobin. The heme group, shown in color, has
an iron atom to which oxygen binds.

The designations α- and β- used to
describe the subunits of hemoglobin
do not refer to types of secondary
structure.

Only when the four peptides are bonded to one another is the protein molecule functional. The
binding of several peptides to produce a functional protein defines the **quaternary structure** of
a protein.

The forces that hold the quaternary structure of a protein are the same as those that hold the
tertiary structure. These include hydrogen bonds between polar amino acids, ionic bridges
between oppositely charged amino acids, hydrophobic attraction between nonpolar amino acids,
and disulfide bridges.

In some cases a functional protein must be bound to something extra in order for it to be
functional. This additional group is called a **prosthetic group,** and the functional protein carrying a prosthetic group is called a **conjugated protein.** Many of the receptor proteins on cell
surfaces are **glycoproteins.** These are conjugated proteins with sugar groups covalently attached. Hemoglobin is also a conjugated protein. Each of the subunits is bound to an iron-
containing heme group. As in the case of hemoglobin, the prosthetic group often determines the
function of a protein. For instance, in hemoglobin it is the iron-containing heme groups that have
the ability to bind reversibly to oxygen.

The four levels of protein structure are summarized in Figure 15.14 using the protein
hemoglobin as an example.

QUESTION 15.5

Describe the four levels of protein structure.

QUESTION 15.6

What are the weak interactions that maintain the tertiary structure of a protein?

15.3 MYOGLOBIN AND HEMOGLOBIN

Myoglobin and oxygen storage

The cells of our bodies are buried in the interior of the body and cannot get food molecules or
eliminate waste directly. The circulatory system solves this problem by delivering nutrients and
oxygen to body cells and carrying away wastes. Our cells require a steady supply of oxygen, but
oxygen is only slightly soluble in aqueous solutions. To overcome this solubility problem, we
have an oxygen transport protein, **hemoglobin.** Hemoglobin is found in red blood cells and is

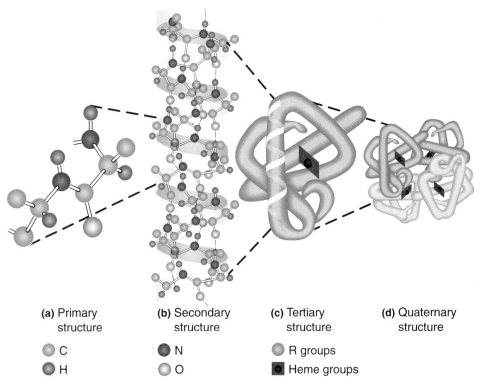

(a) Primary
structure

(b) Secondary
structure

(c) Tertiary
structure

(d) Quaternary
structure

○ C

● N

○ R groups

● H

○ O

◆ Heme groups

FIGURE 15.14
Summary of the four levels of protein structure, using hemoglobin as an example.

the oxygen transport protein of higher animals. **Myoglobin** is the oxygen storage protein of skeletal muscle.

The structure of myoglobin (Mb) is shown in Figure 15.13. The **heme** group (Figure 15.15) is an essential component of this protein. The Fe^{2+} ion in the heme group is the binding site for oxygen in both myoglobin and hemoglobin. Fortunately, myoglobin has a greater attraction for oxygen than does hemoglobin. Thus there is efficient transfer of oxygen from the bloodstream to the cells of the body.

FIGURE 15.15
Structure of the heme prosthetic group bound to myoglobin and hemoglobin.

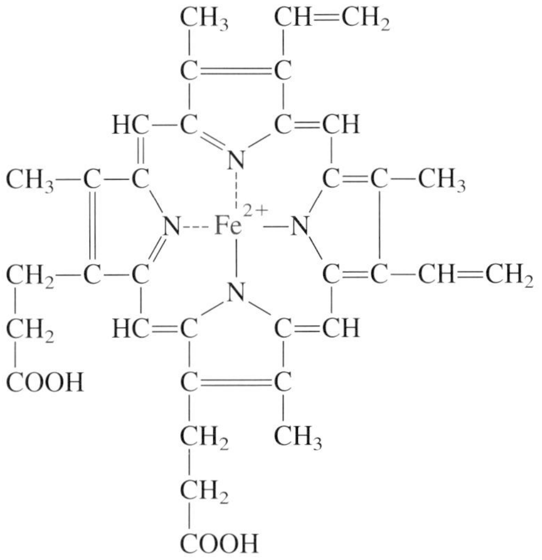

A MEDICAL PERSPECTIVE

Immunoglobulins: Proteins That Defend the Body

A living organism is subjected to a constant barrage of bacterial, viral, parasitic, and fungal diseases. Without a defense against such perils we would soon perish. All vertebrates possess an *immune system.* In humans the immune system is composed of about 10^{12} cells, about as many as the brain or liver, that protect us from foreign invaders. This immune system has three important characteristics.

1. **It is highly specific.** The immune response to each infection is specific to, or directed against, only one disease organism or similar, related organisms.

2. **It has a memory.** Once the immune system has responded to an infection, the body is protected against reinfection by the same organism. This is the reason that we seldom suffer from the same disease more than once. Most of the diseases that we suffer recurrently, such as the common cold and flu, are actually caused by many different strains of the same virus. Each of these strains is "new" to the immune system.

3. **It can recognize "self" from "nonself."** When we are born, our immune system is already aware of all the antigens of our bodies. These it recognizes as "self" and will not attack. Every antigen that is not classified as "self" will be attacked by the immune system when it is encountered. Some individuals suffer from a defect of the immune response that allows it to attack the cells of one's own body. The result is an *autoimmune reaction* that can be fatal.

One facet of the immune response is the synthesis of *immunoglobulins,* or *antibodies,* that specifically bind a single macromolecule called an *antigen.* These antibodies are produced by specialized white blood cells called *B-lymphocytes.* We are born with a variety of B-lymphocytes that are capable of producing antibodies against perhaps a million different antigens. When a foreign antigen enters the body, it binds to the B-lymphocyte that was preprogrammed to produce antibodies to destroy it. This stimulates the B-cell to grow and divide. Then all of these new B-cells produce antibodies that will bind to the disease agent and facilitate its destruction.

Each B-cell produces only one type of antibody with an absolute specificity for its target antigen. Many different B-cells respond to each infection because the disease-causing agent is made up of many different antigens. Antibodies are made that bind to all of the antigens of the invader. This primary immune response is rather slow. It can take a week or two before there are enough B-cells to produce a high enough level of antibodies in the blood to combat an infection.

Because the immune response has a memory, the second time we encounter a disease-causing agent the antibody response is immediate. This is why it is extremely rare to suffer from mumps, measles, or chickenpox a second time. We take advantage of this property of the immune system to protect ourselves against many diseases. In the process of *vaccination* a person can be immunized against an infectious disease by injection of a small amount of the antigens of the virus or microorganism (the vaccine). The B-lymphocytes of the body then manufacture antibodies against the antigens of the infectious agent. If the individual comes into contact with the disease-causing microorganism at some later time, the sensitized B-lymphocytes "remember" the antigen and very quickly produce a large amount of specific antibody to overwhelm the microorganism or virus before it can cause overt disease.

Immunoglobulin molecules contain four peptide chains that are connected by disulfide bonds and arranged in a Y-shaped quaternary structure.

Each immunoglobulin has two identical antigen-binding sites located at the tips of the Y and is therefore bivalent. Since most antigens have three or more antigen-binding sites, immunoglobulins can form large cross-linked antigen-antibody complexes that precipitate from solution.

Immunoglobulin G (IgG) is the major serum immunoglobulin. Some immunoglobulin G molecules can cross cell membranes and thus can pass between mother and fetus through the placenta, before birth. This is important because the immune system of a fetus is immature and cannot provide adequate protection from disease. Fortunately, the IgG acquired from the mother protects the fetus against most bacterial and viral infections that it might encounter before birth.

Hemoglobin and oxygen transport

Hemoglobin (Hb) is a tetramer composed of four peptide subunits: two α-subunits and two β-subunits (Figure 15.16). Because each subunit of hemoglobin contains a heme group, a hemoglobin molecule can bind four molecules of oxygen:

$$Hb \quad + 4O_2 \longrightarrow \quad Hb(O_2)_4$$

Deoxyhemoglobin   Oxyhemoglobin

Oxygen transport from mother to fetus

A fetus receives its oxygen from its mother by simple diffusion across the placenta. If both the fetus and the mother had the same type of hemoglobin, this transfer process would not be efficient, since the hemoglobin of the fetus and the mother would have the same affinity for

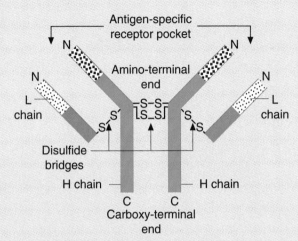

Schematic diagram of a Y-shaped immunoglobulin molecule. The binding sites for antigens are at the tips of the Y.

There are four additional types of antibody molecules that vary in their protein composition, but all have the same general Y shape. One of these is IgM, which is the first antibody produced in response to an infection. Secondarily, the B cell produces IgG molecules with the same antigen-binding region but a different protein composition in the rest of the molecule. IgA is the immunoglobulin responsible for protecting the body surfaces, such as the mucous membranes of the

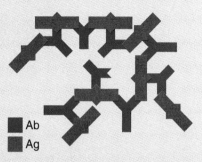

Schematic diagram of cross-linked immunoglobulin-antigen lattice. From Robert M. Coleman, Mary F. Lombard, Raymond E. Sicard, and Nicholas J. Rencricca, *Fundamental Immunology*. Copyright © 1989 Wm. C. Brown Communications, Inc., Dubuque, Iowa. All Rights Reserved. Reprinted by permission.

gut, the oral cavity, and the genitourinary tract. IgA is also found in mother's milk, protecting the newborn against diseases during the first few weeks of life. IgD is found in very small amounts and is thought to be involved in the regulation of antibody synthesis. The last type of immunoglobulin is IgE. For many years the function of IgE was unknown. It is found in large quantities in the blood of people suffering from allergies and is therefore thought to be responsible for this "overblown" immunological reaction to dust particles and pollen grains.

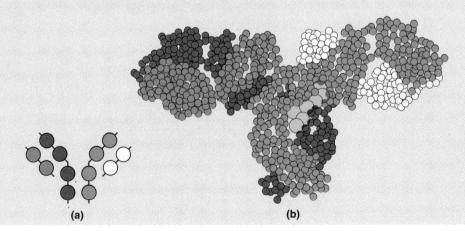

(a) Sketch of immunoglobulin G showing the two heavy chains (red and blue) and the two light chains (green and yellow). (b) Space-filling model of immunoglobulin G. The color code is the same as in (a). The gray balls represent sugar groups attached to the immunoglobulin molecule. From Robert F. Weaver and Philip W. Hedrick, *Genetics*. Copyright © 1989 Wm. C. Brown Communications, Inc., Dubuque, Iowa. All Rights Reserved. Reprinted by permission.

oxygen. The fetus, however, has a unique type of hemoglobin, called *fetal hemoglobin*. This unique hemoglobin molecule has a greater affinity for oxygen than does the mother's hemoglobin. Oxygen is therefore efficiently transported, via the circulatory system, from the lungs of the mother to the fetus. The biosynthesis of fetal hemoglobin stops shortly after birth when the genes encoding fetal hemoglobin are switched ''off'' and the genes coding for adult hemoglobin are switched ''on.''

See "Wake Up, Sleeping Gene," the Chemistry Connection in Chapter 12.

QUESTION 15.7

Why is oxygen efficiently transferred from hemoglobin in the blood to myoglobin in the muscles?

Hemoglobin

⬛ Alpha chains
⬜ Beta chains
◈ Heme groups

FIGURE 15.16
Structure of hemoglobin. The protein contains four subunits, designated α and β. The α- and β-subunits face each other across a central cavity. Each subunit in the tetramer contains a heme group that binds oxygen.

QUESTION 15.8

How is oxygen efficiently transferred from mother to fetus?

15.4 THE EFFECT OF TEMPERATURE AND pH ON PROTEINS

We have mentioned that the shape of a protein is absolutely essential to its function. We have also noted that life can exist only within a rather narrow range of temperature and pH. How are these two ideas related? Extremes of pH or temperature cause proteins to lose their characteristic three-dimensional shape. When the organized structures of a protein—the α-helix, the β-pleated sheet, and tertiary folds—become completely disorganized, the protein is said to be **denatured.** Denaturation of an α-helical protein is shown in Figure 15.17.

The effect of temperature

Consider the effect of increasing temperature on a solution of proteins, for instance egg white. At first, increasing the temperature simply increases the rate of molecular movement, the movement of the individual molecules within the solution. Then, as the temperature continues to increase, the weak interactions, like the hydrogen bonds, that preserve the protein structure are disrupted. The protein molecules are denatured as they lose their characteristic three-dimensional shape and become completely disorganized. The protein molecules then **coagulate** as

FIGURE 15.17
The denaturation of proteins by heat. (a) The α-helical proteins are in solution. (b) As heat is applied, the hydrogen bonds maintaining the secondary structure are disrupted, and the protein structure becomes disorganized. The protein is denatured. (c) The denatured proteins clump together, or coagulate, and are now in an insoluble form.

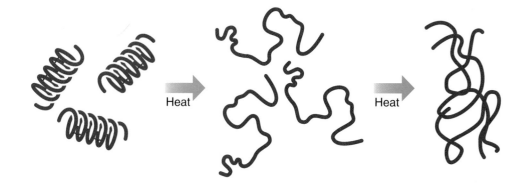

(a)   (b)   (c)

they clump together. At this point they are no longer in solution; they have aggregated to become a solid (Figure 15.17c). Our egg white began as a viscous solution of egg proteins; but when we finished cooking it, the proteins had been denatured and had coagulated to become solid.

Many of the proteins of our cells—for instance, the enzymes—are in the same kind of viscous solution within the cytoplasm. To continue to function properly, they must remain in solution and maintain the correct three-dimensional shape. If the body temperature becomes too high, or if local regions of the body are subjected to very high temperatures, as when you touch a hot cookie sheet, cellular proteins become denatured. They lose their function, and the cell, or the organism, dies.

Because of the R groups of the amino acids, all proteins have a characteristic electric charge. Since every protein has a different amino acid composition, each will have a different net electric charge on its surface. The positively and negatively charged R groups on the surface of the molecule interact with ions and water molecules, and these interactions keep the protein in solution within the cytoplasm.

The protein shown in Figure 15.18a has a net charge of 2+ because it has two extra $-N^+H_3$ groups. If we add a base, like NaOH, the protonated amino groups lose their protons and thus become electrically neutral. Now the net charge of the protein is zero. When the polypeptide has an equal number of positive and negative charges, it is said to be **isoelectric.** The protein shown in Figure 15.18b has a net charge of 2− because of two additional carboxylate groups. When an acid is added, the carboxylate groups become protonated. They are now electrically neutral, and the net charge on the protein is zero. As in the above example, the protein is now isoelectric.

Once a protein has no net charge on its surface, it no longer has a means of interacting with the surrounding water molecules, and it cannot remain in solution. Under these conditions the protein molecules clump together, and coagulation occurs.

This is a reaction that you have probably observed in your own kitchen. When milk sits in the refrigerator too long, the bacteria in the milk begin to grow and produce lactic acid as a by-product of their metabolism. As the concentration of lactic acid increases, the pH decrease causes the protonation of exposed carboxylate groups on the surface of the dissolved milk proteins. They become isoelectric and coagulate into a solid curd.

Imagine for a moment what would happen if the pH of the blood were to become too acidic or too basic. Blood is a fluid that contains water and dissolved electrolytes, a variety of cells, including the red blood cells responsible for oxygen transport, and many different proteins. These proteins include fibrinogen, which is involved in the clotting reaction; immunoglobulins, which protect us from disease; and albumins, which carry hydrophobic molecules in the blood.

The effect of pH

Section 16.4

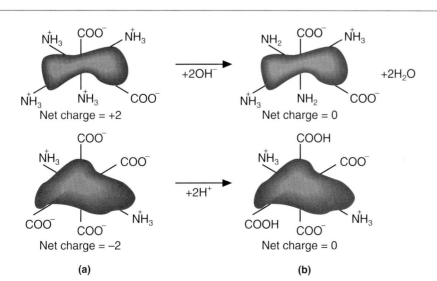

Net charge = +2

Net charge = 0

Net charge = −2

Net charge = 0

(a)   (b)

FIGURE 15.18
The effect of pH on proteins.
(a) This protein has an overall charge of 2+. When a base is added, some of the protonated amino groups lose their protons. Now the protein is isoelectric; it has an equal number of positive and negative charges. (b) This protein has an overall charge of 2−. As acid is added, some of the carboxylate groups are protonated. The result is that the protein becomes isoelectric.

Section 7.5 If the pH of the blood were to become too acidic or too basic, the proteins dissolved in the blood and the proteins of the cells in the blood would become isoelectric. In this extreme condition the blood proteins would denature and would no longer be able to carry out their required functions. The blood cells would also die as their critical enzymes were denatured. The hemoglobin in the red blood cells would become denatured and would no longer be able to transport oxygen. Fortunately, the body has a number of mechanisms to avoid the radical changes in the blood pH that can occur as a result of metabolic or respiratory difficulties.

Temperature and pH changes are only two of the means by which proteins can be denatured. Ultraviolet light and organic solvents, such as alcohols, also denature proteins and are used in the health care field as sterilizing agents and disinfectants. In addition, whipping or shaking can also denature proteins. This is the reason that whipping egg whites produces a stiff meringue.

QUESTION 15.9

How does high temperature denature proteins?

QUESTION 15.10

How does extremely low pH cause proteins to coagulate?

15.5 ENZYMES: NOMENCLATURE AND CLASSIFICATION

An enzyme is a biological catalyst. Without enzymes to speed up biochemical reactions, life could not exist. Enzyme-catalyzed reactions often occur from 1 million to 100 million times faster than the uncatalyzed reaction. The enzyme *catalase* is a spectacular example. Hydrogen peroxide (H_2O_2) is a by-product of our metabolism. However, it is toxic and must be destroyed. One molecule of catalase converts *40 million* molecules of hydrogen peroxide to harmless water and oxygen every second:

$$2H_2O_2 \xrightarrow[\text{(an enzyme)}]{\text{Catalase}} 2H_2O + O_2$$

Reaction occurs 40 million times every second!

This is the reaction that you see when you pour hydrogen peroxide on a wound. Catalase released from injured cells rapidly breaks down the hydrogen peroxide. The bubbles that you see are oxygen gas released as a product of the reaction.

Nomenclature of enzymes

One of the easiest concepts in chemistry is enzyme nomenclature. The common name of an enzyme is derived from the name of the **substrate** (the reactant that binds to the enzyme and is converted to product) with which the enzyme interacts and/or the type of reaction that it catalyzes. Because of this, the function of the enzyme is generally conveyed directly by its common name.

Let's look at a few examples of this simple concept. *Urea* is the substrate acted on by the enzyme *urease:*

$$\text{Urea} - \text{a} + \text{ase} = \text{Urease}$$
$$\text{(substrate)} \qquad \text{(enzyme)}$$

Lactose is the substrate of *lactase:*

$$\text{Lactose} - \text{ose} + \text{ase} = \text{Lactase}$$
$$\text{(substrate)} \qquad \text{(enzyme)}$$

Other enzymes may be named for the reactions they catalyze. For example:

Dehydrogenases remove hydrogen.

Decarboxylases remove carboxyl groups.

The prefix *de-* indicates that a functional group is being removed. Hydrogenases and carboxylases, on the other hand, add hydrogen or carboxyl groups. Some enzyme names include *both* the substrate and reaction type. For example, *lactate dehydrogenase* removes hydrogen atoms from lactate ions, and *pyruvate decarboxylase* removes carboxyl groups from pyruvate.

As in other areas of chemistry, historical names, having no relationship to either substrate or reaction, continue to be used. In these cases the substrates and reactions must simply be memorized. Examples of some historical common names include catalase, pepsin, chymotrypsin, and trypsin.

QUESTION 15.11

What is the substrate for each of the following enzymes?

a. Sucrase

b. Pyruvate decarboxylase

c. Succinate dehydrogenase

QUESTION 15.12

What chemical reaction is mediated by each of the enzymes in Question 15.11?

Enzymes may be classified according to the type of reaction in which they are involved. The six classes are as follows.

Classification of enzymes

Oxireductases

Oxireductases are enzymes that catalyze oxidation-reduction (redox) reactions. *Lactate dehydrogenase* is an oxireductase that removes hydrogen from a molecule of lactate. Other subclasses of the oxireductases include oxidases and reductases.

Recall that redox reactions involve electron transfer from one substance to another (Section 7.6).

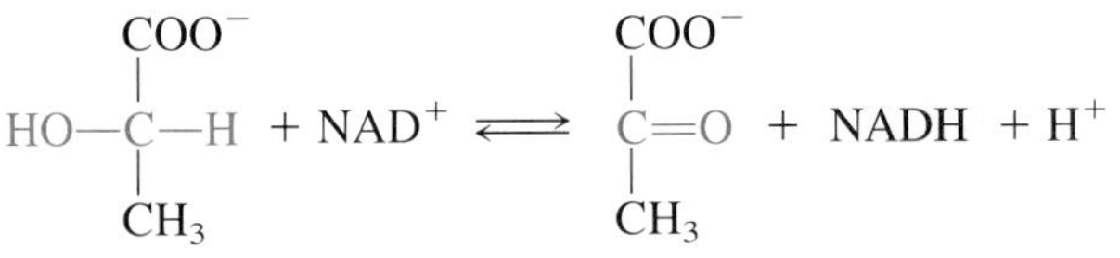

$$
\begin{array}{ccc}
\text{COO}^- & & \text{COO}^- \\
| & & | \\
\text{HO—C—H} + \text{NAD}^+ \rightleftharpoons & \text{C=O} + \text{NADH} + \text{H}^+ \\
| & & | \\
\text{CH}_3 & & \text{CH}_3 \\
\text{Lactate} & & \text{Pyruvate}
\end{array}
$$

Transferases

Transferases are enzymes that catalyze the transfer of functional groups from one molecule to another. For example, a *transaminase* catalyzes the transfer of an amine functional group, and a *kinase* catalyzes the transfer of a phosphate group. Kinases play a major role in energy production processes involving ATP. In the adrenal glands, norepinephrine is converted to epinephrine by the enzyme *phenylethanolamine-N-methyltransferase* (PNMT), a *transmethylase*.

Sections 16.1 and 16.3

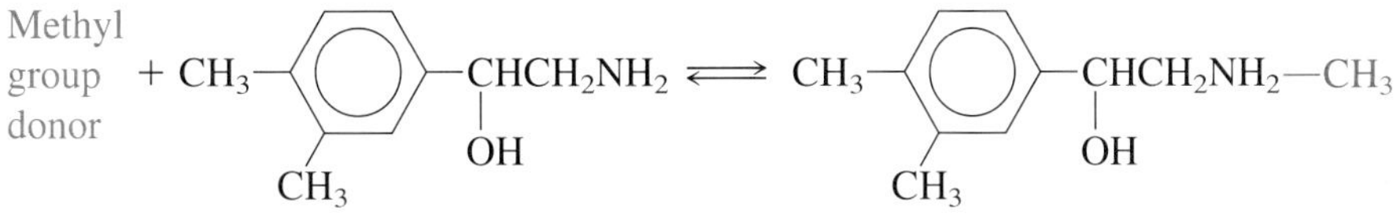

Methyl group donor $+ \text{CH}_3-$⟨◯⟩$-\text{CHCH}_2\text{NH}_2 \rightleftharpoons \text{CH}_3-$⟨◯⟩$-\text{CHCH}_2\text{NH}_2-\text{CH}_3$

Norepinephrine   Epinephrine

Hydrolases

Hydrolases catalyze hydrolysis reactions, that is, the addition of a water molecule to a bond resulting in bond breakage. These reactions are of importance in the digestive process. For

See "A Human Perspective: Amines and the Central Nervous System" in Chapter 14.

example, *lipases* catalyze the hydrolysis of triglycerides:

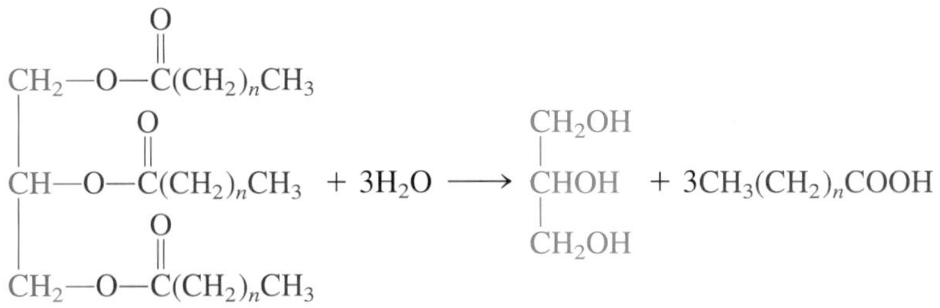

$$
\begin{array}{l}
CH_2-O-\overset{\overset{O}{\|}}{C}(CH_2)_nCH_3 \\[4pt]
CH-O-\overset{\overset{O}{\|}}{C}(CH_2)_nCH_3 \quad + 3H_2O \longrightarrow \quad
\begin{array}{l}
CH_2OH \\
CHOH \\
CH_2OH
\end{array}
\quad + 3CH_3(CH_2)_nCOOH \\[4pt]
CH_2-O-\overset{\overset{O}{\|}}{C}(CH_2)_nCH_3
\end{array}
$$

Triglyceride   Glycerol   Fatty acids

Lyases

Lyases catalyze the cleavage of C—O, C—C, or C—N bonds. In the process a double bond is formed. *Citrate lyase* catalyzes the removal of an acetate group from a molecule of citrate. The products of this reaction include oxaloacetate, acetyl CoA, ADP, and an inorganic phosphate group (P_i):

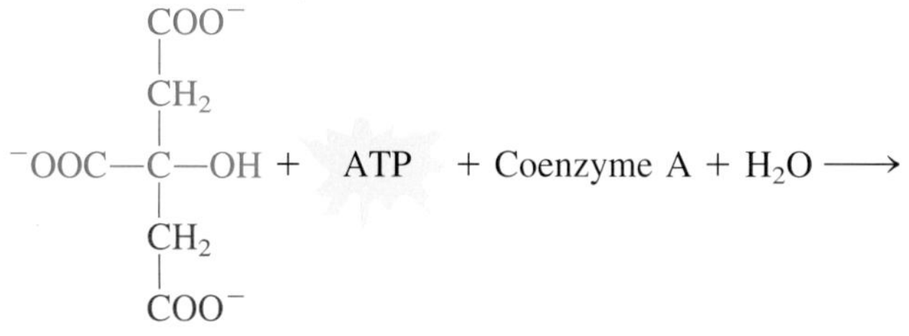

$$
\begin{array}{l}
COO^- \\
CH_2 \\
^-OOC-C-OH \;+\; ATP \;+\; \text{Coenzyme A} \;+\; H_2O \longrightarrow \\
CH_2 \\
COO^-
\end{array}
$$

Citrate

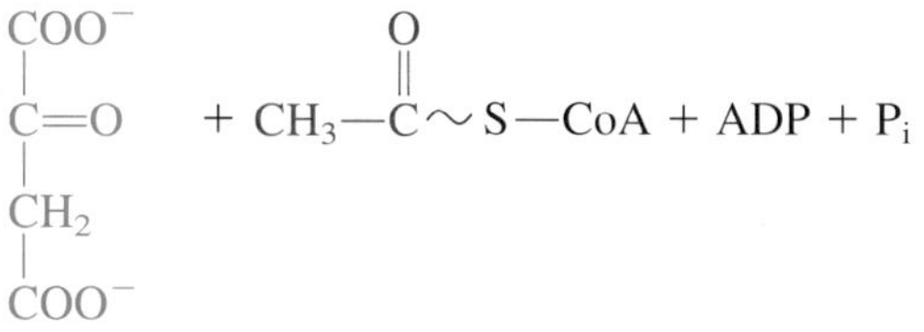

$$
\begin{array}{l}
COO^- \\
C=O \quad + CH_3-\overset{\overset{O}{\|}}{C}\sim S-CoA + ADP + P_i \\
CH_2 \\
COO^-
\end{array}
$$

Oxaloacetate   Acetyl CoA

Isomerases

Isomerases rearrange the functional groups within a molecule and catalyze the conversion of one isomer into another. For example, *phosphoglyceromutase* converts one structural isomer, 3-phosphoglycerate, into another, 2-phosphoglycerate:

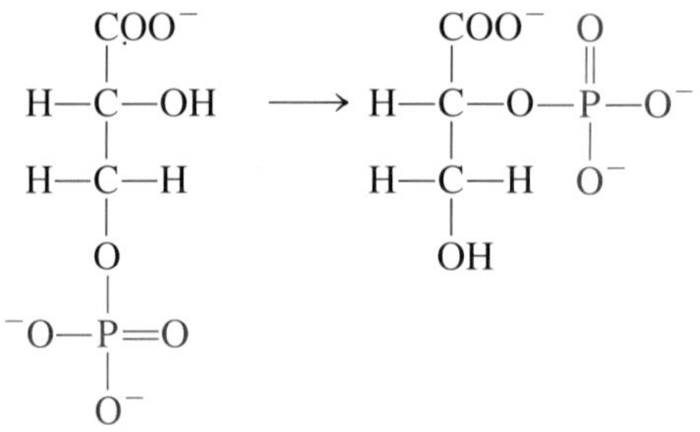

$$
\begin{array}{l}
COO^- \\
H-C-OH \\
H-C-H \\
O \\
^-O-P=O \\
O^-
\end{array}
\longrightarrow
\begin{array}{l}
COO^- \quad O \\
H-C-O-\overset{\overset{O}{\|}}{P}-O^- \\
H-C-H \quad O^- \\
OH
\end{array}
$$

3-Phosphoglycerate   2-Phosphoglycerate

Ligases

Ligases are enzymes that catalyze the condensation or joining of two molecules. For example, *DNA ligase* catalyzes the joining of the hydroxyl group of a nucleotide in a DNA strand with the phosphate group of the adjacent nucleotide to form a phosphoester bond:

Section 19.3

DNA strand —3′—OH + ⁻O—P—O—5′— DNA strand

(top structure with O double bond and ⁻O)

DNA strand —3′—O—P—O—5′— DNA strand

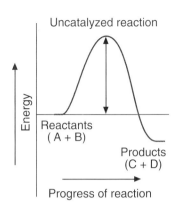

(a)

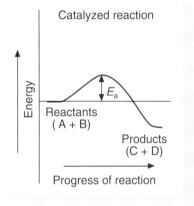

(b)

FIGURE 15.19
Diagram of the difference in energy between the reactants (*A* and *B*) and products (*C* and *D*) for a reaction. Enzymes cannot change this energy difference but act by lowering the activation energy (E_a) for the reaction, thereby speeding up the reaction.

QUESTION 15.13

To which class of enzymes does each of the following belong?

a. Pyruvate kinase
b. RNA ligase
c. Triose isomerase
d. Pyruvate dehydrogenase
e. Pyruvate carboxylase
f. Maltase

QUESTION 15.14

To which class of enzymes does each of the following belong?

a. Phosphofructokinase
b. Lipase
c. Acetoacetate decarboxylase
d. Succinate dehydrogenase
e. Alanine aminotransferase
f. Phosphoglucoisomerase

15.6 ENZYME-CATALYZED REACTIONS

Effect of enzymes on the activation energy of a reaction

Effect of substrate concentration on enzyme-catalyzed reactions

The activation energy (Section 5.3) of a reaction is the threshold energy that must be overcome to produce a chemical reaction.

How does an enzyme speed up a chemical reaction? It changes the path by which the reaction occurs, providing a lower-energy route for the conversion of the substrate into the **product,** the chemical species that results from the enzyme-catalyzed reaction. Thus enzymes speed up reactions by lowering the activation energy of the reaction (Figure 15.19). As we will see below, to lower the activation energy, the enzyme binds the substrate or substrates in a groove or pocket on the enzyme surface. This groove, called the active site, is the location where catalysis occurs.

The rates of uncatalyzed chemical reactions double every time the substrate concentration is doubled. As long as the substrate concentration increases, there is a direct increase in the rate of the reaction (Figure 15.20a). For enzyme-catalyzed reactions this is not the case. Although the rate of the reaction initially increases with increasing substrate concentration, at a certain concentration of substrate the rate of the reaction reaches a maximum. A graph of the rate of reaction, *V*, versus the substrate concentration, [*S*], is shown in Figure 15.20b.

Why does the reaction rate level off at a maximum value? The reason for this is that the active sites of all the enzymes in solution are filled with substrate molecules. A new molecule of substrate cannot bind to an enzyme until the substrate molecule already bound to the enzyme is converted to product. For this reason the rate of the reaction is limited by the speed with which the substrate is converted into product and thus by the availability of the enzyme.

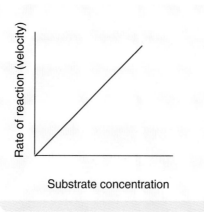

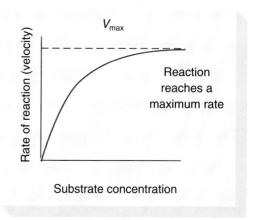

FIGURE 15.20
Plot of the rate or velocity, V, of an enzyme-catalyzed reaction versus the concentration of substrate, [S], for (a) an uncatalyzed reaction and (b) an enzyme-catalyzed reaction. For an enzyme-catalyzed reaction the rate is at a maximum when all of the enzyme molecules are bound to the substrate. Beyond this concentration of substrate, further increases in substrate concentration have no effect on the rate of the reaction.

The enzyme-substrate complex

The following series of reversible reactions represent the steps in an enzyme-catalyzed reaction. The first step (highlighted in purple) involves the encounter of the enzyme with its substrate and the formation of an **enzyme-substrate complex.**

$$E + S \xrightarrow{\text{Step I}} ES \xrightarrow{\text{Step II}} ES* \xrightarrow{\text{Step III}} EP \xrightarrow{\text{Step IV}} E + P$$

| Enzyme + substrate | Enzyme-substrate complex | Transition state | Enzyme product complex | Enzyme + product |

The part of the enzyme that binds with the substrate is called the **active site.** We find that the properties of the active site are crucial to the function of the enzyme and have the following general characteristics:

◆ Enzyme active sites are pockets or clefts in the surface of the enzyme.

◆ The shape of the active site is complementary to the shape of the substrate. That is, the substrate fits neatly into the active site of the enzyme.

◆ An enzyme attracts and holds its substrate by weak, noncovalent interactions.

◆ The conformation of the active site determines the specificity of the enzyme because only the substrate that fits into the active site will be used in a reaction.

The **lock-and-key model** of enzyme activity, shown in Figure 15.21a, was devised by Emil Fischer in 1894. At that time, proteins were considered to be rigid molecules, and it was thought that the substrate simply snapped into place like a piece of a jigsaw puzzle or a key into a lock.

Today we know that proteins are flexible molecules. This has led to a more sophisticated model of the way enzymes and substrates interact. This model, called the **induced fit model,** is shown in Figure 15.21b. In this model the active site of the enzyme is not a rigid pocket into which the substrate fits precisely; rather, it is a flexible pocket that *approximates* the shape of the substrate. When the substrate enters the pocket, the active site "molds" itself around the substrate. This produces the perfect enzyme-substrate "fit" (Figure 15.21b).

The overall shape of a protein is maintained by many weak interactions. At any time a few of these weak interactions may be broken by heat energy or a local chemical change in pH. If only a few bonds are broken, they will reform very quickly. The overall result is that there is a brief change in the shape of the enzyme. Thus the protein or enzyme can be viewed as a flexible molecule, changing shape slightly in response to minor local changes.

substrate and the final product. This transition state favors the conversion of the substrate into product (step III). The product remains bound to the enzyme for a very brief time, then in step IV the product and enzyme dissociate from one another, leaving the enzyme completely unchanged.

Conjugated proteins require an additional nonprotein prosthetic group in order to function. The same is true of some enzymes. The protein portion of such an enzyme is called the **apoenzyme,** and the nonprotein prosthetic group is called the **cofactor.** Cofactors are generally metal ions that must be bound to the enzyme to maintain the correct shape of the active site (Figure 15.22). When the cofactor is bound and the active site is in the proper conformation, the enzyme can bind the substrate and catalyze the reaction.

Cofactors and coenzymes

Other enzymes require the temporary binding of a **coenzyme.** Coenzymes are organic groups that generally serve as carriers of electrons or chemical groups. In chemical reactions they may either donate chemical groups to the substrate or accept chemical groups that are removed from the substrate (Figure 15.23).

Often coenzymes contain modified **vitamins** as part of their structure. A vitamin is an organic substance that is required in the diet in only small amounts. Of the water-soluble vitamins, only vitamin C has not been associated with a coenzyme. Table 15.2 is a summary of some coenzymes and the water-soluble vitamins from which they are made.

Water-soluble vitamins are discussed in greater detail in Appendix E.

Nicotinamide adenine dinucleotide (NAD$^+$), seen in Figure 15.24a, and nicotinamide adenine dinucleotide phosphate (NADP$^+$), seen in Figure 15.24b, are coenzymes made from the vitamin **niacin.** They are needed for the many oxidation-reduction reactions in the cell. NAD$^+$ and NADP$^+$ accept a hydride ion (H : $^-$, a hydrogen atom with two electrons) from the substrate of the reaction. The substrate is oxidized, and NAD$^+$ (or NADP$^+$) is reduced to produce NADH (or NADPH). The NADH (or NADPH) later donates the hydride ion in another chemical

FIGURE 15.22
(a) The apoenzyme is unable to bind to its substrate. (b) When the required cofactor, in this case a copper ion, Cu^{2+}, is available, it binds to the apoenzyme. Now the active site takes on the correct configuration, the enzyme-substrate complex forms, and the reaction occurs.

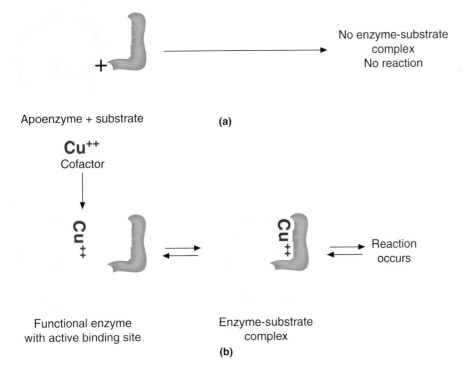

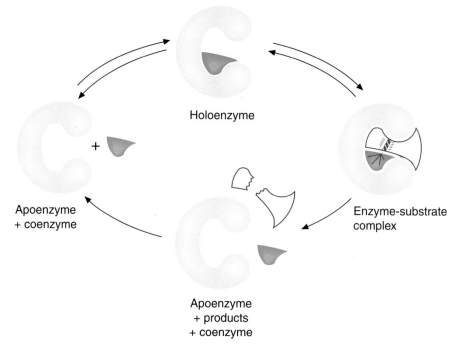

FIGURE 15.23
Some enzymes require a coenzyme to facilitate the reaction. The apoenzyme binds the coenzyme and then the substrate. The coenzyme is a part of the catalytic domain and will either donate or accept functional groups, allowing the reaction to occur. Once the product is formed, both the product and the coenzyme are released.

TABLE 15.2   **Water-Soluble Vitamins Required by Humans and Coenzymes Derived from Them**

Vitamin	Coenzyme	Function
Thiamine (B_1)	Thiamine pyrophosphate	Decarboxylation reactions
Riboflavin (B_2)	Flavin mononucleotide (FMN)	Carriers of H atoms
	Flavin adenine dinucleotide (FAD)	
Niacin (B_3)	Nicotinamide adenine dinucleotide (NAD^+)	Carriers of hydride ions
	Nicotinamide adenine dinucleotide phosphate ($NADP^+$)	
Pyridoxine (B_6)	Pyridoxal phosphate	Carriers of amino and carboxyl groups
	Pyridoxamine phosphate	
Cyanocobalamin (B_{12})	Deoxyadenosyl cobalamin	Coenzyme in amino acid metabolism
Folic acid	Tetrahydrofolic acid	Coenzyme for 1-C transfer
Pantothenic acid	Coenzyme A	Acyl group carrier
Biotin	Biocytin	Coenzyme in CO_2 fixation
Ascorbic acid (C)	Unknown	Hydroxylation of proline and lysine in collagen

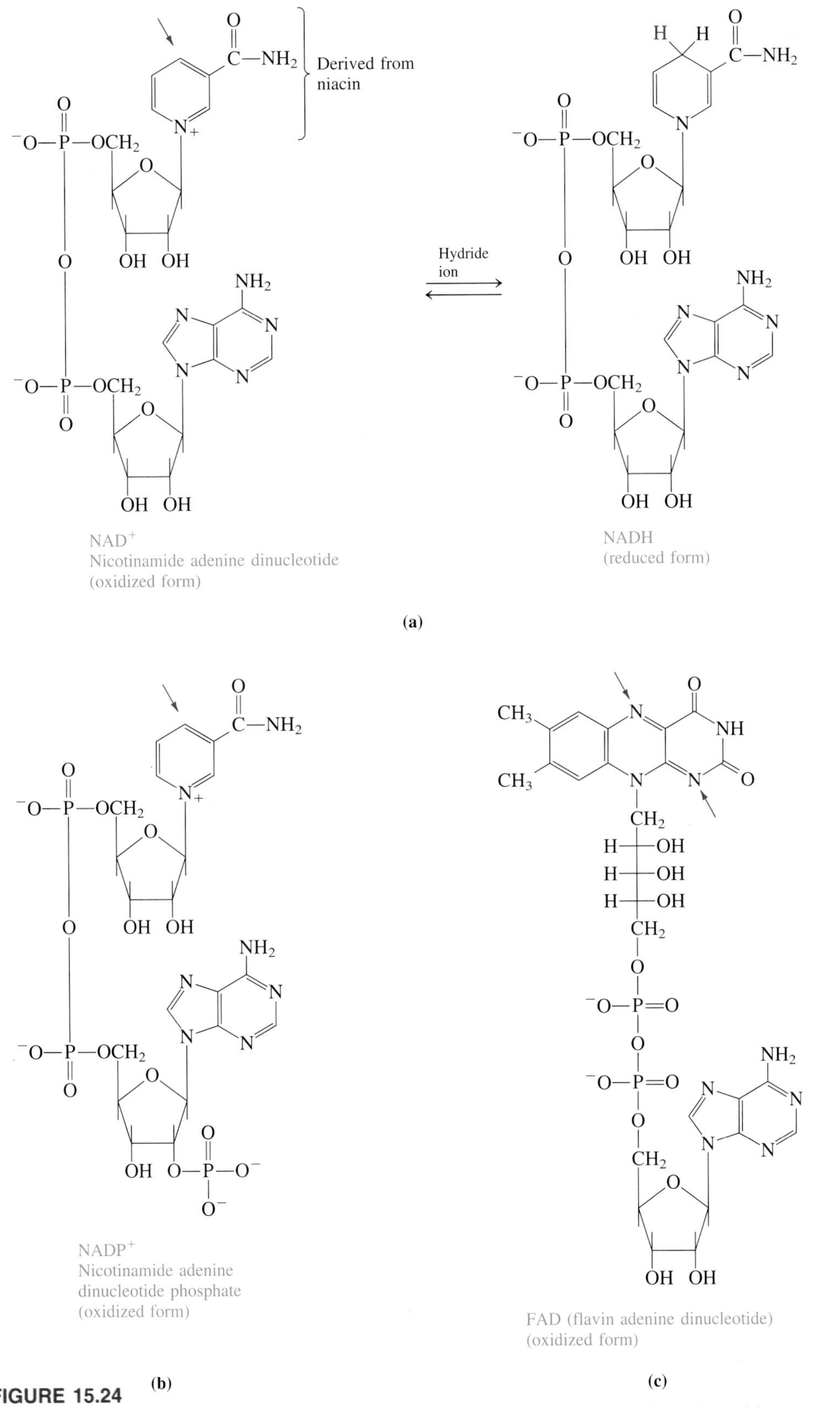

FIGURE 15.24
The structure of three coenzymes. (a) The oxidized and reduced forms of nicotinamide adenine dinucleotide. (b) The oxidized form of the closely related hydride ion carrier nicotinamide adenine dinucleotide phosphate (NADP$^+$) accepts hydride ions at the same position as NAD$^+$ (red arrow). (c) The oxidized form of flavin adenine dinucleotide (FAD) accepts hydrogen atoms at the positions indicated by the red arrows.

A CLINICAL PERSPECTIVE

Enzymes, Isoenzymes, and Myocardial Infarction

A patient is brought into the emergency room with acute, squeezing chest pains; shallow, irregular breathing; and pale, clammy skin. The immediate diagnosis is myocardial infarction, a heart attack. The first thoughts of the attending nurses and physicians concern the series of treatments and procedures that will save the patient's life. It is a short time later, when the patient's condition has stabilized, that the doctor begins to consider the battery of enzyme assays that will confirm the diagnosis and perhaps even help to predict the prognosis.

Myocardial infarction occurs when the blood supply to the heart muscle is blocked for an extended period of time. If this lack of blood supply, called *ischemia,* is prolonged, the myocardium suffers irreversible cell damage and muscle death, or infarction. When this happens, the concentration of cardiac enzymes in the blood rises dramatically as the dead cells release their contents into the bloodstream. Although many enzymes are liberated, three are of prime importance. These three enzymes, creatine phosphokinase (CPK), lactate dehydrogenase (LDH), and aspartate aminotransferase/serum glutamate–oxaloacetate transaminase (AST/SGOT), show a very characteristic sequential rise in blood serum level following myocardial infarction and then return to normal. This enzyme profile, seen in the accompanying figure, is characteristic of, and is the basis for the diagnosis of, a heart attack.

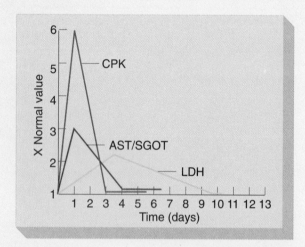

Characteristic pattern of serum cardiac enzyme concentrations following a myocardial infarction.

To ensure against misdiagnosis due to tissue damage in other organs, the levels of other serum enzymes, including alanine aminotransferase/serum glutamate–pyruvate transaminase (ALT/SGPT) and isocitrate dehydrogenase (ICD), are also measured. ALT and AST are usually determined simultaneously to differentiate between cardiac and hepatic disease. The concentration of ALT is higher in liver disease, while the serum concentration of AST is higher following acute myocardial infarction. ICD is found primarily in the liver, and serum levels would not be elevated after a heart attack.

The use of LDH and CPK levels alone can also lead to a misdiagnosis because these enzymes are produced by many tissues. How can a clinician diagnose heart disease with confidence when the elevated serum enzyme levels could indicate coexisting disease in another tissue? The physician is able to make such a decision because of the presence of *isoenzymes,* which provide diagnostic accuracy because they reveal the tissue of origin.

Isoenzymes are forms of the same enzyme with slightly different amino acid sequences. The binding and catalytic sites are the same, but there are differences in the scaffolding sequences of the enzyme that maintain the three-dimensional structure of the protein. Each of the cells of the body contains the genes that could direct the production of all the different forms of these enzymes, yet the expression is *tissue-specific.* This means that the genes for certain isoenzymes are expressed preferentially in different types of tissue.

It is not clear why a certain isoenzyme is "turned on" in the liver while another predominates in the heart, but it is known that we can distinguish among the different forms in the laboratory on the basis of their migration through a gel placed in an electric field. This process is called *gel electrophoresis.* This test is based on the fact that each protein has a characteristic surface charge resulting from the R groups of the amino acids. If these proteins are placed in a gel matrix and an electrical current is applied, the proteins will migrate as a function of that charge. In the figure on the next page, we see the position of the five isoenzymes of LDH following electrophoresis.

Imagine a mixture of serum proteins, each with a different overall charge, subjected to an electric field. The proteins with the greatest negative charge will be most strongly attracted to the positive pole and will migrate rapidly toward it, while those with a lesser negative charge will migrate much more slowly. Once electrophoresis is terminated, the enzyme assay is carried out within the gel. The result is a stained band that can be seen visually and measured spectrophotometrically. By inspecting the positions of the bands of enzymatic activity, one can determine which tissue isoenzymes are present. This gives the clinician a very accurate picture of the nature of the diseased tissues. The accompanying table shows the serum enzyme and isoenzyme changes that follow an acute myocardial infarction.

The physician also has enzymes available to treat a heart attack patient. Most myocardial infarctions are the result of a *thrombus,* or clot, within a coronary blood vessel. The clot restricts blood flow to the heart muscle. One technique that shows promise for treatment following a coronary thrombosis, a heart attack caused by the formation of a clot, is destruction of the clot by intravenous or intracoronary injection of an enzyme called *streptokinase.* This enzyme, formerly purified from the pathogenic bacterium *Streptococcus pyogenes* but now available through recombinant DNA techniques, catalyzes the production of the proteolytic enzyme plasmin. Plas-

Serum Isoenzymes Characteristic of Myocardial Infarction

Enzyme	Normal Values*	% Normal Values	Period of Elevation	Peak	Primary Site of Production
Creatine phosphokinase (CPK)	80–780		4–72 hr	12–36 hr	
Isoenzymes:					
CPK I		0–3%	0	0	Brain
CPK II		0–5%	4–72 hr	12–36 hr	Heart
CPK III		90–100%	0	0	Skeletal muscle
Aspartate transaminase (AST)	117–450		6 hr–6 d	36–48 hr	Heart
Lactate dehydrogenase (LDH)	750–1500		12 hr–14 d	24–96 hr	
Isoenzymes:					
LDH1		20–27%	12 hr–14 d	24–96 hr	Heart, RBC
LDH2		25–37%	0	0	Immune system
LDH3		16–25%	0	0	Lungs
LDH4		3–8%	0	0	Kidney Pancreas Brain
LDH5		0–5%	0	0	Liver Skeletal muscle

*Normal values are expressed in nmol $\times$ s^{-1}/L and are given for an adult male. CPK and AST levels are somewhat lower for normal females, and the values for children and newborns are generally much higher.

min has the ability to degrade a fibrin clot into subunits. Of course, this has the effect of dissolving the clot that is responsible for restricted blood flow to the heart, but there is an additional protective function as well. The subunits produced by plasmin degradation of fibrin clots are able to inhibit further clot formation by inhibiting thrombin.

Recombinant DNA technology has provided medical science with yet another, perhaps more promising, clot-dissolving enzyme. *Tissue-type plasminogen activator (TPA)* is an enzyme that occurs naturally in the body as a part of the anticlotting mechanisms. Injection of TPA within two hours of the initial chest pain can significantly improve the circulation to the heart and greatly improve the patient's chances of survival.

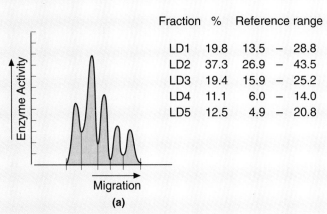

Fraction	%	Reference range
LD1	19.8	13.5 – 28.8
LD2	37.3	26.9 – 43.5
LD3	19.4	15.9 – 25.2
LD4	11.1	6.0 – 14.0
LD5	12.5	4.9 – 20.8

(a)

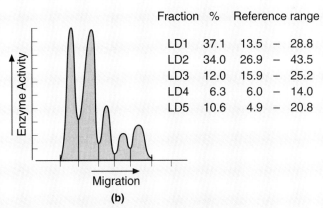

Fraction	%	Reference range
LD1	37.1	13.5 – 28.8
LD2	34.0	26.9 – 43.5
LD3	12.0	15.9 – 25.2
LD4	6.3	6.0 – 14.0
LD5	10.6	4.9 – 20.8

(b)

A profile of the isoenzymes of lactate dehydrogenase. (a) The pattern of LDH isoenzymes from a normal individual. (b) The pattern of LDH isoenzymes of an individual suffering from a myocardial infarction.

reaction. FAD, another hydride ion carrier seen in Figure 15.24c, is made from the vitamin **riboflavin.**

Why does the body require the water-soluble vitamins?

What are the coenzymes formed from each of the following vitamins?

a.   Pantothenic acid

b.   Niacin

c.   Riboflavin

Factors that affect enzyme activity

Effect of pH

Most enzymes are active only within a very narrow range of pH. The cellular cytoplasm has a pH near 7, and most cytoplasmic enzymes function at a maximum efficiency at this pH. A typical plot of the relative rate of an enzyme-catalyzed reaction versus pH is provided in Figure 15.25.

The pH at which an enzyme is most active is called the **pH optimum.** Making the solution more basic or more acidic sharply decreases the rate of the reaction. At extremes of pH the enzyme actually loses its biologically active shape and is denatured. When this happens, all enzyme activity is destroyed.

Although the pH optima for most cellular enzymes are near pH 7, there are areas in the body where the pH is far from 7. For instance, the pH of the stomach is approximately 2 as a result of the secretion of hydrochloric acid by specialized cells of the stomach lining. The proteolytic digestive enzyme *pepsin* is able to degrade proteins at this extreme pH. Thus pepsin has a pH optimum of 2. *Trypsin* degrades dietary protein in the intestine where the pH is high. It has a pH optimum of 8.5.

Effect of temperature

Enzymes are rapidly destroyed if the temperature of the solution rises much above 37°C, but they remain stable at much lower temperatures. This is why solutions of enzymes used for clinical assays are stored in refrigerators or freezers. Figure 15.26 shows the effects of temperature on enzyme-catalyzed and uncatalyzed reactions.

FIGURE 15.25
Effect of pH on the rate of an enzyme-catalyzed reaction. The enzyme functions most efficiently at pH 7. The rate of the reaction falls rapidly as the solution is made either more acidic or more basic.

FIGURE 15.26
Effect of temperature on (a) uncatalyzed reactions and (b) enzyme-catalyzed reactions.

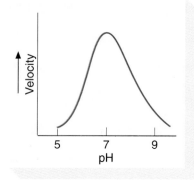

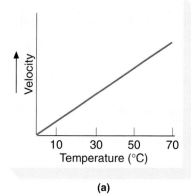

(a)

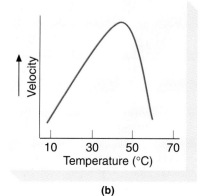

(b)

The rate of the uncatalyzed reaction steadily increases with increasing temperature. This is because there are more collisions between reactants with enough energy to overcome the activation energy. The rate of an enzyme-catalyzed reaction also increases as the temperature increases because there are more collisions between the enzyme and the substrate. But before long, increasing temperature denatures the enzyme, and the reaction stops.

Since enzymes and other proteins are denatured by high heat, cells cannot survive very high temperatures. Thus heat is an effective way to sterilize medical instruments and solutions for transfusion or clinical tests. Instruments can be sterilized by dry heat (160°C) applied for at least 2 hours in a dry air oven. However, autoclaving is a quicker, more reliable procedure. The autoclave works on the principle of the pressure cooker. Air is pumped out of the chamber, and steam under pressure is pumped into the chamber until the pressure reaches 15 lb/in^2 above atmospheric pressure. The pressure causes the temperature of the steam, which would be 100°C at atmospheric pressure, to rise to 121°C. Within 20 minutes, all the bacteria and viruses are killed. This is the most effective means of destroying the very heat-resistant endospores that are formed by many bacteria of clinical interest.

Recall that the boiling point of a liquid is a function of the pressure of the surrounding atmosphere (Section 6.1).

Endospore-producing bacteria include the genera *Bacillus* and *Clostridium*, which are responsible for such unpleasant and deadly diseases as anthrax, gas gangrene, tetanus, and botulism food poisoning.

15.7 INHIBITION OF ENZYME ACTIVITY

Many chemicals can bind to enzymes and either eliminate or drastically reduce their activity. These chemicals, called *enzyme inhibitors,* have been used for hundreds of years. When she poisoned her victims with arsenic, Lucretia Borgia was unaware that it was binding to the sulfhydryl groups of cysteine in the proteins of her victims and thus interfering with the formation of disulfide bonds needed to stabilize the tertiary structure of enzymes. However, she was well aware of the deadly toxicity of heavy metal salts such as arsenic and mercury. When we take penicillin for a bacterial infection, we are taking another enzyme inhibitor. Penicillin inhibits several enzymes involved in the synthesis of bacterial cell walls.

The two major types of enzyme inhibitors are irreversible inhibitors and competitive inhibitors.

Irreversible inhibitors, such as arsenic, usually bind very tightly, sometimes even covalently, to the enzyme. This may involve binding of the inhibitor to one of the R groups of an amino acid in the active site. Inhibitor binding may block the active site so that the enzyme-substrate complex cannot form. Alternatively, an inhibitor may remove a required cofactor and in this way stop enzyme activity. Irreversible inhibitors generally inhibit many different enzymes. Because they severely disrupt so many biochemical reactions, they may cause serious illness or death. As a result, irreversible inhibitors are considered to be *poisons.*

Irreversible inhibition

Competitive inhibitors are often referred to as **structural analogs,** that is, they are molecules that resemble the natural substrate for a particular enzyme. Because of this resemblance, the inhibitor can occupy the enzyme active site. However, no reaction can occur, and enzyme activity is inhibited. This inhibition is said to be **competitive** because the enzyme-inhibitor complex is maintained by weak interactions and readily dissociates. The empty active site is now available for substrate binding. Thus the active site can alternatively bind the inhibitor or the normal substrate. The two will compete for this binding, and thus the degree of inhibition depends on their relative concentrations. If the inhibitor is in excess, it will occupy the active site more frequently, and enzyme activity will be greatly decreased. If, on the other hand, the natural substrate is present in excess, it will more frequently occupy the active site, and there will be little inhibition.

The sulfa drugs, the first antibiotics to be discovered, are competitive inhibitors of a bacterial enzyme needed for the synthesis of the vitamin folic acid. **Folic acid** is a vitamin required for the transfer of methyl groups in the biosynthesis of methionine and nitrogenous bases. Humans cannot synthesize folic acid and must obtain it from the diet. Bacteria, on the other hand, must make folic acid because they cannot take it in from the environment.

Para-aminobenzoic acid (PABA) is the substrate for an early step in folic acid synthesis. The sulfa drugs, the prototype for which was discovered by Gerhard Domagk in the 1930s, are

Competitive inhibition

See ''A Human Perspective: Fooling the AIDS Virus with 'Look-Alike' Nucleotides'' in Chapter 19.

In addition to the folic acid supplied in the diet, we obtain folic acid from our intestinal bacteria.

structural analogs of PABA and thus competitive inhibitors of the enzyme that uses PABA as its normal substrate.

$$H_2N\!-\!\langle\bigcirc\rangle\!-\!\overset{\displaystyle O}{\overset{\|}{C}}\!-\!OH \qquad\qquad H_2N\!-\!\langle\bigcirc\rangle\!-\!\overset{\displaystyle O}{\underset{\displaystyle O}{\overset{\|}{\underset{\|}{S}}}}\!-\!NH_2$$

p-Aminobenzoic acid   Sulfanilamide

If the correct substrate (PABA) is bound by the enzyme, the reaction occurs, and the bacterium lives. However, if the sulfa drug is present in excess over PABA, it will bind more frequently to the active site of the enzyme. No folic acid will be produced, and the bacterial cell will die.

Since we obtain our folic acid from our diets, sulfa drugs do not harm us. However, bacteria will be selectively killed. Luckily, we can capitalize on this property for the treatment of bacterial infections, and as a result, sulfa drugs have saved countless lives. Although bacterial infection was the major cause of death before the discovery of sulfa drugs and other antibiotics, death caused by bacterial infection is relatively rare at present.

15.8 USE OF ENZYMES IN MEDICINE

Analysis of blood serum for levels (concentrations) of certain enzymes can provide a wealth of information about a patient's medical condition. Often, such tests are used to confirm a preliminary diagnosis based on the disease symptoms or clinical picture.

For example, when a heart attack occurs, a lack of blood supplied to the heart muscle causes some of the heart muscle cells to die. These cells release their contents, including their enzymes, into the bloodstream. Simple tests can be done to measure the amounts of certain enzymes in the blood. Such tests, called *enzyme assays,* are very precise and specific because they are based on the specificity of the enzyme-substrate complex. If you wish to test for the enzyme lactate dehydrogenase (LDH), you need only to add the appropriate substrate, in this case pyruvate and NADH. The reaction that occurs is the oxidation of NADH to NAD^+ and the reduction of pyruvate to lactate. To measure the rate of the chemical reaction, one can measure the disappearance of the substrate or the accumulation of one of the products. In the case of LDH, spectrophotometric methods are available to measure the rate of production of NAD^+. The role of LDH and other enzymes in disease diagnosis is discussed in "A Clinical Perspective: Enzymes, Isoenzymes, and Myocardial Infarction." The choice of substrate determines what enzyme activity is to be measured.

Elevated blood serum concentrations of the enzymes amylase and lipase are indications of pancreatitis, an inflammation of the pancreas. Liver diseases such as cirrhosis and hepatitis result in elevated levels of one of the isoenzymes of lactate dehydrogenase (LDH_5), as well as elevated levels of alanine aminotransferase/serum glutamate–pyruvate transaminase (ALT/SGPT) and aspartate aminotransferase/serum glutamate–oxaloacetate transaminase (AST/SGOT) in blood serum. In fact, these latter two enzymes also increase in concentration following heart attack, but the physician can differentiate between these two conditions by considering the relative increase in the two enzymes. If ALT/SGPT is elevated to a greater extent than AST/SGOT, it can be concluded that the problem is liver dysfunction.

Enzymes are also used as analytical reagents in the clinical laboratory owing to their specificity. They will often selectively react with one substance of interest, producing a product that is easily measured. An example of this is the clinical analysis of urea in blood. The measurement of urea levels in blood is difficult because of the complexity of blood. However, if urea is converted to ammonia, the ammonia becomes an *indicator* of urea, since it is produced from urea, and it is easily measured. This test, called the *blood urea nitrogen (BUN) test,* is useful in the diagnosis of kidney malfunction and serves as one example of the utility of enzymes in clinical chemistry.

Proteins are the third major type of energy source in the diet. As do carbohydrates and fats, proteins serve several dietary purposes. They can be oxidized to provide energy. In addition, the amino acids liberated by the hydrolysis of proteins are used directly in biosynthesis. The protein synthetic machinery of the cell can incorporate amino acids, released by the digestion of dietary protein, directly into the cellular proteins. Amino acids are also used in the biosynthesis of a large number of important molecules called the *nitrogen compounds.* This group includes some hormones and the heme groups of hemoglobin and myoglobin.

Amino acids can be divided into two major nutritional classes. **Essential amino acids** are those that cannot be synthesized by the body and are required in the diet. **Nonessential amino acids** are those amino acids that can be synthesized by the body and need not be included in the diet. Table 15.3 lists the essential and nonessential amino acids.

Proteins are also classified as **complete** or **incomplete.** Protein derived from animal sources is generally complete. That is, it provides all of the essential and nonessential amino acids in approximately the correct amounts for biosynthesis. In contrast, proteins derived from vegetable sources are generally incomplete because they are lacking a sufficient amount of one or more amino acids. People who want to maintain a strictly vegetarian diet or for whom animal protein is often not available have the problem that no single high-protein vegetable has all of the essential amino acids to ensure a sufficient daily intake. For example, the major protein of beans contains abundant lysine and tryptophan but very little methionine, whereas corn contains considerable methionine but very little tryptophan or lysine. A mixture of corn and beans, however, satisfies both requirements. This combination, called *succotash,* was a staple of the diet of Native Americans for centuries.

A few vegetarian meals each week can provide all the required amino acids and simultaneously help reduce the amount of saturated fats in the diet. Many enjoyable ethnic foods apply the principle of mixing protein sources. Mexican foods such as tortillas and refried beans, Cajun dishes of spicy beans and rice, Indian cuisine of rice and lentils, and even the traditional American peanut butter sandwich are examples of ways to mix foods to provide complete protein.

15.9 DIETARY PROTEIN AND PROTEIN DIGESTION

Section 17.5
Section 19.6

QUESTION 15.19

Why must vegetable sources of protein be mixed to provide an adequate diet?

QUESTION 15.20

What are some common sources of dietary protein?

TABLE 15.3 The Essential and Nonessential Amino Acids

Essential Amino Acids	Nonessential Amino Acids
Isoleucine	Alanine
Leucine	Arginine
Lysine	Asparagine
Methionine	Aspartate
Phenylalanine	Cysteine[2]
Threonine	Glutamate
Tryptophan	Glutamine
Valine	Glycine
	Histidine[1]
	Proline
	Serine
	Tyrosine[2]

[1]Histidine is an essential amino acid for infants but not for adults.
[2]Cysteine and tyrosine are considered to be semiessential amino acids. They are required by premature infants and adults who are ill.

A CLINICAL PERSPECTIVE

The AIDS Test

In 1981 the Centers for Disease Control in Atlanta, Georgia, recognized a new disease syndrome, Acquired Immune Deficiency Syndrome (AIDS). The syndrome is characterized by an impaired immune system, a variety of opportunistic infections and cancers, and brain damage that results in dementia. It soon became apparent that the disease was being transmitted by blood and blood products, as well as by sexual contact. The threat of contamination of blood supplies worldwide resulted in a multinational effort to elucidate the cause of AIDS and to develop a suitable test for the presence of the virus. As a part of this effort, Francoise Barre-Sinoussi and her colleagues at the Pasteur Institute first isolated the virus, now called human immunodeficiency virus, in 1983.

By April 1985 a test for virus infection was available for testing blood products. The test, called an *enzyme-linked immunosorbent assay (ELISA)*, is based on the specificity of antigen-antibody binding and uses a specific enzyme reaction to detect the presence of the virus in the blood. Because it is quite difficult and expensive to test for the virus itself, scientists actually test for the presence of the antibodies *produced* by the body in response to the virus infection.

The ELISA test is performed by coating the wells of a plastic microtiter plate with viral antigens (see the figure at right). These protein antigens are produced by growing the virus in tissue culture and purifying the viral proteins. A series of dilutions of the patient serum is prepared and placed in the wells of the microtiter plate. All samples are tested in duplicate, consistent with good analytical technique. If there are antibodies against HIV in the blood, they will bind to the viral antigens on the surface of the plastic. However, this binding is invisible. How can we visualize whether or not the binding reaction has occurred? This involves the use of an additional antibody to which an enzyme has been covalently linked. The second antibody reacts with human IgG antibody molecules. Thus antibodies from the blood that have bound to the viral antigen on the plate will now bind to the second antibody-enzyme. Enzymes that are commonly used for this are horseradish peroxidase and alkaline phosphatase. A substrate for the enzyme is chosen that will produce a colored product. For horseradish peroxidase the substrate is orthophenylenediamine, and the product is blue. For alkaline phosphatase the substrate is para-nitrophenylphosphate, and

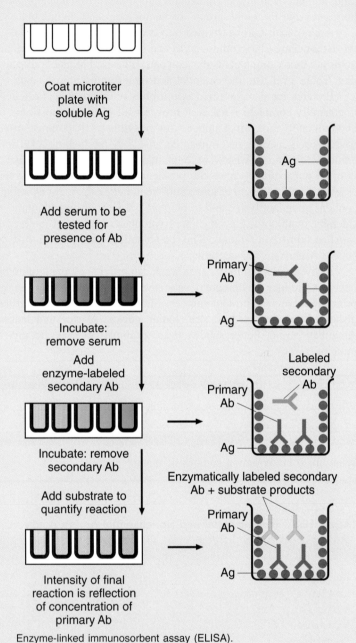

Coat microtiter plate with soluble Ag

Add serum to be tested for presence of Ab

Ag

Incubate: remove serum

Add enzyme-labeled secondary Ab

Primary Ab

Ag

Incubate: remove secondary Ab

Add substrate to quantify reaction

Labeled secondary Ab

Primary Ab

Ag

Enzymatically labeled secondary Ab + substrate products

Primary Ab

Ag

Intensity of final reaction is reflection of concentration of primary Ab

Enzyme-linked immunosorbent assay (ELISA).

Digestion of dietary proteins begins in the stomach. The stomach enzyme pepsin degrades the proteins that we eat into amino acids that can be taken up by the cells of the small intestine. Pepsin and other **proteolytic enzymes** catalyze the hydrolysis of peptide bonds of the protein. Production of proteolytic digestive enzymes must be carefully controlled because the active enzyme could digest and destroy the cell that produces it. Thus the cells of the stomach that produce pepsin actually produce an inactive form called *pepsinogen*. Pepsinogen has an addi-

the product is yellow. If the second antibody-enzyme has been bound by the sample, a colored product will appear when the substrate is added, and it can be concluded that the test is positive for the presence of HIV infection. If no color change is observed, the patient has not been exposed to HIV, and the test is negative. The more intense the color observed, the greater the amount of HIV antibodies in the test serum.

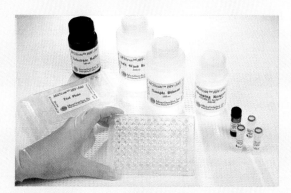

ELISA test for the presence of HIV antibodies in the blood serum. The more intense the color reaction, the greater the concentration of antibodies in the serum.

It would seem that the advent of this test would remove all threat of a contaminated blood supply, but this is unfortunately not the case. Sometimes, individuals who are not infected with the virus show positive results with the test: false positives. This is caused by other antibodies in the blood of the individual that react with other antigens that contaminate the HIV protein preparation. Other individuals who are infected demonstrate a negative result: false negatives. One reason for a false negative is the fact that it can take up to six months before the body produces antibodies against the virus. (The longest lag reported was 42 months.) During this period the individual tests negative but is infectious. Such an individual could donate contaminated blood that would then be available for transfusion.

Because of the incidence of false positive results, any blood that tests positive is tested, in duplicate, a second

time. If the result is positive in the second test, then a more accurate test is done to determine with certainty whether the subject has been infected with HIV. This test is called a *Western blot* and relies on the use of gel electrophoresis to separate HIV proteins according to their size. The proteins are then detected by using antigen-antibody binding and enzyme assays, as with the ELISA test. Proteins of the HIV virus are electrophoresed and transferred to a membrane. The membrane is then covered with the serum of the test subject. If antibodies are present that can bind to the individual HIV proteins on the membrane, antigen-antibody complexes will form. The membrane is then treated with an antibody-enzyme complex similar to that used in the ELISA test. Finally, the enzyme substrate is added. At any position on the membrane where the necessary antigen-antibody-antibody-enzyme complexes have formed, a colored band will appear, as seen in the figure below:

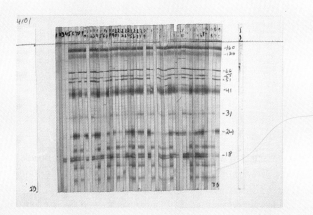

Western blot analysis of serum for the presence of HIV antibodies.

Seven different tests are on the market for HIV testing, and at least ten new tests are undergoing clinical trials. Many of these new generation tests will use HIV proteins that have been produced by recombinant DNA technology. These antigens will be much purer than those prepared from whole virus particles. It is hoped that, with fewer nonviral antigens present in the test, the incidence of false positives will dramatically decrease.

tional 42 amino acids. In the presence of stomach acid and previously activated pepsin, the extra 42 amino acids are cleaved off, and the inactive enzyme is transformed into the active enzyme. Table 15.4 lists several digestive enzymes that are produced in an inactive form.

Protein digestion continues in the small intestine. There the enzymes chymotrypsin, trypsin, elastase, and others all catalyze the hydrolysis of peptide bonds, but each cuts the protein chain at a different location. For instance, chymotrypsin catalyzes cleavage of peptide bonds on the

TABLE 15.4 Zymogens of the Digestive Tract

Zymogen	Activator	Enzyme
Proelastase	Trypsin	Elastase
Trypsinogen	Trypsin	Trypsin
Chymotrypsinogen A	Trypsin + chymotrypsin	Chymotrypsin
Pepsinogen	Acid pH + pepsin	Pepsin
Procarboxypeptidases	Trypsin	Carboxypeptidase A, carboxypeptidase B

carbonyl side of aromatic amino acids; trypsin cleaves peptide bonds on the carbonyl side of basic amino acids; and elastase cleaves peptide bonds on the carbonyl side of glycine and alanine.

Each of these enzymes has a different pocket in the active site for the side chains of its particular substrate; *different keys fit different locks.* As a result, each catalyzes cleavage of proteins at different sites, and together they are able to degrade large proteins into amino acids.

QUESTION 15.21

Why must synthesis of digestive enzymes be carefully controlled?

QUESTION 15.22

What is the relationship between pepsin and pepsinogen?

SUMMARY

15.1 Cellular Functions of Proteins

Proteins serve as biological catalysts (enzymes) and protective *antibodies. Transport proteins* carry materials throughout the body. Protein hormones regulate conditions in the body. Proteins also provide mechanical support and are needed for movement.

15.2 The Complex Design of Proteins

Proteins are made from 20 different *amino acids,* each having an α-COO$^-$ group and an α-N$^+$H$_3$ group. They differ only by their side-chain R groups. All α-*amino acids* are chiral except glycine. Naturally occurring amino acids have the same chirality, designated L. Amino acids are joined by *peptide bonds* to produce peptides and proteins. Proteins are linear polymers of amino acids. The linear sequence of amino acids defines the *primary structure* of the protein. The *secondary structure* of a protein consists of α-*helix* and β-*pleated sheet.* Usually, *structural proteins,* such as α-*keratins* and silk fibroin, are composed almost entirely of α-helix or β-pleated sheet. *Globular proteins* contain varying amounts of α-helix and β-pleated sheets folded into higher levels of structure called the *tertiary structure.* Some proteins are composed of more than one peptide. They are said to have *quaternary structure.* The forces that maintain tertiary and quaternary structure are a variety of weak interactions between the R groups of the constituent amino acids. *Conjugated proteins* require an attached, nonprotein *prosthetic group.*

15.3 Myoglobin and Hemoglobin

Myoglobin, the oxygen storage protein of skeletal muscle, is a conjugated protein with a prosthetic group called the *heme group.* The heme group is the site of oxygen binding. *Hemoglobin* consists of four peptides. It transports oxygen from the lungs to the tissues. Myoglobin has a greater affinity for oxygen than does hemoglobin, and so oxygen is efficiently transferred from hemoglobin in the blood to myoglobin in tissues. Fetal hemoglobin has a greater affinity for oxygen than does maternal hemoglobin, and oxygen transfer occurs efficiently across the placenta from the mother to the fetus.

15.4 The Effect of Temperature and pH on Proteins

When a protein is subjected to very high temperatures or extremes of pH, the well-ordered secondary, tertiary, and quaternary structure is destroyed. When a protein loses its structural organization, it is *denatured.* Such denatured proteins can then aggregate into an insoluble form; they become coagulated.

15.5 Enzymes: Nomenclature and Classification

Enzymes are most frequently named by using the common system of nomenclature. The names are useful because they are often derived from the name of the substrate and/or the reaction of the substrate that is catalyzed by the enzyme. Enzymes are classified according to function. The six general classes include *oxireductases, transferases, hydrolases, lyases, isomerases,* and *ligases.*

15.6 Enzyme-Catalyzed Reactions

Enzymes are the biological catalysts that lower the activation energies of the reactions that they catalyze. Formation of an *enzyme-substrate complex* is the first step of an enzyme-catalyzed reaction. This involves the binding of the substrate to the active site of the enzyme. The chemical reaction is then mediated through a *transition state.* Enzymes are also classified on the basis of their specificity. The four classifications of specificity are *absolute, group, linkage,* and *stereochemical specificity.*

Enzymes are sensitive to pH and temperature. High temperatures or extremes of pH rapidly inactivate most enzymes by denaturing them.

15.7 Inhibition of Enzyme Activity

Enzyme activity can be destroyed by a variety of inhibitors. *Irreversible inhibitors,* or poisons, bind tightly to enzymes and destroy their activity permanently. *Competitive inhibitors* are generally *structural analogs* of the natural substrate for the enzyme. They compete with the normal substrate for binding to the active site. When the competitive inhibitor is bound by the active site, the reaction cannot occur, and no product is produced.

15.8 Use of Enzymes in Medicine

Analysis of blood serum for unusually high levels of certain enzymes provides valuable information on a patient's condition. Such analysis is used to diagnose heart attack, liver disease, and pancreatitis. Enzymes are also used as analytical reagents, as in the blood urea nitrogen (BUN) test.

15.9 Dietary Protein and Protein Digestion

Essential amino acids must be acquired in the diet; *nonessential amino acids* can be synthesized by the body. *Complete proteins* contain all the essential and nonessential amino acids. *Incomplete proteins* are missing one or more amino acids. Protein digestion begins in the stomach, where proteins are degraded by the enzyme pepsin. Further digestion occurs in the small intestine by enzymes such as trypsin and chymotrypsin.

KEY TERMS

absolute specificity (15.6)
active site (15.6)
α-amino acid (15.2)
antibodies (15.1)
antigen (15.1)
apoenzyme (15.6)
C-terminal amino acid (15.2)

coagulation (15.4)
coenzyme (15.6)
cofactor (15.6)
competitive inhibition (15.7)
competitive inhibitor (15.7)
complete protein (15.9)
conjugated protein (15.6)

denaturation (15.4)
enzyme (15.1)
enzyme specificity (15.6)
enzyme-substrate complex (15.6)
essential amino acids (15.9)
fibrous protein (15.2)
folic acid (15.7)
globular protein (15.2)
glycoprotein (15.2)
group specificity (15.6)
α-helix (15.2)
heme (15.3)
hemoglobin (15.3)
hydrolase (15.5)
hydrophilic (15.2)
hydrophobic (15.2)
incomplete protein (15.9)
induced fit model (15.6)
irreversible inhibitor (15.7)
isoelectric (15.4)
isomerase (15.5)
α-keratin (15.2)
ligase (15.5)
linkage specificity (15.6)
lock-and-key model (15.6)
lyase (15.5)
myoglobin (15.3)
myosin (15.2)
N-terminal amino acid (15.2)

niacin (15.6)
nonessential amino acids (15.9)
oxireductases (15.5)
peptide bond (15.2)
pH optimum (15.6)
β-pleated sheet (15.2)
primary protein structure (15.2)
product (15.6)
prosthetic group (15.2)
protein (Introduction)
proteolytic enzymes (15.9)
quaternary protein structure (15.2)
regulatory proteins (15.1)
riboflavin (15.6)
secondary protein structure (15.2)
stereochemical specificity (15.6)
structural analog (15.7)
structural proteins (15.1)
substrate (15.5)
tertiary protein structure (15.2)
transferase (15.5)
transition state (15.6)
transport proteins (15.1)
vitamin (15.6)

QUESTIONS AND PROBLEMS

The Cellular Functions of Proteins

15.23 List five biological functions of proteins.

15.24 Provide an example of a protein that carries out each of the functions listed in answer to Question 15.23.

The Complex Design of Proteins

15.25 Write the basic general structure of an L-α-amino acid.

15.26 Why are all of the α-amino acids except glycine chiral?

15.27 What is the importance of the R groups of the amino acids?

15.28 Describe the classification of the R groups of the amino acids, and provide an example of each class.

15.29 Write the structure of the amino acid produced by the oxidation of cysteine.

15.30 What is the role of cystine in maintaining protein structure?

15.31 Write the structure of each of the following peptides:
   a. His-trp-cys
   b. Gly-leu-ser
   c. Arg-ile-val

15.32 Write the structure of each of the following peptides:
   a. Ile-leu-phe
   b. His-arg-lys
   c. Asp-glu-ser

15.33 What type of secondary structure is characteristic of
  a. The α-keratins?
  b. Silk fibroin?

15.34 Describe the forces that maintain the two types of secondary structure: α-helix and β-pleated sheet.

15.35 What is a conjugated protein?

15.36 What is a prosthetic group?

15.37 Why is heat an effective means of sterilization?

15.38 Yogurt is produced from milk by the action of dairy bacteria. These bacteria produce lactic acid as a by-product of their metabolism. The pH decrease causes the milk proteins to coagulate. Why are food preservatives not required to inhibit the growth of bacteria in yogurt?

Myoglobin and Hemoglobin

15.39 What is the function of heme in hemoglobin and myoglobin?

15.40 Write an equation representing the binding to and release of oxygen from hemoglobin.

Enzymes: Nomenclature and Classification

15.41 Match each of the following substrates with its corresponding enzyme:
  1. Urea   **a.** Lipase
  2. Hydrogen peroxide   **b.** Glucose-6-phosphatase
  3. Lipid   **c.** Peroxidase
  4. Aspartic acid   **d.** Sucrase
  5. Glucose-6-phosphate   **e.** Urease
  6. Sucrose   **f.** Aspartase

15.42 Give a systematic name for the enzyme that would act upon each of the following substrates:
  a. Alanine
  b. Citrate
  c. Ampicillin
  d. Ribose
  e. Methyl amine

15.43 Describe the function implied by the name of each of the following enzymes:
  a. Citrate decarboxylase
  b. Adenosine diphosphate phosphorylase
  c. Oxalate reductase
  d. Nitrite oxidase
  e. *cis-trans* Isomerase

15.44 List the six classes of enzymes based on the type of reaction catalyzed. Briefly describe the function of each class, and provide an example of each.

Enzyme-Catalyzed Reactions

15.45 What is the activation energy of a reaction?

15.46 What is the effect of an enzyme on the activation energy of a reaction?

15.47 Why doesn't the rate of an enzyme-catalyzed reaction increase indefinitely when the substrate concentration is made very large?

15.48 **a.** Draw a graph that describes the effect of increasing the concentration of the substrate on the rate of an enzyme-catalyzed reaction.

  b. What does this graph tell us about the nature of enzyme-catalyzed reactions?

15.49 List and define four classes of enzyme specificities.

15.50 Give an example of an enzyme that has each of the four types of specificity.

15.51 Outline the four general stages in an enzyme-catalyzed reaction.

15.52 Describe the transition state.

15.53 What is the role of a cofactor in enzyme activity?

15.54 How does a coenzyme function in an enzyme-catalyzed reaction?

15.55 Why does an enzyme lose activity when the pH is drastically changed from optimum pH?

15.56 Define the optimum pH for enzyme activity.

15.57 High temperature is an effective mechanism for killing bacteria on surgical instruments. How does high temperature result in cellular death?

15.58 An increase in temperature will increase the rate of a reaction if a nonenzymatic catalyst is used; however, an increase in temperature will eventually *decrease* the rate of a reaction when an enzyme catalyst is used. Explain the apparent contradiction of these two statements.

Inhibition of Enzyme Activity

15.59 Define *competitive enzyme inhibition.*

15.60 How do the sulfa drugs selectively kill bacteria while causing no harm to humans?

15.61 What is a structural analog?

15.62 How can structural analogs serve as enzyme inhibitors?

15.63 Define *irreversible enzyme inhibition.*

15.64 Why are irreversible enzyme inhibitors often called poisons?

Dietary Protein and Protein Digestion

15.65 Why is it necessary to mix vegetable proteins to provide an adequate vegetarian diet?

15.66 Name some ethnic foods that apply the principle of mixing vegetable proteins to provide all of the essential amino acids.

15.67 What is the difference between essential and nonessential amino acids?

15.68 What is the difference between a complete protein and an incomplete protein?

Further Problems

15.69 List the enzymes whose levels are elevated in blood serum following a myocardial infarction.

15.70 Why are enzymes that are used for clinical assays in hospitals stored in refrigerators?

15.71 Ethylene glycol is a poison that causes about 50 deaths a year in the United States. Treating people who have drunk ethylene glycol with massive doses of ethanol can save their lives. The structures of ethylene glycol and ethanol are shown below. Suggest a reason for the effect of ethanol.

$$HO—CH_2—CH_2—OH \qquad CH_3—CH_2—OH$$

Ethylene glycol   Ethanol

15.72 Suppose that a certain drug company manufactured a compound that had nearly the same structure as a substrate for a certain enzyme but that could not be acted upon chemically by the enzyme. What type of interaction would the compound have with the enzyme?

15.73 The addition of phenylthiourea to a preparation of the enzyme polyphenoloxidase completely inhibits the activity of the enzyme. Knowing that phenylthiourea binds all copper ions, what conclusion can you draw about whether polyphenoloxidase requires a cofactor? What kind of inhibitor is phenylthiourea?

15.74 Carbon monoxide binds tightly to the heme groups of hemoglobin and myoglobin. How does this affinity reflect the toxicity of carbon monoxide?

VOCABULARY QUIZ

15.1 The _active site_ is the groove or cleft in the surface of an enzyme that is the site of substrate binding.

15.2 The chemical group that is found attached to a conjugated protein is called the _____.

15.3 The _____ is the theory of enzyme-substrate binding that assumes that the enzyme is a flexible molecule and that both the substrate and the enzyme change their shapes to accommodate one another as the enzyme-substrate complex forms.

15.4 The process by which the organized structure of a protein is disrupted resulting in a completely disorganized, nonfunctional form of the protein is called _____.

15.5 The _____ is the globular, three-dimensional structure of a protein that results from folding the regions of secondary structure. This folding occurs spontaneously as a result of interactions of the side chains or R groups of the amino acids.

15.6 The _____ is the covalent linkage between two amino acids in a peptide chain. It is formed by a condensation reaction.

15.7 An enzyme that catalyzes the transfer of a functional group from one molecule to another is called a(n) _____.

15.8 A(n) _____ is the protein portion of an enzyme that requires a cofactor in order to function in catalysis.

15.9 A common secondary structure that resembles the pleats of an oriental fan is called _____.

15.10 _____ is a vitamin that is essential for the energy-generating reactions of the cell. It is a component of two coenzymes: nicotinamide adenine dinucleotide and nicotinamide adenine dinucleotide phosphate.

16

Carbohydrate Metabolism

L E A R N I N G   G O A L S

◆ Understand the importance of ATP in cellular energy transfer processes.

◆ Describe the three stages of catabolism of dietary proteins, carbohydrates, and fats.

◆ Discuss glycolysis in terms of its two major segments.

◆ Understand the practical and metabolic roles of fermentation reactions.

◆ Compare glycolysis and gluconeogenesis.

◆ Summarize the regulation of blood glucose levels by glycogenesis and glycogenolysis in the liver.

CHEMISTRY CONNECTION

The Man Who Got Tipsy from Eating Pasta

Imagine becoming drunk after eating a plate of spaghetti or a bag of potato chips. That is exactly what happened to Charles Swaart while he was stationed in Tokyo after World War II. Suddenly, he would be completely drunk—without having swallowed a drop of alcohol.

During the next two decades, Swaart continued to have unexplainable bouts of drunkenness and horrible hangovers. The problem was so serious that his liver was being destroyed. But in 1964, Swaart heard of a man in Japan who suffered from the same mysterious—and embarrassing—symptoms. After 25 years, physicians diagnosed the problem. There was a mutant strain of the yeast *Candida albicans* living in the gastrointestinal tract of the Japanese gentleman. These yeast cells were using carbohydrates from the man's diet to make ethanol. The metabolic pathways used by these yeast were glycolysis and alcohol fermentation, two of the pathways that we will study in this chapter.

Swaart took advantage of the therapy used in Japan. He had to try several antibiotics over the years. But finally, in 1975, all of the mutant yeast cells in his intestine were killed, and his life returned to normal.

Why was it so difficult for physicians to solve this medical mystery? Normal, nonfermenting *Candida albicans* is a regular inhabitant of the human gut. It took some very clever scientific detective work to find this mutant ethanol-producing strain. The scientists even have a hypothesis about where the mutant yeast comes from. They think that the radiation released in one of the atomic bomb blasts at Nagasaki or Hiroshima may have caused the mutation.

In this chapter we begin our study of the chemical reactions used by all organisms to provide energy for cellular work. In Chapter 19 we will look at the kinds of DNA damage (mutations) that can produce changes in the structure or function of an organism.

INTRODUCTION

Just as we need energy to run, jump, and think, the cell needs a ready supply of cellular energy for the many functions that support these activities. Cells need energy for *active transport,* to move molecules between the environment and the cell. Energy is also needed for *biosynthesis* of small metabolic molecules and production of macromolecules from these intermediates. Finally, energy is required for *mechanical work,* including muscle contraction and motility of sperm cells. Table 16.1 lists some examples of each of these energy-requiring processes.

We need a supply of energy-rich food molecules that can be degraded, or *oxidized,* to provide this needed cellular energy. Our diet includes three major sources of energy: carbohydrates, fats, and proteins. Each of these types of large biological molecules must be broken down into its basic subunits—simple sugars, fatty acids and glycerol, and amino acids—before they can be taken into the cell and used to produce cellular energy. Of these classes of food molecules, carbohydrates are the most readily used. The pathway for the first stages of carbohydrate breakdown, called *glycolysis,* was the first successful energy-generating pathway on earth. It is so successful that we find the same pathway in organisms as different as the simple bacterium and human beings.

In this chapter we are going to examine the steps of this ancient energy-generating pathway. We will see that it is responsible for the capture of some of the bond energy of carbohydrates and the storage of that energy in the molecular form of *adenosine triphosphate (ATP).* Glycolysis actually releases and stores very little (2.2%) of the potential energy of glucose, but the pathway also serves as a source of biosynthetic building blocks. It also modifies the carbohydrates in such a way that other pathways are able to release as much as 40% of the potential energy.

Recall that the potential energy of a compound is the chemical bond energy of that compound.

The degradation of fuel molecules, called **catabolism,** provides the energy that enables the cell to function. The energy of a food source, such as the simple sugar glucose, is released by the step-by-step oxidation of glucose. These reactions are accompanied by the release of small amounts of energy at several points in the pathway. To oxidize food molecules and harvest the

16.1 ATP: THE CELLULAR ENERGY CURRENCY

TABLE 16.1   The Types of Cellular Work That Require Energy

Biosynthesis: Synthesis of Metabolic Intermediates and Macromolecules
Synthesis of glucose from CO_2 and H_2O in the process of photosynthesis in plants Synthesis of amino acids Synthesis of nucleotides Synthesis of lipids Protein synthesis from amino acids Synthesis of nucleic acids Synthesis of organelles and membranes

Active Transport: Movement of Ions and Molecules
Transport of H^+ to maintain constant pH Transport of food molecules into the cell Transport of Na^+ and K^+ into and out of nerve cells for transmission of nerve impulses Secretion of HCl from parietal cells into the stomach Transport of waste from the blood into the urine in the kidneys Transport of amino acids and most hexose sugars into the blood from the intestines Accumulation of calcium ions in the mitochondria

Motility
Contraction and flexion of muscle cells Separation of chromosomes during cell division Ability of sperm to swim via flagella Movement of foreign substances out of the respiratory tract by cilia on the epithelial lining of the trachea Translocation of eggs into the fallopian tubes by cilia in the female reproductive tract

Recall that energy-releasing reactions are called exothermic reactions and energy-requiring reactions are called endothermic reactions (Section 5.1).

energy released, the cell needs enzymes to catalyze the reactions and a means of saving the released chemical energy so that it can be used in energy-requiring reactions.

The chemical energy released during the breakdown of fuel molecules is stored by producing **adenosine triphosphate (ATP).** Because ATP is the major energy storage form in all living cells, it is often called the *universal energy currency* (Figure 16.1).

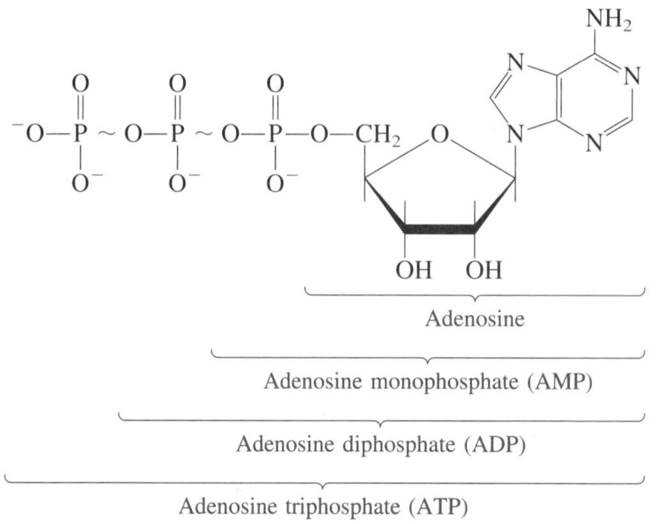

FIGURE 16.1
The structure of the universal energy currency, ATP.

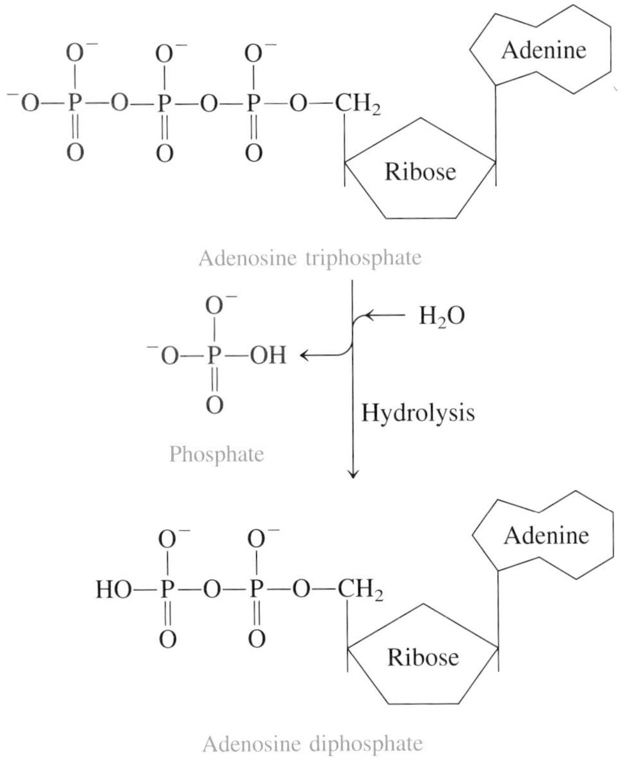

FIGURE 16.2
Hydrolysis of ATP to ADP breaks the phosphoanhydride linkage and releases an inorganic phosphate group.

ATP is a **nucleotide.** Nucleotides are molecules composed of a nitrogenous base, a five-carbon sugar, and one, two, or three phosphoryl groups. ATP is composed of the nitrogenous base adenine bonded in N-glycosidic linkage to the sugar ribose. Ribose in turn is bonded to one (AMP), two (ADP), or three (ATP) phosphoryl groups by a phosphoester bond. The molecule is a high-energy compound because of the phosphoanhydride bonds holding the terminal phosphate groups. When these bonds are broken, or hydrolyzed, they release a large amount of energy that can be used for cellular work. For this reason they are called *high-energy bonds.* The high-energy bonds of the ATP molecule are indicated as squiggles (~) in Figure 16.1.

Hydrolysis of ATP yields adenosine diphosphate (ADP), an inorganic phosphate group (P_i), and energy (Figure 16.2). The energy released by this hydrolysis of ATP is then used to drive biological processes.

An example of the way in which the energy of ATP is used can be seen in the first reaction of glycolysis. This reaction involves the transfer of a phosphoryl group, $-PO_3^{2-}$, from ATP to the C-6 hydroxyl group of glucose (Figure 16.3). This reaction is catalyzed by the enzyme hexokinase.

Although this is a coupled reaction, we can think of it as a two-step process. In the first step, ATP is hydrolyzed to produce ADP and a phosphoryl group (Figure 16.2). In the second step,

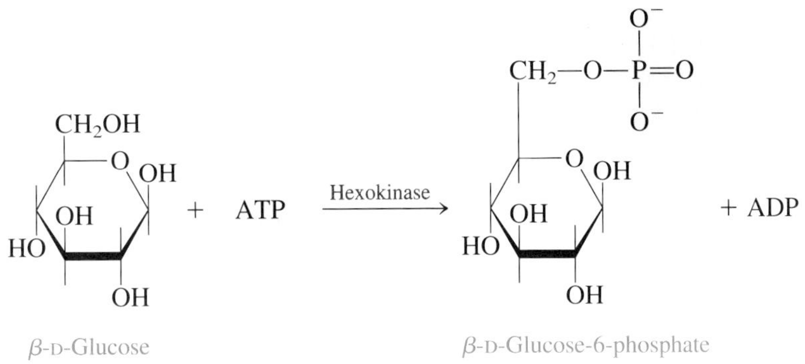

An N-glycosidic bond results when a carbon from a cyclic sugar is linked to an amine nitrogen. In the case of ATP, that sugar is ribose, and the amine nitrogen is part of the heterocyclic amine, adenine (Sections 14.2 and 19.1).

Sections 12.3 and 19.1

β-D-Glucose   +   ATP   →[Hexokinase]   *β-D-Glucose-6-phosphate*   +   ADP

FIGURE 16.3
Phosphoryl group transfer from ATP to the C-6 hydroxyl group of glucose.

the phosphoryl group reacts with the C-6 hydroxyl group of glucose, producing glucose-6-phosphate. This product has more energy than the reactant, glucose, because it now carries some of the energy from the original phosphoanhydride bond of ATP.

The primary function of all catabolic pathways is to harvest the chemical energy of fuel molecules and to store that energy by the production of ATP. This continuous production of ATP is what provides the stored potential energy that is used to power most cellular functions.

QUESTION 16.1

Why is ATP called the universal energy currency?

QUESTION 16.2

List five biological activities that require ATP.

16.2 OVERVIEW OF CATABOLIC PROCESSES

Although carbohydrates, fats, and proteins can all be degraded to release energy, carbohydrates are the most readily used energy source. We will begin by examining the oxidation of the hexose glucose. In Chapters 17 and 18 we will see the way in which the pathways of glucose oxidation are also used for the degradation of fats and proteins.

Any catabolic process must begin with a supply of nutrients. When we eat a meal, we are eating quantities of carbohydrates, fats, and proteins. From this point the catabolic processes can be broken down into a series of stages. The three stages of catabolism are summarized in Figure 16.4.

Stage I: Hydrolysis of dietary macromolecules into small subunits

The purpose of this stage of catabolism is to degrade large food molecules into their component subunits. These subunits—simple sugars, amino acids, fatty acids, and glycerol—are then taken into the cells of the body for use as an energy source. The process of digestion is summarized in Figure 16.5.

Polysaccharides are hydrolyzed to monosaccharides. This process begins in the mouth, where the enzyme amylase begins the hydrolysis of starch. Digestion continues in the small intestine, where pancreatic amylase further hydrolyzes the starch into maltose (a disaccharide of glucose). Maltase catalyzes the hydrolysis of maltose, producing two glucose molecules. Similarly, sucrose is hydrolyzed to glucose and fructose by the enzyme sucrase, and lactose (milk sugar) is degraded into the monosaccharides glucose and galactose by the enzyme lactase. The monosaccharides are taken up by the epithelial cells of the intestine in an energy-requiring process called *active transport*.

In the laboratory, strong acid or base and high temperatures are required for hydrolysis of amide bonds (Section 14.3). However, this reaction proceeds quickly under physiological conditions when catalyzed by enzymes.

Section 15.9

The digestion of proteins begins in the stomach, where the low pH denatures the proteins so that they are more easily hydrolyzed by the enzyme pepsin. They are further degraded in the small intestine by trypsin, chymotrypsin, elastase, and other proteases. The products of protein digestion—amino acids and short oligopeptides—are taken up by the cells lining the intestine. This uptake also involves an active transport mechanism.

The digestion and transport of fats are considered in greater detail in Chapter 18.

Digestion of fats does not begin until the food reaches the small intestine, even though there are lipases in both the saliva and stomach fluid. Fats arrive in the duodenum, the first portion of the small intestine, in the form of large fat globules. Bile salts produced by the liver break these up into an emulsion of tiny fat droplets. Because the small droplets have a greater surface area, the lipids are now more accessible to the action of pancreatic lipase. This enzyme hydrolyzes the fats into fatty acids and glycerol, which are taken up by intestinal cells by a transport process that does not require energy. This process is called *passive transport*. A summary of these hydrolysis reactions is shown in Figure 16.6.

Stage II: Conversion of monomers into a form that can be completely oxidized

The monosaccharides, amino acids, fatty acids, and glycerol must now be assimilated into the pathways of energy metabolism. The two major pathways are glycolysis and the citric acid cycle (Figure 16.4). Sugars usually enter the glycolysis pathway in the form of glucose or fructose. They are eventually converted to acetyl CoA, which is a form that can be completely oxidized in

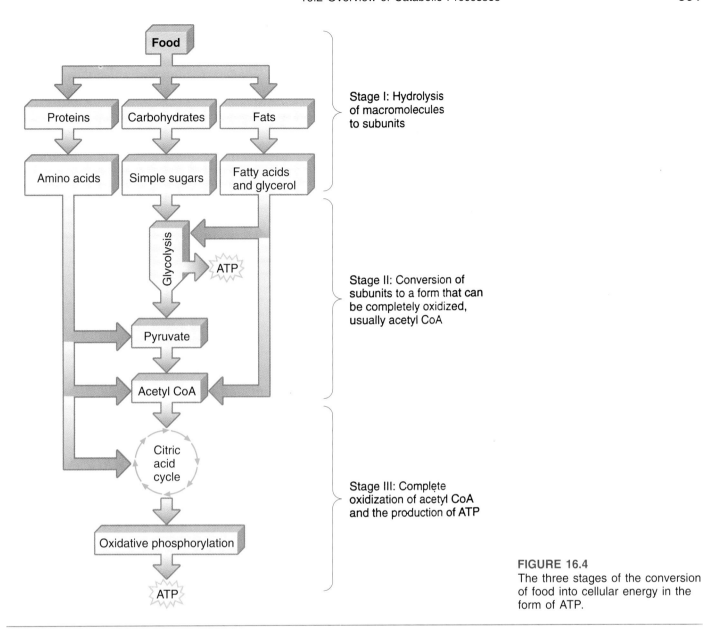

FIGURE 16.4
The three stages of the conversion of food into cellular energy in the form of ATP.

the citric acid cycle. Amino groups are removed from amino acids, and the remaining carbon skeletons enter the catabolic processes at many steps of glycolysis and the citric acid cycle. Fatty acids are converted to acetyl CoA and enter the citric acid cycle in that form. Glycerol, produced by the hydrolysis of fats, is converted to glyceraldehyde-3-phosphate, one of the intermediates of glycolysis, and enters energy metabolism at that level.

The citric acid cycle will be considered in detail in Section 17.3.

Section 16.7

Acetyl CoA carries two carbon remnants of the nutrients, acetyl groups, to the citric acid cycle. Here electrons and hydrogen atoms are harvested during the complete oxidation of the nutrients to CO$_2$. These electrons and hydrogen atoms are used in the process of oxidative phosphorylation to produce ATP.

Stage III: The complete oxidation of nutrients and the production of ATP
Section 17.4

QUESTION 16.3

Briefly describe the three stages of catabolism.

QUESTION 16.4

Discuss the digestion of dietary carbohydrates, lipids, and proteins.

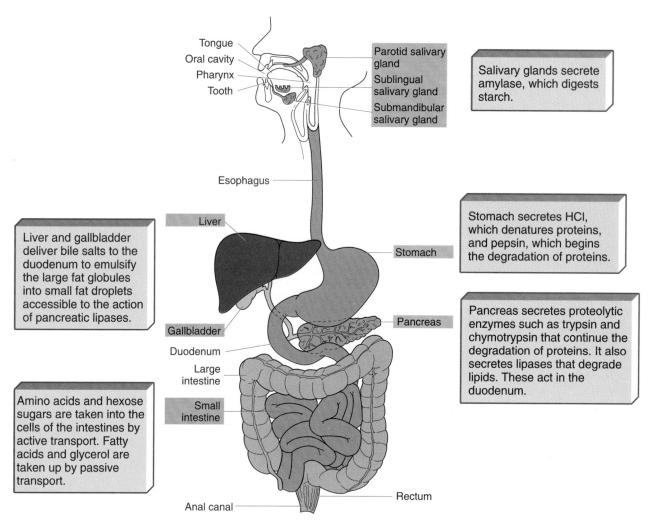

Tongue
Oral cavity
Pharynx
Tooth

Parotid salivary gland
Sublingual salivary gland
Submandibular salivary gland

Salivary glands secrete amylase, which digests starch.

Esophagus

Liver

Stomach

Stomach secretes HCl, which denatures proteins, and pepsin, which begins the degradation of proteins.

Liver and gallbladder deliver bile salts to the duodenum to emulsify the large fat globules into small fat droplets accessible to the action of pancreatic lipases.

Gallbladder
Duodenum
Large intestine
Small intestine

Pancreas

Pancreas secretes proteolytic enzymes such as trypsin and chymotrypsin that continue the degradation of proteins. It also secretes lipases that degrade lipids. These act in the duodenum.

Amino acids and hexose sugars are taken into the cells of the intestines by active transport. Fatty acids and glycerol are taken up by passive transport.

Anal canal

Rectum

FIGURE 16.5
An overview of the digestive processes that hydrolyze carbohydrates, proteins, and fats.

16.3 GLYCOLYSIS

An overview

Glycolysis is the first stage of carbohydrate catabolism. The first substrate in the pathway is D-glucose. The very fact that all organisms can use glucose as an energy source for glycolysis suggests that glycolysis was the first successful pathway for energy generation that evolved on the earth. The pathway evolved at a time when the earth's atmosphere was *anaerobic;* no free oxygen was available. As a result, glycolysis requires no oxygen; it is an anaerobic process. Further, it must have evolved in very simple, single-celled organisms, much like the bacteria. These organisms did not have complex organelles in the cytoplasm to carry out specific cellular functions. Thus glycolysis was a process carried out by enzymes that were free in the cytoplasm. To this day, glycolysis remains an anaerobic process carried out by cytoplasmic enzymes, even in cells as complex as our own.

An outline of the nine steps of glycolysis is seen in Figure 16.7. The first substrate in the pathway is the hexose sugar glucose. Nine enzymes are needed to carry out the nine reactions of the pathway. The first reactions of glycolysis involve an energy investment. ATP is hydrolyzed, and high-energy phosphoryl groups are added to the hexose sugars. In the remaining steps of glycolysis, energy is harvested.

The three major products of glycolysis are seen in Figure 16.7. These are chemical energy in the form of ATP, chemical energy in the form of NADH, and two three-carbon pyruvate molecules. Each of these products is considered below:

◆ **Chemical energy as ATP.** Four ATP molecules are formed by the process of **substrate-level phosphorylation.** This means that high-energy phosphoryl groups from one of the

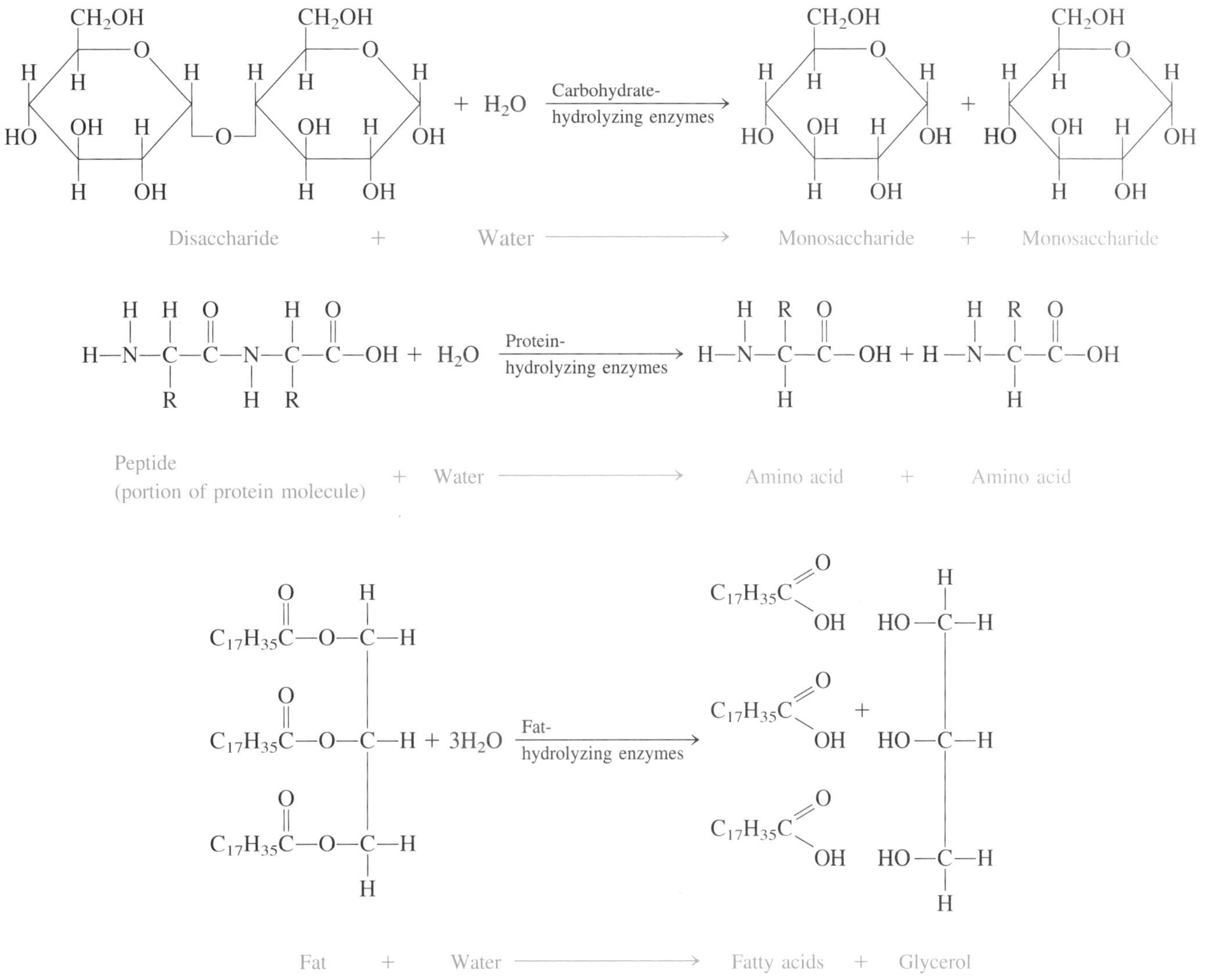

FIGURE 16.6
A summary of the hydrolysis reactions of carbohydrates, proteins, and fats.

---

substrates in glycolysis are transferred to ADP to form ATP. The two substrates involved in these transfer reactions are 1,3-bisphosphoglycerate and phosphoenolpyruvate (Figure 16.7, steps 6 and 9). Although four ATP molecules are produced during glycolysis, the *net* gain is only two ATP molecules because two ATP molecules are used early in glycolysis (Figure 16.7, steps 1 and 3). The two ATP molecules produced represent only 2.2% of the potential energy of the glucose molecule. Thus glycolysis is not a very efficient energy-harvesting process.

◆ **Chemical energy in the form of reduced NAD^+, NADH. Nicotinamide adenine dinucleotide (NAD^+)** is a coenzyme derived from the vitamin niacin. The reduced form of NAD^+, NADH, carries hydride anions, hydrogen atoms with two electrons ($H:^-$), removed during the oxidation of one of the substrates, glyceraldehyde-3-phosphate (Figure 16.7, step 5). Under aerobic conditions the electrons and hydrogen atom are donated to an electron transport system for the generation of ATP by **oxidative phosphorylation.** Under anaerobic conditions, NADH is used as a source of electrons in fermentation reactions.

The structure of NAD^+ and the way it functions as a hydride anion carrier are shown in Figure 15.24 and described in Section 15.6.

Section 17.4

◆ **Two pyruvate molecules.** At the end of glycolysis the six-carbon glucose molecule has been converted into two three-carbon pyruvate molecules. The fate of the pyruvate also

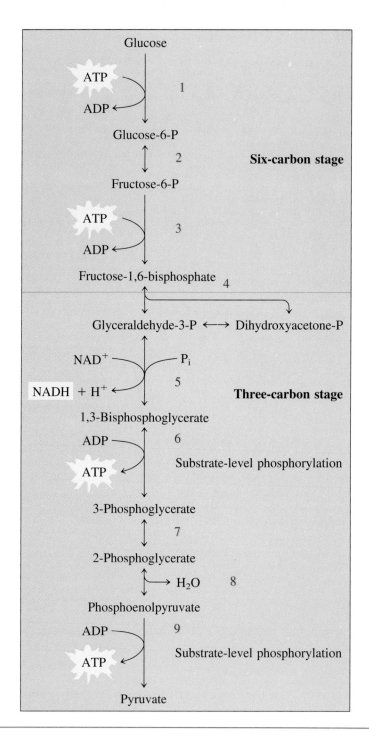

FIGURE 16.7
A summary of the nine reactions of glycolysis.

depends on whether the reactions are occurring in the presence or absence of oxygen. Under aerobic conditions it will be used to produce acetyl CoA destined for the citric acid cycle and complete oxidation. Under anaerobic conditions it will be used as the substrate in fermentation reactions.

In any event these last two products must be used in some way so that glycolysis can continue to function and produce ATP. There are two reasons for this. First, if pyruvate were allowed to build up, it would cause glycolysis to stop, thereby stopping the production of ATP. Thus pyruvate must be used in some kind of follow-up reaction, aerobic or anaerobic. Second, in step 5 we see that glyceraldehyde-3-phosphate is oxidized and NAD^+ is reduced (accepts the hydride anion). The cell has only a small supply of NAD^+. If all the NAD^+ is reduced, none will be available for this reaction, and glycolysis will stop. Therefore NADH must be reoxidized so that glycolysis can continue to produce ATP for the cell.

The structures of the intermediates of glycolysis are seen in Figure 16.8, along with a concise description of the reactions that occur at each step and the names of the enzymes that catalyze each reaction.

Reactions of glycolysis

Glycolysis can be divided into two major segments. The first is the investment of ATP energy. Without this investment, glucose would not have enough energy for glycolysis to continue, and there would be no ATP produced. This segment includes the first four reactions of the pathway. The second major segment involves the remaining reactions of the pathway (steps 5–9), those that result in a net energy yield.

Reaction 1

The substrate, glucose, is phosphorylated by the enzyme *hexokinase*. The name hexokinase tells us that this is an enzyme that adds phosphoryl groups to a six-carbon sugar, glucose. The source of the phosphoryl group is ATP. At first this reaction seems contrary to the overall purpose of catabolism, the *production* of ATP. The expenditure of ATP in these early reactions must be thought of as an "investment." The cell actually goes into energy "debt" in these early reactions, but this is absolutely necessary to get the pathway started.

Reaction 2

The glucose-6-phosphate formed in the first reaction is rearranged to produce the structural isomer fructose-6-phosphate. The enzyme *phosphoglucoisomerase* catalyzes this isomerization.

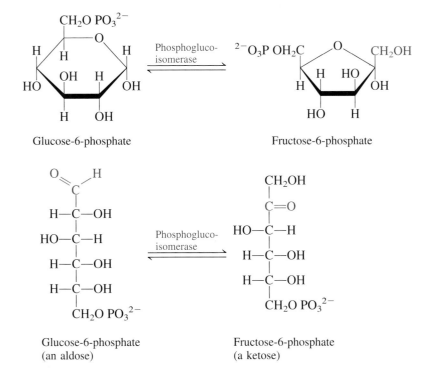

Reaction 3

A second energy "investment" is catalyzed by the enzyme *phosphofructokinase*. ATP is hydrolyzed, and a phosphoester linkage between the phosphoryl group and the C-1 hydroxyl group of fructose-6-phosphate is formed. The product is fructose-1,6-bisphosphate.

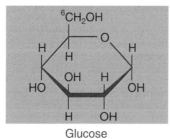

Glucose

ATP

Hexokinase (1)

ADP

1. Glucose is phosphorylated at the expense of ATP to produce glucose-6-phosphate.

Glucose-6-phosphate

Phosphogluco-isomerase (2)

2. Glucose-6-phosphate is rearranged to produce fructose-6-phospate.

Fructose-6-phosphate

ATP

Phospho-fructokinase (3)

ADP

3. Fructose-6-phosphate is phosphorylated to produce fructose-1,6-bisphosphate at the expense of another ATP. The expenditure of 2 ATP represents an energy investment to "activate" the glucose for its eventual oxidation.

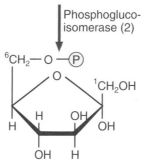

Fructose-1,6-bisphosphate

Aldolase (4)

4. Aldolase cleaves the six carbon fructose-1,6-bisphosphate into two nonidentical three-carbon molecules, dihydroxyacetone phosphate and glyceraldehyde-3-phosphate. The dihydroxyacetone phosphate is converted to glyceraldehyde-3-phosphate by the enzyme triose isomerase.

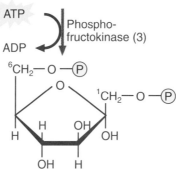

Dihydroxyacetone phosphate

Glyceraldehyde-3-phosphate

FIGURE 16.8
The intermediates and enzymes of glycolysis.

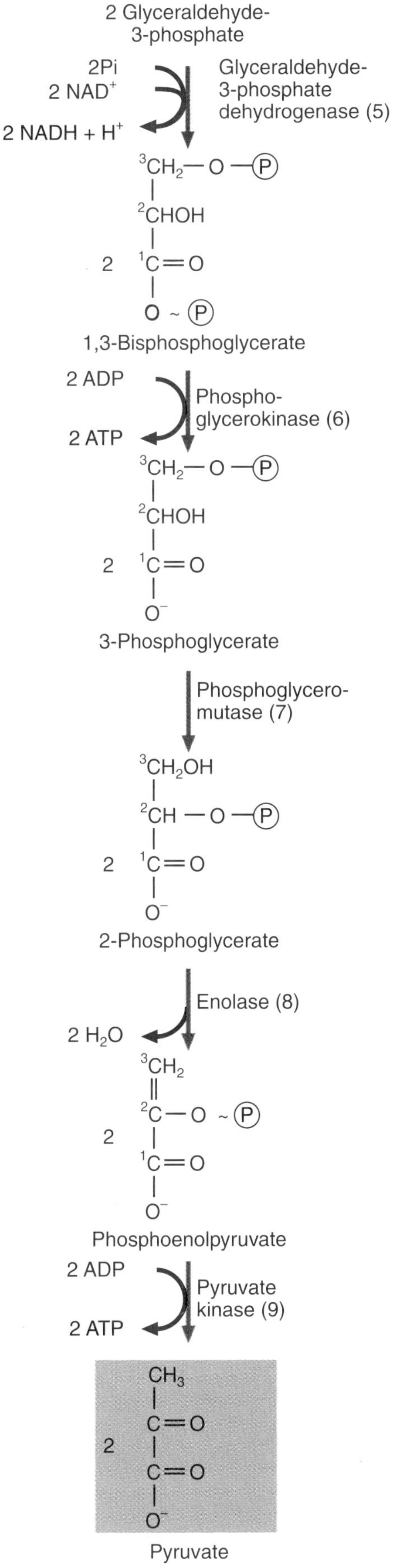

2 Glyceraldehyde-
3-phosphate

2Pi
2 NAD⁺

Glyceraldehyde-
3-phosphate
dehydrogenase (5)

2 NADH + H⁺

$^3CH_2-O-$(P)
$\vert$
^2CHOH
$\vert$
2 $^1C=O$
$\vert$
O ~ (P)

1,3-Bisphosphoglycerate

2 ADP

Phospho-
glycerokinase (6)

2 ATP

$^3CH_2-O-$(P)
$\vert$
^2CHOH
$\vert$
2 $^1C=O$
$\vert$
O⁻

3-Phosphoglycerate

Phosphoglycero-
mutase (7)

$^3CH_2OH$
$\vert$
$^2CH-O-$(P)
$\vert$
2 $^1C=O$
$\vert$
O⁻

2-Phosphoglycerate

Enolase (8)

2 H₂O

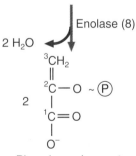

Phosphoenolpyruvate

2 ADP

Pyruvate
kinase (9)

2 ATP

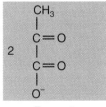

Pyruvate

5. Glyceraldehyde-3-phosphate is oxidized and NADH is produced. An inorganic phosphate group is transferred to the carboxylate group to produce 1,3-bisphosphoglycerate.

6. ATP is produced in the first substrate level phosphorylation in the pathway. The phosphoryl group is transferred from the substrate to ADP to produce ATP.

7. The C-3 phosphoryl group of 3-phosphoglycerate is transferred to the second carbon.

8. Dehydration of 2-phosphoglycerate generates the energy-rich molecule phosphoenolpyruvate.

9. The final substrate level phosphorylation produces ATP and pyruvate.

$$^{2-}O_3P\ OH_2C \quad\overset{O}{\diagup} \quad CH_2OH \qquad + \quad ATP \quad \xrightarrow{\text{Phosphofructokinase}} \quad ^{2-}O_3P\ OH_2C \quad\overset{O}{\diagup} \quad CH_2O\ PO_3{}^{2-} \qquad + \ ADP + H^+$$

Fructose-6-phosphate　　　　　　　　　　　　　　　　　　Fructose-1,6-disphosphate

Reaction 4

Fructose-1,6-bisphosphate is split into two three-carbon intermediates in a reaction catalyzed by the enzyme *aldolase*. The products are glyceraldehyde-3-phosphate (G3P) and dihydroxyacetone phosphate. Since G3P is the only substrate that can be used by the next enzyme in the pathway, the dihydroxyacetone phosphate is rearranged to become a second molecule of G3P. The enzyme that mediates this isomerization is *triose isomerase*.

Fructose-1,6-bisphosphate　　Dihydroxyacetone phosphate　　Glyceraldehyde-3-phosphate

Dihydroxyacetone phosphate　　　　Glyceraldehyde 3-phosphate

Reaction 5

In this reaction the aldehyde glyceraldehyde-3-phosphate is oxidized to a carboxylic acid in a reaction catalyzed by *glyceraldehyde-3-phosphate dehydrogenase*. This is the first step in glycolysis that harvests energy, and it involves the reduction of the coenzyme nicotinamide adenine dinucleotide (NAD^+). This reaction occurs in two steps. First, NAD^+ is reduced to NADH as the aldehyde group of glyceraldehyde-3-phosphate is oxidized to a carboxyl group. Second, an inorganic phosphate group is transferred to the carboxyl group to give 1,3-bisphosphoglycerate. Notice that the phosphoester bond is denoted with a squiggle ($\sim$), indicating that this is a high-energy bond.

Glyceraldehyde 3-phosphate　　　　　　　　　　　1,3-Bisphosphoglycerate

Reaction 6

In this reaction, energy is harvested in the form of *ATP*. The enzyme *phosphoglycerokinase* catalyzes the transfer of the phosphoryl group of 1,3-bisphosphoglycerate to ADP. This is the first substrate-level phosphorylation of glycolysis, and it produces ATP and 3-phosphoglycerate.

1,3-Bisphosphoglycerate   3-Phosphoglycerate

Reaction 7

3-Phosphoglycerate is isomerized to produce 2-phosphoglycerate in a reaction catalyzed by the enzyme *phosphoglyceromutase*. The phosphoryl group attached to the third carbon of 3-phosphoglycerate is transferred to the second carbon.

3-Phosphoglycerate   2-Phosphoglycerate

Reaction 8

In this step the enzyme *enolase* catalyzes the dehydration (removal of a water molecule) of 2-phosphoglycerate. The energy-rich product is phosphoenolpyruvate.

2-Phosphoglycerate   Phosphoenolpyruvate

Reaction 9

Here we see the final substrate-level phosphorylation in the pathway, which is catalyzed by *pyruvate kinase*. Phosphoenolpyruvate serves as a donor of the phosphoryl group that is transferred to ADP to produce ATP. The final product of glycolysis is pyruvate.

Phosphoenolpyruvate   Pyruvate

It should be noted that reactions 5 through 9 occur twice per glucose molecule, since the starting six-carbon sugar is split into two three-carbon molecules. Thus in reaction 5, two

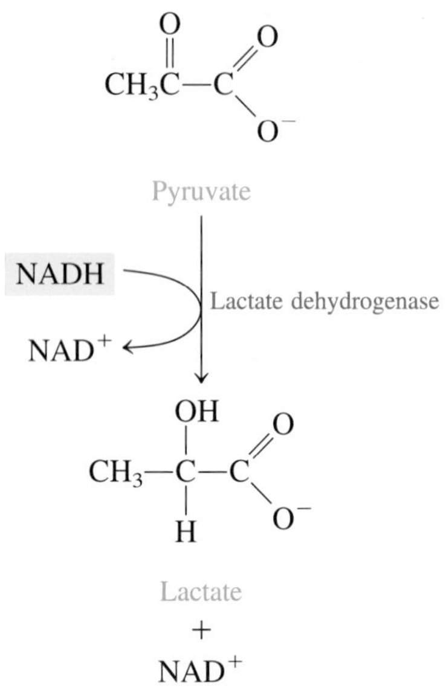

O   O
‖   ‖
CH₃C—C
          \
           O⁻

Pyruvate

NADH ⌐
         ⌐ Lactate dehydrogenase
NAD⁺ ←

OH   O
| ‖
CH₃—C—C
     | \
     H   O⁻

Lactate
+
NAD⁺

FIGURE 16.9
Lactate fermentation.

NADH molecules are generated, and a total of four ATP molecules are made (steps 6 and 9). The net ATP gain from this pathway is, however, only two ATP molecules because there was an energy investment of two ATP molecules in the early steps of the pathway. This investment was paid back by the two ATP molecules produced by substrate-level phosphorylation in step 6. The actual energy yield is produced by substrate-level phosphorylation in reaction 9.

QUESTION 16.5

What is substrate-level phosphorylation?

QUESTION 16.6

What are the major products of glycolysis?

QUESTION 16.7

Describe an overview of the reactions of glycolysis.

QUESTION 16.8

How do the names of the first three enzymes of the glycolytic pathway relate to the reactions they catalyze?

16.4 FERMENTATIONS

Chapter 17

In the overview of glycolysis we noted that the pyruvate produced must be used up in some way so that the pathway will continue to produce energy. Similarly, the NADH produced by glycolysis in step 5 (see Figure 16.8) must be reoxidized at a later time, or glycolysis will grind to a halt as the available NAD⁺ is used up. If the cell is functioning under aerobic conditions, NADH will be reoxidized, and pyruvate will be completely oxidized by aerobic respiration. Under anaerobic conditions, however, different types of fermentation reactions accomplish these purposes. **Fermentations** are catabolic reactions that occur with no net oxidation. Pyruvate or an organic compound produced from pyruvate is reduced as NADH is oxidized. We will examine two types of fermentation pathways in detail: lactate fermentation and alcohol fermentation.

Lactate fermentation

As we saw in "A Human Perspective: Simple Sugars and Tooth Decay" (Chapter 11), the lactate produced by oral bacteria is responsible for the gradual removal of calcium from tooth enamel and the resulting dental cavities.

Chapter 17

The Cori Cycle is described in Section 16.5 and shown in Figure 16.12.

Lactate fermentation is familiar to anyone who has performed strenuous exercise. If you exercise so hard that your lungs and circulatory system can't deliver enough oxygen to the working muscles, your aerobic (oxygen-requiring) energy-generating pathways will not be able to supply enough ATP to your muscles. But they still demand energy. Under these anaerobic conditions the lactate fermentation begins. In this reaction the enzyme *lactate dehydrogenase* reduces pyruvate to lactate. NADH is the reducing agent for this process (Figure 16.9). As pyruvate is reduced, NADH is oxidized, and NAD⁺ is again available, permitting glycolysis to continue.

The lactate produced in the working muscle passes into the blood. Eventually, if strenuous exercise is continued, the concentration of lactate becomes so high that this fermentation can no longer continue. Glycolysis, and thus energy production, stops. The muscle, deprived of energy, can no longer function. This point of exhaustion is called the **anaerobic threshold.**

Of course, most of us do not exercise to this point. When exercise is finished, the body begins the process of reclaiming all of the potential energy that was lost in the form of lactate. The liver takes up the lactate from the blood and converts it back to pyruvate. Now that a sufficient supply of oxygen is available, the pyruvate can be completely oxidized in the much more efficient aerobic energy-harvesting reactions to replenish the store of ATP. Alternatively, the pyruvate may be used to restore the supply of liver and muscle glycogen through the Cori Cycle.

A variety of bacteria are able to carry out lactate fermentation under anaerobic conditions. This is of great importance in the dairy industry, since these organisms are used to produce yogurt and some cheeses. The tangy flavor of yogurt is contributed by the lactate produced by these bacteria. Unfortunately, similar organisms also cause milk to spoil.

Alcohol fermentation has been appreciated, if not understood, since the dawn of civilization. The fermentation process itself was discovered by Louis Pasteur during his studies of the chemistry of wine making and "diseases of wines." Under anaerobic conditions, yeast are able to ferment the sugars produced by fruit and grains. The sugars are broken down to pyruvate by glycolysis. This is followed by the two reactions of the alcohol fermentation. First, *pyruvate decarboxylase* removes CO_2 from the pyruvate producing acetaldehyde (Figure 16.10). Second, *alcohol dehydrogenase* catalyzes the reduction of acetaldehyde to ethanol but, more important, reoxidizes NADH in the process. The regeneration of NAD^+ allows glycolysis to continue, just as in the case of lactate fermentation.

The two products of alcohol fermentation, then, are ethanol and CO_2. We take advantage of this fermentation in the production of wines and other alcoholic beverages and in the process of bread making.

Alcohol fermentation

These applications and other fermentations are described in "A Human Perspective: Fermentations: The Good, the Bad, and the Ugly."

QUESTION 16.9

How is the alcohol fermentation in yeast similar to lactate production in skeletal muscle?

QUESTION 16.10

Why must pyruvate be used and NADH be reoxidized so that glycolysis can continue?

Under normal conditions we have enough glucose to satisfy our needs. However, under some conditions the body must make glucose. This is necessary following strenuous exercise to replenish the liver and muscle supplies of glycogen. It also occurs during starvation so that the body can maintain adequate blood glucose levels to supply the brain cells and red blood cells. Under normal conditions these two tissues use only glucose for energy.

Glucose is produced by the process of **gluconeogenesis,** the production of glucose from noncarbohydrate starting materials (Figure 16.11). Gluconeogenesis occurs primarily in the liver. Lactate, all the amino acids except leucine and lysine, and glycerol from fats can all be used to make glucose. However, the amino acids and glycerol are generally used only under starvation conditions.

At first glance, gluconeogenesis appears to be simply the reverse of glycolysis (compare Figures 16.11 and 16.7), because the intermediates of the two pathways are identical. But this is not the case, because steps 1, 3, and 9 of glycolysis are irreversible, and therefore the reverse reactions must be carried out by other enzymes. In step 1 of glycolysis, hexokinase catalyzes the phosphorylation of glucose. In gluconeogenesis the dephosphorylation of glucose-6-phosphate is carried out by the enzyme *glucose-6-phosphatase,* which is found in the liver but not in muscle. Similarly, in reaction 3 the phosphorylation of fructose-6-phosphate mediated by phosphofructokinase is irreversible. That step is bypassed in gluconeogenesis by using the enzyme *fructose bisphosphatase.* Finally, the phosphorylation of ADP catalyzed by pyruvate kinase, step 9 of glycolysis, cannot be reversed. The conversion of pyruvate to phosphoenolpyruvate actually involves two enzymes and some unusual reactions. First, the enzyme *pyruvate carboxylase* adds atmospheric CO_2 to pyruvate. The product is the four-carbon compound oxaloacetate. Then *phosphoenolpyruvate carboxykinase* removes the CO_2 and adds a phosphoryl group. The donor of the phosphoryl group in this unusual reaction is **guanosine triphosphate (GTP).** This is a nucleotide like ATP, except that the nitrogenous base is guanine.

As we have seen, the conversion of lactate into glucose is important in mammals. As the muscles work, they produce lactate, which is converted back to glucose in the liver. The glucose is transported into the blood and from there back to the muscle. In the muscle it can be used to generate energy, or it can be used to replenish the muscle stores of glycogen. This cyclic process between the liver and skeletal muscles is called the **Cori Cycle** and is shown in Figure 16.12. Through this cycle, gluconeogenesis produces enough glucose to restore the depleted muscle glycogen reservoir within 48 hours.

16.5 GLUCONEOGENESIS: THE SYNTHESIS OF GLUCOSE

Under extreme conditions of starvation the brain eventually switches to the use of ketone bodies. Ketone bodies are produced, under certain circumstances, from the breakdown of lipids (Section 18.3).

Section 19.1

FIGURE 16.10
Alcohol fermentation.

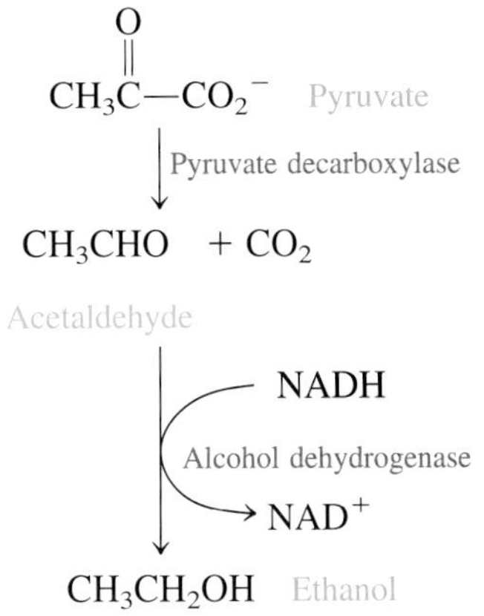

$$\underset{\text{Pyruvate}}{CH_3\overset{\overset{\textstyle O}{\|}}{C}-CO_2^-}$$

Pyruvate decarboxylase

$$CH_3CHO \ + CO_2$$
Acetaldehyde

Alcohol dehydrogenase

NADH

NAD^+

$$CH_3CH_2OH \quad \text{Ethanol}$$

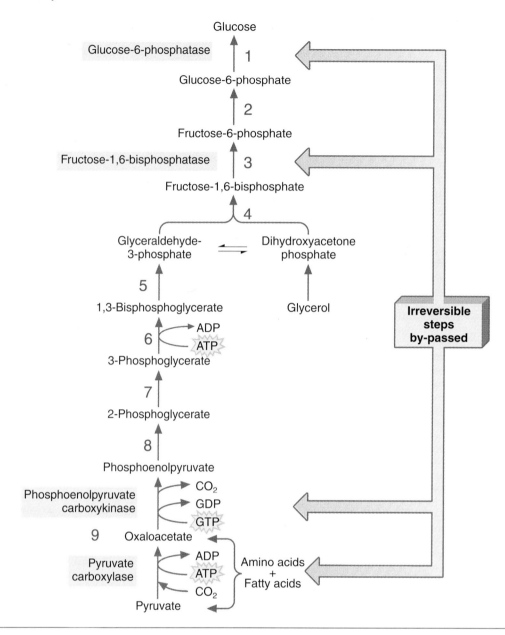

FIGURE 16.11
Comparison of glycolysis and gluconeogenesis.

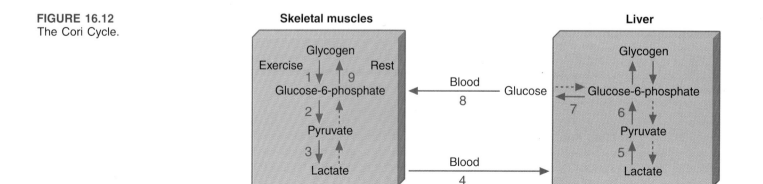

FIGURE 16.12
The Cori Cycle.

What are the major differences between gluconeogenesis and glycolysis?

What do the three irreversible reactions of glycolysis have in common?

Glycogen is a long, branched polymer of glucose that is stored in the liver and skeletal muscle in the form of complexes of glycogen polymers and the enzymes responsible for glycogen synthesis and degradation. These complexes are called **glycogen granules.** The structure of the glycogen granule is shown in Figure 16.13.

16.6 GLYCOGEN SYNTHESIS AND DEGRADATION

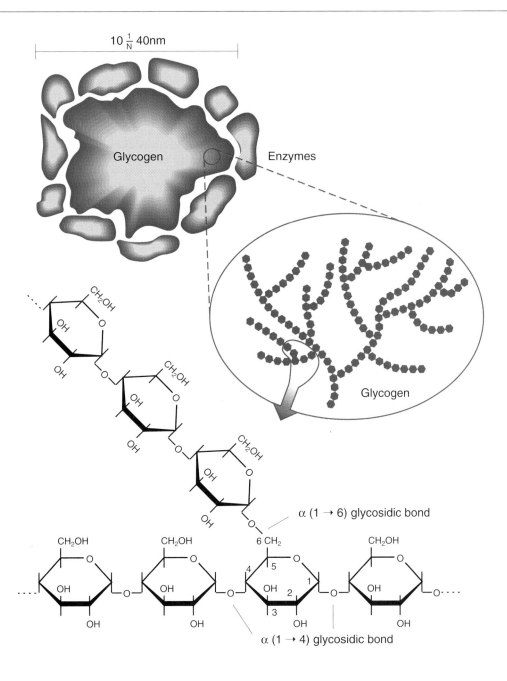

FIGURE 16.13
The structure of glycogen and a glycogen granule.

A HUMAN PERSPECTIVE

Fermentations: The Good, the Bad, and the Ugly

In this chapter we have seen that fermentation is an anaerobic, cytoplasmic process that allows continued ATP generation by glycolysis. ATP production can continue because the pyruvate produced by the pathway is utilized in the fermentation and because NAD^+ is regenerated.

The stable end products of alcohol fermentation are CO_2 and ethanol. These have been used by humankind in a variety of ways, including the production of alcoholic beverages, bread making, and alternative fuel sources.

The production of bread, wine, and cheese depends on the fermentation process.

If alcohol fermentation is carried out by using fruit juices in a vented vat, the CO_2 will escape, and the result will be a still wine (not bubbly). But conditions must remain anaerobic; otherwise, fermentation will stop, and aerobic energy-harvesting reactions will ruin the wine. Fortunately for vintners (wine makers), when a vat is fermenting actively, enough CO_2 is produced to create a layer that keeps the oxygen-containing air away from the fermenting juice, thus maintaining an anaerobic atmosphere.

Now suppose we want to make a sparkling wine, such as champagne. To do this, we simply have to trap the CO_2 produced. In this case the fermentation proceeds in a sealed bottle, a very strong bottle. Both the fermentation products, CO_2 and ethanol, accumulate. Under pressure within the sealed bottle the CO_2 remains in solution. When the top is "popped," the pressure is released, and the CO_2 comes out of solution in the form of bubbles.

In either case the fermentation continues until the alcohol concentration reaches 12–13%. At that point the yeast "stews in its own juices"! That is, 12–13% ethanol kills the yeast cells that produce it. This points out a last generalization about fermentations. The stable fermentation end product, whether it is lactate or ethanol, eventually accumulates to a concentration that is toxic to the organism. Muscle fatigue is the early effect of lactate buildup in the working muscle. In the same way, continued accumulation of the fermentation product can lead to concentrations that are fatal if there is no means of getting rid of the toxic product or of getting away from it. For single-celled organisms the result is generally death. Our bodies have evolved in such a way that lactate buildup contributes to muscle fatigue that causes the

Glycogenolysis: glycogen degradation

Under normal physiological conditions, glucose is the sole source of energy of mammalian red blood cells and the major source of energy for the brain. Neither red blood cells nor the brain can store glucose; therefore a constant supply must be available as blood glucose. The liver supply of glycogen is important in the regulation of blood glucose levels, because liver glycogen can be broken down to produce glucose, which is then released into the bloodstream.

Glycogen degradation is called **glycogenolysis.** It occurs in a series of reactions, each of which is catalyzed by an enzyme. The steps in glycogen degradation that produce glucose are summarized below and in Figure 16.14.

The reaction is termed *phosphorolysis* because the inorganic phosphate group directly breaks the bond between two glucose units and is simultaneously added to the glucose molecule that was removed. This is also a clever energy savings for the cell because no ATP is required to phosphorylate the glucose before it enters glycolysis.

Step 1: The enzyme *glycogen phosphorylase* catalyzes the removal of a glucose molecule at one end of a glycogen polymer. The $\alpha(1{\rightarrow}4)$ glycosidic bond is broken, and a phosphate group is attached at C-1 of glucose, producing glucose-1-phosphate.

Step 2: Glycogen contains many branches bound to the $\alpha(1{\rightarrow}4)$ backbone by $\alpha(1{\rightarrow}6)$ glycosidic bonds. These branches must be removed to allow the complete degradation of glycogen. The *debranching enzyme* catalyzes hydrolysis of the $\alpha(1{\rightarrow}6)$ glycosidic bond at a branchpoint. Hydrolysis of the branch bond liberates another stretch of $\alpha(1{\rightarrow}4)$-linked glucose for the action of glycogen phosphorylase.

exerciser to stop the exercise. Then the lactate is removed from the blood by the process of gluconeogenesis.

Another application of the alcohol fermentation is the use of yeast in bread making. When we mix the water, sugar, and dried yeast, the yeast cells begin to grow and carry out the process of fermentation. This mixture is then added to the flour, milk, shortening, and salt, and the dough is placed in a warm place to rise. The yeast continues to grow and ferment the sugar, producing CO_2 that causes the bread to rise. Of course, when we bake the bread, the yeast cells are killed, and the ethanol evaporates, but we are left with a light and airy loaf of bread.

Today, alcohol produced by fermentation is being considered as an alternative fuel to replace the use of some fossil fuels. Geneticists and bioengineers are trying to develop strains of yeast that can survive higher alcohol concentrations and thus convert more of the sugar of corn and other grains into alcohol.

Bacteria perform a variety of other fermentations. The propionibacteria produce propionic acid and CO_2. The acid gives Swiss cheese its characteristic flavor, and the CO_2 gas produces the characteristic holes in the cheese. Other bacteria, the clostridia, perform a fermentation that is responsible in part for the horrible symptoms of gas gangrene. When these bacteria are inadvertently introduced into deep tissues by a puncture wound, they find a nice anaerobic environment in which to grow. In fact, these organisms are *obligate anaerobes,* that is, they are killed by even a small amount of oxygen. As they grow, they perform a fermentation called the butyric acid, butanol, acetone fermentation. This results in the formation of CO_2, the gas associated with gas gangrene. The CO_2 infiltrates the local tissues and helps to maintain an anaerobic environment because oxygen from the local blood supply cannot enter the area of the wound. Now able to grow well, these bacteria produce a variety of toxins and enzymes that cause extensive tissue death and necrosis. In addition, the fermentation produces acetic acid, ethanol, acetone, isopropanol, butanol, and butyric acid (which is responsible, along with the necrosis, for the characteristic foul smell of gas gangrene). Certainly, the presence of these organic chemicals in the wound causes enhanced tissue death.

Gas gangrene is very difficult to treat. Because the bacteria establish an anaerobic region of cell death and cut off the local circulation, systemic antibiotics do not infiltrate the wound and kill the bacteria. Even our immune response is stymied. Treatment usually involves surgical removal of the necrotic tissue accompanied by antibiotic therapy. In some cases a hyperbaric oxygen chamber is employed. The infected extremity is placed in an environment with a very high partial pressure of oxygen. The oxygen forced into the tissues is poisonous to the bacteria, and they die.

These are but a few examples of the fermentations that have an impact on humans. Regardless of the specific chemical reactions, all fermentations share the following traits:

◆ They use pyruvate produced in glycolysis.

◆ They reoxidize the NADH.

◆ They are self-limiting because the accumulated stable fermentation end product eventually kills the cell that produces it.

Step 3: Glucose-1-phosphate is converted to glucose-6-phosphate in a reaction catalyzed by the enzyme *phosphoglucomutase.* Glucose-6-phosphate may enter glycolysis directly, or it may be dephosphorylated for transport into the bloodstream.

Glycogen synthesis, termed **glycogenesis,** is a very complex set of reactions. These reactions are summarized below and are also seen in Figure 16.14.

Glycogenesis: glycogen synthesis

Step 1: The enzyme *glucokinase* traps glucose within the cell by catalyzing the addition of a phosphoryl group donated by ATP. Glucose-6-phosphate is formed.

Step 2: The glucose-6-phosphate formed in the first step is isomerized to glucose-1-phosphate in a reaction catalyzed by the enzyme *phosphoglucomutase.*

Step 3: The glucose-1-phosphate must now be ''activated'' before it can be added to the growing glycogen chain. The high-energy compound that does this is the nucleotide **uridine triphosphate (UTP).** The enzyme *pyrophosphorylase* catalyzes bond formation between glucose-phosphate and UTP to produce UDP-glucose.

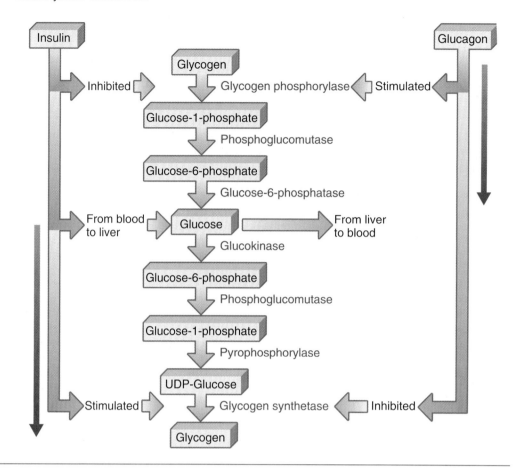

FIGURE 16.14
The opposing effects of the hormones insulin and glucagon on glycogen metabolism.

Step 4: The UDP-glucose can now be used to extend glycogen chains. The enzyme *glycogen synthetase* catalyzes breakage of the phosphoester bond of UDP-glucose and formation of an $\alpha(1\rightarrow4)$ glycosidic bond between the glucose and the growing glycogen chain. UDP is released in the process.

Step 5: Finally, we must introduce the $\alpha(1\rightarrow6)$ glycosidic linkages to form the branches that are quite important to proper glycogen utilization. This is catalyzed by the *branching enzyme,* which removes a section of the linear $\alpha(1\rightarrow4)$ linked glycogen and reattaches it in $\alpha(1\rightarrow6)$ glycosidic linkage at another point in the chain.

Compatibility of glycogenesis and glycogenolysis

It would be senseless for the cell to simultaneously carry out glycogen synthesis and degradation. The results achieved by the action of one pathway would be undone by the other glycogenesis. Since glycogenesis and glycogenolysis are essential for the regulation of blood glucose levels, the rates of the two pathways must be carefully controlled. Thus, blood glucose levels are regulated by a series of hormonal controls that indirectly activate the enzymes of one pathway while simultaneously inhibiting the enzymes of the other pathway.

When the blood glucose level is too high, a condition called **hyperglycemia,** the hormone **insulin** stimulates the uptake of glucose into cells. It further aids trapping of glucose within those cells by stimulating the activity of glucokinase. Finally, insulin activates glycogen synthetase, the last enzyme in the synthesis of glycogen chains. To further accelerate storage, insulin *inhibits* the first enzyme in glycogen degradation, glycogen phosphorylase. The net effect, seen in Figure 16.14, is that glucose is removed from the bloodstream and converted into glycogen in the liver. When the glycogen stores are filled, excess glucose is converted to fat and stored in adipose tissue.

A HUMAN PERSPECTIVE

Glycogen Storage Diseases

Glycogen metabolism is important for the proper function of many aspects of cellular metabolism. Many diseases of glycogen metabolism have been discovered. Generally, these are diseases that result in the excessive accumulation of glycogen in the liver, muscle, and tubules of the kidneys. Often they are caused by defects in one of the enzymes involved in the degradation of glycogen.

One example is an inherited defect of glycogen metabolism known as von Gierke's disease. This disease results from a defective gene for glucose-6-phosphatase, which catalyzes the final step of gluconeogenesis. People who lack glucose-6-phosphatase cannot convert glucose-6-phosphate to glucose. As we have seen, the liver is the primary source of blood glucose, and much of this glucose is produced by gluconeogenesis. Glucose-6-phosphate, unlike glucose, cannot cross the cell membrane, and the liver of a person suffering from von Gierke's disease cannot provide the individual with glucose. The blood sugar level falls precipitously low between meals. In addition, the lack of glucose-6-phosphatase also affects glycogen metabolism. Since glucose-6-phosphatase is absent, the supply of glucose-6-phosphate in the liver is large. This glucose-6-phosphate can also be converted to glycogen. A person suffering from von Gierke's disease has a massively enlarged liver as a result of enormously increased stores of glycogen.

Defects in other enzymes of glycogen metabolism also exist. Cori's disease is caused by a genetic defect in the debranching enzyme. As a result, individuals who have this disease cannot completely degrade glycogen and thus use their glycogen stores very inefficiently.

On the other side of the coin, Andersen's disease results from a genetic defect in the branching enzyme. Individuals who have this disease produce very long, unbranched glycogen chains. These unbranched chains cannot be properly degraded by the glycogenolytic enzymes, again resulting in inefficient use of glycogen stores.

One final example of a glycogen storage disease is McArdle's disease. In this syndrome the muscle cells lack the enzyme glycogen phosphorylase and cannot degrade glycogen to glucose. Individuals who have this disease have little tolerance for physical exercise because their muscles cannot provide enough glucose for the production of ATP. It is interesting to note that the glycogen phosphorylase found in the liver functions normally. As a result, these people respond appropriately with a rise of blood glucose levels under the influence of glucagon or epinephrine.

Glucagon is produced in response to low blood glucose levels, a condition known as **hypoglycemia,** and has an effect opposite to that of insulin. It stimulates glycogen phosphorylase, which catalyzes the first reaction of glycogen degradation. This accelerates glycogenolysis and release of glucose into the bloodstream. The effect is further enhanced because glucagon *inhibits* glycogen synthetase. The opposing effects of insulin and glucagon are summarized in Figure 16.14.

This elegant system of hormonal control ensures that the reactions involved in glycogen degradation and synthesis *do not* compete with one another. In this way, they provide glucose when the blood level is too low, and they cause the storage of glucose in times of excess.

QUESTION 16.13

Explain how glucagon affects the synthesis and degradation of glycogen.

QUESTION 16.14

How does insulin affect the storage and degradation of glycogen?

As we have seen, under anaerobic conditions, glucose is metabolized to two pyruvate molecules that are then converted to a stable fermentation product. This limited degradation of glucose releases very little of the potential energy of glucose. Under aerobic conditions the cells can use oxygen and completely oxidize glucose to CO_2 in a metabolic pathway called the *citric acid cycle.* We now look at the production of the intermediate that carries two carbon fragments, acetyl groups, from pyruvate into the aerobic energy-harvesting pathways. That intermediate is **acetyl CoA.**

16.7 CONVERSION OF PYRUVATE TO ACETYL CoA

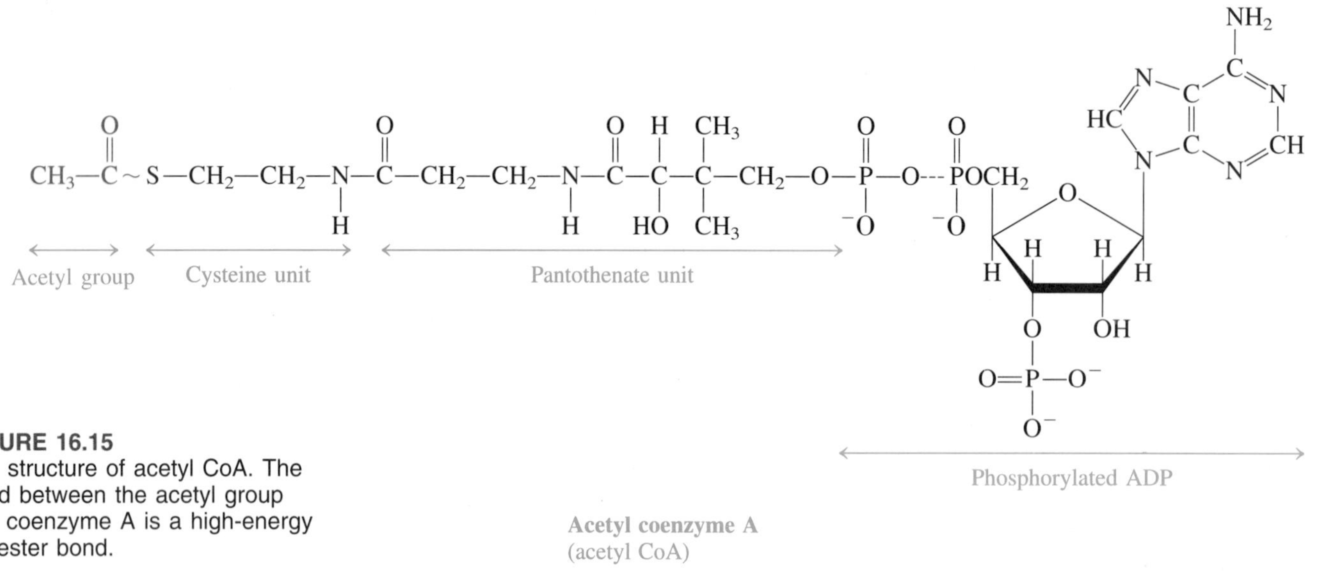

FIGURE 16.15
The structure of acetyl CoA. The bond between the acetyl group and coenzyme A is a high-energy thioester bond.

Section 10.4

Section 12.3

The structure of acetyl CoA is seen in Figure 16.15. The **coenzyme A** portion of this molecule is derived from ATP, the vitamin pantothenic acid, and the amino acid cysteine. It serves as an acceptor of acetyl groups, shown in red in Figure 16.15, that are linked to the cysteine part of the molecule by a thioester bond. We can consider acetyl CoA to be an "activated" form of the acetyl group.

The reaction that converts pyruvate to acetyl CoA is shown in Figure 16.16. The pyruvate is decarboxylated, which liberates a molecule of CO_2. It is also oxidized, and the hydride anion that is removed is accepted by NAD^+, which is thus reduced. Finally, the remaining acetyl group, $CH_3CO_2^-$, is linked to coenzyme A by a thioester bond. This very complex reaction is

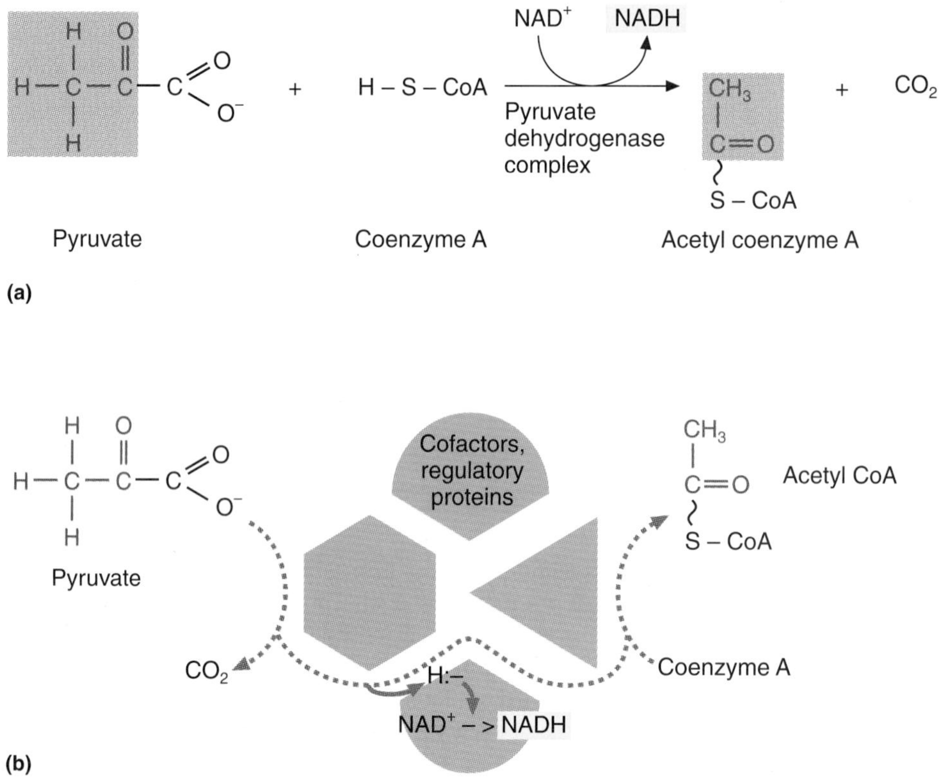

FIGURE 16.16
The decarboxylation and oxidation of pyruvate to produce acetyl CoA. (a) The overall reaction in which CO_2 and an $H:^-$ are removed from pyruvate and the remaining acetyl group is attached to coenzyme A. This requires the concerted action of three enzymes and five coenzymes. (b) The pyruvate dehydrogenase complex that carries out this reaction is actually a cluster of enzymes and coenzymes. The substrate is passed from one enzyme to the next as the reaction occurs.

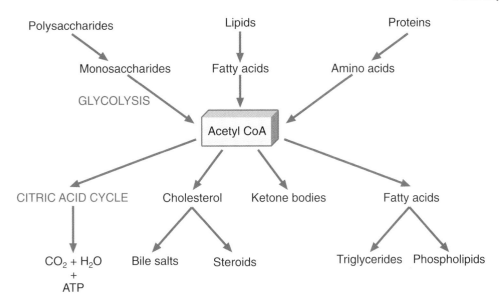

FIGURE 16.17
The central role of acetyl CoA in cellular metabolism.

carried out by three enzymes and four coenzymes. To economize the process, these enzymes and coenzymes are all localized in a single bundle called the **pyruvate dehydrogenase complex** (Figure 16.16b). In this way the substrate can be passed from one enzyme to the next as each modification occurs. A schematic representation of this "disassembly line" is shown in Figure 16.16.

This single reaction requires four coenzymes made from four different vitamins. These are thiamine pyrophosphate, derived from thiamine (vitamin B_1); FAD, derived from riboflavin (vitamin B_2); NAD^+, derived from niacin; and coenzyme A, derived from pantothenic acid. Obviously, a deficiency in any of these vitamins would seriously reduce the amount of acetyl CoA that our cells could produce. This, in turn, would limit the amount of ATP that the body could make and would contribute to vitamin-deficiency diseases. Fortunately, a well-balanced diet provides an adequate supply of these and other vitamins.

In Figure 16.17 we see that acetyl CoA is a central character in cellular metabolism. It is produced by the degradation of glucose, fatty acids, and some amino acids. The major function of acetyl CoA in energy-harvesting pathways is to carry the acetyl group to the citric acid cycle, where it will be used to produce large amounts of ATP. In addition to these catabolic duties, the acetyl group of acetyl CoA can also be used for *anabolic* or biosynthetic reactions to produce cholesterol and fatty acids. It is through this intermediate, acetyl CoA, that all the energy sources (fats, proteins, and carbohydrates) are interconvertible.

The citric acid cycle and the electron transport system responsible for making large quantities of ATP are discussed in detail in Chapter 17.

QUESTION 16.15

What vitamins are required for acetyl CoA production from pyruvate?

QUESTION 16.16

What is the major role of coenzyme A in catabolic reactions?

SUMMARY

16.1 ATP: The Cellular Energy Currency

Adenosine triphosphate, ATP, is a *nucleotide* composed of adenine, the sugar ribose, and a triphosphate group. The energy released by the hydrolysis of the phosphoanhydride bond be-

tween the second and third phosphoryl groups provides the energy for most cellular work.

16.2 Overview of Catabolic Processes

The body needs a supply of ATP to carry out life processes. To provide this ATP, we consume a variety of energy-rich food molecules: carbohydrates, lipids, and proteins. In the digestive tract these large molecules are degraded into smaller molecules (monosaccharides, glycerol, fatty acids, and amino acids) that are absorbed by our cells. These molecules are further broken down to generate ATP.

16.3 Glycolysis

Glycolysis is the pathway for the *catabolism* of glucose that leads to pyruvate. It is an anaerobic process carried out by enzymes in the cytoplasm of the cell. The net harvest of ATP during glycolysis is two molecules of ATP per molecule of glucose. Two molecules of NADH are also produced.

16.4 Fermentation

Under anaerobic conditions the NADH produced by glycolysis is used to reduce pyruvate to lactate in skeletal muscle (lactate *fermentation*) or to convert acetaldehyde to ethanol in yeast (alcohol fermentation).

16.5 Gluconeogenesis: The Synthesis of Glucose

Gluconeogenesis is the pathway for glucose synthesis from noncarbohydrate starting materials. It occurs in mammalian liver. Glucose can be made from lactate, all the amino acids except lysine and leucine, and glycerol. Gluconeogenesis is not simply the reversal of glycolysis. Three steps in glycolysis in which ATP is produced or consumed are bypassed by different enzymes in gluconeogenesis. All other enzymes in gluconeogenesis are shared with glycolysis.

16.6 Glycogen Synthesis and Degradation

Glycogenesis is the pathway for the synthesis of glycogen, and *glycogenolysis* is the pathway for the degradation of glycogen. The concentration of blood glucose is controlled by the liver. A high blood glucose level causes secretion of *insulin*. This hormone stimulates glycogenesis and inhibits glycogenolysis. When blood glucose levels are too low, the hormone *glucagon* stimulates gluconeogenesis and glycogen degradation in the liver.

16.7 Conversion of Pyruvate to Acetyl CoA

Under aerobic conditions, pyruvate is oxidized by the pyruvate dehydrogenase complex. *Acetyl CoA,* formed in this reaction, is a central molecule in both catabolism and anabolism.

KEY TERMS

acetyl CoA (16.7)
adenosine triphosphate (ATP)
  (16.1)
anaerobic threshold (16.4)

catabolism (16.1)
coenzyme A (16.7)
Cori Cycle (16.5)
fermentation (16.4)

glucagon (16.6)
gluconeogenesis (16.5)
glycogen (16.6)
glycogen granule (16.6)
glycogenesis (16.6)
glycogenolysis (16.6)
glycolysis (16.3)
guanosine triphosphate (GTP)
  (16.5)
hyperglycemia (16.6)
hypoglycemia (16.6)

insulin (16.6)
nicotinamide adenine
  dinucleotide (NAD$^+$) (16.3)
nucleotide (16.1)
oxidative phosphorylation
  (16.3)
substrate-level
  phosphorylation (16.3)
uridine triphosphate (UTP)
  (16.6)

QUESTIONS AND PROBLEMS

ATP: The Cellular Energy Currency

16.17 What molecule is primarily responsible for conserving the energy released in catabolism?

16.18 Describe the structure of ATP.

16.19 Write a reaction showing the hydrolysis of the terminal phosphoanhydride bond of ATP.

16.20 What is meant by the term *high-energy bond?*

Glycolysis

16.21 Why does glycolysis require a supply of NAD$^+$ to function?

16.22 Why must the NADH produced in glycolysis be reoxidized to NAD$^+$?

16.23 What is the net energy yield of ATP in glycolysis?

16.24 How many molecules of ATP are produced by substrate-level phosphorylation during glycolysis?

16.25 Explain how muscle is able to carry out rapid contraction for prolonged periods even though its supply of ATP is sufficient only for a fraction of a second of rapid contraction.

16.26 Where in the muscle cell does glycolysis occur?

16.27 Write the balanced chemical equation for glycolysis.

16.28 Write a chemical equation for the transfer of a phosphoryl group from ATP to fructose-6-phosphate.

Fermentation

16.29 Write a balanced chemical equation for the conversion of acetaldehyde to ethanol.

16.30 Write a balanced chemical equation for the conversion of pyruvate to lactate.

16.31 After running a 100-yard dash, a sprinter had a high concentration of muscle lactate. What process is responsible for production of lactate?

16.32 If the muscle of an organism had no lactate dehydrogenase, could anaerobic glycolysis occur in those muscle cells? Explain your answer.

16.33 What food products are the result of lactate fermentation?

16.34 Explain the value of alcohol fermentation in bread making.

Gluconeogenesis

16.35 What organ is primarily responsible for gluconeogenesis?

16.36 What is the physiological function of gluconeogenesis?

16.37 Lactate can be converted to glucose by gluconeogenesis. To what metabolic intermediate must lactate be converted so that it can be a substrate for the enzymes of gluconeogenesis?

16.38 L-Alanine can be converted to pyruvate. Can L-alanine also be converted to glucose? Explain your answer.

16.39 Explain why gluconeogenesis is not simply the reversal of glycolysis.

16.40 In step 9 of glycolysis, phosphoenolpyruvate is converted to pyruvate, and ATP is produced by substrate-level phosphorylation. How is this reaction bypassed in gluconeogenesis?

Glycogen Synthesis and Degradation

16.41 What organ is primarily responsible for maintaining the proper blood glucose level?

16.42 Why must the blood glucose level be carefully regulated?

16.43 What does the term *hypoglycemia* mean?

16.44 What does the term *hyperglycemia* mean?

16.45 What enzymes involved in glycogen metabolism are stimulated by insulin? What effect does this have on glycogen metabolism? What effect does this have on blood glucose levels?

16.46 What enzyme is stimulated by glucagon? What effect does this have on glycogen metabolism? What effect does this have on blood glucose levels?

Conversion of Pyruvate to Acetyl CoA

16.47 Under what metabolic conditions is pyruvate converted to acetyl CoA?

16.48 Write a chemical equation for the production of acetyl CoA from pyruvate. Under what conditions does this reaction occur?

16.49 How could a deficiency of riboflavin, thiamine, niacin, or pantothenic acid reduce the amount of energy the body can produce?

16.50 In what form are the vitamins riboflavin, thiamine, niacin, and pantothenic acid needed by the pyruvate dehydrogenase complex?

Further Problems

16.51 Define each of the following terms:
  a. Gluconeogenesis
  b. Catabolism
  c. Glycolysis
  d. Aerobic energy metabolism
  e. Anaerobic energy metabolism
  f. Fermentation

16.52 Which glycolysis reactions are catalyzed by each of the following enzymes?
  a. Hexokinase
  b. Pyruvate kinase
  c. Phosphoglyceromutase
  d. Glyceraldehyde-3-phosphate dehydrogenase

16.53 Fill in the blanks:
  a. _____ molecules of ATP are produced per molecule of glucose that is converted to pyruvate.
  b. Two molecules of ATP are consumed in the conversion of _____ to fructose-1,6-bisphosphate.

  c. NAD^+ is _____ to NADH in the first energy-releasing step of glycolysis.
  d. The second substrate-level phosphorylation in glycolysis is phosphoryl group transfer from phosphoenolpyruvate to _____.

16.54 Label each of the following statements as true or false:
  a. Glycolysis is an aerobic process.
  b. The metabolism of most organisms revolves around the synthesis and hydrolysis of ATP.
  c. In the first step of glycolysis, a phosphoryl group, PO_3^{2-}, is transferred from ATP to the C-6 hydroxyl group of glucose.
  d. The enzyme that catalyzes the first step of glycolysis is called hexokinase.
  e. Hydrolysis of ATP absorbs energy.

16.55 Which steps in the glycolysis pathway are irreversible?

16.56 What enzymatic reactions of gluconeogenesis bypass the irreversible steps of glycolysis?

16.57 What enzyme catalyzes the reduction of pyruvate to lactate?

16.58 What enzymes catalyze the conversion of pyruvate to ethanol and carbon dioxide?

16.59 A child was brought to the doctor's office suffering from a strange set of symptoms. When the child exercised hard, she became giddy and behaved as though drunk. What do you think is the metabolic basis of these symptoms?

16.60 A family started a batch of wine by adding yeast to grape juice and placing the mixture in a sealed bottle. Two weeks later, the bottle exploded. What metabolic reactions—and specifically, what product of those reactions—caused the bottle to explode?

VOCABULARY QUIZ

16.1 _____ is a nucleotide composed of the purine adenine, the sugar ribose, and a triphosphate group. It serves as the major energy storage form of the cell.

16.2 The enzymatic pathway that converts a glucose molecule into two molecules of pyruvate is called _____. This anaerobic process generates energy in the form of two ATP molecules and two NADH molecules per glucose molecule.

16.3 _____ is the synthesis of glucose from noncarbohydrate precursors.

16.4 _____ is the production of ATP by the transfer of a phosphoryl group from the substrate of a reaction to ADP.

16.5 A molecule that is derived from ATP, the vitamin pantothenic acid, and the amino acid cysteine and that functions in the transfer of acetyl groups is _____.

16.6 The condition in which blood glucose levels are higher than normal is called _____.

16.7 The degradation of fuel molecules and production of ATP for cellular functions is called _____.

16.8 _____ is a long, branched polymer of glucose stored in the liver and in muscles.

16.9 _____ is a molecule that is synthesized from the vitamin niacin and the nucleotide ATP and that serves as a carrier of hydride anions.

16.10 _____ is a molecule composed of coenzyme A and an acetyl group. This intermediate provides acetyl groups for complete oxidation by aerobic respiration.

Aerobic Respiration and Energy Production

LEARNING GOALS

◆ Define metabolism, including catabolism and anabolism.

◆ Name the regions of the mitochondria and the function of each region.

◆ Summarize the reactions of the citric acid cycle.

◆ Describe oxidative phosphorylation.

◆ Describe the conversion of amino acids to molecules that can enter the citric acid cycle.

◆ Know the cause and effect of hyperammonemia.

◆ Understand the importance of the urea cycle and describe its essential steps.

◆ Summarize the role of the citric acid cycle in catabolism and anabolism.

Mitochondria from Mom

In this chapter we will be studying the amazing, intricate set of reactions that allow us to completely degrade fuel molecules such as sugars and amino acids. These oxygen-requiring reactions occur in cellular organelles called mitochondria.

We are used to thinking of the organelles as a collection of membrane-bound structures that are synthesized under the direction of the genetic information in the nucleus of the cell. Not so with the mitochondria. These organelles have their own genetic information and are able to make some of their own proteins. They grow and multiply in a way very similar to the simple bacteria. This, along with other information on the structure and activities of mitochondria, has led researchers to conclude that the mitochondria are actually the descendants of bacteria captured by eukaryotic cells millions of years ago.

Recent studies of the mitochondrial genetic information (DNA) have revealed fascinating new information. For instance, although each of us inherited half our genetic information from our mothers and half from our fathers, each of us inherited all of our mitochondria from our mothers. The reason for this is that when the sperm fertilizes the egg, only the sperm nucleus enters the cell.

The observation that all of our mitochondria are inherited from our mothers led Dr. A. Wilson to study the mitochondrial DNA of thousands of women around the world. He thought that by looking for similarities and differences in the mitochondrial DNA he would be able to identify a "Mitochondrial Eve"—the mother of all humanity. He didn't really think that he could identify a single woman who would have lived tens of thousands of years ago. But he hoped to determine the location of the first population of human women to help answer questions about the origin of humankind. Although the idea was a good one, the study had a number of experimental flaws. Currently, a hot debate is going on among hundreds of scientists about the Mitochondrial Eve. Hopefully, this controversy will encourage better experiments and analysis to help us identify our origins and to better understand the workings of the mitochondria.

Like the mitochondria themselves, some genetic diseases of energy metabolism are maternally inherited. One such disease, Leber's hereditary optic neuropathy (LHON), causes blindness and heart problems. People with LHON have a reduced ability to make ATP. As a result, sensitive tissues that demand a great deal of energy eventually die. LHON sufferers eventually lose their sight because the optic nerve dies from lack of energy.

Researchers have identified and cloned a mutant mitochondrial gene that is responsible for LHON. The defect is a mutant form of *NADH dehydrogenase*. NADH dehydrogenase is a huge, complex enzyme that accepts electrons from NADH and sends them on through an electron transport system. Passage of electrons through the electron transport system allows the synthesis of ATP. If NADH dehydrogenase is defective, passage of electrons through the electron transport system is less efficient, and less ATP is made. In LHON sufferers the result is eventual blindness.

In this chapter and the next, we will study some of the important biochemical reactions that occur in the mitochondria. A better understanding of the function of healthy mitochondria will eventually allow us to help those suffering from LHON and other mitochondrial genetic diseases.

INTRODUCTION

As we have seen, the anaerobic glycolysis pathway begins the breakdown of glucose and produces a small amount of ATP and NADH. But it is aerobic metabolic pathways that complete the oxidation of glucose to CO_2 and H_2O and provide most of the ATP needed by the body. In fact, this process, called *aerobic respiration,* produces 36 ATP molecules from each glucose molecule that is used. These reactions occur in metabolic pathways located in *mitochondria,* the cellular "power plants." Mitochondria are a type of membrane-enclosed cell *organelle.*

Here, in the mitochondria, the final oxidations of carbohydrates, lipids, and proteins occur. Here, also, the electrons that are harvested in these oxidation reactions are used to make ATP. In these remarkably efficient reactions, nearly 40% of the potential energy of glucose is stored as ATP.

An organelle is a compartment within the cytoplasm that has a specialized function.

Mitochondria are football-shaped organelles that are roughly the size of a bacterial cell. They are bounded by an **outer membrane** and an **inner membrane** (Figure 17.1). The region between the two membranes is known as the **intermembrane space,** and the region enclosed by the inner membrane is known as the **matrix space.** The enzymes of the citric acid cycle, of the β-oxidation pathway for the breakdown of fatty acids, and for the degradation of amino acids are all found in the mitochondrial matrix space.

17.1 THE MITOCHONDRIA

Structure and function

A HUMAN PERSPECTIVE

Exercise and Energy Metabolism

The Olympic sprinters get set in the blocks. The gun goes off, and roughly ten seconds later the 100-m dash is over. Elsewhere, the marathoners line up. They will run 26 miles and 385 yards in a little over 2 hours. Both these sports involve running, but they utilize very different sources of energy.

Let's look at the sprinter first. The immediate source of energy for the sprinter is stored ATP. But the quantity of stored ATP is very small, only about three ounces. This allows the sprinter to run as fast as he or she can for about 3 seconds. Obviously, another source of stored energy must be tapped, and that energy store is *creatine phosphate:*

$$\text{-O-P-N-C-N-CH}_2\text{-C}$$

The structure of creatine phosphate.

Creatine phosphate, stored in the muscle, donates its high-energy phosphate to ADP to produce new supplies of ATP.

This will keep our runner in motion for another 5 or 6 seconds before the store of creatine phosphate is also depleted. This is almost enough energy to finish the 100-m dash, but in reality, all the runners are slowing down, owing to energy depletion, and the winner is the sprinter who is slowing down the least!

Consider a longer race, the 400-meter or the 800-meter. These runners run at maximum capacity for much longer times. When they have depleted their ATP and creatine phosphate stores, they must synthesize more ATP. Of course, the cells have been making ATP all the time, but now the demand for energy is much greater. To supply this increased demand, the anaerobic energy-generating reactions (glycolysis and lactate fermentation, Chapter 16) and aerobic processes (citric acid cycle and oxidative phosphorylation) begin to function much more rapidly. Often, however, these athletes are running so strenuously that they cannot provide enough oxygen to the exercising muscle to allow oxidative phosphorylation to function efficiently. When this happens, the muscles must rely on glycolysis and lactate fermentation to provide *most* of the energy requirement. The chemical by-product of these anaerobic processes, lactate, builds up in the muscle and diffuses into the bloodstream.

Phosphoryl group transfer from creatine phosphate to ADP is catalyzed by the enzyme creatine kinase.

The outer mitochondrial membrane is freely permeable to substances of molecular weight less than 10,000. Small molecules to be oxidized for the production of energy, such as the pyruvate produced by glycolysis, can freely enter the intermembrane space through pores in the outer membrane.

The inner membrane is highly folded, which greatly increases the surface area. The folded membranes are known as **cristae.** The inner mitochondrial membrane is almost completely impermeable to most substances. For this reason it has many transport proteins to bring particular fuel molecules into the matrix space. Also embedded within the inner mitochondrial membrane are the protein electron carriers of the *electron transport system* and *ATP synthase.* ATP synthase is a large complex of many proteins that catalyzes the synthesis of ATP.

Origin of the mitochondria

As we will see in Chapter 19, ribosomes are complexes of protein and RNA that serve as small platforms for protein synthesis.

Not only are mitochondria roughly the size of bacteria, they have several other features that have led researchers to suspect that they may once have been free-living bacteria that were "captured" by eukaryotic cells. They have their own genetic information (DNA). They also make their own ribosomes that are very similar to those of bacteria. These ribosomes allow the mitochondria to synthesize some of their own proteins. Finally, mitochondria are actually self-replicating; they grow in size and divide to produce new mitochondria. All of these characteris-

However, the concentration of lactate inevitably builds up in the working muscle and causes muscle fatigue and, eventually, muscle failure. Thus exercise that depends primarily on anaerobic energy generation cannot continue for very long periods.

The marathoner presents us with a different scenario. This runner will deplete his or her stores of ATP and creatine phosphate as quickly as a short-distance runner. The anaerobic glycolytic pathway will begin to degrade glucose provided by the blood at a more rapid rate, as will the citric acid cycle and oxidative phosphorylation. The major difference in energy generation between the long-distance runner and the short- or middle-distance runner is that the muscles of the long-distance runner derive almost all the energy through aerobic pathways. These individuals continue to run long distances at a pace that allows them to supply virtually all the oxygen needed by the exercising muscle. In fact, only aerobic pathways can provide a constant supply of ATP for exercise that goes on for hours. Theoretically, under such conditions our runner could run indefinitely, utilizing first his or her stored glycogen and eventually stored lipids. Of course, in reality, other factors such as dehydration and fatigue place limits on the athlete's ability to continue.

We have seen, then, that long-distance runners must have a great capacity to produce ATP aerobically, in the mitochondria, while short- and middle-distance runners need a great capacity to produce energy anaerobically, in the cytoplasm of the muscle cells. It is interesting to note that the muscles of these runners reflect these diverse needs.

When one examines muscle tissue that has been surgically removed, one finds two predominant types of muscle fibers. *Fast twitch muscle fibers* are large, relatively plump cells that are pale in color. These cells have only a few mitochondria but contain a large reserve of glycogen and high concentrations of the enzymes that are needed for glycolysis and lactate fermentation. These muscle fibers fatigue rather quickly because fermentation is inefficient, quickly depleting the cell's glycogen store and causing the accumulation of lactate.

Slow twitch muscle fiber cells are about half the diameter of fast twitch muscle cells and are red in color. The red color is a result of the high concentrations of myoglobin in these cells. Recall that myoglobin stores oxygen for the cell (Section 15.3) and facilitates rapid diffusion of oxygen throughout the cell. In addition, slow twitch muscle fiber cells are packed with mitochondria. With this abundance of oxygen and mitochondria these cells have the capacity for extended ATP production via aerobic pathways—ideal for endurance sports like marathon racing.

It is not surprising, then, that researchers have found that the muscles of sprinters have many more fast twitch muscle fibers and those of endurance athletes have many more slow twitch muscle fibers. One question that many researchers are trying to answer is whether the type of muscle fibers an individual has is a function of genetic makeup or training. Is a marathon runner born to be a long-distance runner, or are his or her abilities due to the type of training the runner undergoes? There is no doubt that the training regimen for an endurance runner does indeed increase the number of slow twitch muscle fibers and that of a sprinter increases the number of fast twitch muscle fibers. But there is intriguing new evidence to suggest that the muscles of endurance athletes have a greater proportion of slow twitch muscle fibers before they ever begin training. It appears that some of us truly were born to run.

tics suggest that the mitochondria that produce the majority of the ATP for our cells evolved from bacteria "captured" perhaps as long as 1.5×10^9 years ago.

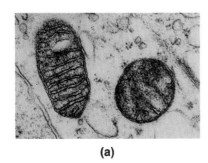

(a)

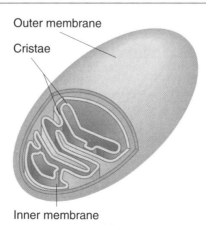

Outer membrane

Cristae

Inner membrane

(b)

FIGURE 17.1
Structure of the mitochondrion. (a) Electron micrograph of mitochondria. (b) Schematic drawing of the mitochondrion.

What is the function of the mitochondria?

How do the mitochondria differ from the other components of eukaryotic cells?

Draw a schematic diagram of a mitochondrion, and label the parts of this organelle.

Describe the evidence that suggests that mitochondria evolved from free-living bacteria.

17.2 AN OVERVIEW OF AEROBIC RESPIRATION

Remember (Section 15.6) that it is really the hydride anion with its pair of electrons ($H:^-$) that is transferred to NAD^+ to produce NADH. Similarly, a pair of hydrogen atoms (and thus two electrons) are transferred to FAD to produce $FADH_2$.

The structure of the mitochondrion is very complex, but each region of the mitochondrion has an important role to play in the process of **aerobic respiration.** Aerobic respiration is the oxygen-requiring breakdown of food molecules and production of ATP.

The enzymes for the citric acid cycle are found in the mitochondrial matrix space. The first of these enzymes catalyze a reaction that joins the acetyl group of acetyl CoA (two carbons) to a four-carbon molecule (oxaloacetate) to produce citrate (six carbons). The remaining enzymes catalyze a series of rearrangements, decarboxylations (removal of CO_2), and oxidation-reduction reactions. The eventual products of this cyclic pathway are two CO_2 molecules and oxaloacetate—the molecule we began with.

At several steps in the citric acid cycle a substrate is oxidized. In three of these steps a pair of electrons is transferred from the substrate to NAD^+, producing NADH (three NADH molecules per turn of the cycle). At another step a pair of electrons is transferred from a substrate to FAD, producing $FADH_2$ (one $FADH_2$ molecule per turn of the cycle).

The electrons are passed from NADH or $FADH_2$, through an electron transport system located in the inner mitochondrial membrane, and finally to the terminal electron acceptor, molecular oxygen (O_2). The transfer of electrons through the electron transport system causes protons (H^+) to be pumped from the mitochondrial matrix into the intermembrane compartment. The result is a high-energy H^+ reservoir.

In the final step the energy of the H^+ reservoir is used to make ATP. This last step is carried out by the enzyme complex ATP synthase. As protons flow back into the mitochondrial matrix through a pore in the ATP synthase complex, the enzyme catalyzes the synthesis of ATP.

This long, involved process is called *oxidative phosphorylation,* because the energy of electrons from the *oxidation* of substrates in the citric acid cycle is used to *phosphorylate* ADP and produce ATP. The details of each of these steps will be examined in upcoming sections.

What is meant by the term *oxidative phosphorylation?*

What does the term *aerobic respiration* mean?

17.3 THE CITRIC ACID CYCLE (THE KREBS CYCLE)

The **citric acid cycle** is sometimes called the *Krebs Cycle,* in honor of its discoverer, Sir Hans Krebs. It is the final stage of the breakdown of carbohydrates, fats, and amino acids released from dietary proteins (Figure 17.2).

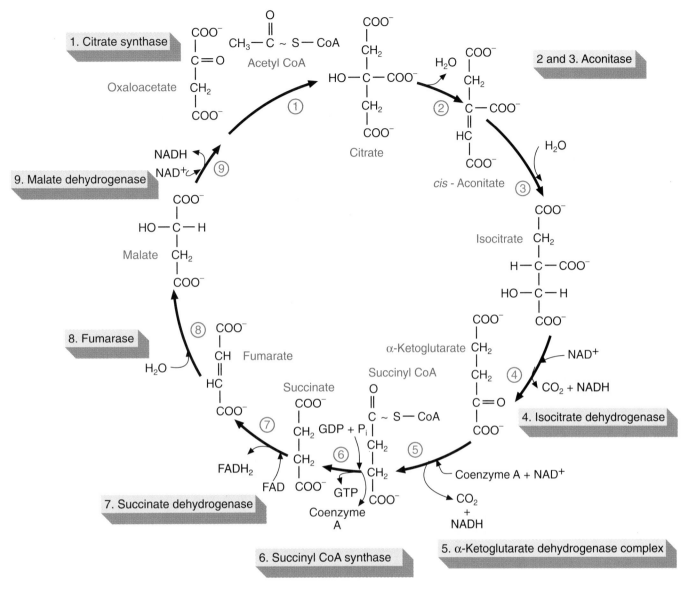

FIGURE 17.2
The reactions of the citric acid cycle.

To understand this important cycle, let us follow the fate of an acetyl group of acetyl CoA as it passes through the citric acid cycle. The numbered steps listed below correspond to the steps in the citric acid cycle that are summarized in Figure 17.2.

Reactions of the citric acid cycle

Step 1: The acetyl group of acetyl CoA is transferred to oxaloacetate in a reaction catalyzed by the enzyme *citrate synthase*. The product that is formed is citrate:

The formation of acetyl CoA was described in Section 16.7.

$$
\begin{array}{ccc}
\text{COO}^- \\
| \\
\text{C}=\text{O} \\
| \\
\text{CH}_2 \\
| \\
\text{COO}^-
\end{array}
\quad + \; \text{H}_3\text{C}-\overset{\displaystyle O}{\overset{\displaystyle \|}{\text{C}}}\sim\text{S}-\text{CoA} + \text{H}_2\text{O}
\xrightarrow{\text{Citrate synthase}}
\begin{array}{c}
\text{COO}^- \\
| \\
\text{CH}_2 \\
| \\
\text{HO}-\text{C}-\text{COO}^- \\
| \\
\text{H}-\text{C}-\text{H} \\
| \\
\text{COO}^-
\end{array}
+ \; \text{HS}-\text{CoA} + \text{H}^+
$$

Oxaloacetate   Acetyl CoA   Citrate   Coenzyme A

Step 2: The enzyme *aconitase* catalyzes the dehydration of citrate, producing *cis*-aconitate:

$$
\begin{array}{ccc}
\text{COO}^- & & \text{COO}^- \\
| & & | \\
\text{CH}_2 & & \text{CH}_2 \\
| & \xrightarrow{\text{Aconitase}} & | \\
\text{HO}-\text{C}-\text{COO}^- & & \text{C}-\text{COO}^- + \text{H}_2\text{O} \\
\| & & \| \\
\text{H}-\text{C}-\text{H} & & \text{C}-\text{H} \\
| & & | \\
\text{COO}^- & & \text{COO}^- \\
\text{Citrate} & & \textit{cis}\text{-Aconitate}
\end{array}
$$

Step 3: The same enzyme, aconitase, then catalyzes addition of a water molecule to the *cis*-aconitate, converting it to isocitrate. The net effect of the last two steps is the isomerization of citrate to isocitrate:

$$
\begin{array}{ccc}
\text{COO}^- & & \text{COO}^- \\
| & & | \\
\text{CH}_2 & & \text{CH}_2 \\
| & \xrightarrow{\text{Aconitase}} & | \\
\text{C}-\text{COO}^- + \text{H}_2\text{O} & & \text{H}-\text{C}-\text{COO}^- \\
\| & & | \\
\text{C}-\text{H} & & \text{HO}-\text{C}-\text{H} \\
| & & | \\
\text{COO}^- & & \text{COO}^- \\
\textit{cis}\text{-Aconitate} & & \text{Isocitrate}
\end{array}
$$

Step 4: The first oxidative step of the citric acid cycle is catalyzed by *isocitrate dehydrogenase*. It is a complex reaction in which three things happen:
a. the hydroxyl group of isocitrate is oxidized to a ketone,
b. carbon dioxide is released, and
c. NAD^+ is reduced to NADH.
The product of this oxidative decarboxylation reaction is α-ketoglutarate:

The structure of NAD^+ and its reduction to NADH are shown in Figure 15.24.

$$
\begin{array}{ccc}
\text{COO}^- & & \text{COO}^- \\
| & & | \\
\text{CH}_2 & & \text{CH}_2 \\
| & \xrightarrow[\text{dehydrogenase}]{\text{Isocitrate}} & | \\
\text{H}-\text{C}-\text{COO}^- + NAD^+ & & \text{CH}_2 \qquad + CO_2 + \textbf{NADH} \\
| & & | \\
\text{HO}-\text{C}-\text{H} & & \text{C}=\text{O} \\
| & & | \\
\text{COO}^- & & \text{COO}^- \\
\text{Isocitrate} & & \alpha\text{-Ketoglutarate}
\end{array}
$$

The pyruvate dehydrogenase complex was described in Section 16.7 and shown in Figure 16.16.

Step 5: Coenzyme A enters the picture again in this step of the citric acid cycle. The α-*ketoglutarate dehydrogenase* complex carries out this series of reactions. This complex is very similar to the pyruvate dehydrogenase complex and requires the same coenzymes. Once again, three chemical events occur:
a. α-ketoglutarate loses a carboxylate group as CO_2,
b. NAD^+ is reduced to NADH, and
c. coenzyme A combines with the product, succinate, to form succinyl CoA. The bond thus formed between succinate and coenzyme A is a high-energy thioester linkage.

$$
\begin{array}{c}
\text{COO}^- \\
|\\
\text{CH}_2 \\
|\\
\text{CH}_2 \\
|\\
\text{C}{=}\text{O} \\
|\\
\text{COO}^-
\end{array}
\quad + \text{NAD}^+ + \text{Coenzyme A}
\xrightarrow[\text{complex}]{\substack{\alpha\text{-Ketoglutarate} \\ \text{dehydrogenase}}}
\begin{array}{c}
\text{COO}^- \\
|\\
\text{CH}_2 \\
|\\
\text{CH}_2 \\
|\\
\text{C}{\sim}\text{S—CoA} \\
||\\
\text{O}
\end{array}
\quad + \text{CO}_2 + \text{NADH}
$$

α-Ketoglutarate   Succinyl CoA

Step 6: Succinyl CoA is converted to succinate in this step, which once more is chemically very involved. The enzyme *succinyl CoA synthase* catalyzes a coupled reaction in which the high-energy thioester bond of succinyl CoA is broken and an inorganic phosphate group is added to GDP to make GTP:

$$
\begin{array}{c}
\text{COO}^- \\
|\\
\text{CH}_2 \\
|\\
\text{CH}_2 \\
|\\
\text{C}{\sim}\text{S—CoA} \\
||\\
\text{O}
\end{array}
\quad + \text{GDP} + \text{P}_i
\xrightarrow[\text{synthase}]{\text{Succinyl CoA}}
\begin{array}{c}
\text{COO}^- \\
|\\
\text{CH}_2 \\
|\\
\text{CH}_2 \\
|\\
\text{COO}^-
\end{array}
\quad + \quad \text{GTP} \quad + \text{Coenzyme A}
$$

Succinyl CoA   Succinate

Another enzyme *dinucleotide diphosphokinase*, then catalyzes the transfer of a phosphoryl group from GTP to ADP to make ATP:

$$
\text{GTP} \quad + \text{ADP}
\xrightarrow[\text{diphosphokinase}]{\text{Nucleotide}}
\text{GDP} + \quad \text{ATP}
$$

Step 7: *Succinate dehydrogenase* then catalyzes the oxidation of succinate to fumarate in the next step. The oxidizing agent, *flavin adenine dinucleotide (FAD)*, is reduced in this step:

The structure of FAD was shown in Figure 15.24.

$$
\begin{array}{c}
\text{COO}^- \\
|\\
\text{CH}_2 \\
|\\
\text{CH}_2 \\
|\\
\text{COO}^-
\end{array}
\quad + \text{FAD}
\xrightarrow[\text{dehydrogenase}]{\text{Succinate}}
\begin{array}{c}
\text{COO}^- \\
|\\
\text{C—H} \\
||\\
\text{H—C} \\
|\\
\text{COO}^-
\end{array}
\quad + \text{FADH}_2
$$

Succinate   Fumarate

Step 8: Addition of H_2O to the double bond of fumarate gives malate. The enzyme *fumarase* catalyzes this reaction:

$$
\begin{array}{c}
\text{COO}^- \\
|\\
\text{C—H} \\
||\\
\text{H—C} \\
|\\
\text{COO}^-
\end{array}
\quad + \text{H}_2\text{O}
\xrightarrow{\text{Fumarase}}
\begin{array}{c}
\text{COO}^- \\
|\\
\text{HO—C—H} \\
|\\
\text{H—C—H} \\
|\\
\text{COO}^-
\end{array}
$$

Fumarate   Malate

Step 9: In the final step of the citric acid cycle, *malate dehydrogenase* catalyzes the reduction of NAD^+ to NADH and the oxidation of malate to oxaloacetate. Since the citric acid cycle "began" with the addition of an acetyl group to oxaloacetate, we have come full circle.

$$\begin{array}{c}
COO^- \\
| \\
HO-C-H \\
| \\
CH_2 \\
| \\
COO^-
\end{array} + NAD^+ \xrightarrow{\text{Malate dehydrogenase}} \begin{array}{c}
COO^- \\
| \\
C=O \\
| \\
CH_2 \\
| \\
COO^-
\end{array} + NADH$$

Malate   Oxaloacetate

Summary of the energy yield

One turn of the citric acid cycle results in the production of two CO_2 molecules, three NADH molecules, one $FADH_2$ molecule, and one ATP molecule. Oxidative phosphorylation will yield three ATP molecules per NADH molecule and two ATP molecules per $FADH_2$ molecule. The only exception to these energy yields is the NADH produced in the cytoplasm during glycolysis. Oxidative phosphorylation yields only two ATP molecules per cytoplasmic NADH molecule. The reason for this is that energy must be expended to shuttle electrons from NADH in the cytoplasm to $FADH_2$ in the mitochondrion.

Knowing this information and keeping in mind that two turns of the citric acid cycle are required, we can sum up the total energy yield that results from the complete oxidation of one glucose molecule. The net result of the complete oxidation of glucose is production of 36 molecules of ATP (Figure 17.3). This represents an energy harvest of about 40% of the potential energy of glucose.

EXAMPLE 17.1

Determining the Yield of ATP Produced by the Complete Oxidation of One Molecule of Glucose

Solution

Glycolysis:
Substrate-level phosphorylation	2 ATP
2 NADH × 2 ATP/cytoplasmic NADH	4 ATP

Conversion of 2 pyruvate molecules to 2 acetyl CoA molecules:
2 NADH × 3 ATP/NADH	6 ATP

Citric acid cycle (two turns):
2 GTP × 1 ATP/GTP	2 ATP
6 NADH × 3 ATP/NADH	18 ATP
2 $FADH_2$ × 2 ATP/$FADH_2$	4 ATP
	36 ATP

Aerobic metabolism is very much more efficient than anaerobic metabolism. The abundant energy harvested by aerobic metabolism has had enormous consequences for the biological world. Much of the energy released by the oxidation of fuels is not lost as heat but conserved in the form of ATP. Organisms that possess abundant energy have evolved into multicellular organisms and developed specialized functions. As a consequence of their energy requirements, all multicellular organisms are aerobic.

17.4 OXIDATIVE PHOSPHORYLATION

In the preceding section we noted that NADH can be used to produce three ATP molecules and $FADH_2$ to produce two ATP molecules. What is the process by which the energy of electrons carried by these coenzymes is converted to ATP energy? It is a series of reactions called

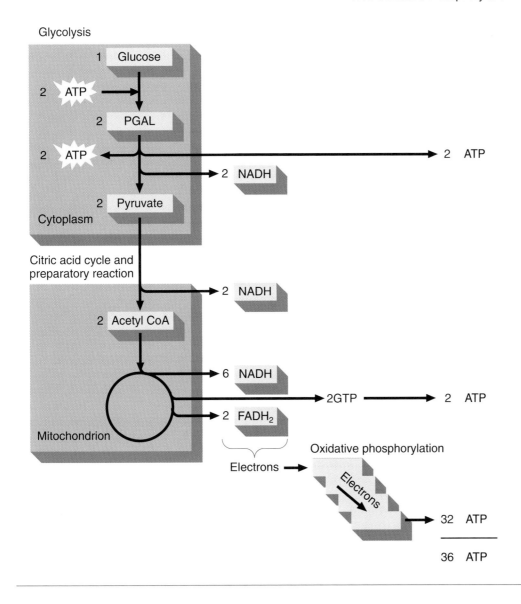

FIGURE 17.3
Thirty-six molecules of ATP are generated by the complete oxidation of glucose via the combined action of glycolysis, the citric acid cycle, and oxidative phosphorylation.

oxidative phosphorylation, which couples the oxidation of NADH and FADH$_2$ to the phosphorylation of ADP to generate ATP.

Before we try to understand the mechanism of oxidative phosphorylation, let us first look at the molecules that carry out this complex process. Embedded within the mitochondrial inner membrane are **electron transport systems.** These are made up of a series of electron carriers, including coenzymes and cytochromes. All these molecules are located within the membrane in an arrangement that allows them to pass electrons from one to the next. This array of electron carriers is called the respiratory electron transport system (Figure 17.4). As you would expect in such sequential oxidation-reduction reactions, the electrons lose some energy with each transfer. Some of this energy will be used to make ATP.

At three sites in the electron transport system, protons can be pumped from the mitochondrial matrix to the intermembrane space. These protons contribute to a high-energy H$^+$ reservoir. At each of the three sites, enough H$^+$ are pumped into the H$^+$ reservoir to produce one ATP molecule. The first site is NADH dehydrogenase. Since electrons from NADH enter the electron transport system by being transferred to NADH dehydrogenase, all three sites actively pump protons, and three ATP molecules are made (Figure 17.4). FADH$_2$ is a less powerful electron donor. It transfers its electrons to an electron carrier that follows NADH dehydrogen-

Electron transport systems and the hydrogen ion gradient

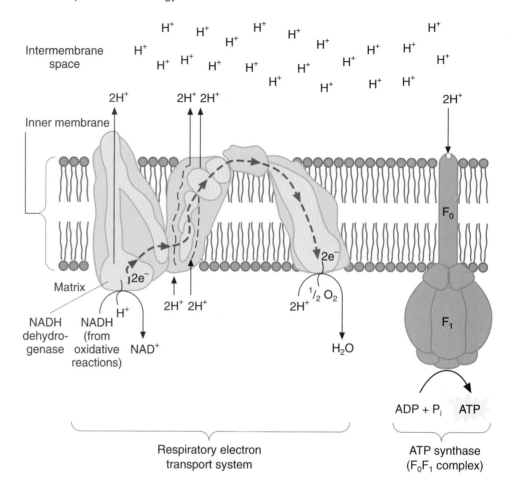

FIGURE 17.4
Electrons flow from NADH to molecular oxygen through a series of electron carriers embedded in the inner mitochondrial membrane. Protons are pumped out of the mitochondrial matrix space, generating a proton gradient between the matrix and intermembrane space. As protons pass through the channel in ATP synthase, their energy is used to phosphorylate ADP and produce ATP.

ase. As a result, when $FADH_2$ is oxidized, only the second and third sites pump protons, and only two ATP molecules are made. The electron transport system is seen in Figure 17.4.

The last component needed for oxidative phosphorylation is a multiprotein complex called **ATP synthase,** also called the **F_0F_1 complex** (Figure 17.4). Spanning the inner mitochondrial membrane is a protein complex (F_0) that provides a channel through which protons may pass. Protruding into the mitochondrial matrix is a spherical protein complex (F_1) with the enzymatic ability to phosphorylate ADP to produce ATP.

ATP synthase and the production of ATP

How does all this complicated machinery actually function? NADH carries electrons, originally from glucose, to the first carrier of the electron transport system, NADH dehydrogenase (Figure 17.4). There, NADH is oxidized to NAD^+, which returns to the site of the citric acid cycle to be reduced again. As Figure 17.4 shows (dashed red line), the pair of electrons is passed to the next electron carrier, and protons are pumped to the intermembrane compartment. The electrons are passed sequentially through the electron transport system, and at two additional sites, protons from the matrix are pumped into the intermembrane compartment. With each transfer the electrons lose some of their potential energy. Some of the energy of the electrons is used to transport H^+ across the inner mitochondrial membrane and into the H^+ reservoir. Finally, the electrons arrive at the last carrier. They now have too little energy to accomplish any more work, but they *must* be donated to some final electron acceptor so that the electron transport system can continue to function. In aerobic organisms the **terminal electron acceptor** is molecular oxygen, O_2, and the product is water.

Thus the electron transport system carries out the oxidation of NADH and $FADH_2$ with molecular oxygen as the final electron acceptor. As noted above, $FADH_2$ donates its electrons to a carrier of lower energy. The result of this is that fewer protons are pumped into the H^+ reservoir and less ATP is produced.

As the electron transport system continues to function, a high concentration of protons builds up in the intermembrane space. This creates a hydrogen ion (H^+) reservoir. Such a reservoir is an enormous energy source, like water stored behind a dam. The mitochondria make use of the potential energy of the reservoir to synthesize ATP energy.

It is the ATP synthase that harvests the energy of this gradient to produce ATP. Although the inner mitochondrial membrane is quite impermeable, the ATP synthase provides a channel (F_0) through which the protons can return to the matrix. As protons pass through F_0, the enzymatic portion of ATP synthase (F_1) undergoes a shape change and catalyzes the phosphorylation of ADP to produce ATP. In this way the energy of the H^+ reservoir is harvested to make ATP.

QUESTION 17.7

Write a balanced chemical equation for the reduction of NAD^+.

QUESTION 17.8

Write a balanced chemical equation for the reduction of FAD.

17.5 THE DEGRADATION OF AMINO ACIDS

Carbohydrates are not our only source of energy. As we saw in Chapter 16, dietary protein is digested to amino acids that can also be used as an energy source, although this is not their major metabolic function. Most of the amino acids used for energy come from the diet. In fact, it is only under starvation conditions, when stored glycogen and lipid have been depleted, that the body begins to burn its own protein, for instance from muscle, as a fuel.

The fate of the mixture of amino acids provided by digestion of protein depends upon a balance between the need for amino acids for biosynthesis and the need for cellular energy. Only those amino acids that are not needed for protein synthesis are eventually converted into citric acid cycle intermediates and used as fuel.

The degradation of amino acids occurs primarily in the liver and takes place in two stages. The first stage is the removal of the α-amino group, and the second is the degradation of the carbon skeleton. In land mammals the amino group generally ends up in urea, which is excreted in the urine. The carbon skeletons can be converted into a variety of compounds, including citric acid cycle intermediates, pyruvate, acetyl CoA, or acetoacetyl CoA. The degradation of the carbon skeletons is summarized in Figure 17.5. Deamination reactions and the fate of the carbon skeletons of amino acids are described in detail below.

Removal of α-amino groups: transamination

The first stage of amino acid degradation, the removal of the α-amino group, is usually accomplished by a **transamination** reaction. **Aminotransferases,** also called **transaminases,** catalyze the transfer of the α-amino group from an α-amino acid to an α-keto acid:

$$\underset{\substack{\text{Donor} \\ \text{amino} \\ \text{acid}}}{H\overset{\overset{+}{N}H_3}{\underset{R_1}{-C}}-COO^-} + \underset{\substack{\text{Acceptor} \\ \text{keto} \\ \text{acid}}}{\overset{O}{\underset{R_2}{\overset{\|}{C}}}-COO^-} \underset{}{\overset{\text{Transaminase}}{\rightleftharpoons}} \underset{\substack{\text{Carbon} \\ \text{skeleton} \\ \text{of amino acid}}}{\overset{O}{\underset{R_1}{\overset{\|}{C}}}-COO^-} + \underset{\substack{\text{New} \\ \text{amino} \\ \text{acid}}}{H\overset{\overset{+}{N}H_3}{\underset{R_2}{-C}}-COO^-}$$

The α-amino group of a great many amino acids is transferred to α-ketoglutarate to produce the amino acid glutamate and a new keto acid. This glutamate family of aminotransferases is especially important because the α-keto acid corresponding to glutamate is α-ketoglutarate, a citric acid cycle intermediate. The glutamate aminotransferases thus provide a direct link between amino acid degradation and the citric acid cycle.

A HUMAN PERSPECTIVE

Brown Fat: The Fat That Makes You Thin?

Humans have two types of fat, or adipose, tissue. *White fat* is distributed throughout the body and is composed of aggregations of cells having membranous vacuoles containing stored triglycerides. The size and number of these storage vacuoles determine whether a person is overweight or not. The other type of fat is *brown fat.* Brown fat is a specialized tissue for heat production, called *nonshivering thermogenesis.* As the name suggests, this is a means of generating heat in the absence of the shivering response. The cells of brown fat look nothing like those of white fat. They do contain small fat vacuoles; however, the distinguishing feature of brown fat is the huge number of mitochondria within the cytoplasm. In addition, brown fat tissue contains a great many blood vessels. These provide oxygen for the thermogenic metabolic reactions.

(a)

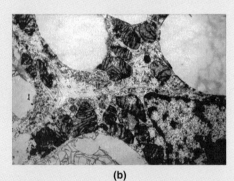

(b)

(a) A light micrograph of white fat cells. (b) An electron micrograph of brown fat cells. The cytoplasm contains few lipid storage vacuoles and a large number of mitochondria.

Brown fat is most pronounced in newborns, cold-adapted mammals, and hibernators. One major difficulty faced by a newborn is temperature regulation. The baby leaves an environment in which he or she was bathed in fluid of a constant 37°C, body temperature. Suddenly, the child is thrust into a world that is much colder and in which he or she must gen-

erate his or her own warmth internally. By having a good reserve of active brown fat to generate that heat, the newborn is protected against cold shock at the time of birth. However, this thermogenesis literally burns up most of the brown fat tissue, and adults typically have so little brown fat that it can be found only by using a special technique called thermography, which detects temperature differences throughout a body. However, in some individuals, brown fat is very highly developed. For instance, the Korean diving women who spend 6–7 hours every day diving for pearls in cold water have a massive amount of brown fat to warm them by nonshivering thermogenesis. Thus development of brown fat is a mechanism of cold adaptation.

When it was noticed that such cold-adapted individuals were seldom overweight, a correlation was made between the amount of brown fat in the body and the tendency to become overweight. Studies done with rats suggest that, to some degree, fatness is genetically determined. In other words, you are as lean as your genes allow you to be. In these studies, cold-adapted and non-cold-adapted rats were fed cafeteria food—as much as they wanted—and their weight gain was monitored. In every case the cold-adapted rats, with their greater quantity of brown fat, gained significantly less weight than their non-cold-adapted counterparts, despite the fact that they ate as much as the non-cold-adapted rats. This and other studies led researchers to conclude that brown fat burns excess fat in a highly caloric diet.

How does brown fat generate heat and burn excess calories? For the answer we must turn to the mitochondrion. In addition to the ATP synthase and the electron transport system proteins that are found in all mitochondria, there is a protein in the inner mitochondrial membrane of brown fat tissue called *thermogenin.* This protein has a channel in the center through which the protons (H^+) of the intermembrane space could pass back into the mitochondrial matrix. Under normal conditions this channel is plugged by a GDP molecule so that it remains closed and the proton gradient can continue to drive ATP synthesis by oxidative phosphorylation.

When brown fat is turned on, by cold exposure or in response to certain hormones, there is an immediate increase in the rate of glycolysis and β-oxidation of the stored fat (Chapter 18). These reactions produce acetyl CoA, which then fuels the citric acid cycle. The citric acid cycle, of course, produces NADH and $FADH_2$, which carry electrons to the electron transport system. Finally, the electron transport system pumps protons into the intermembrane space. Under usual conditions the energy of the proton gradient would be used to synthesize ATP. However, when brown fat is stimulated, the GDP that had plugged the pore in thermogenin is lost. Now protons pass freely back into the matrix space, and the proton gradient is dissipated. The energy of the gradient, no longer useful for generating ATP, is released as *heat,* the heat that warms and protects newborns and cold-adapted individuals.

Brown fat is just one of the body's many systems for maintaining a constant internal environment regardless of the conditions in the external environment. Such mechanisms, called *homeostatic mechanisms,* are absolutely essential to allow the body to adapt to and survive in an ever-changing environment.

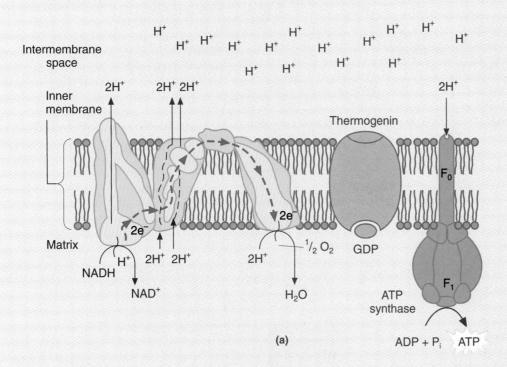

(a)

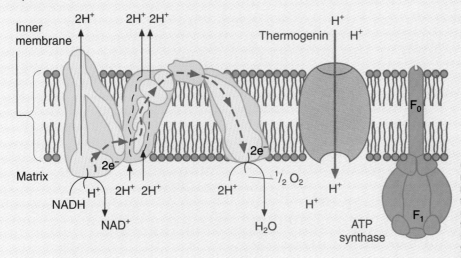

(b)

(a) The inner membrane of brown fat mitochondria contains thermogenin. In the normal state the pore in the center of thermogenin is plugged by a GDP molecule. (b) When brown fat is activated for thermogenesis, the GDP molecule is removed from the pore, and the protons from the H$^+$ reservoir are free to flow back into the matrix of the mitochondrion. As the gradient dissipates, heat energy is released.

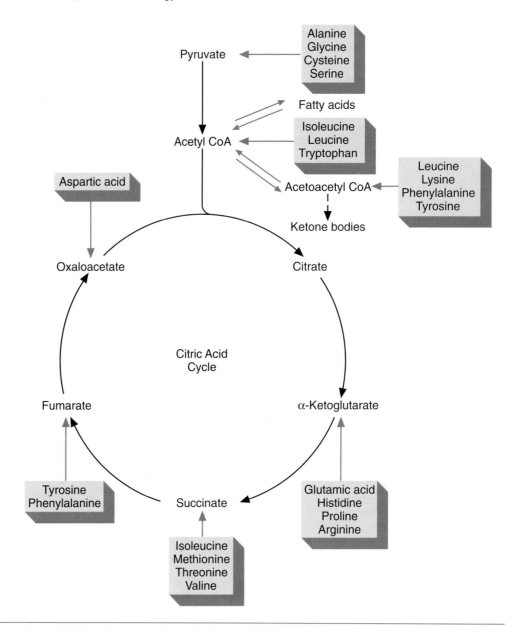

FIGURE 17.5
The carbon skeletons of amino acids can be converted to citric acid cycle intermediates and completely oxidized to produce ATP energy.

One of the most important aminotransferases is *aspartate aminotransferase*, which catalyzes the transfer of the α-amino group of aspartate to α-ketoglutarate, producing oxaloacetate and glutamate:

$$
\begin{array}{cccc}
\overset{+}{N}H_3 & O & O & \overset{+}{N}H_3 \\
H-C-COO^- + & C-COO^- \rightleftharpoons & C-COO^- + & H-C-COO^- \\
H-C-H & H-C-H & H-C-H & H-C-H \\
COO^- & H-C-H & COO^- & H-C-H \\
& COO^- & & COO^- \\
\text{Aspartate} & \text{α-Ketoglutarate} & \text{Oxaloacetate} & \text{Glutamate}
\end{array}
$$

Another important transaminase in mammalian tissues is *alanine aminotransferase,* which catalyzes the transfer of the α-amino group of alanine to α-ketoglutarate and produces pyruvate and glutamate:

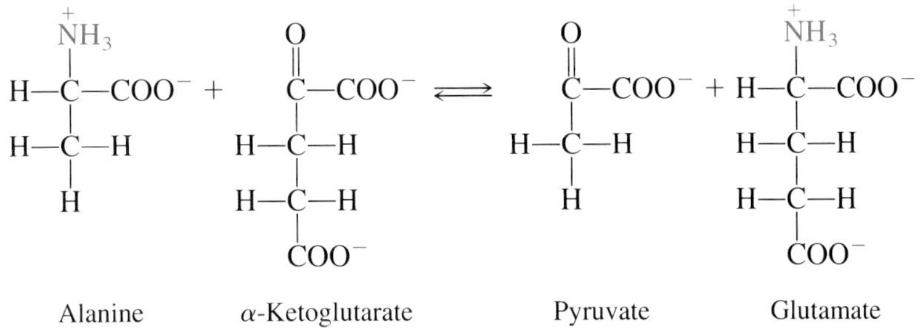

Alanine α-Ketoglutarate   Pyruvate   Glutamate

All of the more than 50 aminotransferases that have been discovered require the coenzyme **pyridoxal phosphate.** This coenzyme is derived from vitamin B_6 (pyridoxine).

See Appendix E, "Water-Soluble Vitamins," for more information on these vitamins and the coenzymes that are made from them.

QUESTION 17.9

What is the role of pyridoxal phosphate in transamination reactions?

QUESTION 17.10

What is the function of an aminotransferase?

In the next stage of amino acid degradation, ammonium ion is liberated from the glutamate formed by the aminotransferase. This breakdown of glutamate, catalyzed by the enzyme *glutamate dehydrogenase,* is shown below:

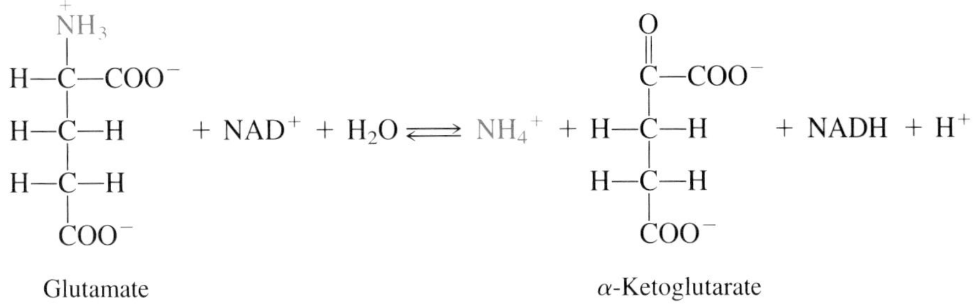

Removal of α-amino groups: oxidative deamination

Glutamate α-Ketoglutarate

This is an example of an **oxidative deamination,** an oxidation-reduction process in which NAD^+ is reduced to NADH and the amino acid is deaminated (the amino group is removed). A summary of the deamination reactions described above is shown in Figure 17.6.

The carbon skeletons produced by these and other deamination reactions enter glycolysis or the citric acid cycle at many steps. For instance, we have seen that transamination converts aspartate to oxaloacetate and alanine to pyruvate. The positions at which the carbon skeletons of various amino acids enter the energy-harvesting pathways are summarized in Figure 17.5.

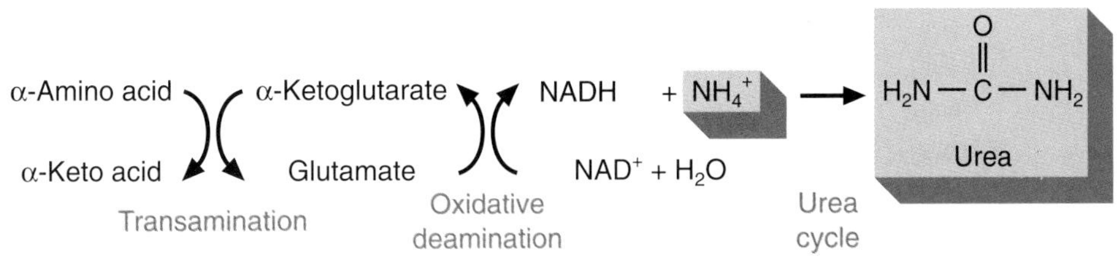

The fate of amino acid carbon skeletons

FIGURE 17.6
Summary of the deamination of an α-amino acid and the fate of the ammonium ion (NH_4^+).

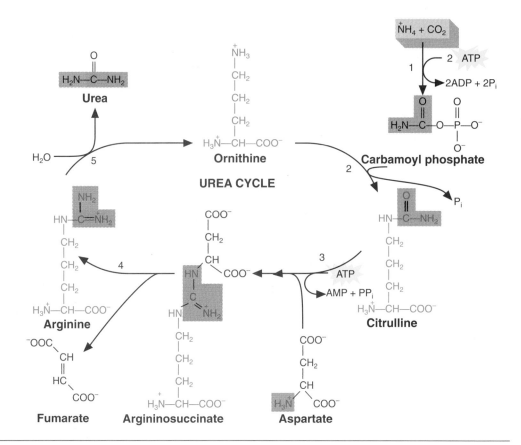

FIGURE 17.7
The reactions of the urea cycle.

17.6 THE UREA CYCLE

Oxidative deamination produces large amounts of ammonium ion. If this were not incorporated into a biological molecule and removed from the body, it would quickly reach toxic levels. Thus it is of critical importance to the survival of the organism to have a pathway for the excretion of ammonium ions, regardless of the energy required. In humans and most terrestrial vertebrates the means of ammonium ion removal is the urea cycle.

As was noted above, ammonium ions are extremely toxic. They are detoxified in the liver by converting the ammonium ions into urea. This pathway, called the **urea cycle,** is the method by which toxic ammonium ions are kept out of the blood. The excess ammonium ions incorporated in urea are excreted in the urine (Figure 17.7).

Reactions of the urea cycle

The five reactions of the urea cycle are shown in Figure 17.7, and details of the reactions are summarized below.

Step 1:   The first step of the cycle is a reaction in which CO_2 and NH_4^+ form carbamoyl phosphate. This reaction also requires ATP and H_2O.

$$CO_2 + NH_4^+ + 2ATP + H_2O \longrightarrow H_2N-\overset{O}{\overset{\|}{C}}-O-\overset{O}{\underset{O^-}{\overset{\|}{P}}}-O^- + 2ADP + P_i + 3H^+$$

Carbamoyl phosphate

The urea cycle involves several un-usual amino acids that are not found in polypeptides.

Step 2:   The carbamoyl phosphate thus produced condenses with the amino acid ornithine to produce the amino acid citrulline:

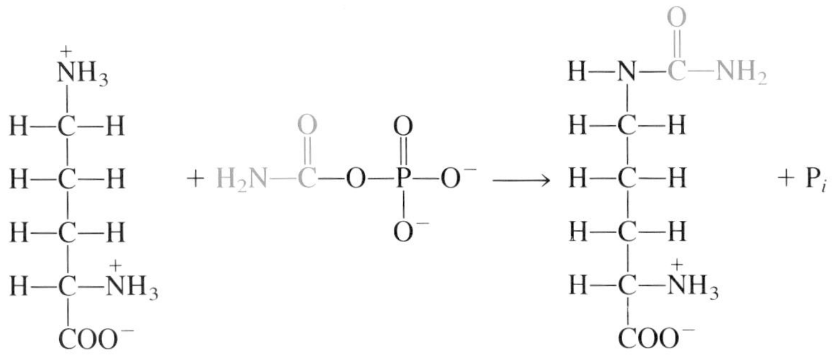

Ornithine   Carbamoyl phosphate   Citrulline

Step 3: Citrulline now condenses with aspartate to produce argininosuccinate. This reaction requires energy released by the hydrolysis of ATP.

The abbreviation PP_i represents the pyrophosphate group, which consists of two phosphate groups joined by a phosphoanhydride bond:

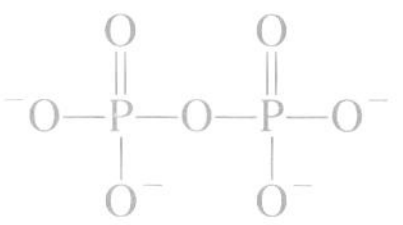

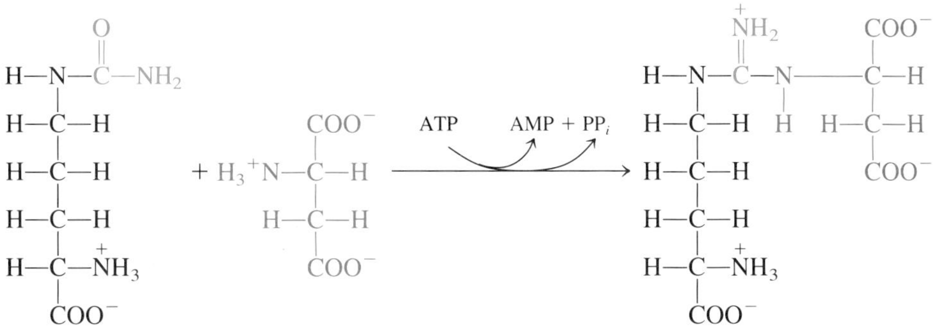

Citrulline   Aspartate   Argininosuccinate

ATP → AMP + PP_i

Step 4: Now the argininosuccinate is cleaved to produce the amino acid arginine and the citric acid cycle intermediate fumarate:

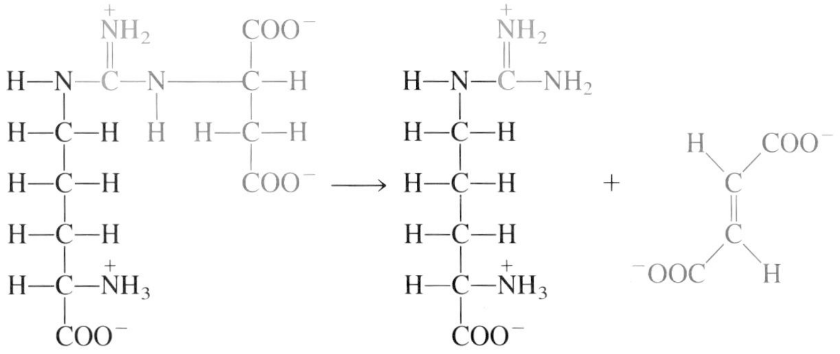

Argininosuccinate   Arginine   Fumarate

Step 5: Finally, arginine is hydrolyzed to generate urea, the product of the reaction to be excreted, and ornithine, the original reactant in the cycle:

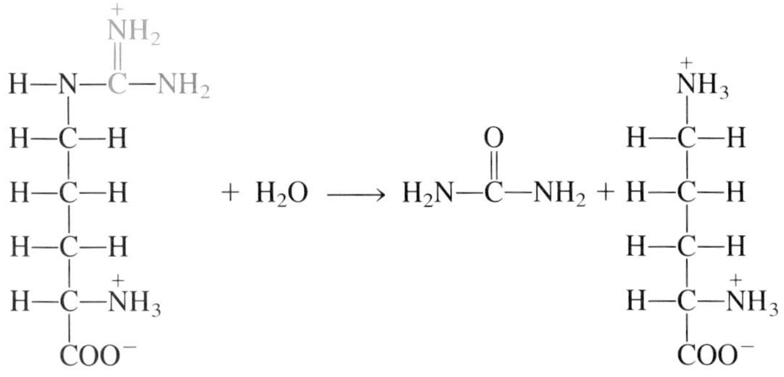

$+ H_2O \longrightarrow$

Arginine   Water   Urea   Ornithine

Note that one of the amino groups in urea is derived from the ammonium ion and the second is derived from the amino acid aspartate.

There are genetically transmitted diseases that result from a deficiency of one of the enzymes of the urea cycle. The importance of the urea cycle is apparent when we consider the terrible symptoms suffered by afflicted individuals. A deficiency of urea cycle enzymes causes an elevation of the concentration of NH_4^+, a condition known as **hyperammonemia.** If there is a complete deficiency of one of the enzymes of the urea cycle, the result is death in early infancy. If there is a partial deficiency of one of the enzymes of the urea cycle, the result may be retardation, convulsions, and vomiting. In these milder forms of hyperammonemia a low-protein diet leads to a lower concentration of NH_4^+ in blood and less severe clinical symptoms.

QUESTION 17.11

What is the purpose of the urea cycle?

QUESTION 17.12

Where do the reactions of the urea cycle occur?

17.7 OVERVIEW OF ANABOLISM: THE CITRIC ACID CYCLE AS A SOURCE OF BIOSYNTHETIC INTERMEDIATES

So far, we have talked about the citric acid cycle only as an energy-harvesting mechanism. We have seen that dietary carbohydrates and amino acids enter the pathway at various stages and are oxidized to generate NADH and $FADH_2$, which, by means of oxidative phosphorylation, are used to make ATP.

However, the role of the citric acid cycle in cellular metabolism involves more than just **catabolism.** It plays a key role in **anabolism,** or biosynthesis, as well. Figure 17.8 shows the central role of glycolysis and the citric acid cycle as energy-harvesting reactions, as well as sources of major biosynthetic precursors.

As you may already suspect from the fact that amino acids can be converted into citric acid cycle intermediates, these same citric acid cycle intermediates can also be used as starting materials for the synthesis of amino acids. Oxaloacetate provides the carbon skeleton for the one-step synthesis of the amino acid aspartate by the transamination reaction shown below:

$$\text{Oxaloacetate} + \text{glutamate} \rightleftharpoons \text{aspartate} + \alpha\text{-ketoglutarate}$$

Aside from providing aspartate for protein synthesis, this reaction provides aspartate for the urea cycle.

Asparagine is made from aspartate by the amidation reaction shown below:

$$\text{Aspartate} + NH_4^+ + \text{ATP} \longrightarrow \text{asparagine} + \text{AMP} + PP_i + H^+$$

α-Ketoglutarate serves as the starting carbon chain for the family of amino acids including glutamate, glutamine, proline, and arginine. Glutamate is especially important because it serves as the donor of the α-amino group of almost all other amino acids. It is synthesized from NH_4^+ and α-ketoglutarate in a reaction mediated by glutamate dehydrogenase. This is the reverse of the reaction shown in Figure 17.6 and described above. In this case the coenzyme that serves as the reducing agent is NADPH in the reaction that is summarized below:

$$NH_4^+ + \alpha\text{-ketoglutarate} + \text{NADPH} \rightleftharpoons \text{L-glutamate} + NADP^+ + H_2O$$

Glutamine, proline, and arginine are synthesized from glutamate.

Examination of Figure 17.8 reveals that serine, glycine, and cysteine are synthesized from 3-phosphoglycerate; alanine is synthesized from pyruvate; and tyrosine is produced from phosphoenolpyruvate and the four-carbon sugar erythrose-4-phosphate, which, in turn, is synthesized from glucose-6-phosphate. In addition to the amino acid precursors, glycolysis and the citric acid cycle also provide precursors for lipids and the nitrogenous bases that are required to make

The nine amino acids not shown in Figure 17.8 (histidine, isoleucine, leucine, lysine, methionine, phenylalanine, threonine, tryptophan, and valine) are called the essential amino acids (Section 15.9) because they cannot be synthesized by humans.

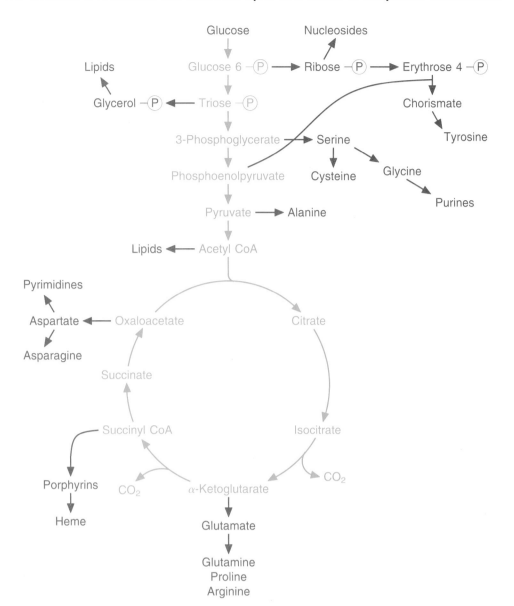

FIGURE 17.8
Glycolysis and the citric acid cycle also provide a variety of precursors for the biosynthesis of amino acids, nitrogenous bases, and porphyrins.

DNA, the molecule that carries the genetic information. They also generate precursors for heme, the prosthetic group that is required for hemoglobin, myoglobin, and the cytochromes.

Clearly, the reactions of glycolysis and the citric acid cycle are central to both anabolic and catabolic cellular activities. Metabolic pathways that function in both anabolism and catabolism are termed **amphibolic pathways.** Consider for a moment the difficulties that the dual nature of these pathways could present to the cell. When the cell is actively growing, there is a great demand for biosynthetic precursors to build new cell structures. The demand for amino acids may draw a great deal of oxaloacetate and α-ketoglutarate away from the citric acid cycle. The dilemma that arises is that periods of active cell growth also demand enormous amounts of energy, but depletion of mitochondrial oxaloacetate would reduce the cell's capacity to produce ATP.

The solution to this problem is to have an alternative pathway for oxaloacetate synthesis that can produce enough oxaloacetate to supply the anabolic and catabolic requirements of the cell. Although bacteria and plants have several mechanisms, the only way that mammalian cells can produce more oxaloacetate is by the carboxylation of pyruvate, a reaction that is also important in gluconeogenesis. This reaction is summarized below:

Section 16.5

$$\text{Pyruvate} + CO_2 + \text{ATP} \longrightarrow \text{oxaloacetate} + \text{ADP} + P_i$$

The enzyme that catalyzes this reaction is *pyruvate carboxylase*. It is a conjugated protein having as its covalently linked prosthetic group the vitamin *biotin*. This enzyme is "turned on" by high levels of acetyl CoA. A high concentration of acetyl CoA is a signal that the cell requires high levels of the citric acid cycle intermediates, particularly oxaloacetate, the beginning substrate.

The reaction catalyzed by pyruvate carboxylase is called an **anaplerotic reaction.** The term "anaplerotic" means to fill up. Indeed, this critical enzyme must constantly replenish the oxaloacetate and thus indirectly all the citric acid cycle intermediates that are withdrawn as biosynthetic precursors for the reactions summarized in Figure 17.8.

QUESTION 17.13

Explain how the citric acid cycle serves as an amphibolic pathway.

QUESTION 17.14

What is the function of an anaplerotic reaction?

SUMMARY

17.1 The Mitochondria

The *mitochondria* are aerobic cell organelles that are responsible for most of the ATP production in eukaryotic cells. They are enclosed by a double membrane. The outer membrane permits low-molecular-weight molecules to pass through. The *inner mitochondrial membrane,* by contrast, is almost completely impermeable to most molecules. The inner mitochondrial membrane is the site where *oxidative phosphorylation* occurs. The enzymes of the *citric acid cycle,* of amino acid catabolism, and of fatty acid oxidation are located in the *matrix space* of the mitochondrion.

17.2 An Overview of Aerobic Respiration

Aerobic respiration is the oxygen-requiring degradation of food molecules and production of ATP. *Oxidative phosphorylation* is the process that uses the high-energy electrons harvested by oxidation of substrates of the citric acid cycle to produce ATP.

17.3 The Citric Acid Cycle (The Krebs Cycle)

The *citric acid cycle* is the final pathway for the degradation of carbohydrates, amino acids, and fatty acids. The citric acid cycle occurs in the matrix of the mitochondria. It is a cyclic series of biochemical reactions that accomplishes the complete oxidation of the carbon skeletons of food molecules.

17.4 Oxidative Phosphorylation

Oxidative phosphorylation is the process by which NADH and $FADH_2$ are oxidized and ATP is produced. Two molecules of ATP are produced when $FADH_2$ is oxidized, and three molecules of ATP are produced when NADH is oxidized. The complete oxidation of one glucose molecule by glycolysis, the citric acid cycle, and oxidative phosphorylation yields 36 molecules of ATP versus two molecules of ATP for anaerobic degradation of glucose by glycolysis and fermentation.

17.5 Degradation of Amino Acids

Amino acids are oxidized in the mitochondria. The first step of amino acid catabolism is deamination, the removal of the amino group. The carbon skeletons of amino acids are converted into molecules that can enter the citric acid cycle.

17.6 The Urea Cycle

In the *urea cycle* the toxic ammonium ions released by deamination of amino acids are incorporated in urea which is excreted in the urine.

17.7 Overview of Anabolism: The Citric Acid Cycle as a Source of Biosynthetic Intermediates

In addition to its role in *catabolism,* the citric acid cycle also plays an important role in cellular *anabolism,* or biosynthetic reactions. Many of the citric acid cycle intermediates are precursors for the synthesis of amino acids and macromolecules required by the cell. A pathway that functions in both catabolic and anabolic reactions is called an *amphibolic pathway.*

KEY TERMS

aerobic respiration (17.2)
aminotransferase (17.5)
amphibolic pathways (17.7)
anabolism (17.7)
anaplerotic reactions (17.7)
ATP synthase (17.4)
catabolism (17.7)
citric acid cycle (17.3)
cristae (17.1)
electron transport system (17.4)
F_0F_1 complex (17.4)
hyperammonemia (17.6)
inner mitochondrial membrane (17.1)

intermembrane space (17.1)
matrix space (17.1)
mitochondria (17.1)
outer mitochondrial membrane (17.1)
oxidative deamination (17.5)
oxidative phosphorylation (17.4)
pyridoxal phosphate (17.5)
terminal electron acceptor (17.4)
transaminase (17.5)
transamination (17.5)
urea cycle (17.6)

QUESTIONS AND PROBLEMS

The Mitochondria

17.15 What is the function of the intermembrane compartment of the mitochondria?

17.16 What biochemical processes occur in the matrix space of the mitochondria?

17.17 In what important way do the inner and outer mitochondrial membranes differ?

17.18 What kinds of proteins are found in the inner mitochondrial membrane?

The Citric Acid Cycle

17.19 Label each of the following statements as true or false:
   a. Both glycolysis and the citric acid cycle are aerobic processes.
   b. Both glycolysis and the citric acid cycle are anaerobic processes.
   c. Glycolysis occurs in the cytoplasm, and the citric acid cycle occurs in the mitochondria.
   d. The inner membrane of the mitochondria is virtually impermeable to most substances.

17.20 Fill in the blanks:
   a. The proteins of the electron transport system are found in the _____, the enzymes of the citric acid cycle are found in the _____, and the hydrogen ion reservoir is found in the _____ of the mitochondria.
   b. The infoldings of the inner mitochondrial membrane are called _____.
   c. Energy released by oxidation in the citric acid cycle is conserved in the form of phosphoanhydride bonds in _____.
   d. The purpose of the citric acid cycle is the _____ of the acetyl group.

17.21 To what metabolic intermediate is the acetyl group of acetyl CoA transferred in the citric acid cycle? What is the product of this reaction?

17.22 To what final products is the acetyl group of acetyl CoA converted during oxidation in the citric acid cycle?

17.23 How many ions of NAD^+ are reduced to molecules of NADH during one turn of the citric acid cycle?

17.24 How many molecules of FAD are converted to $FADH_2$ during one turn of the citric acid cycle?

17.25 What is the net yield of ATP for anaerobic glycolysis?

17.26 How many molecules of ATP are produced by the complete degradation of glucose via glycolysis, the citric acid cycle, and oxidative phosphorylation?

17.27 What is the function of acetyl CoA in the citric acid cycle?

17.28 What is the function of oxaloacetate in the citric acid cycle?

17.29 GTP is formed in one step of the citric acid cycle. How is this GTP converted into ATP?

17.30 What is the chemical meaning of the term *decarboxylation?*

Oxidative Phosphorylation

17.31 How many molecules of ATP are produced when one molecule of NADH is oxidized by oxidative phosphorylation?

17.32 How many molecules of ATP are produced when one molecule of $FADH_2$ is oxidized by oxidative phosphorylation?

17.33 What is the source of energy for the synthesis of ATP in mitochondria?

17.34 What is the name of the enzyme that catalyzes ATP synthesis in mitochondria?

17.35 What is the function of the electron transport systems of the mitochondria?

17.36 What is the cellular location of the electron transport systems?

Amino Acid Metabolism

17.37 What chemical transformation is carried out by aminotransferases?

17.38 Write a chemical equation for an aminotransferase that transfers an amino group from alanine to α-ketoglutarate.

17.39 Why is the glutamate family of aminotransferases so important?

17.40 What biochemical reaction is catalyzed by glutamate dehydrogenase?

17.41 What is the net yield of ATP for degradation of alanine by the citric acid cycle and oxidative phosphorylation?

17.42 Into which amino acid cycle intermediate is each of the following amino acids converted?
   a. Alanine
   b. Glutamate
   c. Aspartate
   d. Phenylalanine
   e. Threonine
   f. Arginine

Urea Cycle

17.43 What metabolic condition is produced if the urea cycle does not function properly?

17.44 What is hyperammonemia? How are mild forms of this disease treated?

17.45 The structure of urea is given below:

$$NH_2-\overset{\overset{\textstyle O}{\|}}{C}-NH_2$$

   a. What substances are the sources of each of the amino groups in the urea molecule?
   b. What substance is the source of the carbonyl group?

17.46 What is the energy source used for the urea cycle?

Overview of Anabolism: The Citric Acid Cycle as a Source of Biosynthetic Intermediates

17.47 From which citric acid cycle intermediate is the amino acid glutamate synthesized?

17.48 What amino acids are synthesized from α-ketoglutarate?

17.49 What is the role of the citric acid cycle in biosynthesis?

17.50 How are citric acid cycle intermediates replenished when they are in demand for biosynthesis?

17.51 What is meant by the term *essential amino acid?*

17.52 What are the nine essential amino acids?

Further Problems

17.53 Compare the number of molecules of ATP produced by glycolysis to the number of ATP molecules produced by oxidation of glucose via the citric acid cycle. Which pathway produces more energy? Explain.

17.54 At which steps in the citric acid cycle do oxidation-reduction reactions occur?

17.55 Write a balanced equation for the synthesis of glutamate that is mediated by the enzyme glutamate dehydrogenase.

17.56 Write a balanced equation for the transamination of aspartate.

17.57 Write a balanced equation for the reaction catalyzed by pyruvate carboxylase.

17.58 How does the reaction described in Problem 17.57 allow the citric acid cycle to fulfill its roles in both catabolism and anabolism?

VOCABULARY QUIZ

17.1 A(n) _____ is an enzyme that catalyzes the transfer of an amino group from one molecule to another.

17.2 Metabolic pathways that function in both anabolism and catabolism are called _____ _____.

17.3 _____ is the series of reactions that couples the oxidation of NADH and $FADH_2$ to the phosphorylation of ADP to produce ATP.

17.4 The _____ is the series of electron transport proteins embedded in the inner mitochondrial membrane that accept high-energy electrons from NADH and $FADH_2$.

17.5 The cellular ''power plants'' in which the reactions of the citric acid cycle, the electron transport system, and ATP synthase function to produce ATP are called _____.

17.6 The _____ is the final electron acceptor in an electron transport system that removes the low-energy electrons from the system. In aerobic organisms it is molecular oxygen.

17.7 _____ is the multiprotein complex within the inner mitochondrial membrane that uses the energy of the proton gradient to produce ATP.

17.8 The _____ is the region of the mitochondrion within the inner membrane. It is the location of the enzymes that carry out the reactions of the citric acid cycle.

17.9 The _____ is a cyclic series of reactions that detoxifies ammonium ions by incorporating them into urea, which is excreted from the body.

17.10 The _____ is the cyclic biochemical pathway that is the final stage of degradation of carbohydrates, fats, and amino acids. It results in the complete oxidation of acetyl groups derived from these dietary fuels.

18

Fatty Acid Metabolism

OUTLINE

LEARNING GOALS

- Summarize the digestion and storage of lipids.
- Understand the role of acetyl CoA in fatty acid metabolism.
- Describe the degradation of fatty acids by β-oxidation.
- Compare β-oxidation of fatty acids and fatty acid biosynthesis.
- Understand the role of ketone body production in β-oxidation.
- Describe the regulation of lipid and carbohydrate metabolism in relation to the liver, adipose tissue, muscle tissue, and the brain.
- Summarize the antagonistic effects of glucagon and insulin.

INTRODUCTION

The metabolism of fatty acids and lipids revolves around the fate of acetyl CoA. We saw in Chapter 16 that, under aerobic conditions, pyruvate is converted to acetyl CoA and in Chapter 17 that the acetyl CoA feeds into the citric acid cycle. Fatty acids are also degraded to acetyl CoA and oxidized by the citric acid cycle, as are certain amino acids. Moreover, acetyl CoA is itself the starting material for the biosynthesis of fatty acids, fully half of the amino acids, cholesterol, and steroid hormones. Acetyl CoA is thus one of the major metabolites of intermediary metabolism.

18.1 LIPID METABOLISM IN ANIMALS

Digestion and absorption of dietary fats

See Sections 12.1 and 13.2 for a more complete discussion of micelles.

Fats are highly hydrophobic ("water fearing"). Because of this they must be processed before they can be digested, absorbed, and metabolized. As a result the **lipases,** enzymes that hydrolyze fats, that are found in the stomach and in the saliva are not very effective. In fact, most dietary fat arrives in the duodenum, the first part of the small intestine, in the form of fat globules. These fat globules stimulate the secretion of bile from the gallbladder. **Bile** is composed of micelles of lecithin, cholesterol, protein, bile salts, inorganic ions, and bile pigments. **Micelles** (Figure 18.1) are aggregations of molecules having a polar region and a nonpolar region. The nonpolar ends of bile salts tend to bunch together when placed in water. The hydrophilic ("water loving") regions of these molecules will interact with water. Bile salts are made in the liver and stored in the gallbladder, awaiting the stimulus to be secreted into the duodenum. The major bile salts in humans are cholic acid and chenodeoxycholic acid (Figure 18.2).

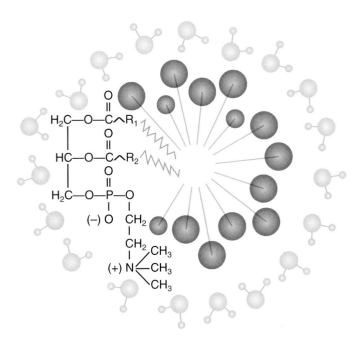

FIGURE 18.1
The structure of a micelle formed from the phospholipid lecithin. The straight lines represent the long hydrophobic fatty acid tails, and the spheres represent the hydrophilic heads of the phospholipid.

Cholesterol is almost completely insoluble in water, but the conversion of cholesterol to bile salts creates detergents whose polar heads make them soluble in the aqueous phase of the cytoplasm and whose hydrophobic tails bind lipids. After a meal is eaten, bile flows through the common bile duct into the duodenum, where bile salts emulsify the fat globules into tiny droplets. This increases the surface area of the lipid molecules, allowing them to be more easily digested (Figure 18.3).

Much of the lipid in these droplets is in the form of **triglycerides,** or triacylglycerols, which are fatty acyl esters of glycerol. A protein called **colipase** binds to the surface of the lipid droplets and helps pancreatic lipases to stick to the surface and hydrolyze the ester bonds between the glycerol and fatty acids of the triglycerides (Figure 18.4). In this process, two of the three fatty acids are liberated, and the monoglycerides and free fatty acids produced mix freely

Section 13.3

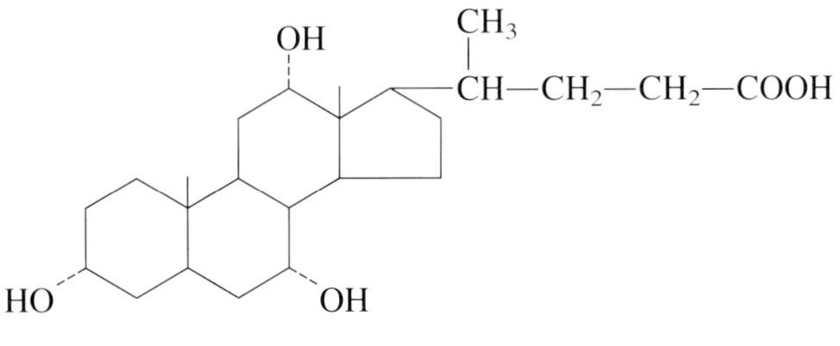

FIGURE 18.2
Structures of the most common bile acids in human bile: cholic acid and chenodeoxycholic acid.

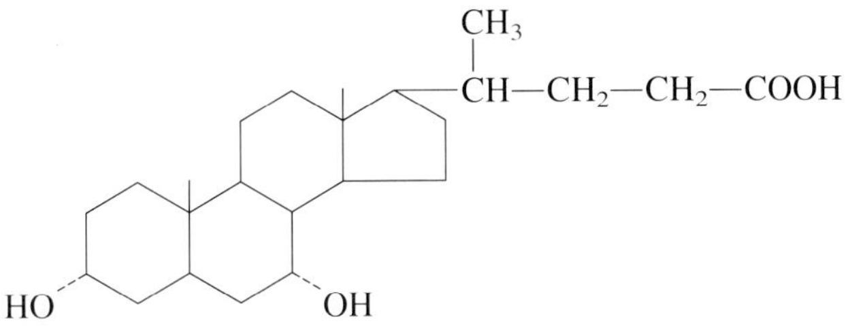

Cholic acid

Chenodeoxycholic acid

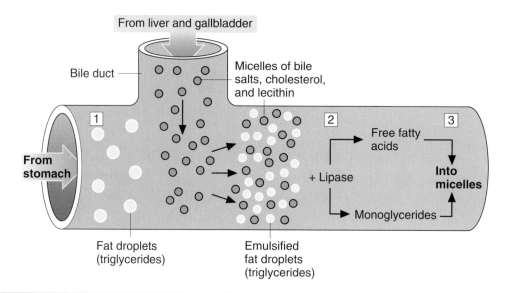

FIGURE 18.3
Stages of lipid digestion in the intestinal tract. Step 1 is the emulsification of fat droplets by bile salts. Step 2 is the hydrolysis of triglycerides in emulsified fat droplets into fatty acids and monoglycerides. Step 3 involves dissolving fatty acids and monoglycerides into micelles to produce "mixed micelles."

Section 13.5

with the micelles of bile. These micelles are readily absorbed through the membranes of the intestinal epithelial cells (Figure 18.5).

Surprisingly, the monoglycerides and fatty acids are then reassembled into triglycerides that are combined with protein to produce the class of plasma lipoproteins called **chylomicrons** (Figure 18.5). These collections of lipid and protein are secreted into small lymphatic vessels and eventually arrive in the bloodstream. In the bloodstream the triglycerides are once again hydrolyzed to produce glycerol and free fatty acids that are then absorbed by the cells. If the body needs energy, these molecules are degraded to produce ATP. If the body does not need energy, these energy-rich molecules are stored.

Lipid storage

See "A Human Perspective: Brown Fat: The Fat That Makes You Thin?" in Chapter 17.

Fatty acids are stored in the form of triglycerides. Most of the body's triglyceride molecules are stored as fat droplets in the cytoplasm of **adipocytes** (fat cells) that make up **adipose tissue.** Each adipocyte contains a large fat droplet that accounts for nearly the entire volume of the cell. Other cells, such as those of cardiac muscle, contain a few small fat droplets. In these cells the fat droplets are surrounded by mitochondria. When the cells need energy, triglycerides are hydrolyzed to release fatty acids that are transported into the matrix space of the mitochondria. There the fatty acids are completely oxidized, and ATP is produced.

FIGURE 18.4
The action of pancreatic lipase in the hydrolysis of dietary lipids.

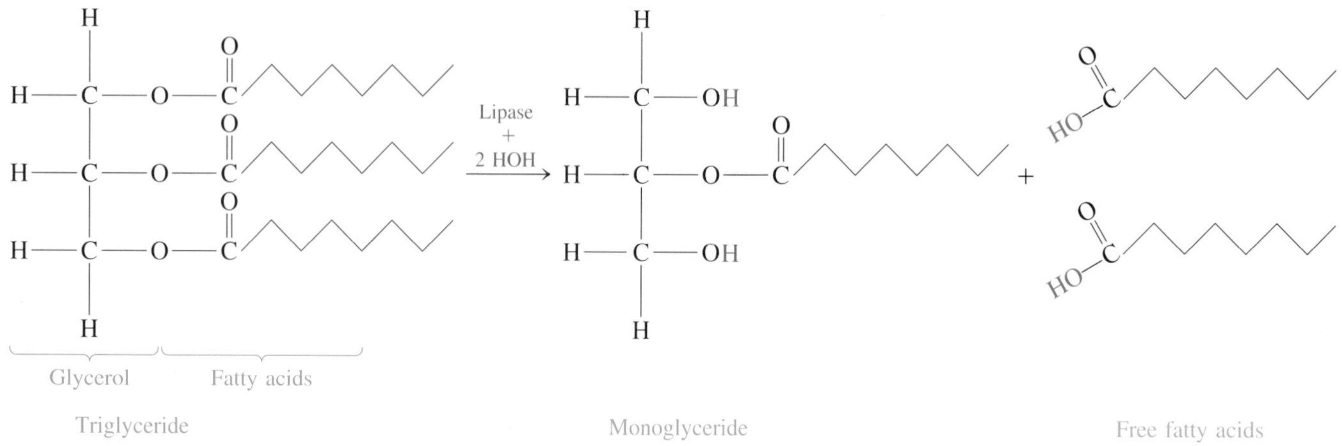

Glycerol   Fatty acids

Triglyceride   Monoglyceride   Free fatty acids

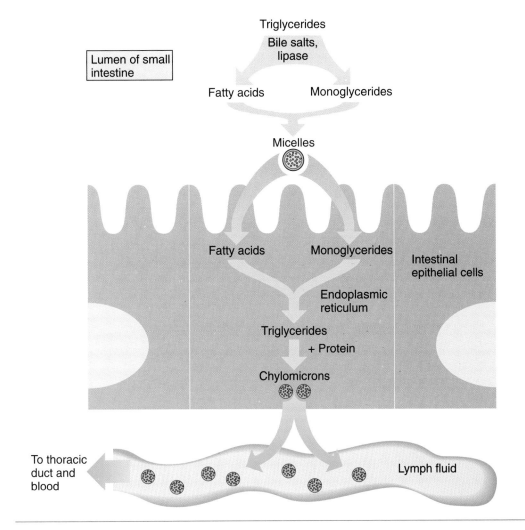

FIGURE 18.5
Passage of triglycerides in micelles into the cells of the intestinal epithelium.

The fatty acids provided by the hydrolysis of triglycerides are a very rich energy source for the body. The complete oxidation of fatty acids releases much more energy than the oxidation of a comparable amount of glycogen.

QUESTION 18.1

How do bile salts aid in the digestion of dietary lipids?

QUESTION 18.2

Why must dietary lipids be processed before enzymatic digestion can be effective?

18.2 FATTY ACID DEGRADATION

An overview of fatty acid degradation

Early in the twentieth century, a very clever experiment was done to determine how fatty acids are degraded. Recall from Chapter 8 that radioactive elements can be attached to biological molecules and followed through the body. A German biochemist, Franz Knoop, devised a similar kind of labeling experiment long before radioactive tracers were available. Knoop fed dogs fatty acids in which the usual terminal methyl group had a phenyl group substituent. Such molecules are called ω-labeled (omega-labeled) fatty acids (Figure 18.6). He found that phenyl acetate was formed when the fatty acid had an even number of carbon atoms in the chain. But benzoate was formed when the fatty acid had an odd number of carbon atoms. Knoop interpreted these data to mean that the degradation of fatty acids occurs by the removal of two-carbon

A HUMAN PERSPECTIVE

Losing Those Unwanted Pounds of Adipose Tissue

Weight, or overweight, is a topic of great concern to the American populace. A glance through almost any popular magazine quickly informs us that by today's standards, "beautiful" is synonymous with "thin." The models in all these magazines are extremely thin, and there are literally dozens of ads for weight-loss programs. Americans spend millions of dollars each year trying to attain this slim ideal of the fashion models.

Studies have revealed that this slim ideal is often below a desirable, healthy body weight. In fact, the suggested weight for a 6 foot tall male between 18 and 39 years of age is 179 pounds. For a 5'6'' female in the same age range, the desired weight is 142 pounds. For a 5'1'' female, 126 pounds is recommended. Just as being too thin can cause health problems, so too can obesity.

What is obesity, and does it have disadvantages beyond aesthetics? An individual is considered to be obese if his or her body weight is more than 20% above the ideal weight for his or her height. The accompanying table lists desirable body weights, according to sex, age, height, and body frame.

Overweight carries with it a wide range of physical problems, including elevated blood cholesterol levels; high blood pressure; increased incidence of diabetes, cancer, and heart disease; and increased probability of early death. It often causes psychological problems as well, such as guilt and low self-esteem.

Many factors may contribute to obesity. These include genetic factors, a sedentary lifestyle, and a preference for high-calorie, high-fat foods. However, the real concern is how to lose weight. How can we lose weight wisely and safely and keep the weight off for the rest of our lives? Unfortunately, the answer is *not* the answer that most people want to hear. The prevalence and financial success of the quick-weight-loss programs suggest that the majority of people want a program that is rapid and effortless. Unfortunately, most programs that promise dramatic weight reduction with little effort are usually ineffective or, worse, unsafe. The truth is that weight loss and management are best obtained by a program involving three elements.

1. *Reduced caloric intake.* A pound of body fat is equivalent to 3500 Calories (kilocalories). So if you want to lose 2 pounds each week, a reasonable goal, you must reduce your caloric intake by 1000 Calories per day. Remember

	Men*						Women**		
Height					**Height**				
Feet	*Inches*	*Small Frame*	*Medium Frame*	*Large Frame*	*Feet*	*Inches*	*Small Frame*	*Medium Frame*	*Large Frame*
5	2	128–134	131–141	138–150	4	10	102–111	109–121	118–131
5	3	130–136	133–143	140–153	4	11	103–113	111–123	120–134
5	4	132–138	135–145	142–156	5	0	104–115	113–126	122–137
5	5	134–140	137–148	144–160	5	1	106–118	115–129	125–140
5	6	136–142	139–151	146–164	5	2	108–121	118–132	128–143
5	7	138–145	142–154	149–168	5	3	111–124	121–135	131–147
5	8	140–148	145–157	152–172	5	4	114–127	124–138	134–151
5	9	142–151	148–160	155–176	5	5	117–130	127–141	137–155
5	10	144–154	151–163	158–180	5	6	120–133	130–144	140–159
5	11	146–157	154–166	161–184	5	7	123–136	133–147	143–163
6	0	149–160	157–170	164–188	5	8	126–139	136–150	146–167
6	1	152–164	160–174	168–192	5	9	129–142	139–153	149–170
6	2	155–168	164–178	172–197	5	10	132–145	142–156	152–173
6	3	158–172	167–182	176–202	5	11	135–148	145–159	155–176
6	4	162–176	171–187	181–207	6	0	138–151	148–162	158–179

*Weights at ages 25–59 based on lowest mortality. Weight in pounds according to frame (in indoor clothing weighing 5 lb, shoes with 1'' heels).
**Weights at ages 25–59 based on lowest mortality. Weight in pounds according to frame (in indoor clothing weighing 3 lb, shoes with 1'' heels).
Reprinted with permission of the Metropolitan Insurance Companies.

Activity	Kilocalories per Hour*
Badminton, competitive singles	480
Basketball	360–660
Bicycling	
10 mph	420
11 mph	480
12 mph	600
13 mph	660
Calisthenics, heavy	600
Handball, competitive	660
Rope skipping, vigorous	800
Rowing machine	840
Running	
5 mph	600
6 mph	750
7 mph	870
8 mph	1,020
9 mph	1,130
10 mph	1,285
Skating, ice or roller, rapid	700
Skiing, downhill, vigorous	600
Skiing, cross-country	
2.5 mph	560
4 mph	600
5 mph	700
8 mph	1,020
Swimming, 25–50 yards per min.	360–750
Walking	
Level road, 4 mph (fast)	420
Upstairs	600–1,080
Uphill, 3.5 mph	480–900
Gardening, much lifting, stooping, digging	500
Mowing, pushing hand mower	450
Sawing hardwood	600
Shoveling, heavy	660
Wood chopping	560

*Caloric expenditure is based on a 150-lb person. There is a 10% increase in caloric expenditure for each 15 lb over this weight and a 10% decrease for each 15 lb under.
From E. L. Wynder, *The Book of Health: The American Health Foundation.* ©1981 Franklin Watts, Inc., New York. Used with permission.

that diets recommending fewer than 1200 Calories per day are difficult to maintain because they are not very satisfying and may be unsafe because they don't provide all the required vitamins and minerals. The best way to decrease Calories is to reduce fat and increase complex carbohydrates in the diet.

2. *Exercise.* Increase energy expenditures by 200–400 Calories each day. You may choose walking, running, or mowing the lawn; the type of activity doesn't matter, as long as you get moving. Exercise has additional benefits. It increases cardiovascular fitness, provides a psychological lift, and may increase the base rate at which you burn calories after exercise is finished. The accompanying table summarizes the caloric expenditure of several activities.

3. *Behavior modification.* Overweight is as much a psychological problem as it is a physical problem, and half the battle is learning to recognize the triggers that cause eating behavior. Several principles of behavior modification have been found to be very helpful.

   a. Keep a diary. Record the amount of foods eaten and the circumstances—for instance, a meal at the kitchen table or a bag of chips in the car on the way home.

   b. Identify your eating triggers. Do you eat when you feel stress, boredom, fatigue, joy?

   c. Develop a plan for avoiding or coping with your trigger situations or emotions. You might exercise when you feel that stress-at-the-end-of-the-day trigger or carry a bag of carrot sticks for the midmorning-boredom trigger.

   d. Set realistic goals, and reward yourself when you reach them. The reward should be a new necklace or a movie, not a hot fudge sundae.

As you can see, there is no "quick fix" for safe, effective weight control. A commitment must be made to modify existing diet and exercise habits. Most important, those habits must be avoided forever and replaced by new, healthier behaviors and attitudes.

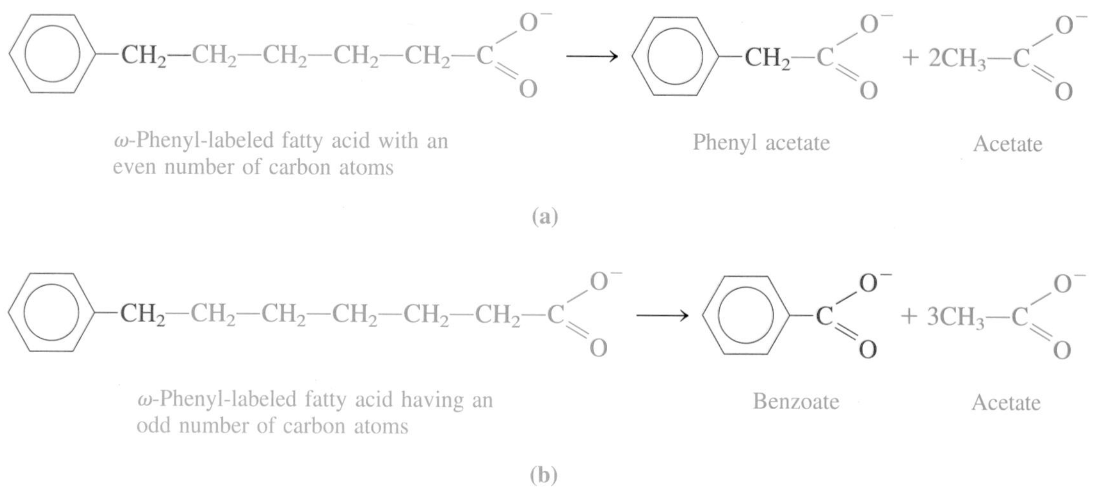

ω-Phenyl-labeled fatty acid with an
even number of carbon atoms

Phenyl acetate   Acetate

(a)

ω-Phenyl-labeled fatty acid having an
odd number of carbon atoms

Benzoate   Acetate

(b)

FIGURE 18.6
The last carbon of the chain is called the ω-carbon (omega-carbon), so the attached phenyl group is an ω-phenyl group. (a) Oxidation of ω-phenyl-labeled fatty acids occurs two carbons at a time. Fatty acids having an even number of carbon atoms are degraded to phenyl acetate and "acetate." (b) Oxidation of ω-phenyl-labeled fatty acids that contain an odd number of carbon atoms yields benzoate and "acetate."

acetate groups from the carboxyl end of the fatty acid. We now know that the two-carbon fragments produced by the degradation of fatty acids are not acetate, but acetyl CoA. The pathway for the breakdown of fatty acids into acetyl CoA is called **β-oxidation.**

The β-oxidation cycle consists of a set of five repeated reactions whose overall form is similar to the reactions of the citric acid cycle (Figure 18.7). Each trip through the set of five reaction releases acetyl CoA and returns a fatty acyl CoA molecule that has two fewer carbons. One molecule of FADH$_2$, equivalent to two ATP molecules, and one molecule of NADH, equivalent to three ATP molecules, are produced for each cycle of β-oxidation.

EXAMPLE 18.1

What Products Would Be Produced by the β-Oxidation of 10-Phenyldecanoic Acid?

Solution

Since this is a ten-carbon fatty acid, it would be broken down into four acetyl CoA molecules and one phenyl acetate molecule. Since four cycles through β-oxidation are required to break down a ten-carbon fatty acid, four NADH molecules and four FADH$_2$ molecules would also be produced.

QUESTION 18.3

What products would be formed by β-oxidation of each of the following fatty acids? (*Hint:* Refer to Example 18.1.)

a.   9-Phenylnonanoic acid

b.   8-Phenyloctanoic acid

c.   7-Phenylheptanoic acid

d.   12-Phenyldodecanoic acid

QUESTION 18.4

What does ω refer to in the naming of ω-phenyl-labeled fatty acids?

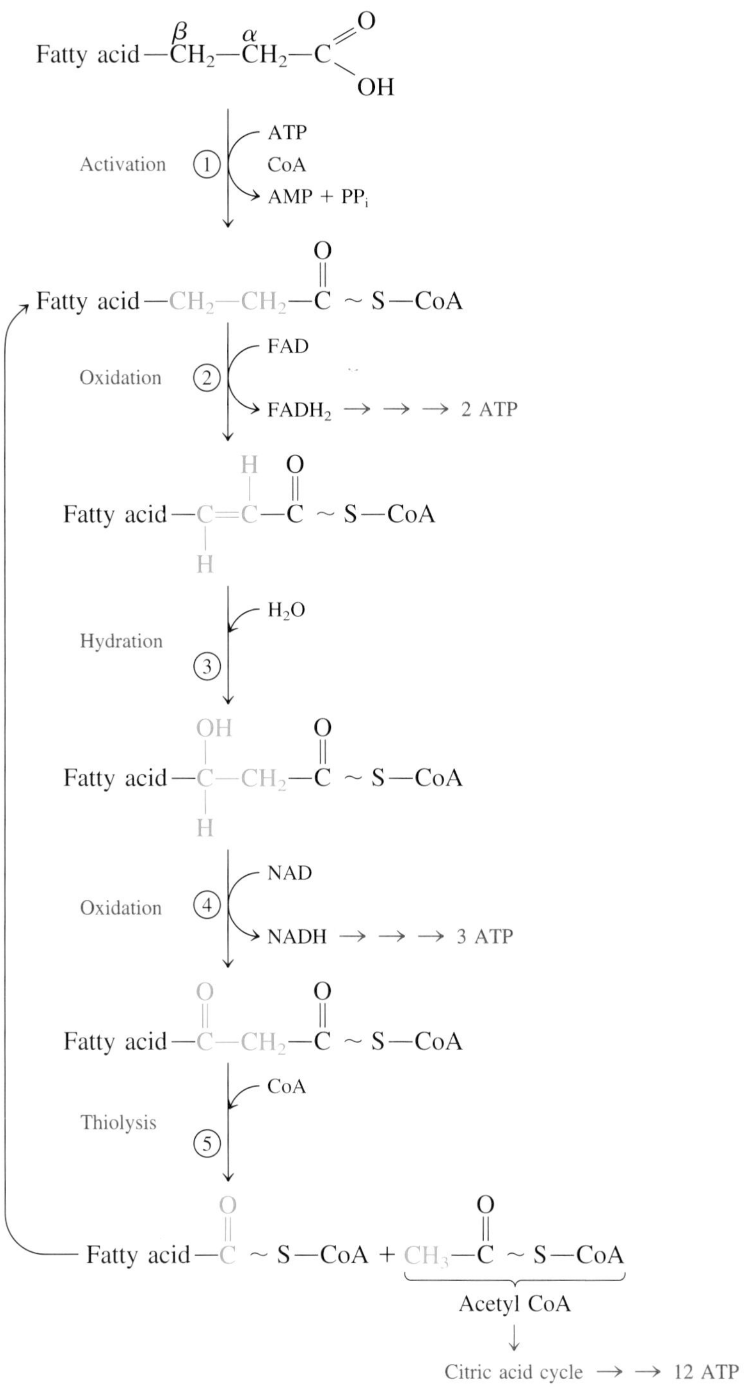

FIGURE 18.7
The cycle of reactions in β-oxidation of fatty acids.

The enzymes that catalyze the β-oxidation of fatty acids are located in the matrix space of the mitochondria. Special transport mechanisms are required to bring fatty acid molecules into the mitochondrial matrix. Once inside, the fatty acids are degraded by the reactions of β-oxidation. As we will see, these reactions interact with oxidative phosphorylation and the citric acid cycle to produce ATP.

The reactions of β-oxidation

Step 1: The first step is an *activation* reaction that results in the production of a fatty acyl CoA molecule. A thioester bond is formed between coenzyme A and the fatty acid:

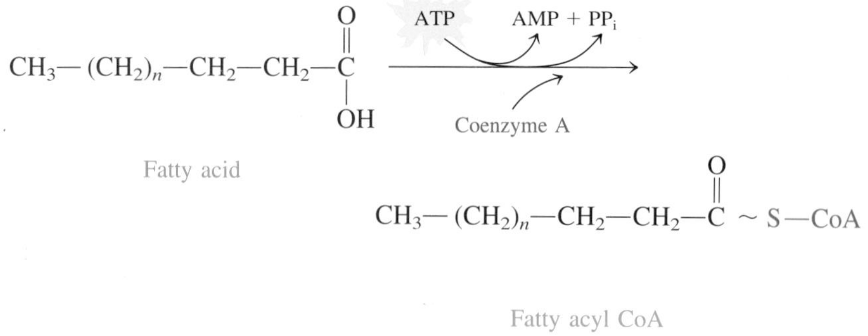

$$CH_3-(CH_2)_n-CH_2-CH_2-\overset{\overset{O}{\|}}{\underset{OH}{C}}$$

ATP   AMP + PP$_i$

Coenzyme A

Fatty acid

$$CH_3-(CH_2)_n-CH_2-CH_2-\overset{\overset{O}{\|}}{C} \sim S-CoA$$

Fatty acyl CoA

This reaction requires energy in the form of ATP, which is cleaved to AMP and pyrophosphate. Here again we see the need to invest a small amount of energy so that a much greater amount of energy can be harvested later in the pathway. Coenzyme A is also required for this step. The product, a fatty acyl CoA, has a *high-energy* thioester bond between the fatty acid and coenzyme A.

Step 2: The second reaction is an *oxidation* reaction that removes a pair of hydrogen atoms from the fatty acid. These are used to reduce FAD to produce FADH$_2$:

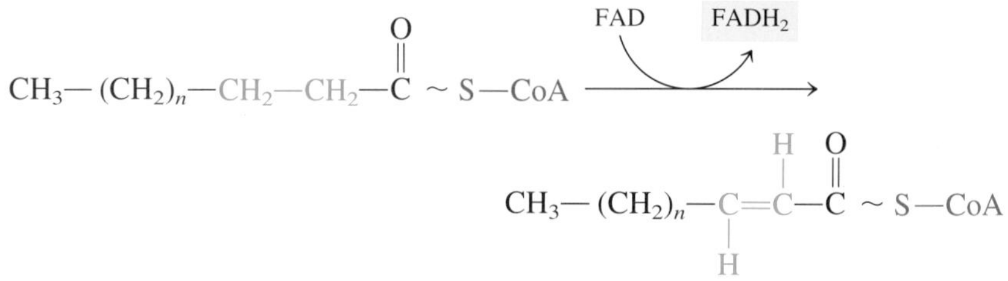

$$CH_3-(CH_2)_n-CH_2-CH_2-\overset{\overset{O}{\|}}{C} \sim S-CoA$$

FAD   FADH$_2$

$$CH_3-(CH_2)_n-\overset{\overset{H}{|}}{C}=\overset{\overset{H}{}}{\underset{\underset{H}{|}}{C}}-\overset{\overset{O}{\|}}{C} \sim S-CoA$$

Oxidative phosphorylation yields two ATP molecules for each molecule of FADH$_2$ produced by this reaction.

Step 3: This reaction involves the *hydration* of the double bond produced in step 2. As a result the β-carbon is hydroxylated:

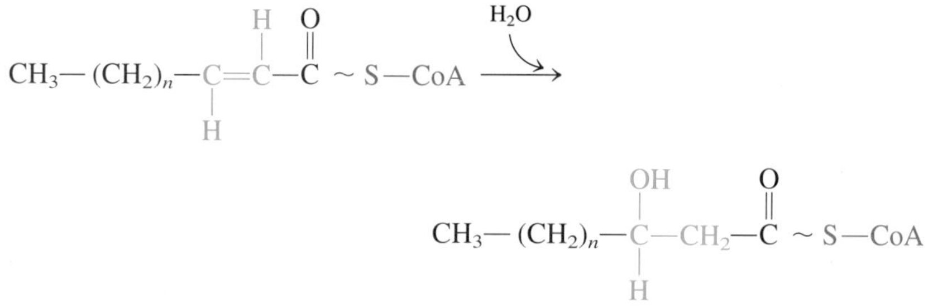

$$CH_3-(CH_2)_n-\overset{\overset{H}{|}}{C}=\overset{\overset{}{}}{\underset{\underset{H}{|}}{C}}-\overset{\overset{O}{\|}}{C} \sim S-CoA$$

H$_2$O

$$CH_3-(CH_2)_n-\overset{\overset{OH}{|}}{\underset{\underset{H}{|}}{C}}-CH_2-\overset{\overset{O}{\|}}{C} \sim S-CoA$$

Step 4: In this *oxidation* reaction the hydroxyl group of the β-carbon is now dehydrogenated. NAD$^+$ is reduced to form NADH that is subsequently used to produce three ATP molecules by oxidative phosphorylation:

$$CH_3-(CH_2)_n-\overset{\overset{OH}{|}}{\underset{\underset{H}{|}}{C}}-CH_2-\overset{\overset{O}{\|}}{C} \sim S-CoA$$

NAD$^+$ NADH

$$CH_3-(CH_2)_n-\overset{\overset{O}{\|}}{C}-CH_2-\overset{\overset{O}{\|}}{C} \sim S-CoA$$

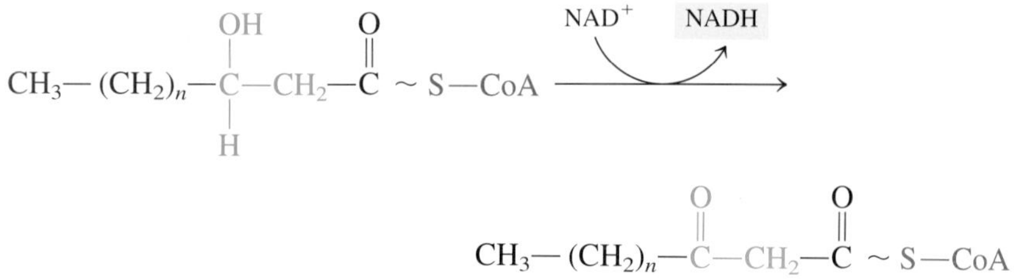

Step 5: The final step is the cleavage that releases acetyl CoA. This is accomplished by *thiolysis*, attack of a molecule of coenzyme A on the β-carbon. The result is the release of acetyl CoA and a fatty acyl CoA that is two carbons shorter than the beginning fatty acid:

$$CH_3-(CH_2)_n-\overset{\overset{O}{\|}}{C}-CH_2-\overset{\overset{O}{\|}}{C}\sim S-CoA \xrightarrow{\quad CoA \quad}$$

$$CH_3-(CH_2)_{n-2}-CH_2-CH_2-\overset{\overset{O}{\|}}{C}\sim S-CoA$$

$$+$$

$$\overset{\overset{O}{\|}}{C}-CH_3$$
$$\overset{\wr}{S}-CoA$$

The shortened fatty acyl CoA is further oxidized by cycling through steps 2–5 until the fatty acid carbon chain is completely degraded to acetyl CoA. The acetyl CoA produced by β-oxidation of fatty acids then enters the reactions of the citric acid cycle. Of course, this eventually results in the production of 12 ATP molecules per molecule of acetyl CoA released during β-oxidation.

The balance sheet for ATP production of the C_{16}-fatty acid palmitic acid when it is degraded by β-oxidation is summarized in Figure 18.8. Complete oxidation of palmitate results in

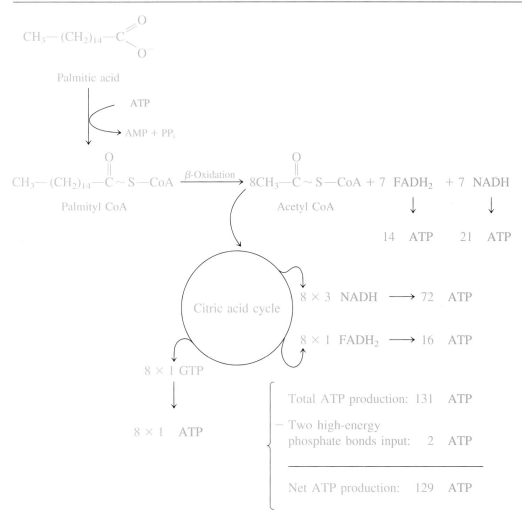

FIGURE 18.8
Complete oxidation of palmitic acid yields 129 molecules of ATP.

production of 129 molecules of ATP, *three and a half times more energy than results from the complete oxidation of an equivalent amount of glucose.*

EXAMPLE 18.2

Calculating the Amount of ATP Produced in Complete Oxidation of a Fatty Acid

How many molecules of ATP are produced in the complete oxidation of stearic acid, an 18-carbon saturated fatty acid?

Solution

Step 1 (activation)	−2 ATP

Steps 2–5:

8 FADH$_2$ × 2 ATP/FADH$_2$	16 ATP
8 NADH × 3 ATP/NADH	24 ATP

9 acetyl CoA (to citric acid cycle):

9 × 1 GTP × 1 ATP/GTP	9 ATP
9 × 3 NADH × 3 ATP/NADH	81 ATP
9 × 1 FADH$_2$ × 2 ATP/FADH$_2$	18 ATP
	146 ATP

QUESTION 18.5

Write out the sequence of steps for β-oxidation of butyryl CoA.

QUESTION 18.6

What is the energy yield from the complete degradation of butyryl CoA via β-oxidation, the citric acid cycle, and oxidative phosphorylation?

18.3 KETONE BODIES

Section 17.7

For the acetyl CoA produced by the β-oxidation of fatty acids to efficiently enter the citric acid cycle, there must be an adequate supply of oxaloacetate. If glycolysis and β-oxidation are occurring at the same rate, there will be a steady supply of pyruvate (from glycolysis) that can be converted to oxaloacetate. But what happens if the supply of oxaloacetate is too low to allow all of the acetyl CoA to enter the citric acid cycle? Under these conditions, acetyl CoA is converted to the so-called **ketone bodies:** β-hydroxybutyrate, acetone, and acetoacetate (Figure 18.9).

Ketosis

Ketosis, abnormally high levels of blood ketone bodies, is a situation that arises under some pathological conditions, such as starvation, a diet that is extremely low in carbohydrates (as with the high-protein liquid diets), or uncontrolled **diabetes mellitus.** The carbohydrate intake of a diabetic is normal, but the carbohydrates cannot get into the cell to be used as fuel. Thus diabetes amounts to starvation in the midst of plenty. In diabetes the very high concentration of ketone acids in the blood leads to **ketoacidosis.** The ketone acids are relatively strong acids and therefore readily dissociate to release H$^+$. Under these conditions the blood pH becomes acidic.

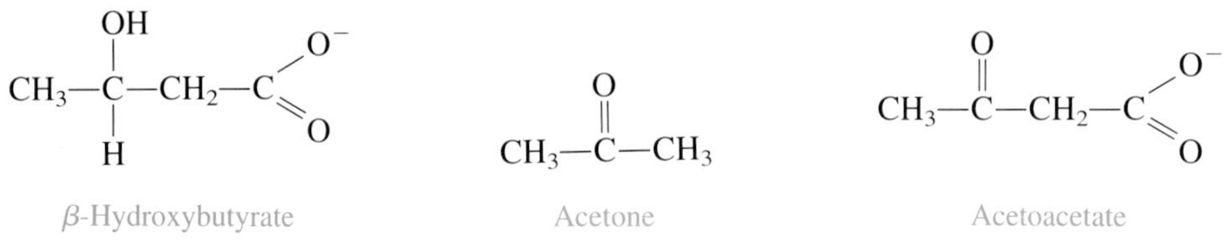

FIGURE 18.9
Structures of ketone bodies.

β-Hydroxybutyrate   Acetone   Acetoacetate

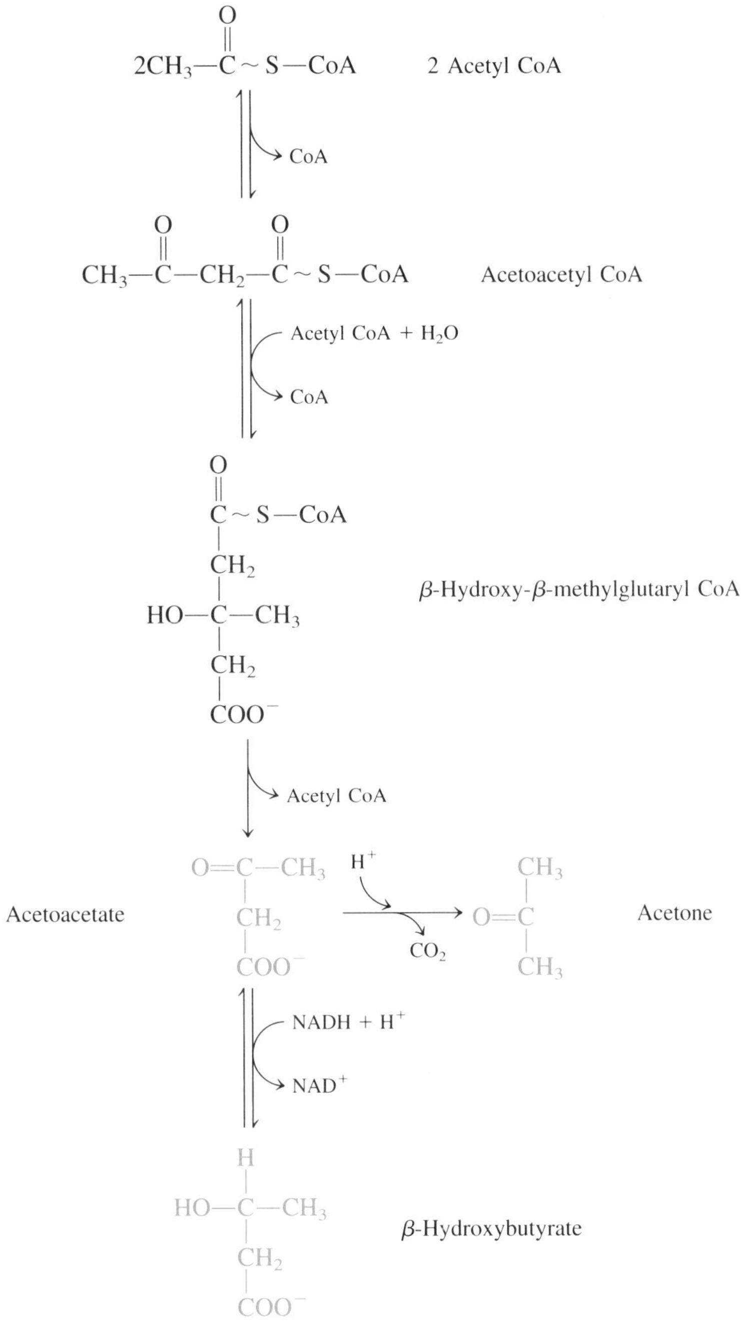

FIGURE 18.10
Summary of the reactions involved in ketogenesis.

The pathway for the production of ketone bodies (Figure 18.10) begins with a "reversal" of the last step of β-oxidation. When oxaloacetate levels are low, the enzyme that normally carries out the last reaction of β-oxidation now catalyzes the fusion of two acetyl CoA molecules to produce acetoacetyl CoA:

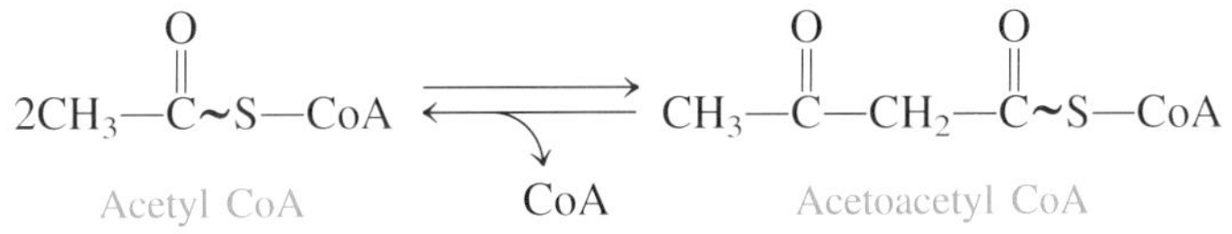

Ketogenesis

Acetoacetyl CoA can react with a third acetyl CoA molecule to yield β-hydroxy-β-methylglutaryl CoA (HMG-CoA):

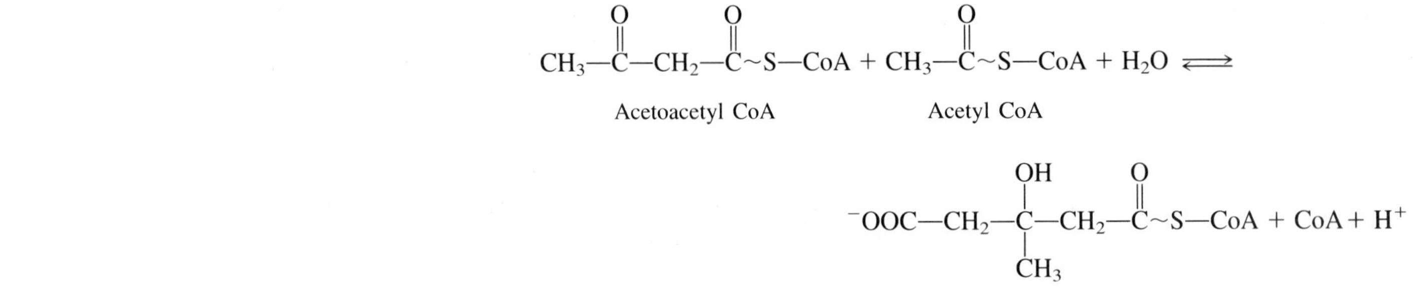

$$CH_3-\overset{\overset{\displaystyle O}{\|}}{C}-CH_2-\overset{\overset{\displaystyle O}{\|}}{C}\sim S-CoA + CH_3-\overset{\overset{\displaystyle O}{\|}}{C}\sim S-CoA + H_2O \rightleftharpoons$$

Acetoacetyl CoA   Acetyl CoA

$$^-OOC-CH_2-\underset{\underset{\displaystyle CH_3}{|}}{\overset{\overset{\displaystyle OH}{|}}{C}}-CH_2-\overset{\overset{\displaystyle O}{\|}}{C}\sim S-CoA + CoA + H^+$$

HMG-CoA

If HMG-CoA were formed in the cytoplasm, it would serve as a precursor for cholesterol biosynthesis. But ketogenesis, like β-oxidation, occurs in the mitochondrial matrix, and here HMG-CoA is cleaved to yield acetoacetate and acetyl CoA:

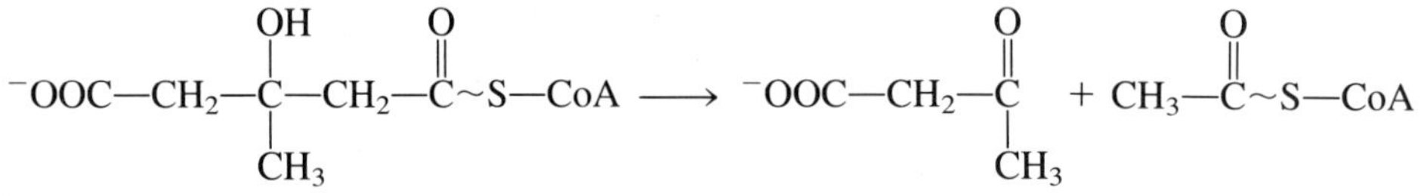

$$^-OOC-CH_2-\underset{\underset{\displaystyle CH_3}{|}}{\overset{\overset{\displaystyle OH}{|}}{C}}-CH_2-\overset{\overset{\displaystyle O}{\|}}{C}\sim S-CoA \longrightarrow {}^-OOC-CH_2-\underset{\underset{\displaystyle CH_3}{|}}{\overset{\overset{\displaystyle O}{\|}}{C}} + CH_3-\overset{\overset{\displaystyle O}{\|}}{C}\sim S-CoA$$

HMG-CoA   Acetoacetate   Acetyl CoA

In very small amounts, acetoacetate spontaneously loses carbon dioxide to give acetone. This is the reaction that causes the "acetone breath" that is often associated with diabetes mellitus. More frequently, it undergoes NADH-dependent reduction to produce β-hydroxybutyrate:

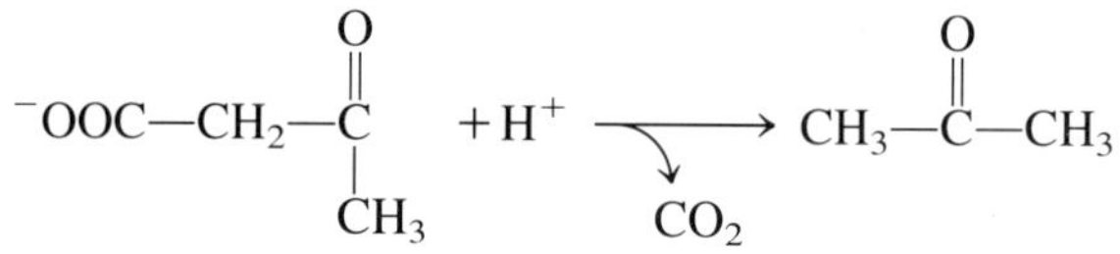

$$^-OOC-CH_2-\underset{\underset{\displaystyle CH_3}{|}}{\overset{\overset{\displaystyle O}{\|}}{C}} + H^+ \xrightarrow{} CH_3-\overset{\overset{\displaystyle O}{\|}}{C}-CH_3$$

$$CO_2$$

Acetoacetate   Acetone

or

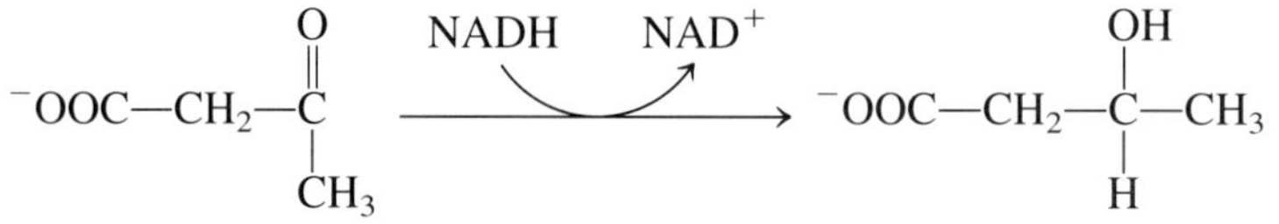

$$^-OOC-CH_2-\underset{\underset{\displaystyle CH_3}{|}}{\overset{\overset{\displaystyle O}{\|}}{C}} \xrightarrow{\text{NADH} \quad \text{NAD}^+} {}^-OOC-CH_2-\underset{\underset{\displaystyle H}{|}}{\overset{\overset{\displaystyle OH}{|}}{C}}-CH_3$$

Acetoacetate β-Hydroxybutyrate

Acetoacetate and β-hydroxybutyrate are produced primarily in the liver. These metabolites diffuse into the blood and are circulated to other tissues, where they may be reconverted to acetyl CoA and used to produce ATP. In fact, the heart muscle derives most of its metabolic energy from the oxidation of ketone bodies, not from the oxidation of glucose. Other tissues that are best adapted to the use of glucose will increasingly rely on ketone bodies for energy when glucose becomes unavailable or limited. This is particularly true of the brain.

QUESTION 18.7

What conditions lead to excess production of ketone bodies?

QUESTION 18.8

What is the cause of the characteristic "acetone breath" that is associated with uncontrolled diabetes mellitus?

All organisms possess the ability to synthesize fatty acids. In humans the excess acetyl CoA produced by carbohydrate degradation is used to make fatty acids that are then stored as triglycerides.

On first examination, fatty acid synthesis appears to be simply the reverse of β-oxidation. Specifically, the fatty acid chain is constructed by the sequential addition of two-carbon acetyl groups (Figure 18.11). Although the chemistry of fatty acid synthesis and breakdown are similar, there are several major differences between β-oxidation and fatty acid biosynthesis. These are summarized below.

18.4 FATTY ACID SYNTHESIS

A comparison of fatty acid synthesis and degradation

◆ **Intracellular location.** The enzymes responsible for fatty acid biosynthesis are located in the cytoplasm of the cell, whereas those responsible for the degradation of fatty acids are in the mitochondria.

◆ **Acyl group carriers.** The activated intermediates of fatty acid biosynthesis are bound to a carrier molecule called the **acyl carrier protein (ACP)** (Figure 18.12). In β-oxidation the acyl group carrier was coenzyme A. However, there are important similarities between these two carriers. Both contain the **phosphopantetheine** group, which is made up of the vitamin pantothenic acid and the amino acid cysteine. In both cases the fatty acyl group is bound by a thioester bond to the phosphopantetheine group.

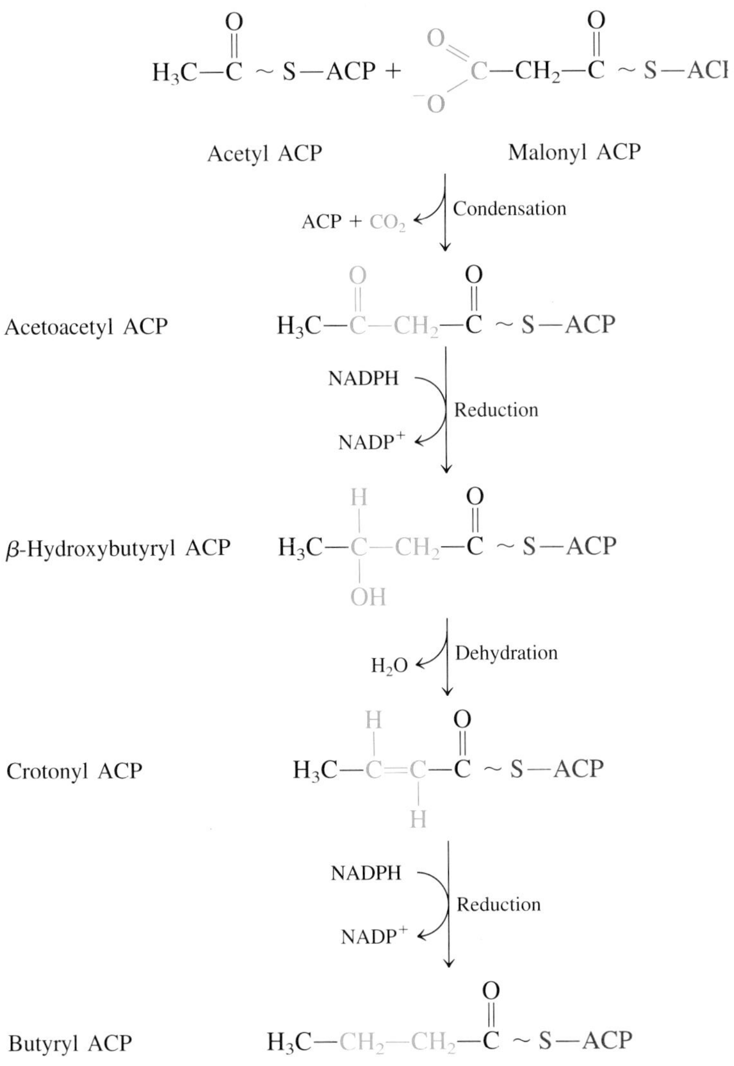

FIGURE 18.11
Summary of the reactions of fatty acid synthesis.

A CLINICAL PERSPECTIVE

Diabetes Mellitus and Ketone Bodies

More than one person, found unconscious on the streets of some metropolis, has been carted to jail only to die of complications arising from uncontrolled diabetes mellitus. Others are fortunate enough to arrive in hospital emergency rooms. A quick test for diabetes mellitus—induced coma is the odor of acetone on the breath of the afflicted person. Acetone is one of several metabolites produced by diabetics that are known collectively as *ketone bodies.*

The term "diabetes" was used by the ancient Greeks to designate diseases in which excess urine is produced. Two thousand years later, in the eighteenth century, the urine of certain individuals was found to contain sugar, and the name "diabetes mellitus" (Latin: *mellitus,* sweetened with honey) was given to this disease. People suffering from diabetes mellitus waste away as they excrete large amounts of sugar-containing urine.

The cause of insulin-dependent-diabetes mellitus is an inadequate production of insulin by the body. Insulin is secreted in response to high blood glucose levels. It binds to the membrane receptor protein on its target cells. Binding increases the rate of transport of glucose across the membrane and stimulates glycogen synthesis, lipid biosynthesis, and protein synthesis. As a result, the blood glucose level is reduced. Clearly, the inability to produce sufficient insulin seriously impairs the body's ability to regulate metabolism.

Individuals suffering from diabetes mellitus do not produce enough insulin to properly regulate blood glucose levels. This generally results from the destruction of the β-cells of the islets of Langerhans. One theory to explain the mysterious disappearance of these cells is that a virus infection stimulates the immune system to produce antibodies that cause the destruction of the β-cells.

In the absence of insulin the uptake of glucose into the tissues is not stimulated, and a great deal of glucose is eliminated in the urine. Without insulin, then, adipose cells are unable to take up the glucose required to synthesize triglycerides. As a result, the rate of fat hydrolysis is much greater than the rate of fat resynthesis, and large quantities of free fatty acids are liberated into the bloodstream. Because glucose is not being efficiently taken into cells, carbohydrate metabolism slows, and there is an increase in the rate of lipid catabolism. In the liver this lipid catabolism results in the production of ketone bodies: acetone, acetoacetate, and β-hydroxybutyrate.

A similar situation can develop from improper eating, fasting, or dieting—any situation in which the body is not provided with sufficient energy in the form of carbohydrates. These ketone bodies cannot all be oxidized by the citric acid cycle, which is limited by the supply of oxaloacetate. The acetone concentration in blood rises to levels so high that acetone can be detected in the breath of untreated diabetics. The elevated concentration of ketones in the blood can overwhelm the buffering capacity of the blood, resulting in ketoacidosis. Ketones, too, will be excreted through the kidney. In fact, the presence of excess ketones in the urine can raise the osmotic concentration of the urine so that it behaves as an "osmotic diuretic," causing the excretion of enormous amounts of water. As a result, the patient may become severely dehydrated. In extreme cases the combination of dehydration and ketoacidosis may lead to coma and death.

It has been observed that diabetics also have a higher than normal level of glucagon in the blood. As we have seen, glucagon stimulates lipid catabolism and ketogenesis. It may be that the symptoms described above may result from both the deficiency of insulin and the elevated glucagon levels. The absence of insulin may cause the elevated blood glucose and fatty acid levels, while the glucagon, by stimulating ketogenesis, may be responsible for the ketoacidosis and dehydration.

There is no cure for diabetes. However, when the problem is the result of the inability to produce active insulin, blood glucose levels can be controlled moderately well by the injection of either animal insulin or human insulin produced from the cloned insulin gene (see "A Medical Perspective: The New Genetics and Human Genetic Disease" in Chapter 19). Unfortunately, one or even a few injections of insulin each day cannot mimic the precise control of blood glucose accomplished by the pancreas.

As a result, diabetics suffer progressive tissue degeneration that leads to early death. One primary cause of this degeneration is atherosclerosis, the deposition of plaque on the walls of blood vessels. This causes a high frequency of strokes, heart attack, and gangrene of the feet and lower extremities, often necessitating amputation. Kidney failure causes the death of about 20% of diabetics under 40 years of age, and diabetic retinopathy (various kinds of damage to the retina of the eye) ranks fourth among the leading causes of blindness in the United States. Nerves are also damaged,

◆ **Enzymes involved.** The seven steps of fatty acid biosynthesis are carried out by a multienzyme complex known as *fatty acid synthase.* The enzymes responsible for fatty acid degradation are not physically associated in such complexes.

◆ **Electron carriers.** NADH and $FADH_2$ are produced by fatty acid oxidation, whereas NADPH is the reducing agent for fatty acid biosynthesis. As a general rule, *NADH is produced by catabolic reactions, and NADPH is the reducing agent of biosynthetic reactions.* These two coenzymes differ only by the presence of a phosphate group bound to the

resulting in neuropathies that can cause pain or numbness, particularly of the feet.

There is no doubt that insulin injections prolong the life of diabetics, but only the presence of a fully functioning pancreas can allow a diabetic to live a life free of the complica-

tions noted here. At present, pancreas transplants do not have a good track record. Only about 50% of the transplants are functioning after one year. It is hoped that improved transplantation techniques will be developed so that diabetics can live a normal life span, free of debilitating disease.

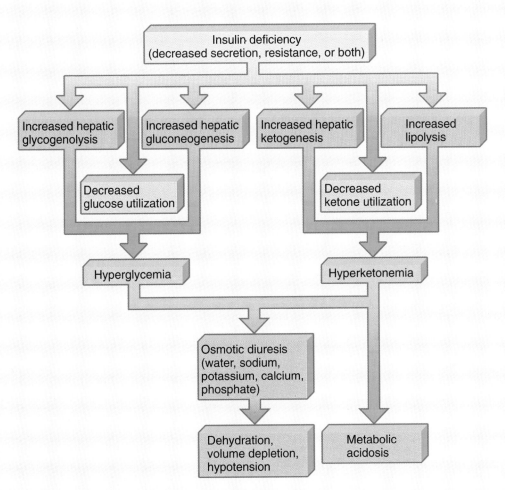

The array of metabolic events that occur in uncontrolled diabetes that can lead to coma and death.

ribose ring of NADPH (Figure 18.13). The enzymes that use these coenzymes, however, are easily able to distinguish them on this basis.

QUESTION 18.9

List the four major differences between β-oxidation and fatty acid biosynthesis that reveal that the two processes are not just the reverse of one another.

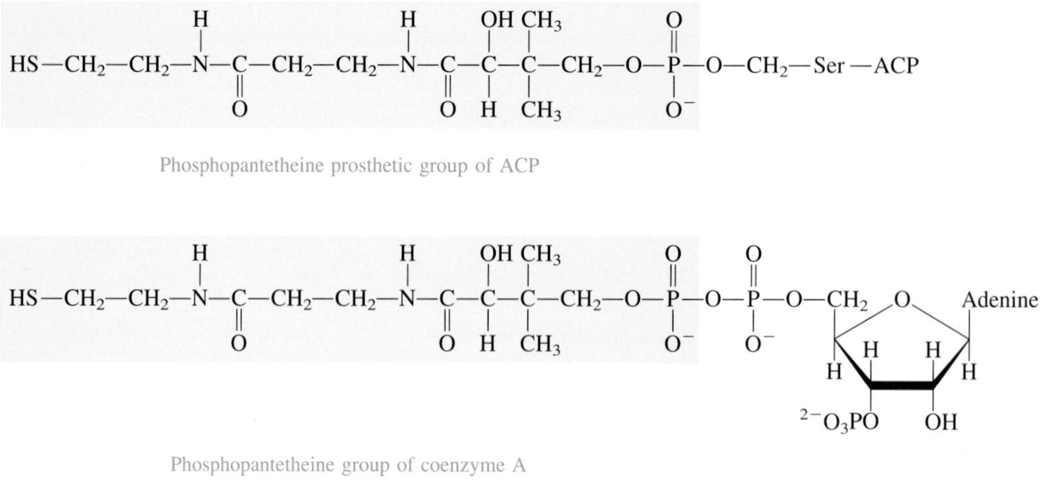

Phosphopantetheine prosthetic group of ACP

FIGURE 18.12
The structure of the phosphopantetheine group, the reactive group common to coenzyme A and acyl carrier protein, is highlighted in yellow.

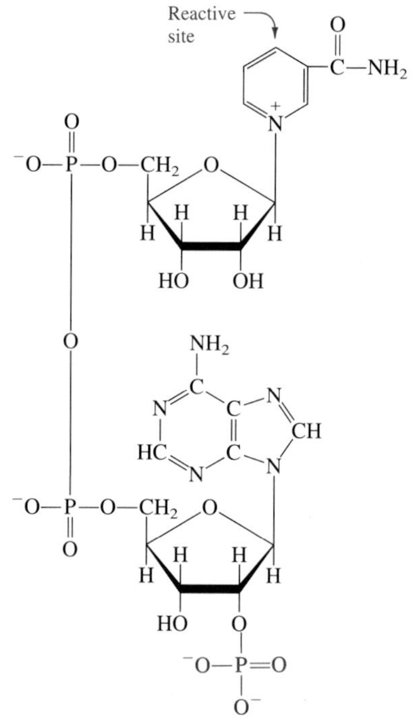

Phosphopantetheine group of coenzyme A

FIGURE 18.13
Structure of NADPH. The phosphate group shown in blue is the structural feature that distinguishes NADPH from NADH.

What chemical group is part of coenzyme A and acyl carrier protein and allows both molecules to form thioester bonds to fatty acids?

18.5 THE REGULATION OF LIPID AND CARBOHYDRATE METABOLISM

The liver

Section 16.6

The metabolism of fatty acids and carbohydrates occurs to a different extent in different organs. As we will see in this section, the regulation of these two related aspects of metabolism is of great physiological importance.

The liver provides a steady supply of glucose for muscle and brain and plays a major role in the regulation of blood glucose concentration. This regulation is under hormonal control. Recall that the hormone insulin causes blood glucose to be taken up by the liver and stored as glycogen (glycogenesis). In this way the liver reduces the blood glucose levels when they are too high.

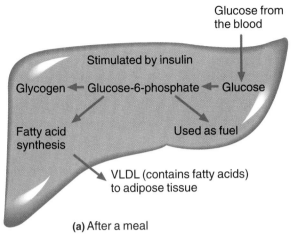
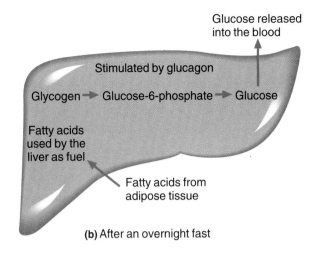

(a) After a meal

(b) After an overnight fast

FIGURE 18.14
The liver controls the concentration of blood glucose.

The hormone glucagon, on the other hand, stimulates the breakdown of glycogen and the release of glucose into the bloodstream. Lactate produced by muscles under anaerobic conditions is also taken up by liver cells and is converted to glucose by gluconeogenesis. Both glycogen degradation (glycogenolysis) and gluconeogenesis are pathways that produce glucose for export to other organs when energy is needed (Figure 18.14).

The liver also plays a central role in lipid metabolism. When excess fuel is available, the liver synthesizes fatty acids. These are used to produce triglycerides that are transported from the liver to adipose tissues by very low density lipoprotein (VLDL) complexes. In fact, VLDL complexes provide adipose tissue with its major source of fatty acids. This transport is particularly active when more Calories are eaten than are burned! During fasting or starvation conditions, however, the liver converts fatty acids to acetoacetate and other ketone bodies. The liver cannot use these ketone bodies because it lacks an enzyme for the conversion of acetoacetate to acetyl CoA. Therefore the ketone bodies produced by the liver are exported to other organs. Surprisingly, the preferred fuel for the liver is not glucose. Rather, the liver obtains most of its metabolic energy from the carbon skeletons of such amino acids as alanine.

Section 13.5

Adipose tissue

Adipose tissue is the major storage depot of fatty acids. Triglycerides produced by the liver are transported through the bloodstream as components of VLDL complexes. The triglycerides are hydrolyzed by the same lipases that act on chylomicrons, and the fatty acids are absorbed by adipose tissue. The synthesis of triglycerides in adipose tissue requires glycerol-3-phosphate. However, adipose tissue is unable to make glycerol-3-phosphate and depends upon glycolysis for its supply of this molecule. Thus adipose cells must have a ready source of glucose in order to synthesize and store triglycerides.

Triglycerides are constantly being hydrolyzed and resynthesized in the cells of adipose tissue. Lipases that are under hormonal control determine the rate of hydrolysis of triglycerides into fatty acids and glycerol. If glucose is in limited supply, there will not be sufficient glycerol-3-phosphate for the resynthesis of triglycerides, and the fatty acids and glycerol are exported to the liver for further processing (Figure 18.15).

$$
\begin{array}{l}
\quad\ \ \overset{\displaystyle H}{|} \\
H-\overset{|}{C}-OH \\
\quad\ \ | \\
H-\overset{|}{C}-OH \quad\ \ O \\
\quad\ \ | \qquad\qquad \| \\
H-\overset{|}{C}\ \ \ \ -O-P-O^{-} \\
\quad\ \ | \qquad\qquad | \\
\quad\ \ H \qquad\qquad O^{-}
\end{array}
$$

Glycerol-3-phosphate

Muscle tissue

The energy demand of *resting* muscle is generally supplied by the β-oxidation of fatty acids. The heart muscle actually prefers ketone bodies over glucose.

Working muscle, however, obtains energy by degradation of its own supply of glycogen. Glycogen degradation produces glucose-6-phosphate, which is directly funneled into glycolysis. If the muscle is working so hard that it doesn't get enough oxygen, it produces large amounts of lactate. This fermentation end product, as well as alanine (from catabolism of proteins and

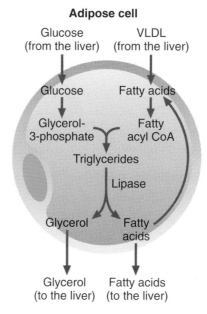

FIGURE 18.15
Synthesis and degradation of triglycerides in adipose tissue.

Section 17.7

transamination of pyruvate), is exported to the liver. Here they are converted to glucose by gluconeogenesis (Figure 18.16).

The brain

Under normal conditions the brain uses glucose as its sole source of metabolic energy. When the body is in the resting state, about 60% of the free glucose of the body is used by the brain. Starvation depletes glycogen stores, and the amount of glucose available to the brain drops sharply. The ketone bodies acetoacetate and β-hydroxybutyrate are then used by the brain as an alternative energy source. Fatty acids themselves are transported in the blood in complexes with the protein serum albumin and cannot cross the blood-brain barrier. But ketone bodies, which have a free carboxyl group, are soluble in blood and can enter the brain. This allows the body to degrade lipids before proteins during starvation.

FIGURE 18.16
Metabolic relationships between liver and muscle.

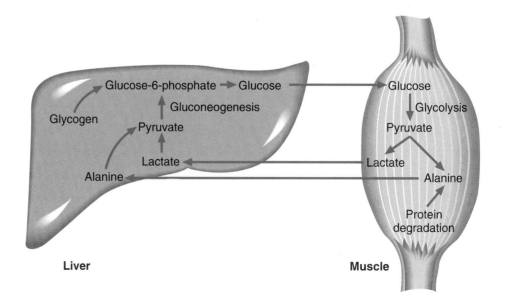

How does the liver regulate blood glucose levels?

Why is regulation of blood glucose levels important to the efficient function of the brain?

The hormone **insulin** is produced by the β-cells of the islets of Langerhans in the pancreas. It is secreted from these cells in response to an increase in the blood glucose level. Insulin lowers the concentration of blood glucose by causing a number of changes in metabolism (Table 18.1).

The simplest way to lower blood glucose levels is to stimulate storage of glucose, both as glycogen and as triglycerides. *Insulin therefore activates biosynthetic processes and inhibits catabolic processes.*

Insulin acts only on those cells, known as *target cells*, that possess a specific insulin receptor protein in their plasma membranes. The major target cells for insulin are liver, adipose, and muscle cells.

The blood glucose level is normally about 10 mM. However, a substantial meal increases the concentration of blood glucose considerably and stimulates insulin secretion. Subsequent binding of insulin to the plasma membrane insulin receptor protein increases the rate of transport of glucose across the membrane and into cells.

Insulin exerts a variety of effects on all aspects of cellular metabolism:

◆ **Carbohydrate metabolism.** Insulin stimulates glycogen synthesis. At the same time it inhibits glycogenolysis and gluconeogenesis. The overall result of these activities is the storage of excess glucose.

◆ **Protein metabolism.** Insulin stimulates transport and uptake of amino acids, as well as the incorporation of amino acids into proteins.

◆ **Lipid metabolism.** Insulin stimulates uptake of glucose by adipose cells, as well as the synthesis and storage of triglycerides. As we have seen, storage of lipids requires a source of glucose, and insulin helps the process by increasing the available glucose. At the same time, insulin inhibits the breakdown of stored triglycerides.

As you may have already guessed, insulin is only part of the overall regulation of cellular metabolism in the body. A second hormone, **glucagon,** is secreted by the α-cells of the islets of Langerhans in response to decreased blood glucose levels. The effects of glucagon, generally the opposite of the effects of insulin, are summarized in Table 18.1. Although it has no direct effect on glucose uptake, glucagon inhibits glycogen synthesis and stimulates glycogenolysis and gluconeogenesis. It also stimulates the breakdown of fats and ketogenesis.

The antagonistic effects of these two hormones, seen in Figure 18.17, are critical for the maintenance of adequate blood glucose levels. During fasting, low blood glucose levels stimu-

18.6 THE EFFECT OF INSULIN AND GLUCAGON ON CELLULAR METABOLISM

Section 16.6

Sections 16.5 and 16.6

FIGURE 18.17
A summary of the antagonistic effects of insulin and glucagon.

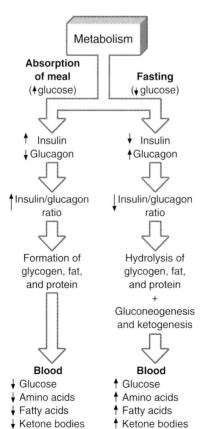

TABLE 18.1 Comparison of the metabolic effects of insulin and glucagon

Actions	Insulin	Glucagon
Cellular glucose transport	Increased	No effect
Glycogen synthesis	Increased	Decreased
Glycogenolysis in liver	Decreased	Increased
Gluconeogenesis	Decreased	Increased
Amino acid uptake and protein synthesis	Increased	No effect
Inhibition of amino acid release and protein degradation	Decreased	No effect
Lipogenesis	Increased	No effect
Lipolysis	Decreased	Increased
Ketogenesis	Decreased	Increased

late production of glucagon, which increases blood glucose by stimulating the breakdown of glycogen and the production of glucose by gluconeogenesis. This ensures a ready supply of glucose for the tissues, especially the brain. On the other hand, when blood glucose levels are too high, insulin is secreted. It stimulates the removal of the excess glucose by enhancing uptake and inducing pathways for storage.

QUESTION 18.13

Summarize the effects of the hormone insulin on carbohydrate, lipid, and amino acid metabolism.

QUESTION 18.14

Summarize the effects of the hormone glucagon on carbohydrate and lipid metabolism.

SUMMARY

18.1 Lipid Metabolism in Animals

Dietary lipids *(triglycerides)* are emulsified into tiny fat droplets in the intestine by the action of *bile* salts. Pancreatic *lipase* catalyzes the hydrolysis of triglycerides into monoglycerides and fatty acids. These are absorbed by intestinal epithelial cells, reassembled into triglycerides, and combined with protein to form *chylomicrons*. Chylomicrons are transported to the cells of the body through the bloodstream. Fatty acids are stored as triglycerides (triacylglycerols) in fat droplets in the cytoplasm of *adipocytes*.

18.2 Fatty Acid Degradation

Fatty acids are degraded to acetyl CoA in the mitochondria by the *β-oxidation* pathway, which involves five steps: (1) the production of a fatty acyl CoA molecule, (2) oxidation of the fatty acid by an FAD-dependent dehydrogenase, (3) hydration, (4) oxidation by an NAD^+-dependent dehydrogenase, and (5) cleavage of the chain with release of acetyl CoA and a fatty acyl CoA that is two carbons shorter than the beginning fatty acid. The last four reactions are repeated until the fatty acid is completely degraded.

18.3 Ketone Bodies

Under some conditions, fatty acid degradation occurs more rapidly than glycolysis. As a result, a large amount of acetyl CoA is produced from fatty acids, but little oxaloacetate is generated from pyruvate. When oxaloacetate levels are too low, the excess acetyl CoA is converted to the *ketone bodies* acetone, acetoacetate, and *β*-hydroxybutyrate.

18.4 Fatty Acid Synthesis

Fatty acid biosynthesis occurs by the sequential addition of acetyl groups and, on first inspection, appears to be a simple reversal of the *β*-oxidation pathway. Although the biochemical reactions are similar, fatty acid synthesis differs from *β*-oxidation in the following ways: It occurs in the cytoplasm, utilizes *acyl carrier protein* and NADPH, and is carried out by a multienzyme complex, fatty acid synthase.

18.5 The Regulation of Lipid and Carbohydrate Metabolism

Lipid and carbohydrate metabolism occur to different extents in different organs. The liver regulates the flow of metabolites to brain, muscle, and adipose tissue and ultimately controls the concentration of blood glucose. *Adipose tissue* is the major storage depot for fatty acids. Triglycerides are constantly hydrolyzed and resynthesized in adipose tissue. Muscle oxidizes glucose, fatty acids, and ketone bodies. The brain uses glucose as a fuel except in prolonged fasting or starvation, when it will use ketone bodies as an energy source.

18.6 The Effects of Insulin and Glucagon on Cellular Metabolism

Insulin stimulates biosynthetic processes and inhibits catabolism in liver, muscle, and adipose tissue. Insulin is synthesized in the *β*-cells of the pancreas and is secreted when the blood glucose levels become too high. The insulin receptor protein binds to the insulin and mediates a variety of responses in target tissues. The effects of insulin encourage the storage of glucose and lipids. *Glucagon* is secreted when blood glucose levels are too low. It has the opposite effects on metabolism, including the breakdown of lipids and glycogen.

KEY TERMS

acyl carrier protein (ACP) (18.4)
adipocyte (18.1)
adipose tissue (18.1)
bile (18.1)
chylomicron (18.1)
colipase (18.1)
diabetes mellitus (18.3)
glucagon (18.6)
insulin (18.6)
ketoacidosis (18.3)
ketone bodies (18.3)
ketosis (18.3)
lipase (18.1)
micelle (18.1)
β-oxidation (18.2)
phosphopantetheine (18.4)
triglyceride (18.1)

QUESTIONS AND PROBLEMS

Lipid Metabolism

18.15 What is the major storage form of fatty acids?

18.16 What tissue is the major storage depot for lipids?

18.17 What is the outstanding structural feature of an adipocyte?

18.18 What is the major metabolic function of adipose tissue?

18.19 What is the general reaction catalyzed by lipases?

18.20 Why are the lipases that are found in saliva and in the stomach not very effective at digesting triglycerides?

18.21 List three major biological molecules for which acetyl CoA is a precursor.

18.22 Why are triglycerides more efficient energy-storage molecules than glycogen?

18.23 What are chylomicrons, and what is their function?

18.24 What are very low density lipoproteins? Compare the function of VLDLs with that of chylomicrons.

18.25 What is the function of the bile salts in the digestion of dietary lipids?

18.26 What is the function of colipase in the digestion of dietary lipids?

Fatty Acid Degradation

18.27 What products are formed when the ω-phenyl-labeled carboxylic acid 12-phenyldodecanoic acid is degraded by β-oxidation?

18.28 What products are formed when the ω-phenyl-labeled carboxylic acid 5-phenylpentanoic acid is degraded by β-oxidation?

18.29 Calculate the number of ATP molecules produced for complete β-oxidation of the 14-carbon saturated fatty acid tetradecanoic acid (common name: myristic acid).

18.30 Write the sequence of steps that would be followed for one round of β-oxidation of hexanoic acid. Calculate the number of ATP molecules produced for complete β-oxidation of hexanoic acid.

18.31 How many molecules of ATP are produced for each molecule of $FADH_2$ that is generated by β-oxidation?

18.32 How many molecules of ATP are produced for each molecule of NADH generated by β-oxidation?

18.33 What is the fate of the acetyl CoA produced by β-oxidation?

18.34 How many ATP molecules are produced from each acetyl CoA molecule generated in β-oxidation that enters the citric acid cycle?

Ketone Bodies

18.35 Draw the structures of acetoacetate and β-hydroxybutyrate.

18.36 Describe the relationship between the formation of ketone bodies and β-oxidation.

18.37 Why do uncontrolled diabetics produce large amounts of ketone bodies?

18.38 How does the presence of ketone bodies in the blood lead to ketoacidosis?

18.39 When does the heart use ketone bodies?

18.40 When does the brain use ketone bodies?

Fatty Acid Synthesis

18.41 What is the role of the phosphopantetheine group in fatty acid biosynthesis? From what molecules is phosphopantetheine made?

18.42 What molecules involved in fatty acid degradation and fatty acid biosynthesis contain the phosphopantetheine group?

18.43 How does the structure of fatty acid synthase differ from that of the enzymes that carry out β-oxidation?

18.44 In what cellular compartments do fatty acid biosynthesis and β-oxidation occur?

Regulation of Lipid and Carbohydrate Metabolism

18.45 What is the major metabolic function of the liver?

18.46 What is the fate of lactate produced in skeletal muscle during rapid contraction?

18.47 What are the major fuels of the heart, brain, and liver?

18.48 Why can't the brain use fatty acids as fuel?

18.49 Briefly describe triglyceride metabolism in an adipocyte.

18.50 What is the source of the glycerol molecule that is used in the synthesis of triglycerides?

The Effects of Insulin and Glucagon on Cellular Metabolism

18.51 Where is insulin produced?

18.52 Where is glucagon produced?

18.53 How does insulin affect carbohydrate metabolism?

18.54 How does glucagon affect carbohydrate metabolism?

18.55 How does insulin affect lipid metabolism?

18.56 How does glucagon affect lipid metabolism?

Further Problems

18.57 Fill in the blanks:
   a. Fatty acids are stored as _____ in adipose tissue.
   b. The enzyme that catalyzes the release of fatty acids from triglycerides is called _____.
   c. For each acetyl CoA produced by β-oxidation, _____ ATP are produced.
   d. Glucose, fatty acids, and ketone bodies are all energy sources that can be used by _____ tissue.

18.58 Label each of the following statements as true or false:
   a. Insulin-dependent diabetes mellitus is caused by insulin deficiency.
   b. Acetyl CoA is one of the minor products of β-oxidation of fatty acids.
   c. The complete oxidation of fatty acids releases more energy than the oxidation of a comparable mass of glycogen.
   d. β-oxidation of fatty acids involves the sequential removal of single carbon fragments.

18.59 Describe the stages of lipid digestion.

18.60 Describe the transport of lipids digested in the lumen of the intestines to the cells of the body.

18.61 Why is it said that diabetes mellitus amounts to starvation in the midst of plenty?

18.62 What is the role of the insulin receptor in controlling blood glucose levels?

VOCABULARY QUIZ

18.1 _____ is fatty tissue that stores most of the body lipids.

18.2 A(n) _____ is a molecule composed of glycerol esterified to three fatty acids.

18.3 _____ consists of micelles of lecithin, cholesterol, bile salts, protein, inorganic ions, and bile pigments that aid in lipid digestion by emulsifying fat droplets.

18.4 A(n) _____ is an aggregate of protein and triglycerides that carries triglycerides from the intestines to all body tissues via the bloodstream.

18.5 The biochemical pathway that results in the oxidation of fatty acids and the production of acetyl CoA is called _____.

18.6 The molecule that serves as a carrier of acetyl groups in lipid and carbohydrate metabolism is _____.

18.7 _____ is a peptide hormone synthesized by the α-cells of the islets of Langerhans in the pancreas and secreted in response to low blood glucose levels.

18.8 The peptide hormone secreted by the β-cells of the islets of Langerhans in the pancreas in response to high blood glucose levels is _____.

18.9 A(n) _____ is an enzyme that hydrolyzes the ester linkage between glycerol and the fatty acids of triglycerides.

18.10 Acetone, acetoacetone, and β-hydroxybutyrate produced from fatty acids in the liver are referred to as _____.

19

Introduction to Molecular Genetics

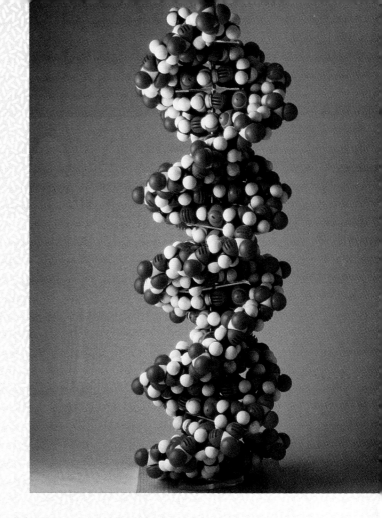

LEARNING GOALS

◆ Describe the structure of DNA and RNA.

◆ Understand DNA replication.

◆ Explain the role of DNA in the transmission of genetic information.

◆ Describe the essential elements of the genetic code, and develop a "feel" for its elegance.

◆ List three classes of RNA molecules.

◆ Explain the processes of transcription and translation.

◆ Define mutation and understand how mutations cause cancer and cell death.

◆ Describe the tools used in the study of DNA and in genetic engineering.

◆ Recognize the potential of pharmaceuticals produced by recombinant DNA.

CHEMISTRY CONNECTION

A World Without Human Genetic Disease?

It is estimated that 3–5% of the human population suffers from a serious genetic defect. That's 200 million people! But imagine a world with no human genetic disease. Two new technologies, *gene therapy* and *preimplantation diagnosis,* may help us realize this dream.

For a couple with a history of genetic disease in the family, pregnancy is a time of anxiety. Through *genetic counseling* these couples can learn the probability that their child has the disease. For about 200 genetic diseases the uncertainty can be eliminated. *Amniocentesis* (removal of 10–20 mL of fluid from the sac around the fetus) and *chorionic villus sampling* (removal of fetal cells from a fetal membrane) are two procedures that are used to obtain fetal cells for genetic testing. Fetal cells are cultured and tested by enzyme assays and DNA tests to look for genetic diseases. If a genetic disease is diagnosed, the parents must make a difficult decision: to abort the fetus or to carry the child to term and deal with the effects of the genetic disease.

The power of modern molecular genetics is obvious in our ability to find a "bad" gene from just a few cells. But scientists have developed an even more impressive way to test for genetic disease before the embryo implants into the uterine lining. This technique, called preimplantation diagnosis, involves fertilizing a human egg and allowing the resulting con-

ceptus to divide in a sterile petri dish. When the conceptus consists of 8–16 cells, *one* cell is removed for genetic testing. Only genetically normal embryos are implanted in the mother. To date, five babies tested by this procedure have been born. Thus the genetic diseases that we can detect could be eliminated from the population by preimplantation diagnosis because only a conceptus with "good" genes is used.

Gene therapy is a second way in which genetic diseases may one day be eliminated. Foreign genes, including growth hormone, have been introduced into fertilized mouse eggs and the conceptuses implanted in female mice. The baby mice born with the foreign growth hormone gene were about three times larger than their normal litter mates! One day, this kind of technology may be used to introduce normal genes into human fertilized eggs carrying a defective gene, thereby replacing the defective gene with a normal one.

In this chapter we will examine the molecules that carry and express our genetic information, DNA and RNA. Only by understanding the structure and function of these molecules have we been able to develop the amazing array of genetic tools that currently exists. We hope that as we continue to learn more about human genetics, we will be able to detect and one day correct most of the known genetic diseases.

INTRODUCTION

Deoxyribonucleic acid (DNA) carries all the genetic information in the cell. DNA is a polymer of many subunits called nucleotides. However, as we have seen in previous chapters, it is proteins that carry out the work for the cell. Thus the DNA carries the information to produce the proteins that will serve as enzymes and structural elements of the cell. The sequence of the nucleotides in the DNA dictates the sequence of amino acids in the primary structure of each protein. The sequence of nucleotides that carries the code for one protein is called a gene.

Ribonucleic acid (RNA) molecules are also polymers of nucleotides. There are three types of RNA: messenger RNA, transfer RNA, and ribosomal RNA. These are the molecules that carry out the translation of the genetic code into the structure of a protein.

19.1 THE STRUCTURE OF THE NUCLEOTIDE

Chemical Composition of DNA and RNA

Section 11.2

Deoxyribonucleic acid (DNA) and **ribonucleic acid (RNA)** are long polymers of **nucleotides.** Every nucleotide is composed of three units: a five-carbon sugar, a nitrogenous base, and either one, two, or three phosphoryl groups. Nitrogenous bases are heterocyclic ring structures having backbones consisting of carbon and nitrogen atoms. There are two classes of nitrogenous bases. The **purine** nitrogenous bases consist of a six-membered ring fused to a five-membered ring. The **pyrimidine** nitrogenous bases consist of a single six-membered ring. The structures are seen in Figure 19.1.

The five-carbon sugar in RNA is ribose, and the sugar in DNA is 2′-deoxyribose. The only difference between these two sugars is the absence of an hydroxyl group on the 2′ carbon of 2′-deoxyribose. The purines in both DNA and RNA are adenine and guanine. Both DNA and

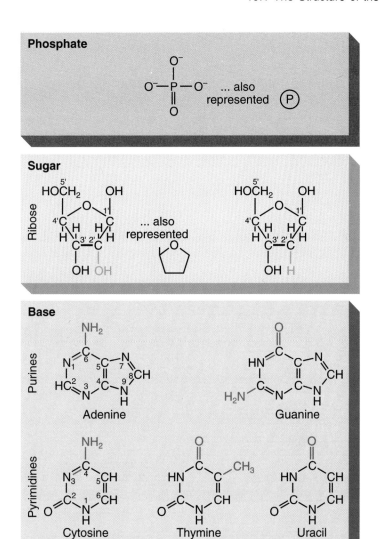

FIGURE 19.1
The components of nucleic acids include phosphate groups, the five-carbon sugars ribose and deoxyribose, and purine and pyrimidine nitrogenous bases. The ring positions of the sugars are designated with primes to distinguish them from the ring positions of the bases.

RNA contain the pyrimidine cytosine; however, the fourth base is thymine in DNA and uracil in RNA. The chemical compositions of DNA and RNA are summarized in Table 19.1.

In addition, the nucleotides that make up DNA and RNA contain phosphoryl groups. Nucleotides may contain one, two, or three phosphoryl groups.

The carbon atoms of the sugars found in nucleic acids are indicated with a prime: 1′, 2′, 3′, and so on. This is to distinguish them from the ring atoms of the nitrogenous bases.

Nucleotides are produced by the combination of a sugar, a nitrogenous base, and at least one phosphoryl group, as shown in Figure 19.2. Because this large structure contains two cyclic molecules, the sugar and the base, we must have an easy way to describe the ring atoms of each.

Nucleotide structure

TABLE 19.1 Chemical Composition of Nucleic Acids

	DNA	RNA
Sugar	2′-Deoxyribose	Ribose
Purine nitrogenous bases	Adenine (A)	Adenine (A)
	Guanine (G)	Guanine (G)
Pyrimidine nitrogenous bases	Cytosine (C)	Cytosine (C)
	Thymine (T)	Uracil (U)

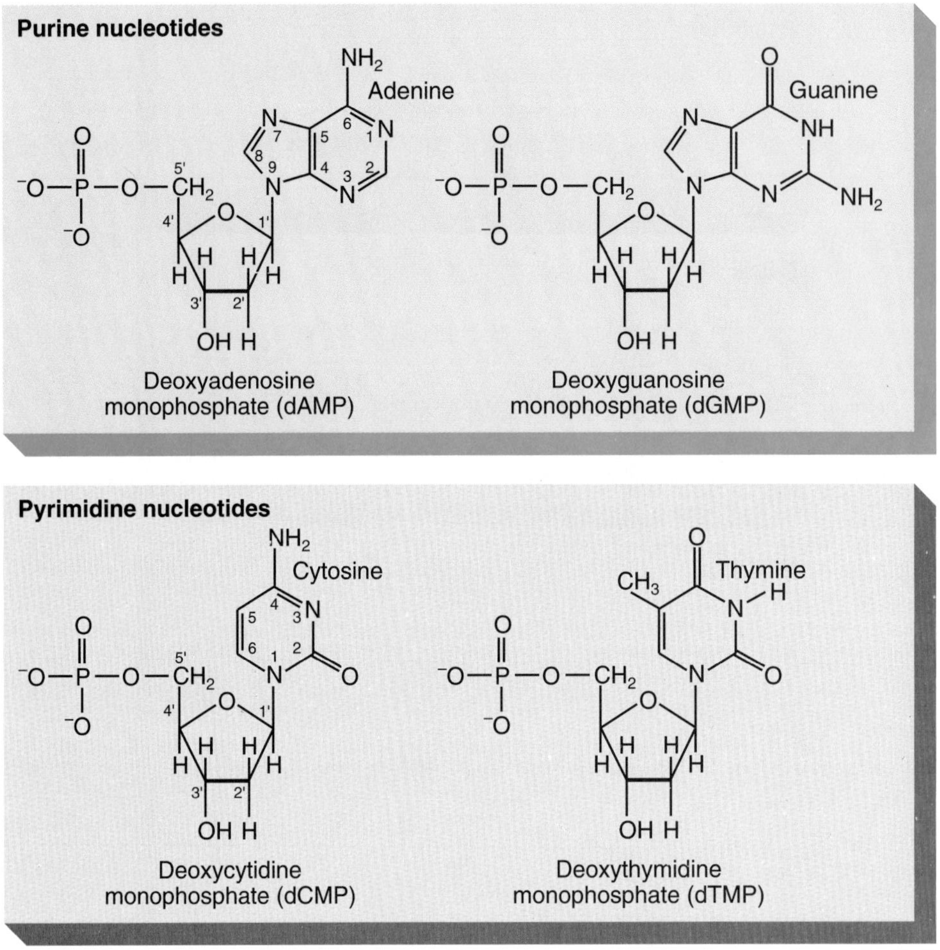

FIGURE 19.2
Structures and names and common abbreviations of four deoxyribonucleotides or deoxyribonucleoside 5′-phosphates.

For this reason the ring atoms of the sugar are designated with a prime to distinguish them from atoms in the base. The covalent bond between the sugar and the phosphoryl group is a phospho-ester linkage formed by a dehydration reaction between the 5′-OH of the sugar and an —OH of the phosphoryl group. The bond between the base and the sugar is called a β-N-glycosidic linkage, and it joins the 1′-carbon of the sugar and a nitrogen atom of the nitrogenous base (N-9 of purines and N-1 of pyrimidines).

To name a nucleotide, simply begin with the name of the nitrogenous base, and apply the following simple rules:

◆ Remove the -ine ending, and replace it with either -osine for purines or -idine for pyrimidines. Uracil is the one exception to this rule. In this case the -acil ending is replaced with -idine, producing the name uridine.

◆ Nucleotides with the sugar ribose are **ribonucleotides,** and those having the sugar 2′-deoxyribose are **deoxyribonucleotides.** For a deoxyribonucleotide, the prefix deoxy- is placed before the modified nitrogenous base name. No prefix is required for ribonucleotides.

In diphosphates and triphosphates the phosphoryl groups are bonded to one another through phosphoanhydride bonds (Section 12.3).

◆ Add a prefix to indicate the number of phosphoryl groups that are attached. A monophosphate carries one phosphoryl group; a diphosphate carries two phosphoryl groups; and a triphosphate carries three phosphoryl groups.

TABLE 19.2   Names and Abbreviations of the Ribonucleotides and Deoxyribonucleotides Containing Adenine

Nucleotide	Abbreviation
Deoxyadenosine monophosphate	dAMP
Deoxyadenosine diphosphate	dADP
Deoxyadenosine triphosphate	dATP
Adenosine monophosphate	AMP
Adenosine diphosphate	ADP
Adenosine triphosphate	ATP

QUESTION 19.1

Referring to the structures in Figures 19.1 and 19.2, draw the structures and write the names for nucleotides consisting of the following units:

a.   Ribose, adenine, two phosphoryl groups

b.   2′-Deoxyribose, guanine, three phosphoryl groups

QUESTION 19.2

Referring to the structures in Figures 19.1 and 19.2, draw the structures and write the names for nucleotides consisting of the following units:

a.   2′-Deoxyribose, thymine, one phosphoryl group

b.   Ribose, cytosine, three phosphoryl groups

c.   Ribose, uracil, one phosphoryl group

Because the full names of the nucleotides are so cumbersome, a simple abbreviation is generally used. These abbreviations are summarized in Table 19.2.

QUESTION 19.3

Write the names and abbreviations of the deoxyribonucleotides and ribonucleotides of guanine.

QUESTION 19.4

Write the names and abbreviations of the deoxyribonucleotides and ribonucleotides of cytosine.

19.2 THE STRUCTURE OF DNA AND RNA

DNA structure: the double helix

A single strand of DNA is a polymer of nucleotides bonded to one another by 3′–5′ phosphodiester bonds. The backbone of the polymer is called the sugar-phosphate backbone because it is composed of alternating units of the five-carbon sugar 2′-deoxyribose and phosphoryl groups in phosphodiester linkage. A nitrogenous base is bonded to each sugar by an N-glycosidic linkage (Figure 19.3).

James Watson and Francis Crick were the first to describe the three-dimensional structure of DNA in 1953. DNA, they concluded, is a **double helix** of two strands of DNA wound around one another. It is useful to compare the structure of the double helix to a spiral staircase. The sugar-phosphate backbones of the two strands of DNA spiral around the outside of the helix like the handrails on a spiral staircase. The nitrogenous bases extend into the center at right angles to the axis of the helix. You can imagine the nitrogenous bases forming the steps of the staircase. The structure of this elegant molecule is shown in Figure 19.4.

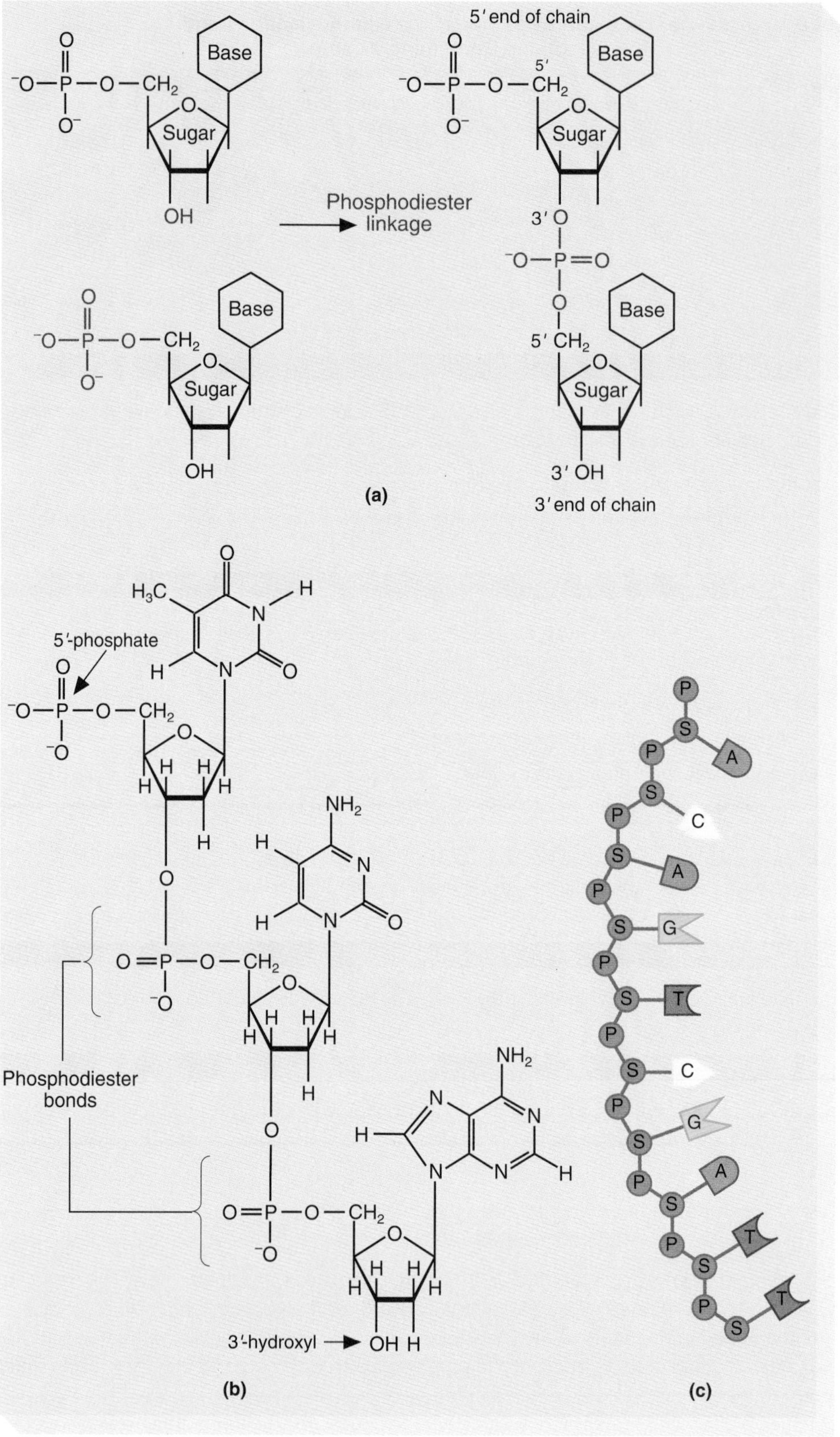

FIGURE 19.3

The covalent, primary structure of DNA. (a) The esterification reaction by which two nucleotides become linked by a phosphodiester bond. (b) A series of three covalently linked deoxyribonucleotides. (c) A stylized representation of the covalent primary structure of a longer piece of DNA.

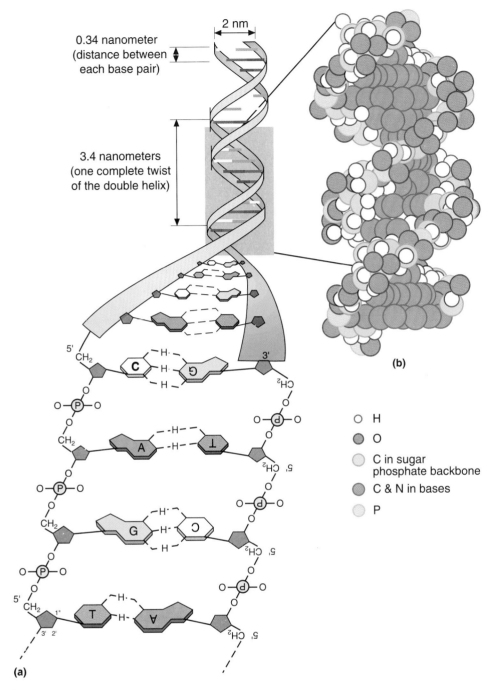

FIGURE 19.4
The DNA double helix. (a) Schematic ribbon diagram of the DNA double helix showing the dimensions of the DNA molecule and the antiparallel orientation of the two strands. (b) Space-filling model of a portion of a DNA molecule.

The two strands of DNA are held together by hydrogen bonds between the nitrogenous bases in the center of the helix. Adenine forms two hydrogen bonds with thymine, and cytosine forms three hydrogen bonds with guanine (Figure 19.5). These are called **base pairs.** The two strands of DNA are **complementary** because the sequence of bases on one strand automatically determines the sequence of bases on the opposite strand. When there is an adenine on one strand, there will always be a thymine in the same location on the opposite strand.

A CLINICAL PERSPECTIVE

Fooling the AIDS Virus with "Look-Alike" Nucleotides

The virus that is responsible for the acquired immune deficiency syndrome (AIDS) is called the human immunodeficiency virus, or HIV. Members of this family of viruses, *retroviruses,* have single-stranded RNA as their genetic material. The RNA is copied by a viral enzyme called reverse transcriptase into a double-stranded DNA molecule. This process is the opposite of the central dogma, which states that the flow of genetic information is from DNA to RNA. But these viruses reverse that flow, RNA to DNA. For this reason these viruses are called retroviruses, which literally means "backward viruses." The process of producing a DNA copy of the RNA is called reverse transcription.

Because our genetic information is DNA and it is expressed by the classical DNA → RNA → protein pathway, our cells have no need for a reverse transcriptase enzyme. Thus the HIV reverse transcriptase is a good target for antiviral chemotherapy because inhibition of the reverse transcriptase should kill the virus but have no effect on the human host. Many drugs have been tested for the ability to selectively inhibit the HIV reverse transcriptase. Among these is 3'-azido-2',3'-dideoxythymidine, commonly called AZT or zidovudine.

How does AZT work? It is one of many drugs that looks like one of the normal nucleosides. These are called *nucleoside analogs.* A nucleoside is just a nucleotide without any phosphate groups attached. The analog is phosphorylated by the cell and then tricks a polymerase, in this case viral reverse transcriptase, into incorporating it into the growing DNA chain in place of the normal phosphorylated nucleoside. AZT is a nucleoside analog that looks like the nucleoside thymidine except that in the 3' position of the ribose sugar there is an azido group (—N₃) rather than the 3'-OH group. Compare the structures of thymidine and AZT shown in the accompanying figure. The 3'-OH group is necessary for further DNA

Comparison of the structures of the normal nucleoside, 2'-deoxythymidine, and the nucleoside analog, 3'-azido-2',3'-dideoxythymidine.

polymerization because it is there that the phosphodiester linkage must be made between the growing DNA strand and the next nucleotide. If an azido group or some other group is present at the 3' position, the nucleotide analog can be incorporated into the growing DNA strand, but further chain elongation is blocked, as seen in the accompanying figure. If the viral RNA cannot be reverse transcribed into the DNA form, the virus will not be able to replicate and can be considered to be dead.

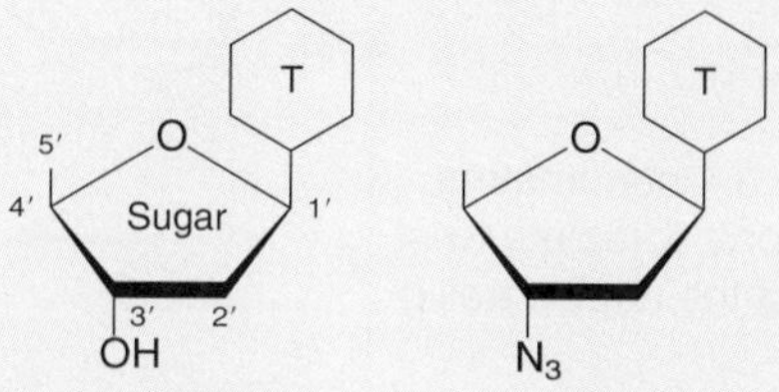

AZT is particularly effective because the HIV reverse transcriptase actually prefers it over the normal nucleotide, thymidine. Nonetheless, AZT is not a cure. At best it prolongs the life of a person with AIDS for a year or two. Eventually, however, AZT has a negative effect on the body. The cells of our bone marrow are constantly dividing to produce new blood cells: red blood cells to carry oxygen to the tissues, white blood cells of the immune system, and platelets for blood clotting. For cells to divide, they must replicate their DNA. The DNA polymerases of these dividing cells also acciden-

---

One last important feature of the DNA double helix is that the two strands are **antiparallel** to one another, as this example shows:

$$5' \text{ P—S—P—S—P—S—P—S—P—S—P—S—OH } 3'$$

```
5' P—S—P—S—P—S—P—S—P—S—P—S—OH 3'
       |       |       |       |       |       |
       A       T       G       C       G       A
       :       :       :       :       :       :
       T       A       C       G       C       T
       |       |       |       |       |       |
3'OH—S—P—S—P—S—P—S—P—S—P—S—P  5'
```

In other words, the two strands of the helix run in opposite directions (Figure 19.4). Only when the two strands are antiparallel can the base pairs form the hydrogen bonds that hold the two strands together.

tally incorporate AZT into the growing DNA chains with the result that cells of the bone marrow begin to die. This can result in anemia and even further depression of the immune response.

Another problem that has arisen with prolonged use of AZT is that AZT-resistant mutants of the virus appear. It is well known that HIV is a virus that mutates rapidly. Some of these mutant forms of the virus have an altered reverse tran-

scriptase that will no longer use AZT. When these mutants appear, AZT is no longer useful in treating the infection.

It is hoped that research with other nucleoside analogs and alternative types of antiviral treatments will provide a means of effectively treating HIV infection. Such a therapy must have fewer toxic side-effects while stopping the replication of the virus and the progress of the disease.

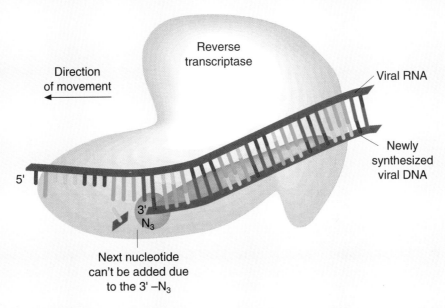

The mechanism by which AZT inhibits HIV reverse transcriptase. Incorporation of AZT into the growing HIV DNA strand in place of deoxythymidine results in DNA chain termination; the azido group on the 3′ carbon of the sugar cannot react to produce the phosphodiester linkage required to add the next nucleotide.

RNA structure

The sugar-phosphate backbone of RNA consists of ribonucleotide residues, also linked by 3′–5′ phosphodiester bonds. These phosphodiester bonds are identical to those found in DNA. However, RNA molecules differ from DNA molecules in three basic properties.

◆ RNA molecules are usually single-stranded.

◆ The sugar-phosphate backbone of RNA consists of *ribonucleotides* linked by 3′–5′ phosphodiester bonds. Thus the sugar ribose is found in place of 2′-deoxyribose.

◆ The nitrogenous base uracil (U) replaces thymine (T).

Even though RNA molecules are single-stranded, base pairing between uracil and adenine and between guanine and cytosine can still occur. This property will become very important as we examine the way in which RNA molecules are involved in the expression of the genetic information in DNA.

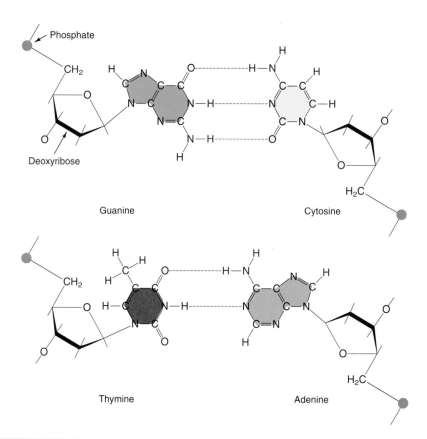

FIGURE 19.5
Base pairing in DNA. Adenine is always paired with thymine (A—T), and guanine is paired with cytosine (G—C).

19.3 DNA REPLICATION

FIGURE 19.6
The semiconservative model of DNA replication.

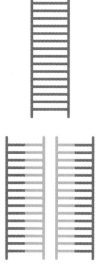

DNA must be replicated before a cell divides so that each daughter cell inherits a copy of each gene. A cell that is missing a critical gene will die, just as an individual with a genetic disease, a defect in an important gene, may die early in life. Thus it is essential that the process of DNA replication produces an absolutely accurate copy of the original genetic information. If mistakes are made in critical genes, the result may be lethal mutations.

The first step in DNA replication is the separation of the strands of DNA. Proteins do this by breaking the hydrogen bonds between the base pairs. Then the enzyme **DNA polymerase** ''reads'' each parental strand, also called the *template,* and catalyzes the polymerization of a complementary daughter strand. Deoxyribonucleotide triphosphate molecules are the precursors for DNA replication. However, the last two phosphoryl groups are cleaved away in the process. This cleavage releases the energy needed by DNA polymerase to form the phosphoester linkage between the 3'-OH of 2'-deoxyribose and the 5'-phosphoryl group of the deoxyribonucleotide monophosphate to be added to the DNA chain.

Because DNA polymerase ''reads'' each parental strand and produces a new complementary daughter DNA strand, each new DNA molecule consists of one parental strand and one newly synthesized daughter strand. This mode of DNA replication is called **semiconservative replication** (Figure 19.6).

Because it is critical to produce an accurate copy of the parental DNA, it is very important to avoid errors in the replication process. In addition to catalyzing the replication of new DNA strands, DNA polymerase is able to *proofread* the newly synthesized strand. If the wrong nucleotide has been added to the growing DNA strand, it is removed and replaced with the correct one. In this way a faithful copy of the parental DNA is ensured.

Bacterial chromosomes are circular DNA molecules. Replication begins at a **replication origin** and proceeds bidirectionally around the circular chromosome (Figure 19.7). The site at which the new DNA is being synthesized is called the **replication fork.** As this huge circular DNA molecule is replicated, it takes on the appearance of the Greek letter theta (Θ). Therefore this replicating structure is called a *theta structure.*

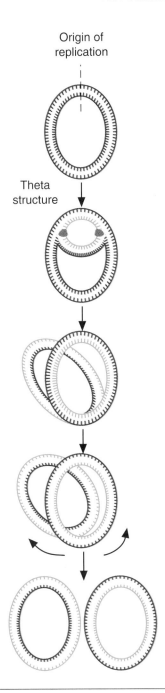

Origin of replication

Theta structure

FIGURE 19.7
Summary of the events of DNA replication. The DNA replication enzyme complex recognizes a specific DNA sequence called the *origin of replication.* An enzyme in the replication complex opens the DNA strands so that the DNA polymerase will be able to read the sequence of nucleotides and produce a complementary daughter strand. Replication proceeds bidirectionally, with two growing forks proceeding in opposite directions. This generates a DNA molecule that resembles the Greek letter theta (Θ). Eventually, the two replication forks collide, releasing two circular daughter DNA molecules.

The genetic information in the DNA must be expressed to produce the proteins that actually carry out the work of the cell. Gene expression involves two steps. First, DNA is transcribed to produce a variety of RNA molecules. This process is called **transcription.** Then the RNA molecules participate in **translation,** a process in which proteins are produced. This unidirectional expression of the genetic information is called the **central dogma** of molecular biology (Figure 19.8) and can be summarized as follows:

$$DNA \longrightarrow RNA \longrightarrow PROTEIN$$

Three classes of RNA molecules are produced by transcription: messenger RNA, transfer RNA, and ribosomal RNA.

1. **Messenger RNA (mRNA)** carries the genetic information for a protein from DNA to the ribosomes. It is a complementary RNA copy of a gene on the DNA.

19.4 INFORMATION FLOW IN BIOLOGICAL SYSTEMS

Classes of RNA molecules

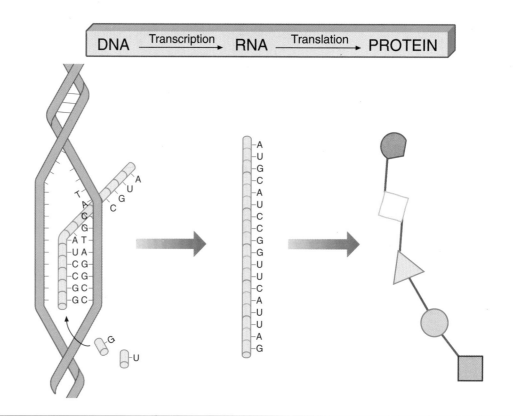

FIGURE 19.8
The central dogma of molecular biology. Information flows from DNA to RNA to protein. All the genetic information for all the structures and functions of the cell is carried by the DNA. The process of transcription copies a portion of the genetic information into a messenger RNA (mRNA) molecule. In the process of translation the genetic code carried by the mRNA is decoded into a linear sequence of amino acids. Each group of three nucleotides is called a codon, and each codes for a particular amino acid.

Eukaryotes are organisms, such as humans, that have cells containing a true nucleus enclosed by a nuclear membrane and that have a variety of membrane-bound organelles.

2. **Ribosomal RNA (rRNA)** is a structural and functional component of the ribosomes, which are "platforms" on which protein synthesis occurs. There are three rRNA molecules in bacterial ribosomes and four rRNA species in the ribosomes of eukaryotes.

3. **Transfer RNA (tRNA)** translates the genetic code of the mRNA into the primary sequence of amino acids in the protein. In addition to the primary structure, tRNA molecules have a cloverleaf-shaped secondary structure resulting from base pair hydrogen bonding (A—U and G—C) and a roughly L-shaped tertiary structure (Figure 19.9). The sequence CCA is found at the 3′ end of the tRNA. The A part of this sequence can be covalently attached to an amino acid. Three nucleotides at the base of the cloverleaf structure form the **anticodon.** As we will discuss in more detail in Section 19.6, this triplet of bases forms hydrogen bonds to a **codon** (complementary sequence of bases) on a messenger RNA (mRNA) molecule on the surface of a ribosome during protein synthesis. This hydrogen bonding of codon and anticodon brings the correct amino acid to the site of protein synthesis at the appropriate location in the growing peptide chain (Figure 19.10).

Transcription

Transcription, shown in Figure 19.11, is catalyzed by the enzyme **RNA polymerase.** The process occurs in three stages. The first, called initiation, involves binding of RNA polymerase to a specific nucleotide sequence, the **promoter,** at the beginning of a gene. This interaction of RNA polymerase with specific promoter DNA sequences allows RNA polymerase to recognize the start point for transcription, the beginning of a gene. As it binds to the DNA, RNA polymerase separates or melts the two strands of DNA so that it can "read" the base sequence of the DNA.

The second stage, chain elongation, begins as the RNA polymerase "reads" the DNA template strand and catalyzes the polymerization of a complementary RNA copy. With each catalytic step, RNA polymerase transfers a complementary ribonucleotide to the end of the growing RNA chain and catalyzes the formation of a 3′–5′ phosphodiester bond between the 5′

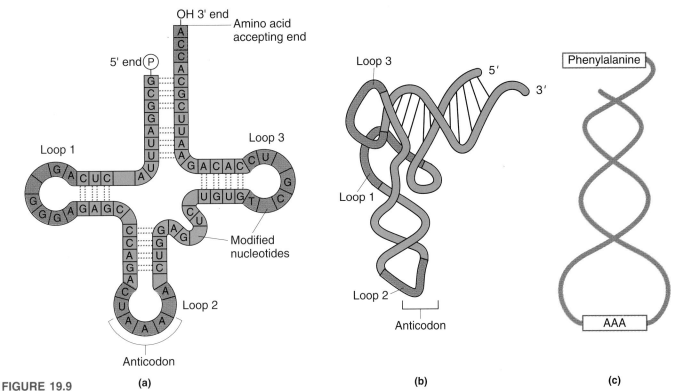

FIGURE 19.9
Structure of tRNA. (a) The primary structure of a tRNA is the linear sequence of ribonucleotides. Here we see the hydrogen-bonded secondary structure of a tRNA showing the three loops and the amino acid-accepting end. (b) The three-dimensional structure of a tRNA. (c) A schematic diagram that will be used to represent a tRNA throughout the chapter.

FIGURE 19.10
Codon-anticodon binding.

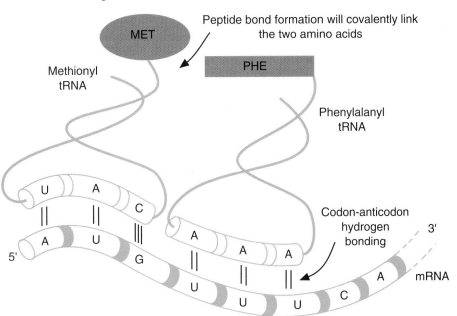

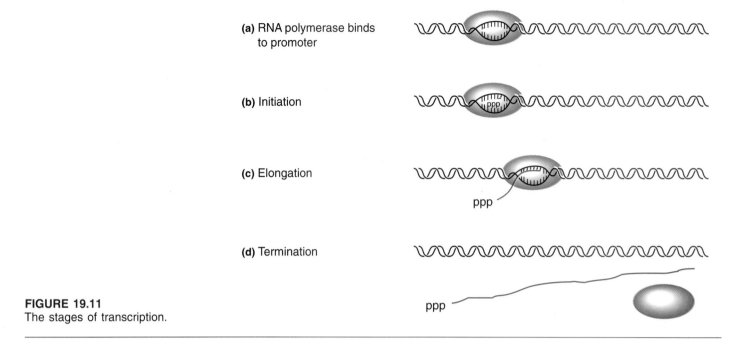

(a) RNA polymerase binds
      to promoter

(b) Initiation

(c) Elongation

ppp

(d) Termination

ppp

FIGURE 19.11
The stages of transcription.

phosphoryl group of the incoming ribonucleotide and the 3′ hydroxyl group of the last ribonucleotide of the growing RNA chain. This reaction is seen in Figure 19.12.

The final stage of transcription is termination. The RNA polymerase finds a termination
sequence at the end of the gene and releases the newly formed RNA molecule.

QUESTION 19.5

What is the function of RNA polymerase in the process of transcription?

QUESTION 19.6

What is the function of the promoter sequence in the process of transcription?

RNA splicing

Bacterial genes are continuous; all the nucleotide sequences of the gene are found in the mRNA.
However, study of the gene structure of eukaryotes revealed a fascinating difference. Eukaryotic
genes are discontinuous; there are *extra* DNA sequences within these genes that do not encode
any amino acid sequences for the protein. These sequences are termed *intervening sequences* or
introns. As you might suspect, the presence of introns in the mRNA would make it impossible
for the process of translation to synthesize the correct protein. Therefore they must be removed.
This is done by the process of *RNA splicing.*

In eukaryotic cells the first product of transcription is called the *primary transcript.* It
carries both the protein coding sequences, termed **exons,** and the introns. The primary transcript,
carrying the introns, is folded into a looped structure that brings together the coding sequences
to be spliced together. The introns are then perfectly cut out, and the protein coding exons are
sealed back together.

This mechanism is summarized for β-globin mRNA in Figure 19.13. In fact, one of the first
eukaryotic genes shown to contain introns was the gene for the β subunit of adult hemoglobin.
On the DNA the gene for β-hemoglobin is 1200 nucleotides long, but only 438 nucleotides carry
the genetic information for protein. The remaining sequences are found in two introns of 116
and 646 nucleotides that are removed by splicing before translation. It is interesting that the
larger intron is longer than the final β-globin mRNA! In the genes that have been studied,

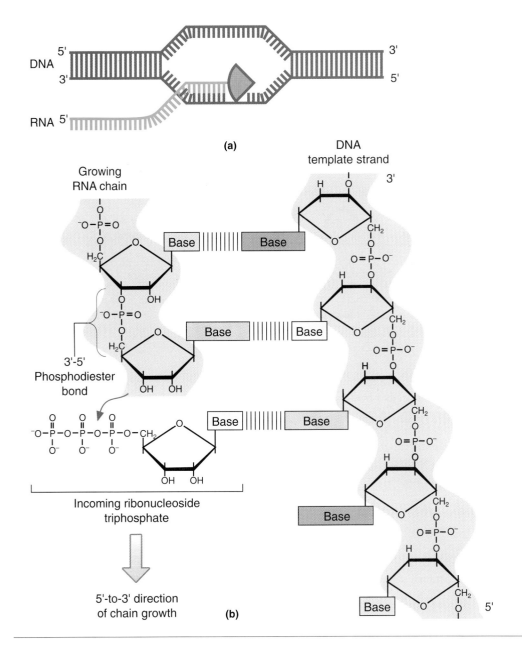

FIGURE 19.12
The reaction catalyzed by RNA polymerase. (a) RNA polymerase separates the two strands of DNA and produces an RNA copy of one of the two DNA strands. (b) Phosphodiester bond formation occurs as a nucleotide is added to the growing RNA chain.

introns have been found to range in size from 50 to 20,000 nucleotides in length, and there may be many throughout a gene. Thus a typical human gene might be 10–30 times longer than the final mRNA.

19.5 THE GENETIC CODE

The mRNA carries the genetic code for a protein. But what is the nature of this code? In 1954, George Gamow proposed that since there are only four "letters" in the DNA alphabet (A, T, G, and C) and since there are 20 amino acids, the genetic code must contain words made of at least three letters taken from the four letters in the DNA alphabet. How did he come to this conclusion? He reasoned that a code of two-letter words constructed from any combination of the four letters has a "vocabulary" of only 16 words (4^2). In other words, there are only 16 different ways to put A, T, C, and G together two bases at a time (AA, AT, AC, AG, TT, TA, etc.). That is not enough to encode all 20 amino acids. A code of four-letter words gives 256 words (4^4), far more than are needed. A code of three-letter words, however, has a possible vocabulary of 64 words (4^3), sufficient to encode the 20 amino acids but not too excessive.

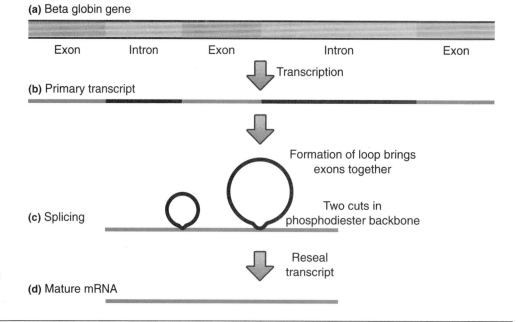

FIGURE 19.13

Schematic diagram of mRNA splicing. (a) The β-globin gene contains protein coding exons, as well as noncoding sequences called introns. (b) The primary transcript of the DNA carries both the introns and the exons. (c) The introns are looped out, the phosphodiester backbone of the mRNA is cut twice, and the pieces are tied together. (d) The final mature mRNA now carries only the coding sequences (exons) of the gene.

A series of elegant experiments proved that Gamow was correct by demonstrating that the genetic code is, indeed, a triplet code. Mutations were introduced into the DNA of a bacterial virus that inserted (or deleted) one, two, or three nucleotides into a gene. The researchers then looked for the protein encoded by that gene. When one or two nucleotides were inserted, no protein was produced. However, when a third base was inserted, the sense of the mRNA was restored, and the protein was made. You can imagine this experiment by using a sentence composed of only three-letter words. For instance,

THE CAT RAN OUT

What happens to the ''sense'' of the sentence if we insert one letter?

THE FCA TRA NOU T

The reading frame of the sentence has been altered, and the sentence is now nonsense. Can we now restore the sense of the sentence by inserting a second letter?

THE FAC ATR ANO UT

No, we have not restored the sense of the sentence. Once again, we have altered the reading frame, but since our code has only three-letter words, the sentence is still nonsense. If we now insert a third letter, it should restore the correct reading frame:

THE FAT CAT RAN OUT

Indeed, by inserting three new letters we have restored the sense of the message by restoring the reading frame. This is exactly the way in which the message of the mRNA is interpreted. Each group of three nucleotides in the sequence of the mRNA is called a codon, and each codes for a single amino acid. If the sequence is interrupted or changed, it can change the amino acid composition of the protein that is produced or even result in the production of no protein at all.

We noted above that a three-letter genetic code contains 64 words, called codons, but there are only 20 amino acids. Thus there are 44 more codons than are required to specify all of the amino acids found in proteins. Three of the codons—UAA, UAG, and UGA—specify termination signals for the process of translation. But this still leaves us with 41 additional codons. What is the function of the ''extra'' code words? Crick (recall Watson and Crick and the double helix) proposed that the genetic code is **degenerate.** The term ''degenerate'' is used to indicate that different triplet codons may serve as code words for the same amino acid.

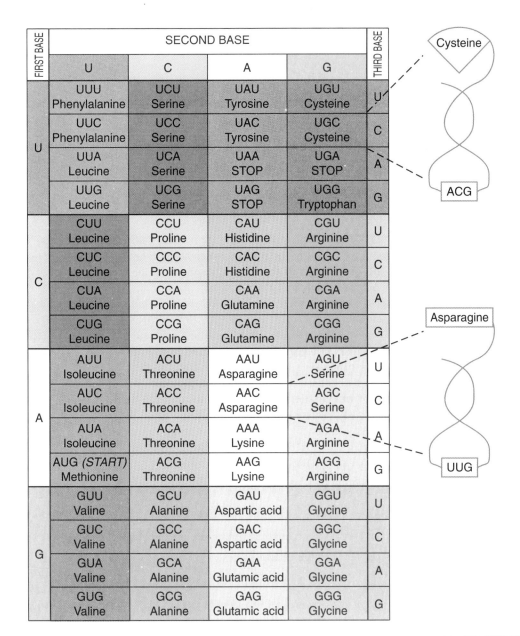

FIGURE 19.14
The genetic code. The table shows the possible codons found in mRNA. To read the universal biological language from this chart, find the first base in the column on the left, the second base from the row across the top, and the third base from the column to the right. This will direct you to one of the 64 squares in the matrix. Within that square you will find the codon and the amino acid that it specifies. In the cell this message is decoded by tRNA molecules like those shown to the right of the table.

The complete genetic code is shown in Figure 19.14. We can make several observations about the genetic code. First, methionine and tryptophan are the only amino acids that have a single codon. All others have at least two codons, and serine and leucine have six codons each. The genetic code is also somewhat mutation-resistant. For those amino acids that have multiple codons the first two bases are often identical and thus identify the amino acid, and only the third position is variable. Mutations—changes in the nucleotide sequence—in the third position therefore often have no effect on the amino acid that is incorporated into a protein.

QUESTION 19.7

Why is the genetic code said to be degenerate?

QUESTION 19.8

Why is the genetic code said to be mutation-resistant?

19.6 PROTEIN SYNTHESIS

The process of protein synthesis is called *translation*. It involves translating the genetic information from the sequence of nucleotides into the sequence of amino acids in the primary structure of a protein. Translation is carried out on **ribosomes,** which are complexes of ribosomal RNA (rRNA) and proteins. Each ribosome is made up of two subunits: a small and a large ribosomal subunit (Figure 19.15). In eukaryotic cells the small ribosomal subunit contains one rRNA molecule and 33 different ribosomal proteins, and the large subunit contains three rRNA molecules and about 49 different proteins.

Protein synthesis involves the simultaneous action of many ribosomes on a single mRNA molecule. These complexes of many ribosomes along a single mRNA are known as *polyribosomes* or **polysomes** (Figure 19.15b). Each ribosome is synthesizing one copy of the protein molecule encoded by the mRNA. Thus many copies of a protein are simultaneously produced.

The role of transfer RNA

The codons of mRNA must be read if the genetic message is to be translated into protein. The molecule that decodes the information in the mRNA molecule into the primary structure of a protein is transfer RNA (tRNA). To decode the genetic message into the primary sequence of a protein, the tRNA must faithfully perform two functions.

First, the tRNA must covalently bind one, and only one, specific amino acid. There is at least one transfer RNA for each amino acid. As seen in Figure 19.9, all tRNA molecules have the sequence CCA at their 3′ ends. This is the site where the amino acid will be covalently attached to the tRNA molecule. Each tRNA is specifically recognized by the active site of an enzyme called an **aminoacyl tRNA synthetase.** This enzyme also recognizes the correct amino acid and covalently links the amino acid to the 3′ end of the tRNA molecule. Figure 19.16 shows the recognition of the amino acid methionine and its tRNA by the methionyl tRNA synthetase. The resulting structure is called an **aminoacyl tRNA,** in this case methionyl tRNA. In Figure 19.16b the reaction that results in the attachment of the aminoacyl group to the tRNA is shown. This amino acid will be transferred from the tRNA to a growing polypeptide chain during protein synthesis.

FIGURE 19.15
Structure of the ribosome. (a) The large and small subunits form the functional complex in association with an mRNA molecule. (b) A polyribosome translating the mRNA for a β-globin chain of hemoglobin.

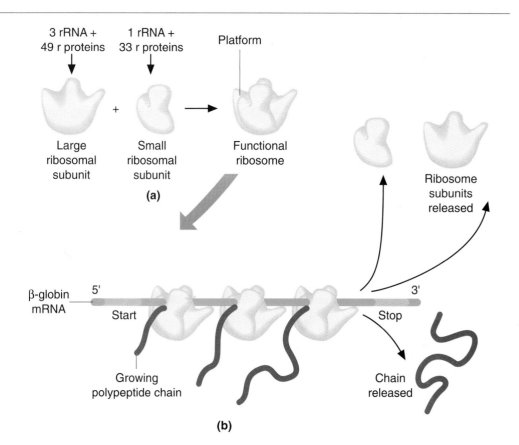

3 rRNA + 49 r proteins   1 rRNA + 33 r proteins   Platform

Large ribosomal subunit   +   Small ribosomal subunit   →   Functional ribosome

(a)

Ribosome subunits released

β-globin mRNA   5′   Start   3′   Stop

Growing polypeptide chain   Chain released

(b)

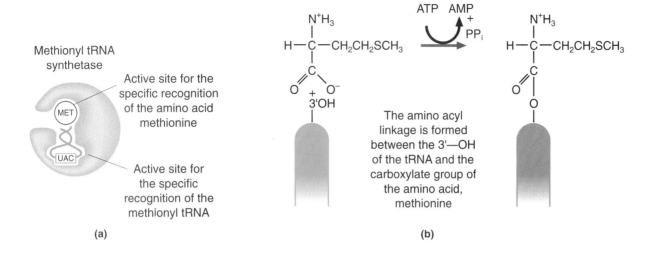

(a)

(b)

(c)

FIGURE 19.16
Methionyl tRNA synthetase.
(a) The enzyme specifically
recognizes the amino acid
methionine in one region of the
active site and the methionyl tRNA
in another. (b) The acylation
reaction that results in a covalent
linkage of the amino acid to the
tRNA. (c) Molecular model of a
tRNA bound to its aminoacyl tRNA
synthetase.

Second, the tRNA must be able to recognize the appropriate codon on the mRNA that calls for that amino acid. This is mediated through a sequence of three bases called the anticodon, which is located at the bottom of the tRNA cloverleaf (refer to Figure 19.9). The anticodon sequence for each tRNA is complementary to the codon on the mRNA that specifies a particular amino acid. As you can see in Figure 19.10, the anticodon-codon complementary hydrogen bonding will bring the correct amino acid to the site of protein synthesis.

How are codons related to anticodons?

If the sequence of a codon on the mRNA is 5′-AUG-3′, what will the sequence of the anticodon be? Remember that the hydrogen bonding rules require antiparallel strands. It is easiest to write the anticodon first 3′ → 5′ and then reverse it to the 5′ → 3′ order.

The process of translation

Initiation

The first stage of protein synthesis is *initiation.* Proteins called **initiation factors** are required to mediate the formation of a translation complex composed of an mRNA molecule, the small and large ribosomal subunits, and the initiator tRNA. This initiator tRNA recognizes the codon AUG and carries the amino acid methionine.

The ribosome has two sites for binding tRNA molecules. The first site, called the **peptidyl tRNA binding site (P-site),** holds the peptidyl tRNA, the growing peptide bound to a tRNA molecule. The second site, called the **aminoacyl-tRNA binding site (A-site),** holds the aminoacyl tRNA carrying the next amino acid to be added to the peptide chain. Each of the tRNA molecules is hydrogen bonded to the mRNA molecule by codon-anticodon complementarity. The entire complex is further stabilized by the fact that the mRNA is also bound to the ribosome. Figure 19.17a shows the series of events that result in the formation of the initiation complex. The initiator methionyl tRNA occupies the P-site in this complex.

Chain elongation

The second stage of translation is *chain elongation.* This occurs in three steps that are repeated until protein synthesis is complete. We enter the action after a tetrapeptide has already been assembled, and a peptidyl tRNA occupies the P-site (Figure 19.17b).

The first event is binding of an aminoacyl-tRNA molecule to the empty A-site. Next, peptide bond formation occurs. This is catalyzed by an enzyme on the ribosome called *peptidyl transferase.* Now the peptide chain is shifted to the tRNA that occupies the A-site. Finally, the tRNA in the P-site falls away, and the ribosome changes positions so that the next codon on the mRNA occupies the A-site. This movement of the ribosome is called **translocation.** The process shifts the new peptidyl tRNA from the A-site to the P-site.

Recent evidence indicates that the peptidyl transferase is a catalytic region of the 28S ribosomal RNA.

Termination

The last stage of translation is *termination.* There are three **termination codons**—UAA, UAG, and UGA—for which there are no corresponding tRNA molecules. When one of these ''stop'' codons is encountered, translation is terminated. A **release factor** binds the empty A-site. The peptidyl transferase that had previously catalyzed peptide bond formation hydrolyzes the ester bond between the peptidyl tRNA and the last amino acid of the newly synthesized protein (Figure 19.17c). At this point the tRNA, the newly synthesized peptide, and the two ribosomal subunits are released.

What is the function of the ribosomal P-site in protein synthesis?

What is the function of the ribosomal A-site in protein synthesis?

Section 15.9
Section 15.3

The peptide that is released following translation is not necessarily in its final functional form. In some cases the peptide is proteolytically cleaved before it becomes functional. An example of this is the digestive enzymes. Sometimes the protein must associate with other

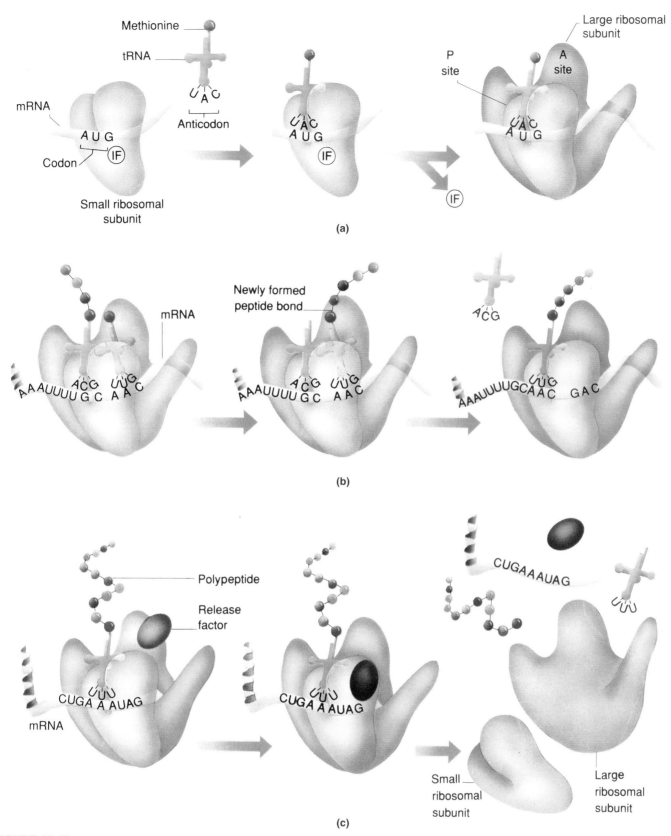

FIGURE 19.17
(a) Formation of an initiation complex sets protein synthesis in motion. The mRNA and proteins called initiation factors bind to the small ribosomal subunit. Next, a charged methionyl tRNA molecule binds, and finally, the initiation factors are released, and the large subunit binds. (b) The elongation phase of protein synthesis involves addition of new amino acids to the C-terminus of the growing peptide. An aminoacyl tRNA molecule binds at the empty A-site, and the peptide bond is formed. The uncharged tRNA molecule is released, and the peptidyl tRNA is shifted to the P-site as the ribosome moves along the mRNA. (c) Termination of protein synthesis occurs when a release factor binds the stop codon on mRNA. This leads to the hydrolysis of the ester bond linking the peptide to the peptidyl tRNA molecule in the P-site. The ribosome then dissociates into its two subunits, releasing the mRNA and the newly synthesized peptide.

peptides to form a functional protein, as in the case of hemoglobin. Cellular enzymes add carbohydrate or lipid groups to some proteins, especially those that will end up on the cell surface. These final modifications are specific for particular proteins and, like the sequence of the protein itself, are directed by the cellular genetic information.

19.7 MUTATION, ULTRAVIOLET LIGHT, AND DNA REPAIR

The nature of mutations

Changes can occur in the nucleotide sequence of a DNA molecule. Such a genetic change is called a **mutation.** Mutations can arise from mistakes made by DNA polymerase during DNA replication. They also result from the action of chemicals, called **mutagens,** that damage the DNA.

Mutations are classified by the kind of change that occurs in the DNA. The substitution of a single nucleotide for another is called a **point mutation:**

> ATG<u>G</u>ACTTC: normal DNA sequence
>
> ATG<u>C</u>ACTTC: point mutation

Sometimes a single nucleotide or even large sections of DNA are lost. These are called **deletion mutations:**

> ATGG<u>AC</u>TTC: normal DNA sequence
>
> ATGTTC: deletion mutation

Occasionally, one or more nucleotides are added to a DNA sequence. These are **insertion mutations:**

> ATGGACTTC: normal DNA sequence
>
> ATGC<u>TC</u>GACTTC: insertion mutation

The results of mutations

Some mutations are **silent;** that is, they cause no change in the organism. Often, however, a mutation has a negative effect on the health of the organism. The effect of a mutation depends on how it alters the genetic code for a protein. Consider the two codons for glutamic acid: GAA and GAG. A point mutation that alters the third nucleotide of GA<u>A</u> to GA<u>G</u> will still result in the incorporation of glutamic acid at the correct position in the protein. Similarly, a GA<u>G</u> to GA<u>A</u> mutation will also be silent.

There are approximately 4000 human genetic diseases that result from mutations. These occur because the mutation in the DNA changes the codon and results in incorporation of the wrong amino acid into the protein. This causes the protein to be nonfunctional or to function improperly.

Consider the human genetic disease sickle cell anemia. In the normal β-chain of hemoglobin the sixth amino acid is glutamic acid. In the β-chain of sickle cell hemoglobin the sixth amino acid is valine. How did this amino acid substitution arise? The answer lies in examination of the codons for glutamic acid and valine:

> Glutamic acid: GAA or GAG
>
> Valine: GUG, GUC, GUA, or GUU

A point mutation of A → U in the second nucleotide changes some codons for glutamic acid into codons for valine:

> G<u>A</u>A   ⟶   G<u>U</u>A
>
> G<u>A</u>G   ⟶   G<u>U</u>G
>
> Glutamic acid codon   Valine codon

This mutation in a single codon leads to the change in amino acid sequence at position 6 in the β-chain of human hemoglobin from glutamic acid to valine. The result of this seemingly minor change is sickle cell anemia in individuals who inherit two copies of the mutant gene.

A CLINICAL PERSPECTIVE

The Ames Test for Carcinogens

Each day we come into contact with a variety of chemicals, including insecticides, food additives, hair dyes, automobile emissions and cigarette smoke. Some of these chemicals have the potential to cause cancer. How do we determine whether these agents are harmful? More particularly, how do we determine whether they cause cancer?

If we consider the example of cigarette smoke, we see that it can be years, even centuries, before a relationship is seen between a chemical and cancer. Europeans and Americans have been smoking since Sir Walter Raleigh introduced tobacco into England in the seventeenth century. However, it was not until three centuries later that physicians and scientists demonstrated the link between smoking and lung cancer. Obviously, this epidemiological approach takes too long, and too many people die. Alternatively, we can test chemicals by treating laboratory animals, such as mice, and observing them for various kinds of cancer. However, this, too, can take years, is expensive, and requires the sacrifice of many laboratory animals. How, then, can chemicals be tested for carcinogenicity (the ability to cause cancer) quickly and inexpensively? In the 1970s it was recognized that most carcinogens are also mutagens. That is, they cause cancer by causing mutations in the DNA, and the mutations cause the cells of the body to lose growth control. Bruce Ames, a biochemist and bacterial geneticist, developed a test using mu-tants of the bacterium *Salmonella typhimurium* that can demonstrate in 48–72 hours whether a chemical is a mutagen and thus a suspected carcinogen.

Ames chose several mutants of *S. typhimurium* that cannot grow unless the amino acid histidine is added to the growth medium. The Ames Test involves subjecting these bacteria to a chemical and determining whether the chemical causes reversion of the mutation. In other words, the researcher is looking for a mutation that reverses the original mutation. When a reversion occurs, the bacteria will be able to grow in the absence of histidine.

The details of the Ames Test are shown in the accompanying figure. Both an experimental and a control test are done. The control test contains no carcinogen and will show the number of spontaneous revertants that occur in the culture. If there are many colonies on the surface of the experimental plate and only a few colonies on the negative control plate, it can be concluded that the chemical tested is a mutagen. It is therefore very likely that the chemical is also a carcinogen.

The Ames Test has greatly accelerated our ability to test new compounds for mutagenic and possibly carcinogenic effects. However, once the Ames Test identifies a mutagenic compound, testing in animals must be done to show conclusively that the compound also causes cancer.

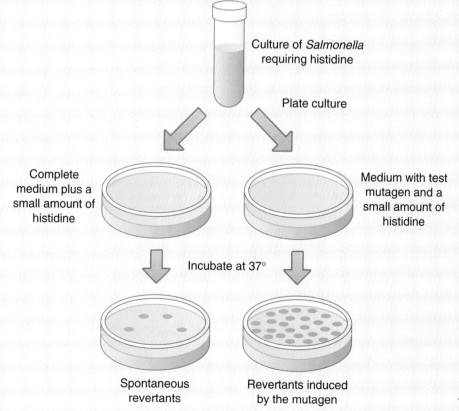

Culture of *Salmonella* requiring histidine

Plate culture

Complete medium plus a small amount of histidine

Medium with test mutagen and a small amount of histidine

Incubate at 37°

Spontaneous revertants

Revertants induced by the mutagen

The Ames Test for carcinogenic compounds.

QUESTION 19.13

The sequence of a gene on the mRNA is normally AUGCCCGACUUU. A point mutation in the gene results in the mRNA sequence AUGC<u>G</u>CGACUUU. What are the amino acid sequences of the normal and mutant proteins? Would you expect this to be a silent mutation?

QUESTION 19.14

The sequence of a gene on the mRNA is normally AUGCCCGACUUU. A point mutation in the gene results in the mRNA sequence AUGCC<u>G</u>GACUUU. What are the amino acid sequences of the normal and mutant proteins? Would you expect this to be a silent mutation?

Mutagens and carcinogens

Any chemical that causes a change in the DNA sequence is called a mutagen. Often, mutagens are also **carcinogens,** cancer-causing chemicals. Most cancers result from one or more mutations in a single normal cell. These mutations result in the loss of normal growth control, causing the abnormal cell to proliferate. If that growth is not controlled or destroyed, it will result in the death of the individual. We are exposed to many carcinogens in the course of our lives. Sometimes we are exposed to a carcinogen by accident, but in some cases it is by choice. There are about 3000 chemical components in cigarette smoke, and several are potent mutagens. As a result, people who smoke have a much greater chance of lung cancer than those who don't.

Ultraviolet light, mutation, and DNA repair

Ultraviolet (UV) light is another agent that causes damage to DNA. Absorption of UV light by DNA causes adjacent thymine bases to become covalently linked to one another. The product (seen in Figure 19.18) is called a **thymine dimer.** As a result of thymine dimer formation, there is no hydrogen bonding between these thymine molecules and the complementary adenine bases. This stretch of DNA cannot be replicated or transcribed!

Bacteria such as *Escherichia coli* have four different mechanisms to repair ultraviolet light damage. However, even a repair process can make a mistake. Mutations occur when the UV damage repair system makes an error and causes a change in the nucleotide sequence of the DNA.

In medicine the thymine dimerization reaction is used to advantage in hospitals where germicidal (UV) light is used to kill bacteria in the air and on environmental surfaces, such as

FIGURE 19.18
Photodimerization of adjacent thymines results from the absorption of ultraviolet light.

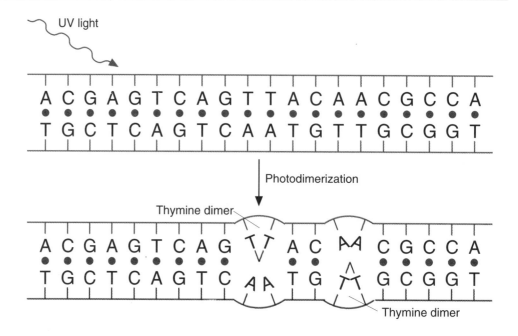

in a vacant operating room. This cell death is caused by thymine dimer formation on a massive scale. The repair systems of the bacteria are overwhelmed, and the cells die.

Of course, the same type of thymine dimer formation can occur in human cells as well. Lying out in the sun all day to acquire a fashionable tan exposes the skin to large amounts of UV light. This damages the skin by formation of many thymine dimers. Exposure to high levels of UV from sunlight or tanning booths has been linked to a rising incidence of skin cancer in human populations.

Consequences of defects in DNA repair

The human repair system for thymine dimers is quite complex, requiring at least five enzymes. The first step in repair of the thymine dimer is the cleavage of the sugar-phosphate backbone of the DNA near the site of the damage. The enzyme that performs this cleavage of the sugar-phosphate backbone is called a repair endonuclease. If the gene encoding this enzyme is defective, thymine dimers cannot be repaired. The accumulation of mutations combined with a simultaneous decrease in the efficiency of DNA repair mechanisms leads to an increased incidence of cancer. For example, a mutation in the repair endonuclease gene and in other genes in the repair pathway results in the genetic skin disorder called *xeroderma pigmentosum*. People who suffer from xeroderma pigmentosum are extremely sensitive to the ultraviolet rays of sunlight and develop multiple skin cancers, usually before the age of 20.

19.8 RECOMBINANT DNA

Tools used in the study of DNA

Scientists are often asked why they study such seemingly unimportant subjects as bacterial DNA replication. One very good reason is that such studies often lend insight into the workings of human genetic systems. A second is that such research often produces the tools that allow great leaps into new technologies. Nowhere is this more true than in the development of recombinant DNA technology. Many of the techniques and tools used in recombinant DNA studies were developed or discovered during basic studies on bacterial DNA replication and gene expression. These include many enzymes that catalyze reactions of DNA molecules, gel electrophoresis, cloning vectors, and hybridization techniques.

Restriction enzymes

Restriction enzymes are bacterial enzymes that "cut" the sugar-phosphate backbone of DNA molecules at specific nucleotide sequences. The first of these enzymes to be purified and studied was called EcoR1. The name is derived from the genus and species name of the bacteria from which it was isolated, in this case *E. coli*. The following is the specific nucleotide sequence recognized by EcoR1:

$$5'-----------GAATTC---------3'$$

$$3'-----------CTTAAG---------5'$$

When EcoR1 cuts the DNA at this site, it does so in a staggered fashion. Specifically, it cuts between the G and the first A on both strands. Cutting produces two DNA fragments with the following structure:

$$5'-----------G \qquad AATTC---------3'$$

$$3'-----------CTTAA \qquad G---------5'$$

These staggered termini are called *sticky ends* because they can reassociate with one another by hydrogen bonding. This is a property of the DNA fragments generated by restriction enzymes that is very important to gene cloning.

Examples of other restriction enzymes and their specific recognition sequences are seen in Table 19.3. The sites on the sugar-phosphate backbone that are cut by the enzymes are indicated by slashes.

These enzymes are used to digest large DNA molecules into smaller fragments of specific size. Because a restriction enzyme always cuts at the same site, DNA from a particular individ-

TABLE 19.3 Some Common Restriction Enzymes and Their Recognition Sequences

Restriction Enzyme	Recognition Sequence
BamHI	5'-G/GATCC-3' 3'-CCTAG/G-5'
HindIII	5'-A/AGCTT-3' 3'-TTCGA/A-5'
SalI	5'-G/TCGAC-3' 3'-CAGCT/G-3'
BglII	5'-A/GATCT-3' 3'-TCTAG/A-5'
PstI	5'-CTGCA/G-3' 3'-G/ACGTC-5'

ual will generate a reproducible set of DNA fragments. This is convenient for the study or cloning of DNA from any source.

Agarose gel electrophoresis

One means of studying the DNA fragments produced by restriction enzyme digestion is agarose gel electrophoresis. The digested DNA sample is placed in a sample well in the gel, and an electric current is applied. Owing to the negative charge of the phosphoryl groups in the sugar-phosphate backbone, the DNA fragment will move through the gel away from the negative electrode (cathode) and toward the positive electrode (anode). The smaller DNA fragments move more rapidly than the larger ones, and as a result the DNA fragments end up distributed throughout the gel according to their size. The sizes of each fragment can be determined by comparison with the migration pattern of DNA fragments of known size. An agarose gel showing the DNA bands of different sizes is shown in Figure 19.19.

Hybridization

Agarose gel electrophoresis allows the determination of the size of a DNA fragment. However, in recombinant DNA research it is also important to identify what gene is carried by a particular DNA fragment.

Hybridization is a technique used to identify the presence of a gene on a particular DNA fragment. This technique is based on the fact that complementary DNA sequences will hydrogen bond, or hybridize, to one another. It doesn't matter whether the complementary single-stranded sequences come from the same DNA molecule or from DNA molecules from two different kinds of organisms. If the DNA sequences are complementary, they will hybridize with one another.

In fact, even RNA can be used in hybridization studies. RNA can hybridize to DNA molecules or to other RNA molecules. Again, the only important criterion for hybridization is the presence of complementary nucleic acid sequences on the two strands.

One hybridization technique, called Southern blotting, involves hybridization of DNA fragments from an agarose gel (Figure 19.20). The first step of the procedure is digestion of the DNA with a restriction enzyme. Then the fragments are separated by size on an agarose gel. Next the DNA fragments are transferred by blotting onto a special membrane filter. The DNA molecules on the filter are "melted" into single DNA strands so that they are ready for hybridization.

The next requirement for the procedure is a probe that will detect the particular gene sequence of interest. A probe is a radioactively labeled DNA or RNA molecule that can be used to detect a specific gene. Once the probe has been made, it is placed in a solution in contact with the membrane filter. The probe will hybridize only with those DNA fragments on the filter that have sequences complementary to it.

FIGURE 19.19
DNA fragments (pink) shown in an electrophoresis gel-rendered fluorescent by ultraviolet light.

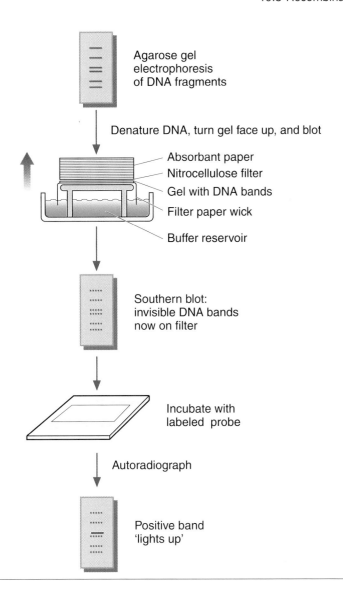

Agarose gel
electrophoresis
of DNA fragments

Denature DNA, turn gel face up, and blot

Absorbant paper
Nitrocellulose filter
Gel with DNA bands
Filter paper wick
Buffer reservoir

Southern blot:
invisible DNA bands
now on filter

Incubate with
labeled probe

Autoradiograph

Positive band
'lights up'

FIGURE 19.20
Southern blot hybridization.

To detect which DNA bands on the gel have hybridized, the filter is placed on a piece of X-ray film. Following exposure and development the X-ray film will show a black band or bands at any site where hybridization has occurred. In this way, scientists can identify which DNA fragments are carrying the gene of interest.

DNA cloning vectors

DNA cloning experiments combine these technologies with a few additional tricks to isolate single copies of a gene and then produce billions of copies. To produce multiple copies of a gene, it must be joined to a **cloning vector.** A cloning vector is a piece of DNA having its own replication origin so that it can be replicated inside a host cell. Often the bacterium *E. coli* serves as the host cell in which the vector carrying the cloned DNA is replicated in abundance.

There are two major kinds of cloning vectors. The first are bacterial virus or phage vectors. These are bacterial viruses that have been genetically altered to allow the addition of cloned DNA fragments. These viruses have not only an origin of replication, but also all the other genes required to replicate 100–200 copies of the virus (and cloned fragment) per infected cell.

The second commonly used vector is a plasmid vector. Plasmids are extra pieces of circular DNA found in most kinds of bacteria. They have their own replication origins; however, it is replication enzymes of the host cell that are responsible for the replication of plasmids.

A HUMAN PERSPECTIVE

DNA Fingerprints: Admissible in Court?

On a hot August night in 1990 a young woman in Parkville, Maryland, fell asleep on her couch while watching TV. As she slept, a man entered her apartment, put a pillowcase over her head, beat her, and raped her. As the man fled, she got a brief glimpse of him in the dim light of the TV screen. She identified her assailant as her former boyfriend. Certainly, on the basis of eyewitness identification by a woman who knew him well, it was expected that the ex-boyfriend would be convicted and sentenced to a long prison term. Nonetheless, the young man insisted that he was innocent and submitted to DNA fingerprint analysis.

DNA fingerprinting has become a valuable tool for forensic scientists. The technique was developed in the 1980s as a result of basic molecular genetic studies of the human genome. In the course of these studies it was observed that some DNA sequences vary greatly from one person to the next. These hypervariable regions are composed of multiple repeats of short DNA sequences and are found at many loci on different chromosomes. Different individuals have different numbers of repeats. As a result, when a person's DNA is digested with restriction enzymes, a unique set of fragments is generated. Alec Jeffries at the University of Leicester in England developed a set of DNA probes that can detect these variable number tandem repeats (VNTRs) at numerous loci on different chromosomes.

Although several variations on DNA fingerprinting exist, the basic technique is quite simple. DNA from human cells (blood, semen, etc.) is digested with restriction enzymes, producing a set of DNA fragments. These are separated according to size by electrophoresis through an agarose gel. The DNA fragments are then transferred to a special membrane and hybridized with the radioactive probe DNA. This involves melting the complementary strands of the genomic DNA fragments on the membrane and allowing them to hydrogen bond to complementary sequences of the single-stranded DNA probes. The bands to which the radioactive probe has hybridized can be visualized by exposing the membrane to X-ray film and developing a "picture" of the gel. The result is a set of 25–60 DNA bands that are unique to an individual. Jeffries called this set of fragments a *DNA fingerprint*.

It was originally estimated that the odds of two individuals (excluding identical twins) having the same DNA fingerprint were less than 1 in 100 million or even 1 in a billion. Foren-sic scientists were quick to perceive the value of such a technique for the positive identification of criminals. As a result, it has been used as evidence in rape and murder trials, paternity and maternity suits, and immigration disputes.

Very recently, the technique has come under intense scrutiny. Some scientists have questioned the statistical methods used to calculate the odds of the individuality of a DNA fingerprint, concerned that within particular ethnic groups the variability may be much lower than was previously claimed. Others argued that slightly different methodologies used in different labs could lead to different results. Still others were concerned that the DNA obtained from a crime scene sampling may be partially degraded and thus yield misleading results.

In 1989 the National Academy of Sciences (NAS) established a committee to investigate concerns about DNA fingerprint technology. In April 1992 the committee reported its findings. First and foremost, the committee supported the use of DNA fingerprint evidence in legal proceedings. However, it stated that there must be stringent quality control. Laboratories must be accredited, and scientists (not simply practitioners) must oversee the process of testing. The committee also established a far more conservative means for calculating probability estimates. The probability estimates based on this new means of statistical analysis will be in the range of 1 in several hundred thousand to 1 in a million—still impressive odds! Finally, the committee recommended an extensive study of the degree of variability of these VNTRs in various ethnic groups and populations. Implementation of these recommendations will improve DNA fingerprint technology and will ensure that it is performed properly and that the data are interpreted correctly.

DNA fingerprinting is certainly a powerful tool in forensic science. As the Maryland rape case showed, it has the ability to demonstrate innocence and to prove guilt. Comparison of the DNA fingerprint of the ex-boyfriend with that obtained from the semen of the rapist demonstrated conclusively that he was innocent. Almost a year after the attack, DNA fingerprint analysis proved the guilt of another man, one who bore an uncanny resemblance to the accused ex-boyfriend.

From *Strategies for Success*, Fall 1992, Number 10. Copyright © 1992 by The Benjamin/Cummings Publishing Company. Reprinted by permission.

Antibiotic resistance causes countless problems in the treatment of bacterial infections.

Plasmids in nature often carry genes for antibiotic resistance. Thus the cells having the plasmids become resistant to the action of one or more antibiotics. The plasmids that are used as cloning vectors have also been altered to accept cloned DNA fragments. It is interesting to note that they often contain antibiotic resistance genes that are useful in the selection of cells containing a plasmid.

One such plasmid is pBR322. The restriction enzyme map of pBR322 is seen in Figure

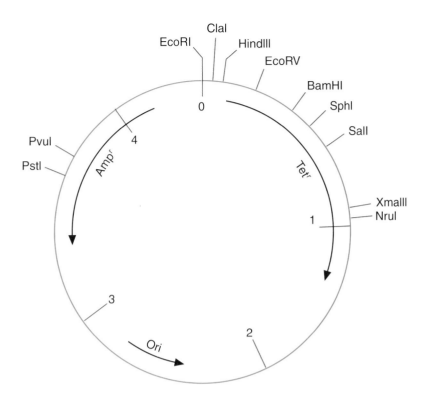

FIGURE 19.21
A restriction enzyme map of the plasmid cloning vector pBR322. Restriction enzyme cleavage sites for 11 enzymes are shown, along with the location of the ampicillin resistance gene (red arrow) and the tetracycline resistance gene (blue arrow). "Ori" is the origin of DNA replication of the plasmid.

19.21. This plasmid has two antibiotic resistance genes: one for ampicillin and one for tetracycline. Within the antibiotic resistance genes are several restriction enzyme sites that are convenient for cloning.

Genetic engineering

Most of the tools needed for a cloning experiment having been assembled, the next decision to be made is which gene to clone. The example that we will use is the cloning of the β-globin genes for normal and sickle cell hemoglobin. DNA from an individual with normal hemoglobin is digested with a restriction enzyme, perhaps BamHI. This is the target DNA. The vector DNA must be digested with the same enzyme (Figure 19.22). In our example we will use the plasmid vector pBR322.

The digested vector and target DNA are mixed together under conditions that encourage the BamHI sticky ends of the target and vector DNA to hybridize with one another. Since the sticky ends are held together by only a few hydrogen bonds, we must covalently link the target and vector DNA before placing them into a bacterial cell. This is easily accomplished by using the enzyme DNA ligase. DNA ligase is another enzyme discovered during basic studies of DNA replication and repair. It catalyzes the formation of phosphoester bonds between the two pieces of DNA.

Now it is time to introduce the recombinant DNA molecules into a bacterial cell. One means of doing this is transformation, a process by which *E. coli* cells are treated under conditions that favor the entry of DNA into the cells. The cells of the transformation mixture are plated on a solid nutrient agar medium. Each individual cell will grow into a colony of cells on this agar medium. Unfortunately, transformation is not very efficient, and most of the cells in the transformation mixture do not carry a plasmid. These are of no interest, but how can they be eliminated? As it turns out, with pBR322 it is very simple. If the cells are plated on an agar medium containing ampicillin, all the cells that did not acquire a plasmid will be killed by the antibiotic.

Now hybridization can be used to detect the clones that carry the β-globin gene. A radioactive probe is prepared by extracting β-globin mRNA from red blood cells. These cells contain

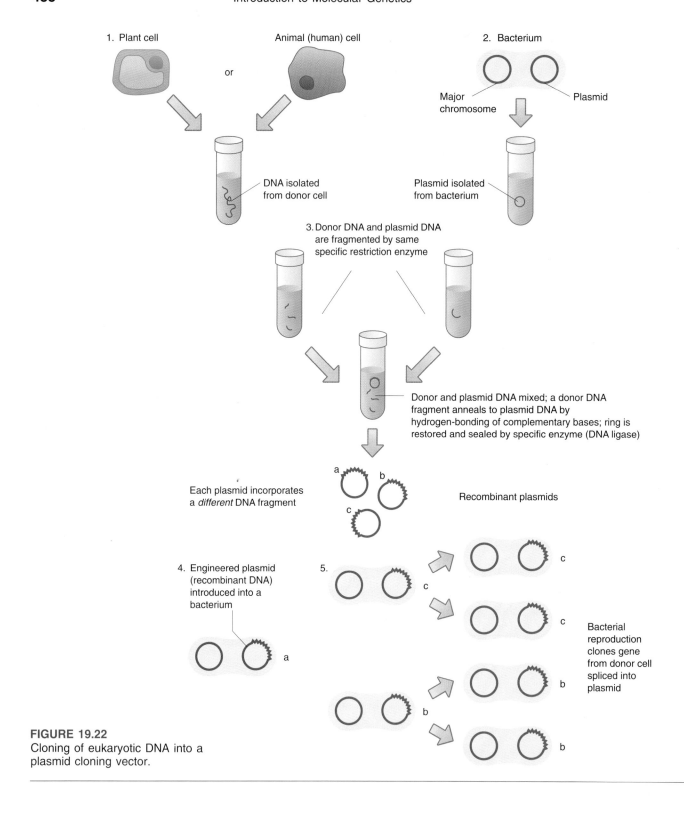

1. Plant cell

Animal (human) cell

or

2. Bacterium

Major chromosome

Plasmid

DNA isolated from donor cell

Plasmid isolated from bacterium

3. Donor DNA and plasmid DNA are fragmented by same specific restriction enzyme

Donor and plasmid DNA mixed; a donor DNA fragment anneals to plasmid DNA by hydrogen-bonding of complementary bases; ring is restored and sealed by specific enzyme (DNA ligase)

Each plasmid incorporates a *different* DNA fragment

a
b
c

Recombinant plasmids

4. Engineered plasmid (recombinant DNA) introduced into a bacterium

5.

c

c

c

a

b

b

b

b

Bacterial reproduction clones gene from donor cell spliced into plasmid

FIGURE 19.22
Cloning of eukaryotic DNA into a plasmid cloning vector.

little nucleic acid other than globin mRNAs. The β-globin mRNA is radioactively labeled and used as a probe to detect those colonies that contain the desired cloned DNA.

A replica of the experimental plate is made by pressing sterile velveteen fabric onto the surface. The velveteen, carrying cells from the original colonies, is pressed onto the surface of a fresh agar plate, producing a precise replica. A membrane filter is placed on the colonies on the agar plate. Cells from each colony will be transferred to the membrane filter. These cells are gently broken open by treatment with detergents and enzymes, and the filter is treated so that the released DNA becomes attached to the membrane. When hybridization is carried out on these filters, the radioactive probe will hybridize only to the complementary sequences of the β-globin gene. When the membrane filter is exposed to X-ray film, a "spot" will appear on the developed film only at the site of a colony carrying the desired clone. By going back to the original plate, cells from that colony can be selected and the cells grown for further study (Figure 19.23).

The same procedure can be used to clone the β-chain gene of sickle cell hemoglobin. Then the two can be studied and compared to determine the nature of the genetic defect.

This simple example makes it appear that all gene cloning is very easy and straightforward. This has proved to be far from the truth. Genetic engineers have had to overcome many obstacles to clone eukaryotic genes of special interest medically. One of the first obstacles encountered was the presence of introns within eukaryotic genes. Bacteria that are used for cloning lack the enzymatic machinery to splice out introns. Molecular biologists found that a DNA copy of a eukaryotic mRNA could be made by using the enzyme reverse transcriptase from a family of viruses called retroviruses (see "A Clinical Perspective: Fooling the AIDS Virus with Look-Alike Nucleotides"). Such a DNA copy of the mRNA carries all the protein-coding sequences of a gene but none of the intron sequences. Thus bacteria are able to transcribe and translate the cloned DNA and produce valuable products for use in medicine and other applications.

This is only one of the many technical problems that have been overcome by the amazing developments in recombinant DNA technology. A brief but impressive list of medically important products of genetic engineering is found in Table 19.4.

While great progress has been made in applying genetic engineering to important medical problems, most of these products represent only a treatment, not a cure. The ultimate dream for the future is to intervene more absolutely, to remove "bad" genes from the human population

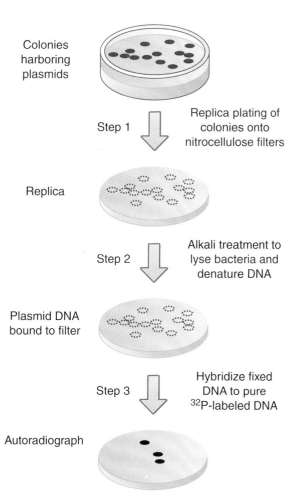

Colonies harboring plasmids

Step 1 — Replica plating of colonies onto nitrocellulose filters

Replica

Step 2 — Alkali treatment to lyse bacteria and denature DNA

Plasmid DNA bound to filter

Step 3 — Hybridize fixed DNA to pure ^{32}P-labeled DNA

Autoradiograph

FIGURE 19.23
Colony blot hybridization for detection of cells carrying a plasmid clone of the β-chain gene of hemoglobin.

A MEDICAL PERSPECTIVE

The New Genetics and Human Genetic Disease

It is estimated that about half a million babies are born each year suffering from one of almost 4000 known genetic defects. The care and treatment of these children cause a tremendous drain on both the parents and health care systems.

The revolution in molecular genetics that began in the early 1960s has led to important advances in our understanding of human genetics and human genetic diseases. As a result, genetic counseling has become a major component of the health care system, and through genetic screening, about 250 of these genetic defects can be detected in fetuses, children, and adults.

Recombinant DNA technology has been a critical component of these advances. For instance, the genes for human insulin, human growth hormone (HGH), and the blood-clotting protein Factor VIII have been cloned, and the protein products have been purified and are available for the treatment of insulin-dependent diabetes, pituitary dwarfism, and hemophilia. The significance of the availability of these human gene products is made more evident when we consider some of the problems faced by sufferers of these genetic defects.

Many diabetics are insulin-dependent; in other words, they require injections of insulin to control their blood glucose levels. Previously, only insulin from the pancreas of pigs and cows was available. These hormones differ from the human hormone by only a few amino acids, but this slight difference caused many diabetics to develop immunity to their insulin. As a result, the hormone could not control blood glucose. This problem has been alleviated by the fact that the human insulin gene was cloned and human insulin (Humalin) was approved for human use in 1982.

At least 3500 children in the United States suffer from pituitary dwarfism. Without treatment these children can expect to grow to no more than four feet in height. However, treatment with human growth hormone purified from the pituitary glands of cadavers allows these children to attain nearly normal height. In 1985 a medical crisis arose. Some of the cadavers were infected with the virus that causes Creutzfeldt-Jacob syndrome, a degenerative brain infection, and children receiving HGH from these cadavers were contracting this fatal disease. HGH produced from recombinant DNA was immediately approved by the FDA for safe treatment of these individuals.

It is estimated that 1 in 10,000 males is born with classical hemophilia. The disease primarily affects males because the gene for the defect is on the X chromosome. These individuals were faced with a dilemma similar to that of the children with pituitary dwarfism. The preparation of Factor VIII needed to arrest severe bleeding from even minor wounds is purified from human blood plasma. In the early 1980s this plasma supply became contaminated with the virus that causes acquired immune deficiency syndrome (AIDS) with the result that a great many hemophiliacs contracted this fatal disease. Factor VIII produced from recombinant DNA is currently being tested for use by hemophiliacs.

Recently, scientists have been allowed to conduct clinical trials involving introducing recombinant DNA molecules into humans. In one such trial the goal is to treat the genetic disease cystic fibrosis. This disease, which affects about 1 of every 20,000 babies born, is a defect in the gene that codes for a channel protein that controls the movement of chloride ions out of cells. One of the problems that arises when this gene is defective is that chloride is not removed from cells in the lungs. As a result, there is a buildup of thick mucus in the lungs. This makes it difficult to breath and increases the chances of lung infections. A recombinant adenovirus has been constructed that carries the normal gene. Adenovirus is a virus that causes the common cold. A group of cystic fibrosis sufferers have received the recombinant advenovirus by inhalation. It is hoped that the virus will infect the cells of the lungs and the recombinant gene will produce the needed chloride channel protein. This would alleviate the respiratory symptoms of cystic fibrosis.

In another exciting clinical trial, researchers are treating a rare genetic disorder of the immune system. Adenine deaminase is an enzyme involved in nucleotide metabolism. Children born with a defect in the gene for this enzyme suffer from a syndrome called *severe combined immune deficiency*. Because their immune systems do not function, these children suffer repeated infections and generally die at a very young age. Researchers have cloned the normal gene for adenine deaminase into white blood cells from children suffering from this genetic disease. They have then transfused these white blood cells back into the child. Early results are encouraging. The children who have undergone the treatment have responded by producing elevated levels of the normal enzyme. Although they must have transfusions of their own cells every few months, they are able to lead a more normal life, without the constant threat of a fatal infection.

These examples clearly demonstrate the value of recombinant DNA technology to human populations. Many different strategies are being tried by genetic engineers working to clone genes to detect and treat human genetic diseases. The eventual goal of this type of research is to actually replace the mutated gene that is responsible for the genetic defect with a normal functional copy of the gene. This ultimate goal is many years in the future. We must first have a better understanding of the way normal genes are controlled by the cell before we can begin to tamper with genes in the intact organism.

TABLE 19.4   A Brief List of Medically Important Proteins Produced by Genetic Engineering

Protein	Medical Condition Treated
Insulin	Insulin-dependent diabetes
Human growth hormone	Pituitary dwarfism
Factor VIII	Type A hemophilia
Factor IX	Type B hemophilia
Tissue plasminogen factor	Stroke, myocardial infarction
Streptokinase	Myocardial infarction
Interferon	Cancer, some virus infection
Interleukin-2	Cancer
Tumor necrosis factor	Cancer
Atrial natriuretic factor	Hypertension
Erythropoetin	Anemia
Thymosin α-1	Stimulate immune system
Hepatitis B virus (HBV) vaccine	Prevent HBV viral hepatitis
Influenza vaccine	Prevent influenza infection

entirely. Replacing a mutant gene in a fertilized egg with a normal gene is one approach to this goal. However, realization of that dream in humans is years, perhaps decades, away. Meanwhile, molecular biologists continue to work toward that goal by studying the normal structure and expression of DNA and by working to develop safe delivery systems for the introduction of new DNA into cells such as the fragile human fertilized egg.

SUMMARY

19.1 The Structure of the Nucleotide

DNA and RNA are polymers of *nucleotides,* which are composed of a five-carbon sugar (ribose in RNA and 2′-deoxyribose in DNA), a nitrogenous base, and one, two, or three phosphoryl groups. There are two kinds of nitrogenous bases, the *purines* (adenine and guanine) and the *pyrimidines* (cytosine, thymine, and uracil). *Deoxyribonucleotides* are the subunits of DNA. *Ribonucleotides* are the subunits of RNA.

19.2 The Structure of DNA and RNA

Nucleotides are joined by 3′–5′ phosphodiester bonds in both DNA and RNA. DNA is a *double helix,* two strands of DNA wound around one another. The sugar-phosphate backbone is on the outside of the helix, and complementary pairs of bases extend into the center of the helix. The *base pairs* are held together by hydrogen bonds. Adenine base pairs with thymine, and cytosine base pairs with guanine. The two strands of DNA in the helix are antiparallel to one another. RNA is single-stranded.

19.3 DNA Replication

DNA replication involves synthesis of a faithful copy of the DNA molecule. It is *semiconservative;* each daughter molecule consists of one parental strand and one newly synthesized strand.

DNA polymerase "reads" each parental strand and synthesizes the complementary daughter strand according to the rules of base pairing.

19.4 Information Flow in Biological Systems

The *central dogma* states that the flow of biological information in cells is DNA → RNA → protein. There are three classes of RNA: *messenger RNA, transfer RNA,* and *ribosomal RNA. Transcription* is the process by which RNA molecules are synthesized. *RNA polymerase* catalyzes the synthesis of RNA. Transcription occurs in three stages: initiation, elongation, and termination. Eukaryotic genes contain *introns,* sequences that do not encode protein. These are removed from the primary transcript by the process of RNA splicing. The final mRNA contains only the protein coding sequences or *exons.*

19.5 The Genetic Code

The genetic code is a triplet code. Each code word is called a *codon* and consists of three nucleotides. There are 64 codons in the genetic code. Of these, three are *termination codons* (UAA, UAG, and UGA), and the remaining 61 specify an amino acid. Most amino acids have several codons. As a result, the genetic code is said to be *degenerate.*

19.6 Protein Synthesis

The process of protein synthesis is called *translation.* The genetic code words on the mRNA are decoded by tRNA. Each tRNA has an *anticodon* that is complementary to a codon on the mRNA. In addition the tRNA is covalently linked to its correct amino acid. Thus hydrogen bonding between codon and anticodon brings the correct amino acid to the site of protein synthesis. Translation also occurs in three stages called initiation, chain elongation, and termination.

19.7 Mutation, Ultraviolet Light, and DNA Repair

Any change in a DNA sequence is a *mutation.* Mutations are classified according to the type of DNA alteration, including *point mutations, deletion mutations,* and *insertion mutations.* Mutations are also classified by their biological effect. Some are *silent,* and others have negative biological consequences. Ultraviolet light (UV) causes formation of *thymine dimers.* Mistakes can be made during thymine dimer repair, causing UV-induced mutations. Germicidal (UV) lamps are used to kill bacteria on environmental surfaces. The large UV dose causes extreme DNA damage that kills the bacteria. UV damage to skin can result in skin cancer. Humans have a complex DNA repair system. A defect in that system, such as in the genetic disease xeroderma pigmentosum, results in cancer at an early age.

19.8 Recombinant DNA

Several tools are required for genetic engineering, including *restriction enzymes, agarose gel electrophoresis, hybridization,* and *cloning vectors.* Cloning a DNA fragment involves digestion of the target and vector DNA with a restriction enzyme. DNA ligase joins the target and vector DNA covalently, and the recombinant DNA molecules are introduced into bacterial cells by transformation. The desired clone is located by using antibiotic selection and hybridization. Many eukaryotic genes have been cloned for the purpose of producing medically important proteins.

KEY TERMS

aminoacyl tRNA (19.6)
aminoacyl tRNA binding site
    of ribosome (A-site) (19.6)
aminoacyl tRNA synthetase
    (19.6)
anticodon (19.4)
antiparallel (19.2)
base pair (19.2)
carcinogen (19.7)
central dogma (19.4)
cloning vector (19.8)
codon (19.4)
complementary strands (19.2)
degenerate code (19.5)
deletion mutation (19.7)

deoxyribonucleic acid (DNA)
    (19.1)
deoxyribonucleotide (19.1)
DNA polymerase (19.3)
double helix (19.2)
exon (19.4)
hybridization (19.8)
initiation factors (19.6)
insertion mutation (19.7)
intron (19.4)
messenger RNA (mRNA)
    (19.4)
mutagen (19.7)
mutation (19.7)
nucleotide (19.1)

peptidyl tRNA binding site of
    ribosome (P-site) (19.6)
point mutation (19.7)
polysome (19.6)
promoter (19.4)
purine (19.1)
pyrimidine (19.1)
release factors (19.6)
replication fork (19.3)
replication origin (19.3)
restriction enzyme (19.8)
ribonucleic acid (RNA) (19.1)
ribonucleotide (19.1)

ribosomal RNA (rRNA) (19.4)
ribosome (19.6)
RNA polymerase (19.4)
semiconservative DNA
    replication (19.3)
silent mutation (19.7)
termination codon (19.6)
thymine dimers (19.7)
transcription (19.4)
transfer RNA (tRNA) (19.4,
    19.6)
translation (19.4)
translocation (19.6)

QUESTIONS AND PROBLEMS

The Structure of the Nucleotide

19.15 Draw the structure of the purine ring, and indicate the nitrogen that is bound to sugars in nucleotides.

19.16 Draw the ring structure of the pyrimidines. In a nucleotide, which nitrogen atom of pyrimidine rings is bound to the sugar?

19.17 How many hydrogen bonds link the adenine-thymine base pair?

19.18 How many hydrogen bonds link the guanine-cytosine base pair?

19.19 Write the structure that results when deoxycytosine-5'-monophosphate is linked by a $3' \rightarrow 5'$ phosphodiester bond to deoxythymidine-5'-monophosphate.

19.20 Write the structure that results when adenosine-5'-monophosphate is linked by a $3' \rightarrow 5'$ phosphodiester bond to uridine-5'-monophosphate.

DNA Replication

19.21 What is meant by semiconservative DNA replication?

19.22 What are the two primary functions of DNA polymerase?

19.23 If a DNA strand had the nucleotide sequence 5'-ATGCGGCTAGAATATTCCA-3', what would the sequence of the complementary daughter strand be?

19.24 If the sequence of a double-stranded DNA is

what would the sequence of the two daughter DNA molecules be after DNA replication? Indicate which strands are newly synthesized and which are parental.

Information Flow in Biological Systems

19.25 What is the central dogma of molecular biology?

19.26 What are the roles of DNA, RNA, and protein in information flow in biological systems?

19.27 On what molecule is the anticodon found?

19.28 On what molecule is the codon found?

19.29 If a gene had the nucleotide sequence 5'-TACCTAGCTCTGGTCATTAAGGCAGTA-3', what would the sequence of the mRNA be?

19.30 If a mRNA had the nucleotide sequence 5'-AUGCCCUUUCAUUACCCGGUA-3', what was the sequence of the DNA strand that was transcribed?

19.31 What is meant by the term *RNA splicing?*

19.32 The following is the unspliced transcript of a eukaryotic gene:

exon 1   intron A   exon 2   intron B   exon 3   intron C   exon 4

What would the structure of the final mature mRNA look like, and which of the above sequences would be found in the mature mRNA?

The Genetic Code

19.33 How many codons constitute the genetic code?

19.34 What is meant by a triplet code?

Protein Synthesis

19.35 What is the function of ribosomes?

19.36 What are the two tRNA binding sites on the ribosome?

19.37 Briefly describe the three stages of translation: initiation, elongation, and termination.

19.38 What peptide sequence would be formed from the mRNA 5'-AUGUGUAGUGACCAACCGAUUUCACUGUGA-3'?

Mutation, Ultraviolet Light, and DNA Repair

19.39 What damage does UV light cause in DNA, and how does this lead to mutations?

19.40 Explain why UV lights are effective germicides on environmental surfaces.

19.41 What is a carcinogen? Why are carcinogens also mutagens?

19.42 What causes the genetic disease xeroderma pigmentosum? Why are people who suffer from xeroderma pigmentosum prone to cancer?

Recombinant DNA

19.43 What is a restriction enzyme?

19.44 Of what value are restriction enzymes in recombinant DNA research?

19.45 Describe the molecular basis of hybridization.

19.46 What is a cloning vector?

19.47 Name three products of recombinant DNA that are of value in the field of medicine.

19.48 What is the ultimate goal of genetic engineering? What ethical issues does this goal raise?

Further Problems

19.49 ATP is the universal energy currency of the cell. What components make up the ATP nucleotide?

19.50 One of the energy harvesting steps of the citric acid cycle results in the production of GTP. What is the structure of the GTP nucleotide?

19.51 The two strands of a DNA molecule are antiparallel. What is meant by this description?

19.52 List three differences between DNA and RNA.

19.53 What is the replication origin of a DNA molecule?

19.54 What is occurring at the replication fork?

19.55 List the three classes of RNA molecules.

19.56 What is the function of each of the classes of RNA molecules?

VOCABULARY QUIZ

19.1   The _____ is composed of a five-carbon sugar, a nitrogenous base, and one, two, or three phosphoryl groups.

19.2   The term _____ describes the double-stranded spiral nature of the DNA molecule.

19.3   The unidirectional flow of biological information (DNA → RNA → protein) is called _____.

19.4   The class of RNA that carries the genetic code for a protein is _____.

19.5   The process of protein synthesis is called _____.

19.6   The platform on which protein synthesis occurs is called the _____.

19.7   Any change in the sequence of DNA is called a(n) _____.

19.8   The enzyme that is responsible for transcription is _____.

19.9   An enzyme that cuts DNA molecules at specific DNA sequences is _____.

19.10 A mutation that results in no change in the sequence of amino acids in the protein is called a(n) _____.

A Review of Mathematics Applied to Problem Solving in Chemistry

ALGEBRAIC EQUATIONS

Many of the problems and examples discussed in the text involve one or more of a limited number of algebraic equations. If you are having difficulty with the mathematics rather than the chemistry, this algebra review may prove useful. Let's consider a variety of common algebraic relationships and their application to chemistry problem-solving.

One common algebraic equation that is often applied in chemical problem solving is

$$a = \frac{b}{c}$$

The expression for density, $d = \dfrac{m}{V}$, is one common example of this type of relationship.

Let's compare the similarity between the pure algebraic manipulation (left column) and the relationship between density (d), mass (m), and volume (V).

Mathematical Function	Chemistry Connection
To solve for a, divide b by c.	To solve for d, divide m by V.
To solve for b, multiply both sides of the equation by c:	To solve for m, multiply both sides of the equation by V:
$$a \times c = \frac{b}{\cancel{c}} \times \cancel{c}$$	$$d \times V = \frac{m}{\cancel{V}} \times \cancel{V}$$
$$b = a \times c$$	$$m = d \times V$$

This can be applied to problems such as those in Examples 1.14 and 1.15 in the text. A typical problem involving the concept of density is shown below.

EXAMPLE A.1

Calculating Mass from Volume Using Density

Pure oxygen has a density of 0.0014 g/mL at 273 K. What is the mass of an 8.0-L sample of oxygen?

Solution

Recall that a number such as 0.0014 g/mL can be expressed as

$$1.4 \times 10^{-3} \text{ g/mL}.$$

(The decimal point is moved three positions to the right.) Also, using a conversion factor to make the volume units consistent, we have

$$8.0 \; \cancel{\text{L oxygen}} \times \frac{10^3 \text{ mL oxygen}}{1 \; \cancel{\text{L oxygen}}} = 8.00 \times 10^3 \text{ mL oxygen}$$

This problem can be solved by rearranging the expression for density, $d = m/V$, to the form

$$m = d \times V$$

as we have done above. Substituting the data that we have for density and volume,

$$\frac{1.4 \times 10^{-3} \text{ g oxygen}}{\text{mL oxygen}} \times 8.00 \times 10^3 \text{ mL oxygen} = 11.2 \text{ g oxygen}$$

We can use the density to calculate the mass of a liquid as well.

EXAMPLE A.2

Calculating Mass from Volume Using Density

A certain thermometer contains 0.500 mL of mercury. Calculate the mass, in grams, of the mercury in the thermometer. The density of mercury is 13.5 g/mL.

Solution

Using the density as a conversion factor from volume to mass, we have

$$m = d \times V$$

$$m = (0.500 \text{ mL mercury})\left(\frac{13.5 \text{ g mercury}}{\text{mL mercury}}\right)$$

$$m = 6.75 \text{ g mercury}$$

If we wish to solve the same general expression, $a = \dfrac{b}{c}$, for c or in the specific case of the density expression, $d = \dfrac{m}{V}$, for V, we may use the following approach:

Mathematical Function	Chemistry Connection
To solve for c, multiply both sides of the equation by $\dfrac{c}{a}$:	To solve for V, multiply both sides of the equation by $\dfrac{V}{d}$:
$$a \times \frac{c}{a} = \frac{b}{c} \times \frac{c}{a}$$	$$d \times \frac{V}{d} = \frac{m}{V} \times \frac{V}{d}$$
$$c = \frac{b}{a}$$	$$V = \frac{m}{d}$$

This approach is useful in solving problems such as the one in Example 1.16. For instance, we can use the density to calculate the volume of a liquid.

EXAMPLE A.3

Calculating Volume from Mass Using Density

Calculate the volume, in milliliters, of a liquid that has a density of 1.30 g/mL and a mass of 9.00 g.

Solution

Using the density as a conversion factor from mass to volume and following the algebraic solution

$$c = \frac{b}{a}$$

It follows that

$$V = \frac{m}{d}$$

and

$$V = \frac{9.00 \text{ g liquid}}{1.30 \text{ g/mL liquid}}$$

$$V = 6.92 \text{ mL liquid}$$

Another frequently used algebraic expression is

$$\frac{a}{b} = \frac{c}{d}$$

The expression for Charles's Law, relating initial and final volumes and temperatures, depends on this algebraic form for its solution. One form of Charles's Law follows this algebraic form:

$$\frac{V_i}{T_i} = \frac{V_f}{T_f}$$

Mathematical Function	Chemistry Connection
To solve for a, multiply both sides of the equation by b: $$\frac{a}{\cancel{b}} \times \cancel{b} = \frac{c}{d} \times b$$ $$a = \frac{c \times b}{d}$$	To solve for V_i, multiply both sides of the equation by T_i: $$\frac{V_i}{\cancel{T_i}} \times \cancel{T_i} = \frac{V_f}{T_f} \times T_i$$ $$V_i = \frac{V_f \times T_i}{T_f}$$
To solve for b, multiply both sides of the equation by $\frac{b \times d}{c}$: $$\frac{a}{\cancel{b}} \times \frac{\cancel{b} \times d}{c} = \frac{\cancel{c}}{\cancel{d}} \times \frac{b \times \cancel{d}}{\cancel{c}}$$ $$\frac{a \times d}{c} = b \quad \text{or} \quad b = \frac{a \times d}{c}$$	To solve for T_i, multiply both sides of the equation by $\frac{T_i \times T_f}{V_f}$: $$\frac{V_i}{\cancel{T_i}} \times \frac{\cancel{T_i} \times T_f}{V_f} = \frac{\cancel{V_f}}{\cancel{T_f}} \times \frac{T_i \times \cancel{T_f}}{\cancel{V_f}}$$ $$\frac{V_i \times T_f}{V_f} = T_i \quad \text{or} \quad T_i = \frac{V_i \times T_f}{V_f}$$
To solve for c, multiply both sides of the equation by d: $$\frac{a}{b} \times d = \frac{c}{\cancel{d}} \times \cancel{d}$$ $$\frac{a \times d}{b} = c \quad \text{or} \quad c = \frac{a \times d}{b}$$	To solve for V_f, multiply both sides of the equation by T_f: $$\frac{V_i}{T_i} \times T_f = \frac{V_f}{\cancel{T_f}} \times \cancel{T_f}$$ $$\frac{V_i \times T_f}{T_i} = V_f \quad \text{or} \quad V_f = \frac{V_i \times T_f}{T_i}$$

This equation is used in solving the problem in Example 5.4. We can use this equation to calculate the final volume of a balloon after it has undergone a change in temperature.

EXAMPLE A.4

Calculating a New Volume after a Temperature Change

A balloon filled with helium has a volume of 10.0×10^3 L at 298 K. What would the balloon's volume be, at 255 K, if the pressure surrounding the balloon remained constant?

Solution

We use the Charles's Law relationship:

$$\frac{V_i}{T_i} = \frac{V_f}{T_f}$$

and substitute our data into the Charles's Law expression, rearranged as

$$c = \frac{a \times d}{b}$$

$$V_f = \frac{V_i \times T_f}{T_i}$$

$$V_f = \frac{(10.0 \times 10^3 \text{ L})(255 \text{ K})}{(298 \text{ K})}$$

$$V_f = 8.56 \times 10^3 \text{ L}$$

Mathematical Function	Chemistry Connection
To solve for d, multiply both sides of the equation by $\dfrac{b \times d}{a}$:	To solve for T_f, multiply both sides of the equation by $\dfrac{T_i \times T_f}{V_i}$:
$\dfrac{d}{b} \times \dfrac{b \times d}{d} = \dfrac{c}{d} \times \dfrac{b \times d}{a}$	$\dfrac{V_i}{T_i} \times \dfrac{T_i \times T_f}{V_i} = \dfrac{V_f}{T_f} \times \dfrac{T_i \times T_f}{V_i}$
$d = \dfrac{b \times c}{a}$	$T_f = \dfrac{V_f \times T_i}{V_i}$

This expression is useful in the calculation of temperature-volume problems such as the following.

EXAMPLE A.5

Calculating a New Temperature after a Volume Change

Calculate the final temperature of the gas in a balloon that was observed to expand from 3.00 L to 6.00 L as the balloon was heated from an initial temperature of 325 K.

Solution

As we have shown,

$$T_f = \frac{V_f \times T_i}{V_i}$$

$$T_f = \frac{(6.00 \text{ L})(325 \text{ K})}{3.00 \text{ L}}$$

$$T_f = 650 \text{ K}$$

Another useful algebraic expression takes the form

$$a \times b = c \times d$$

The expression for Boyle's Law, relating pressure to the initial and final volumes of a gas, depends on this algebraic form for its solution:

$$P_i V_i = P_f V_f$$

Mathematical Function	Chemistry Connection
To solve for a, divide both sides of the equation by b: $$\frac{a \times \cancel{b}}{\cancel{b}} = \frac{c \times d}{b}$$ $$a = \frac{c \times d}{b}$$ By using the same logic, expressions for b, c, or d may be derived: $$b = \frac{c \times d}{a}$$ $$c = \frac{a \times b}{d}$$ $$d = \frac{a \times b}{c}$$	To solve for P_i, divide both sides of the equation by V_i: $$\frac{P_i \times \cancel{V_i}}{\cancel{V_i}} = \frac{P_f \times V_f}{V_i}$$ $$P_i = \frac{P_f \times V_f}{V_i}$$ By using the same logic expressions for V_i, P_f, and V_f, may be derived: $$V_i = \frac{P_f \times V_f}{P_i}$$ $$P_f = \frac{P_i \times V_i}{V_f}$$ $$V_f = \frac{P_i \times V_i}{P_f}$$

This can be applied to the solution of problems such as that found in Example 5.3. The determination of a final pressure is illustrated below.

EXAMPLE A.6

Calculating the Pressure Needed to Compress a Gas

A certain mass of air, at 25°C, occupies a volume of 8.00×10^2 mL at 2.75 atm pressure. What pressure must be applied to compress the gas to a volume of 1.00×10^2 mL, assuming no temperature change?

Solution

Boyle's Law applies directly, as there is no change in temperature or number of moles (the mass remains constant). Begin by identifying each term in the Boyle's Law expression:

$$P_i = 2.75 \text{ atm}$$
$$V_i = 8.00 \times 10^2 \text{ mL}$$
$$V_f = 1.00 \times 10^2 \text{ mL}$$
$$P_i V_i = P_f V_f$$

and solve using the algebraic form $c = \dfrac{a \times b}{d}$:

$$P_f = \frac{P_i \times V_i}{V_f}$$

$$P_f = \frac{(2.75 \text{ atm air})(8.00 \times 10^2 \text{ mL air})}{(1.00 \times 10^2 \text{ mL air})}$$

$$P_f = 22.0 \text{ atm air}$$

(*Note:* The calculation can be done with volume units of milliliters or liters. It is important only that the units be the *same* on both sides of the equation.)

The last algebraic form that we consider is

$$e = \frac{a(b - c)}{d}$$

The expression relating temperature to Celsius and Fahrenheit units is a practical example of this algebraic form:

$$°C = \frac{5(°F - 32)}{9}$$

Mathematical Function	Chemistry Connection
To solve for b, multiply both sides of the equation by d/a:	To solve for F, multiply both sides of the equation by 9/5:
$$\frac{\cancel{d}}{\cancel{a}} \times \frac{\cancel{a}(b - c)}{\cancel{d}} = \frac{d}{a} \times e$$	$$\frac{\cancel{9}}{\cancel{5}} \times \frac{\cancel{5}(°F - 32)}{\cancel{9}} = \frac{9}{5} \times °C$$
$$b - c = \frac{d \times e}{a}$$	$$°F - 32 = \frac{9 \times °C}{5}$$
Then add c to both sides of the equation:	Then add 32 to both sides of the equation:
$$b - c + c = \frac{(d \times e)}{a} + c$$	$$°F - 32 + 32 = \frac{(9 \times °C)}{5} + 32$$
$$b = \frac{(d \times e)}{a} + c$$	$$°F = \frac{(9 \times °C)}{5} + 32$$

Consider the following example.

EXAMPLE A.7

Converting Temperature Units

A patient has a temperature of 40°C. Calculate the corresponding temperature in units of degrees Fahrenheit.

Solution

By following the steps outlined above, the equation

$$°C = \frac{5(°F - 32)}{9}$$

can be solved for F:

$$°F = \frac{(9 \times °C)}{5} + 32$$

Substituting, we have

$$°F = \frac{(9 \times 40)}{5} + 32$$

$$F = 104°F$$

In scientific calculations, data, results, and physical constants are often either very large or very small numbers. For example, Avogadro's number is

$$602,000,000,000,000,000,000,000 \text{ particles}$$

EXPONENTIAL NOTATION

and the atomic mass unit (amu), expressed in units of grams, is

$$0.0000000000000000000000000166 \text{ g}$$

Chapter 1 describes the use of scientific notation (exponential notation) to represent such numbers more conveniently. The rules for scientific notation, as summarized in our first chapter, are as follows:

1. To convert a number greater than 1 to scientific notation, the original decimal point is moved x places to the left, and the resulting number is multiplied by 10^x. The exponent (x) is a *positive* number equal to the number of places the original decimal point was moved.

    Avogadro's number is represented as 6.02×10^{23}. The decimal point is moved 23 places to the *left*.

2. To convert a number less than 1 to scientific notation, the original decimal point is moved x places to the right, and the resulting number is multiplied by 10^{-x}. The exponent ($-x$) is a *negative* number equal to the number of places the original decimal point was moved.

    The atomic mass unit is represented as 1.66×10^{-24} g. The decimal point is moved 24 places to the *right*.

Addition and subtraction using exponents

Consider the following:

$$(6.52 \times 10^{-3}) - (4.87 \times 10^{-4}) = ?$$

Note that the exponents are not identical. To use a calculator to solve this problem, simply enter the data in a format that is consistent with the way that your calculator is designed to function. The answer is displayed with the correct numerical value and exponent.

If you do not have access to a calculator, you must make both exponents identical before attempting to subtract the numbers. It makes no difference which exponent you choose to change; in this example, let's change the first exponent to agree with the second:

$$6.52 \times 10^{-3} \quad \text{is also} \quad 65.2 \times 10^{-4}$$

Moving the decimal point one place to the right
makes the exponent one unit more negative.

Subtract (or add) the numerical portions of each and carry the exponential term:

$$(65.2 \times 10^{-4}) - (4.87 \times 10^{-4}) = 60.3 \times 10^{-4}$$

$$60.3 \times 10^{-4} \quad \text{is also} \quad 6.03 \times 10^{-3}$$

Moving the decimal point one place to the left
makes the exponent one unit more positive.

Perhaps the most common error made in these calculations is one of omission; after subtraction of the nonexponential terms we may forget to carry along the exponent. This small oversight can have great consequences. In the preceding example, omitting the power of ten would produce a thousandfold error.

Multiplication and division using exponents

To multiply numbers with exponents, carry out the following steps:

◆   Change all numbers to powers of 10.

◆   To determine the numerical value, multiply the numerical portion.

◆   To determine the exponent, algebraically add the exponents of 10.

EXAMPLE A.8

Multiplying Numbers with Positive Exponents

$$220 \times 3500 = ?$$

Solution

$$2.2 \times 10^2 \times 3.5 \times 10^3 = 7.7 \times 10^{(2+3)} = 7.7 \times 10^5$$

EXAMPLE A.9

Multiplying Numbers with Negative Exponents

$$220 \times 0.000035 = ?$$

$$2.2 \times 10^{2} \times 3.5 \times 10^{-5} = 7.7 \times 10^{[2+(-5)]} = 7.7 \times 10^{-3}$$

To divide numbers with exponents, carry out the following steps:

- Change all numbers to powers of 10.
- To determine the numerical value, divide the numerical portion.
- To determine the exponent, algebraically subtract the exponents of 10. Note that the exponents in the denominator are subtracted from the exponents in the numerator.

EXAMPLE A.10

Dividing Numbers with Positive Exponents

$$\frac{770{,}000}{220} = ?$$

Solution

$$\frac{7.7 \times 10^{5}}{2.2 \times 10^{2}} = ?$$

$$\frac{7.7 \times 10^{5}}{2.2 \times 10^{2}} = 3.5 \times 10^{(5-2)} = 3.5 \times 10^{3}$$

EXAMPLE A.11

Dividing Numbers with Negative Exponents

$$\frac{0.0077}{220} = ?$$

Solution

$$\frac{7.7 \times 10^{-3}}{2.20 \times 10^{2}} = ?$$

$$\frac{7.7 \times 10^{-3}}{2.20 \times 10^{2}} = 3.5 \times 10^{[-3-(+2)]} = 3.5 \times 10^{-5}$$

PROPORTIONALITY

Experiments in chemistry, and in science in general, often look for relationships between two or more variable quantities. For example, Charles's Law resulted from the observation that gas volumes increase as the temperature of the gas increases when the pressure and number of moles of the gas remain constant.

Direct proportionality

The following data were obtained to illustrate Charles's Law:

Experiment	*T* (K)	*V* of Helium (L)
1	300	1.00
2	600	2.00
3	900	3.00

Doubling the temperature (from 300 K to 600 K) causes the volume of helium to double. Tripling the temperature (from 300 K to 900 K) causes the volume of helium to triple. If we begin with a temperature of 600 K, decreasing the temperature by one-half also decreases the volume by one-half.

Because this is true, the temperature and volume of a gas are *directly proportional*. This relationship is expressed as

$$V \propto T$$

where the symbol $\propto$ is shorthand for the words *proportional to;* it reads: *Volume is proportional to temperature.* Use of a proportionality constant, k, and an equality sign to replace $\propto$ results in a valid mathematical equation:

$$V = kT$$

In this example, k is the Charles's Law constant. Graphical representation of a direct proportion results in a straight-line (linear) relationship between variables:

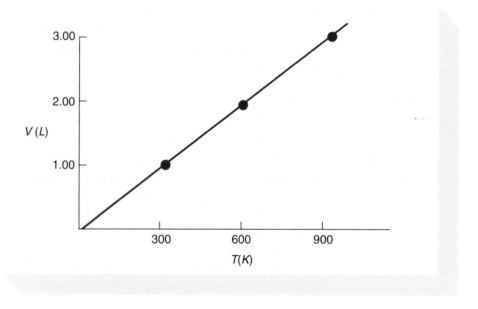

Graphs of this type allow prediction of the volume at *any* temperature within the range in which Charles's Law applies.

Inverse proportionality

Boyle's Law resulted from the observation that gas volumes decrease as the pressure of the gas increases when the temperature and number of moles of the gas remain constant. The following data were obtained to illustrate Boyle's Law:

Experiment	P (atm)	V of Helium (L)
1	2.00	6.00
2	4.00	3.00
3	6.00	2.00

Doubling the pressure (from 2 atm to 4 atm) causes the volume of helium to decrease by a factor of one-half. Tripling the pressure (from 2 atm to 6 atm) decreases the volume to one-third of the original value (from 6 L to 2 L).

Pressure and volume are *inversely proportional.* This relationship is expressed as

$$V \propto \frac{1}{P}$$

where the symbol $\propto$ is short for the words *proportional to;* it reads: *Volume is inversely proportional to pressure.* Use of a proportionality constant, k, and an equality sign to replace $\propto$ results in a valid mathematical equation:

$$V = \frac{k}{P}$$

The proportionality constant, k, is the Boyle's Law constant. The graphical representation of the data is as follows:

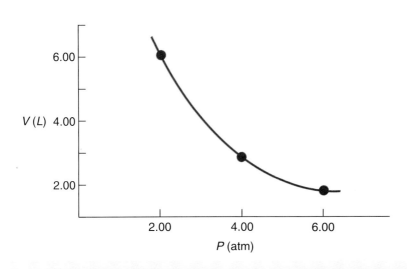

A curved relationship, such as that shown above, is not ideal for predicting other pairs of values from the graph. However, regraphing the data as follows:

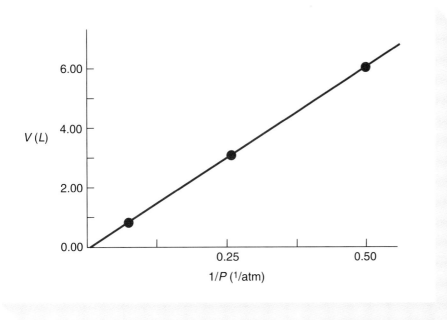

results in a linear relationship that is useful for predicting the volume at *any* pressure.

APPENDIX B   Table of Formula Weights

The following list of names, formulas, and formula weights may be useful in solving many of the problems found in Chapters 4–7.

Name	Formula	Formula Weight
Acetic acid	CH_3COOH	60.05 g/mol
Acetylene	C_2H_2	26.04 g/mol
Aluminum carbonate	$Al_2(CO_3)_3$	233.99 g/mol
Aluminum oxide	Al_2O_3	101.96 g/mol
Ammonia	NH_3	17.03 g/mol
Ammonium chloride	NH_4Cl	53.49 g/mol
Ammonium nitrate	NH_4NO_3	80.05 g/mol
Aspirin	$C_9H_8O_4$	180.15 g/mol
Barium carbonate	$BaCO_3$	197.35 g/mol
Boron oxide	B_2O_3	69.62 g/mol
Bromine	Br_2	159.82 g/mol
Calcium carbonate	$CaCO_3$	100.09 g/mol
Calcium hydride	CaH_2	42.10 g/mol
Calcium nitrate	$Ca(NO_3)_2$	164.10 g/mol
Calcium phosphate	$Ca_3(PO_4)_2$	310.18 g/mol
Carbon dioxide	CO_2	44.01 g/mol
Carbon disulfide	CS_2	76.13 g/mol
Chromium oxide (chromium(III)oxide)	Cr_2O_3	152.00 g/mol
Chromium trichloride (chromium(III)chloride)	$CrCl_3$	158.35 g/mol
Diborane	B_2H_6	27.67 g/mol
Ethyl alcohol	C_2H_5OH	46.07 g/mol
Glucose	$C_6H_{12}O_6$	180.16 g/mol
Hydrogen	H_2	2.016 g/mol
Iron oxide (iron(III)oxide)	Fe_2O_3	159.7 g/mol
Lithium chloride	$LiCl$	42.39 g/mol
Lithium nitrate	$LiNO_3$	68.95 g/mol
Magnesium chloride	$MgCl_2$	95.21 g/mol
Magnesium sulfate	$MgSO_4$	120.37 g/mol
Mercury oxide	HgO	216.59 g/mol
Methane	CH_4	16.04 g/mol
Methionine	$C_5H_{11}NO_2S$	149.21 g/mol
Nitrogen	N_2	28.02 g/mol
Nitrous oxide	N_2O	44.02 g/mol
Octane	C_8H_{18}	114.2 g/mol
Oxygen	O_2	32.00 g/mol
Phosphorous acid	H_3PO_3	82.00 g/mol
Potassium bromide	KBr	119.01 g/mol
Potassium chloride	KCl	74.55 g/mol
Potassium hydroxide	KOH	56.11 g/mol
Silicon dioxide	SiO_2	60.09 g/mol
Silver chloride	$AgCl$	143.3 g/mol
Silver nitrate	$AgNO_3$	169.9 g/mol
Sodium bromide	$NaBr$	102.9 g/mol
Sodium chloride	$NaCl$	58.44 g/mol
Sodium hydroxide	$NaOH$	40.00 g/mol
Sodium sulfate	Na_2SO_4	142.04 g/mol
Strontium hydroxide	$Sr(OH)_2$	121.64 g/mol
Sucrose	$C_{12}H_{22}O_{11}$	342.3 g/mol
Sulfur dioxide	SO_2	64.06 g/mol
Sulfuric acid	H_2SO_4	98.08 g/mol
Water	H_2O	18.02 g/mol

APPENDIX C

Stereochemistry and Stereoisomers Revisited

INTRODUCTION TO ISOMERS

Section 9.2

Compounds with identical molecular formulas but different structures are called *isomers*. Many types of isomers exist, and several of them are discussed throughout this text. *Structural isomers* differ from one another in configuration, that is, they differ in which atoms are bonded to one another. Structural isomers can be interconverted only by breaking bonds within the molecule and forming new bonds. *Functional group isomers* are molecules having the same molecular formula but different functional groups. For instance, alcohols and ethers having the same number of carbon atoms are functional group isomers. Consider the following examples:

$$CH_3CH_2CH_2OH \qquad\qquad CH_3CH_2OCH_3$$

1-Propanol (C_3H_8O)   Ethylmethyl ether (C_3H_8O)

Section 9.3

Section 11.2

Similarly, carboxylic acids and esters having the same number of carbon atoms are also functional group isomers, as are aldehydes and ketones. *Geometric isomers,* also called *cis-trans* isomers, differ from one another in the placement of substituents on a double bond or ring.

    Stereoisomers are the major focus of this appendix. By definition, stereoisomers are molecules that have the same structural formulas but differ in the arrangement of the atoms in space. Stereoisomers may be distinguished from one another by their different optical properties. They rotate plane-polarized light in different directions.

ROTATION OF PLANE-POLARIZED LIGHT

White light is a form of electromagnetic (EM) radiation and thus consists of waves in motion. In fact, white light is made up of many different wavelengths (colors) of light. The light waves vibrate in all directions, or *planes,* but are always perpendicular to the direction of the light beam (Figure C.1). Special light sources, such as sodium or mercury lamps, and filters can be used to produce *monochromatic light,* light consisting of only a single wavelength.

FIGURE C.1
Light as a wave motion.
(a) Viewed from the end of the axis of propagation, light contains waves traveling in many planes.
(b) Plane-polarized light contains only light traveling in one plane.

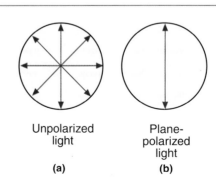

Unpolarized light

Plane-polarized light

(a)   (b)

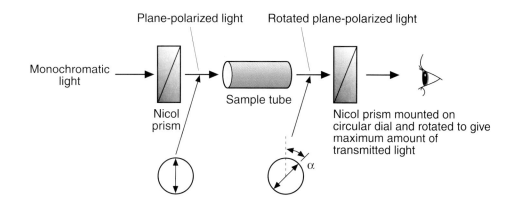

Plane-polarized light   Rotated plane-polarized light

Monochromatic light

Sample tube

Nicol prism

Nicol prism mounted on circular dial and rotated to give maximum amount of transmitted light

α

FIGURE C.2
Schematic drawing of a polarimeter.

When monochromatic light is passed through a polarizing material, such as a polaroid lens, only light waves in one plane can pass through; all others are filtered out. The light that emerges from the lens is called *plane-polarized light*. Polaroid lenses, like those found in polaroid sunglasses, consist of parallel arrays of crystals that can be imagined to look like the slats of Venetian blinds. When light interacts with this material, the emerging light beam is plane-polarized by the regular crystalline structure.

Applying these principles, scientists have developed an instrument called a *polarimeter* that is used to measure the optical activity of molecules. Specifically, the polarimeter measures the ability of a compound to change the angle of the plane of plane-polarized light (Figure C.2).

The monochromatic light source of a polarimeter is generally a sodium lamp. The light waves are directed through a *polarizer,* and the emerging plane-polarized light passes through the sample. Finally, the light passes through an *analyzer.* If the plane of the light is not altered by the sample, the compound is *optically inactive.* However, if the plane of light is rotated in either a clockwise or a counterclockwise direction, the sample is *optically active.*

The angle and direction of rotation are determined by rotating the analyzer, which is attached to a round dial graduated in degrees. First, the zero point is determined by passing light through the polarimeter without the sample present. The position that allows the maximum amount of light to pass through is the zero point. Next, the sample is placed in the polarimeter, and the analyzer is again rotated to allow the maximum amount of light to pass through. The *angle of rotation,* or *optical rotation,* is the difference between the zero point and the new angle obtained with the sample in place.

The observed angles of rotation are proportional to the number of optically active molecules in the sample that interact with light. Thus, optical rotation is proportional to the concentration of the sample and to the length of the sample tube, since both affect the total number of molecules in the light path. To compare values from different laboratories using different concentrations and apparatus, a standard reference, the specific rotation, was developed. Chemists have defined *specific rotation* [α], as the amount of rotation produced by 1.00 g of substance in 1.00 mL of solution and in a sample tube that is 1.00 decimeters (dm) in length. Because rotation is also a function of the temperature, the wavelength of monochromatic light, and the solvent used (if any), these experimental variables must also be reported. The following equation is used to calculate and express specific rotation:

$$[\alpha]_D^t = \frac{[\alpha_{obs}]}{l \times c}$$

where

$[\alpha]$ = specific rotation
$[\alpha_{obs}]$ = observed rotation
l = sample tube length (dm)
c = concentration of sample (expressed as g/mL)
t = temperature (°C)
D = the D line of the Na spectrum (589.3 nm)

THE RELATIONSHIP BETWEEN MOLECULAR STRUCTURE AND OPTICAL ACTIVITY

As was noted in Section 11.2 of the text, some optically active compounds rotate plane-polarized light in a clockwise direction. These are said to be *dextrorotatory* and are denoted by a plus sign (+) before the specific rotation value. Substances that rotate plane-polarized light in a counterclockwise direction are called *levorotatory* and are designated by a minus sign (−) before the specific rotation value.

In 1848, Louis Pasteur was the first to see a relationship between the structure of a compound and the effect of that compound on plane-polarized light. In his studies of wine making, Pasteur noticed that salts of tartaric acid were formed as a by-product. It is a tribute to his extraordinary powers of observation that he noticed that two types of crystals were formed and that they were mirror images of one another.

Using a magnifying glass and forceps, Pasteur separated the left-handed and right-handed crystals into separate piles. When he measured the optical activity of each of the mirror-image forms and of the original mixed sample, he obtained the following results:

◆   A solution of the original mixture of crystals was optically inactive.

◆   But *both* of the mirror-image crystals were optically active. In fact, the specific rotation produced by each was identical in magnitude but was of opposite sign.

Although Pasteur's work opened the door to understanding the relationship between structure and optical activity, it was not until 1874 that the Dutch chemist van't Hoff and the French chemist LeBel independently came up with a basis for the observed optical activity: tetrahedral carbon atoms bonded to four different atoms or groups of atoms.

In Section 9.2 we saw that a carbon atom involved in four single bonds has tetrahedral geometry. If the carbon atom is bonded to two identical substituents and two nonidentical substituents, the resulting molecule is *symmetrical* (Figure C.3). In other words, a plane of symmetry can be drawn through this molecule. Furthermore, this molecule is superimposable on its mirror image. (Prove this to yourself by building the molecules with molecular models or toothpicks and gumdrops.)

Compare the structure in Figure C.3 with that seen in Figure 11.3 of the text. In the molecule seen in Figure 11.3 the tetrahedral carbon is bonded to four nonidentical groups. The resulting molecule is *asymmetric*. There is no plane of symmetry that can be drawn through the molecule, nor can it be superimposed on its mirror image. (Build the molecules to demonstrate these characteristics.)

As was discussed in Section 11.2, the analogy can be made between these mirror-image molecules and your left and right hands. Your hands are, indeed, mirror images of one another; however, you cannot draw a plane of symmetry through your hand, nor can you superimpose your left and right hands on one another.

A molecule that cannot be superimposed on its mirror image is said to be *chiral*. When a carbon atom is bonded to four different atoms or groups of atoms, it is called a *chiral carbon*. Two stereoisomers that are nonsuperimposable mirror images of one another are a pair of

---

FIGURE C.3
A pair of superimposable mirror images. These molecules have an internal plane of symmetry that can be drawn through atoms a-C-c.

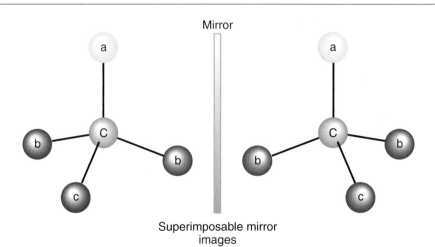

Mirror

Superimposable mirror images

enantiomers. As was mentioned in Section 11.2, the chemical and physical properties of enanti-omers are identical, with the exception that they rotate plane-polarized light to the same degree but in opposite directions. This is exactly the phenomenon that Pasteur observed with the mirror-image crystals of tartaric acid salts.

Refer to Figure 11.4 in the text for the structures of the enantiomers of glyceraldehyde. It would be useful at this point to review the use of the *Fischer projection* to draw these three-dimensional structures in two dimensions. Note that when you are comparing two Fischer projections to determine whether two molecules are enantiomers, you may rotate the structures as much as 180°, but you may never "flip" the structure out of the plane of the page. Always remember: If you are in doubt about the three-dimensional structure of a molecule, build it with a molecular model kit. This is particularly useful as you begin your study of organic chemistry, and it will help you in your future study of biochemistry.

RACEMIC MIXTURES

When Louis Pasteur measured the specific rotation of the mixture of tartaric acid salt crystals, he observed that it was optically inactive. The reason for this was that the mixture contained equal amounts of the (+) enantiomer and the (−) enantiomer. A mixture of equal amounts of a pair of enantiomers is called a *racemic mixture,* or simply a *racemate.* The prefix (±) is used to designate a racemic mixture. Consider the following situation:

$$50\% \text{ (+) tartrate} \quad + 50\% \text{ (−) tartrate} \quad = \text{ (±) tartrate}$$
$$[\alpha]_D^{20} = +4.7 \qquad\qquad [\alpha]_D^{20} = -4.7 \qquad\qquad [\alpha]_D^{20} = 0$$
$$50\% \text{ (+) enantiomer} + 50\% \text{ (−) enantiomer} = \text{racemic mixture}$$

In this situation the specific rotation is zero because the rotation caused by one enantiomer is canceled by the opposite rotation caused by the mirror-image enantiomer.

DIASTEREOMERS

So far, we have looked only at molecules containing a single carbon. In this case only two enantiomers are possible. However, it is quite common to find molecules with two or more chiral carbons. For a molecule of n chiral carbons the maximum possible number of different configurations is 2^n. Note that this formula predicts the *maximum* number of configurations. As we will see, there may actually be fewer.

EXAMPLE C.1

Drawing Stereoisomers for Compounds with More Than One Chiral Carbon

Draw all the possible stereoisomers of 2,3,4-trichlorobutanal.

Solution

1. There are two chiral carbons in this molecule, C-2 and C-3. Thus there are 2^2 or 4 possible stereoisomers.

2. There are two possible configurations for each of the chiral carbons (Cl on the left or on the right). Begin by drawing an isomer with both Cl atoms on the right (a). Now draw the mirror image (b). You have now generated the first pair of enantiomers (a and b).

(a)   (b)

Enantiomers

3. Next, change the location of one of the two Cl atoms bonded to a chiral carbon to produce another possible isomer (c). Finally, draw the mirror image of (c) to produce the second set of enantiomers (c and d).

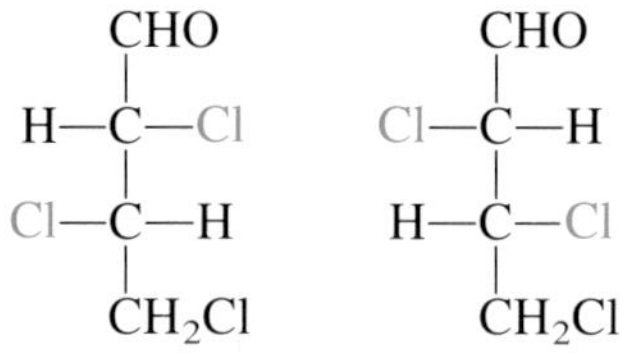

$$
\begin{array}{cc}
\text{CHO} & \text{CHO} \\
| & | \\
\text{H—C—Cl} & \text{Cl—C—H} \\
| & | \\
\text{Cl—C—H} & \text{H—C—Cl} \\
| & | \\
\text{CH}_2\text{Cl} & \text{CH}_2\text{Cl} \\
\text{(c)} & \text{(d)}
\end{array}
$$

Enantiomers

4. By this systematic procedure we have drawn the four possible isomers of 2,3,4-trichlorobutanal.

In the example, structures (a) and (b) are clearly enantiomers, as are (c) and (d). But how do we describe the relationship between structure (a) and (c) or any of the pairs of stereoisomers that are *not* enantiomers? The term *diastereomers* is used to describe a pair of stereoisomers that are not enantiomers.

While enantiomers differ from one another only in the direction of rotation of plane-polarized light, diastereomers are different in their chemical and physical properties.

MESO COMPOUNDS

As was mentioned above, the maximum number of configurations for a molecule with two chiral carbons is 2^2, or 4. However, if each of the two chiral carbons is bonded to the same four nonidentical groups, fewer than four stereoisomers exist. The example of tartaric acid, studied by Pasteur, helps to explain this phenomenon.

EXAMPLE C.2

Drawing Stereoisomers of Compounds with More Than One Chiral Carbon

Draw all the possible stereoisomers of tartaric acid, HOOC—CHOH—CHOH—COOH.

Solution

1. Proceed in exactly the same fashion that was used in Example C.1, and you will generate the following four structures:

$$
\begin{array}{cccc}
\text{COOH} & \text{COOH} & \text{COOH} & \text{COOH} \\
| & | & | & | \\
\text{H—C—OH} & \text{HO—C—H} & \text{H—C—OH} & \text{HO—C—H} \\
| & | & | & | \\
\text{H—C—OH} & \text{HO—C—H} & \text{HO—C—H} & \text{H—C—OH} \\
| & | & | & | \\
\text{COOH} & \text{COOH} & \text{COOH} & \text{COOH} \\
\text{(a)} & \text{(b)} & \text{(c)} & \text{(d)}
\end{array}
$$

Identical   Enantiomers

2. Careful examination of pair (c) and (d) reveals that these molecules are nonsuperimposable mirror images. Thus they are enantiomers.

3. Similar inspection of structures (a) and (b) reveals that although they are mirror images, they are identical. Structure (b) can simply be rotated 180° to produce structure (a); therefore they are identical.

Notice that if you draw a line between chiral carbon-2 and chiral carbon-3 of structure (a) or (b), the top half of the molecule is the mirror image of the bottom half. There is a plane of symmetry within the molecule:

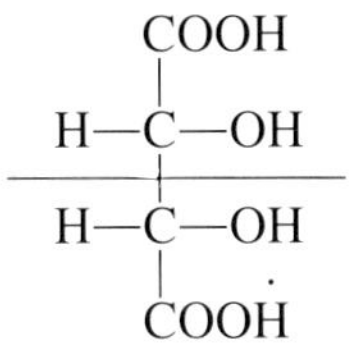

$$
\begin{array}{c}
\text{COOH} \\
| \\
\text{H—C—OH} \\
\overline{\phantom{\text{H—C—OH}}} \\
\text{H—C—OH} \\
| \\
\text{COOH}
\end{array}
$$

As a result, structure (a) is optically inactive. Even though there are two chiral carbons, the rotation of plane-polarized light by chiral carbon-2 is canceled by the opposite rotation of plane-polarized light caused by chiral carbon-3. This molecule is *achiral* and is termed *meso*-tartaric acid. Any compound with an internal plane of symmetry (i.e., that can be superimposed on its mirror image) is optically inactive and is termed a *meso*-compound.

Absolute configuration is the actual arrangement of the four groups around a chiral carbon atom. The *(R) and (S) System* indicates the absolute configuration for any chiral carbon. In this system, (R) stands for a right-handed configuration (Latin, *rectus*), and (S) stands for a left-handed configuration (Latin, *sinister*).

To assign an (R) or (S) configuration to a chiral carbon, the following set of rules is used:

ASSIGNMENT OF ABSOLUTE CONFIGURATION: THE (R) AND (S) SYSTEM

1. Priority rank the atoms or groups of atoms attached to the chiral carbon according to the sequence rules listed in Table C.1.

2. Draw the molecule with the lowest priority group projecting to the rear.

3. Draw a circular arrow from the group of highest priority to the group with the next highest priority.

4. If the arrow points in a clockwise direction (right), the configuration of the chiral carbon is (R); if the arrow points counterclockwise (left), it is (S).

TABLE C.1   Sequence Rules for Order of Priority

Rule	Example
1. For atoms, those with the highest atomic number are given the highest priority.	$F < Cl < Br < I$
2. If two isotopes of an element are present, the isotope of higher mass is given the higher priority.	$^1H < {}^2H < {}^3H$
3. If two atoms are identical, the atomic numbers of the next atoms are used to assign priority.	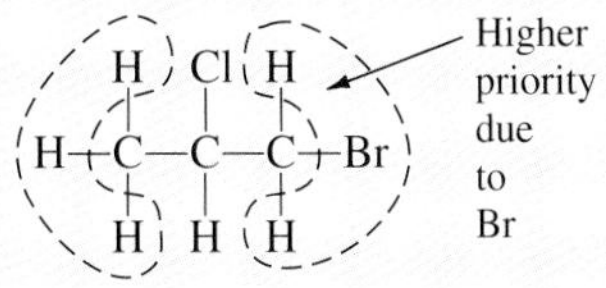
4. Atoms attached by double or triple bonds are assigned single bond equivalences. Every double-bonded atom is duplicated, and every triple-bonded atom is triplicated.	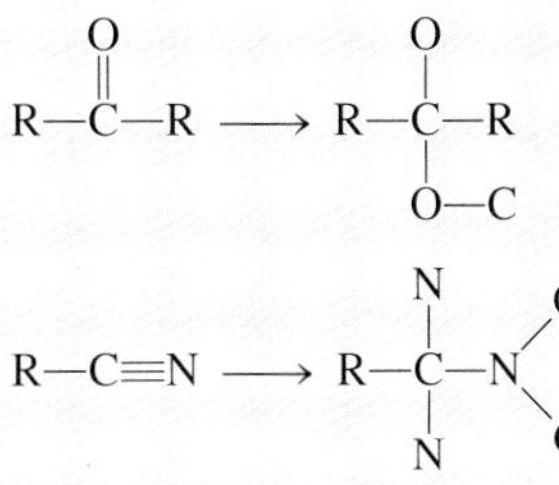

Lipid-Soluble Vitamins

Vitamins are organic substances, required in the diet, that promote a variety of essential reactions in cells. Since they are not an energy source, they are required only in small amounts. However, if a vitamin is absent from the diet, the results are often catastrophic.

Vitamins A, D, E; and K are soluble in lipids and in biological membranes. Many of the functions of the lipid-soluble vitamins are intimately involved in metabolic processes that occur in membranes. The common sources and functions of the lipid-soluble vitamins are summarized in Table D.1.

The Food and Nutrition Board of the National Research Council of the National Academy of Sciences publishes information on the quantities of vitamins and minerals that are required in the diet. These are called *recommended dietary allowances (RDA)* and are defined as ''the levels of intake of essential nutrients considered adequate to meet the known nutritional needs of practically all healthy persons.'' The RDA is determined by obtaining an estimate of the range of normal human needs. The value at the high end of the range is chosen, and an additional safety factor is added. Thus the RDA is by no means a minimum value, but rather a high estimate of daily requirements. It is important to remember that serious physical problems can follow ingestion of megadoses of many minerals or vitamins.

In some cases the RDA of a mineral or a vitamin cannot be determined owing to insufficient information. In those cases the Food and Nutrition Board expresses the suggested daily dose as the *estimated safe and adequate daily dietary intake (ESADDI)*.

Recently, a great deal of emphasis has been placed on vitamin supplements to combat stress, prevent the common cold, protect against various kinds of cancer and heart disease, offset the symptoms of premenstrual syndrome, delay the aging process, and improve one's sex life! Most nutritionists believe that a well-balanced diet provides all the nutrients, including the vitamins, required by the body. Indeed, when associations such as the American Cancer Society suggest that certain vitamins might help prevent cancers, they recommend that they be obtained from the natural food sources, rather than from vitamin supplements.

TABLE D.1 Nutritional Sources, Functions, and Symptoms of Deficiency of the Lipid-Soluble Vitamins

Vitamin	Source	Function	Symptoms of Deficiency
A, carotene	Egg yolk, liver, green and yellow vegetables, fruits	Synthesis of visual pigments	Night blindness and blindness in children
D_3, calciferol	Milk, action of sunlight on the skin	Regulation of calcium metabolism	Rickets (malformation of the bones)
E	Vegetable oil	Antioxidant, protection of cell membranes	Fragile red blood cells
K	Leafy vegetables, intestinal bacteria	Required for the carboxylation of prothrombin and other blood-clotting factors	Blood-clotting disorders

Vitamin A is obtained in the active form called *retinol,* from animal sources such as liver and egg yolks. It is also acquired in the precursor form, *provitamin A* or *carotene,* from plant foods. Green and yellow vegetables and fruits are good sources of vitamin A. Carrots are especially rich in this vitamin.

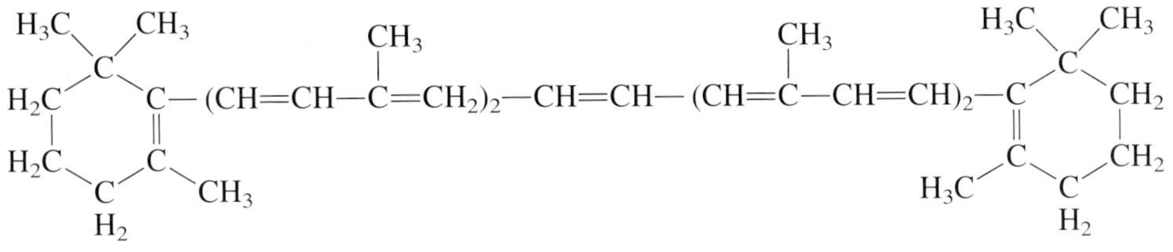

VITAMIN A

Beta-carotene

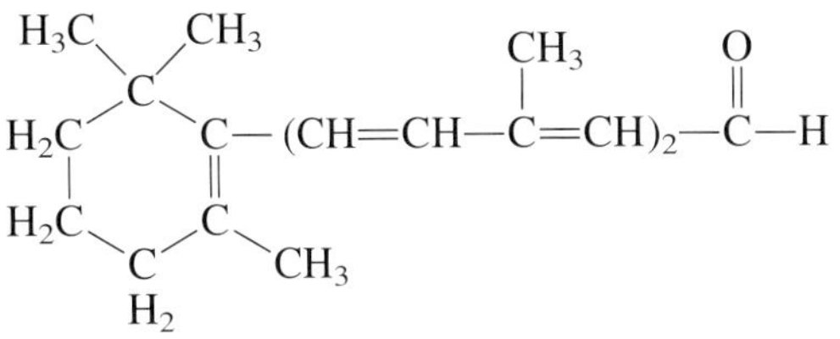

Retinal

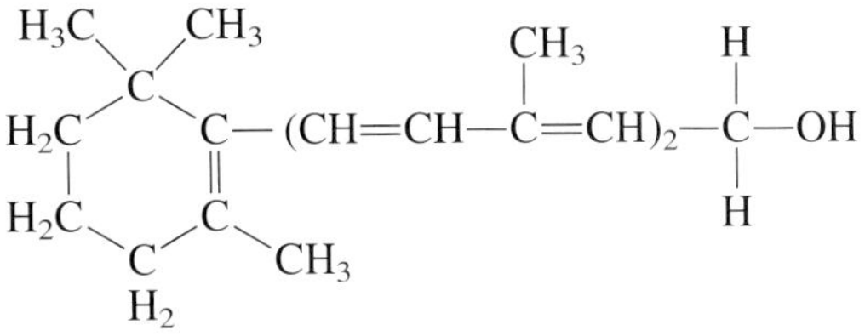

Retinol (vitamin A)

Vitamin A helps maintain the skin and mucous membranes of the oral cavity and the digestive, respiratory, reproductive, and urinary tracts. Vitamin A is also critical for vision. The aldehyde form of Vitamin A, called *retinal,* binds to a protein called opsin to form the visual pigment *rhodopsin.* This pigment is found in the *rod* cells of the retina of the eye. These cells are responsible for black-and-white vision. As you might expect, a deficiency of vitamin A can have terrible consequences. In children, lack of vitamin A leads to *xerophthalmia,* an eye disease that results first in night blindness and eventually in total blindness. The disease can be prevented by an adequate dietary or supplementary supply of this vitamin. Because vitamin A is stored in the liver, a dose of 0.03 mg will protect a child for six months. Yet in countries that have suffered from cruel famines, even this amount of vitamin A is unavailable, and the burdens of malnutrition and disease lead to total blindness in thousands of children.

The current recommended dietary allowance (RDA) for vitamin A is expressed in international units (I.U.). The RDA for vitamin A is 5000 I.U., which is equal to 1 μg of retinol or 6 μg of β-carotene. Since vitamin A is a lipid-soluble vitamin that is stored in the liver, it is dangerous to ingest quantities larger than the RDA. Symptoms of vitamin A poisoning include elevated pressure of the spinal fluid and the fluid around the brain, as well as swelling around the optic nerve. These result in severe headaches. Other symptoms include anorexia, swelling of the spleen and liver, irritability, hair loss, and scaly dermatitis. It is interesting to note that early Arctic explorers suffered from vitamin A poisoning. Later it was found that this was the result of eating polar bear liver, which has an unusually high concentration of vitamin A.

The formation of a blood clot in response to a wound is an intricate process that involves at least a dozen proteins in the blood serum. *Vitamin K* is involved in blood clotting.

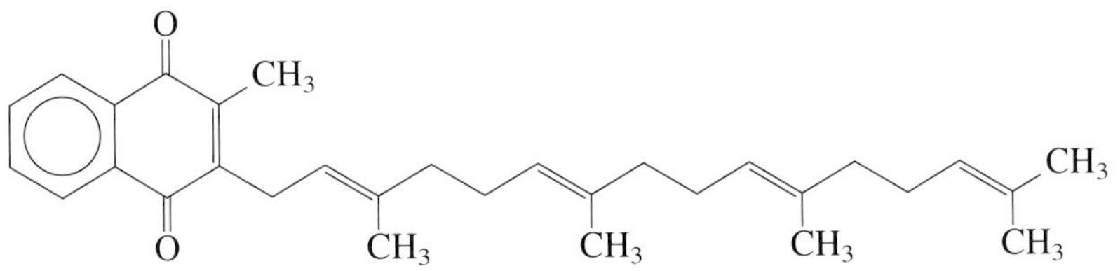

VITAMIN K

Vitamin K

In clot formation, molecules of the serum protein *prothrombin* must be activated to produce *thrombin,* which then initiates the final stages of clot formation. This requires binding of Ca^{2+} ions to the unusual amino acid γ-carboxyglutamate, in prothrombin. Vitamin K is required as a coenzyme by the enzyme that adds the carboxyl groups to the normal amino acid glutamate to form γ-carboxyglutamate. Thus a deficiency of vitamin K in the diet leads to poor blood clotting.

The estimated safe and adequate daily dietary intake (ESADDI) for vitamin K is 70–140 μg/day. This is easily obtained in the diet by eating leafy vegetables. In addition, vitamin K is manufactured by our normal intestinal bacteria. It is extremely rare for adults to suffer from vitamin K deficiency, but it is observed in some individuals on antibiotic therapy or with fat absorption problems. However, newborns frequently suffer from vitamin K deficiency because they lack intestinal bacteria. They are often administered injections of vitamin K to prevent excessive bleeding in the early days of their lives.

Since vitamin K is another lipid-soluble vitamin, it is possible to suffer from hypervitaminosis K. The symptoms include gastrointestinal disturbances and anemia.

VITAMIN D

Vitamin D plays a major role in the regulation of calcium levels and therefore is required for the proper formation of bone and teeth.

Vitamin D₃

The RDA for vitamin D is 10 μg/day for children and 5 μg/day for adults. Milk, liver, and fish oils are rich in this vitamin. It is also produced by the action of sunlight on the skin.

In children, vitamin D deficiency causes *rickets,* a disease that results in soft, deformed, and poorly calcified bones. Vitamin D deficiency is almost totally confined to children. However, the home-bound elderly who are not able to get outside and may drink little milk may suffer from vitamin D deficiency.

The vitamin D produced in the skin results from the action of ultraviolet light on 7-dehydrocholesterol. This series of reactions is diagrammed in Figure D.1. Ultraviolet light causes the conversion of 7-dehydrocholesterol to vitamin D₃ (cholecalciferol). This alcohol is then hydroxylated in the liver to produce 25-hydroxyvitamin D₃, also called 25-hydroxycholecalciferol. In the kidney a final hydroxylation produces the hormone 1,25-dihydroxyvitamin D₃ (1,25-dihydroxycholecalciferol), the active form of the vitamin. 1,25-dihydroxyvitamin D₃ is classified as a hormone because it is synthesized in one part of the body but exerts its effects elsewhere. Only about 1% of the body's calcium exists outside of bone, but regulating the concentration of calcium ions in the blood is critical because these soluble calcium ions are involved in many physiological processes from blood clotting to muscle contraction. When the level of calcium in the blood is low, 1,25-dihydroxyvitamin D₃ stimulates the uptake of calcium from the intestines and its transport into the blood. In the kidneys this hormone, along with parathyroid hormone, stimulates the reabsorption of calcium so that it is not lost in the urine. If the blood level of calcium is low enough, 1,25-dihydroxyvitamin D₃ even stimulates the removal of calcium from the bone. This, of course, leads to the weakening of the bone that can result in *osteomalacia—* very brittle, decalcified bones—later in life.

Ingestion of excess vitamin D can result in hypervitaminosis with the presentation of the following symptoms: renal failure, weight loss, and calcification of soft tissues of the body.

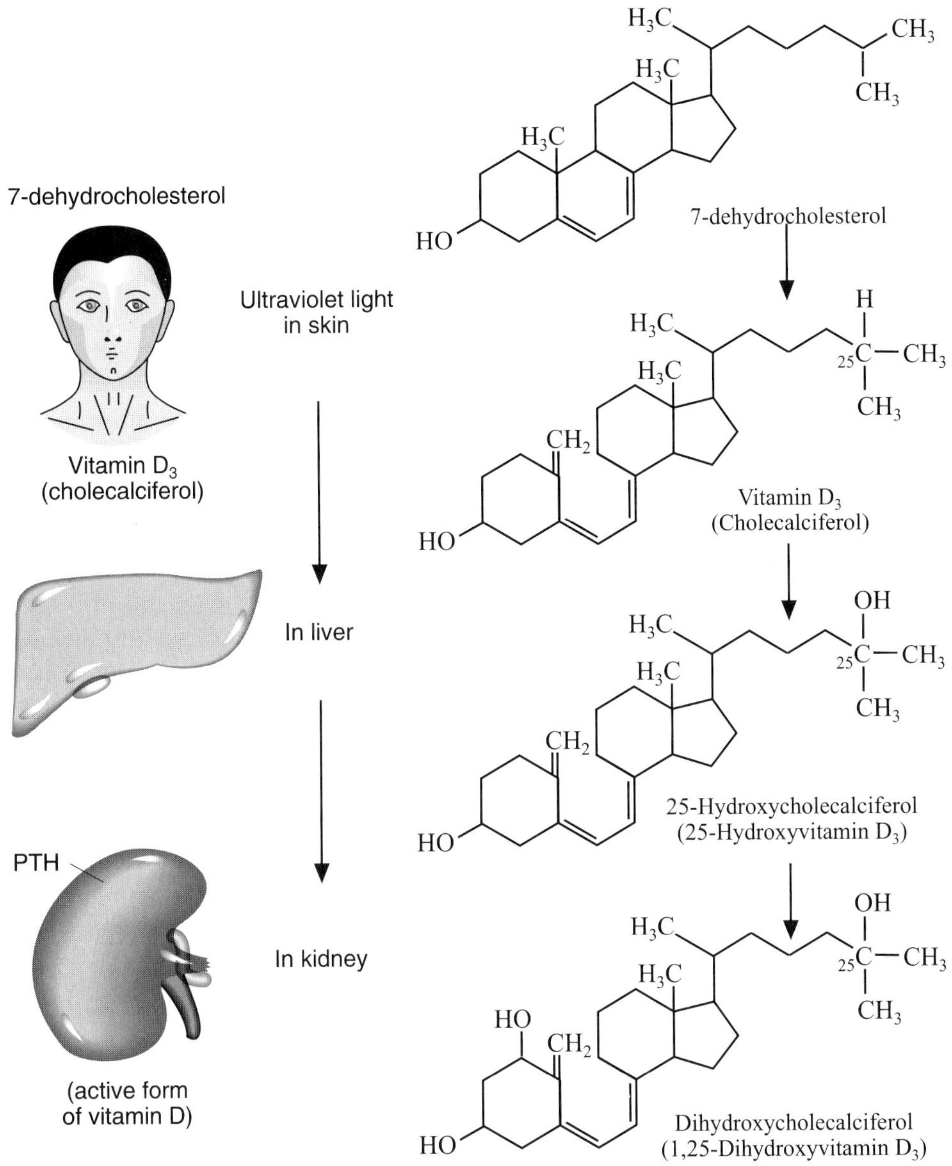

7-dehydrocholesterol

Ultraviolet light
in skin

Vitamin D₃
(cholecalciferol)

In liver

PTH

In kidney

(active form
of vitamin D)

7-dehydrocholesterol

Vitamin D₃
(Cholecalciferol)

25-Hydroxycholecalciferol
(25-Hydroxyvitamin D₃)

Dihydroxycholecalciferol
(1,25-Dihydroxyvitamin D₃)

FIGURE D.1
The pathway of the synthesis of vitamin D₃ in the skin and its conversion to the hormone that is active in calcium metabolism.

Vitamin E is the least well understood of the lipid-soluble vitamins. In fact, the term vitamin E actually refers to a family of eight compounds called the *tocopherols*.

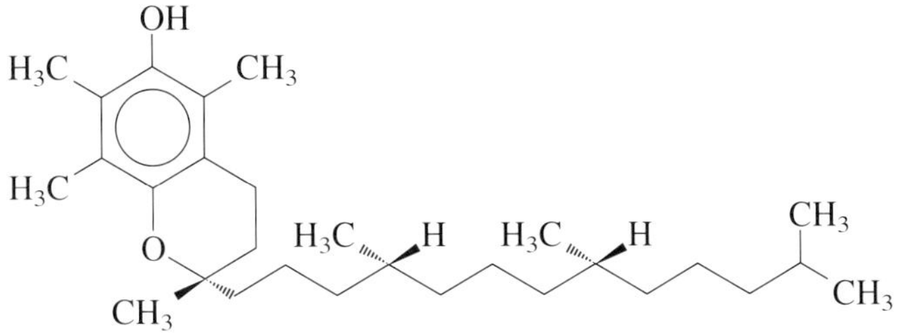

VITAMIN E

Vitamin E

Rats that are deprived of vitamin E become infertile, but the reasons for this are unknown. Vitamin E is known to prevent the oxidation of double bonds in the hydrocarbon tails of membrane lipids, and this may be its major function. Since oxidation reactions accelerate aging, some researchers believe that vitamin E may help to retard the aging process. The RDA for vitamin E is expressed in α-tocopherol equivalents (α-TE) because this is the most active form of vitamin E. The recommended daily intake is 10 α-TE for males and 8 α-TE for females. This is roughly the amount of vitamin E in a tablespoon of vegetable oil.

Compared to vitamins A and D, vitamin E is relatively nontoxic at high levels. However, it is unwise to drastically exceed the RDA because high levels of vitamin E may cause diarrhea, nausea, headache, and fatigue.

The *water-soluble vitamins* are organic substances that are required in small amounts in the diet because they are required for a variety of essential enzymatic reactions in cells. The water-soluble vitamins are components of many coenzymes that are required by enzymes to carry out a variety of important biochemical reactions. Once ingested, these vitamins undergo chemical modifications that convert them into coenzymes. However, it serves no purpose to consume vast quantities of water-soluble vitamins by taking enormous doses of vitamin tablets because they are not stored in the body. Since they are soluble in water, the excess is simply excreted in the urine. Table 15.2 lists the coenzymes derived from the water-soluble vitamins and their chemical functions. Table E.1 provides the major nutritional sources of the water-soluble vitamins and the clinical conditions that result from their deficiency.

PANTOTHENIC ACID

Pantothenic acid is essential for the normal metabolism of fats and carbohydrates. Like many other vitamins, pantothenic acid is abundant in meat, fish, poultry, whole-grain cereals, and legumes. The recommended daily allowance (RDA) of pantothenic acid is 4–7 mg per day. Pantothenic acid deficiency, which is rather rare in the United States except among alcoholics,

TABLE E.1   Major Nutritional Sources of Water-Soluble Vitamins Required by Humans and Some Physiological Effects of Deficiencies

Vitamin	Source	Symptoms of Deficiency
Thiamine (B_1)	Brain, liver, heart, whole grains	Beriberi, neuritis, mental disturbance
Riboflavin (B_2)	Milk, eggs, liver	Photophobia, dermatitis
Niacin (B_3)	Whole grains, liver	Pellagra, dermatitis, digestive problems
Pyridoxine (B_6)	Whole grains, liver, fish, kidney	Dermatitis, nervous disorders
Cobalamin (B_{12})	Liver, kidney, brain	Pernicious anemia
Folic acid	Liver, leafy vegetables, intestinal bacteria	Anemia
Pantothenic acid	Most foods	Neuromotor and cardiovascular disorders
Biotin	Egg yolk, intestinal bacteria	Scaly dermatitis, muscle pains, weakness
Ascorbic acid (C)	Citrus fruits, green leafy vegetables, tomatoes	Scurvy, failure to form collagen

manifests itself as gastrointestinal, neuromotor, and cardiovascular disorders. Pantothenic acid is converted to its biologically functional form, known as *coenzyme A,* in the body. Coenzyme A is important for the transfer of acyl groups in the metabolism of fatty acids and carbohydrates.

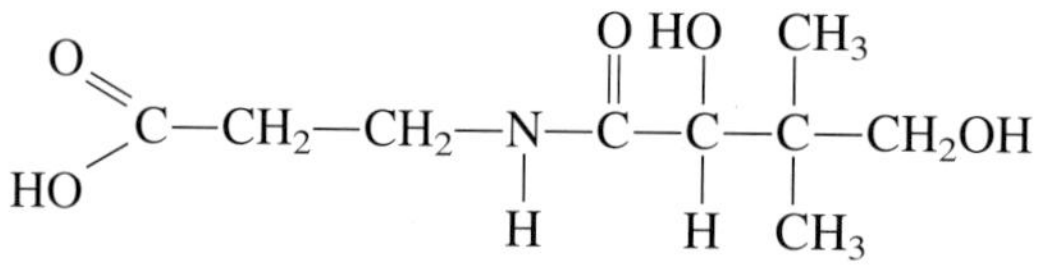

Pantothenic acid

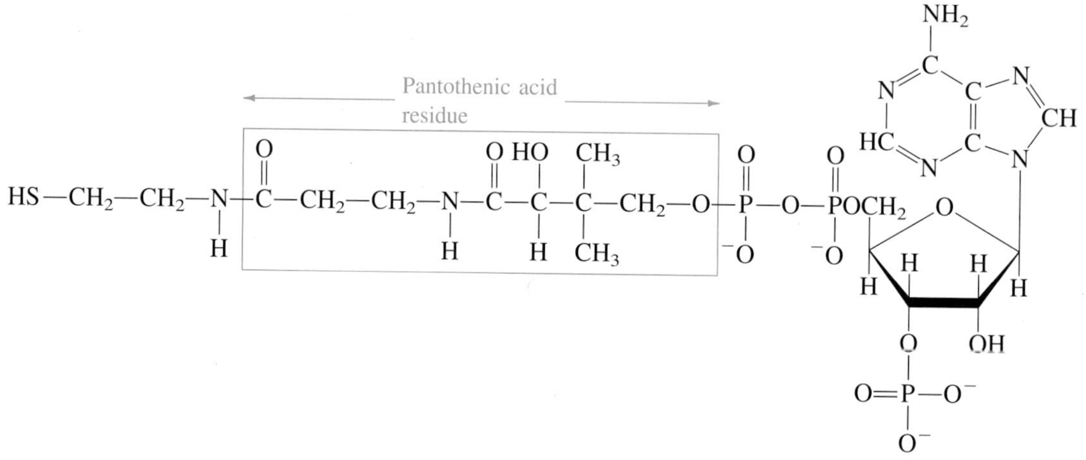

Coenzyme A
(CoA)

NIACIN

Niacin (vitamin B_3) refers to both nicotinic acid and nicotinamide. Nicotinamide is an essential precursor for the coenzyme nicotinamide adenine nucleotide (NAD^+).

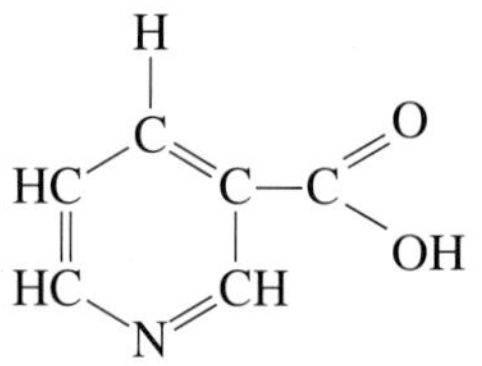

Nicotinic acid 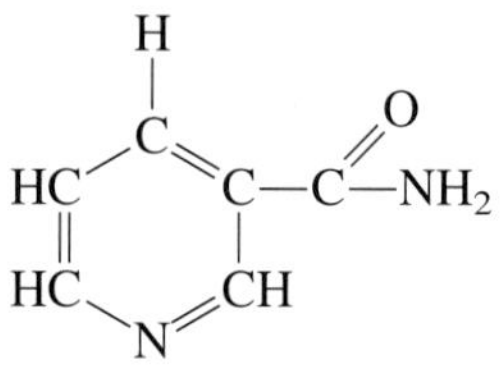   Nicotinamide

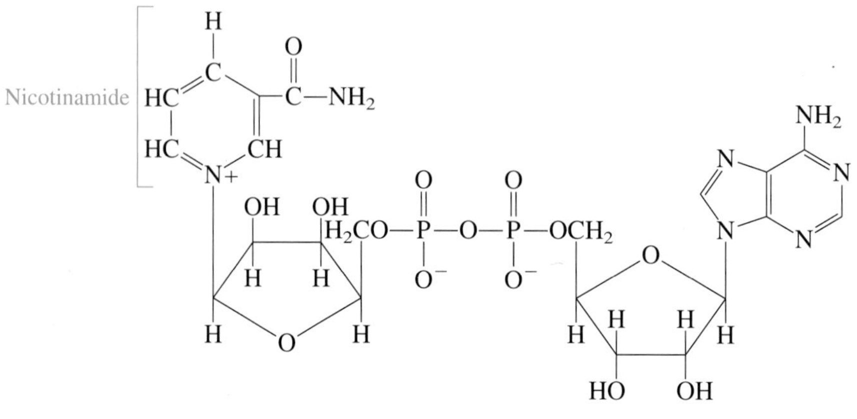

NAD^+ or nicotinamide adenine dinucleotide

Niacin is found in fish, lean meat, legumes, milk, and whole-grain and enriched cereals. The RDA for niacin is 20 mg per day. Niacin deficiency leads to dermatitis, diarrhea, dementia, and death. The most common illness that develops from niacin deficiency is *pellagra,* a form of dermatitis. This nutritional disease is found where corn is abundant in the diet and meat is scarce.

Corn actually contains a rather large amount of niacin, but it is present in a form that is not made available to the body simply by cooking. American and South American Indians discovered centuries ago that soaking cornmeal in lime water (dilute calcium hydroxide) proved to be beneficial. The lime water releases nicotinamide in a form that can then be absorbed through the intestines.

Riboflavin, or *vitamin B₂,* is abundant in milk, eggs, and dark green leafy vegetables.

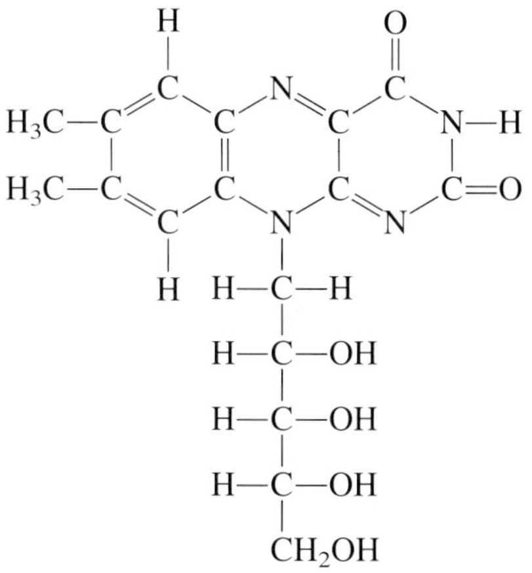

RIBOFLAVIN

Riboflavin
(Vitamin B₂)

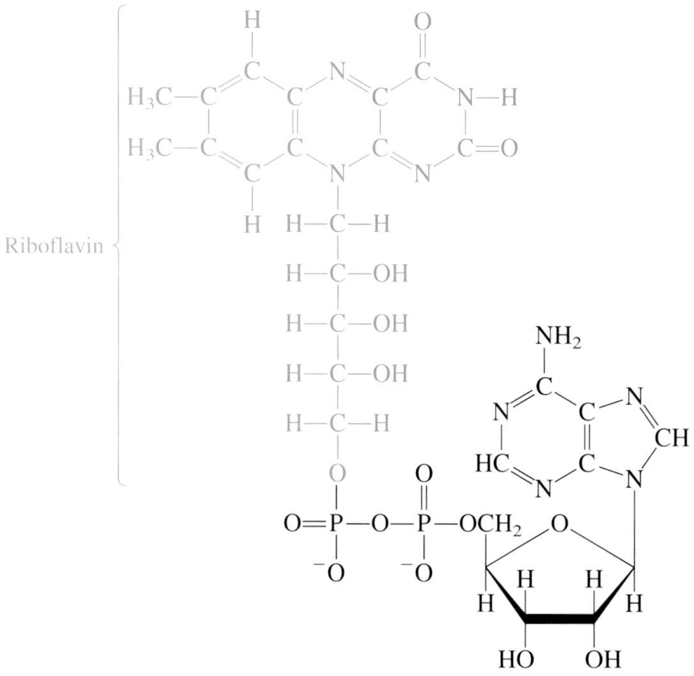

Flavin adenine dinucleotide
(FAD)

As a component of the coenzyme flavin adenine dinucleotide (FAD), riboflavin is essential for the energy-releasing reactions of the cell. The RDA for riboflavin is about 1.7 mg. Severe riboflavin deficiency is rare in most parts of the world, but a marginal deficiency of this vitamin is common even in the United States. Mild riboflavin deficiency leads to dry, cracked lips and other mild forms of dermatitis. In severe cases, however, riboflavin deficiency leads to extreme sensitivity to sunlight and retarded growth in children.

Thiamine, also known as *vitamin B₁,* is required in the diet of all animals. Its biologically active form is the coenzyme thiamine pyrophosphate. This coenzyme is required for many decarboxylation reactions, including the decarboxylation of pyruvate to form CO_2 and acetyl coenzyme A in the transition reaction between glycolysis and the citric acid cycle.

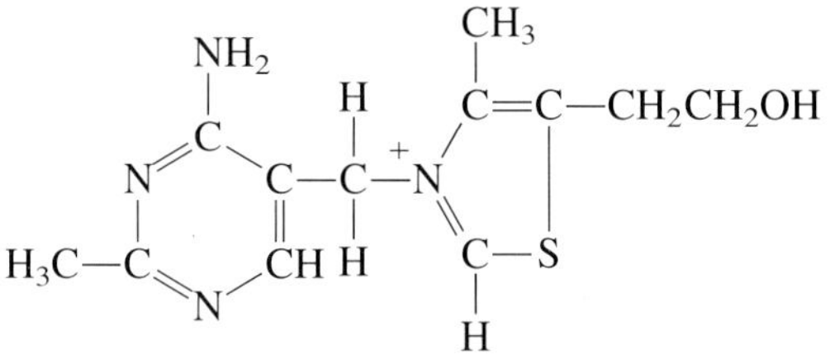

THIAMINE

Thiamine (vitamin B₁)

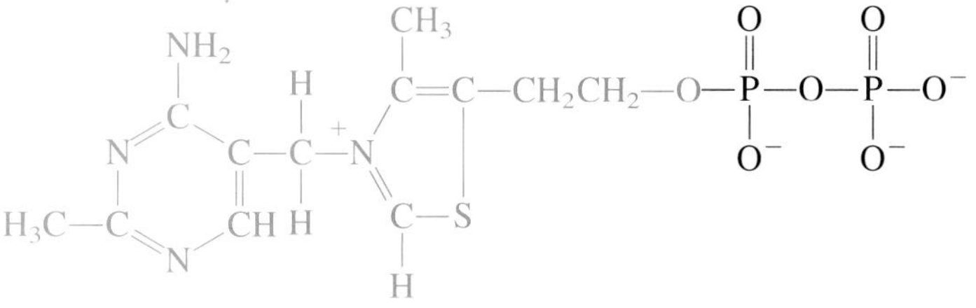

Thiamine pyrophosphate (TPP)

Thiamine is abundant in whole-grain and enriched cereals, meats, legumes, and green leafy vegetables. The RDA for thiamine is about 1.5 mg. Thiamine is lost from whole grains during the refining process. However, thiamine deficiency is largely prevented because many foods, including bread and cereal products, contain thiamine as an additive.

Dietary deficiency leads to *beriberi,* a disease characterized by muscle weakness and mental instability. Sudden recovery from the effects of beriberi is observed within hours of administration of thiamine.

PYRIDOXINE

Pyridoxine, also known as *vitamin B₆,* is required for the synthesis and breakdown of amino acids.

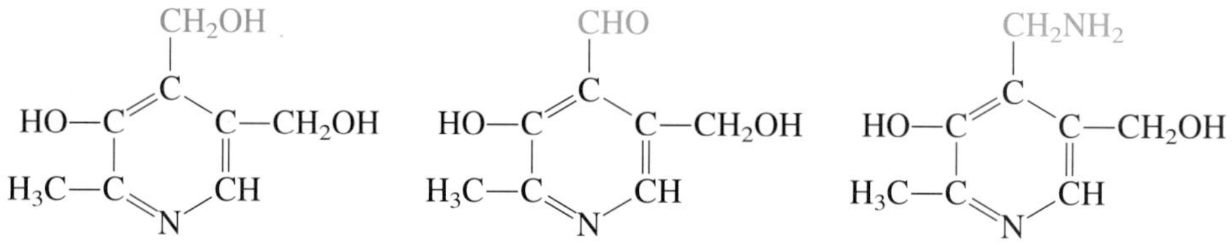

Pyridoxine   Pyridoxal   Pyridoxamine

Vitamin B_6

It is found in many foods, such as fish, meat, poultry, and leafy green vegetables, which are excellent sources of vitamin B_6. Because this vitamin is so readily available in a variety of foods, its deficiency is relatively rare. When it does occur, the symptoms include nervousness and muscular weakness. The RDA for vitamin B_6 is 2.0 mg.

Since vitamin B_6 is a water-soluble vitamin, one would expect that the ingestion of excessive amounts would result simply in the excretion of the excess. However, excess vitamin B_6 (50–100 times the RDA) taken to reduce the symptoms of premenstrual syndrome has resulted in peripheral neuropathy in several young women. This is characterized by a numbness in the limbs and a clumsy, stumbling walk.

FOLIC ACID

Folic acid is a complicated molecule whose structure consists of three components: a heterocyclic ring system known as *pterin, p-aminobenzoic acid,* and the amino acid *glutamic acid.*

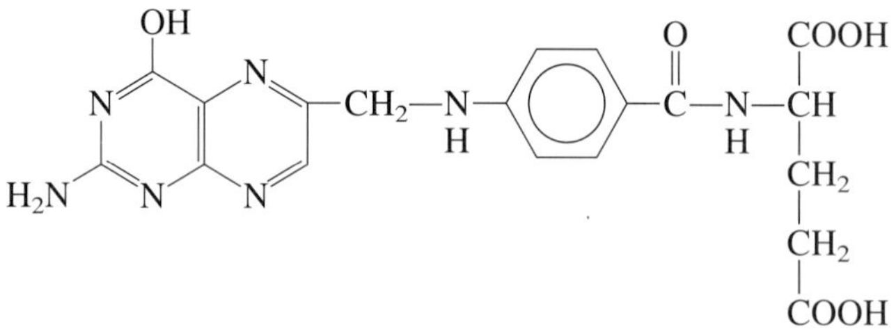

Folic acid

It is required for the synthesis of the amino acid methionine and the nucleic acid precursors: the purines and pyrimidines. The RDA for folic acid is only about 0.4 mg. Since such a small amount is required daily, it might be thought that folic acid deficiency would be rare. The opposite is true: Folic acid deficiency is a very common vitamin deficiency. Green vegetables, whole-grain cereals, and meat contain abundant folic acid, but it is destroyed by cooking. Because a deficiency of folic acid results in anemia and growth failure, folic acid is especially necessary for children and pregnant women.

Biotin is involved in carboxylation and decarboxylation reactions in the metabolism of fats, carbohydrates, and proteins. Liver, egg yolks, cheese, and peanuts are excellent sources of biotin. In addition, it is produced by bacteria in the intestines.

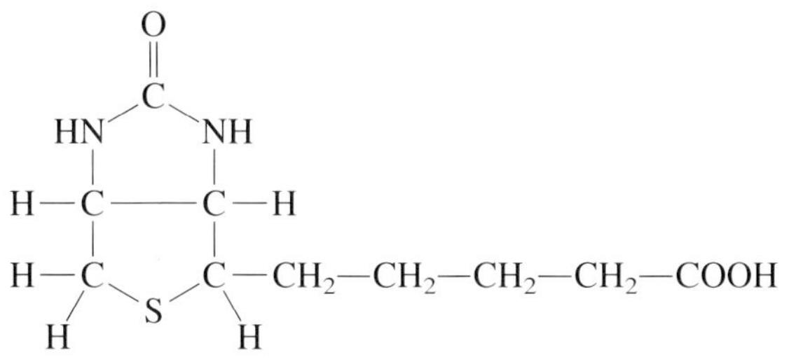

BIOTIN

Biotin

The estimated safe and adequate daily dietary intake (ESADDI) for biotin is 0.30 mg, and in a normal diet, biotin deficiency is almost unknown. However, when it does occur, the symptoms include dermatitis (scaling and hardening of the skin), loss of appetite and nausea, muscle pain, and elevated levels of blood cholesterol.

The extraordinary chemical structure of *vitamin B$_{12}$* is shown below:

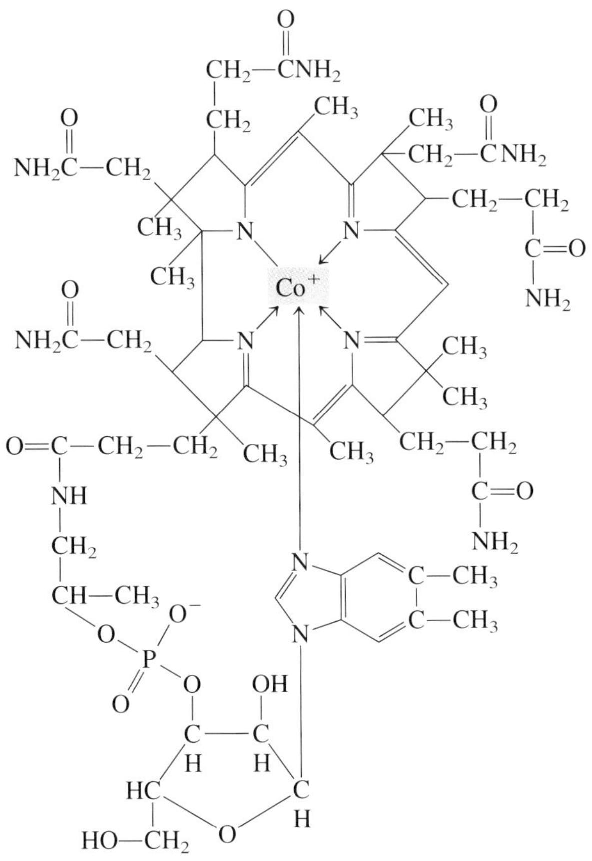

VITAMIN B$_{12}$

Vitamin B$_{12}$ (cobalamin)

B$_{12}$ is a very important vitamin needed for the production of red and white blood cells and the normal growth and maintenance of nerve tissue.

A defective mechanism for the uptake of vitamin B_{12} results in *pernicious anemia,* a disease that is characterized by the presence of large, immature red blood cells in the blood. Symptoms include a sore tongue, weight loss, and mental and nervous disorders. The damage to the central nervous system can even cause demyelination of the peripheral nerves in the arms and legs. Eventually, this can progress to the spinal cord. The requirement for vitamin B_{12} is only about 6 μg per day. Since many foods, including meats, eggs, and dairy products, contain this vitamin, nearly all diets, except those that are completely devoid of animal products, provide a sufficient amount of vitamin B_{12}. In fact, bacteria in the human intestine produce enough vitamin B_{12} to satisfy the normal daily requirement.

VITAMIN C

Vitamin C is important in the growth and repair of connective tissue, teeth, bones, and cartilage. In addition, it promotes wound healing, enhances absorption of iron, and functions in the biosynthesis of several hormones. Vitamin C also serves as an antioxidant in many biological processes. It is almost a part of folk medicine that large doses of vitamin C, or *ascorbic acid,* can prevent, or cure, the common cold and a host of other ailments.

Vitamin C
(ascorbic acid)

The many claims made for the powers of vitamin C have not, however, been substantiated in extensive clinical testing. Although many individuals recommend megadoses of vitamin C, the RDA is only 60 mg. In fact, the ingestion of large doses, more than 1–2 g daily, has been reported to cause intestinal cramps, nausea, diarrhea, and kidney stones. Fresh fruits, especially citrus fruits, and vegetables, among them potatoes, are rich dietary sources of vitamin C. However, extensive cooking of vegetables or fruits destroys vitamin C.

A deficiency of vitamin C leads to *scurvy,* a disorder that is characterized by bleeding gums, loss of teeth, sore joints, and slow wound healing.

APPENDIX F | Minerals and Cellular Function

Many minerals are required in the human diet, and these may be divided into two nutritional classes. The *major minerals* must be consumed in amounts greater than 100 mg/day. The *trace minerals* are required in much smaller amounts (less than 100 mg/day). In some cases the required levels are so small that they cannot be very accurately measured.

Calcium and *phosphorus* are major minerals that are needed for the development of healthy bones and teeth. These two minerals are found in a crystalline calcium phosphate mineral known as *hydroxyapatite*, $[Ca_{10}(PO_4)_6(OH)_2]$, that makes up the mineral matrix of bone and teeth. In addition, calcium is required for normal blood clotting and muscle function. The RDA for calcium is 1200 mg/day for adults between 19 and 24 years of age and 800 mg/day for adults over age 25. Milk, cheese, canned salmon, and dark green leafy vegetables are all rich sources of dietary calcium.

THE MAJOR MINERALS

Phosphorus is required not only as a component of hydroxyapatite in bone, but also as a component of nucleic acids and many other biologically important molecules. Without phosphorus we would have no energy storage molecules, such as ATP and creatine phosphate, for the energy derived from glycolysis and the citric acid cycle. The RDA for phosphorus is the same as that for calcium. Because it is abundant in most foods, a deficiency of phosphorus in the presence of an otherwise adequate diet is virtually impossible.

Sodium, potassium, and *chloride* ions are all required in the human diet. When dissolved in water, sodium and potassium are positively charged ions (cations), while chloride is a negatively charged ion (anion). These three minerals are called blood electrolytes because the ions can conduct electrical currents. Sodium is found primarily in the extracellular fluids, and potassium is found predominantly within the cell. Both of these elements are needed to maintain a proper fluid balance inside and outside of the cell. Because these three minerals are found in most foods, deficiency is rare.

The Food and Nutrition Board has removed the three electrolytes from its table of estimated safe and adequate daily dietary intake because there is not sufficient information available to establish a recommended amount. The major dietary source of sodium and chloride is table salt (40% sodium and 60% chloride). Physicians still recommend that the intake of sodium be restricted to 1–2 g daily. The recommended intake of chloride is approximately 1.7–5.1 g daily. However, getting enough sodium and chloride is not a problem. In fact, sodium intake in the United States is about 5–7 g/day, far in excess of the 1–2 g/day required by a normal adult.

Potassium is the major intracellular cation. It is found in citrus fruits, bananas, and tomatoes. Dietary intake of potassium is about 1.9–5.6 g/day in the United States. Potassium deficiency is rare, but loss of potassium in severe diarrhea, such as can occur in cholera, and the excretion of potassium by a person suffering from diabetes mellitus can lead to a debilitating deficiency. However, potassium deficiency is seen most commonly in individuals who are taking diuretics.

A high intake of table salt, sodium chloride, the major source of sodium in the diet, is one factor that may cause high blood pressure, *hypertension,* in susceptible individuals. There has been considerable emphasis on ''low-salt'' diets as a means of avoiding hypertension. However, it appears that sodium is not the only culprit. It is the sodium-to-potassium ratio that appears to be important in controlling blood pressure. Ideally, the Na/K ratio should be about 0.6, but the Na/K ratio consumed by the average American is greater than 1.0. To avoid hypertension in later life, it is important to both reduce the amount of sodium in the diet *and* increase the amount of potassium.

Magnesium ions are vital to cellular metabolism. They are required for the reactions in the liver that convert glycogen to glucose. They are also important in normal muscle function, nerve conductance, and bone development. Mg^{2+} ions bind to AMP, ADP, and ATP and to nucleic acids. Many enzymes that are involved in the catabolic breakdown of glucose require magnesium ions as cofactors. A typical adult contains about 25 g of magnesium, and the recommended daily intake is about 300 mg/day. Magnesium is plentiful in leafy green vegetables, legumes, cereal grains, and lean meats.

TRACE MINERALS

Iron is a required mineral for heme-containing proteins and is an element that is absolutely essential for normal physiological functioning. It is found in the oxygen transport and storage proteins, hemoglobin and myoglobin, and is also a component of the cytochromes that participate in the respiratory electron transport chain. The requirement for iron is so well known that it might be thought that no one would suffer the effects of iron deficiency. In fact, however, iron deficiency is rather common in the United States, especially among women. Iron can be absorbed by the body only in its ferrous, Fe^{2+}, oxidation state. The iron in meat is absorbed more efficiently than that in most other foods. Vegetarians, whose protein intake is mostly in the form of cereal grains, run a risk of iron deficiency because iron in grains is absorbed poorly by the body.

Hemoglobin, myoglobin, and the cytochromes of the respiratory electron transport chain all contain heme. Heme, of course, contains iron, and it is this need that must be satisfied by the diet. Deficiency of iron leads to *iron-deficiency anemia,* a condition in which the amount of hemoglobin in red blood cells is abnormally low.

Copper is a mineral that is required for many essential enzymes. The respiratory electron transport chain contains an enzyme, *cytochrome oxidase,* that contains both heme groups and copper ions. Copper is therefore required in the diet for the function of this essential enzyme. Copper is also required by some of the enzymes that are responsible for the synthesis of connective tissue proteins. Seafood, vegetables, nuts, and meats such as liver are excellent sources of copper ions. The ESADDI for adults is 1.5–3.0 mg. Copper ions in high concentrations are also toxic. In fact, mental retardation and death in early adolescence result from an inability to remove excess copper ions from the body. Here, as everywhere in life, it is the balance of the system that is critical to its function.

Iodine is a mineral that is required for the proper function of the thyroid gland. The thyroid gland extracts iodine from nutrients and incorporates it into various hormones. The once-common condition of goiter, an enlargement of the thyroid gland, is an abnormality that results from an effort to compensate for low iodine intake. Goiter can be prevented if iodine is included in the diet. Seafood is one of the best sources of iodine. In areas where seafood is not available, dietary iodine is easily obtained in the form of iodized salt, found in most grocery stores.

Fluoride aids in the prevention of dental caries (cavities). The presence of fluoride ions in the water supplies of many cities has dramatically reduced the incidence of cavities, the most widespread ''disease'' in the United States. Unfortunately, resistance to water fluoridation, largely as a result of insufficient information, has caused many municipalities to abandon this practice. An excess of fluoride is, in fact, toxic, but at the level found in fluoridated water supplies, approximately 1 part per million, no toxic effects are observed. Fluoride works by displacing hydroxide in calcium hydroxyapatite to give a crystalline mineral in teeth known as *fluorapatite,* $[Ca_3(PO_4)_2 \cdot CaF_2]$, that is far more resistant to the acid produced by oral bacteria than is hydroxyapatite itself.

Many other *trace minerals* are required in the diet. Among these are zinc, nickel, vanadium, tin, silicon, molybdenum, chromium, selenium, and cobalt. Zinc and molybdenum are required by various enzymes, while cobalt is a component of vitamin B_{12}.

Deficiencies of trace minerals are virtually nonexistent, since they are needed in such small quantities that requirements for them are likely to be met in nearly every diet. As in the case of copper, however, most trace minerals are extremely toxic if ingested in large quantities, and "heavy metal poisoning" has been a scourge of industrial cities throughout the world.

Glossary

absolute specificity (15.6) the property of an enzyme that allows it to bind and catalyze the reaction of only one substrate

accuracy (1.5) the nearness of an experimental value to the true value

acetal (10.5) the family of organic compounds formed via the reaction of two molecules of alcohol with an aldehyde in the presence of an acid catalyst; acetals have the following general structure:

$$R_1-\overset{\displaystyle OR_2}{\underset{\displaystyle H}{\overset{|}{\underset{|}{C}}}}-OR_3$$

acetyl coenzyme A (acetyl CoA) (12.3, 16.7) a molecule composed of coenzyme A and an acetyl group; the intermediate that provides acetyl groups for complete oxidation by aerobic respiration

acid-base reaction (7.2) reactions that involve the transfer of a hydrogen ion (H^+) from one reactant to another

actinide series (2.5) the 14 elements from thorium (Th) though lawrencium (Lr)

activated complex (5.3) the arrangement of atoms at the top of the potential energy barrier as a reaction proceeds

activation energy (5.3) the threshold energy that must be overcome to produce a chemical reaction

active site (15.6) the cleft in the surface of an enzyme that is the site of substrate binding

acyl carrier protein (ACP) (18.4) the protein that forms a thioester linkage with fatty acids during fatty acid synthesis

acyl group (Chapter 12, Introduction) the functional group found in the carboxylic acid derivatives that contains the carbonyl group attached to one alkyl or aryl group:

$$\text{(Ar) } R-\overset{\displaystyle O}{\overset{\|}{C}}-$$

addition reaction (9.3, 10.5) a reaction in which two molecules add together to form a new molecule; often involves the addition of one molecule to a double or triple bond in an unsaturated molecule; e.g., the addition of alcohol to an aldehyde or ketone to form a hemiacetal or hemiketal

adenosine triphosphate (ATP) (12.3, 16.1) a nucleotide composed of the purine adenine, the sugar ribose, and three phosphoryl groups; the primary energy storage and transport molecule used by the cells in cellular metabolism

adipocyte (18.1) a fat cell

adipose tissue (18.1) fatty tissue that stores most of the body lipids

aerobic respiration (17.2) the oxygen-requiring degradation of food molecules and production of ATP

alcohol (10.1) an organic compound that contains a hydroxyl group (—OH) attached to an alkyl group

aldehyde (10.5) a class of organic molecules characterized by a carbonyl group; the carbonyl carbon is bonded to a hydrogen atom and to another hydrogen or an alkyl or aryl group. Aldehydes have the following general structure:

$$\text{(Ar)}-\overset{\displaystyle O}{\overset{\|}{C}}-H \qquad R-\overset{\displaystyle O}{\overset{\|}{C}}-H$$

aldose (11.2) a sugar that contains an aldehyde (carbonyl) group

aliphatic hydrocarbon (9.1) any member of the alkanes, alkenes, and alkynes or the substituted alkanes, alkenes, and alkynes

alkali metal (2.5) an element within group IA of the periodic table

alkaline earth metal (2.5) an element within group IIA of the periodic table

alkaloid (14.2) a class of naturally occurring compounds that contain one or more nitrogen heterocyclic rings; many of the alkaloids have medicinal and other physiological effects

alkane (9.2) a hydrocarbon that contains only carbon and hydrogen and is bonded together through carbon-hydrogen and carbon-carbon single bonds; a saturated hydrocarbon with the general molecular formula C_nH_{2n+2}

alkene (9.3) a hydrocarbon that contains one or more carbon-carbon double bonds; an unsaturated hydrocarbon with the general formula C_nH_{2n}

alkyl group (9.2) a hydrocarbon group that results from the removal of one hydrogen from the original hydrocarbon (e.g., methyl, CH_3—; ethyl, CH_3CH_2—)

alkyl halide (9.2) a substituted hydrocarbon with the general structure R—X, where R— represents any alkyl group and X = a halogen (F—, Cl—, Br—, or I—)

alkylammonium ion (14.1) the ion formed when the lone pair of electrons of the nitrogen atom of an amine is shared with a proton (H^+) from a water molecule

alkyne (9.3) a hydrocarbon that contains one or more carbon-carbon triple bonds; an unsaturated hydrocarbon with the general formula C_nH_{2n-2}.

alpha particle (8.1) a particle consisting of two protons and two neutrons; the alpha particle is identical to a helium nucleus

amidation (14.3) the reaction between a carboxylic acid and ammonia or an amine that produces an amide

amide bond (14.3) the bond between the carbonyl carbon of a carboxylic acid and the amino nitrogen of an amine

amide group (14.3) the functional group characteristic of amides and having the following general structure:

$$R-\overset{\displaystyle O}{\overset{\|}{C}}-NH_2 \qquad \text{(Ar)}-\overset{\displaystyle O}{\overset{\|}{C}}-NH_2$$

amides (14.3) the family of organic compounds formed by the reaction between a carboxylic acid and an amine and characterized by the amide group

amines (14.1) the family of organic molecules with the general formula RNH_2, R_2NH, or R_3N (R— can represent either an alkyl or aryl group); they may be viewed as substituted ammonia molecules in which one or more of the ammonia hydrogens has been substituted by a more complex organic group

α-amino acid (15.2) the subunits of proteins composed of an α-carbon bonded to a carboxylate group, a protonated amino group, a hydrogen atom, and a variable R group

aminoacyl tRNA (19.6) the transfer RNA covalently linked to the correct amino acid

aminoacyl tRNA binding site of ribosome (A-site) (19.6) a pocket on the surface of a ribosome that holds the amino acyl tRNA during translation

aminoacyl tRNA synthetase (19.6) an enzyme that recognizes one tRNA and covalently links the appropriate amino acid to it

aminotransferase (17.5) an enzyme that catalyzes the transfer of an amino group from one molecule to another

amorphous solid (5.8) a solid with no organized, regular structure

amphibolic pathway (17.7) a metabolic pathway that functions in both anabolism and catabolism

amylopectin (11.4) a highly branched form of amylose; the branches are attached to the C-6 hydroxyl by $\alpha(1 \rightarrow 6)$ glycosidic linkage; a component of starch

amylose (11.4) a linear polymer of α-D-glucose molecules bonded in $\alpha(1 \rightarrow 4)$ glycosidic linkage that is a major component of starch; a polysaccharide storage form

anabolism (17.7) all of the cellular energy-requiring biosynthetic pathways

anaerobic threshold (16.4) the point at which the level of lactate in the exercising muscle inhibits glycolysis and the muscle, deprived of energy, ceases to function

analgesic (14.2) any drug that acts as a pain-killer, e.g., aspirin, acetaminophen

analytical chemistry (1.1) a branch of chemistry involving the determination of the identity, structure, and composition of matter

anaplerotic reaction (17.7) a reaction that replenishes a substrate needed for a biochemical pathway

anesthetic (14.2) a drug that causes a lack of sensation in part of the body (local anesthetic) or causes unconsciousness (general anesthetic)

angular molecule (3.4) a planar molecule with bond angles other than 180°

anion (2.2) a negatively charged atom or group of atoms

antibodies (15.1) immunoglobulins; specific glycoproteins produced by cells of the immune system in response to invasion by infectious agents

anticodon (19.4) a sequence of three ribonucleotides on a tRNA that are complementary to a codon on the mRNA; codon-anticodon binding results in delivery of the correct amino acid to the site of protein synthesis

antigen (15.1) any substance that is able to stimulate the immune system; generally a protein or large carbohydrate

antiparallel (19.2) a term describing the polarities of the two strands of the DNA double helix; on one strand the sugar-phosphate backbone advances in the $5' \rightarrow 3'$ direction; on the opposite, complementary strand the sugar phosphate backbone advances in the $3' \rightarrow 5'$ direction

apoenzyme (15.6) the protein portion of an enzyme that requires a cofactor to function in catalysis

aqueous solution (6.1) any solution in which the solvent is water

arachidonic acid (13.2) a fatty acid derived from linoleic acid; the precursor of the prostaglandins

aromatic hydrocarbon (9.1) an organic compound that contains the benzene ring or a derivative of the benzene ring

Arrhenius theory (7.3) a theory that defines an acid as a substance that dissociates to produce H^+ and a base as a substance that dissociates to produce OH^-

artificial radioactivity (8.4) radiation that results from the conversion of a stable nucleus to another, unstable nucleus

aryl halide (11.9) a benzene ring or other aromatic compound in which a hydrogen on the ring has been substituted by a halogen atom (F^-, Cl^-, Br^-, or I^-)

asymmetric carbon (11.2) a chiral carbon; a carbon bonded to four different groups

atherosclerosis (13.4) deposition of excess plasma cholesterol and other lipids and proteins on the walls of arteries, resulting in a decreased artery diameter and increased blood pressure

atom (2.2) the smallest unit of an element that retains the properties of that element

atomic mass (2.2) the mass of an atom expressed in atomic mass units

atomic mass unit (4.1) 1/12 of the mass of ^{12}C atom, equivalent to 1.6606×10^{-24} gram

atomic number (2.2) the number of protons in the nucleus of an atom. It is a charactristic identifier of an element

ATP synthase (17.4) a multiprotein complex within the inner mitochondrial membrane that uses the energy of the proton (H^+) gradient to produce ATP

autoionization (7.4) also known as self-ionization, the reaction of a substance, such as water, with itself to produce a positive and a negative ion

Avogadro's Law (5.6) a law that states that the volume is directly proportional to the number of moles of gas particles, assuming that the pressure and temperature are constant

Avogadro's number (4.1) 6.02×10^{23} particles of matter contained in 1 mole of a substance

background radiation (8.5) the radiation that emanates from natural sources

barometer (5.6) a device for measuring pressure

base pair (19.2) a hydrogen-bonded pair of bases within the DNA double helix. The standard base pairs always involve a purine and a pyrimidine; in particular, adenine always base pairs with thymine and cytosine with guanine

Benedict's reagent (11.2) a buffered solution of Cu^{2+} ions that can be used to test for reducing sugars or to distinguish between aldehydes and ketones

Benedict's test (10.5) a test used to determine the presence of reducing sugars or to distinguish between aldehydes and ketones. It requires a buffered solution of Cu^{2+} ions that are reduced to Cu^+, which precipitates as brick-red Cu_2O

beta particle (8.1) an electron formed in the nucleus by the conversion of a neutron into a proton

bile (18.1) micelles of lecithin, cholesterol, bile salts, protein, inorganic ions, and bile pigments that aid in lipid digestion by emulsifying fat droplets

binding energy (8.3) the energy required to break down the nucleus into its component parts

biochemistry (1.1) the study of the chemistry of living systems

boiling point (3.3) the temperature at which the vapor pressure of a liquid is equal to the atmospheric pressure

bond energy (3.4) the amount of energy necessary to break a chemical bond

Boyle's Law (5.6) a law stating that the volume of a gas varies inversely with the pressure exerted if the temperature and number of moles of gas are constant

breeder reactor (8.3) a nuclear reactor that produces its own fuel in the process of providing electrical energy

Brönsted-Lowry theory (7.3) a theory that describes an acid as a proton donor and a base as a proton acceptor

buffer solution (7.5) a solution containing a weak acid or base and its salt that is resistant to large changes in pH upon addition of strong acids or bases

buret (7.4) a device calibrated to deliver accurately known volumes of liquid, as in a titration

C-terminal amino acid (15.2) the amino acid

in a peptide that has a free α-CO_2^- group; the last amino acid in a peptide

calorimetry (5.2) the measurement of heat energy changes during a chemical reaction

carbohydrate (11.1) an organic compound usually characterized by the general formula $(CH_2O)_n$; generally sugars and polymers of sugars; the primary source of energy for the cell

carbonyl group (10.5) the functional group that contains a carbon-oxygen double bond: —C=O; the functional group found in aldehydes and ketones

carboxyl group (12.1) the —COOH functional group; the functional group found in carboxylic acids

carboxylic acid (12.1) a member of the family of organic compounds that contain the —COOH functional group

carboxylic acid derivative (12.2) any of several families of organic compounds, including the esters and amides, that are derived from carboxylic acids and have the general formula

$$(Ar)-\overset{\overset{\displaystyle O}{\|}}{C}-Z \qquad R-\overset{\overset{\displaystyle O}{\|}}{C}-Z$$

Z = —OR or OAr for the esters, and Z = NH_2 for the amides

carcinogen (19.7) any chemical or physical agent that causes mutations in the DNA that lead to uncontrolled cell growth or cancer

catabolism (16.1, 17.7) the degradation of fuel molecules and production of energy for cellular functions

catalyst (5.3) any substance that increases the rate of a chemical reaction (by lowering the activation energy of the reaction) and that is not destroyed in the course of the reaction

cation (2.2) a positively charged atom or group of atoms

cellulose (11.4) a polymer of β-D-glucose linked by $\beta(1 \rightarrow 4)$ glycosidic bonds

central dogma (19.4) a statement of the directional transfer of the genetic information in cells: DNA → RNA → Protein

Charles's Law (5.6) a law stating that the volume of a gas is directly proportional to the temperature of the gas, assuming that the pressure and number of moles of the gas are constant

chemical bond (3.1) the attractive force holding two atomic nuclei together in a chemical compound

chemical equation (4.4) a record of chemical change, showing the conversion of reactants to products

chemical formula (4.2) the representation of a compound or ion in which elemental symbols represent types of atoms and subscripts show the relative numbers of atoms

chemical properties (2.1) properties of a substance that relate to the substance's participation in a chemical reaction

chemical reaction (2.1) a process in which atoms are rearranged to produce new combinations

chemistry (1.1) the study of matter and the changes that matter undergoes

chiral (11.2) molecules capable of existing in mirror-image forms

cholesterol (13.4) a 27-carbon steroid ring structure that serves as the precursor of the steroid hormones

chylomicron (13.5, 18.1) a plasma lipoprotein (aggregate of protein and triglycerides) that carries triglycerides from the intestine to all body tissues via the bloodstream

citric acid cycle (17.3) a cyclic biochemical pathway that is the final stage of degradation of carbohydrates, fats, and amino acids. It results in the complete oxidation of acetyl groups derived from these dietary fuels

cloning vector (19.8) a DNA molecule that can carry a cloned DNA fragment into a cell and that has a replication origin that allows the DNA to be replicated abundantly within the host cell

coagulation (15.4) the process by which proteins in solution are denatured and aggregate with one another to produce a solid

codon (19.4) a group of three ribonucleotides on the mRNA that specifies the addition of a specific amino acid onto the growing peptide chain

coenzyme (15.6) an organic group required by some enzymes; they generally serve as donors or acceptors of electrons or functional groups in a reaction

coenzyme A (16.7) a molecule derived from ATP, the vitamin pantothenic acid, and the amino acid cysteine. Coenzyme A functions in the transfer of acetyl groups in lipid and carbohydrate metabolism

cofactor (15.6) an inorganic group, usually a metal ion, that must be bound to an apoenzyme to maintain the correct configuration of the active site

colipase (18.1) a protein that aids in lipid digestion by binding to the surface of lipid droplets and facilitating binding of pancreatic lipase

colligative properties (6.4) properties of solutions that are dependent only on the concentration of solute particles

colloidal suspension (6.1) a nonhomogeneous mixture of solute particles in a solvent; distribution of solute particles is not uniform because of the size of the particles

combination reaction (7.1) a reaction in which two substances join to form another substance

combustion (9.2) the oxidation of hydrocarbons by burning in the presence of air to produce carbon dioxide and water

common system of nomenclature (9.4) the nonsystematic, though older and well-established, system of nomenclature

competitive inhibition (15.7) a molecule with structure very similar to the natural substrate of an enzyme competes with the natural substrate for binding to the enzyme active site and inhibits the reaction

competitive inhibitor (15.7) a structural analog; a molecule that has a structure very similar to the natural substrate of an enzyme, competes with the natural substrate for binding to the enzyme active site, and inhibits the reaction

complementary strands (19.2) the opposite strands of the double helix are hydrogen-bonded to one another such that adenine and thymine or guanine and cytosine are always paired

complete protein (15.9) a protein source that contains all the essential and nonessential amino acids

complex lipid (13.5) a lipid bonded to other types of molecules

compound (2.1) a substance that is characterized by constant composition and that can be chemically broken down into elements

concentration (1.7, 6.2) a measure of the number of particles or the mass of a substance contained in a specified volume

condensation (5.7) the conversion of a gas to a liquid

condensed formula (9.2) a structural formula showing all of the atoms in a molecule and placing them in a sequential arrangement that details which atoms are bonded to each other; the bonds themselves are not shown

conjugated protein (15.6) a protein that is functional only when it carries other chemical groups attached by covalent linkages or by weak interactions

conversion factor (1.4) an equivalence statement or multiplier consisting of a ratio of two equivalent quantities in different units, used to convert a quantity from one unit to another

Cori cycle (16.5) a metabolic pathway in which the lactate produced by working muscle is converted back to glucose by gluconeogenesis in the liver

covalent bond (3.1) a pair of electrons shared between two atoms

covalent solid (5.8) a collection of atoms held together by covalent bonds

crenation (6.4) the shrinkage of red blood cells due to water loss to the surrounding medium

cristae (17.1) the folds of the inner membrane of the mitochondria

crystal lattice (3.2) a unit of a solid characterized by a regular arrangement of components

crystalline solid (5.8) a solid having a regular repeating atomic structure

curie (8.7) the quantity of radioactive material that produces 3.7×10^{10} nuclear disintegrations per second

cycloalkane (9.2) a cyclic alkane; a saturated hydrocarbon that has the general formula C_nH_{2n}

Dalton's Law (5.6) also called the Law of Partial Pressures; states that the total pressure exerted by a gas mixture is the sum of the partial pressures of the component gases

data (1.3) a group of facts resulting from an experiment

decomposition reaction (7.1) the breakdown of a substance into two or more substances

degenerate code (19.5) a term used to describe the fact that several triplet codons may be used to specify a single amino acid in the genetic code

dehydration (of alcohols) (10.1) a reaction that involves the loss of a water molecule, in this case the loss of water from an alcohol and the simultaneous formation of an alkene

deletion mutation (19.7) a mutation that results in the loss of one or more nucleotides from a DNA sequence

denaturation (15.4) the process by which the organized structure of a protein is disrupted, resulting in a completely disorganized, nonfunctional form of the protein

density (1.7) mass per unit volume of an object

deoxyribonucleic acid (DNA) (19.1) the nucleic acid molecule that carries all of the genetic information of an organism; the DNA molecule is a double helix composed of two strands, each of which is composed of phosphate groups, deoxyribose, and the nitrogenous bases thymine, cytosine, adenine, and guanine

deoxyribonucleotide (19.1) a nucleoside phosphate or nucleotide composed of a nitrogenous base in β-N-glycosidic linkage to the 1′ carbon of the sugar 2′-deoxyribose and with one, two, or three phosphoryl groups esterified at the hydroxyl of the 5′ carbon

diabetes mellitus (18.3) a disease caused by the production of insufficient levels of insulin and characterized by the appearance of very high levels of glucose in the blood and urine

diglyceride (13.3) the product of esterification of glycerol at two positions

disaccharide (11.1, 11.3) a sugar composed of two monosaccharides joined through an oxygen atom bridge

dissociation (3.3) formation of positive and negative ions when an ionic compound dissolves in water

disulfide (10.4) an organic compound that contains a disulfide group (—S—S—)

DNA polymerase (19.3) the enzyme that catalyzes the polymerization of daughter DNA strands using the parental strand as a template

double bond (3.4) a bond in which two pairs of electrons are shared by two atoms

double helix (19.2) the spiral staircase-like structure of the DNA molecule characterized by two sugar-phosphate backbones wound around the outside and nitrogenous bases extending into the center

double-replacement reaction (7.1) a chemical change in which cations and anions "exchange partners"

dynamic equilibrium (5.4) the state that exists when the rate of change in the concentration of products and reactants is equal, resulting in no net concentration change

electrolyte (3.3, 6.1) a material that dissolves in water to produce a solution that conducts an electrical current

electrolytic solution (3.3) a solution composed of an electrolytic solute dissolved in water

electron (2.2) a negatively charged particle outside of the nucleus of an atom

electron affinity (2.7) the energy released when an electron is added to an isolated atom

electron configuration (2.3, 2.6) the arrangement of electrons around a nucleus of an atom, ion, or a collection of nuclei of a molecule

electron transport system (17.4) the series of electron transport proteins embedded in the inner mitochondrial membrane that accept high-energy electrons from NADH and $FADH_2$ and transfer them in stepwise fashion to molecular oxygen (O_2)

electronegativity (3.4) a measure of the tendency of an atom in a molecule to attract shared electrons

electronic transition (2.3) the movement of an electron from one energy level to another within an atom

element (2.1) a substance that cannot be decomposed into simpler substances by chemical or physical means

emulsifying agent (13.3) a bipolar molecule that aids in the suspension of fats in water

enantiomers (11.2) stereoisomers that are nonsuperimposable mirror images of one another

endothermic reaction (5.1) a chemical or physical change in which energy is absorbed

energy (1.1) the capacity to do work

energy level (2.3) one of numerous atomic regions where electrons may be found

enthalpy (5.1) a term that represents heat energy

entropy (5.1) a tendency toward randomness or disorder

enzyme (15.1) a protein that serves as a biological catalyst

enzyme specificity (15.6) the ability of an enzyme to bind to only one, or a very few, substrates and thus catalyze only a single reaction

enzyme-substrate complex (15.6) a molecular aggregate formed when the substrate binds to the active site of the enzyme

equilibrium (5.4) a reaction that has a measurable quantity of reactants and products and their concentrations remain constant over time

equivalence point (7.4) the situation in which reactants have been mixed in the molar ratio corresponding to the balanced equation

equivalent (6.3) the number of grams of an ion corresponding to Avogadro's number of electrical charges

error (1.5) the difference between the true value and the experimental value for data or results

essential amino acids (15.9) amino acids that cannot be synthesized by the body and must therefore be supplied by the diet

essential fatty acids (13.2) the fatty acids linolenic and linoleic acids that must be supplied in the diet because they cannot be synthesized by the body

ester (12.2) a carboxylic acid derivative formed by the reaction of a carboxylic acid and an alcohol. Esters have the following general formula:

$$R-\overset{\overset{\displaystyle O}{\|}}{C}-OR \quad R-\overset{\overset{\displaystyle O}{\|}}{C}-O \; (Ar) \quad (Ar)-\overset{\overset{\displaystyle O}{\|}}{C}-O(Ar)$$

ether (10.3) an organic compound that contains two alkyl and/or aryl groups attached to an oxygen atom; R—O—R, Ar—O—R, and Ar—O—Ar

evaporation (5.7) the conversion of a liquid to a gas below the boiling point of the liquid

excited state (2.3) a condition in which an atom has one or more of its electrons in an energy state higher than the ground state

exon (19.4) the protein-coding sequences of a gene that are found on the final mature mRNA

exothermic reaction (5.1) a chemical or physical change that releases energy

extensive property (2.1) a property of a substance that depends on the mass

F_0F_1 complex (17.4) an alternative term for the ATP synthase, the multiprotein complex in the inner mitochonrial membrane that uses the energy of the proton gradient to produce ATP

family (2.5) any of the 18 vertical columns of elements in the periodic table; also called a group

fatty acid (12.1, 13.2) any member of the family of continuous-chain carboxylic acids that generally contain 4 to 20 carbon atoms; the most concentrated source of energy used by the cell

fermentation (10.1, 16.4) anaerobic (in the absence of oxygen) catabolic reactions that occur with no net oxidation. Pyruvate or an organic compound produced from pyruvate is reduced as NADH is oxidized

fibrous protein (15.2) proteins composed of peptides arranged in long sheets or fibers

Fischer projection (11.2) a two-dimensional formula used to designate the three-dimensional structure of a molecule. It is drawn as a cross with the chiral carbon in the center

fission process (8.3) the splitting of heavy nuclei into lighter nuclei accompanied by the release of large quantities of energy

fluid mosaic model (13.3) the model of membrane structure that describes the fluid nature of the lipid bilayer and the presence of numerous proteins embedded within the membrane

folic acid (15.7) a vitamin required for the transfer of one carbon group for the synthesis of methionine, purines, and pyrimidines

formula (3.2) the representation of the fundamental compound unit using chemical symbols and numerical subscripts

formula unit (4.2) the smallest collection of atoms from which the formula of a compound can be established

formula weight (4.3) the mass of a formula unit of a compound relative to a standard (carbon-12)

free energy (5.1) the combined contribution of entropy and enthalpy for a chemical reaction

fructose (11.2) a ketohexose that is also called levulose and fruit sugar; the sweetest of all sugars, abundant in honey and fruits

fuel value (5.2) the amount of energy derived from a given mass of material

functional group (9.1) an atom (or group of atoms and their bonds) that imparts specific chemical and physical properties to a molecule

fusion process (8.3) the joining of light nuclei to form heavier nuclei, accompanied by the release of large amounts of energy

galactose (11.2) an aldohexose that is a component of lactose (milk sugar)

galactosemia (11.3) a human genetic disease caused by the inability to convert galactose to a phosphorylated form of glucose (glucose-1-phosphate) that can be used in cellular metabolic reactions

gamma ray (8.1) a high-energy emission from nuclear processes, traveling at the speed of light; the high energy region of the electromagnetic spectrum

gaseous state (2.1) a physical state of matter characterized by the lack of fixed shape or volume and ease of compressibility

geometric isomer (9.3) an isomer that differs from another isomer in the placement of substituents on a double bond or a ring

globular protein (15.2) a protein composed of polypeptide chains that are tightly folded into a compact spherical shape

glucagon (16.6, 18.6) a peptide hormone synthesized by the α-cells of the islets of Langerhans in the pancreas and secreted in response to low blood glucose levels; glucagon promotes glycogenolysis and gluconeogenesis and thereby increases the concentration of blood glucose

gluconeogenesis (16.5) the synthesis of glucose from noncarbohydrate precursors

glucose (11.2) an aldohexose, the most abundant monosaccharide; it is a component of many disaccharides, such as lactose and sucrose, and of polysaccharides, such as cellulose, starch, and glycogen

glyceraldehyde (11.2) an aldotriose that is the simplest carbohydrate; phosphorylated forms of glyceraldehyde are important intermediates in cellular metabolic reactions

glyceride (13.3) a lipid that contains glycerol

glycogen (11.4, 16.6) a long, branched polymer of glucose stored in liver and muscles of animals; it consists of a linear backbone of α-D-glucose in $\alpha(1 \rightarrow 4)$ linkage, with numerous short branches attached to the C-6 hydroxyl group by $\alpha(1 \rightarrow 6)$ linkage

glycogen granule (16.6) a core of glycogen surrounded by enzymes responsible for glycogen synthesis and degradation

glycogenesis (16.6) the metabolic pathway that results in the addition of glucose to growing glycogen polymers when blood glucose levels are high

glycogenolysis (16.6) the biochemical pathway that results in the removal of glucose molecules from glycogen polymers when blood glucose levels are low

glycolysis (16.3) the enzymatic pathway that converts a glucose molecule into two molecules of pyruvate. This anaerobic process generates energy in the form of 2 molecules of ATP and 2 molecules of NADH

glycoprotein (15.2) proteins conjugated with sugar groups

glycosidic bond (11.1, 11.3) the bond between the hydroxyl group of the C-1 carbon of one sugar and a hydroxyl group of another sugar

ground state (2.3) a condition in which an atom is in its lowest energy state

group (2.5) any one of 18 vertical columns of elements; often referred to as a family

group specificity (15.6) an enzyme that catalyzes reactions involving similar substrate molecules having the same functional groups

guanosine triphosphate (GTP) (16.5) a nucleotide composed of the purine guanosine, the sugar ribose, and three phosphoryl groups; it serves as a phosphoryl group donor in the conversion of oxaloacetate to phosphoenolpyruvate during gluconeogenesis

half-life ($t_{1/2}$) (8.3) the length of time required for one-half of the initial mass of an isotope to decay to products

halogen (2.5) an element found in group VIIA of the periodic table

halogenation (9.2, 9.3) a reaction in which one of the C—H bonds of a hydrocarbon is replaced with a C—X bond of a halogen atom (X = Br or Cl generally)

Haworth projection (11.2) a means of representing the orientation of substituent groups around a cyclic sugar molecule

α-helix (15.2) a right-handed coiled secondary structure maintained by hydrogen bonds between the amide hydrogen of one amino acid and the carbonyl oxygen of an amino acid four residues away

heme (15.3) the chemical group found in hemoglobin and myoglobin that is responsible for the ability to carry oxygen

hemiacetal (10.5, 11.2) the family of organic compounds formed via the reaction of one molecule of alcohol with an aldehyde in the presence of an acid catalyst; hemiacetals have the following general structure:

$$R_1 - \overset{\displaystyle OH}{\underset{\displaystyle H}{C}} - OR_2$$

hemiketal (10.5, 11.2) the family of organic compounds formed via the reaction of one molecule of alcohol with a ketone in the presence of an acid catalyst; hemiketals have the following general structure:

$$R_1 - \overset{\displaystyle OH}{\underset{\displaystyle R_2}{C}} - OR_3$$

hemoglobin (15.3) the major protein component of red blood cells; the function of this red, iron-containing protein is transport of oxygen

hemolysis (6.4) the rupture of red blood cells resulting from transfer of water from the surrounding medium

Henry's Law (6.1) a law stating that the number of moles of a gas dissolved in a liquid at a given temperature is proportional to the partial pressure of the gas

heterocyclic amines (14.2) heterocyclic compounds that contain nitrogen in at least one position in the ring skeleton

heterogeneous mixture (2.1) a mixture of two or more substances characterized by nonuniform composition

hexose (11.2) a six-carbon monosaccharide

high-density lipoprotein (HDL) (13.5) a plasma lipoprotein that transports cholesterol from peripheral tissue to the liver

homogeneous mixture (2.1) a mixture consisting of two or more substances and characterized by uniform composition

hybridization (19.8) a technique for identifying DNA or RNA sequences that is based on specific hydrogen bonding between a radioactive probe and complementary DNA or RNA sequences

hydrate (7.1) any substance that has water molecules incorporated in its structure

hydration (9.3, 10.1) a reaction in which water is added to a molecule, e.g., the addition of water to an alkene to form an alcohol

hydrocarbon (9.1) a compound composed solely of the elements carbon and hydrogen

hydrogen bonding (5.2, 6.5) the attractive force between a hydrogen atom covalently bonded to a highly electronegative atom and another atom containing an unshared pair of electrons

hydrogenation (9.3, 10.5, 13.2) a reaction in which hydrogen (H_2) is added to a double or a triple bond

hydrohalogenation (9.3) the addition of a hydrohalogen (HCl, HBr, or HI) to an unsaturated bond

hydrolase (15.5) an enzyme that catalyzes hydrolysis reactions

hydrolysis (12.2, 13.2) a chemical reaction that involves the reaction of a molecule with water; the process by which molecules are broken into their constituents by addition of water

hydronium ion (7.3) a protonated water molecule, H_3O^+

hydrophilic (15.2) ''water loving''; polar and ionic substances that have a high affinity for water

hydrophobic (15.2) ''water fearing''; a nonpolar substance that prefers contact with other nonpolar substances over contact with water

hydroxyl group (10.1) the —OH functional group that is characteristic of alcohols

hyperammonemia (17.6) a genetic defect in one of the enzymes of the urea cycle that results in toxic or even fatal elevation of the concentration of ammonium ions in the body

hyperglycemia (16.6) blood glucose levels that are higher than normal

hypertonic solution (6.4) the more concentrated solution of two separated by a semipermeable membrane

hypoglycemia (16.6) blood glucose levels that are lower than normal

hypothesis (1.2) an ''educated guess'' at the explanation of observed behavior of our surroundings

hypotonic solution (6.4) the more dilute solution of two separated by a semipermeable membrane

ideal gas (5.6) a gas in which gas particles do not interact and the volume of the individual gas particles is assumed to be negligible

ideal gas law (5.6) a law stating that for an ideal gas the product of pressure and volume is proportional to the product of the number of moles of the gas and its temperature; the proportionality constant for an ideal gas is symbolized R

incomplete protein (15.9) a protein source that does not contain all the essential and nonessential amino acids

indicator (7.4) a solute that shows some condition of a solution (such as acidity or basicity) by its color

induced fit model (15.6) the theory of enzyme-substrate binding that assumes that the enzyme is a flexible molecule and that both the substrate and the enzyme change their shapes to accommodate one another as the enzyme-substrate complex forms

initiation factors (19.6) proteins that are required for formation of the translation initiation complex, which is composed of the large and small ribosomal subunits, the mRNA, and the initiator tRNA, *N*-formylmethionyl tRNA

inner mitochondrial membrane (17.1) the highly folded, impermeable membrane within the mitochondrion that is the location of the electron transport system and ATP synthase

inorganic chemistry (1.1) the study of all the elements and their compounds, excluding the compounds of carbon (organic chemistry)

insertion mutation (19.7) a mutation that results in the addition of one or more nucleotides to a DNA sequence

insulin (16.6, 18.6) a hormone released from the pancreas in response to high blood glucose levels. Insulin stimulates glycogenesis, fat storage, and cellular uptake and storage of glucose from the blood

intensive property (2.1) a property of a substance that is independent of the quantity of the substance

intermembrane space (17.1) the region between the outer and inner mitochondrial membranes, which is the location of the proton (H^+) reservoir that drives ATP synthesis

intermolecular force (3.5) the attractive forces that occur between molecules

intramolecular force (3.5) the attractive forces that occur within molecules

intron (19.4) a noncoding sequence within a eukaryotic gene that must be removed from the primary transcript to produce a functional mRNA

ion (2.2) an electrically charged particle formed by the gain or loss of electrons

ion pair (3.1) the empirical formula unit for an ionic compound

ion product for water (7.4) the product of the hydronium and hydroxide ion concentrations in pure water at a specified temperature

ionic bond (3.1) an electrostatic attractive force between ions resulting from electron transfer

ionic solid (5.8) a solid composed of positive and negative ions in a regular three-dimensional crystalline arrangement

ionization energy (2.7) the energy needed to remove an electron from an atom in the gas phase

ionizing radiation (8.4) radiation that is sufficiently high in energy to cause ion formation upon impact with an atom

irreversible inhibitor (15.7) a chemical that binds strongly to the R-groups of an amino acid in the active site and eliminates enzyme activity

isoelectric (15.4) a situation in which a protein has an equal number of positive and negative charges and therefore has an overall net charge of zero

isoelectronic (2.6) atoms and ions containing the same number of electrons

isomerase (15.5) an enzyme that catalyzes the conversion of one isomer to another

isotonic solution (6.4) a solution that has the same solute concentration (water activity and osmotic pressure) as another solution with which it is being compared; a solution that has the same osmotic pressure as a solution existing within a cell

isotopes (2.2) atoms of the same element that differ in mass because they contain different numbers of neutrons

I.U.P.A.C. Nomenclature System (9.2) the International Union of Pure and Applied Chemistry (I.U.P.A.C.) standard, universal system for the nomenclature of organic compounds

α-keratins (15.2) a family of fibrous proteins that form the covering of most land animals; major components of fur, skin, beaks, and nails

ketal (10.5) the family of organic compounds formed via the reaction of two molecules of alcohol with a ketone in the presence of an acid catalyst; ketals have the following general structure:

$$R_1 - \overset{\displaystyle OR_3}{\underset{\displaystyle R_2}{C}} - OR_4$$

ketoacidosis (18.3) a drop in the pH of the blood caused by elevated ketone levels

ketone (10.5) a family of organic molecules characterized by a carbonyl group; the carbonyl carbon is bonded to two alkyl groups, two aryl groups, or one alkyl and one aryl group; ketones have the following general structures:

$$\underset{R-\overset{\displaystyle O}{\overset{\|}{C}}-R}{} \quad \underset{R-\overset{\displaystyle O}{\overset{\|}{C}}-(Ar)}{} \quad \underset{(Ar)-\overset{\displaystyle O}{\overset{\|}{C}}-(Ar)}{}$$

ketone bodies (18.3) acetone, acetoacetone, and β-hydroxybutyrate produced from fatty acids in the liver via acetyl CoA

ketose (11.2) a sugar that contains a ketone (carbonyl) group

ketosis (18.3) an abnormal rise in the level of ketone bodies in the blood

kinetic energy (1.7) the energy resulting from motion of an object [K.E. = 1/2 (mass)(velocity)^2]

kinetic-molecular theory (5.6) the fundamental model of particle behavior in the gas phase

kinetics (5.3) the study of rates of chemical reactions

lactose (11.3) a disaccharide composed of β-D-galactose and either α- or β-D-glucose in β(1 → 4) glycosidic linkage; milk sugar

lactose intolerance (11.3) the inability to produce the enzyme lactase, which degrades lactose to galactose and glucose

lanthanide series (2.5) the rare earth elements, the 14 elements from cerium (Ce) to lutetium (Lu)

law (1.2) a statement of observed behavior for which no exceptions have been found

law of conservation of mass (4.4) a law stating that, in chemical change, matter cannot be created or destroyed

LeChatelier's Principle (5.4) a law stating that when a system in equilibrium is disturbed, the equilibrium shifts in the direction that minimizes the disturbance

lethal dose (LD$_{50}$) (8.7) the quantity of toxic material (such as radiation) that causes the death of 50% of a population of an organism

Lewis symbol (3.1) representation of an atom or ion using the atomic symbol (for the nucleus and core electrons) and dots to represent valence electrons

ligase (15.5) an enzyme that catalyzes the joining of two molecules

linear molecule (3.4) a molecule in which the bond angles about the central atom(s) is (are) 180°

linkage specificity (15.6) the property of an enzyme that allows it to catalyze reactions involving only one kind of bond in the substrate molecule

lipase (18.1) an enzyme that hydrolyzes the ester linkage between glycerol and the fatty acids of triglycerides

lipid (13.1) a member of the group of biological molecules of varying composition that are classified together on the basis of their solubility in nonpolar solvents

liquid state (2.1) a physical state of matter characterized by a fixed volume and the absence of a fixed shape

lock-and-key model (15.6) the theory of enzyme-substrate binding that depicts enzymes as inflexible molecules; the substrate fits into the rigid active site in the same way a key fits into a lock

lone pair (3.4) an electron pair that is not involved in bonding

low-density lipoprotein (LDL) (13.5) a plasma lipoprotein that carries cholesterol to peripheral tissues and helps to regulate cholesterol levels in those tissues

lyase (15.5) an enzyme that catalyzes a reaction involving double bonds

maltose (11.3) a disaccharide composed of α-D-glucose and a second glucose molecule in α(1 → 4) glycosidic linkage

Markovnikov's Rule (9.3) the rule stating that a hydrogen atom, adding to a carbon-carbon double bond, will add to the carbon having the larger number of hydrogens attached to it

mass (1.7) a quantity of matter

mass number (2.2) the sum of the number of protons and neutrons in an atom

matrix space (17.1) the region of the mitochondrion within the inner membrane; the location of the enzymes that carry out the reactions of the citric acid cycle and β-oxidation of fatty acids

matter (1.1) the material component of the universe

melting point (3.3, 5.8) the temperature at which a solid converts to a liquid

messenger RNA (19.4) an RNA species produced by transcription and that specifies the amino acid sequence for a protein

metallic bond (5.8) a bond that results from the orbital overlap of metal atoms

metallic solid (5.8) a solid composed of metal atoms held together by metallic bonds

metalloid (2.5) an element along the "staircase" boundary between metals and nonmetals; metalloids exhibit both metallic and nonmetallic properties

metal (2.5) an element located on the left side of the periodic table (left of the "staircase" boundary)

metastable isotope (8.2) an isotope that will give up some energy to produce a more stable form of the same isotope

micelle (18.1) an aggregation of molecules having a nonpolar and a polar region; the nonpolar regions of the molecules aggregate, leaving the polar regions facing the surrounding water

mitochondria (17.1) the cellular "power plants" in which the reactions of the citric acid cycle, the electron transport system, and ATP synthase function to produce ATP

mixture (2.1) a material composed of two or more substances

molality (6.4) the number of moles of solute per kilogram of solvent

molar volume of a gas (5.6) the volume occupied by one mole of any gas

molarity (6.3) the number of moles of solute per liter of solution

mole (4.1) the amount of substance containing Avogadro's number of particles

molecular formula (9.2) a formula that provides the atoms and number of each type of atom in a molecule but gives no information regarding the bonding pattern involved in the molecule's structure

molecular solid (5.8) a solid in which the molecules are held together by dipole-dipole and London forces

molecular weight (4.3) the mass of a molecule relative to a standard (carbon-12)

molecule (3.2) a unit in which the atoms of two or more elements are held together by chemical bonds

monatomic ion (3.2) an ion formed by electron gain or loss from a single atom

monoglyceride (13.3) the product of the esterification of glycerol at one position

monosaccharide (11.1, 11.2) the simplest type of carbohydrate consisting of a single saccharide unit

mutagen (19.7) any chemical or physical agent that causes changes in the nucleotide sequence of a gene

mutation (19.7) any change in the nucleotide sequence of a gene

myoglobin (15.3) the oxygen storage protein found in muscle

myosin (15.2) one of the major proteins of muscle tissue. It has a rodlike structure of two α-helices coiled around one another

N-terminal amino acid (15.2) the amino acid in a peptide that has a free α-N$^+$H$_3$ group; the first amino acid of a peptide

natural radioactivity (8.4) the spontaneous decay of a nucleus to produce high-energy particles or rays

neutral glyceride (13.3) the product of the esterification of glycerol at one, two, or three positions

neutralization (7.4) the reaction between an acid and a base

neutron (2.2) an uncharged particle, with the same mass as the proton, in the nucleus of an atom

niacin (15.6) vitamin B$_3$, a vitamin essential for the energy-generating reactions of the cell. It is a component of two coenzymes, nicotinamide adenine dinucleotide and nicotinamide adenine dinucleotide phosphate

nicotinamide adenine dinucleotide (NAD$^+$) (16.3) a molecule synthesized from the vitamin niacin and the nucleotide ATP and that serves as a carrier of hydride anions; a coenzyme that is an oxidizing agent used in a variety of metabolic processes

noble gas (2.5) elements in Group VIIIA of the periodic table

nomenclature (3.2) a system for naming chemical compounds

nonelectrolyte (3.3, 6.1) a substance that, when dissolved in water, produces a solution that does not conduct an electrical current

nonessential amino acid (15.9) any amino acid that can be synthesized by the body

nonmetal (2.5) an element located on the right side of the periodic table (right of the "staircase" boundary)

nonreducing sugar (11.3) a sugar that cannot be oxidized by Benedict's or Tollens' reagent

normal boiling point (5.7) the temperature at which a substance will boil at one atmosphere of pressure

nuclear equation (8.2) a balanced equation accounting for the products and reactants in a nuclear reaction

nuclear imaging (8.4) the generation of images of components of the body (organs, tissues) using techniques based on the measurement of radiation

nuclear medicine (8.4) a field of medicine that uses radioisotopes for diagnostic and therapeutic purposes

nuclear reactor (8.4) a device for conversion of nuclear energy into electrical energy

nucleotide (16.1, 19.1) a molecule composed of a nitrogenous base, a five-carbon sugar, and one, two, or three phosphoryl groups

nucleus (2.2) the small, dense center of positive charge in the atom

nutritional Calorie (5.2) equivalent to one kilocalorie (1000 calories); also known as a large Calorie

octet rule (2.6) a rule predicting that atoms form the most stable molecules or ions when they are surrounded by eight electrons in their highest occupied energy level

oligosaccharide (11.1, 11.3) an intermediate-sized carbohydrate composed of from two to ten monosaccharides

orbit (2.3) according to the Bohr theory, a region of the atom where electrons may be found

organic chemistry (1.1) the study of carbon-containing compounds and their properties

osmolarity (6.4) molarity of particles in solution; this value is used for osmotic pressure calculations

osmosis (6.4) net flow of a solvent across a semipermeable membrane in response to a concentration gradient

osmotic pressure (6.4) the net force with which water enters a solution through a semipermeable membrane; alternatively, the pressure required to stop net transfer of solvent across a semipermeable membrane

outer mitochondrial membrane (17.1) the membrane that surrounds the mitochondrion and separates it from the contents of the cytoplasm; it is highly permeable to small "food" molecules

β-oxidation (18.2) the biochemical pathway that results in the oxidation of fatty acids and the production of acetyl CoA

oxidation (7.6, 12.1) a loss of electrons or hydrogen atoms or the gain of oxygen

oxidation-reduction reaction (7.2) also called redox reaction, a reaction involving the transfer of one or more electrons from one reactant to another

oxidative deamination (17.5) an oxidation-reduction reaction in which NAD$^+$ is reduced and the amino acid is deaminated

oxidative phosphorylation (16.3, 17.4) production of ATP using the energy of electrons harvested during biological oxidation-reduction reactions

oxidizing agent (7.6) a substance that oxidizes, or removes electrons from, another substance; the oxidizing agent is reduced in the process

oxireductase (15.5) an enzyme that catalyzes an oxidation-reduction reaction

parent compound or parent chain (9.2) in the I.U.P.A.C. Nomenclature System the parent compound is the longest carbon-carbon chain containing the principal functional group in the molecule that is being named

partial pressure (5.6) the pressure exerted by one compound of a gas mixture

particle accelerator (8.4) a device for production of high-energy nuclear particles based on the interaction of charged particles with magnetic and electrical fields

pentose (11.2) a five-carbon monosaccharide

peptide bond (14.3, 15.2) the covalent linkage between two amino acids in a peptide chain, formed by a condensation reaction

peptidyl tRNA binding site of ribosome (P-site) (19.6) a pocket on the surface of the ribosome that holds the tRNA bound to the growing peptide chain

period (2.5) any one of seven horizontal rows of elements in the periodic table

periodic law (2.5) a law stating that properties of elements are periodic functions of their atomic numbers (Note that Mendeleev's

original statement was based on atomic masses.)

peripheral protein (13.3) a protein bound to either the inner or the outer surface of a membrane

pH optimum (15.6) the pH at which an enzyme catalyzes the reaction at maximum efficiency

pH scale (7.4) a numerical representation of acidity or basicity of a solution; pH = $-\log [H^+]$

phenol (10.2) an organic compound that contains a hydroxyl group (—OH) attached to a benzene ring

phosphatidate (13.3) a molecule of glycerol with fatty acids esterified to C-1 and C-2 of glycerol and a free phosphoryl group esterified at C-3

phosphoester (12.3) the product of the reaction between phosphoric acid and an alcohol

phosphoglyceride (13.3) a molecule with fatty acids esterified at the C-1 and C-2 positions of glycerol and a phosphoryl group esterified at the C-3 position

phospholipid (13.3) a lipid containing a phosphoryl group

phosphopantetheine (18.4) the portion of coenzyme A and the acyl carrier protein that is derived from the vitamin pantothenic acid and the amino acid cysteine; it forms a thioester linkage with fatty acids

phosphoric anhydride (12.3) the bond formed when two phosphate groups react with one another and a water molecule is lost

physical change (2.1) a change in the form of a substance but not in its chemical composition; no chemical bonds are broken in a physical change

physical chemistry (1.1) a subdiscipline of chemistry involving the development of theoretical aspects of chemistry

physical property (2.1) a characteristic of a substance that can be observed without the substance undergoing change (examples include color, density, melting and boiling points)

plasma lipoprotein (13.5) a complex composed of lipid and protein that is responsible for the transport of lipids throughout the body

β-pleated sheet (15.2) a common secondary structure of a peptide chain that resembles the pleats of an Oriental fan

point mutation (19.7) the substitution of a single base in a codon; it may or may not alter the genetic code of the mRNA, resulting in the substitution of one amino acid in the protein

polar covalent bond (3.4) a covalent bond in which the electrons are not equally shared

polar covalent molecule (3.4) a molecule that has a permanent electric dipole moment resulting from an unsymmetrical electron distribution; a dipolar molecule

polyatomic ion (3.2) an ion containing a number of atoms

polysaccharide (11.1, 11.4) a large, complex carbohydrate composed of long chains of monosaccharides

polysome (19.6) complexes of many ribosomes all simultaneously translating a single mRNA

potential energy (1.7) stored energy or energy due to position or composition

precipitate (6.1) an insoluble substance formed and separated from a solution

precision (1.5) the degree of agreement between replicate measurements of the same quantity

pressure (5.6) a force per unit area

primary (1°) alcohol (10.1) an alcohol with the general formula RCH_2OH

primary (1°) amine (14.1) an amine with the general formula RNH_2

primary protein structure (15.2) the linear sequence of amino acids in a protein chain determined by the genetic information of the gene for each protein

product (2.1, 4.4, 15.6) the chemical species that results from a chemical reaction and that appears on the right side of a chemical equation

promoter (19.4) the sequence of nucleotides immediately before a gene that is recognized by the RNA polymerase and signals the start point and direction of transcription

promotion (2.3) an electron transition from a lower to a higher energy level, resulting from absorption of energy

prostaglandins (13.2) a family of hormone-like substances derived from the 20-carbon fatty acid, arachidonic acid; produced by many cells of the body, they regulate many body functions

prosthetic group (15.2) the nonprotein portion of a conjugated protein that is essential to the biological activity of the protein; often a complex organic compound

protein (Chapter 15 Introduction) a macromolecule whose primary structure is a linear sequence of α-amino acids and whose final structure results from folding of the chain into a specific three-dimensional structure; proteins serve as catalysts, structural components, and nutritional elements for the cell

proteolytic enzyme (15.9) an enzyme that hydrolyzes the peptide bonds between amino acids in a protein chain

proton (2.2) a positively charged particle in the nucleus of an atom

pure substance (2.1) a substance with constant composition

purine (19.1) a family of nitrogenous bases that are components of DNA and RNA and

consist of a six-sided ring fused to a five-sided ring; the common purines in nucleic acids are adenine and guanine

pyramidal molecule (3.4) a nonplanar structure involving three groups bonded to a central atom in which each group is equidistant from the central atom

pyridoxal phosphate (17.5) a coenzyme derived from vitamin B_6 that is required for all transamination reactions

pyrimidine (19.1) a family of nitrogenous bases that are components of nucleic acids and consist of a single six-sided ring; the common pyrimidines of DNA are cytosine and thymine; the common pyrimidines of RNA are cytosine and uracil

quantum level (2.3) a specific energy state or energy level in an atom

quantum number (2.3) an integer used to describe the orbitals of an atom

quaternary ammonium salt (14.1) an amine salt with the general formula $R_4N^+A^-$ (in which R— can be an alkyl or aryl group or a hydrogen atom and A^- can be any anion

quaternary protein structure (15.2) aggregation of more than one folded peptide chain to yield a functional protein

rad (8.7) abbreviation for *radiation absorbed dose,* the absorption of 2.4×10^{-3} calories of energy per kilogram of absorbing tissue

radioactivity (8.1) the process by which atoms emit high-energy particles or rays; the spontaneous decomposition of a nucleus to produce a different nucleus

radiocarbon dating (8.3) the estimation of the age of objects through measurement of isotopic ratios of carbon

Raoult's law (6.4) a law stating that the vapor pressure of a component is equal to its mole fraction times the vapor pressure of the pure component

rate of a reaction (5.3) the change in concentration of a reactant or product per unit time

reactant (2.1, 4.4) starting material for a chemical reaction, appearing on the left side of a chemical equation

reducing agent (7.6) a substance that reduces, or donates electrons to, another substance; the reducing agent is itself oxidized in the process

reducing sugar (11.2) a sugar that can be oxidized by Benedict's or Tollens' reagents; includes all monosaccharides and most disaccharides

reduction (7.6) the gain of electrons, gain of hydrogen, or loss of oxygen

regulatory proteins (15.1) proteins that control cell functions such as metabolism and reproduction

relaxation (2.3) an electron transition from a higher to a lower energy level, accompanied by a release of energy

release factor (19.6) a protein that binds to the termination codon in the empty A-site of the ribosome and causes the peptidyl transferase to hydrolyze the bond between the peptide and the peptidyl tRNA

rem (8.7) abbreviation for *roentgen equivalent for man,* the product of rads and RBE

replication fork (19.3) the point at which new nucleotides are added to the growing daughter DNA strand

replication origin (19.3) the region of a DNA molecule where DNA replication always begins

representative elements (2.5) those members of the groups of the periodic table designated as "A"

restriction enzymes (19.8) bacterial enzymes that recognize specific nucleotide sequences on a DNA molecule and cut the sugar-phosphate backbone of the DNA at or near that site

results (1.3) the outcome of a designed experiment, often calculated from individual bits of data

reversible reaction (5.4) a reaction that will proceed in either direction, reactants to products or products to reactants

riboflavin (15.6) vitamin B_2, a vitamin required by the energy-releasing reactions of the cell; a component of the coenzyme flavin adenine dinucleotide

ribonucleic acid (RNA) (19.1) single-stranded nucleic acid molecules that are composed of phosphoryl groups, ribose, and the nitrogenous bases uracil, cytosine, adenine, and guanine

ribonucleotide (19.1) a ribonucleoside phosphate or nucleotide composed of a nitrogenous base in β-N-glycosidic linkage to the $1'$ carbon of the sugar ribose and with one, two, or three phosphoryl groups esterified at the hydroxyl of the $5'$ carbon of the ribose

ribose (11.2) a five-carbon monosaccharide that is a component of RNA and many coenzymes

ribosomal RNA (rRNA) (19.4) the RNA species that are structural and functional components of the small and large ribosomal subunits

ribosome (19.6) an organelle composed of a large and a small subunit, each of which is made up of ribosomal RNA and proteins; the platform on which translation occurs and that carries the enzymatic activity that forms peptide bonds

RNA polymerase (19.4) the enzyme that catalyzes the synthesis of RNA molecules using DNA as the template

roentgen (8.7) the dose of radiation producing 2.1×10^9 ions in 1 cm^3 of air at 0°C and 1 atmosphere of pressure

saccharide (11.1) a sugar molecule

saponification (12.2, 13.2) a reaction in which a soap is produced; more generally, the hydrolysis of an ester by an aqueous base

saturated fatty acid (13.2) a long-chain monocarboxylic acid in which each carbon of the chain is bonded to the maximum number of hydrogen atoms

saturated hydrocarbon (9.1) an alkane; a hydrocarbon that contains only carbon and hydrogen bonded together through carbon-hydrogen and carbon-carbon single bonds

saturated solution (6.1) one in which undissolved solute is in equilibrium with the solution

scientific method (1.2) the process of studying our surroundings that is based on experimentation

scientific notation (1.6) a system used to represent numbers as powers of 10

secondary (2°) alcohol (10.1) an alcohol with the general formula R_2CHOH

secondary (2°) amine (14.1) an amine with the general formula R_2NH

secondary protein structure (15.2) folding of the primary structure of a protein into an α-helix or a β-pleated sheet; folding is maintained by hydrogen bonds between the amide hydrogen and the carbonyl oxygen of the peptide bond

semiconservative DNA replication (19.3) DNA polymerase ''reads'' each parental strand of DNA and produces a complementary daughter strand; thus, all newly synthesized DNA molecules consist of one parental and one daughter strand

semipermeable membrane (6.4) a membrane permeable to the solvent but not the solute; a material that allows the transport of certain substances from one side of the membrane to the other

shielding (8.5) material used to provide protection from radiation

significant figures (1.6) all digits in a number known with certainty and the first uncertain digit

silent mutation (19.7) a mutation that changes the sequence of the DNA but does not alter the amino acid sequence of the protein encoded by the DNA

single bond (3.4) a bond in which one pair of electrons is shared by two atoms

single-replacement reaction (7.1) also called substitution reaction, one in which one atom in a molecule is displaced by another

soap (12.1) any of a variety of the alkali metal salts of fatty acids

solid state (2.1) a physical state of matter characterized by its rigidity and fixed volume and shape

solubility (3.5, 6.1) the amount of a substance that will dissolve in a given volume of solvent at a specified temperature

solute (6.1) a component of a solution that is present in lesser quantity than the solvent

solution (6.1) a homogeneous (uniform) mixture of two or more substances

solvent (6.1) the solution component that is present in the largest quantity

specific gravity (1.7) the ratio of the density of a substance to the density of water at 4°C

specific heat of water (5.2) the quantity of heat (calories) required to raise the temperature of 1 gram of water 1 degree Celsius

sphingolipid (13.4) a phospholipid that is derived from the amino alcohol sphingosine rather than from glycerol

sphingomyelin (13.4) a sphingolipid found in abundance in the myelin sheath that surrounds and insulates cells of the central nervous system

standard solution (7.4) a solution whose concentration is accurately known

standard temperature and pressure (STP) (5.6) defined as 273 K and 1 atmosphere

states of matter (2.1) the three different forms in which matter can exist (solid, liquid, and gas)

stereochemical specificity (15.6) the property of an enzyme that allows it to catalyze reactions involving only one stereoisomer of the substrate

stereochemistry (11.2) the study of the spatial arrangement of atoms in a molecule

stereoisomers (11.2) a pair of molecules having the same structural formulas and bonding patterns but differing in the arrangement of the atoms in space

steroid (13.4) a lipid derived from cholesterol and composed of one five-sided ring and three six-sided rings; the steroids include sex hormones and anti-inflammatory compounds

structural analog (15.7) a chemical having a structure and charge distribution very similar to those of a natural enzyme substrate

structural formula (9.2) a formula showing all of the atoms in a molecule and exhibiting all bonds as lines

structural isomers (9.2) two molecules having the same molecular formulas but different chemical structures

structural protein (15.1) a protein that provides mechanical support for large plants and animals

substituted hydrocarbon (9.1) a hydrocarbon in which one or more hydrogen atoms is replaced by another atom or group of atoms

substitution reaction (9.2) a reaction that results in the replacement of one group for another

substrate (15.5) the reactant in a chemical reaction that binds to an enzyme active site and is converted to product

substrate-level phosphorylation (16.3) the production of ATP by the transfer of a phosphoryl group from the substrate of a reaction to ADP

sucrose (11.3) a disaccharide composed of α-D-glucose and β-D-fructose in α,β-glycosidic linkage; table sugar

supersaturated solution (6.1) a solution that is more concentrated than a saturated solution (Note that such a solution is not at equilibrium.)

surface tension (5.7) a measure of the strength of the attractive forces at the surface of a liquid

surfactant (5.7) a substance that decreases the surface tension of a liquid

thermodynamics (5.1) the study of energy and its interconversions

technology (1.2) the conversion of matter from its current form to a more useful form

temperature (1.7) a measure of the relative ''hotness'' or ''coldness'' of an object

terminal electron acceptor (17.4) the final electron acceptor in an electron transport system that removes the low-energy electrons from the system; in aerobic organisms the terminal electron acceptor is molecular oxygen

termination codon (19.6) a triplet of ribonucleotides with no corresponding anticodon on a tRNA; as a result, translation will end, since there is no amino acid to transfer to the peptide chain

terpene (13.4) the general term for lipids that are synthesized from isoprene units; the terpenes include steroids, bile salts, lipid-soluble vitamins, and chlorophyll

tertiary (3°) alcohol (10.1) an alcohol with the general formula R_3COH

tertiary (3°) amine (14.1) an amine with the general formula R_3N

tertiary protein structure (15.2) the globular, three-dimensional structure of a protein that results from folding the regions of secondary structure; this folding occurs spontaneously as a result of interactions of the side chains or R groups of the amino acids

tetrahedral molecule (3.4) a molecule consisting of four groups, attached to a central atom, that occupy the four corners of an imagined tetrahedron

tetrose (11.2) a four-carbon monosaccharide

theory (1.2) a hypothesis developed to explain observed behavior of matter that has been verified by using the scientific method

thermodynamics (5.1) the branch of science that deals with the relationship between energies of systems, work, and heat

thioester (12.3) the product of a reaction between a thiol and a carboxylic acid

thiol (10.4) an organic compound that contains a thiol group (—SH)

thymine dimers (19.7) ultraviolet light–induced covalent bonding of two adjacent thymine bases in a strand of DNA

titration (7.4) the process of adding a solution from a buret to a sample until a reaction is complete, at which time the volume is accurately measured and the concentration of the sample is calculated

Tollens' Test (10.5) a test reagent (silver nitrate in ammonium hydroxide) used to test for the carbonyl functional group; also called the Tollens' silver mirror test

tracer (8.4) a radioisotope that is rapidly and selectively transmitted to the part of the body for which diagnosis is desired

transaminase (17.5) aminotransferase; an enzyme that catalyzes the transfer of an amino group from one molecule to another

transamination (17.5) a reaction in which an amino group is transferred from one molecule to another

transcription (19.4) the synthesis of RNA from a DNA template

transfer RNA (tRNA) (19.4, 19.6) small RNAs that bind to a specific amino acid at the 3′ end and mediate its addition at the appropriate site in a growing peptide chain; accomplished by recognition of the correct codon on the mRNA by the complementary anticodon on the tRNA

transferase (15.5) an enzyme that catalyzes the transfer of a functional group from one molecule to another

transition element (2.5) any element located between groups IIA and IIIA in the long period of the periodic table

transition state (15.6) the unstable intermediate in catalysis in which the enzyme has altered the form of the substrate so that it now shares properties of both the substrate and the product

translation (19.4) the synthesis of a protein from the genetic code carried on the mRNA

translocation (19.6) movement of the ribosome along the mRNA during translation

transmembrane protein (13.3) a protein that is embedded within a membrane and crosses the lipid bilayer, protruding from the membrane both inside and outside the cell

transport protein (15.1) a protein that transports materials across the cell membrane or throughout the body

triglyceride (13.3, 18.1) triacylglycerol; a molecule composed of glycerol esterified to three fatty acids

triose (11.2) a three-carbon monosaccharide

triple bond (3.4) a bond in which three pairs of electrons are shared by two atoms

uncertainty (1.5) the degree of doubt in a single measurement

unit (1.3) a determinate quantity (of length, time, etc.) that has been adopted as a standard of measurement

unsaturated fatty acid (13.2) a long-chain monocarboxylic acid having at least one carbon-to-carbon double bond

unsaturated hydrocarbon (9.1) a hydrocarbon containing at least one multiple (double or triple) bond

urea cycle (17.6) a cyclic series of reactions that detoxifies ammonium ions by incorporating them into urea, which is excreted from the body

uridine triphosphate (UTP) (16.6) a nucleotide composed of the pyrimidine uracil, the sugar ribose, and three phosphoryl groups and that serves as a carrier of glucose-1-phosphate in glycogenesis

valence electrons (2.6) electrons in the outermost shell (principal quantum level) of an atom

vapor pressure of a liquid (5.7) the pressure exerted by the vapor at the surface of a liquid at equilibrium

very low density lipoprotein (VLDL) (13.5) a plasma lipoprotein that binds triglycerides synthesized by the liver and carries them to adipose tissue for storage

viscosity (5.7) a measure of the resistance to flow of a substance at constant temperature

vitamin (15.6) an organic substance that is required in the diet in small amounts; water-soluble vitamins are used in the synthesis of coenzymes required for the function of cellular enzymes; lipid-soluble vitamins are involved in calcium metabolism, vision, and blood clotting

volume/volume percent (% (V/V)) (6.2) the concentration of a solution expressed as a ratio of volume of solute to volume of solution times 10^2

wax (13.4) a collection of lipids that are generally considered to be esters of long-chain alcohols

weight (1.7) the force exerted on an object by gravity

weight/volume percent (% (W/V)) (6.2) the concentration of a solution expressed as a ratio of grams of solute to milliliters of solution times 10^2

weight/weight percent (% (W/W)) (6.2) the concentration of a solution expressed as a ratio of mass of solute to mass of solution times 10^2

Answers to End-of-Chapter Vocabulary Quizzes

Chapter 1

1.1 accuracy
1.2 chemistry
1.3 data
1.4 hypothesis
1.5 law
1.6 potential energy
1.7 precision
1.8 specific gravity
1.9 theory
1.10 weight

Chapter 2

2.1 alkali metals
2.2 cation
2.3 chemical
2.4 electron
2.5 element
2.6 gaseous
2.7 homogeneous mixture (or solution)
2.8 isotopes
2.9 neutron
2.10 proton

Chapter 3

3.1 orbital
3.2 crystal
3.3 electrolyte
3.4 intermolecular forces
3.5 Lewis symbol
3.6 lone pair
3.7 polar covalent
3.8 polyatomic ion
3.9 tetrahedral
3.10 triple bond

Chapter 4

4.1 Avogadro's number
4.2 chemical equation
4.3 formula
4.4 the formula unit
4.5 the formula weight
4.6 law of conservation of mass
4.7 mole
4.8 molecular weight
4.9 products
4.10 reactants

Chapter 5

5.1 activation energy
5.2 amorphous
5.3 barometer
5.4 calorimeter
5.5 catalyst
5.6 condensation
5.7 endothermic
5.8 entropy
5.9 evaporation
5.10 ideal

Chapter 6

6.1 crenation
6.2 electrolyte
6.3 hypertonic solution
6.4 hypotonic solution
6.5 molarity
6.6 osmosis
6.7 osmotic pressure
6.8 saturated solution
6.9 solute
6.10 supersaturated solution

Chapter 7

7.1 Brönsted-Lowry
7.2 autoionization (or self-ionization)
7.3 buffer (or buffer solution)
7.4 decomposition
7.5 combination
7.6 oxidation
7.7 oxidizing agent
7.8 pH
7.9 standard
7.10 titration

Chapter 8

8.1 alpha particle
8.2 beta particle
8.3 binding energy

8.4 Einstein's equation ($E = mc^2$)
8.5 fusion
8.6 gamma radiation
8.7 half-life
8.8 ionizing radiation
8.9 lethal dose (LD_{50})
8.10 tracer

Chapter 9

9.1 alkane
9.2 isomers
9.3 geometric isomers
9.4 alkyl group
9.5 parent compound
9.6 unsaturated hydrocarbon
9.7 alkene
9.8 hydrocarbon
9.9 functional group
9.10 substitution reaction

Chapter 10

10.1 alcohols
10.2 thiols
10.3 dehydration
10.4 carbonyl group
10.5 Benedict's test
10.6 hemiacetal
10.7 ketal
10.8 hydrogen (H_2)
10.9 oxidation
10.10 tertiary

Chapter 11

11.1 galactosemia
11.2 Fischer projection
11.3 chiral, asymmetric
11.4 enantiomers
11.5 glycogen
11.6 hyperglycemia
11.7 Haworth projection
11.8 reducing sugar
11.9 stereochemistry
11.10 aldopentose

Chapter 12

12.1 ATP
12.2 hydrolysis
12.3 saponification
12.4 fatty acids
12.5 oxidation
12.6 thioester
12.7 acyl group
12.8 carboxyl group
12.9 phosphoester
12.10 soap

Chapter 13

13.1 cholesterol
13.2 fluid mosaic model
13.3 phospholipids
13.4 triglyceride (triacylglycerol)

13.5 fatty acid
13.6 sphingomyelin
13.7 chylomicron
13.8 essential fatty acid
13.9 low-density lipoprotein
13.10 emulsifying agent

Chapter 14

14.1 peptide bond
14.2 primary amine
14.3 amide
14.4 tertiary amine
14.5 heterocyclic amine
14.6 analgesic
14.7 alkaloids
14.8 alkylammonium ion
14.9 quaternary ammonium salt
14.10 amine

Chapter 15

15.1 active site
15.2 prosthetic group
15.3 induced fit model
15.4 denaturation
15.5 tertiary structure
15.6 peptide bond
15.7 transferase
15.8 apoenzyme
15.9 β-pleated sheet
15.10 niacin

Chapter 16

16.1 ATP
16.2 glycolysis
16.3 gluconeogenesis
16.4 substrate-level phosphorylation
16.5 coenzyme A
16.6 hyperglycemia
16.7 catabolism
16.8 glycogen
16.9 NAD^+ (nicotine adenine dinucleotide)
16.10 acetyl CoA

Chapter 17

17.1 aminotransferase (transaminase)
17.2 amphibolic pathways
17.3 oxidative phosphorylation
17.4 electron transport system
17.5 mitochondria
17.6 terminal electron acceptor
17.7 ATP synthase (F_0F_1 complex)
17.8 matrix space
17.9 urea cycle
17.10 citric acid cycle

Chapter 18

18.1 adipose tissue
18.2 triglyceride (triacylglycerol)
18.3 bile
18.4 chylomicron
18.5 β-oxidation

18.6 coenzyme A
18.7 glucagon
18.8 insulin
18.9 lipase
18.10 ketone bodies

Chapter 19

19.1 nucleotide
19.2 double helix

19.3 central dogma of molecular biology
19.4 messenger RNA
19.5 translation
19.6 ribosome
19.7 mutation
19.8 RNA polymerase
19.9 restriction enzyme
19.10 silent mutation

Chapter 1

1.1 **a.** 1×10^3 mL
b. 1×10^6 μL
c. 1×10^{-3} kL
d. 1×10^2 cL
e. 1×10^{-1} daL

1.3 **a.** 1.3×10^{-2} m
b. 0.71 L
c. 2.00 oz

1.5 **a.** Three
b. Three
c. Four
d. Two
e. Three

1.7 **a.** 2.4×10^{-3}
b. 1.80×10^{-2}
c. 2.24×10^2

1.9 **a.** 8.09
b. 5.9
c. 20.19

1.11 **a.** 51
b. 8.0×10^1
c. 1.6×10^2

1.13 **a.** 61.4
b. 6.17
c. 6.65×10^{-2}

1.15 **a.** 0°C
b. 273 K

1.17 23.7 g

1.19 **a.** the study of matter and the changes that matter undergoes
b. the material component of the universe
c. the ability to do work
d. an "educated guess" at the explanation of observed behavior of our surroundings
e. a hypothesis developed to explain behavior of matter that has been verified by using the scientific method
f. a statement of observed behavior for which no exceptions have been found

1.21 **a.** gram
b. liter
c. meter

1.23 Weight is the force exerted on a body by gravity; mass is a quantity of matter. Mass is an independent quantity while weight is dependent on gravity which may differ from location to location.

1.25 Density is mass per volume. Specific gravity is the ratio of the density of a substance to the density of water at 4°C.

1.27 The scientific method is an organized way of doing science. It uses carefully planned experimentation to study our surroundings.

1.29 **a.** 32 oz
b. 1.0×10^{-3} t
c. 9.1×10^2 g
d. 9.1×10^5 mg
e. 9.1×10^1 da

1.31 **a.** 6.6×10^{-3} lb
b. 1.1×10^{-1} oz
c. 3.0×10^{-3} kg
d. 3.0×10^2 cg
e. 3.0×10^3 mg

1.33 **a.** 10°C
b. 283 K

1.35 **a.** 293 K
b. 68°F

1.37 4 L

1.39 101°F

1.41 **a.** three
b. three
c. three
d. four
e. four
f. three

1.43 **a.** 3.87×10^{-3}
b. 5.20×10^{-2}
c. 2.62×10^{-3}
d. 2.43×10^{-1}
e. 2.40×10^2
f. 2.41×10^0

1.45 **a.** 1.5×10^4
b. 2.41×10^{-1}

c. 5.99
d. 1139.42
e. 7.21×10^3

1.47 **a.** 1.23×10^1
b. 5.69×10^{-2}
c. -1.527×10^3
d. 7.89×10^{-7}
e. 9.2×10^7
f. 5.280×10^{-3}
g. 1.279×10^0
h. -5.3177×10^2

1.49 **a.** 3,240
b. 0.000150
c. 0.4579
d. −683,000
e. −0.0821
f. 299,790,000
g. 1.50
h. 602,000,000,000,000,000,000,000

1.51 6.00 g/mL

1.53 1.08×10^3 g

1.55 9.8×10^{-1} g/cm^3 (teak)

1.57 0.789

1.59 $d_{lead} = 7.9$ g/cm^3
$d_{uranium} = 19$ g/cm^3
$d_{platinum} = 21.4$ g/cm^3; Lead has the lowest density and platinum has the greatest density.

Chapter 2

2.1 **a.** physical property
b. chemical property
c. physical property
d. physical property
e. physical property

2.3 **a.** pure substance
b. heterogeneous mixture
c. homogeneous mixture
d. pure substance

2.5 **a.** 16 protons; 16 electrons; 16 neutrons
b. 11 protons; 11 electrons; 12 neutrons

2.7 **a.** Zr (zirconium)
b. 22.99
c. Cr (chromium)
d. Bi (bismuth)

2.9 **a.** helium, atomic number = 2, mass = 4.00 amu
b. fluorine, atomic number = 9, mass = 19.00 amu
c. manganese, atomic number = 25, mass = 54.94 amu

2.11 **a.** total electrons = 11, valence electrons = 1
b. total electrons = 12, valence electrons = 2
c. total electrons = 16, valence electrons = 6
d. total electrons = 17, valence electrons = 7
e. total electrons = 18, valence electrons = 8

2.13 **a.** Ca^{2+} and Ar
b. Sr^{2+} and Kr
c. S^{2-} and Ar
d. Mg^{2+} and Ne
e. P^{-3} and Ar

2.15 **a.** (smallest) F, N, Be (largest)
b. (lowest) Be, N, F (highest)
c. (lowest) Be, N, F (highest)

2.17 a characteristic of a substance that can be observed without the substance undergoing a change in chemical composition

2.19 **a.** chemical change
b. physical change
c. physical change
d. chemical change
e. chemical change

2.21 flammability and toxicity

2.23 A pure substance has constant composition with only a single substance whereas a mixture is composed of two or more substances.

2.25 Mixtures are composed of two or more substances. A homogeneous mixture has uniform composition while a heterogeneous mixture has nonuniform composition.

2.27 **a.** 8 protons; 8 electrons; 8 neutrons
b. 15 protons; 15 electrons; 16 neutrons

2.29 atoms of the same element that differ in mass due to the fact that they contain different numbers of neutrons

2.31 All matter consists of tiny particles called atoms. Atoms cannot be created, divided, destroyed, or converted to any other type of atom. All atoms of a particular element have identical properties. Atoms of different elements have different properties. Atoms combine in simple whole-number ratios. Chemical change involves joining, separating, or rearranging atoms.

2.33

$^{23}_{11}Na$	11	**12**	11	0
$^{32}_{16}S^{2-}$	16	16	**18**	2−
$^{16}_{8}O$	8	8	8	0
$^{24}_{12}Mg^{2+}$	**12**	12	10	2+
$^{39}_{19}K^+$	19	20	18	**1+**

2.35 **a.** true
b. true
c. false

2.37 **a.** sodium
b. potassium
c. magnesium

2.39 Group IA; lithium, sodium, potassium, rubidium, cesium, and francium

2.41 **a.** one
b. one
c. three
d. seven
e. eight
f. two

2.43 **a.** *are* isoelectronic
b. *are* isoelectronic
c. *are not* isoelectronic
d. *are* isoelectronic

2.45 **a.** (lowest) O, N, F (highest) [NOTE exception to trend.]
b. (lowest) Cs, K, Li (highest)
c. (lowest) I, Br, Cl (highest)

2.47 **a.** (smallest) F, O, N (largest)
b. (smallest) Li, K, Cs (largest)
c. (smallest) Cl, Br, I (largest)

2.49 color, odor, taste, hardness, density, melting temperature, and boiling temperature

2.51 flammability and toxicity

2.53 loss of one or more electrons from an atom

2.55 An atom cannot be created, divided, destroyed, or converted to any other type of atom. All atoms of a particular element have identical properties.

Chapter 3

3.1 **a.** LiBr
b. $CaBr_2$
c. Ca_3N_2

3.3 **a.** potassium cyanide
b. magnesium sulfide
c. lithium acetate

3.5 **a.** $CaCO_3$
b. $NaHCO_3$

3.7 **a.** diboron trioxide
b. nitrogen oxide
c. iodine chloride
d. phosphorus trichloride

3.9 **a.** P_2O_5
b. SiO_2

3.11 **a.**
b.

3.13 **a.**
b.

3.15 **a.** The bonded nuclei are closer together when a double bond exists, in comparison to a single bond.
b. a double bond is stronger than a single bond

3.17 **a.**
b.

3.19 **a.** Oxygen is more electronegative than sulfur; the bond is polar. The electrons are pulled toward the oxygen atom.
b. Nitrogen is more electronegative than carbon; the bond is polar. The electrons are pulled toward the nitrogen atom.
c. There is no electronegativity difference between two identical atoms; the bond is nonpolar.
d. Chlorine is more electronegative than iodine; the bond is polar. The electrons are pulled toward the chlorine atom.

3.21 **a.** The molecule is nonpolar.
b. The molecule is polar.
c. The molecule is polar.
d. The molecule is nonpolar.

3.23 **a.** H_2O
b. CO
c. NH_3
d. ICl

3.25 **a.** Ionic
b. Covalent
c. Covalent
d. Covalent

3.27 **a.** $Li^+ + \left[:\ddot{Br}: \right]^-$
b. $Mg^{2+} + \left[:\ddot{Cl}: \right]^-$

3.29 **a.**
b.
c.

3.31 **a.** Sodium ion
b. Copper(I) ion
c. Magnesium ion
d. Iron(II) ion
e. Iron(III) ion

3.33 **a.** K^+
b. Br^-
c. Ca^{2+}
d. Cr^{6+}

3.35 **a.** NaCl
b. $MgBr_2$
c. CuO
d. Fe_2O_3
e. $AlCl_3$

3.37 **a.** Magnesium chloride
b. Aluminum chloride
c. Calcium sulfide
d. Sodium oxide
e. Iron(III) hydroxide

3.39 **a.** Al_2O_3
b. Li_2S
c. BH_3
d. Mg_3P_2

3.41 Ionic solid state compounds exist in regular, repeating, three-dimensional structures; the crystal lattice. The crystal lattice is made up of positive and negative ions. Solid state covalent compounds are made up of molecules which may be arranged in a regular crystalline pattern or in an irregular (amorphous) structure. The melting points of ionic solids are generally much higher than those of covalent solids.

3.43 **a.** $H\cdot$
b. $He:$
c. $\cdot\ddot{C}\cdot$
d. $\cdot\ddot{N}\cdot$

3.45 **a.** Li^+
b. Mg^{2+}
c. $\left[:\ddot{Cl}: \right]^-$
d. $\left[:\ddot{P}: \right]^{3-}$

3.47 A molecule containing no polar bonds *must* be nonpolar. A molecule containing polar bonds may be either polar or nonpolar. It depends upon the number and arrangement of the bonds.

3.49 We predict higher melting points for polar compounds when compared to nonpolar compounds.

3.51 a.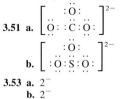

c. $\left[\begin{array}{c} H \\ H:\overset{\cdot\cdot}{N}:H \\ H \end{array}\right]^{+}$

b.

3.53 a. 2^{-}
    b. 2^{-}
    c. 3^{-}
    d. 1^{-}

Chapter 4

4.1 a. 1.51×10^{24}
    b. 3.01×10^{24}

4.3 14.0 g

4.5 a. 17.04 g/mol
    b. 180.18 g/mol
    c. 237.95 g/mol

4.7 a. $4Fe(s) + 3O_2(g) \rightarrow 2Fe_2O_3(s)$
    b. $C_6H_6(l) + 6O_2(g) \rightarrow 6CO_2(g) + 3H_2(g)$

4.9 a. 90.1 g H_2O
    b. 0.590 mol LiCl

4.11 a. 3 mol O_2
    b. 96 g O_2

4.13 a. $4Fe(s) + 3O_2(g) \rightarrow 2Fe_2O_3(s)$
    b. 3.50 g Fe

4.15 4.00g/mol

4.17 a. 5.00 mol He
    b. 1.7 mol Na
    c. 8.5×10^{-2} mol Cl

4.19 A molecule is a single unit composed of atoms joined by covalent bonds. An ion-pair is composed of positively and negatively charged ions joined by electrostatic attraction, the ionic bond.

4.21 a. 58.44 g/mol
    b. 142.04 g/mol
    c. 357.49 g/mol

4.23 a. 0.257 mol NaCl
    b. 0.106 mol Na_2SO_4

4.25 a. 18.02 g H_2O
    b. 116.9 g NaCl

4.27 a. 40.0 g He
    b. 2.02×10^2 g H_2

4.29 a. 2.43 g Mg
    b. 10.0 g $CaCO_3$
    c. 18.0 g $C_6H_{12}O_6$
    d. 5.84 g NaCl

4.31 a. 0.420 mol KBr
    b. 0.415 mol $MgSO_4$
    c. 0.313 mol Br_2
    d. 0.935 mol NH_4Cl

4.33 a. 6.02×10^{22} molecules CO_2
    b. 6.32×10^{22} molecules $C_6H_{12}O_6$

4.35 the law of conservation of mass

4.37 a. $N_2(g) + 3H_2(g) \rightarrow 2NH_3(g)$
    b. $HCl(aq) + NaOH(aq) \rightarrow NaCl(aq) + H_2O(l)$

4.39 a. $C_6H_{12}O_6(s) + 6O_2(g) \rightarrow 6H_2O(l) + 6CO_2(g)$

    b. $Na_2CO_3(s) \xrightarrow{\Delta} Na_2O(s) + CO_2(g)$

4.41 50.3 g B_2O_3

4.43 104 g $CrCl_3$

4.45 a. $N_2(g) + 3H_2(g) \rightarrow 2NH_3(g)$
    b. Three moles of H_2 will react with one mole of N_2.
    c. One mole of N_2 will produce two moles of the product.
    d. 1.50 mol H_2
    e. 17.0 g NH_3

4.47 a. 149.21 g/mol
    b. 1.20×10^{24} O atoms
    c. 32.00 g O
    d. 10.7 g O

4.49 7.39 g O_2

4.51 6.14×10^4 g O_2

4.53 0.5 mole of CCl_4 represents fewer moles of carbon.

4.55 a. 8.0×10^{23} molecules $C_{12}H_{22}O_{11}$
    b. 2.15×10^{25} molecules N_2O

Chapter 5

5.1 13°C

5.3 3.0 nutritional Calories in a 1.0-g sample of candy and 2.1×10^2 nutritional Cal/candy bar

5.5 a. amount of A decreases
    b. amount of A increases
    c. amount of A decreases

5.11 a. 3.76 L
    b. 3.41 L
    c. 2.75 L

5.7 a. 0.954 atm
    b. 0.382 atm
    c. 0.730 atm

5.13 9.00 L

5.15 0.223 mol N_2

5.9 a. P_i = 38 atm
    b. P_f = 25 atm

5.17 a. An exothermic reaction is one in which energy is released during chemical change.
    b. An endothermic reaction is one in which energy is absorbed during chemical change.
    c. A calorimeter is a device for measuring heat absorbed or released during chemical change.

5.19 Enthalpy is a measure of heat energy.

5.21 $Q = 1.20 \times 10^3$ cal

5.23 a. Entropy increases.
    b. Entropy increases.

5.25 An increase in stability is equated with a decrease in energy (reaching a lower energy state). The energy of products is less than that of the reactants in an exothermic reaction; energy is given off in an exothermic reaction.

5.27 Isopropyl alcohol quickly evaporates (liquid → gas) after being applied to the skin. Conversion of a liquid to a gas requires heat energy. The heat energy is supplied by the skin. When this heat is lost, the skin temperature drops.

5.29 a. arrangement of reactants in an unstable transition state as a chemical reaction proceeds
    b. change in concentration of a reactant or product per unit time
    c. The rates of the forward and reverse reactions are equal, resulting in no net concentration change.
    d. a substance formed from reactants during chemical change

5.31 a. False
    b. False

5.33 average distance of separation of particles; strength of attractive forces; compressibility

5.35 a. Gas particles do not interact and individual gas particle volumes are assumed to be negligible.
    b. a device for measuring gas pressure
    c. a measure of a substance's resistance to flow at a specified, constant temperature
    d. a measure of the strength of attractive forces exerted between molecules at the surface of a liquid

5.37 0.700 L SO_2

5.39 12.4 L Ne

5.41 12.2 atm

5.43 a. 44.0 g/mol
    b. 42.1 g/mol

5.45 a. increases
    b. decreases
    c. decreases
    d. decreases
    e. remains the same

5.47 Gas densities are much lower than liquid densities.

5.49 Enthalpy is a measure of heat energy. Free energy includes both the enthalpy term *and* the entropy term. Free energy predicts reaction spontaneity.

Chapter 6

6.1 16.7% NaCl

6.3 7.50% KCl

6.5 5.00% ethyl alcohol

6.7 a. 2.56×10^{-2}% oxygen
    b. 17.9%
    c. 20.0%

6.9 0.125 mol HCl

6.11 To prepare the solution dilute 1.7×10^{-2} L of 12 M HCl with sufficient water to produce 1.0×10^2 mL of total solution.

6.13 1.0×10^{-2} osm

6.15 0.24 atm

6.17 a. 2.00% NaCl
b. 6.60% $C_6H_{12}O_6$

6.19 a. 5.00% ethyl alcohol
b. 10.0% ethyl alcohol

6.21 a. 21.0% NaCl
b. 3.75% NaCl

6.23 a. 2.25 g NaCl
b. 3.13 g $NaC_2H_3O_2$

6.25 a. 0.342 M NaCl
b. 0.367 M $C_6H_{12}O_6$

6.27 a. 1.46 g NaCl
b. 9.00 g $C_6H_{12}O_6$

6.29 0.146 M $C_{12}H_{22}O_{11}$

6.31 5.00×10^{-2} L

6.33 20.0 M

6.35 a solution property that depends on the concentration of solute particles rather than the identity of the particles

6.37 Salt is an ionic substance that dissociates in water to produce positive and negative ions. These ions (or particles) lower the freezing point of water. If the concentration of salt particles is large, the freezing point may be depressed below the surrounding temperature, and the ice would melt.

6.39 a. NaOH is the solute; H_2O is the solvent.
b. 40.0% NaOH

6.41 NaCl would cause the greater freezing point depression, per mole, in water.

6.43 On a weight basis, NaCl is the most efficient road salt because it produces the largest number of particles/gram.

Chapter 7

7.1 a. DR
b. SR
c. DR
d. D

7.3 a. $KCl(aq) + AgNO_3(aq) \rightarrow KNO_3(aq) + AgCl(s)$
b. $CH_3COOK(aq) + AgNO_3(aq) \rightarrow$ no reaction

7.5 A 1.0×10^{-3} M HCl solution corresponds to a pH = 3.00 (Example 7.2). A solution of hydrochloric acid with a pH = 4.00 corresponds to an HCl concentration of 1.0×10^{-4} M (Example 7.3).

7.7 A solution of sodium hydroxide producing $[OH^-] = 1.0 \times 10^{-2}$ M corresponds to a pH of 12.00.

7.9 3.16×10^{-9} M

7.11 0.1000 M NaOH

7.13 This will cause the molar concentration of H_2CO_3 to increase.

7.15 In Question 7.13, the molar concentration of H_3O^+ should increase. In Question 7.14, the molar concentration of H_3O^+ should decrease.

7.17 a. $MgCO_3(s) \xrightarrow{\Delta} MgO(s) + CO_2(g)$
b. $Zn(s) + CuSO_4(aq) \rightarrow ZnSO_4(aq) + Cu(s)$

7.19 $2NaOH(aq) + FeCl_2(aq) \rightarrow Fe(OH)_2(s) + 2NaCl(aq)$

7.21 a. $2C_2H_6(g) + 7O_2(g) \rightarrow 4CO_2(g) + 6H_2O(g)$
b. $6K_2O(s) + P_4O_{10}(l) \rightarrow 4K_3PO_4(s)$
c. $MgBr_2(aq) + H_2SO_4(aq) \rightarrow 2HBr(g) + MgSO_4(aq)$

7.23 a. $Ca(s) + F_2(g) \rightarrow CaF_2(s)$
b. $2Mg(s) + O_2(g) \rightarrow 2MgO(s)$
c. $3H_2(g) + N_2(g) \rightarrow 2NH_3(g)$

7.25 a. a substance that dissociates, producing hydrogen ions
b. a substance that behaves as a proton donor

7.27 a. 1.0×10^{-7} M
b. 1.0×10^{-11} M

7.29 a. neutral
b. basic

7.31 a. 7.00
b. 5.00

7.33 a. $[H_3O^+] = 1.0 \times 10^{-1}$ M; $[OH^-] = 1.0 \times 10^{-13}$ M
b. $[H_3O^+] = 1.0 \times 10^{-9}$ M; $[OH^-] = 1.0 \times 10^{-5}$ M

7.35 a. $[H_3O^+] = 5.0 \times 10^{-2}$ M; $[OH^-] = 2.0 \times 10^{-13}$ M
b. $[H_3O^+] = 2.0 \times 10^{-10}$ M; $[OH^-] = 5.0 \times 10^{-5}$ M

7.37 a reaction in which an acid and a base react to produce water and a salt

7.39 a. NH_3 and NH_4Cl can form a buffer solution.
b. HNO_3 and KNO_3 cannot form a buffer solution.

7.41 a. A buffer solution contains components that enable the solution to resist large changes in pH when acids or bases are added.

b. Acidosis is a medical condition characterized by higher-than-normal levels of CO_2 in the blood and lower-than-normal blood pH.

7.43 a. The equilibrium will shift to the left.
b. The equilibrium will shift to the right.

7.45 a. the loss of electrons, loss of hydrogen atoms, or gain of oxygen atoms
b. removes electrons from another substance

7.47 loses

7.49 reduced

7.51 a. acid-base or double replacement
b. oxidation-reduction or single replacement

7.53 Cl_2 + $2KI$ $\rightarrow 2KCl + I_2$
             ↑   ↑
    Substance reduced   Substance oxidized
    oxidizing agent   reducing agent

7.55 a. $[H_3O^+] = 1.0 \times 10^{-6}$ M; $[OH^-] = 1.0 \times 10^{-8}$ M
b. $[H_3O^+] = 6.3 \times 10^{-6}$ M; $[OH^-] = 1.6 \times 10^{-9}$ M
c. $[H_3O^+] = 1.6 \times 10^{-8}$ M; $[OH^-] = 6.3 \times 10^{-7}$ M

7.57 a. 1×10^2
b. 1×10^4
c. 1×10^{10}

Chapter 8

8.1 x-ray, ultraviolet, visible, infra-red, microwave, and radiowave

8.3 a. $^{85}_{37}Rb$
b. $^{226}_{88}Ra$

8.5 6.3 ng

8.7 $\frac{1}{4}$ of the original amount

8.9 Isotopes with short half-lives release their radiation rapidly. There is much more radiation per unit time observed with short half-life substances; hence, the signal is stronger and the sensitivity of the procedure is enhanced.

8.11 The rem takes into account the relative biological effect of the radiation in addition to the quantity of radiation. This provides a more meaningful estimate of potential radiation damage to human tissue.

8.13 a. the spontaneous decay of a nucleus to produce high-energy particles or rays
b. radiation from natural sources
c. particle composed of two protons and two neutrons
d. the release of alpha particles from an unstable nucleus.

8.15 a. ^4_2He
b. $^{0}_{-1}e$
c. ^1_1p
d. $^{235}_{92}U$

8.17 Alpha and beta particles are matter; gamma radiation is pure energy. Alpha particles are large and relatively slow moving. They are the least energetic and least penetrating. Gamma radiation moves at the speed of light, is highly energetic, and most penetrating.

8.19 $^{60}_{27}Co \rightarrow ^{60}_{28}Ni + ^{0}_{-1}\beta + \delta$

8.21 $^{24}_{11}Na$

8.23 Natural radioactivity is a spontaneous process; artificial radioactivity is nonspontaneous and results from a nuclear reaction that produces an unstable nucleus.

8.25 Nuclei for light atoms tend to be most stable if their neutron/proton ratio is close to 1. Nuclei with more than 84 protons tend to be unstable. Isotopes with a "magic number" of protons or neutrons (2, 8, 20, 50, 82, or 126 protons or neutrons) tend to be more stable. Isotopes with even numbers of protons or neutrons tend to be more stable.

8.27 fission

8.29 Radiocarbon dating is a process used to determine the age of objects. The ratio of the masses of the stable isotope, carbon-12, and unstable isotope, carbon-14, is measured. Using this value and the half-life of carbon-14, the age of the coffin may be calculated.

8.31 0.40 mg of iodine-131 remains after 24 days.

8.33 13 mg of iron-59 remains after 135 days.

8.35 $^{108}_{47}Ag + ^4_2\alpha \rightarrow ^{112}_{49}In$

8.37 a. used to study the heart, kidney, liver, and spleen
b. used to locate regions of reduced ventilation and presence of tumors in the lung

8.39 a. The level of radiation exposure decreases as the distance from the radioactive source increases.
   b. Wearing gloves provides a level of shielding that is very efficient for α and β radiation, but totally ineffective for δ radiation.

8.41 Background radiation is emitted by the sun as cosmic radiation, and from naturally radioactive isotopes found throughout our environment.

8.43 a measure of the damage to biological tissue caused by different forms of radiation

8.45 a. the amount of radioactive material needed to produce 3.7×10^{10} atomic disintegrations per second
   b. the amount of radioactive material needed to produce 2×10^9 ion-pairs when passing through 1 cc of air at 0°C

8.47 13 hours

8.49 The treatment of cancer using cobalt-60 is based on the fact that this isotope emits high energy gamma radiation. Gamma radiation preferentially kills cancer cells. By targeting the infected organ the spread of the disease can be controlled or eliminated.

8.51 A film badge detects gamma radiation by darkening photographic film in proportion to the amount of radiation exposure over time.

Chapter 9

9.1 a. Tetrachloromethane
   b. 2,2-Dimethylpentane
   c. 2,2-Dimethylpropane
   d. 1,2,3-Tribromopropane

9.3 a. The linear isomers of C_4H_9Br:

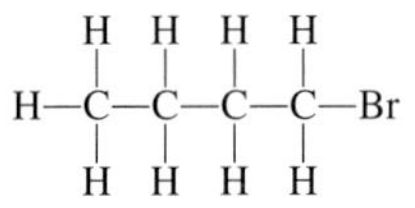

H—C—C—C—C—Br
1-Bromobutane

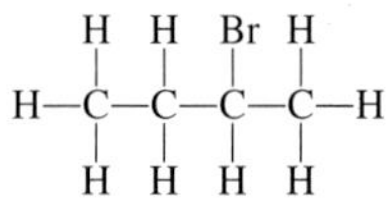

H—C—C—C—C—H
2-Bromobutane

   b. The linear isomers of $C_4H_8Br_2$:

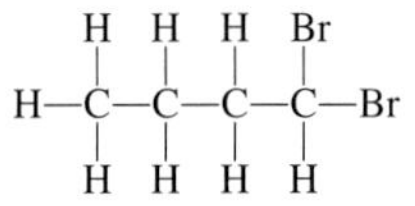

H—C—C—C—C—Br
1,1-Dibromobutane

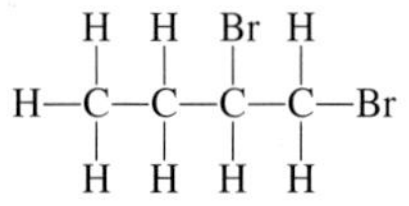

H—C—C—C—C—Br
1,2-Dibromobutane

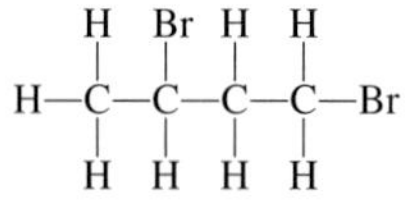

H—C—C—C—C—Br
1,3-Dibromobutane

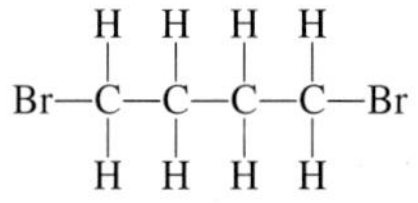

Br—C—C—C—C—Br
1,4-Dibromobutane

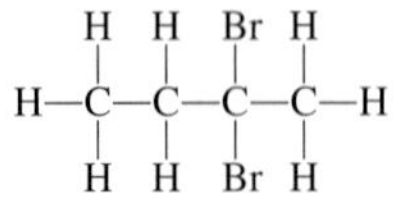

H—C—C—C—C—H
2,2-Dibromobutane

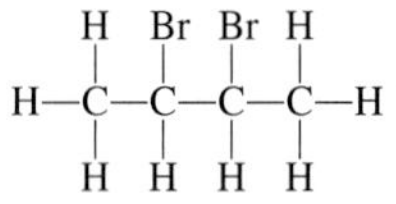

H—C—C—C—C—H
2,3-Dibromobutane

   c. The linear isomers of $C_5H_{11}I$:

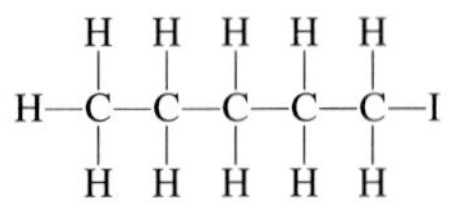

H—C—C—C—C—C—I
1-Iodopentane

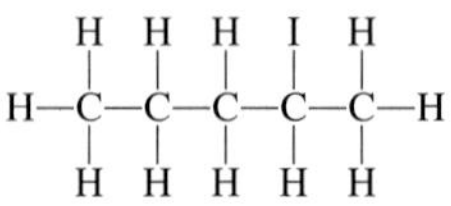

H—C—C—C—C—C—H
2-Iodopentane

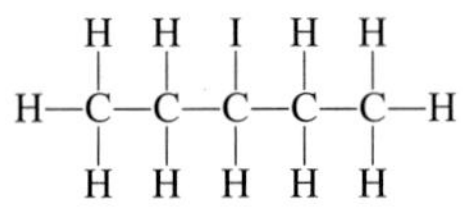

H—C—C—C—C—C—H
3-Iodopentane

9.5 a. 1-Bromo-2-ethylcyclobutane
   b. 1,2-Dimethylcyclopropane
   c. Propylcyclohexane

9.7 a. 1-Bromo-3-hexyne:

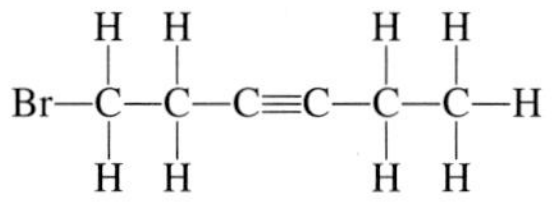

Br—C—C—C≡C—C—C—H

   b. 2-Butyne:

H—C—C≡C—C—H

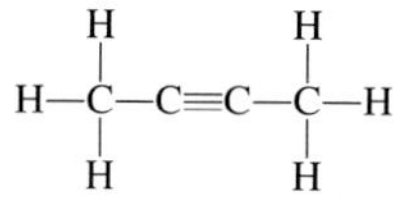

   c. Dichloroethyne:

Cl—C≡C—Cl

   d. 9-Iodo-1-nonyne:

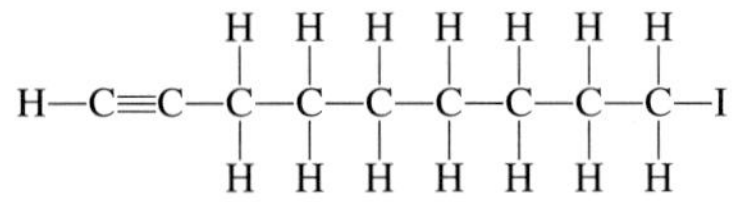

H—C≡C—C—C—C—C—C—C—C—I

9.9 a. cis-3-Octene:

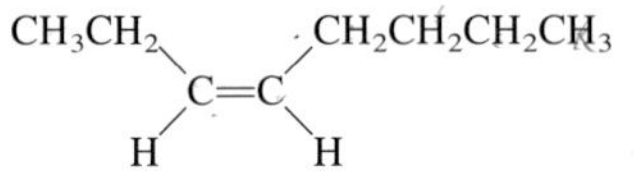

   b. trans-5-Chloro-2-hexene:

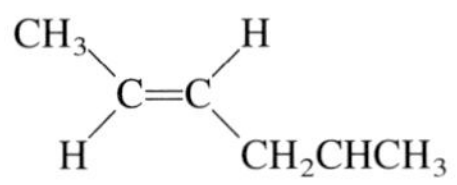

   c. trans-2,3-Dichloro-2-butene:

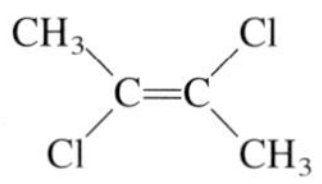

9.11 a. Reactant—cis-2-Butene; only product—Butane
   b. Reactant—1-Butene; major product—2-Butanol
   c. Reactant—2-Butene; only product—2,3-Dichlorobutane
   d. Reactant—1-Pentene; major product—2-Bromopentane

9.13 a. 1,3,5-Trichlorobenzene: **d.** para-Dinitrobenzene:

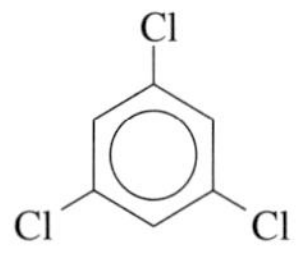

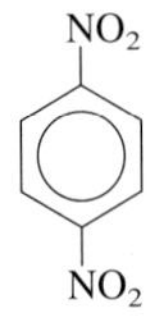

   b. ortho-Cresol: 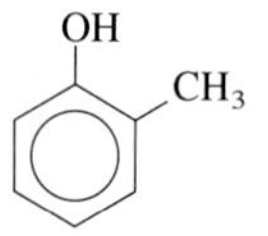   **e.** 2-Nitroaniline:

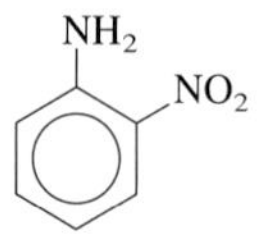

   c. 2,5-Dibromophenol: 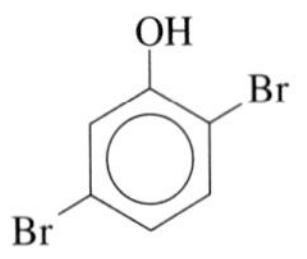   **f.** meta-Nitrotoluene

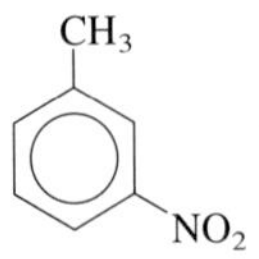

9.15 a. Water-soluble inorganic compounds are good electrolytes because they dissociate into ions in water. The ions conduct an electrical charge.
   b. Inorganic compounds exhibit ionic bonding.
   c. Organic compounds have lower melting points.
   d. Inorganic compounds are more likely to be water-soluble.
   e. Organic compounds are flammable.

9.17 a.

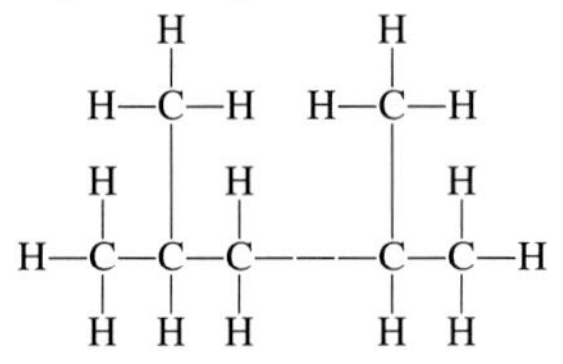

H—C—H   H—C—H

H—C—C—C————C—C—H

b.

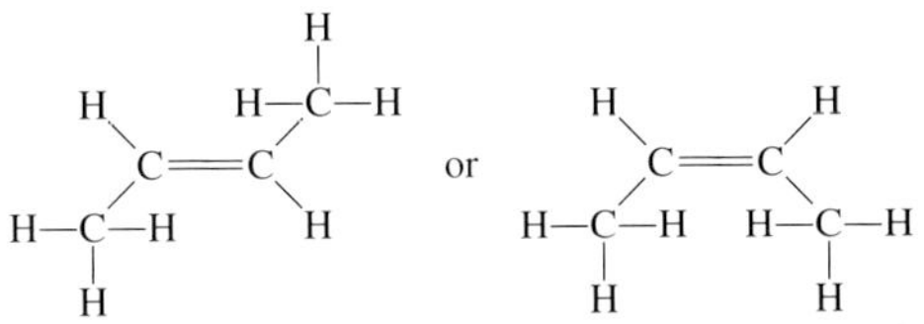

or

c.

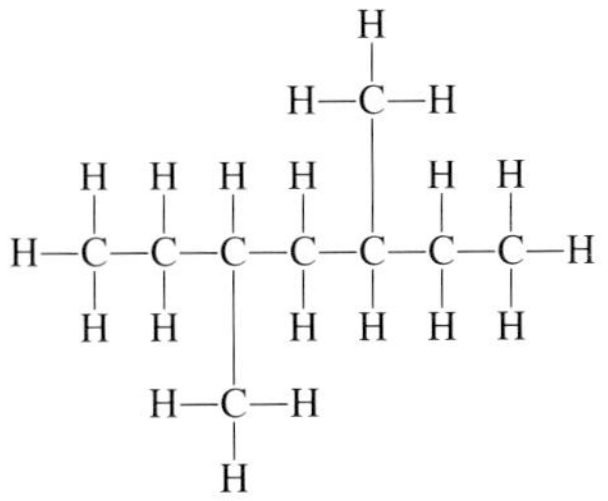

d.

or

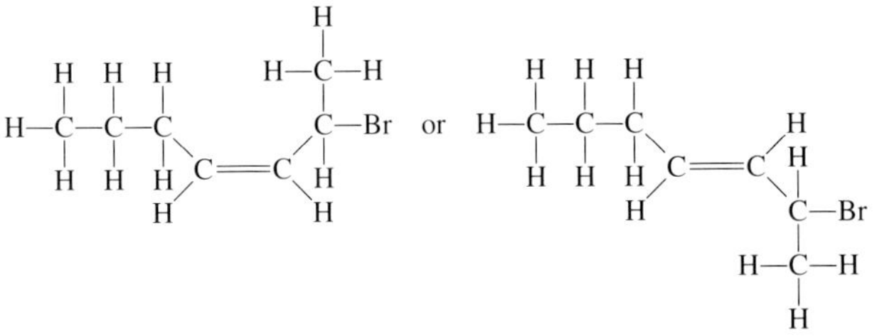

9.19 Structure b is not possible because there are five bonds to carbon-2. Structure d is not possible because there are five bonds to carbon-3. Structure e is not possible because there are five bonds to carbon-2 and carbon-3. Structure f is not possible because there are five bonds to carbon-3.

9.21 an alcohol—Ethanol

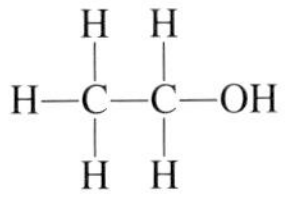

an aldehyde—Ethanal

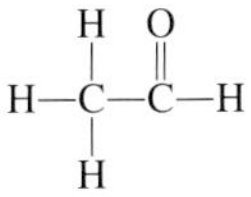

a ketone—Propanone

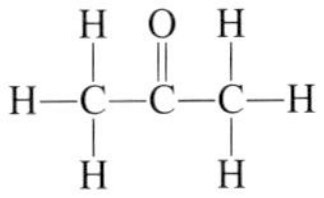

a carboxylic acid—Ethanoic acid

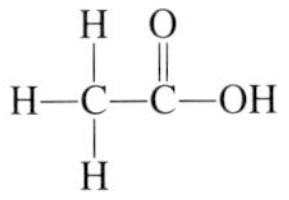

an ester—Methyl ethanoate

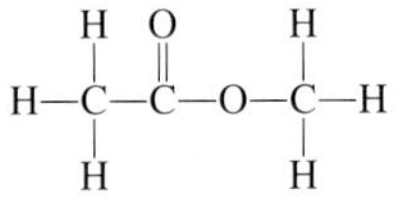

an amine—Ethanamine

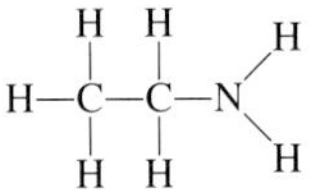

9.23 a. 2-Bromobutane:

$$CH_3CHCH_2CH_3$$

b. 2-Chloro-2-methylpropane:

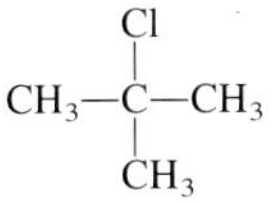

c. 2,2-Dimethylhexane:

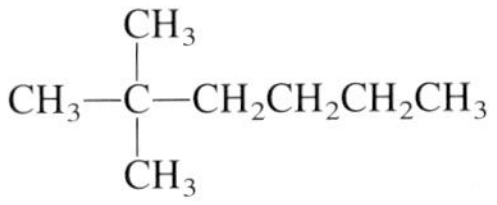

d. Dichlorodiiodomethane:

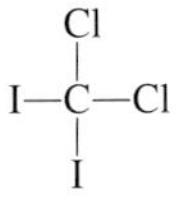

e. 1,4-Diethylcyclohexane:

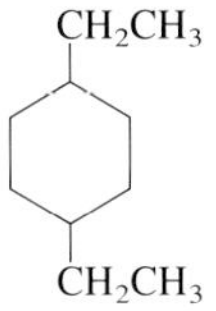

f. 2-Iodo-2,4,4-trimethylpentane:

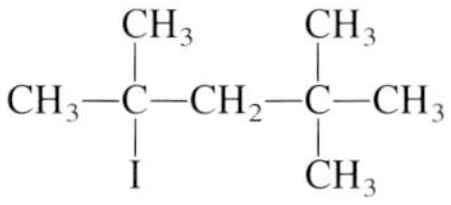

9.25 a. 3-Methylpentane
b. 1-Bromoheptane
c. 3-Ethyl-5-methylheptane
d. 2-Bromo-2-methylpropane
e. 2,5-Dimethylhexane
f. 1-Chloro-3-methylbutane
g. 1,4-Dichloropentane

9.27 a. 1,1,3-Trimethylcyclohexane
b. 1,1-Dimethylcyclopropane
c. 1,3,5,7-Tetramethylcyclooctane
d. 1,2,3,4,5-Pentachlorocyclopentane
e. Ethylcyclopentane
f. 1-Methyl-2-propylcyclobutane
g. 1,2-Dichlorocyclohexane

9.29 a. identical—both are 2-Bromobutane
b. identical—both are 3-Bromo-5-methylhexane
c. identical—both are 2,2-Dibromobutane
d. isomers of molecular formula $C_6H_{12}Br_2$: 1,3-Dibromo-3-methylpentane and 1,4-Dibromo-2-ethylbutane
e. identical—both are Methylcyclopentane
f. isomers of molecular formula $C_6H_{10}Br_2$: 1,3-Dibromocyclohexane and 1,4-Dibromocyclohexane

9.31 a. $8CO_2 + 10H_2O$

b.

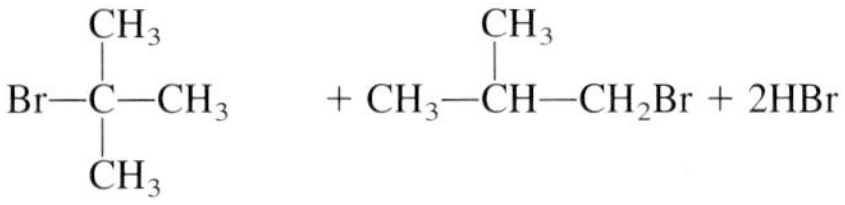

2-Bromo-2-methylpropane + 1-Bromo-2-methylpropane

c. Cl_2 + light

9.33 The following molecules are all isomers of C_6H_{14}:

$$CH_3CH_2CH_2CH_2CH_2CH_3$$
Hexane

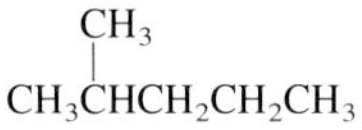

2-Methylpentane

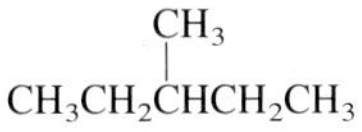

3-Methylpentane

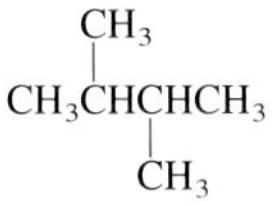

2,3-Dimethylbutane

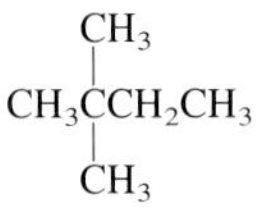

2,2-Dimethylbutane

a. 2,3-Dimethylpentane produces only two monobrominated derivatives: 1-Bromo-2,3-dimethylpentane and 2-Bromo-2,3-dimethylpentane
b. Hexane produces three monobrominated products: 1-Bromohexane, 2-Bromohexane, and 3-Bromohexane. 2,2-Dimethylbutane also produces three monobrominated products, 1-Bromo-2,2-dimethylbutane, 2-Bromo-3,3-dimethylbutane, and 1-Bromo-3,3-dimethylbutane.
c. 3-Methylpentane produces four monobrominated products: 1-Bromo-3-methylpentane, 2-Bromo-3-methylpentane, 3-Bromo-3-methylpentane, and 1-Bromo-2-ethylbutane.

9.35 a. 2-Methyl-2-hexene:

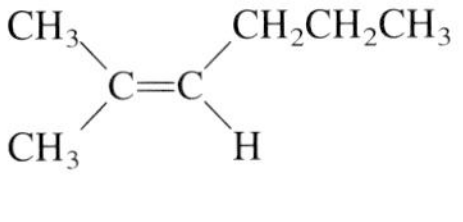

b. *trans*-3-Heptene:

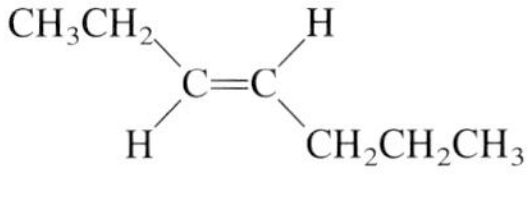

c. *cis*-1-Chloro-2-pentene:

$$\begin{array}{c}
Cl \\
| \\
CH_2 \qquad CH_2CH_3 \\
\backslash \qquad / \\
C=C \\
/ \qquad \backslash \\
H \qquad H
\end{array}$$

d. *cis*-2-Chloro-2-methyl-3-heptene:

$$\begin{array}{c}
CH_3 \\
| \\
CH_3C \qquad CH_2CH_2CH_3 \\
\backslash \qquad / \\
C=C \\
/ \qquad \backslash \\
Cl \qquad H \\
H
\end{array}$$

e. *trans*-5-Bromo-2,6-dimethyl-3-octene:

$$\begin{array}{c}
CH_3 \\
| \\
CH_3-C \qquad H \\
| \qquad \backslash \qquad / \\
H \quad C=C \\
| \qquad \backslash \\
H \qquad CH-CHCH_2CH_3 \\
| \qquad | \\
Br \quad CH_3
\end{array}$$

9.37 Addition of bromine (Br_2) to an alkene results in a color change from red to colorless. If equimolar quantities of Br_2 are added to hexene, the reaction mixture will change from red to colorless. This color change will not occur if cyclohexane is used.

9.39 a. H_2
    b. H_2O
    c. HBr
    d. $19O_2 \rightarrow 12CO_2 + 14H_2O$
    e. Cl_2
    f.

9.41 An addition reaction involves addition of a molecule to a double or triple bond in an unsaturated molecule. In a substitution reaction one chemical group replaces another.

9.43 a. 3-Methyl-1-pentene
    b. 7-Bromo-1-heptene
    c. 5-Bromo-3-heptene
    d. 1-*t*-Butyl-4-methylcyclohexene
    e. 2,5-Dimethyl-2-hexene
    f. 4-Chloro-3-methyl-1-butyne
    g. 6-Chloro-1-heptyne
    h. 1-Bromo-2-chlorocyclopentane

9.45 a. 2.4-Dibromotoluene:

c. Isopropylbenzene:

$$CH_3CHCH_3$$

b. 1,2,4-Triethylbenzene:

d. 2-Bromo-5-chlorotoluene:

9.47 a. C_nH_{2n+2}
    b. C_nH_{2n-2}
    c. C_nH_{2n}
    d. C_nH_{2n}
    e. C_nH_{2n-2}

9.49 Alkanes have only carbon-to-carbon single bonds, as in the molecule ethane:

$$\begin{array}{c}
H \quad H \\
| \quad | \\
H-C-C-H \\
| \quad | \\
H \quad H
\end{array}$$

Alkenes have at least one carbon-to-carbon double bond, as in the molecule ethene:

$$\begin{array}{c}
H \qquad H \\
\backslash \quad / \\
C=C \\
/ \quad \backslash \\
H \qquad H
\end{array}$$

Alkynes have at least one carbon-to-carbon triple bond, as in the molecule ethyne:

$$H-C\equiv C-H$$

9.51 a. a ketone:
$$\begin{array}{c} O \\ \| \\ CH_3-C-CH_3 \end{array}$$

b. an aldehyde:
$$\begin{array}{c} O \\ \| \\ CH_3CH_2-C-H \end{array}$$

c. a carboxylic acid:
$$\begin{array}{c} O \\ \| \\ CH_3CH_2-C-OH \end{array}$$

d. an amide:
$$\begin{array}{c} O \\ \| \\ CH_3CH_2-C-NH_2 \end{array}$$

e. an amine: $CH_3CH_2CH_2-NH_2$

f. an alcohol: $CH_3CH_2CH_2-OH$

g. an ester:
$$\begin{array}{c} O \\ \| \\ CH_3CH_2-C-O-CH_2CH_3 \end{array}$$

h. an ether: $CH_3CH_2-O-CH_2CH_3$

9.53 a. $CH_2=CHCH_2CH_2CH_3$ 1-Pentene
    b. $CH_3CH=CHCH_2CH_3$ 2-Pentene
    c. $CH_3C=CHCH_3$ 2-Methyl-2-butene
$$\qquad\qquad | \atop CH_3$$

9.55 a. 1,3,5-Trifluoropentane:

$$\begin{array}{c}
F \quad H \quad F \quad H \quad F \\
| \quad | \quad | \quad | \quad | \\
H-C-C-C-C-C-H \\
| \quad | \quad | \quad | \quad | \\
H \quad H \quad H \quad H \quad H
\end{array}$$

b. *cis*-2-Octene:

$$\begin{array}{c}
CH_3 \qquad CH_2CH_2CH_2CH_2CH_3 \\
\backslash \qquad / \\
C=C \\
/ \qquad \backslash \\
H \qquad H
\end{array}$$

c. Dipropylacetylene: $CH_3CH_2CH_2-C\equiv C-CH_2CH_2CH_3$

d. 3,3,5-Trimethyl-1-hexene:

$$\begin{array}{c}
CH_3 \quad CH_3 \\
| \\
H \qquad CCH_2CHCH_3 \\
\backslash \qquad / \\
C=C \qquad CH_3 \\
/ \qquad \backslash \\
H \qquad H
\end{array}$$

e. 1-Bromo-3-chloro-1-heptyne:
$$\begin{array}{c}
Cl \\
| \\
Br-C\equiv C-CHCH_2CH_2CH_2CH_3
\end{array}$$

Chapter 10

10.1 a. 4-Methyl-1-pentanol
    b. 4-Methyl-2-hexanol
    c. 1,2,3-Propanetriol
    d. 4-Chloro-3-methyl-1-hexanol

10.3 a. Primary alcohol
    b. Secondary alcohol
    c. Tertiary alcohol
    d. Aromatic alcohol (phenol)
    e. Secondary alcohol

10.5 a. Ethanol
    b. 2-Propanol is the major product. 1-Propanol is the minor product.
    c. 2-Butanol is the major product. 1-Butanol is the minor product.
    d. 2-Butanol
    e. 2-Methyl-2-propanol is the major product. 2-Methyl-1-propanol is the minor product.

10.7 a. 3-Iodo-2-butanone
    b. 3-Methyl-2-butanone
    c. 2-Fluoro-3-pentanone
    d. 3-Methylheptanal
    e. 2-Methylpropanal

10.9 a. Reduction
    b. Reduction
    c. Reduction
    d. Oxidation
    e. Reduction

10.11 a < d < b < c

10.13 a. CH_3CH_2OH
b. CH_2OHCH_2OH
c. $CH_3CH_2CH_2CH_2OH$
d. CH_3CHCH_3
       $\quad\ |$
       $\quad OH$

10.15 a. 1-Heptanol
b. 2-Propanol
c. 2,2-Dimethylpropanol
d. 4-Bromo-1-hexanol
e. 3,3-Dimethyl-2-hexanol
f. 3-Ethyl-3-heptanol

10.17 Denatured alcohol is 100% ethanol to which benzene or methanol is added. The additive makes the ethanol unfit to drink and prevents illegal use of pure ethanol.

10.19 a. Primary alcohol
b. Secondary alcohol
c. Tertiary alcohol
d. Tertiary alcohol
e. Tertiary alcohol

10.21 a. 2-Pentanol is the major product and 1-pentanol is the minor product.
b. 2-Pentanol and 3-pentanol
c. 3-Methyl-2-butanol is the major product and 3-methyl-1-butanol is the minor product.
d. 3,3-Dimethyl-2-butanol is the major product and 3,3-dimethyl-1-butanol is the minor product.

10.23 a. 2-Butanone
b. N.R.
c. Cyclohexanone
d. N.R.

10.25 a. 3-Pentanone
b. Propanal (upon further oxidation, propanoic acid would be formed.)
c. 4-Methyl-2-pentanone
d. N.R.
e. 3-Phenylpropanal

10.27 Picric acid:

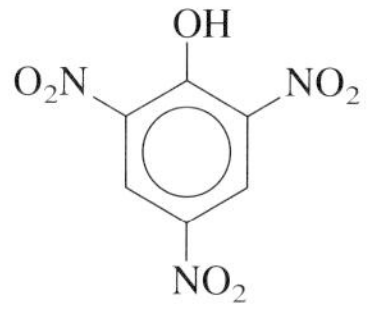

2,4,6-Trinitrotoluene:

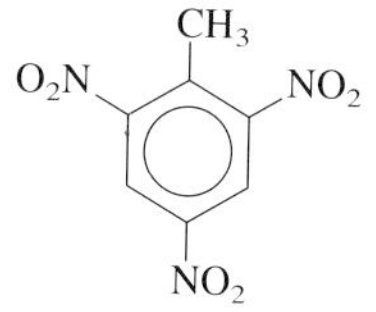

Picric acid is water-soluble because of the polar hydroxyl group that can form hydrogen bonds with water.

10.29 Hexachlorophene, hexylresorcinol, and o-phenylphenol are phenol compounds used as antiseptics or disinfectants.

10.31 Alcohols of molecular formula $C_4H_{10}O$:

$CH_3CH_2CH_2CH_2OH \qquad CH_3\overset{\displaystyle OH}{\underset{\displaystyle |}{C}}HCH_2CH_3$

$CH_3\overset{\ }{\underset{\displaystyle |}{C}}HCH_2OH \qquad CH_3-\overset{\displaystyle OH}{\underset{\displaystyle |}{C}}-CH_3$
$\quad\ \ |\ \qquad\qquad\qquad\quad |$
$\quad\ CH_3 \qquad\qquad\qquad\quad CH_3$

Ethers of molecular formula $C_4H_{10}O$:

$CH_3-O-CH_2CH_2CH_3 \qquad CH_3CH_2-O-CH_2CH_3$

$CH_3-O-\underset{\displaystyle |}{C}HCH_3$
$\qquad\qquad\quad CH_3$

10.33 Penthrane: 2,2-dichloro-1,1-difluoro-1-methoxyethane
Enthrane: 2-chloro-1-(difluoromethoxy)-1,1,2-trifluoroethane

10.35 a. Methanal:

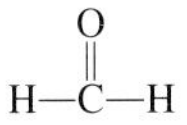

b. 7,8-Dibromooctanal:

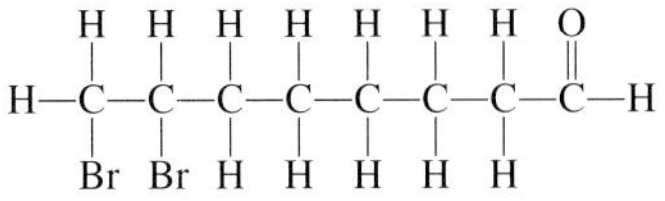

c. Acetone:

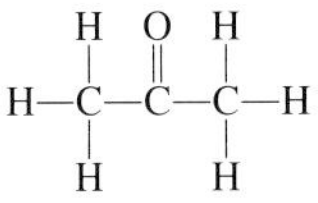

d. Hydroxyethanal:

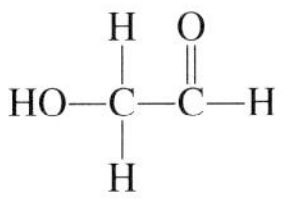

e. 3-Chloro-2-pentanone:

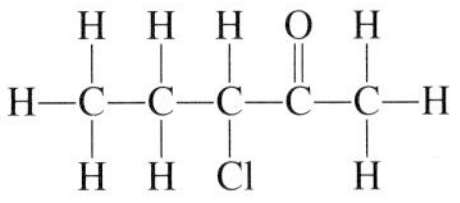

f. Benzaldehyde:

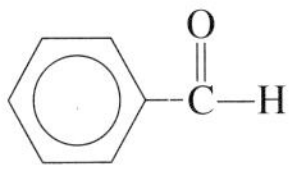

g. 4-Bromo-3-hexanone:

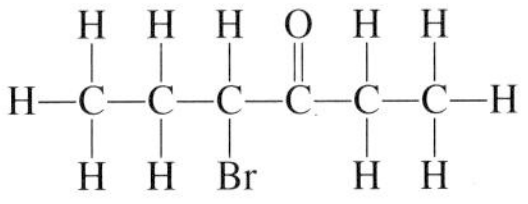

10.37 Cystine:

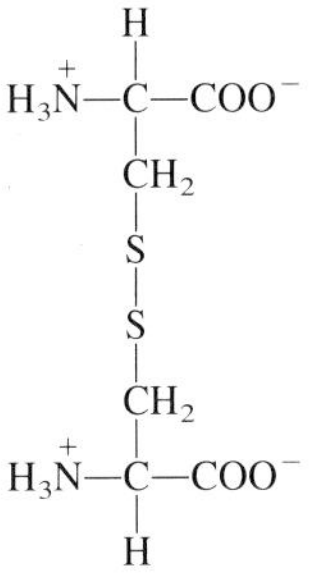

10.39 a.

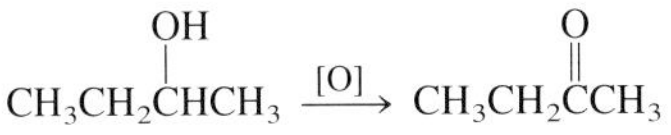

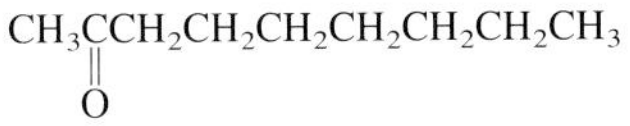

b.

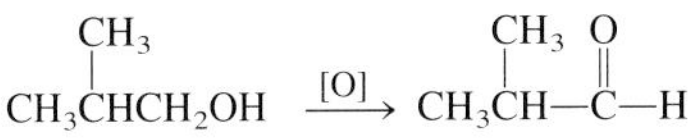

c.

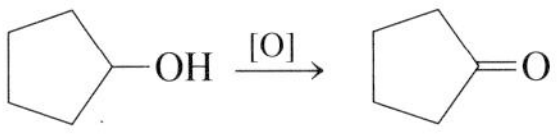

d.

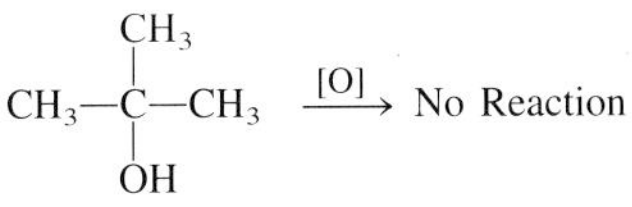

e.

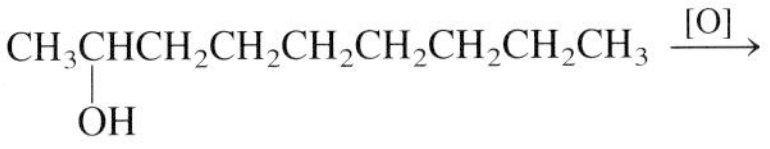

f. $CH_2CH_2CH_2CH_2CH_2CH_2CH_2CH_2CH_2CH_3$
          |
          OH

1-Decanol

↓ [O]

$H-CCH_2CH_2CH_2CH_2CH_2CH_2CH_2CH_2CH_3$
      ‖
      O

Decanal

10.41 a. Reduction reaction

$CH_3-\overset{\overset{\displaystyle O}{\|}}{C}-H \rightarrow CH_3CH_2OH$

Ethanal   Ethanol

b. Reduction reaction

⬡=O → ⬡—OH

Cyclohexanone   Cyclohexanol

c. Oxidation reaction

$\overset{\overset{\displaystyle OH}{|}}{CH_3CHCH_3} \rightarrow CH_3-\overset{\overset{\displaystyle O}{\|}}{C}-CH_3$

2-Propanol   Propanone

10.43 Acetaldehyde and 3-methylbutanal would give a positive Tollens' test.

10.45 a. $CH_3-\overset{\overset{\displaystyle O}{\|}}{C}-CH_3 + CH_3CH_2OH \rightarrow CH_3-\overset{\overset{\displaystyle OH}{|}}{\underset{\underset{\displaystyle OCH_2CH_3}{|}}{C}}-CH_3$

b. $CH_3CH_2-\overset{\overset{\displaystyle O}{\|}}{C}-H + CH_3CH_2OH \rightarrow CH_3CH_2-\overset{\overset{\displaystyle OH}{|}}{\underset{\underset{\displaystyle OCH_2CH_3}{|}}{C}}-H$

c. $CH_3-\overset{\overset{\displaystyle O}{\|}}{C}-H + CH_3CH_2OH \rightarrow CH_3-\overset{\overset{\displaystyle OH}{|}}{\underset{\underset{\displaystyle OCH_2CH_3}{|}}{C}}-H$

d. $CH_3-\overset{\overset{\displaystyle O}{\|}}{C}-CH_2CH_2CH_3 + CH_3CH_2OH \rightarrow CH_3-\overset{\overset{\displaystyle OH}{|}}{\underset{\underset{\displaystyle OCH_2CH_3}{|}}{C}}-CH_2CH_2CH_3$

10.47 An acetal is formed when two molecules of alcohol react with an aldehyde. A ketal is formed when two molecules of an alcohol react with a ketone.

10.49 $CH_3CH_2CH=CH_2 + H_2O \xrightarrow{H^+} CH_3CH_2\overset{\overset{\displaystyle OH}{|}}{C}HCH_3$

1-Butene   2-Butanol

This is a hydration reaction.

10.51 a. Methanal
  b. Propanal
  c. 3-Pentanone
  d. No reaction can occur because 2-methyl-2-butanol is a tertiary alcohol

10.53 a. F **b.** T **c.** F **d.** F

10.55 $CH_3CH_2OH \xrightarrow{liver\ enzymes} CH_3CH_2-\overset{\overset{\displaystyle O}{\|}}{C}-H$

Ethanol   Ethanal

The product, ethanal, is responsible for the symptoms of a hangover.

Chapter 11

11.1 It is currently recommended that 58% of the calories in the diet should be carbohydrates. Of that amount, no more than 10% should be simple sugars.

11.3 An aldose is a sugar with an aldehyde functional group. A ketose is a sugar with a ketone functional group.

11.5 a. ketose
  b. aldose
  c. ketose
  d. aldose
  e. ketose
  f. aldose

11.7

D-Galactose   β-D-Galactose   α-D-Galactose

11.9 α-Amylase and β-amylase are digestive enzymes that break down the starch amylose. α-Amylase cleaves glycosidic bonds of the amylose chain at random, producing shorter polysaccharide chains. β-Amylase sequentially cleaves maltose (a disaccharide of glucose) from the reducing end of the polysaccharide chain.

11.11 A monosaccharide is the simplest sugar and consists of a single saccharide unit. A disaccharide is made up of two monosaccharides joined covalently by a glycosidic bond.

11.13 a. β-D-Glucose is a hemiacetal.
  b. β-D-Fructose is a hemiketal.
  c. α-D-Galactose is a hemiacetal.

11.15

D-glyceraldehyde   L-glyceraldehyde

11.17 Dextrose is a common name used for D-glucose.

11.19 D- and L-Glyceraldehyde are a pair of enantiomers, that is, they are nonsuperimposable mirror images of one another. In D-glyceraldehyde the hydroxyl group on the chiral carbon farthest from the aldehyde group (C-2) is on the right of the structure. In L-glyceraldehyde the hydroxyl group on C-2 is on the left of the structure.

11.21 When the carbonyl group at C-1 of D-glucose reacts with the C-5 hydroxyl group, a new chiral carbon is created (C-1). In the α-isomers of the cyclic sugar the C-1 hydroxyl group is below the ring and in the β-isomers the C-1 hydroxyl group is above the ring.

11.23 β-Maltose and α-lactose would give positive Benedict's tests. Glycogen would give only a weak reaction because it is a long polymer and thus there are fewer reducing ends for a given mass of the carbohydrate.

11.25

β-Maltose

11.27 Milk is the major source of lactose.

11.29 Since galactose is one of the two monosaccharides making up lactose (milk sugar), eliminating milk and milk products from the diet allows the patient to avoid most of the ill-effects of galactosemia.

11.31 Both amylose and cellulose are linear polymers of glucose units. However, the glucose units of amylose are joined by α(1 → 4) glycosidic bonds and those of cellulose are bonded together by β(1 → 4) glycosidic bonds.

11.33 The major physiological purpose of glycogen is to serve as a storage molecule for glucose. This represents an energy reservoir for the body. Glycogen synthesis and degradation in the liver are involved in regulation of blood glucose levels.

11.35 Mashed potato flakes, rice, and corn starch would contain amylose and amylopectin, both of which are polysaccharides. A candy bar contains sucrose, a disaccharide. Orange juice contains fructose, a monosaccharide. It may also contain sucrose if the label indicates that sugar has been added.

11.37 Four kilocalories of energy are released for each gram of carbohydrate "burned" or oxidized.

11.39

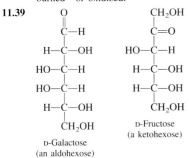

D-Galactose
(an aldohexose)

D-Fructose
(a ketohexose)

11.41 Enantiomers are stereoisomers that are nonsuperimposable mirror images of one another. For instance:

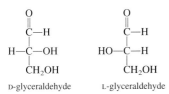

D-glyceraldehyde   L-glyceraldehyde

11.43 α-Amylase and β-amylase are produced in the salivary glands and in the pancreas.

11.45 The linear structure of an aldehyde sugar forms a cyclic structure by formation of an intramolecular hemiacetal. The carbonyl group of the monosaccharide reacts with a hydroxyl group on one of the other carbon atoms. The product is a cyclic intramolecular hemiacetal.

11.47 Lactose intolerance is the inability to produce the enzyme that hydrolyzes the milk sugar lactose into its component monosaccharides, glucose and galactose. As a result of the undigested lactose in the intestine, uncomfortable symptoms, including abdominal cramps and diarrhea, occur.

Chapter 12

12.1
  a. 3-Hexanone
  b. 3-Hexanone
  c. Hexane
  d. Dipropyl ether
  e. Hexanal

12.3
  a. 2,4-Dimethylpentanoic acid
  b. 2,4-Dichlorobutanoic acid
  c. 3-Methylcyclohexanecarboxylic acid
  d. 2-Ethylcyclopentanecarboxylic acid

12.5
  a. o-Toluic acid:

  b. 2,4,6-Tribromobenzoic acid:

c. 2,2,2-Triphenylethanoic acid:

12.7
  a. $CH_3CH_2-\overset{O}{\overset{\|}{C}}-H \rightarrow CH_3CH_2-\overset{O}{\overset{\|}{C}}-OH$

Propanal would be the first oxidation product. However, it would quickly be oxidized further to propanoic acid.

  b. $HO-\overset{O}{\overset{\|}{C}}-CH_2CH_2CH_2CH_3$

  c. $CH_3CH_2-\overset{O}{\overset{\|}{C}}-O^-K^+$

  d. $[CH_3CH_2CH_2-COO]_2^- \ Ba^{2+}$

12.9
  a. $CH_3COOH + CH_3CH_2CH_2OH$
    Ethanoic acid   1-Propanol

  b. $CH_3CH_2CH_2CH_2CH_2-COO^-K^+ + CH_3CH_2CH_2CH_2OH$
    Potassium hexanoate   1-Butanol

  c. $CH_3CH_2CH_2CH_2-COO^-Na^+ + CH_3OH$
    Sodium pentanoate   Methanol

  d. $CH_3CH_2CH_2CH_2CH_2-COOH + CH_3CHCH_2CH_2CH_3$
                                       OH
    Hexanoic acid   2-Pentanol

12.11
  a. 2-Bromopentanoic acid:

  b. 2-Bromo-3-methylbutanoic acid:

  c. 2-Bromocyclohexanecarboxylic acid:

  d. 2,6-Dichlorocyclohexanecarboxylic acid

  e. 2,4,6-Trimethylstearic acid:

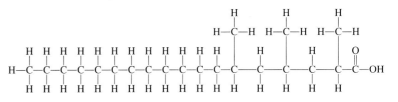

f. Propenoic acid

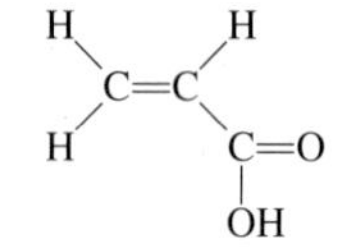

$$
\begin{array}{c}
\text{H} \qquad\qquad \text{H} \\
\diagdown \qquad\qquad \diagup \\
\text{C}=\text{C} \\
\diagup \qquad\qquad \diagdown \\
\text{H} \qquad\qquad \text{C}=\text{O} \\
\qquad\qquad\qquad | \\
\qquad\qquad\qquad \text{OH}
\end{array}
$$

12.13

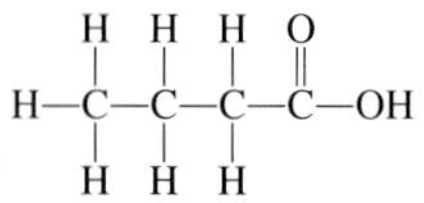

Butanoic acid

$$
\text{H}-\overset{\underset{|}{\text{H}}}{\underset{\underset{|}{\text{H}}}{\text{C}}}-\overset{\underset{|}{\text{H}}}{\underset{\underset{|}{\text{H}}}{\text{C}}}-\overset{\underset{|}{\text{H}}}{\underset{\underset{|}{\text{H}}}{\text{C}}}-\overset{\overset{\text{O}}{\|}}{\text{C}}-\text{OH}
$$

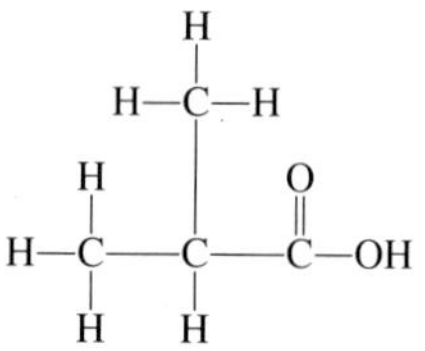

2-Methylpropanoic acid

$$
\text{H}-\overset{\underset{|}{\text{H}}}{\underset{\underset{|}{\text{H}}}{\text{C}}}-\overset{\overset{\underset{|}{\text{H}}}{\overset{|}{\text{C}}-\text{H}}}{\underset{\underset{|}{\text{H}}}{\text{C}}}-\overset{\overset{\text{O}}{\|}}{\text{C}}-\text{OH}
$$

12.15

a. 4,4-Dimethylhexanoic acid:
$$CH_3CH_2-\overset{\overset{\displaystyle CH_3}{|}}{\underset{\underset{\displaystyle CH_3}{|}}{C}}-CH_2CH_2COOH$$

b. 3-Bromo-4-methylpentanoic acid:
$$CH_3\overset{\overset{\displaystyle CH_3}{|}}{C}H\underset{\underset{\displaystyle Br}{|}}{C}HCH_2COOH$$

c. 2,3-Dinitrobenzoic acid:

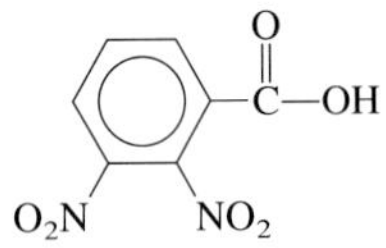

$$
\begin{array}{c}
\overset{\overset{\text{O}}{\|}}{\text{C}}-\text{OH} \\
\text{(benzene ring)} \\
\text{O}_2\text{N} \qquad \text{NO}_2
\end{array}
$$

d. 3-Methylcyclohexanecarboxylic acid:

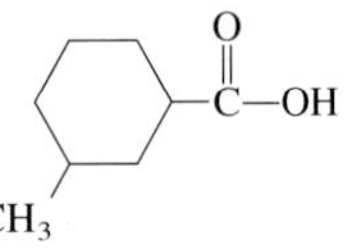

(cyclohexane ring with $\overset{\overset{\text{O}}{\|}}{\text{C}}-\text{OH}$ and CH_3)

12.17
a. Heptanoic acid
b. 1-Propanol
c. Pentanoic acid
d. Butanoic acid

12.19
a. CH_3COOH

b. $CH_3CH_2CH_2-\overset{\overset{\text{O}}{\|}}{\text{C}}-\text{O}-CH_3 + H_2O$

c. CH_3OH

12.21
a. The oxidation of 1-pentanol in the presence of an oxidizing agent yields pentanal.
b. Continued oxidation of pentanal yields pentanoic acid.

12.23
a. Methyl benzoate:

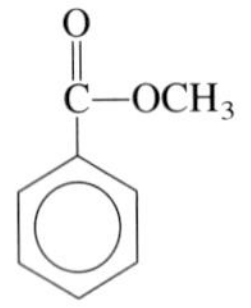

$$\overset{\overset{\text{O}}{\|}}{\text{C}}-OCH_3 \text{ (attached to benzene ring)}$$

b. Butyl decanoate:

$$CH_3CH_2CH_2CH_2CH_2CH_2CH_2CH_2CH_2-\overset{\overset{\text{O}}{\|}}{\text{C}}-\text{O}-CH_2CH_2CH_2CH_3$$

c. Methyl propionate: $\quad CH_3CH_2-\overset{\overset{\text{O}}{\|}}{\text{C}}-\text{O}-CH_3$

d. Ethyl propionate: $\quad CH_3CH_2-\overset{\overset{\text{O}}{\|}}{\text{C}}-\text{O}-CH_2CH_3$

e. Ethyl-*m*-nitrobenzoate:

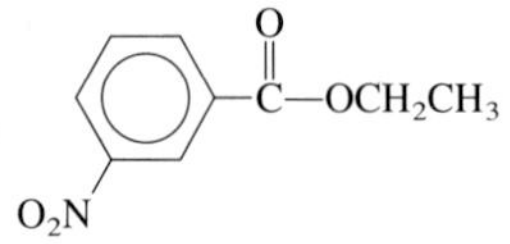

$$\overset{\overset{\text{O}}{\|}}{\text{C}}-OCH_2CH_3 \text{ (benzene ring with } O_2N)$$

f. Isopropyl acetate: $\quad CH_3-\overset{\overset{\text{O}}{\|}}{\text{C}}-\text{O}-\overset{\overset{\displaystyle CH_3}{|}}{\text{C}}HCH_3$

g. Methyl butyrate: $\quad CH_3CH_2CH_2-\overset{\overset{\text{O}}{\|}}{\text{C}}-\text{O}-CH_3$

12.25

a. $CH_3CH_2CH_2-\overset{\overset{\text{O}}{\|}}{\text{C}}-\text{O}-CH_2CH_3$

b. $CH_3CH_2-\overset{\overset{\text{O}}{\|}}{\text{C}}-\text{OH} + CH_3CH_2OH$

c. $CH_3CH_2CH_2OH$

d. $CH_3CH_2\underset{\underset{\displaystyle Br}{|}}{C}HCH_2-\overset{\overset{\text{O}}{\|}}{\text{C}}-\text{O}^- + CH_3CH_2OH$

12.27 Saponification is a reaction in which a soap is produced. More generally, it is the hydrolysis of an ester in the presence of a base. The following reaction shows the base-catalyzed hydrolysis of an ester:

$$CH_3(CH_2)_{14}-\overset{\overset{\text{O}}{\|}}{\text{C}}-\text{O}-CH_3 + NaOH \rightarrow$$

$$CH_3(CH_2)_{14}-\overset{\overset{\text{O}}{\|}}{\text{C}}-\text{O}^-Na^+ + CH_3OH$$

12.29

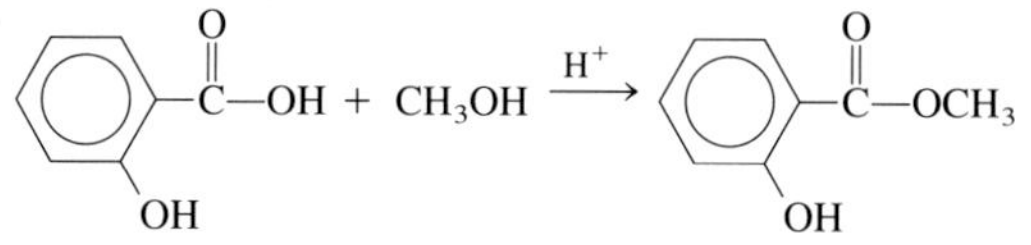

$$\overset{\overset{\text{O}}{\|}}{\text{C}}-\text{OH} + CH_3OH \xrightarrow{\text{H}^+} \overset{\overset{\text{O}}{\|}}{\text{C}}-OCH_3$$

Salicylic acid   Methyl salicylate

(with OH substituents on benzene rings)

12.31 Compound A is $CH_3CH_2CH_2CH_2-\overset{\overset{\text{O}}{\|}}{\text{C}}-\text{O}-CH_3$

Compound B is $CH_3CH_2CH_2CH_2-\overset{\overset{\text{O}}{\|}}{\text{C}}-\text{OH}$

Compound C is CH_3OH

12.33

$$HO-\overset{\overset{\text{O}}{\|}}{\underset{\underset{\displaystyle OH}{|}}{P}}-\text{O}-CH_2CH_3 \quad \text{Monoester}$$

$$HO-\overset{\overset{\text{O}}{\|}}{\underset{\underset{\displaystyle OCH_2CH_3}{|}}{P}}-\text{O}-CH_2CH_3 \quad \text{Diester}$$

$$CH_3CH_2-\text{O}-\overset{\overset{\text{O}}{\|}}{\underset{\underset{\displaystyle OCH_2CH_3}{|}}{P}}-\text{O}-CH_2CH_3 \quad \text{Triester}$$

12.35 ATP is the molecule used to store the energy released in metabolic reactions. The energy is stored in the phosphoanhydride bonds between two phosphoryl groups. The energy is released when the bond is hydrolyzed. A portion of the energy can be transferred to another molecule if the phosphoryl group is transferred from ATP to the other molecule.

12.37 $CH_3-\overset{\overset{\text{O}}{\|}}{\text{C}}\sim\text{S}-\text{Coenzyme A}$

12.39 The structure of nitroglycerine:

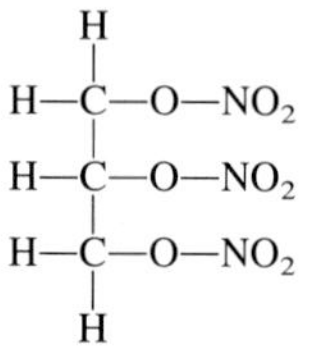

$$
\text{H}-\overset{\underset{|}{\text{H}}}{\text{C}}-\text{O}-NO_2 \\
\text{H}-\overset{}{\text{C}}-\text{O}-NO_2 \\
\text{H}-\overset{\underset{|}{\text{H}}}{\text{C}}-\text{O}-NO_2
$$

12.41 a. I.U.P.A.C. name: 2-Hydroxypropanoic acid
Common name: α-Hydroxypropionic acid

b. I.U.P.A.C. name: 3-Hydroxybutanoic acid
Common name: β-Hydroxybutyric acid

c. I.U.P.A.C. name: 4,4-Dimethylpentanoic acid
Common name: γ,γ-Dimethylvaleric acid

d. I.U.P.A.C. name: 3,3-Dichloropentanoic acid
Common name: β,β-Dichlorovaleric acid

12.43 The smaller carboxylic acids are water-soluble. They have sharp, sour tastes and unpleasant aromas.

12.45 Citric acid is found naturally in citrus fruits. It is added to foods to give them a tart flavor or to act as a food preservative and anti-oxidant. Adipic acid imparts a tart flavor to soft drinks and is a preservative.

12.47 Carboxylic acids are produced commercially by the oxidation of the corresponding alcohol or aldehyde, as seen in the following example:

$$CH_3CH_2OH \xrightarrow{[O]} CH_3-\overset{O}{\overset{\|}{C}}-H \xrightarrow{[O]} CH_3-\overset{O}{\overset{\|}{C}}-OH$$

Ethanol   Ethanal   Ethanoic acid

12.49 Soaps are made from water, a strong base, and natural fats or oils. The fats and oils are triesters of glycerol. In the presence of the strong base, the ester bonds are hydrolyzed and the salts of the long chain fatty acids are formed. The salts of fatty acids are soaps.

Chapter 13

13.1
a. $CH_3(CH_2)_7CH=CH(CH_2)_7COOH$
b. $CH_3(CH_2)_{10}COOH$
c. $CH_3(CH_2)_4CH=CH-CH_2-CH=CH(CH_2)_7COOH$
d. $CH_3(CH_2)_{16}COOH$

13.3
a. Esterification of lauric acid and ethanol

$$CH_3(CH_2)_{10}-\overset{\|}{\underset{O}{C}}-OH + CH_3CH_2OH$$

$$\downarrow$$

$$CH_3(CH_2)_{10}-\overset{\|}{\underset{O}{C}}-OCH_2CH_3 + H_2O$$

b. Reaction of oleic acid with NaOH

$$CH_3(CH_2)_7CH=CH(CH_2)_7-\overset{\|}{\underset{O}{C}}-OH + NaOH$$

$$\downarrow$$

$$CH_3(CH_2)_7CH=CH(CH_2)_7-\overset{\|}{\underset{O}{C}}-O^-Na^+ + H_2O$$

c. Hydrogenation of arachidonic acid

$$CH_3(CH_2)_4CH=CHCH_2CH=CHCH_2CH=CHCH_2CH=CH(CH_2)_3-\overset{\|}{\underset{O}{C}}-OH + 4H_2$$

$$\downarrow$$

$$CH_3(CH_2)_{18}-\overset{\|}{\underset{O}{C}}-OH$$

13.5 a.

$$CH_3(CH_2)_7CH=CH(CH_2)_7-\overset{O}{\overset{\|}{C}}-O-CH_2$$
$$|$$
$$CH-OH$$
$$|$$
$$CH_2-OH$$

$$CH_3(CH_2)_7CH=CH(CH_2)_7-\overset{O}{\overset{\|}{C}}-O-CH_2$$
$$|$$
$$CH_3(CH_2)_7CH=CH(CH_2)_7-\overset{O}{\overset{\|}{C}}-O-CH$$
$$|$$
$$CH_2-OH$$

$$CH_3(CH_2)_7CH=CH(CH_2)_7-\overset{O}{\overset{\|}{C}}-O-CH_2$$
$$|$$
$$CH_3(CH_2)_7CH=CH(CH_2)_7-\overset{O}{\overset{\|}{C}}-O-CH$$
$$|$$
$$CH_3(CH_2)_7CH=CH(CH_2)_7-\overset{O}{\overset{\|}{C}}-O-CH_2$$

b.

$$CH_3(CH_2)_8-\overset{\|}{\underset{O}{C}}-O-CH_2$$
$$|$$
$$CH-OH$$
$$|$$
$$CH_2-OH$$

$$CH_3(CH_2)_8-\overset{\|}{\underset{O}{C}}-O-CH_2$$
$$|$$
$$CH_3(CH_2)_8-\overset{\|}{\underset{O}{C}}-O-CH$$
$$|$$
$$CH_2-OH$$

$$CH_3(CH_2)_8-\overset{\|}{\underset{O}{C}}-O-CH_2$$
$$|$$
$$CH_3(CH_2)_8-\overset{\|}{\underset{O}{C}}-O-CH$$
$$|$$
$$CH_3(CH_2)_8-\overset{\|}{\underset{O}{C}}-O-CH_2$$

c.

$$CH_3(CH_2)_{14}-\overset{\|}{\underset{O}{C}}-O-CH_2$$
$$|$$
$$CH-OH$$
$$|$$
$$CH_2-OH$$

$$CH_3(CH_2)_{14}-\overset{\|}{\underset{O}{C}}-O-CH_2$$
$$|$$
$$CH_3(CH_2)_{14}-\overset{\|}{\underset{O}{C}}-O-CH$$
$$|$$
$$CH_2-OH$$

$$CH_3(CH_2)_{14}-\overset{\|}{\underset{O}{C}}-O-CH_2$$
$$|$$
$$CH_3(CH_2)_{14}-\overset{\|}{\underset{O}{C}}-O-CH$$
$$|$$
$$CH_3(CH_2)_{14}-\overset{\|}{\underset{O}{C}}-O-CH_2$$

d. 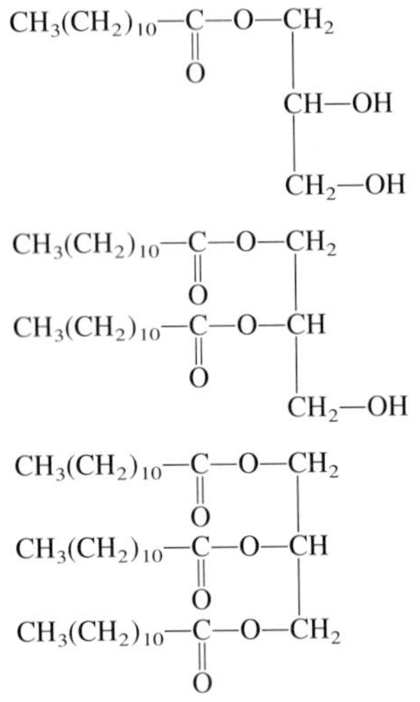 $CH_3(CH_2)_{10}-\overset{O}{\underset{\|}{C}}-O-CH_2$

                           $CH-OH$

                           CH_2-OH

$CH_3(CH_2)_{10}-\overset{}{\underset{}{C}}-O-CH_2$
$\quad\quad\quad\quad\quad\quad\overset{O}{}$
$CH_3(CH_2)_{10}-\overset{}{\underset{}{C}}-O-CH$
$\quad\quad\quad\quad\quad\quad\overset{O}{}\quad\quad\quad CH_2-OH$

$CH_3(CH_2)_{10}-\overset{}{\underset{}{C}}-O-CH_2$
$\quad\quad\quad\quad\quad\quad\overset{O}{}$
$CH_3(CH_2)_{10}-\overset{}{\underset{}{C}}-O-CH$
$\quad\quad\quad\quad\quad\quad\overset{O}{}$
$CH_3(CH_2)_{10}-\overset{}{\underset{}{C}}-O-CH_2$
$\quad\quad\quad\quad\quad\quad\overset{O}{}$

13.7

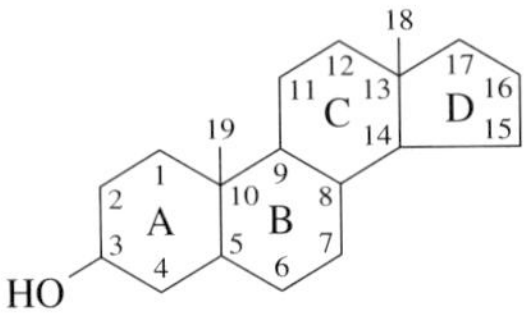

Steroid nucleus

13.9 The four main groups of lipids are fatty acids, glycerides, nonglyceride lipids, and complex lipids.

13.11 A saturated fatty acid has a hydrocarbon tail with only carbon-to-carbon single bonds. In an unsaturated fatty acid the hydrocarbon tail has at least one carbon-to-carbon double bond.

13.13 As the length of the hydrocarbon chains of fatty acids increases, the melting points increase.

13.15 a. Decanoic acid

    $CH_3(CH_2)_8COOH$

b. Stearic acid

    $CH_3(CH_2)_{16}COOH$

c. *trans*-5-Decenoic acid

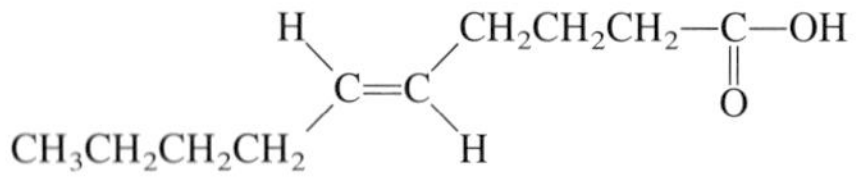

d. *cis*-5-Decenoic acid

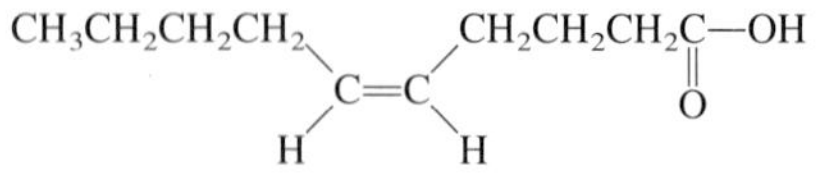

13.17 a.

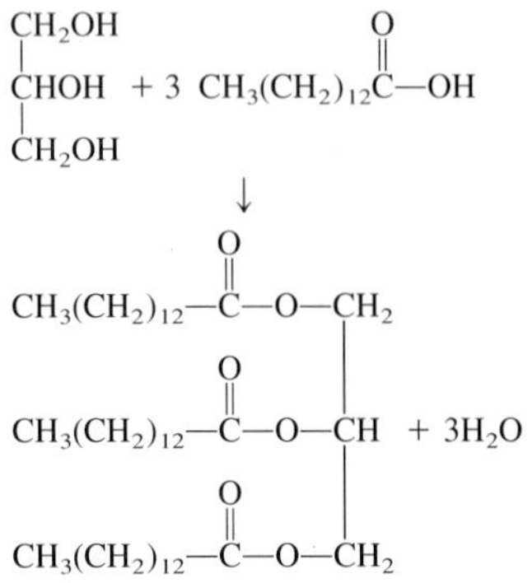

b.

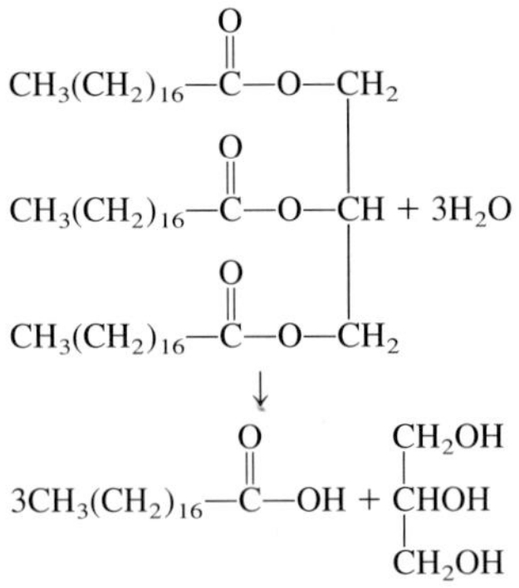

c. 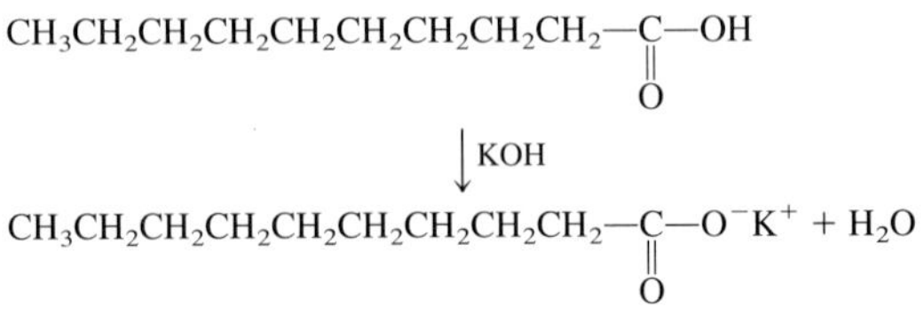 $CH_3CH_2CH_2CH_2CH_2CH_2CH_2CH_2CH_2-\overset{}{\underset{O}{C}}-OH$

    $\downarrow KOH$

$CH_3CH_2CH_2CH_2CH_2CH_2CH_2CH_2CH_2-\overset{}{\underset{O}{C}}-O^-K^+ + H_2O$

d. 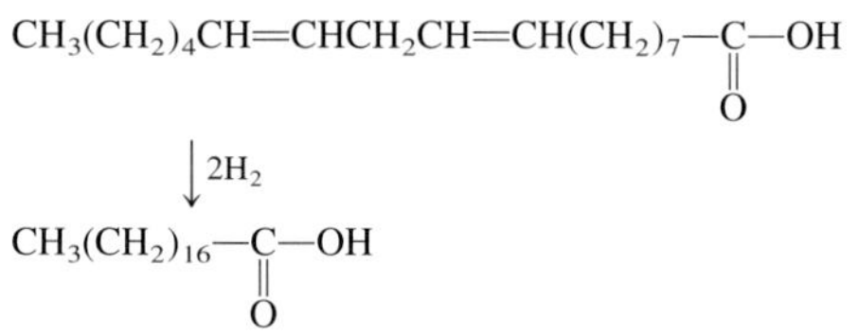 $CH_3(CH_2)_4CH{=}CHCH_2CH{=}CH(CH_2)_7-\overset{}{\underset{O}{C}}-OH$

    $\downarrow 2H_2$

$CH_3(CH_2)_{16}-\overset{}{\underset{O}{C}}-OH$

13.19 The function of essential fatty acids is to form arachidonic acid, a compound that is used by the body to make prostaglandins. The essential fatty acids cannot be manufactured by the body and must be supplied by one's diet.

13.21 Inflammation is a response to tissue damage and results in swelling, redness, fever, and pain. Prostaglandins promote fever and pain of the inflammatory response. Aspirin reduces inflammation by blocking the formation of prostaglandins. An acetyl group from aspirin becomes covalently linked to the enzyme cyclooxygenase, which catalyzes the first step of prostaglandin synthesis in all tissues. This effectively inhibits prostaglandin synthesis.

13.23 Effects of prostaglandins are:
1. promotion of fever and pain in inflammatory response
2. promotion of the onset of labor during childbirth
3. inhibition of platelet aggregation (prevent clotting of blood)
4. inhibition of the secretion of stomach acid
5. dilation of blood vessels
6. promotion of bronchodilation

13.25

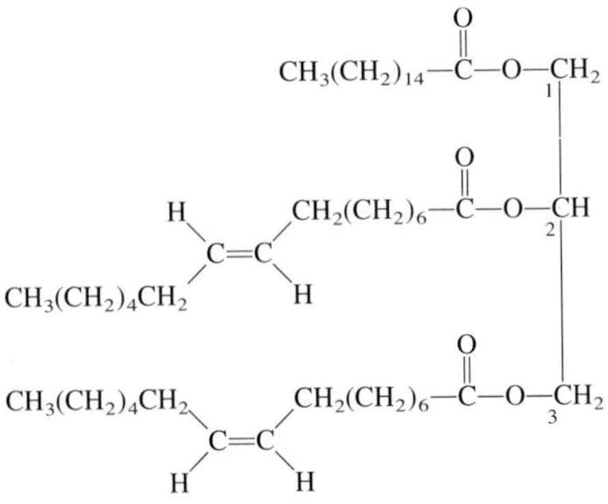

13.27

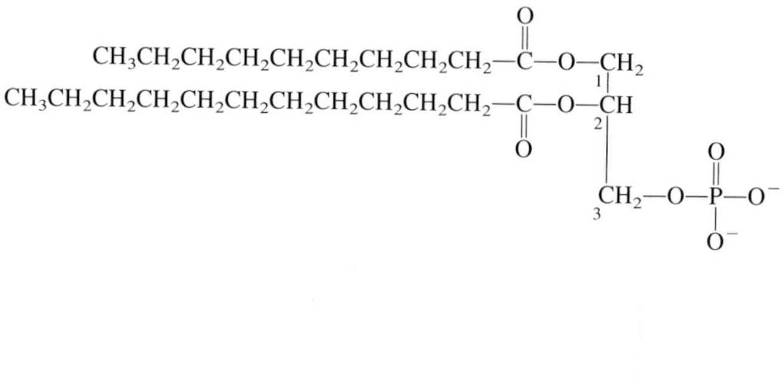

13.29 The membrane will have increased fluidity.

13.31 The basic structure of a cell membrane is a bilayer of phospholipids with the hydrophobic fatty acyl groups facing the center of the bilayer and the polar ''heads'' of the ester portion of the phospholipids lining the exterior and interior of the cell membrane.

13.33 A sphingolipid is a phospholipid derived from the nitrogen-containing (amino) alcohol sphingosine.

13.35 Cholesterol is dissolved in the hydrophobic region of membranes and is involved in regulating the fluidity of the membrane.

13.37 Progesterone is involved in preparation of the lining of the uterus to accept the fertilized egg, development of the fetus, and suppression of ovulation during pregnancy. Testosterone is involved in development of male secondary sexual characteristics. Estrone is involved in development of female secondary sexual characteristics.

13.39 Cortisone is used in treatment of rheumatoid arthritis, asthma, and a variety of other diseases.

13.41 Myricyl palmitate is the ester of the fatty acid palmitic acid, $C_{15}H_{31}COOH$, and the alcohol myricol, $C_{30}H_{61}OH$.

13.43 The four major types of plasma lipoproteins are chylomicrons, very low density lipoproteins, low density lipoproteins, and high density lipoproteins.

13.45 Peripheral membrane proteins are bound to only one surface of the membrane.

13.47 Isoprenoids are a diverse collection of lipids derived from the isoprene unit:

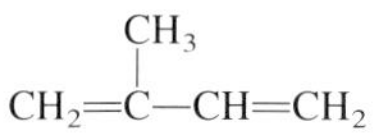

$$CH_2{=}\overset{\overset{\displaystyle CH_3}{|}}{C}{-}CH{=}CH_2$$

13.49 Some biologically important terpenes include the steroids and bile salts, lipid-soluble vitamins, and chlorophyll.

13.51 Atherosclerosis results when cholesterol and other substances coat the arteries causing a narrowing of the passageways. As the passageways become narrower, greater pressure is required to provide adequate blood flow. This results in higher blood pressure (hypertension).

13.53 If the LDL receptor is defective it cannot function to remove cholesterol-bearing LDL from the blood. The excess cholesterol, along with other substances, will accumulate along the walls of the arteries, causing atherosclerosis.

Chapter 14

14.1 **a.** Tertiary amine
   b. Primary amine
   c. Secondary amine

14.3

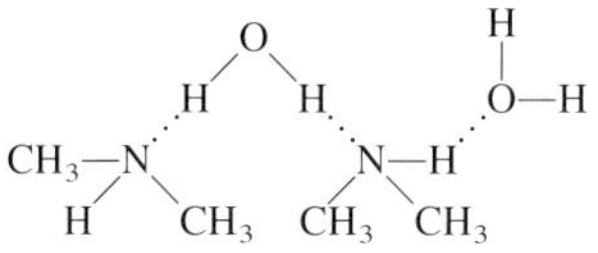

14.5 **a.** *N*-Methylaniline:

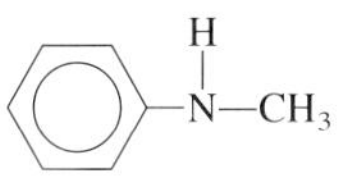

   b. *N,N*-Dimethylaniline:

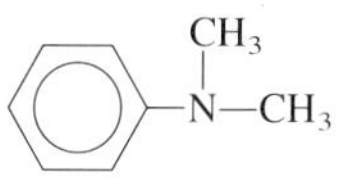

   c. *N*-Ethylaniline:

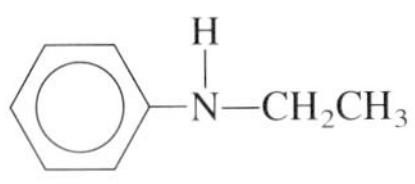

   d. *N*-Isopropylaniline:

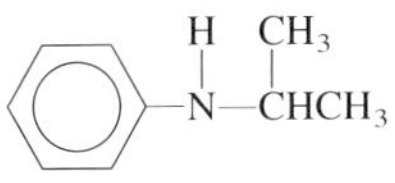

14.7 **a.** 2-Propanamine:

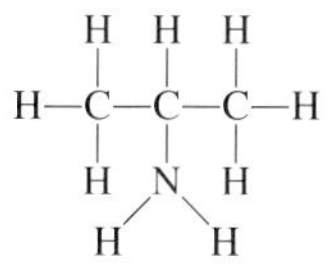

   b. 3-Octanamine:

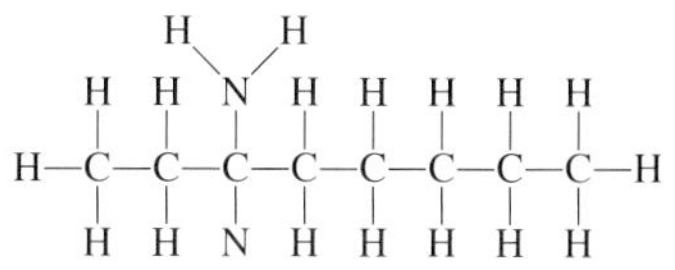

   c. *N*-Ethyl-2-heptanamine:

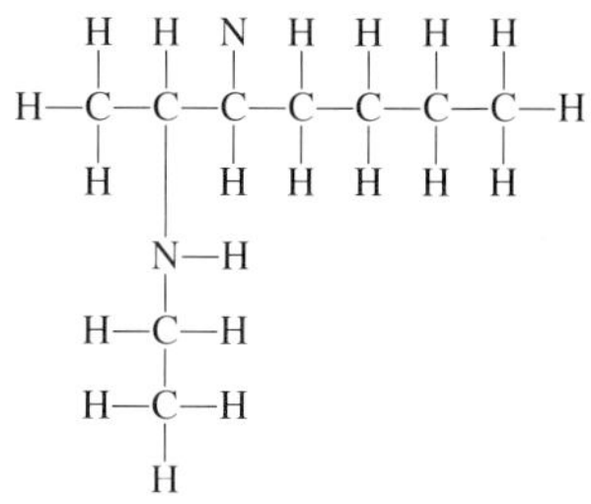

   d. 2-Methyl-2-pentanamine:

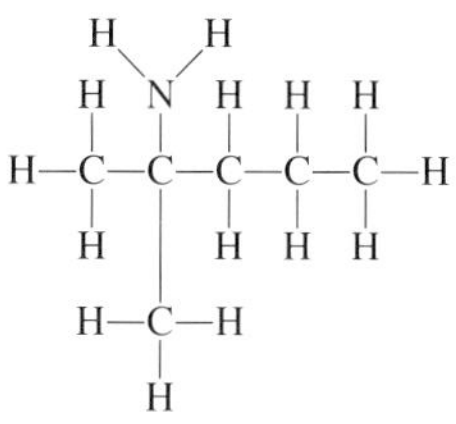

   e. 4-Chloro-5-iodo-1-nonanamine:

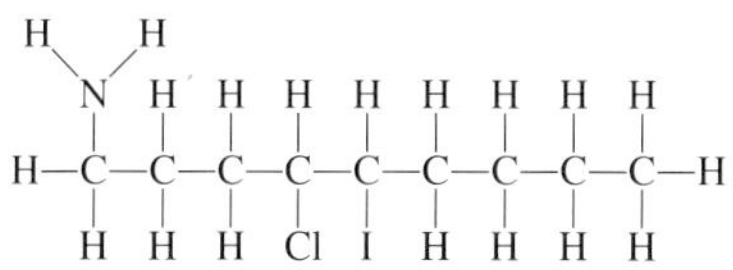

   f. *N,N*-Diethyl-1-pentanamine:

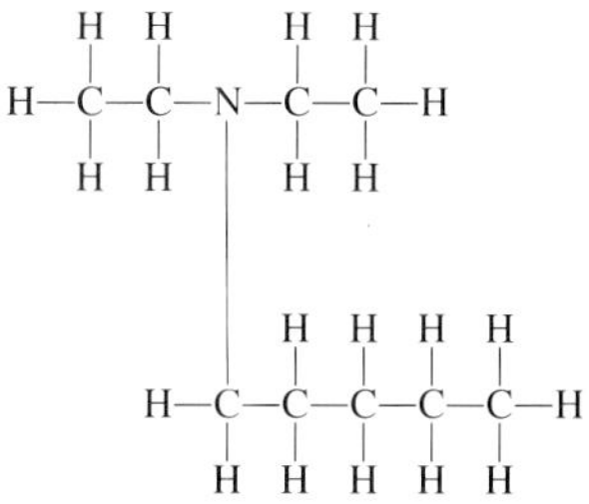

14.9 **a.**

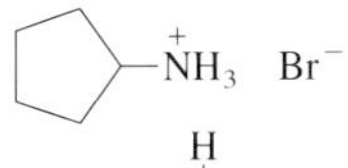

   b. $CH_3CH_2{-}\overset{\overset{\displaystyle H}{|}}{\underset{\underset{\displaystyle H}{|}}{N}}{\overset{+}{}}{-}CH_3 + OH^-$

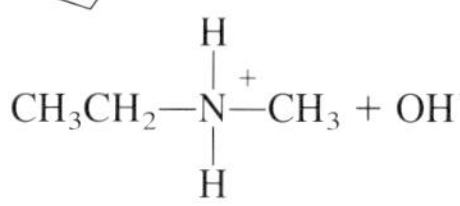

   c. $CH_3{-}N^+H_3 + OH^-$

14.11 **a.** $CH_3{-}NH_2$

   b. $CH_3{-}\overset{\overset{\displaystyle CH_3}{|}}{N}H$ or $(CH_3)_2{-}NH$

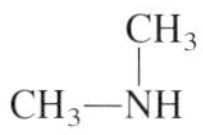

14.13 **a.** 2-Butanamine
   b. 3-Hexanamine
   c. Cyclopentanamine
   d. 2-Methyl-2-propanamine

14.15 **a.** Diethylamine: $CH_3CH_2{-}NH{-}CH_2CH_3$
   b. Butylamine: $CH_3CH_2CH_2CH_2NH_2$
   c. 3-Decanamine: $CH_3CH_2\overset{\underset{\underset{\displaystyle NH_2}{|}}{}}{C}HCH_2CH_2CH_2CH_2CH_2CH_3$
   d. 3-Bromo-2-pentanamine: $CH_3\overset{\overset{\displaystyle Br}{|}}{C}H\overset{\underset{\underset{\displaystyle NH_2}{|}}{}}{C}HCH_2CH_3$
   e. Triphenylamine:

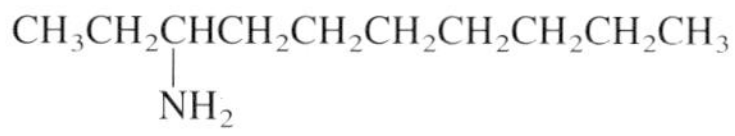

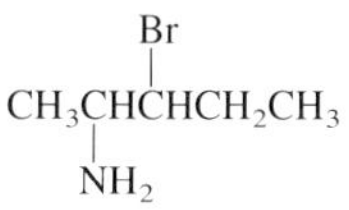

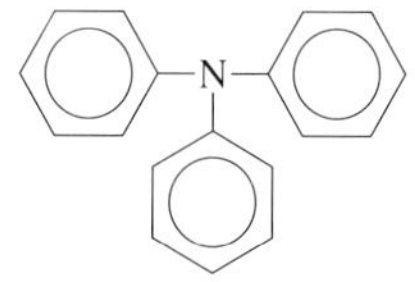

14.17 a. 2-Pentanamine: $CH_3CHCH_2CH_2CH_3$
                        NH_2

b. 2-Bromo-1-butanamine: $CH_3CH_2CHCH_2NH_2$
                                  Br

c. Ethylisopropylamine: $CH_3CH_2-NH-CHCH_3$
                                    CH_3

d. Cyclopentanamine: ⬠—NH_2

14.19
$CH_3CH_2CH_2CH_2NH_2$ $CH_3CH_2CHCH_3$
                                     NH_2
1-Butanamine   2-Butanamine
(Primary amine)   (Primary amine)

$CH_3CHCH_2NH_2$ $CH_3-\overset{CH_3}{\underset{NH_2}{\overset{|}{\underset{|}{C}}}}-CH_3$
       CH_3
2-Methyl-1-propanamine   2-Methyl-2-Propanamine
(Primary amine)   (Primary amine)

$CH_3CH_2-\overset{CH_3}{\underset{}{\overset{|}{N}}}-CH_3$ $CH_3CH_2-NH-CH_2CH_3$
N,N-Dimethylethanamine   *N*-Ethylethanamine
(Tertiary amine)   (Secondary amine)

$\overset{CH_3CHCH_3}{\underset{NH-CH_3}{|}}$ $CH_3CH_2CH_2-NH-CH_3$
N-Methyl-2-propanamine   *N*-Methyl-1-propanamine
(Secondary amine)   (Secondary amine)

14.21 a. Cyclohexanamine is a primary amine.
b. Dibutylamine is a secondary amine.
c. 2-Methyl-2-heptanamine is a primary amine.
d. Tripentylamine is a tertiary amine.

14.23 a. H_2O
b. HBr
c. $CH_3CH_2CH_2-N^+H_3$
d. $CH_3CH_2-\underset{CH_2CH_3}{\overset{}{N^+H_2Cl^-}}$

14.25 a.

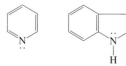

Pyridine   Indole

b. The indole ring is found in lysergic acid diethylamide. The pyridine ring is found in vitamin B_6.

14.27 Morphine has been used as a pain reliever or analgesic. Codeine is used as an analgesic and cough suppressant. Cocaine has been used as an anesthetic for the sinuses and eyes. Quinine is used to treat malaria. Vitamin B_6 is a water-soluble vitamin required by the body.

14.29 a. I.U.P.A.C. name: Propanamide
     Common name: Propionamide
b. I.U.P.A.C. name: Pentanamide
     Common name: Valeramide
c. I.U.P.A.C. name: *N,N*-Dimethylethanamide
     Common name: *N,N*-Diethylacetamide

14.31 a. Ethanamide: $CH_3-\overset{O}{\overset{||}{C}}-NH_2$

b. *N*-Methylpropanamide: $CH_3CH_2-\overset{O}{\overset{||}{C}}-NH-CH_3$
c. *N,N*-Diethylbenzamide:
      ⬡$-\overset{O}{\overset{||}{C}}-\underset{CH_2CH_3}{\overset{}{N}}-CH_2CH_3$

d. 3-Bromo-4-methylhexanamide: $CH_3CH_2-\overset{CH_3}{\overset{|}{C}}HCHCH_2-\overset{O}{\overset{||}{C}}-NH_2$
                                              Br

e. *N,N*-Dimethylacetamide: $CH_3-\overset{O}{\overset{||}{C}}-\underset{CH_3}{\overset{}{N}}-CH_3$

14.33 *N,N*-Diethyl-*m*-toluamide:
      ⬡$-\overset{O}{\overset{||}{C}}-\underset{CH_2CH_3}{\overset{}{N}}-CH_2CH_3$
         CH_3

The carboxylic acid used to form *N,N*-diethyl-*m*-toluamide is *m*-toluic acid and the amine is *N*-ethylethanamide (diethylamine).

14.35 a. $CH_3CH_2-\overset{O}{\overset{||}{C}}-OH + CH_3CH_2CH_2-NH_2 \rightarrow$
      Propanoic acid   1-Propanamine

      $CH_3CH_2CH_2-NH-\overset{O}{\overset{||}{C}}-CH_2CH_3 + H_2O$
                N-Propylpropanamide

b. $CH_3CH_2-\overset{O}{\overset{||}{C}}-OH + NH_3 \rightarrow CH_3CH_2-\overset{O}{\overset{||}{C}}-NH_2 + H_2O$
      Propanoic acid   Ammonia   Propanamide

c. $CH_3CH_2CH_2-\overset{O}{\overset{||}{C}}-OH + CH_3CH_2-NH_2 \rightarrow$
      Butanoic acid   Ethanamine

      $CH_3CH_2CH_2-\overset{O}{\overset{||}{C}}-NH-CH_2CH_3 + H_2O$
                N-Ethylbutanamide

14.37 a. $CH_3-\overset{O}{\overset{||}{C}}-NHCH_3 + H_3O^+ \rightarrow CH_3COOH + CH_3NH_2$
      N-Methylethanamide   Ethanoic acid   Methanamine

b. $CH_3CH_2CH_2-\overset{O}{\overset{||}{C}}-NH-CH_3 + H_3O^+ \rightarrow$
      N-Methylbutanamide

      $CH_3CH_2CH_2-COOH + CH_3NH_2$
            Butanoic acid   Methanamine

c. $CH_3\overset{CH_3}{\overset{|}{C}}HCH_2-\overset{O}{\overset{||}{C}}-NH-CH_2CH_3 + H_3O^+ \rightarrow$
      N-Ethyl-3-methylbutanamide   Hydronium ion
                              (Strong acid)

      $CH_3\overset{}{\overset{|}{C}}HCH_2-COOH + CH_3CH_2NH_2$
        CH_3
      3-Methylbutanoic acid   Ethanamine

14.39
                          Amide group

     $NH-\overset{O}{\overset{||}{C}}-CH_2-\overset{H}{\overset{|}{N^+}}-CH_2CH_3$ Cl^-
   CH_3 CH_3 CH_2CH_3

Lidocaine hydrochloride

14.41

Amide group — Carboxyl group

Penicillin BT

Groups labeled: Amide group, Carboxyl group, COOH, CH₃, CH₃, O, N, S, CH₃(CH₂)₃SCH₂CONH, Amide group

14.43 Lower molecular weight amines are soluble in water because the N—H bond is polar and can form hydrogen bonds with water molecules. As the size of the organic substituents becomes larger, the entire molecule becomes more hydrocarbonlike and, thus, more hydrophobic overall.

14.45 Drugs containing amine groups are generally administered as ammonium salts because the salt is more soluble in water and, hence, in body fluids.

Chapter 15

15.1

a. Glycine (Gly)

b. Proline (Pro)

c. Threonine (Thr)

d. Aspartate (Asp)

e. Lysine (Lys)

15.3 a.

b.

c.

15.5 The primary structure of a protein is the amino acid sequence of the protein chain. Regular, repeating folding of the peptide chain caused by hydrogen bonding between the amide nitrogens and carbonyl oxygens of the peptide bond is the secondary structure of a protein. The two most common types of secondary structure are the α-helix and the β-pleated sheet. Tertiary structure is the further folding of the regions of α-helix and β-pleated sheet into a compact, spherical structure. Formation and maintenance of the tertiary structure results from weak interactions between amino acid R groups. The binding of several peptides to produce a functional protein defines the quaternary structure.

15.7 Oxygen is efficiently transferred from hemoglobin in the blood to myoglobin in the muscle because myoglobin has a greater affinity for oxygen.

15.9 High temperature disrupts the hydrogen bonds and other weak interactions that maintain protein structure. As a result, the protein loses its characteristic three-dimensional shape and becomes denatured.

15.11 a. sucrose **b.** pyruvate **c.** succinate

15.13 a. transferase **b.** ligase **c.** isomerase **d.** oxireductase **e.** transferase **f.** hydrolase

15.15 The induced fit model assumes that the enzyme is flexible. Both the enzyme and the substrate are able to change shape to form the enzyme-substrate complex. The lock-and-key model assumes that the enzyme is inflexible (the lock) and the substrate (the key) fits into a specific rigid site on the enzyme to form the enzyme-substrate complex.

15.17 Water-soluble vitamins are required by the body for the synthesis of coenzymes.

15.19 Vegetables will vary in amino acid composition. Most vegetables lack a sufficient amount of one or more essential amino acids. By eating a variety of vegetables, one can ensure that all amino acid requirements are met.

15.21 Production of proteolytic digestive enzymes must be carefully controlled because the active enzyme could destroy the cell that produces it.

15.23 Five of the biological functions carried out by proteins include serving as enzymes to speed up biochemical reactions, acting as antibodies to protect the body against disease, transport of materials from place to place, regulation of cellular function, and serving as structural support for animals.

15.25

15.27 Interactions between the R groups of the amino acids in a polypeptide chain are important for the formation and maintenance of the tertiary and quaternary structures of proteins.

15.29 The oxidation of two cysteine residues produces cystine:

15.31 a. his-trp-cys:

b. gly-leu-ser:

c. arg-ile-val

15.33 a. α-helix
    b. β-pleated sheet

15.35 A conjugated protein is a protein that requires an additional nonprotein group in order to be functional.

15.37 Heat is an effective means of sterilization because it destroys the proteins of microbial lifeforms, including fungi, bacteria, and viruses.

15.39 The function of the heme group in hemoglobin and myoglobin is to bind to oxygen.

15.41

Substrate	Enzyme
1. urea	e. urease
2. hydrogen peroxide	c. peroxidase
3. lipid	a. lipase
4. aspartic acid	f. aspartase
5. glucose-6-phosphate	b. glucose-6-phosphatase
6. sucrose	d. sucrase

15.43 a. cleaving a carboxylic acid group from citrate **b.** adds a phosphate group to ADP **c.** reduction of oxalate **d.** oxidation of nitrite **e.** interconversion of *cis* and *trans* isomers

15.45 The activation energy of a reaction is the energy required for the reaction to occur.

15.47 The rate of an enzyme-catalyzed reaction does not increase indefinitely with an increase in substrate concentration because at some point every active site is filled with a substrate molecule. At that point the rate of the reaction is limited by the speed with which the substrate is converted into product.

15.49 Absolute specificity: an enzyme catalyzes the reaction of only one substrate
Group specificity: an enzyme catalyzes processes involving similar molecules having the same functional group
Linkage specificity: an enzyme catalyzes formation or breakage of only one type of bond
Stereochemical specificity: an enzyme distinguishes one stereoisomer from another

15.51 $E + S \xrightleftharpoons{\text{Step I}} ES \xrightleftharpoons{\text{Step II}} ES^* \xrightleftharpoons{\text{Step III}} EP \xrightleftharpoons{\text{Step IV}} E + P$

Step I involves the formation of the enzyme-substrate complex. Step II involves the formation of the transition state from the enzyme-substrate complex. Step III involves the formation of the enzyme-product complex from the transition state. Step IV involves the formation and release of the product and regeneration of the enzyme.

15.53 maintaining the proper configuration of the active site

15.55 A drastic change in pH above or below the pH optimum for an enzyme will denature the protein. Since a change in the conformation of the protein will drastically alter its active site, it will no longer be able to bind the substrate for which it was specifically designed, and activity decreases.

15.57 High temperatures denature bacterial enzymes and structural proteins, resulting in cell death.

15.59 Competitive enzyme inhibition occurs when a structural analog of the normal substrate occupies the enzyme active site so that the reaction cannot occur. The structural analog and the normal substrate compete for the active site. Thus, the rate of the reaction will depend on the relative concentrations of the two molecules.

15.61 A structural analog is a molecule that can mimic an enzyme substrate because of the structural similarity of the two molecules. It will act as a competitive inhibitor of the reaction.

15.63 Irreversible inhibitors block the active site of an enzyme and eliminate catalysis at that site. This disrupts the metabolic pathway, and the cell cannot function. The binding of the inhibitor is often tighter than the normal substrate.

15.65 In a vegetarian diet, vegetables are the only source of dietary protein. Since individual vegetable sources do not provide all the needed amino acids, vegetables must be mixed to provide all the essential and nonessential amino acids.

15.67 Nonessential amino acids can be manufactured by one's body. The essential amino acids cannot be made by the body and must be supplied by one's diet.

15.69 creatine phosphokinase (CPK), lactate dehydrogenase (LDH), and aspartate aminotransferase (AST/SGOT)

15.71 Ethanol acts as a competitive inhibitor of the enzyme that would convert ethylene glycol into a toxic metabolite. This allows time for the unreacted ethylene glycol to be removed from the body

15.73 Polyphenoloxidase requires copper ions as a cofactor. Phenylthiourea is an irreversible enzyme inhibitor.

Chapter 16

16.1 ATP is called the universal energy currency because it is the major molecule used by all organisms to store energy. Hydrolysis of the high energy phosphoanhydride bonds releases energy that is used for cellular work.

16.3 The first stage of catabolism is the digestion (hydrolysis) of dietary macromolecules in the stomach and intestine. Polysaccharides are hydrolyzed to monosaccharides; proteins are degraded to amino acids; and triglycerides are broken down into glycerol and fatty acids. The small molecules produced by digestion are taken into the cells lining the intestine by active or passive transport.

In the second stage of catabolism, monosaccharides, amino acids, fatty acids, and glycerol are converted by metabolic reactions into molecules that can be completely oxidized. Often they are converted into acetyl CoA.

In the third stage of catabolism, the two carbon acetyl group of acetyl CoA is completely oxidized by the reactions of the citric acid cycle. The energy of the electrons harvested in these oxidation reactions is used to make ATP.

16.5 Substrate level phosphorylation is one way the cell can make ATP. In this reaction, a high energy phosphoryl group of a substrate in the reaction is transferred to ADP to produce ATP. This kind of reaction can be summarized as follows:

Substrate ~P + ADP → Product + ATP

16.7 Glycolysis is a pathway involving nine reactions. In reactions 1-3 energy is invested in the beginning substrate, glucose. This is done by transferring high energy phosphoryl groups from ATP to the intermediates in the pathway. The product is fructose-1,6-bisphosphate. In the energy producing reactions of glycolysis, fructose-1,6-bisphosphate is split into two three-carbon molecules that begin a series of rearrangement, oxidation-reduction, and substrate level phosphorylation reactions that produce 2 ATP, 2 NADH, and 2 pyruvate molecules.

16.9 Both the alcohol and lactate fermentations are anaerobic reactions that use the pyruvate and re-oxidize the NADH produced in glycolysis. In the alcohol fermentation, pyruvate is first decarboxylated to produce acetaldehyde. The acetaldehyde is then reduced as NADH is oxidized. The products are CO_2, ethanol, and NAD^+. In the lactate fermentation pyruvate is reduced to lactate and NADH is oxidized to NAD^+.

16.11 Gluconeogenesis appears to be the reverse of glycolysis because the intermediates in the two pathways are the same. However, reactions 1, 3, and 9 of glycolysis are not reversible reactions. Thus, the reverse reactions must be carried out by different enzymes. Reaction 1 of glycolysis, the transfer of a high energy phosphoryl group from ATP to glucose, is carried out by the enzyme hexokinase. The reverse reaction in gluconeogenesis is catalyzed by glucose-6-phosphatase. Reaction 3 of glycolysis, the transfer of a high energy phosphoryl group from ATP to fructose-6-phosphate, is catalyzed by phosphofructokinase. The reverse reaction of gluconeogenesis is carried out by fructose bisphosphatase. The final reaction of glycolysis, the transfer of a high energy phosphoryl group from phosphoenolpyruvate to ADP, is catalyzed by pyruvate kinase. This is reversed in gluconeogenesis by the action of two enzymes. Pyruvate carboxylase adds CO_2 to pyruvate to produce oxaloacetate and phosphoenolpyruvate carboxykinase removes the CO_2 and transfers a high energy phosphoryl group from GTP to produce phosphoenolpyruvate.

16.13 Glucagon indirectly stimulates glycogen phosphorylase, the first enzyme of glycogenolysis. This speeds up glycogen degradation. Glucagon also inhibits glycogen synthetase, the first enzyme in glycogenesis. This inhibits glycogen synthesis.

16.15 thiamine; riboflavin; niacin; pantothenic acid

16.17 ATP

16.19

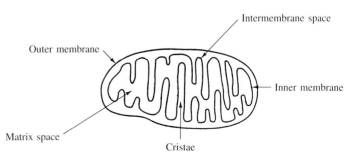

16.21 Glycolysis requires NAD^+ for reaction 5 in which glyceraldehyde-3-phosphate dehydrogenase catalyzes the oxidation of glyceraldehyde-3-phosphate. NAD^+ is reduced and, thus, serves as the electron acceptor in this reaction. If NAD^+ were not available, this reaction would not occur, and glycolysis, and therefore ATP synthesis, would stop.

16.23 2 ATP per glucose molecule

16.25 Although cells only have enough ATP stored for a few seconds of activity, glycolysis speeds up dramatically when there is a demand for more energy. If the cells have a sufficient supply of oxygen, aerobic respiration (the citric acid cycle and oxidative phosphorylation) will contribute large amounts of ATP. If oxygen is limited, the lactate fermentation will speed up. This will use up the pyruvate and re-oxidize the NADH produced by glycolysis and allow the reactions to continue to make ATP for muscle contraction.

16.27

$$C_6H_{12}O_6 + 2ADP + 2P_i + 2NAD^+ \rightarrow$$
Glucose

$$2C_3H_3O_3 + 2ATP + 2NADH + 2H_2O$$
Pyruvate

16.29

$$\underset{\text{Acetaldehyde}}{CH_3-\overset{\overset{\textstyle O}{\|}}{C}-H} + NADH \xrightarrow{\text{Alcohol dehydrogenase}} \underset{\text{Ethanol}}{CH_3CH_2OH} + NAD^+$$

16.31 lactate fermentation

16.33 The tangy flavor of yogurt and some cheeses is the lactate produced by this reaction. It is the pH decrease caused by the lactate build-up that causes milk protein to coagulate. This coagulation produces the soft curd of yogurt and the hard curd of some cheeses.

16.35 the liver

16.37 pyruvate

16.39 Because steps 1, 3, and 9 of glycolysis are irreversible, gluconeogenesis is not simply the reverse of glycolysis. The reverse reactions must be carried out by different enzymes.

16.41 the liver

16.43 Hypoglycemia is the condition in which blood glucose levels are too low.

16.45 Insulin stimulates glycogen synthetase, the first enzyme in glycogen synthesis. It also stimulates uptake of glucose from the bloodstream into cells and phosphorylation of glucose by the enzyme glucokinase. This increases the storage of glucose in the form of glycogen and decreases blood glucose levels.

16.47 under aerobic conditions

16.49 The coenzymes NAD^+, FAD, thiamine pyrophosphate, and coenzyme A are required by the pyruvate dehydrogenase complex for the conversion of pyruvate to acetyl CoA. These coenzymes are synthesized from the vitamins niacin, riboflavin, thiamine, and pantothenic acid, respectively. If the vitamins are not available, the coenzymes will not be available and pyruvate cannot be converted to acetyl CoA. Since the complete oxidation of the acetyl group of acetyl CoA produces the vast majority of the ATP for the body, ATP production would be severely inhibited by a deficiency of any of these vitamins.

16.51 **a.** *gluconeogenesis*—the synthesis of glucose from noncarbohydrate precursors.
    b. *catabolism*—the degradation of fuel molecules and harvesting of energy for cellular functions.
    c. *glycolysis*—the enzymatic pathway that converts a molecule of glucose into two molecules of pyruvate. This anaerobic process generates energy in the form of 2 ATP and 2 NADH.
    d. *aerobic energy metabolism*—metabolic reactions that produce ATP and require oxygen.
    e. *anaerobic energy metabolism*—metabolic reactions that produce ATP and do not require oxygen.
    f. *fermentation*—the anaerobic degradation of sugars.

16.53 **a.** 2
    b. glucose
    c. reduced
    d. ADP

16.55 Steps 1, 3, and 9 of glycolysis are irreversible.

16.57 Lactate dehydrogenase

16.59 This child must have the enzymes to carry out the alcohol fermentation. When the child exercised hard, there was not enough oxygen in the cells to maintain aerobic respiration. As a result, glycolysis and the alcohol fermentation were responsible for the majority of the ATP production by the child. The accumulation of alcohol (ethanol) in the child caused the symptoms of drunkenness.

Chapter 17

17.1 Mitochondria are the organelles responsible for aerobic respiration. They have enzymes that carry out the final oxidations of carbohydrates, amino acids, and fatty acids. They produce the majority of the ATP for the cell.

17.3

Intermembrane space
Outer membrane
Inner membrane
Matrix space
Cristae

17.5 Oxidative phosphorylation is the process by which the energy of electrons harvested from oxidation of a fuel molecule is used to phosphorylate ADP to produce ATP.

17.7 $NAD^+ + H:^- \rightarrow NADH$

17.9 Pyridoxal phosphate is a coenzyme required by all transaminases.

17.11 The purpose of the urea cycle is to convert toxic ammonium ions to urea which is excreted in the urine of land animals. This keeps toxic ammonium ions out of the bloodstream.

17.13 An amphibolic pathway is a metabolic pathway that functions both in anabolism and catabolism. The citric acid cycle is amphibolic because it has a catabolic function; it completely oxidizes the acetyl group carried by acetyl CoA to provide electrons for ATP synthesis. Because citric acid cycle intermediates are precursors for the biosynthesis of many other molecules, it also serves a function in anabolism.

17.15 The intermembrane compartment is the location of the high energy H^+ reservoir produced by the electron transport system. The energy of this H^+ reservoir is used to make ATP.

17.17 The outer mitochondrial membrane is freely permeable to substances of molecular weight less than 10,000. The inner mitochondrial membrane is highly impermeable. Only certain fuel molecules and H^+ are transported through it. Embedded within the inner mitochondrial membrane are the electron carriers of the electron transport system and ATP synthase, the multisubunit enzyme that makes ATP.

17.19
a. False
b. False
c. True
d. True

17.21 The acetyl group of acetyl CoA is transferred to oxaloacetate to produce citrate.

17.23 three

17.25 2 ATP per glucose molecule

17.27 The function of acetyl CoA in the citric acid cycle is to bring the two carbon remnant (acetyl group) of pyruvate from glycolysis and transfer it to oxaloacetate. In this way the acetyl group enters the citric acid cycle for the final stages of oxidation.

17.29 GTP is produced in the citric acid cycle. The high energy phosphoryl group of the GTP is transferred to ADP to produce ATP. This reaction is catalyzed by the enzyme dinucleotide diphosphokinase.

17.31 3 ATP

17.33 The oxidation of a variety of fuel molecules, including carbohydrates, the carbon skeletons of amino acids, and fatty acids provides the electrons. The energy of these electrons is used to produce an H^+ reservoir. The energy of this proton reservoir is used for ATP synthesis.

17.35 The electron transport system passes electrons harvested during oxidation of fuel molecules to molecular oxygen. At three sites protons are pumped from the mitochondrial matrix into the intermembrane compartment. Thus, the electron transport system builds the high energy H^+ reservoir that provides energy for ATP synthesis.

17.37 Aminotransferases (transaminases) transfer amino groups from amino acids to ketoacids.

17.39 The glutamate family of transaminases is very important because the ketoacid corresponding to glutamate is α-ketoglutarate, one of the citric acid cycle intermediates. They provide amino groups for amino acid synthesis and collect amino groups during catabolism of amino acids.

17.41 15 ATP

17.43 hyperammonemia

17.45
a. The source of one amino group of urea is the ammonium ion and the source of the other is the α-amino group of the amino acid aspartate.
b. The carbonyl group of urea is derived from CO_2.

17.47 α-ketoglutarate

17.49 Citric acid cycle intermediates are the starting materials for the biosynthesis of many biological molecules.

17.51 An essential amino acid is one that cannot be synthesized by the body and must be provided in the diet.

17.53 Two ATP (net) per glucose are produced in glycolysis, while the complete oxidation of glucose in the citric acid cycle results in the production of 36 ATP per glucose.

17.55 The synthesis of glutamate catalyzed by glutamate dehydrogenase can be represented by the following equation:

α-Ketoglutarate　　　　Ammonia　　　Glutamate

17.57

Pyruvate　　　　　Oxaloacetate

Chapter 18

18.1 Because dietary lipids are hydrophobic, they arrive in the small intestine as large fat globules. The bile salts emulsify these fat globules into tiny fat droplets. This greatly increases the surface area of the lipids, allowing them to be more accessible to pancreatic lipases and thus more easily digested.

18.3
a. 4 acetyl CoA, 1 benzoate, 4 NADH, and 4 $FADH_2$
b. 3 acetyl CoA, 1 phenyl acetate, 3 NADH, and 3 $FADH_2$
c. 3 acetyl CoA, 1 benzoate, 3 NADH, and 3 $FADH_2$
d. 5 acetyl CoA, 1 phenyl acetate, 5 NADH, and 5 $FADH_2$

18.5

18.7 Starvation, a diet low in carbohydrates, and diabetes mellitus are all conditions that lead to the production of ketone bodies.

18.9 The following are four differences between fatty acid biosynthesis and β-oxidation:
(1) Fatty acid biosynthesis occurs in the cytoplasm while β-oxidation occurs in the mitochondria.
(2) The acyl group carrier in fatty acid biosynthesis is acyl carrier protein while the acyl group carrier in β-oxidation is coenzyme A.
(3) The seven enzymes of fatty acid biosynthesis are associated as a multienzyme complex called fatty acid synthase. The enzymes involved in β-oxidation are not physically associated with one another.
(4) NADPH is the reducing agent used in fatty acid biosynthesis. NADH and $FADH_2$ are produced by β-oxidation.

18.11 The liver regulates blood glucose levels under the control of the hormones insulin and glucagon. When blood glucose levels are too high, insulin stimulates the uptake of glucose by liver cells and the storage of the glucose in glycogen polymers. When blood glucose levels are too low, the hormone glucagon stimulates the breakdown of glycogen and release of glucose into the bloodstream. Glucagon also stimulates the liver to produce glucose for export into the bloodstream by the process of gluconeogenesis.

18.13 Insulin stimulates uptake of glucose and amino acids by cells, glycogen and protein synthesis, and storage of lipids. It inhibits glycogenolysis, gluconeogenesis, breakdown of stored triglycerides, and ketogenesis.

18.15 triglycerides in adipose tissue

18.17 The most outstanding feature of an adipocyte is the large fat globule that takes up nearly the entire cytoplasm.

18.19 Lipases catalyze the hydrolysis of the ester bonds of triglycerides.

18.21 Acetyl CoA is the precursor for fatty acids, several amino acids, cholesterol, and other steroids.

18.23 Chylomicrons are plasma lipoproteins that carry dietary triglycerides from the intestine to all tissues of the body.

18.25 Bile salts serve as detergents. Fat globules stimulate their release from the gall bladder. The bile salts then emulsify the lipids, increasing the surface area and making them more accessible to digestive enzymes (pancreatic lipases).

18.27 5 acetyl CoA, 1 phenyl acetate, 5 NADH, and 5 $FADH_2$

18.29 112 ATP

18.31 Two ATP

18.33 The acetyl CoA produced by β-oxidation will enter the citric acid cycle unless there is too little oxaloacetate available. If that is the case, the acetyl CoA will be used in ketogenesis.

18.35

$$CH_3-\overset{O}{\overset{\|}{C}}-CH_2-\overset{O}{\overset{\|}{C}}-O^- \qquad CH_3-\overset{OH}{\overset{|}{CH}}-CH_2-\overset{O}{\overset{\|}{C}}-O^-$$

Acetoacetate $\qquad\qquad$ β-Hydroxybutyrate

18.37 In those suffering from uncontrolled diabetes, the glucose in the blood cannot get into the cells of the body. The excess glucose is excreted in the urine. Body cells degrade fatty acids because glucose is not available. β-Oxidation of fatty acids yields enormous quantities of acetyl CoA, so much acetyl CoA, in fact, that it cannot all enter the citric acid cycle. Excess acetyl CoA is used for ketogenesis.

18.39 Ketone bodies are the preferred energy source of the heart.

18.41 The phosphopantetheine group allows formation of a high energy thioester bond with a fatty acid. It is derived from the vitamin pantothenic acid and the amino acid cysteine.

18.43 Fatty acid synthase is a huge multienzyme complex consisting of the seven enzymes involved in fatty acid synthesis. It is found in the cell cytoplasm. The enzymes involved in β-oxidation are not physically associated with one another. They are free in the mitochondrial matrix space.

18.45 The major metabolic function of the liver is to regulate blood glucose levels.

18.47 Ketone bodies are the major fuel for the heart. Glucose is the major energy source of the brain, and the liver obtains most of its energy from the oxidation of amino acids carbon skeletons.

18.49 When blood glucose levels are low, glucagon stimulates the hydrolysis of triglycerides in adipocytes. If glucose is limiting, the products, glycerol and three fatty acids, are exported to the liver for further processing. When blood glucose levels are high, insulin stimulates synthesis of triglycerides and uptake of glucose in adipocytes. Glycerol-3-phosphate is produced from glucose. The glycerol-3-phosphate and fatty acids are then assembled into triglycerides.

18.51 Insulin is produced in the β-cells of the islets of Langerhans in the pancreas.

18.53 Insulin stimulates the uptake of glucose from the blood into cells. It enhances glucose storage by stimulating glycogenesis and inhibiting glycogen degradation and gluconeogenesis.

18.55 Insulin stimulates synthesis and storage of triglycerides.

18.57 a. Triglycerides
   b. Lipase
   c. Twelve
   d. Muscle

18.59 When dietary lipids in the form of fat globules reach the duodenum, they are emulsified by bile salts. The triglycerides in the resulting tiny fat droplets are hydrolyzed into monoglycerides and fatty acids by the action of pancreatic lipases, assisted by colipase. The monoglycerides and fatty acids are absorbed by cells lining the intestine. Within intestinal cells triglycerides are reassembled into chylomicrons (lipoprotein particles made up of protein and dietary triglycerides). Chylomicrons are secreted into the lymphatic vessels and eventually reach the bloodstream. In the bloodstream the triglycerides are hydrolyzed once again and the products (glycerol and free fatty acids) are absorbed by the cells of the body.

18.61 Untreated diabetes mellitus is starvation in the midst of plenty because blood glucose levels are very high. However, in the absence of insulin, blood glucose can't be taken up into cells. The excess glucose is excreted into the urine while the cells of the body are starved for energy.

Chapter 19

19.1 a. Adenosine diphosphate:

b. Deoxyguanosine triphosphate

19.3 The deoxyribonucleotides of guanine are:
Deoxyguanosine monophosphate (dGMP)
Deoxyguanosine diphosphate (dGDP)
Deoxyguanosine triphosphate (dGTP)
The ribonucleotides of guanine are:
Guanosine monophosphate (GMP)
Guanosine diphosphate (GDP)
Guanosine triphosphate (GTP)

19.5 The RNA polymerase recognizes the promoter site for a gene, separates the strands of DNA, and catalyzes the polymerization of an RNA strand complementary to the DNA strand that carries the genetic code for a protein. It recognizes a termination site at the end of the gene and releases the RNA molecule.

19.7 The genetic code is said to be degenerate because several different triplet codons may serve as code words for a single amino acid.

19.9 The nitrogenous bases of the codons are complementary to those of the anticodons. As a result they are able to hydrogen bond to one another according to the base pairing rules.

19.11 The ribosomal P-site holds the peptidyl tRNA during protein synthesis. The peptidyl tRNA is the tRNA carrying the growing peptide chain. The only exception to this is during initiation of translation when the P-site holds the initiator tRNA.

19.13 The normal mRNA sequence, AUG-CCC-GAC-UUU, would encode the peptide sequence, methionine-proline-aspartate-phenylalanine. The mutant mRNA sequence, AUG-C*G*C-GAC-UUU, would encode the mutant peptide sequence, methionine-arginine-aspartate-phenylalanine. This would not be a silent mutation because a hydrophobic amino acid (proline) has been replaced by a positively charged amino acid (arginine).

19.15 It is the N-9 of the purine that forms the N-glycosidic bond with C-1 of the five carbon sugar.

19.17 Two hydrogen bonds link the adenine-thymine base pair.

19.19

19.21 The term *semiconservative DNA replication* refers to the fact that each parental DNA strand serves as the template for the synthesis of a daughter strand. As a result, each of the daughter DNA molecules is made up of one strand of the original parental DNA and one strand of newly synthesized DNA.

19.23 If the parental DNA strand had the nucleotide sequence, 5'-ATGCGGCTAGAATATTCCA-3', the sequence of the complementary daughter strand would be 3'-TACGCCGATCTTATAAGGT-5'.

19.25 The central dogma of molecular biology states that information flow in cellular biological systems is unidirectional: DNA → RNA → Protein. The DNA carries the genetic information; RNA molecules carry out the expression of the genetic information for proteins; the final products are proteins which carry out the work of the cell and serve as cellular structural components.

19.27 Anticodons are found on transfer RNA molecules.

19.29 If a gene had the sequence:
5'-TACCTAGCTCTGGTCATTAAGGCAGTA-3',
the mRNA would have the sequence:
3'-AUGGAUCGAGACCAGUAAUUCCGUCAU-5'.

19.31 RNA splicing is the process by which the noncoding sequences (introns) of the primary transcript of a eukaryotic mRNA are removed and the protein coding sequences (exons) are spliced together.

19.33 There are 64 codons in the genetic code.

19.35 The ribosomes serve as a platform on which protein synthesis can occur. They also carry the enzymatic activity that forms peptide bonds.

19.37 In the initiation of translation, initiation factors, methionyl-tRNA (the initiator tRNA), the mRNA, and the small and large ribosomal subunits form the initiation complex. During the elongation stage of translation an aminoacyl-tRNA binds to the A-site of the ribosome. Peptidyl transferase catalyzes the formation of a peptide bond and the peptide chain is transferred to the tRNA in the A-site. Translocation shifts the peptidyl tRNA from the A-site into the P-site, leaving the A-site available for the next aminoacyl tRNA. In the termination stage of translation, a termination codon is encountered. A release factor binds to the empty A-site and peptidyl transferase catalyzes the hydrolysis of the bond between the peptidyl tRNA and the completed peptide chain.

19.39 UV light causes the formation of thymine dimers, the covalent bonding of two adjacent thymine bases. Mutations occur when the UV damage repair system makes an error during the repair process. This causes a change in the nucleotide sequence of the DNA.

19.41 A carcinogen is a compound that causes cancer. Cancers are caused by mutations in the genes responsible for controlling cell division. Carcinogens cause DNA damage that results in changes in the nucleotide sequence of the gene. Thus, carcinogens are also mutagens.

19.43 A restriction enzyme is a bacterial enzyme that "cuts" the sugar-phosphate backbone of DNA molecules at a specific nucleotide sequence.

19.45 Nucleic acid hybridization is based on the fact that complementary DNA or RNA sequences will hydrogen bond to one another according to the base pairing rules.

19.47 Human insulin, interferon, human growth hormone, and human blood clotting factor VIII are protein products of recombinant DNA technology that are of great value in the field of medicine.

19.49 The ATP nucleotide is composed of the five-carbon sugar ribose, the nitrogenous base adenine, and a triphosphate group.

19.51 The term *antiparallel* describes the polarities of the two complementary strands of the DNA double helix. On one strand the sugar-phosphate backbone advances in the 5' → 3' direction, while on the opposite strand the sugar-phosphate backbone advances in the 3' → 5' direction.

19.53 A replication origin is the sequence of nucleotides on a chromosome where DNA replication always begins.

19.55 The three classes of RNA molecules are messenger RNA (mRNA), transfer RNA (tRNA), and ribosomal RNA (rRNA).

Index

565

568

Credits

xi Wm. C. Brown/Louis Rosenstock   **xiv** Wm. C. Brown/Louis Rosenstock   **1** Eric Kamp/PHOTOTAKE   **19** Wm. C. Brown/Louis Rosenstock   **29** Yoav Levy/PHOTOTAKE   **31** *(middle & right)* Wm. C. Brown/Jeff Topping/Louis Rosenstock   **32** Blair Seitz/PHOTO RESEARCHERS   **34** P. Plaily/Science Photo Library/PHOTO RESEARCHERS   **40** Earth Satellite/Science Photo Library/PHOTO RESEARCHERS   **41** *(left)* Wm. C. Brown/Louis Rosenstock; *(right)* Hank Morgan/RAINBOW   **56** Spencer Grant/THE PICTURE CUBE   **61** *(bottom)* Manfred Kage/PETER ARNOLD   **79** *(bottom)* Wm. C. Brown/Louis Rosenstock   **92** *(top)* Custom Medical Stock   **92** *(bottom)* Wm. C. Brown/Louis Rosenstock   **111** Wm. C. Brown/Louis Rosenstock   **114** *(top)* From Stuart Ira Fox, *Human Physiology,* 3d ed. Copyright © 1990 Wm. C. Brown Communications, Inc., Dubuque, Iowa. All Rights Reserved. Reprinted by permission; *(center right)* NASA/PHOTOTAKE.   **121** Courtesy of Robert Shoemaker   **132** Yoav Levy/PHOTOTAKE   **135** Kip & Pat Peticolas/FUNDAMENTAL PHOTOS   **137** J. W. Mowbray/PHOTO RESEARCHERS   **145** From Stuart Ira Fox, *Human Physiology,* 3d ed. Copyright © 1990 Wm. C. Brown Communications, Inc., Dubuque, Iowa. All Rights Reserved. Reprinted by permission.   **148** Wm. C. Brown/Louis Rosenstock   **167** Wm. C. Brown/Louis Rosenstock   **171** Wm. C. Brown/Louis Rosenstock   **172** Wm. C. Brown/Louis Rosenstock   **176** NASA/THE IMAGE WORKS   **184** Gianni Tortoli/PHOTO RESEARCHERS   **185** NASA/THE IMAGE WORKS   **188** Blair Seitz/PHOTO RESEARCHERS   **189** *(right)* DuPont Pharmaceuticals/MEDICUS Intercon   **190** Robert Del Tredici   **192** Scott Camazine/PHOTO RESEARCHERS   **192** *(top)* Wm. C. Brown/Louis Rosenstock   **197** Tom McHugh/PHOTO RESEARCHERS   **204** *(left & right)* Wm. C. Brown/Louis Rosenstock   **205** Wm. C. Brown/Louis Rosenstock   **215** Wm. C. Brown/Louis Rosenstock   **230** Martin Rotker/PHOTOTAKE   **259** Wm. C. Brown/Louis Rosenstock   **261** *(top)* Wm. C. Brown/Louis Rosenstock   **279** *(center left)* R. Feldman & Dan McCoy/RAINBOW   **283** Daniel Brody/STOCK, BOSTON   **292** Wm. C. Brown/Louis Rosenstock   **304** Hans Pfletschinger/PETER ARNOLD   **315** From Stuart Ira Fox, *Human Physiology,* 3d ed. Copyright © 1990 Wm. C. Brown Communications, Inc., Dubuque, Iowa. All Rights Reserved. Reprinted by permission.   **320** *(right)* Wm. C. Brown/Louis Rosenstock   **322** From Stuart Ira Fox, *Human Physiology,* 3d ed. Copyright © 1990 Wm. C. Brown Communications, Inc., Dubuque, Iowa. All Rights Reserved. Reprinted by permission.   **323** *(top)* R. H. Albertin from *Journal of Cellular Science* 39:257–272 (1979); Company of Biologists, Ltd.   **327** Jackie Lewin/Science Photo Library/PHOTO RESEARCHERS   **345** R. Feldman and Dan McCoy/RAINBOW   **354** From *Biochemistry,* Third Edition, by Lubert Stryer. Copyright © 1988 by Lubert Stryer. Reprinted by permission of W. H. Freeman and Company.   **358** From

Robert F. Weaver and Philip W. Hedrick, *Genetics.* Copyright © 1989 Wm. C. Brown Communications, Inc., Dubuque, Iowa. All Rights Reserved. Reprinted by permission.   **362** From Stuart Ira Fox, *Human Physiology,* 3d ed. Copyright © 1990 Wm. C. Brown Communications, Inc., Dubuque, Iowa. All Rights Reserved. Reprinted by permission.   **381** Hank Morgan/PHOTO RESEARCHERS   **392** From Kent M. Van De Graaf, *Human Anatomy,* 3d ed. Copyright © 1992 Wm. C. Brown Communications, Inc., Dubuque, Iowa. All Rights Reserved. Reprinted by permission.   **415** *(left)* CNRI/PHOTOTAKE   **424** *(top)* CNRI/PHOTOTAKE; *(bottom)* Dr. Luz Mangurian/Dept. of Biological Sciences, Towson State University   **435** Wm. C. Brown/Louis Rosenstock   **438** From Stuart Ira Fox, *Human Physiology,* 3d ed. Copyright © 1990 Wm. C. Brown Communications, Inc., Dubuque, Iowa. All Rights Reserved. Reprinted by permission.   **439** From Stuart Ira Fox, *Human Physiology,* 3d ed. Copyright © 1990 Wm. C. Brown Communications, Inc., Dubuque, Iowa. All Rights Reserved. Reprinted by permission.   **440** Courtesy Metropolitan Life Insurance Company, New York.   **441** From E. L. Wynder, *The Book of Health: The American Health Foundation.* © 1981 Franklin Watts, Inc., New York. Reprinted by permission.   **443** From Stuart Ira Fox, *Human Physiology,* 3d ed. Copyright © 1990 Wm. C. Brown Communications, Inc., Dubuque, Iowa. All Rights Reserved. Reprinted by permission.   **472** From Robert F. Weaver and Philip W. Hedrick, *Genetics.* Copyright © 1989 Wm. C. Brown Communications, Inc., Dubuque, Iowa. All Rights Reserved. Reprinted by permission.   **477** From M. G. Rould, J. J. Persona, D. Söll, and T. Steitz, Structure of *E. coli* glutamyl-tRNA synthetics complexed with tRNA^{Gln} and ATP at 2.8-Å resolution: Implications for tRNA discrimination. *Science* 246:1135–42, 1989, © 1989 by the AAAS.   **479** From Sylvia S. Mader, *Biology,* 3d ed. Copyright © 1990 Wm. C. Brown Communications, Inc., Dubuque, Iowa. All Rights Reserved. Reprinted by permission.   **484** Yoav-Simon/PHOTOTAKE   **485** From Robert F. Weaver and Philip W. Hedrick, *Genetics.* Copyright © 1989 Wm. C. Brown Communications, Inc., Dubuque, Iowa. All Rights Reserved. Reprinted by permission.   **486** From *Strategies for Success,* no. 10 (Fall 1992): 1, 3. Reprinted with permission of Benjamin/Cummings Publications.   **487** From Robert F. Weaver and Philip W. Hedrick, *Genetics.* Copyright © 1989 Wm. C. Brown Communications, Inc., Dubuque, Iowa. All Rights Reserved. Reprinted by permission.   **488** From L. R. Maxson and C. H. Daugherty, *Genetics.* Copyright © 1989 Wm. C. Brown Communications, Inc., Dubuque, Iowa. All Rights Reserved. Reprinted by permission.   **489** From G. Zubay, *Biochemistry,* 3d ed. Copyright © 1993 Wm. C. Brown Communications, Inc., Dubuque, Iowa. All Rights Reserved. Reprinted by permission.   **508** From G. Zubay, *Biochemistry,* 3d ed. Copyright © 1993 Wm. C. Brown Communications, Inc., Dubuque, Iowa. All Rights Reserved. Reprinted by permission.

PRINCIPAL FUNCTIONAL GROUPS IN ORGANIC COMPOUNDS

Type of Compound	Structural Formula	Condensed Formula	Chapter Reference	Example Structural Formula	Example IUPAC Name	Example Common Name
Alcohol	R—O—H	ROH	12	CH_3CH_2—O—H	Ethanol	Ethyl alcohol
Aldehyde	$R-\overset{\overset{O}{\|\|}}{C}-H$	RCHO	13, 14	$CH_3\overset{\overset{O}{\|\|}}{C}-H$	Ethanal	Acetaldehyde
Amide	$R-\overset{\overset{O}{\|\|}}{C}-\overset{\overset{H}{\|}}{N}-H$	$RCONH_2$	17	$CH_3\overset{\overset{O}{\|\|}}{C}-\overset{\overset{H}{\|}}{N}-H$	Ethanamide	Acetamide
Amine	$R-\overset{\overset{H}{\|}}{N}-H$	RNH_2	17, 18	$CH_3CH_2\overset{\overset{H}{\|}}{N}-H$	Aminoethane	Ethyl amine
Carboxylic acid	$R-\overset{\overset{O}{\|\|}}{C}-O-H$	RCOOH	15, 16, 18	$CH_3\overset{\overset{O}{\|\|}}{C}-O-H$	Ethanoic acid	Acetic acid
Ester	$R-\overset{\overset{O}{\|\|}}{C}-O-R'$	RCOOR'	15, 16, 23	$CH_3\overset{\overset{O}{\|\|}}{C}-OCH_3$	Methyl ethanoate	Methyl acetate
Ester	R—O—R'	ROR'	12	CH_3OCH_3	Methoxymethane	Dimethyl ether
Halide	—Cl (or —Br, —F, —I)	RCl	10	CH_3CH_2Cl	Chloroethane	Ethyl chloride
Ketone	$R-\overset{\overset{O}{\|\|}}{C}-R'$	RCOR'	13, 14	$CH_3\overset{\overset{O}{\|\|}}{C}CH_3$	Propanone	Acetone